# ENCYCLOPEDIA OF FORENSIC AND LEGAL MEDICINE

# ENCYCLOPEDIA OF
# FORENSIC AND
# LEGAL MEDICINE

EDITED BY

**JASON PAYNE-JAMES**
**ROGER W BYARD**
**TRACEY S COREY**
**CAROL HENDERSON**

ELSEVIER
ACADEMIC
PRESS

AMSTERDAM • BOSTON • HEIDELBERG • LONDON
NEW YORK • OXFORD • PARIS • SAN DIEGO
SAN FRANCISCO • SINGAPORE • SYDNEY • TOKYO

# EDITORS AND EDITORIAL ADVISORY BOARD

# FOREWORD – A FORENSIC PERSPECTIVE

To comprehensively encompass the fields of both forensic medicine and legal medicine is an ambitious project indeed, as conventionally, the two disciplines are usually treated separately. Even "forensic medicine" itself is traditionally divided into autopsy pathology and the clinical aspects, so to produce anything more than an overview of the whole spectrum of the subject, is something that has probably never before been attempted in the English language.

The Editors have assembled an impressive array of contributors, each masters of their own topic and the result is an impressive work which deserves the highest praise, both to the authors and to those who have had to labor at editing to achieve a coherent whole – a feat which personal experience has taught me can be a daunting task. Having myself written about ten books on forensic medical topics, as well as contributions to many more, I can vouch for the fact that the most difficult job of all was editing a couple of multi-author volumes.

The content of this encyclopedia is diverse and comprehensive. The actual range can be seen from the very extensive chapter list and covers virtually every sub-discipline in forensic and legal medicine, from anthropology to botany, from malpractice to substance abuse. Some of the subjects dealt with, would be thought of as "forensic science" in the more compartmentalized attitude of Great Britain, but of course in very many countries, there is not the same demarcation of professional interests within their Institutes of Legal Medicine and thus this book avoids geographical restrictions, which in the past have always raised difficulties in writing for different parts of the world, which have markedly diverse medico-legal systems.

Some of the headings in the list of contents would seem unfamiliar to doctors of previous generations – examples might be "accreditation, digital evidence, crime-scene management, profiling, ritualistic crime, terrorism and torture" – but this underlines the evolutionary nature of all medical disciplines, in which legal medicine is no exception. In former years, many textbooks remained relatively static over numerous editions, following a conventional sequence of topics. Whereas forensic science developed almost explosively, the pace of progress in forensic pathology was slow and it seemed hardly worth buying new editions of established manuals. This has all changed and it is timely that such an ambitious work as this encyclopedia should seek to sweep all current knowledge into its grasp for the benefit of those doctors "at the sharp end" of forensic practice, who need to refer to any part of such a broad field of knowledge that now exists.

Professor Bernard Knight, CBE
Cardiff, UK
January 2005.

# FOREWORD – A LEGAL PERSPECTIVE

Over my judicial career I have observed a tremendous number of changes in the law, scientific and medical practices, and society in general. DNA evidence is now commonplace in many criminal and family cases, domestic violence and child abuse are unfortunately still prevalent, and the notion of personal rights and freedoms for incapacitated children and adults is now becoming widely accepted. The courts are also becoming increasingly involved in difficult cases concerning individuals who, but for advances in life-prolonging technologies, might have reached a natural death much sooner. I am particularly pleased to see a single work that is relevant to all these topics, and with contributions by distinguished practitioners and authors from many disciplines. I am only disappointed that a work of this importance was not available long ago.

The Encyclopedia will be of use and interest to a wide-ranging audience. Judges, lawyers, medical practitioners, scientists and students will be among the many who will benefit from this single repository of knowledge. I especially welcome, as will many, the electronic version which will receive regular updates. This will ensure that the Encyclopedia remains at the forefront of legal, technological and medical developments and will be of continuing use over the years to come.

The number of cases requiring evidence or advice from medical and other forensic experts has increased over recent years. In some cases as many as nine experts have been involved, providing a variety of viewpoints. The Encyclopedia will be a valuable aid in explaining to judges, lawyers and many others engaged in the court process the technical language of forensic and legal medicine and will assist in elucidating the complex issues which arise for resolution in the courts.

Dame Elizabeth Butler-Sloss, GBE
President of the Family Division
London, UK
January 2005.

# PREFACE

The phrase "Forensic and Legal Medicine" may at first appear cumbersome. It does, however, enable all the areas that this Encyclopedia covers to be fully embraced. Global differences in terminology and cross-over with other healthcare and scientific disciplines mean that unlike many other medical specialties such as cardiology or gastroenterology – each with clear boundaries – there may be misunderstanding, both within and without the medical profession as to the vast scope of subject covered. "Forensic medicine" and "legal medicine" are terms that can be used interchangeably, and their specific use may vary from country to country. For many readers, the term "forensic medicine" is synonymous with that of forensic pathology (that specialty of medicine which investigates the cause of death). However, forensic pathology, although part of forensic medicine, is but a small part of the vast range of subjects with which forensic medicine practitioners may be involved. In the broadest terms forensic and legal medicine includes all areas where medicine interacts with the law (including criminal and civil law), judiciary, police bodies, investigative agencies, professional bodies and government or state bodies.

When developing this Enyclopedia the Editors and the Publishers had the objective of providing *the* major reference source of subjects related to forensic and legal medicine. This information is provided in separate chapters generally of about 3–5,000 words. Each chapter gives a source of specific Further Reading to which those requiring even more detailed information can be directed. The degree of interaction of those practising forensic and legal medicine with the law, the judiciary, police bodies, investigative agencies, professional, government and state bodies, will vary from country to country, and from jurisdiction to jurisdiction. Some forensic medicine specialists will be independent of state, government or judiciary, while others will not. Some will work full-time in their field, others part-time. Just a few examples of key areas where differences arise include the investigation of death, approaches to care of detainees in custody, structure of investigative of systems, and interpretation of human rights issues. Clearly it is not possible for a single work, even of this size to illustrate all the differences that exist in our complex world. As Editors, we have sought to identify the most relevant issues and give examples of how such systems, or topics work within a given country or region. There will of course be omissions – and these we apologise for any such in advance. We hope that readers will inform us directly of any information that they feel should have been included. The online version of the Encyclopedia will be updated at timely intervals. Any such suggestions from readers will be assessed and considered as we plan the new material to be included at each update, and will thus help the development and evolution of this work.

The main readership groups of the Encyclopedia are intended to be medical practitioners whose work comprises a forensic element (including forensic pathologists, medical examiners, forensic physicians, forensic odontologists, paediatricians, psychiatrists, psychologists, genitourinary medicine specialists, emergency medicine specialists and primary care physicians), others within the forensic setting (including scientists, toxicologists, anthropologists), legal practitioners (lawyers, advocates, attorneys, coroners, barristers and solicitors), the judiciary, police and related bodies, government and state bodies responsible for – or using the services of – forensic practitioners, research institutes and those undertaking (as educators or students) academic courses or training in medical law, forensic medicine, investigation of crime and related topics. The Editors also hope that those who require authoritative information about the wide range of topics included – such as journalists and campaigning bodies, will find the information contained within as a valuable and indispensable resource.

The Editors have to offer huge thanks to the international spectrum of respected authors of the chapters, for their patience in the production of this substantial work. Each author has been chosen because of their reputation and their expertise in their given topic. Some aspects of some chapters may be controversial – we hope and intend that this is so. Forensic and legal medicine is not a science of absolutes, and its purpose is best served when opinions and approaches to the often complex and sensitive topics of debate can be discussed freely, openly and reasonably without fear of intimidation, retribution or victimisation.

Our thanks must of course go to the publishers – Elsevier – and to the staff of the Major Reference Works Department. In particular, we must congratulate Mark Knowles for his patience and understanding throughout the project, as he as borne the brunt of the development and given the Editors unqualified and unhesitating support. As Editors we have been very grateful for his involvement from shortly after conception, through gestation, to delivery. Assisting Mark have been Tracey Mills, Eleanor Orchard, Sue Stokes, Davinia Hurn-Shanley and Mireille Yanow. Nick Fallon, Mark Listewnik and Carey Chapman were key in establishing and supporting the project through its development. In the production stages Sarah Parkin has been extremely active in identifying any concerns and providing solutions in the production of the work.

Jason Payne-James
Roger W Byard
Tracey S Corey
Carol Henderson
November, 2004

# INTRODUCTION

The need for an understanding of the roles, responsibilities and relationships of practitioners of forensic and legal medicine – and those related specialties – in relation to issues outside the specific medical world has never been greater. There are many issues that are of huge relevance today, where the medical and related professions can have a multiplicity of roles. International terrorism is one example. The medical profession may be involved at a number of levels – the investigation of causes of death after an attack; the identification of human remains; the appropriate sampling of substances that may have evidential value; the care and assessment of terrorist suspects and their victims; the presentation of evidence to courts; and at a more local level, issues of consent for treatment of those unable to consent for themselves; and concern for the treatment of prisoners. Each of these issues requires independent, impartial and objective opinions which allow justice to be pursued appropriately and fairly. With this example the skills of forensic pathologists, forensic physicians, forensic anthropologists, forensic odontologists, forensic psychologists, forensic psychiatrists and forensic scientists may be required. Their findings and conclusions need to be given robustly, with emphasis given where facts or scientific research support an opinion, and clear guidance when such facts or research are either equivocal, or not available.

In some ways the forensic and legal medicine specialist may act as one of the gatekeepers within judicial systems. The recognition of the critical importance of such evidence has been highlighted worldwide where expert evidence has been challenged and impartiality has been questioned. Such challenges and questioning have put much focus on attempting to improve and clarify how, when and to what extent expert opinions in the forensic setting can be utilised, and different judicial systems apply a range of tests to such evidence to assess its integrity. This means that for all those working in forensic and legal medicine and its related specialties, and scientific or healthcare specialties, training, update training and audit and assessment has become a *sine qua non*. "Accreditation", "revalidation" and "standard setting" are terms that are used interchangeably worldwide. Training and education in medical law and forensic aspects of medicine are much more widely available and, increasingly, medical practitioners may be dually trained in medicine and law. However, there are few areas of medicine and healthcare now which are untouched by a need to understand certain aspects of forensic and legal medicine. All healthcare professionals need to be aware of, and put into practice, issues such as consent and confidentiality and apply these into their practice. Every medical or healthcare specialty has some aspect that may require specialist forensic and legal medical knowledge. In many areas this knowledge may be available from a forensic practitioner, but all practitioners need to be able to assist their patients in the absence of such a specialist. To give a number of examples: emergency medicine specialists need to be able to document accurately wounds that present for treatment, so that later interpretation in terms of modes of causation may be undertaken; those caring for the elderly need to recognise and document signs of elder abuse; similarly, paediatricians need to recognise and document signs of child abuse; genitourinary medicine specialists and gynaecologists need to be able to assess, document and provide management plans for victims of sexual assault; primary care physicians need to be able to assess and documents signs of domestic or interpersonal violence; psychiatrists and psychologists need to determine whether mentally vulnerable individuals are responsible for their actions; radiologists need to be able to recognise image appearances of non-accidental injury. All may have to present evidence in court to assist a court with their deliberations. The Encyclopedia provides sources of information to assist in all these functions, as well as giving examples of how court and legal systems compare in different jurisdictions worldwide.

The Encyclopedia endeavours to ensure that the cross-over of boundaries between different related but non-medical specialties, such as forensic toxicology, forensic psychology, forensic anthropology and forensic science are understood and defined. The interrelationship between these specialties is complex and the investigation of issues such as war crimes may require the skills of all these specialties and more.

The work undertaken by forensic practitioners must be based on a bedrock of an understanding of human rights and ethical principles. These principles are identified and referred to in the Encyclopedia; the Editors believe that these ethical principles should guide all those whose careers are primarily or even peripherally involved in the forensic and legal medicine setting.

Jason Payne-James
Roger W Byard
Tracey S Corey
Carol Henderson
November, 2004

# GUIDE TO USE OF THE ENCYCLOPEDIA

## Structure of the Encyclopedia

The material in the Encyclopedia is arranged as a series of entries in alphabetical order. Most entries consist of several articles that deal with various aspects of a topic and are arranged in a logical sequence within an entry. Some entries comprise a single article.

To help you realize the full potential of the material in the Encyclopedia we have provided three features to help you find the topic of your choice: a Contents List, Cross-References and an Index.

## 1. Contents List

Your first point of reference will probably be the contents list. The complete contents lists, which appears at the front of each volume will provide you with both the volume number and the page number of the entry. On the opening page of an entry a contents list is provided so that the full details of the articles within the entry are immediately available.

Alternatively you may choose to browse through a volume using the alphabetical order of the entries as your guide. To assist you in identifying your location within the Encyclopedia a running headline indicates the current entry and the current article within that entry.

You will find 'dummy entries' where obvious synonyms exist for entries or where we have grouped together related topics. Dummy entries appear in both the contents lists and the body of the text.

*Example*
If you were attempting to locate material on hair analysis for drugs via the contents list:

HAIR ANALYSIS *See* DNA: Hair Analysis; SUBSTANCE MISUSE: Hair Analysis

The dummy entry directs you to the Hair Analysis article, in the SUBSTANCE MISUSE entry. At the appropriate location in the contents list, the page numbers for articles under Substance Misuse are given.

If you were trying to locate the material by browsing through the text and you looked up Hair Analysis then the following information would be provided in the dummy entry:

**Hair Analysis** *See* **DNA:** Hair Analysis; **Substance Misuse:** Hair Analysis

Alternatively, if you were looking up Substance Misuse the following infrmation would be provided:

# SUBSTANCE MISUSE

Contents
**Medical Effects**
**Cocaine and Other Stimulants**
**Herbal Medicine**
**Heroin**
**Substitution Drugs**
**Sedatives**
**Miscellaneous Drugs**
**Urine Analysis**
**Hair Analysis**
**Alternative Body Fluids Analysis**
**Patterns and Statistics**
**Crime**

## 2. Cross References

All of the articles in the Encyclopedia have been extensively cross-referenced.

The cross-references, which appear at the end of an article, serve three different functions. For example, at the end of the Anthropology: Archeology, Excavation and Retrieval of Remains article, cross-references are used:

i. To indicate if a topic is discussed in greater detail elsewhere.

### See Also

**Anthropology:** Bone Pathology and Ante-mortem Trauma; Cremated Bones; Overview; Role of DNA; Sex Determination; Taphonomy; **Autopsy:** Procedures and Standards; **Deaths:** Trauma, Musculo-skeletal System; **Death Investigation Systems:** United States of America; **Odontology:** Overview; **Post-mortem Changes:** Overview; **War Crimes:** Pathological Investigation; Site Investigation

ii. To draw the reader's attention to parallel discussions in other articles.

### See Also

**Anthropology:** Bone Pathology and Ante-mortem Trauma; Cremated Bones; Overview; Role of DNA; Sex Determination; Taphonomy; **Autopsy:** Procedures and Standards; **Deaths:** Trauma, Musculo-skeletal System; **Death Investigation Systems:** United States of America; **Odontology:** Overview; **Post-mortem Changes:** Overview; **War Crimes:** Pathological Investigation; Site Investigation

iii. To indicate material that broadens the discussion.

### See Also

**Anthropology:** Bone Pathology and Ante-mortem Trauma; Cremated Bones; Overview; Role of DNA; Sex Determination; Taphonomy; **Autopsy:** Procedures and Standards; **Deaths:**

Trauma, Musculo-skeletal System; **Death Investigation Systems:** United States of America; **Odontology:** Overview; **Post-mortem Changes:** Overview; **War Crimes:** Pathological Investigation; Site Investigation

## 3. Index

The Index will provide you with the page number where the material is located, and the index entries differentiate between material that is a whole article, is part of an article or is data presented in a figure or table. Detailed notes are provided on the opening page of the index.

## 4. Contributors

A full list of contributors appears at the beginning of each volume.

# CONTRIBUTORS

**Aggrawal, A**
Maulana Azad Medical College, New Delhi, India

**Al-Alousi, L M**
Leicester Royal Infirmary, Leicester, UK

**Allden, K**
Dartmouth Medical School, Hanover, NH, USA

**Allison, S P**
Queen's Medical Centre, Nottingham, UK

**Anderson, R A**
University of Glasgow, Glasgow, UK

**Artecona, J**
Tulane University School of Medicine, New Orleans, LA, USA

**Asser, S M**
Hasbro Children's Hospital, Providence, RI, USA

**Baccino, E**
Centre Hospitalier Universitaire de Montpellier, Montpellier, France

**Baldwin, H B**
Forensic Enterprises, Inc., Orland Park, IL, USA

**Ballantyne, J**
University of Central Florida, Orlando, FL, USA

**Barley, V**
National Patient Safety Agency, London, UK

**Bassindale, C**
Lancashire Sexual Assault Forensic Examination Centre, Preston, UK

**Becker, R F**
Chaminade University of Honolulu, Honolulu, HI, USA

**Beh, P S L**
University of Hong Kong, Hong Kong, China

**Bergeron, C E**
American Association of Suicidology, Washington, DC, USA

**Berman, A L**
American Association of Suicidology, Washington, DC, USA

**Betz, P**
University of Erlangen-Nuremberg, Erlangen, Germany

**Black, S M**
University of Dundee, Dundee, UK

**Blackwell, S A**
The University of Melbourne, Melbourne, NSW, and the Victorian Institute of Forensic Medicine, Southbank, VIC, Australia

**Blaho-Owens, K**
University of Tennessee College of Medicine, Memphis, TN, USA

**Blitzer, H L**
Institute for Forensic Imaging, Indianapolis, IN, USA

**Bock, J H**
University of Colorado at Boulder, CO, USA

**Bora, B**
Tulane University School of Medicine, New Orleans, LA, USA

**Briggs, C A**
University of Melbourne, Melbourne, VIC, Australia

**Brown, T**
University of Leicester, Leicester, UK

**Buchino, J J**
University of Louisville, Louisville, KY, USA

**Burbrink II, D F**
Louisville Metropolitan Police Department, Louisville, KY, USA

**Burke, A**
Armed Forces Institute of Pathology, Washington, DC, USA

**Burke, M P**
Victorian Institute of Forensic Medicine, Southbank, VIC, Australia

**Byard, R W**
Forensic Science Centre, Adelaide, SA, Australia

**Campbell, W B**
Royal Devon and Exeter Hospital, Exeter, UK

**Carter, J**
Sussex Forensic Medical Services, Brighton, UK

**Case, M**
St. Louis University Health Sciences Center, St. Louis, MO, USA

**Casey, E**
Stroz Friedberg LLC, Washington, DC, USA

**Cerminara, K L**
Nova Southeastern University, Fort Lauderdale, FL, USA

**Chaturvedi, A K**
Civil Aerospace Medical Institute, Oklahoma City, OK, USA

**Chiamvimonvat, N**
University of California – Davis ACC, Sacramento, CA, USA

**Clark, J**
University of Glasgow, Glasgow, UK

**Clement, J G**
Victorian Institute of Forensic Medicine, Southbank, VIC, Australia

**Collier, S G**
National Drug Recognition Training Unit, Northampton, UK

**Cooper, P N**
University of Newcastle upon Tyne, Newcastle upon Tyne, UK

**Cordner, S**
Victorian Institute of Forensic Medicine, Southbank, VIC, Australia

**Corey, T S**
University of Louisville School of Medicine and Office of the Chief Medical Examiner, Louisville, KY, USA

**Couper, F J**
Office of the Chief Medical Examiner, Washington, DC, USA

**Cox, A R**
West Midlands Centre for Adverse Drug Reaction Reporting, Birmingham, UK

**Crane, J**
Queen's University, Belfast, UK

**Czuzak, M H**
University of Arizona, Tucson, AZ, USA

**D'Arcy, M**
Royal Women's Hospital, Carlton, VIC, Australia

**Dada, M A**
PathCare, Durban, South Africa

**Dargan, P I**
National Poisons Information Service, London, UK

**Davis, D W**
Hennepin County Medical Examiner's Office, Minneapolis, MN, USA

**Dean, P**
Rochford Police Station, Rochford, UK

**DeFreitas, K**
McMaster University, Hamilton, ON, Canada

**Donald, T**
Women's and Children's Hospital, North Adelaide, SA, Australia

**Downs, J C U**
Georgia Bureau of Investigation, Savannah, GA, USA

**Drummer, O H**
Victorian Institute of Forensic Medicine, Southbank, VIC, Australia

**Dworkin, R**
Indiana University School of Law, Bloomington, IN, USA

**Edelmann, R J**
University of Roehampton, London, UK

**El-Fawal, H A N**
Mercy College, Dobbs Ferry, NY, USA

**Ellen, R L**
Monash University, Southbank, VIC, Australia

**Eriksson, A**
Umeå University, Umeå, Sweden

**Ernst, M F**
St. Louis University School of Medicine, St. Louis, MO, USA

**Evans, V**
Ilkley, UK

**Farrell, M**
National Addiction Centre, London, UK

**Fegan-Earl, A W**
Forensic Pathology Services, London, UK

**Ferner, R E**
West Midlands Centre for Adverse Drug Reaction Reporting, Birmingham, UK

**Fernie, C G M**
University of Glasgow, Glasgow, UK

**Ferris, J A J**
Auckland Hospital, Auckland, New Zealand

**Fisher, R P**
Florida International University, North Miami, FL, USA

**Flannery, W**
National Alcohol Unit, London, UK

**Flynn, M**
Nova Southeastern University, Fort Lauderdale, FL, USA

**Foran, D R**
Michigan State University, East Lansing, MI, USA

**Fornes, P**
University of Paris, Paris, France

**Fraser, J**
University of Strathclyde, Glasgow, UK

**Frazer, J**
Cleckheaton, UK

**Freckelton, I**
Monash University, Melbourne, VIC, Australia

**Fung, W K**
University of Hong Kong, Hong Kong, China

**Gaebler, R**
Indiana University School of Law, Bloomington, IN, USA

**Gaensslen, R E**
University of Illinois at Chicago, Chicago, IL, USA

**Gaoling, Z**
Peking University, Beijing, China

**Gatland, D**
Southend Hospital NHS Trust, Essex, UK

**Gerostamoulos, J**
Victorian Institute of Forensic Medicine, Southbank, VIC, Australia

**Glatter, K A**
University of California – Davis ACC, Sacramento, CA, USA

**Goddard, K**
National Fish and Wildlife Services, Ashland, OR, USA

**Goff, M L**
Chaminade University of Honolulu, Honolulu, HI, USA

**Goldberger, B A**
University of Florida College of Medicine, Gainesville, FL, USA

**Golding, S L**
University of Utah, Salt Lake City, UT, USA

**Goodwin, W**
University of Central Lancashire, Preston, UK

**Graffy, E A**
Michigan State University, East Lansing, MI, USA

**Graham, E A M**
University of Leicester, Leicester, UK

**Gregersen, M**
Institute of Forensic Medicine, University of Århus, Århus, Denmark

**Gudjonsson, G H**
Institute of Psychiatry, London, UK

**Gullberg, R G**
Washington State Patrol, Seattle, WA, USA

**Haglund, W D**
Physicians for Human Rights, Washington, DC, USA

**Hall, C M**
Great Ormond Street Hospital for Children, London, UK

**Hayden-Wade, H**
Children's Hospital of San Diego, San Diego, CA, USA

**Healy, T E J**
University of Manchester, Manchester, UK

**Henderson, C**
Stetson University College of Law, Gulfport, FL, USA

**Henry, M M**
Chelsea and Westminster Hospital, London, UK

**Herkov, M J**
University of North Florida, Jacksonville, FL, USA

**Hill, A J**
Victorian Institute of Forensic Medicine, Southbank, VIC, Australia

**Holck, P**
University of Oslo, Oslo, Norway

**Horswell, J**
Forensic Executives, Upper Mt. Gravatt, QLD, Australia

**Houck, M M**
West Virginia University, Morgantown, WV, USA

**Howard, J D**
Tacoma, WA, USA

**Hu, Y-Q**
University of Hong Kong, Hong Kong, China

**Hucker, S J**
McMaster University, Hamilton, ON, Canada

**Hunsaker, D M**
University of Louisville School of Medicine, Louisville, KY, USA

**Hunsaker III, J C**
University of Kentucky College of Medicine, Frankfort, KY, USA

**Hunt, N**
Forensic Pathology Services, Abingdon, UK

**Imwinkelried, E J**
University of California at Davis, Davis, CA, USA

**Ives, N K**
University of Oxford, Oxford, UK

**Jackson, R L**
Pacific Graduate School of Psychology, Palo Alto, CA, USA

**Jawad, R**
King's College Hospital, London, UK

**Jennett, B**
University of Glasgow, Glasgow, UK

**Jenny, C**
Brown Medical School, Providence, RI, USA

**Jones, A L**
National Poisons Information Service, London, UK

**Jones, A W**
University Hospital, Linköping, Sweden

**Jones, G R**
Office of the Chief Medical Examiner, Edmonton, AB, Canada

**Jordan, C E**
University of Kentucky, Lexington, KY, USA

**Josse, S E**
Formerly University of London, London, UK

**Jumbelic, M I**
Upstate Medical University, Syracuse, NY, USA

**Jureidini, J**
Women's and Children's Hospital, Adelaide, SA, Australia

**Kahana, T**
Division of Identification and Forensic Science, Israel
National Police, Israel

**Karch, S B**
Berkeley, CA, USA

**Keeley, S**
Women's and Children's Hospital, North Adelaide,
SA, Australia

**Kelliher, T P**
Niskayuna, NY, USA

**Kennedy, R T**
New Mexico Court of Appeals, Albuquerque,
NM, USA

**Kerrigan, S**
Houston, TX, USA

**Keyser-Tracqui, C**
Institut de Médecine Légale,
Strasbourg, France

**Khanna, A**
Sandwell General Hospital, West Bromwich, UK

**Kibayashi, K**
Saga Medical School, Saga, Japan

**Kirk, G M**
University of KwaZulu Natal, Durban, South Africa

**Koehler, S A**
Allegheny County Coroner, Pittsburgh, PA, USA

**Krous, H F**
Children's Hospital and Health Center, San Diego,
CA, USA

**Langford, N J**
West Midlands Centre for Adverse Drug Reaction
Reporting, Birmingham, UK

**Langlois, N E I**
Westmead Hospital, Wentworthville, NSW, Australia

**Lau, G**
Centre for Forensic Medicine, Health Sciences
Authority, Singapore

**Lazarus, N G**
Path Care, Durban, South Africa

**Lee, H C**
Connecticut Forensic Science Laboratory, Meriden,
CT, USA

**Leslie, L K**
Children's Hospital of San Diego, San Diego, CA, USA

**Levin, R J**
University of Sheffield, Sheffield, UK

**Levine, B**
Office of the Chief Medical Examiner, Baltimore,
MD, USA

**Levinson, J**
John Jay College of Criminal Justice, New York,
NY, USA

**Lewis, A**
McMaster University, Hamilton, ON, Canada

**Liang, B A**
California Western School of Law, San Diego, CA, USA

**Little, D**
Westmead Hospital Wentworthville, NSW, Australia

**Liu, R H**
Fooyin University, Kaohsiung Msien, Taiwan

**Loff, B**
Victorian Institute of Forensic Medicine, Southbank,
VIC, Australia

**Lord, W D**
Serial Killer Unit, FBI Academy, Quantico, VA, USA

**Ludes, B**
Institut de Médecine Légale, Strasbourg, France

**Lunetta, P**
University of Helsinki, Helsinki, Finland

**Luo, B**
Sun Yat Sen Medical School, Gungzhou, China

**Lynch, M J**
Monash University, Southbank, VIC, Australia

**Marc, B**
Compiegne Hospital, Compiegne, France

**Marks, M K**
University of Tennessee, Knoxville, TN, USA

**Marks, P**
The General Infirmary at Leeds, Leeds, UK

**Marrero, L**
Shands at Vista, a University of Florida Affiliate,
Gainesville, FL, USA

**Martrille, L**
Centre Hospitalier Universitaire de Montpellier,
Montpellier, France

**May, C P**
Criminal Justice Institute, Little Rock, AR, USA

**McKelvie, H**
Victorian Institute of Forensic Medicine, Southbank,
VIC, Australia

**McLay, D**
Formerly Strathclyde Police, Glasgow, UK

**McNamara, J J**
Serial Killer Unit, FBI Academy, Quantico, VA, USA

**Meadow, R**
University of Leeds, Leeds, UK

**Mieczkowski, T**
University of South Florida, Tampa, FL, USA

**Millward, M J**
University of Western Australia, Perth, WA, Australia

**Milroy, C M**
University of Sheffield, Sheffield, UK

**Mimasaka, S**
Kumamoto University, Kumamoto, Japan

**Miyaishi, S**
Okayama University Graduate School of Medicine and
Dentistry, Okayama, Japan

**Moore, K A**
Office of the Chief Medical Examiner, Baltimore,
MD, USA

**Moriya, F**
Kochi University, Nankoku, Japan

**Morris, G**
Plantation, FL, USA

**Morton, R J**
Serial Killer Unit, FBI Academy, Quantico, VA, USA

**Mossman, D**
Wright State University School of Medicine, Dayton,
OH, USA

**Mura, P**
Laboratoire Toxicology/Biochimic, France

**Murphy, W A**
MD Anderson Cancer Center, Houston, TX, USA

**Myers, W C**
University of Florida, Gainesville, FL, USA

**Nadesan, K**
University of Malaya, Kuala Lumpur, Malaysia

**Naidoo, S R**
University of KwaZulu Natal, Durban, South Africa

**Nashelsky, M B**
University of Iowa Carver College of Medicine, Iowa City,
IA, USA

**Natarajan, G A**
Chief Medical Examiner's Office, Perth Amboy,
NJ, USA

**Nathan, R**
Merseyside Forensic Psychiatry Service, St Helens, UK

**Nathanson, M**
Compiegne Hospital, Compiegne, France

**Negrusz, A**
University of Illinois at Chicago, Chicago, IL, USA

**Nordby, J J**
Final Analysis Forensics, Tacoma, WA, USA

**Nordrum, I**
Norwegian University of Science and Technology,
Trondheim, Norway

**Norfolk, G A**
Association of Forensic Physicians, Bristol, UK

**Norris, D O**
University of Colorado at Boulder, CO, USA

**Olle, L**
Royal Women's Hospital, Carlton, VIC, Australia

**Ong, B B**
Queensland Health Scientific Services, Brisbane, QLD,
Australia

**Orlando, F**
Nova Southeastern University, Fort Lauderdale, FL, USA

**Pagliaro, E M**
Connecticut Forensic Science Laboratory, Meriden, CT, USA

**Palmbach, T M**
University of New Haven, West Haven, CT, USA

**Park, G**
Addenbrooke's Hospital NHS Trust, Cambridge, UK

**Park, J K**
University of California – Davis ACC, Sacramento, CA, USA

**Parrish, R N**
Office of the Guardian ad Litem, Utah, UT, USA

**Patel, M F**
Royal Berkshire Hospital, Reading, UK

**Payne-James, J**
Forensic Healthcare Services Ltd, London, UK

**Peel, M**
Medical Foundation for the Care of Victims of Torture, London, UK

**Perlmutter, D**
Institute for the Research of Organized and Ritual Violence LLC, Yardley, PA, USA

**Pollak, S**
University of Freiburg, Freiburg, Germany

**Pounder, D J**
University of Dundee, Dundee, UK

**Prahlow, J A**
South Bend Medical Foundation and Indiana University of Medicine – South Bend Center for Medical Education at the University of Notre Dame, South Bend, IN, USA

**Provis, A**
Mount Hospital, Perth, WA, Australia

**Quatrehomme, G**
Laboratoire de Médecine Légale et Anthropologie Médico-légale, and Faculté de Médecine, Nice, France

**Rabinovich, R**
The Hebrew University of Jerusalem, Jerusalem, Israel

**Ratcliff, C**
Thames Valley Police, UK

**Reavis, J A**
Relationship Training Institute, San Diego, CA, USA

**Rebmann, A J**
Connecticut State Police, Kent, WA, USA

**Reeves, R**
University of Medicine and Dentistry of New Jersey, Newark, NJ, USA

**Ren, L**
University of Houston Law Center, Houston, TX, USA

**Rittscher, J**
General Electric, Niskayuna, NY, USA

**Rix, K J B**
Leeds Mental Health Teaching Trust, Leeds, UK

**Robinson, S**
Altrincham, UK

**Rogers, R**
University of North Texas, Denton, TX, USA

**Rognum, T O**
University of Oslo, Oslo, Norway

**Rosner, R**
New York University School of Medicine, and the Forensic Psychiatry Clinic of Bellevue Hospital Center, New York, NY, USA

**Rutty, G N**
Forensic Pathology Unit, Leicester, UK

**Rutty, J E**
DeMonfort University, Leicester, UK

**Sanchez, T L**
New Mexico Court of Appeals, Albuquerque, NM, USA

**Saukko, P**
University of Turku, Turku, Finland

**Saunders, C M**
QEII Medical Centre, Perth, WA, Australia

**Savage, K A**
National Forensic Science Technology Center, Largo, FL, USA

**Sawaguchi, T**
Tokyo Women's Medical University, Tokyo, Japan

**Scheuer, L**
Royal Free and University College Medical School,
London, UK

**Schreiber, N**
University of Miami, Miami, FL, USA

**Schuliar, Y**
Institut de Recherche Criminelle de la Gendarmerie
Nationale, Rosny-sous-Bois, France

**Seals, M**
Nova Southeastern University, Fort Lauderdale, FL, USA

**Sewell, G J**
University of Bath, Bath, UK

**Shapiro, L M**
Papworth Hospital, Cambridge, UK

**Shuttleworth, C**
FGI, Ontario, Canada

**Simmons, T**
University of Central Lancashire, Preston, UK

**Simpson, E K**
Forensic Science Centre, Adelaide, SA, Australia

**Sjøvold, T**
Stockholm University, Stockholm, Sweden

**Smith, J**
Essex, UK

**Smock, W S**
University of Louisville Hospital, Louisville, KY, USA

**Solon, M**
Bond Solon, London, UK

**Sorg, M H**
University of Maine, Orono, ME, USA

**Spivack, B S**
Office of the Chief Medical Examiner, Louisville,
KY, USA

**Stark, M M**
St. George's Hospital Medical School, Epsom, UK

**Sullivan, J E**
University of Louisville, Louisville, KY, USA

**Swift, B**
Forensic Pathology Unit, Leicester, UK

**Synstelien, J A**
University of Tennessee, Knoxville, TN, USA

**Taylor, R**
Royal Cornwall Hospital, Truro, UK

**Tersigni, M A**
University of Tennessee, Knoxville, TN, USA

**Thali, M J**
University of Bern, Bern, Switzerland

**Thatcher, P J**
Forensic Science Center, Darwin, NT, Australia

**Thid, M**
Umeå University, Umeå, Sweden

**Thompson, J W**
Tulane University School of Medicine, New Orleans,
LA, USA

**Tsokos, M**
University of Hamburg, Hamburg, Germany

**Tsunenari, S**
Kumamoto University, Kumamoto, Japan

**Tu, P**
General Electric, Niskayuna, NY, USA

**Tully, B**
Psychologists at Law Group, London, UK

**Tunbridge, R**
Transport Research Laboratory, Wokingham, UK

**Van der Lugt, C**
Dutch National Police Selection and Training Institute,
Zutphen, The Netherlands

**Vanezis, P**
The Forensic Science Service, London, UK

**Vayer, J S**
University of the Health Sciences, Bethesda,
MD, USA

**Vege, Å**
University of Oslo, Oslo, Norway

**Virmani, R**
Armed Forces Institute of Pathology, Washington, DC, USA

**Vock, P**
University of Bern, Bern, Switzerland

**Wagner, G**
Medical Examiner's Office, San Diego, CA, USA

**Walker, A**
University of Sheffield, Sheffield, UK

**Wall, I**
Ruislip, UK

**Weakley-Jones, B**
Office of the Chief Medical Examiner, Louisville, KY, USA

**Wecht, C H**
Allegheny County Coroner, Pittsburgh, PA, USA

**Welch, J**
King's College Hospital, London, UK

**Welner, M**
NYU School of Medicine, New York, NY, USA

**Wetli, C V**
Suffolk County Department of Health Services, Hauppauge, NY, USA

**White, J**
Women's and Children's Hospital, Adelaide, SA, Australia

**Wielbo, D**
National Forensic Science Technology Center, Largo, FL, USA

**Wilets, J D**
Nova Southeastern University, Fort Lauderdale, FL, USA

**Williams, G S**
Northern Illinois University, DeKalb, IL, USA

**Wolff, K**
Kings College, London, UK

**Wolson, T L**
Crime Laboratory Bureau, Miami, FL, USA

**Wright, M G**
London, UK

**Wyatt, J**
Royal Cornwall Hospital, Truro, UK

**Yonemitsu, K**
Kumamoto University, Kumamoto, Japan

**Yoshida, K-I**
University of Tokyo, Tokyo, Japan

**Youyi, H**
Peking University, Beijing, China

# CONTENTS

## VOLUME 1

**A**

ACCREDITATION

Forensic Specialties Accreditation Board     *G R Jones*                                                    1

Crime Scene Investigators     *J Horswell*                                                                         3

Toxicology     *G R Jones*                                                                                                  13

ACCREDITATION *See* DEATH INVESTIGATION SYSTEMS: China; Japan;

Nordic Countries; Certification of Death and the United Kingdom System;

United States of America; FORENSIC PSYCHIATRY AND FORENSIC PSYCHOLOGY:

Forensic Psychology, Education, Training and Certification;

Forensic Psychiatry, Education, Training and Certification

AGE ESTIMATION IN THE LIVING     *L Martrille and E Baccino*                                       17

ALCOHOL

Breath Alcohol Analysis     *R G Gullberg*                                                                       21

Blood and Body Fluid Analysis     *D M Hunsaker and J C Hunsaker III*                        29

Acute and Chronic Use, Postmortem Findings     *A W Jones*                                      39

ALCOHOL BACK-TRACKING CALCULATIONS *See* BACK-TRACKING CALCULATIONS

ALLERGIES     *A Aggrawal*                                                                                                58

ANIMAL ATTACKS AND INJURIES

Fatal and Nonfatal     *A W Fegan-Earl*                                                                          68

Predation     *R Rabinovich and T Kahana*                                                                     71

ANTHROPOLOGY

Overview     *T Kahana*                                                                                                    80

Archeology, Excavation and Retrieval of Remains     *W D Haglund and T Simmons*    89

Taphonomy     *W D Haglund and M H Sorg*                                                                  94

Stature Estimation from the Skeleton     *T Sjøvold*                                                    100

Bone Pathology and Antemortem Trauma     *S M Black*                                           105

Cremated Bones     *P Holck*                                                                                       113

Morphological Age Estimation     *E K Simpson*                                                         119

Pediatric and Juvenile     *L Scheuer*                                                                          123

Sex Determination     *C A Briggs*                                                                              129

Determination of Racial Affinity      *M K Marks and J A Synstelien*                136

Handedness      *M H Czuzak*                142

Role of DNA      *B Ludes and C Keyser-Tracqui*                145

ASPHYXIA      *A Walker, C M Milroy, and J Payne-James*                151

AUTOEROTIC DEATH      *R W Byard*                157

AUTOPSY

Procedures and Standards      *P Saukko and S Pollak*                166

Medico-legal Considerations      *S Cordner and H McKelvie*                171

Pediatric      *H F Krous and T S Corey*                176

Adult      *J A J Ferris*                183

Infectious      *K Kibayashi*                192

AUTOPSY, FINDINGS

Drug Deaths      *S B Karch*                198

Postmortem Drug Measurements, Interpretation of      *B Levine and K A Moore*                203

Postmortem Drug Sampling and Redistribution      *D J Pounder*                211

Organic Toxins      *O H Drummer*                217

Fire      *B Marc*                221

Drowning      *D J Pounder*                227

Sudden Infant Death Syndrome      *R W Byard and T O Rognum*                232

AUTOPSY, FINDINGS, ADULT FALLS FROM HEIGHT *See* FALLS FROM HEIGHT, PHYSICAL
FINDINGS: In Adults

AUTOPSY, FINDINGS, ALCOHOL USE *See* ALCOHOL: Acute and Chronic Use,
Postmortem Findings

AUTOPSY, FINDINGS, ASPHYXIA *See* ASPHYXIA

AUTOPSY, FINDINGS, CARBON MONOXIDE POISONING *See* CARBON MONOXIDE
POISONING: Incidence and Findings at Postmortem

AUTOPSY, FINDINGS, PEDIATRIC FALLS FROM HEIGHT *See* FALLS FROM HEIGHT, PHYSICAL
FINDINGS: In Children

AVIATION ACCIDENTS, ROLE OF PATHOLOGIST      *G Wagner*                243

AVIATION MEDICINE, ILLNESS AND LIMITATIONS FOR FLYING      *K Blaho-Owens*                253

**B**

BACK-TRACKING CALCULATIONS      *R A Anderson*                261

BALLISTIC TRAUMA, OVERVIEW AND STATISTICS      *S R Naidoo*                271

BALLISTIC TRAUMA, INJURIES *See* INJURY, FATAL AND NONFATAL: Explosive Injury; Firearm Injuries;
TACTICAL MEDICINE; TERRORISM: Suicide Bombing, Investigation; WAR INJURIES

BIOTERRORISM *See* TERRORISM: Nuclear and Biological

BLOOD GROUPING      *G S Williams*                283

BODY CAVITY SEARCHES, PRACTICAL ISSUES AND CONSENT      *M M Stark*                289

BODY RECOVERY      *R L Ellen and M J Lynch*                293

BRAIN DEATH *See* MEDICAL DEFINITIONS OF DEATH

**C**

CARBON MONOXIDE POISONING

Clinical Findings, Sequelae In Survivors      *J Payne-James and S Robinson*                301

Incidence and Findings at Postmortem      *J C U Downs*                305

CHEMICAL CROWD CONTROL AGENTS    K Blaho-Owens    319
CHILDREN
    Stages of Development and Growth    H Hayden-Wade and L K Leslie    325
    Legal Protection and Rights of Children    F Orlando and M Seals    338
    Children and Courts    R N Parrish    343
    Emotional Abuse    T Donald    358
    Physical Abuse    C Jenny    363
    Sexual Abuse, Overview    B Marc and M Nathanson    373
    Sexual Abuse, Epidemiology    E Baccino and L Martrille    380
    Sudden Natural Infant and Childhood Death    R W Byard and H F Krous    382
    Non-inflicted Causes of Death    R W Byard and T S Corey    392
CLINICAL TRIALS
    Good Clinical Practice and Ethical Aspects    C M Saunders, M J Millward, and A Provis    399
    Legal Aspects and Consent    K L Cerminara    404
COLD CASE REVIEW - UK EXPERIENCE    J Fraser    410
COMA, DEFINITIONS AND DIFFERENTIAL DIAGNOSES
    Pediatric    S Keeley    415
    Adult    P Marks    419
COMPLAINTS AGAINST DOCTORS, HEALTHCARE WORKERS AND INSTITUTIONS    C G M Fernie    424
COMPUTER CRIME AND DIGITAL EVIDENCE    E Casey    429
CONSENT
    Medical Examination in Custody    C G M Fernie    436
    Treatment Without Consent    C G M Fernie    441
    Confidentiality and Disclosure    I Wall    446
CONSENT, CLINICAL TRIALS See CLINICAL TRIALS: Legal Aspects and Consent
CONSENT, BODY CAVITY SEARCHES See BODY CAVITY SEARCHES, PRACTICAL ISSUES
    AND CONSENT
COURT SYSTEMS
    Jewish (Halacha) Law    J Levinson    452
    Sharii'ah Law    H A N El-Fawal    455
    Law, China    Z Gaoling and H Youyi    463
    Law, Japan    T Sawaguchi    470
    Law, United Kingdom    I Wall    478
    Law, United States of America    R T Kennedy and T L Sanchez    482
COURTS, REPORT WRITING    M Solon    487

VOLUME 2

CRIME-SCENE INVESTIGATION AND EXAMINATION
    Collection and Chain of Evidence    T M Palmbach    1
    Death-scene Investigation, United States of America    M F Ernst    7
    Major Incident Scene Management    J Horswell    12
    Underwater Crime Scene    R F Becker    20
    Recovery of Human Remains    H B Baldwin and C P May    27
    Suspicious Deaths    J Horswell    32

CRIME-SCENE MANAGEMENT, SYSTEMS

    Continental Europe    *Y Schuliar and B Marc*    37

    United Kingdom    *J Fraser and C Ratcliff*    41

    United States of America    *J J Nordby*    46

CRIMINAL PROFILING    *R J Morton and W D Lord*    51

CUSTODY

    Death in, United Kingdom and Continental Europe    *J Payne-James and J Carter*    56

    Death in, United States of America    *C V Wetli and G A Natarajan*    65

**D**

DEATH, POST-MORTEM CHANGES *See* POSTMORTEM CHANGES: Overview

DEATH, POST-MORTEM ELECTROLYTE DISTURBANCES *See* POSTMORTEM

    CHANGES: Electrolyte Disturbances

DEATHS

    Trauma, Head and Spine    *P Marks*    75

    Trauma, Thorax    *A W Fegan-Earl*    81

    Trauma, Abdominal Cavity    *J A Prahlow*    86

    Trauma, Musculo-skeletal System    *P S L Beh*    97

    Trauma, Vascular System    *N Hunt*    103

    Perioperative and Postoperative    *P N Cooper*    107

    Sports    *L M Shapiro*    115

DEATH INVESTIGATION SYSTEMS

    China    *P S L Beh and B Luo*    120

    Japan    *K-I Yoshida*    123

    Nordic Countries    *M Thid, A Eriksson, and T O Rognum*    128

    Certification of Death and the United Kingdom System    *P Dean*    133

    United States of America    *C H Wecht and S A Koehler*    139

DEATH, LEGAL DEFINITIONS OF *See* LEGAL DEFINITIONS OF DEATH

DEATH, MEDICAL DEFINITIONS OF *See* MEDICAL DEFINITIONS OF DEATH

DEATH, POST-MORTEM FINDINGS: ASPHYXIA *See* ASPHYXIA

DEATH, POST-MORTEM FINDINGS: ACUTE AND CHRONIC ALCOHOL USE *See* ALCOHOL:

    Acute and Chronic Use, Postmortem Findings

DEATH, POST-MORTEM FINDINGS, CARBON MONOXIDE POISONING *See* CARBON MONOXIDE

    POISONING: Incidence and Findings at Postmortem

DEATH, POST-MORTEM FINDINGS, DROWNING *See* AUTOPSY, FINDINGS: Drowning

DEATH: POST-MORTEM FINDINGS - FALL FROM HEIGHTS, ADULT *See* FALLS FROM HEIGHT,

    PHYSICAL FINDINGS: In Adults

DEATH: POST-MORTEM FINDINGS - FALL FROM HEIGHTS, PEDIATRIC *See* FALLS FROM HEIGHT,

    PHYSICAL FINDINGS: In Children

DEATH, POST-MORTEM FINDINGS: SUDDEN INFANT DEATH SYNDROME *See* AUTOPSY,

    FINDINGS: Sudden Infant Death Syndrome

DECOMPOSITION, PATTERNS AND RATES    *M K Marks and M A Tersigni*    148

DELIBERATE SELF-HARM, PATTERNS    *J Payne-James*    153

DETAINEES

Care in Police Custody, United Kingdom    *J Payne-James and S Robinson*    158

Care in Prison Custody, United Kingdom    *V Evans*    164

Fitness to be Interviewed    *G H Gudjonsson*    169

DIGITAL EVIDENCE *See* COMPUTER CRIME AND DIGITAL EVIDENCE

DNA

Basic Principles    *B Ludes and C Keyser-Tracqui*    174

Ethics of Forensic Applications and Databanks    *S Cordner*    178

Statistical Analysis    *W K Fung and Y-Q Hu*    184

Risk of Contamination    *G N Rutty and E A M Graham*    189

Mitochondrial    *W Goodwin*    198

Postmortem Analysis for Heritable Channelopathies and Selected Cardiomyopathies    *K A Glatter,
N Chiamvimonvat, and J K Park*    206

Hair Analysis    *E A Graffy and D R Foran*    213

DNA, ANTHROPOLOGICAL USE *See* ANTHROPOLOGY: Role of DNA

DNA, PATERNITY TESTING *See* PARENTAGE TESTING

DOGS, USE IN POLICE INVESTIGATIONS    *B Weakley-Jones and A J Rebmann*    221

DOMESTIC VIOLENCE    *C E Jordan*    223

DROWNING *See* AUTOPSY, FINDINGS: Drowning

DRUG-FACILITATED SEXUAL ASSAULT *See* SEXUAL OFFENSES, ADULT: Drug-Facilitated
Sexual Assault

DRUG-INDUCED INJURY, ACCIDENTAL AND IATROGENIC    *A Aggrawal*    230

DRUGS, PRESCRIBED

Licencing and Registration    *G J Sewell*    239

Product Liability    *A Aggrawal*    243

Testamentary Capacity    *R E Ferner, N J Langford, and A R Cox*    252

DRUGS: BACK-TRACKING CALCULATIONS *See* BACK-TRACKING CALCULATIONS

DYADIC DEATHS *See* MURDER–SUICIDE


# E

ELECTRIC SHOCKS AND ELECTROCUTION, CLINICAL EFFECTS AND PATHOLOGY    *B Marc*    259

ENTOMOLOGY    *M L Goff*    263

EVIDENCE, RULES OF    *I Freckelton*    270

EXCITED DELIRIUM    *C V Wetli*    276

EXHUMATION    *H B Baldwin and C P May*    281

EXPERT WITNESS

Qualifications, Testimony and Malpractice    *C Henderson*    284

Medical    *H F Krous and R W Byard*    290

Daubert and Beyond    *E J Imwinkelried*    294

EXTREMES OF TEMPERATURE    *Å Vege*    300


# F

FALLS FROM HEIGHT, PHYSICAL FINDINGS

In Children    *B S Spivack*    307

In Adults    *G Lau*    310

FEMALE GENITAL ALTERATION    *B Swift and G N Rutty*    320

FIRE INVESTIGATION, EVIDENCE RECOVERY  *P J Thatcher*                                327

FIRE, DEATHS *See* AUTOPSY, FINDINGS: Fire

FIRE, INJURIES *See* INJURY, FATAL AND NONFATAL: Burns and Scalds

FORENSIC BOTANY  *J H Bock and D O Norris*                                          332

FORENSIC JOURNALS, BIBLIOMETRICS AND JOURNAL IMPACT FACTORS  *A W Jones*            335

FORENSIC PSYCHIATRY AND FORENSIC PSYCHOLOGY

    Forensic Psychology, Education, Training and Certification  *S L Golding*       346

    Forensic Psychiatry, Education, Training and Certification  *R Reeves and R Rosner*   350

    Assessment  *R Reeves and R Rosner*                                              355

    Ethics  *D Mossman*                                                              359

    Psychological Autopsy  *A L Berman*                                             364

    Forensic Interviewing  *R P Fisher and N Schreiber*                             371

    Suicide Predictors and Statistics  *A L Berman and C E Bergeron*                378

    Mental Handicap and Learning Disability  *M Welner*                             388

    Drug and Alcohol Addiction  *W Flannery and M Farrell*                          405

    Malingering  *R L Jackson and R Rogers*                                          417

    Personality Disorder  *J Frazer and K J B Rix*                                  424

    Multiple Personality Disorder  *S J Hucker*                                     434

    Stalking  *J A Reavis*                                                           437

    Sex Offenders  *W C Myers, L Marrero, and M J Herkov*                            444

    Criminal Responsibility  *S J Hucker and K DeFreitas*                           451

    Fitness (Competence) To Stand Trial  *S J Hucker and A Lewis*                    455

# H

HAIR ANALYSIS *See* DNA: Hair Analysis; SUBSTANCE MISUSE: Hair Analysis

HEAD TRAUMA

    Pediatric and Adult, Clinical Aspects  *P Marks*                                461

    Neuropathology  *M Case*                                                         472

HEALING AND REPAIR OF WOUNDS AND BONES  *P Betz*                                     480

HISTOPATHOLOGY  *P Fornes*                                                           485

HISTORY OF FORENSIC MEDICINE  *J Payne-James*                                        498

HISTORY OF TORTURE  *M Peel*                                                         520

HISTORY OF TOXICOLOGY  *A Aggrawal*                                                  525

HUMAN RIGHTS, CONTROLS AND PRINCIPLES  *H McKelvie and B Loff*                       538

# VOLUME 3

# I

IDENTIFICATION

    Prints, Finger and Palm  *T P Kelliher, J Rittscher, and P Tu*                    1

    Prints, Challenges To Fingerprints  *P Tu, T P Kelliher, and J Rittscher*         7

    Prints, Footprints  *T Brown and G N Rutty*                                      13

    Prints, Ear  *C Van der Lugt*                                                     18

    Facial  *G Quatrehomme*                                                           28

IMAGING
    Photography    *H L Blitzer*    35
    Radiology, Overview    *W A Murphy*    45
    Radiology, Non-Invasive Autopsies    *M J Thali and P Vock*    57
    Radiology, Pediatric, Scintigraphy and Child Abuse    *C M Hall*    63
IMMUNOASSAYS, FORENSIC APPLICATIONS    *S Miyaishi and F Moriya*    73
INJURY, FATAL AND NONFATAL
    Documentation    *J Payne-James*    80
    Blunt Injury    *T S Corey*    84
    Burns and Scalds    *B B Ong*    90
    Explosive Injury    *J Crane*    98
    Firearm Injuries    *G M Kirk*    110
    Sharp and Cutting-Edge Wounds    *J Payne-James and P Vanezis*    119
INJURY, RECREATIONAL
    Water Sports    *P Lunetta*    130
    Airborne Sports    *K Yonemitsu and S Tsunenari*    135
INJURY, TRANSPORTATION
    Motor Vehicle    *I Nordrum*    141
    Air Disasters    *M Gregersen*    145
INJURIES AND DEATHS DURING POLICE OPERATIONS
    Shootings During Police Stops and Arrests    *T S Corey*    155
    Special Weapons and Training Teams    *T S Corey and D F Burbrink II*    161
INTERNET
    Forensic Medicine    *G N Rutty*    168
    Toxicology    *A Aggrawal*    171

**J**

JUDICIAL PUNISHMENT    *H A N El-Fawal*    183

**L**

LEGAL DEFINITIONS OF DEATH    *R Gaebler and R Dworkin*    191

**M**

MASS DISASTERS
    Role of Forensic Pathologists    *M I Jumbelic*    197
    Organization    *J Levinson*    207
    Principles of Identification    *C M Milroy*    213
MASS DISASTERS, AVIATION *See* AVIATION ACCIDENTS, ROLE OF PATHOLOGIST;
    INJURY, TRANSPORTATION: Air Disasters
MASS DISASTERS, SCENE INVESTIGATION *See* CRIME-SCENE INVESTIGATION
    AND EXAMINATION: Major Incident Scene Management
MASS MURDER    *A Aggrawal*    216
MASS POISONINGS    *A Aggrawal*    223
MEDICAL DEFINITIONS OF DEATH    *B Jennett*    230

MEDICAL MALPRACTICE

Overview    *I Wall*                                                                                                       235

Accident and Emergency    *J Wyatt and R Taylor*                                          238

Anesthesiology    *T E J Healy*                                                                          240

Child and Adolescent Psychiatry    *J Jureidini*                                          251

Colorectal Surgery    *M M Henry*                                                                 254

Ear, Nose and Throat Surgery    *D Gatland*                                              257

Facio-maxillary Surgery    *M F Patel*                                                         261

General Practice    *S E Josse*                                                                       266

Intensive Care    *G Park*                                                                               269

Neonatology    *N K Ives*                                                                               273

Neurosurgery    *P Marks*                                                                             278

Nursing Issues    *J Smith*                                                                             284

Oncology    *V Barley*                                                                                    287

Oral Surgery    *M F Patel*                                                                            290

Plastic and Cosmetic Surgery    *A Khanna*                                              294

Police Surgeon    *G A Norfolk*                                                                     301

Psychiatry    *J W Thompson, J Artecona, and B Bora*                            303

Psychology    *R J Edelmann*                                                                         307

Radiotherapy    *V Barley*                                                                              310

Rheumatology    *M G Wright*                                                                        313

Vascular Surgery    *W B Campbell*                                                             315

MEDICAL MALPRACTICE – MEDICO-LEGAL PERSPECTIVES

Negligence, Standard of Care    *M Flynn*                                                   319

Negligence, Duty of Care    *M Flynn*                                                          324

Negligence, Causation    *M Flynn*                                                               327

Negligence Quantum    *M Flynn*                                                                  333

MEDICAL MISADVENTURE    *J J Buchino and J E Sullivan*                   336

MEDICAL RECORDS, ACCESS TO    *G Morris*                                        339

MEDICAL RECORDS, DOCUMENTATION, CONFIDENTIALITY AND OBLIGATIONS    *B A Liang and L Ren*    346

MUNCHAUSEN-SYNDROME-BY-PROXY    *R Meadow*                         353

MURDER–SUICIDE    *C M Milroy*                                                              358

# N

NEONATICIDE    *R W Byard*                                                                     363
NUCLEAR TERRORISM *See* TERRORISM: Nuclear and Biological

# O

OCCUPATIONAL HEALTH

Police    *D McLay and C Shuttleworth*

Autopsy    *M B Nashelsky*                                                                          379

ODONTOLOGY

Overview    *J G Clement and A J Hill*                                                        386

Bite Mark Analysis    *J G Clement and S A Blackwell*                            395

ORGAN AND TISSUE TRANSPLANTATION, ETHICAL AND PRACTICAL ISSUES    *S Cordner and H McKelvie*    404

# P

PARENTAGE TESTING    *G S Williams*                                        413

PATTERN EVIDENCE    *D W Davis*                                            427

PHARMACOLOGY OF LEGAL AND ILLICIT DRUGS    *K A Savage and D Wielbo*       435

POISONING, OVERVIEW AND STATISTICS    *A L Jones and P I Dargan*           447

POSTMORTEM CHANGES

    Overview    *M Tsokos*                                       456

    Electrolyte Disturbances    *L M Al-Alousi*                   476

    Postmortem Interval    *D J Pounder*                         482

PREPARATION OF WITNESSES

    Scotland    *G Fernie*                                        488

    United States of America    *M M Houck*                       490

PROFESSIONAL BODIES, FRANCE - FORENSIC, MEDICAL AND

    SCIENTIFIC TRAINING    *L Martrille and E Baccino*            495

PROFESSIONAL BODIES

    United Kingdom    *J Payne-James*                            499

    Rest of the World    *S Cordner and H McKelvie*              505

# R

RECOVERED MEMORY    *B Tully*                                              509

REFUGEE MEDICINE    *A Aggrawal*                                           514

RELIGIOUS ATTITUDES TO DEATH    *J E Rutty*                                525

RELIGIOUS EXCEPTION DEFENSE    *S M Asser*                                 536

RESTRAINT TECHNIQUES, INJURIES AND DEATH    *J D Howard*                   541

RESTRAINT, EXCITED DELIRIUM *See* EXCITED DELIRIUM; SUBSTANCE MISUSE:

    Cocaine and other Stimulants

RITUALISTIC CRIME    *D Perlmutter*                                        547

# VOLUME 4

ROAD TRAFFIC ACCIDENTS, AIRBAG-RELATED INJURIES AND DEATHS    *W S Smock*     1

ROAD TRAFFIC, DETERMINATION OF FITNESS TO DRIVE

    Sobriety Tests and Drug Recognition    *R Tunbridge and S G Collier*    12

    General    *C H Wecht and S A Koehler*                        21

    Driving Offense    *C H Wecht and S A Koehler*               32

ROAD TRAFFIC, GLOBAL OVERVIEW OF DRUG AND ALCOHOL STATISTICS    *B Marc and P Mura*    38

# S

SERIAL MURDER    *R J Morton and J J McNamara*                             47

SEROLOGY

    Overview    *J Ballantyne*                                    53

    Blood Identification    *H C Lee and E M Pagliaro*           64

    Bloodstain Pattern Analysis    *T L Wolson*                  70

SEROLOGY, PATERNITY TESTING *See* PARENTAGE TESTING

SEXUAL OFFENSES, ADULT

    Human Normal Sexual Response    *R J Levin*                  81

Injuries and Findings after Sexual Contact    *C Bassindale and J Payne-James*                87

Evidential Sample Collection    *K Nadesan*                91

Management Postassault    *R Jawad and J Welch*                96

Male Sexual Assault    *B Marc*                102

Drug-Facilitated Sexual Assault    *A Negrusz and R E Gaensslen*                107

Global Crime Figures and Statistics    *P S L Beh*                111

SEXUAL OFFENSES, CHILDREN *See* CHILDREN: Sexual Abuse, Overview; Sexual Abuse, Epidemiology

SEXUAL OFFENSES, CHILDREN, DIAGNOSIS *See* IMAGING: Radiology, Pediatric, Scintigraphy and
    Child Abuse

SEXUAL OFFENSES, OFFENDERS *See* FORENSIC PSYCHIATRY AND FORENSIC PSYCHOLOGY:
    Sex offenders

SPOUSAL ABUSE *See* DOMESTIC VIOLENCE

SUDDEN INFANT DEATH SYNDROME, AUTOPSY TECHNIQUES AND FINDINGS *See* AUTOPSY,
    FINDINGS: Sudden Infant Death Syndrome

SUDDEN INFANT DEATH SYNDROME, ETIOLOGY AND EPIDEMIOLOGY    *T O Rognum and R W Byard*                117

STARVATION    *S P Allison*                130

SUBSTANCE MISUSE

Medical Effects    *M M Stark*                137

Cocaine and Other Stimulants    *F J Couper*                141

Herbal Medicine    *S B Karch*                145

Heroin    *O H Drummer and J Gerostamoulos*                152

Substitution Drugs    *K Wolff*                157

Sedatives    *F J Couper*                163

Miscellaneous Drugs    *F J Couper*                165

Urine Analysis    *A K Chaturvedi and R H Liu*                171

Hair Analysis    *T Mieczkowski*                183

Alternative Body Fluids Analysis    *S Kerrigan and B A Goldberger*                192

Patterns and Statistics    *C M Milroy*                201

Crime    *J Payne-James*                206

SUBSTANCE MISUSE, ALCOHOL *See* ALCOHOL: Breath Alcohol Analysis; Blood and Body
    Fluid Analysis; Acute and Chronic Use, Postmortem Findings

SUBSTANCE MISUSE: BACK-TRACKING CALCULATIONS *See* BACK-TRACKING CALCULATIONS

SUDDEN NATURAL DEATH

Cardiovascular    *A Burke and R Virmani*                211

Central Nervous System and Miscellaneous Causes    *M P Burke*                223

Infectious Diseases    *M A Dada and N G Lazarus*                229

SUICIDE

Etiology, Methods and Statistics    *B Marc*                236

Parasuicide    *R Nathan and K J B Rix*                244

Youth Suicide    *R W Byard*                250

SUICIDE, DYADIC DEATH *See* MURDER–SUICIDE

SUICIDE, PREDICTORS AND STATISTICS *See* FORENSIC PSYCHIATRY AND
    FORENSIC PSYCHOLOGY: Suicide Predictors and Statistics

SUICIDE BOMBING *See* TERRORISM: Suicide Bombing, Investigation

# T

TACTICAL MEDICINE      *W S Smock and J S Vayer*                                                255

TATTOOS, MEDICO-LEGAL SIGNIFICANCE      *N E I Langlois and D Little*                           263

TERRORISM

    Medico-legal Aspects      *A Aggrawal*                                                   269

    Nuclear and Biological      *A Aggrawal*                                                 277

    Suicide Bombing, Investigation      *A Aggrawal and M Tsokos*                          289

TORTURE

    Physical Findings      *D J Pounder*                                                     297

    Psychological Assessment      *K Allden*                                                302

TORTURE, HISTORY OF *See* HISTORY OF TORTURE

TOXICOLOGY

    Overview      *O H Drummer*                                                              309

    Methods of Analysis, Antemortem      *O H Drummer*                                      315

    Methods of Analysis, Postmortem      *O H Drummer*                                      322

TOXICOLOGY, ACCREDITATION *See* ACCREDITATION: Toxicology

TOXICOLOGY, HISTORY OF *See* HISTORY: Toxicology

TOXICOLOGY, INTERNET AND *See* INTERNET: Toxicology

# V

VENOM      *J White*                                                                            329

VETERINARY ASPECTS OF FORENSIC MEDICINE, WILD ANIMALS      *K Goddard*                          344

VICTIM SUPPORT      *M D'Arcy and L Olle*                                                       349

# W

WAR CRIMES

    Site Investigation      *W D Haglund*                                                   355

    Pathological Investigation      *J Clark*                                               363

    Tribunals      *J D Wilets*                                                             371

WAR INJURIES      *J Clark*                                                                     377

# Y

YAKUZA      *S T Tsunenari and S Mimasaka*                                                      383

AUTHOR INDEX                                                                                    391

SUBJECT INDEX                                                                                   393

# CRIME-SCENE INVESTIGATION AND EXAMINATION

## Contents
Collection and Chain of Evidence
Death-scene Investigation, United States of America
Major Incident Scene Management
Underwater Crime Scene
Recovery of Human Remains
Suspicious Deaths

## Collection and Chain of Evidence

**T M Palmbach**, University of New Haven, West Haven, CT, USA

### Introduction

Crime-scene investigation is an integral component of many aspects of more general investigations. It can provide investigative leads, aid in the identification of suspect(s) or victim(s), prove or disprove alibis, identify a *modus operandi*, establish the *corpus delicti*, and create linkages and associations among the victim, suspect, scene, and evidence. Evidence may consist of transient, conditional, pattern, transfer, or a diverse variety of physical evidence.

If the full potential of physical evidence is to be achieved there are certain safeguards and standards that must be met. Evidence must be collected in a manner that will preserve the integrity and evidentiary value. In addition, each piece of evidence must be collected and maintained in such a manner that it can be authenticated and proven to be in the substantially same condition as when initially collected. This so-called chain of custody must be established from the moment evidence is first in custody until the conclusion of analysis and legal proceedings.

### Physical Evidence

The role and value of physical evidence to an investigation can be best expressed by the four-way linkage theory (**Figure 1**). This theory postulates that there are four key components in an investigation: (1) suspect; (2) victim; (3) scene; and (4) evidence, and that a reliable and objective means of solving a case is to establish linkages between these components. The more linkages established, the greater the probability of resolving an investigation. No one

component necessarily bears any more weight than another. Ideally, the suspect, victim, scene, and relevant evidence will be identified and associations between them established. However, it is possible to solve a case without locating the primary scene, the actual body of the victim, the exact identity of the offender, or several pieces of key evidence. For example, the trial may proceed without the recovery of the victim's body and only a circumstantial case that established homicide has occurred and an identification of the victim through analysis of partial remains, such as DNA analysis of a blood stain. Moreover, forensic examinations may identify a common perpetrator in a series of cases through methods such as fingerprint, bite mark, or DNA analysis and yet the true identity of the offender remains unknown. Modern mass media exposure and public interest in crime scenes, forensic science, and investigations have created jury pools that hunger for each of the primary four components, and most particularly physical evidence.

What constitutes physical evidence in a particular case will often vary and be difficult to determine. However, recognition that a particular object is to be a piece of physical evidence is only the first step in a sequential process that must be undertaken with each piece of evidence (**Figure 2**). Recognition of an

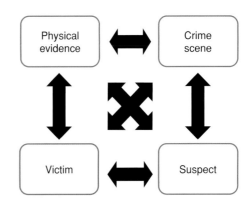

**Figure 1**  Four-way linkage theory.

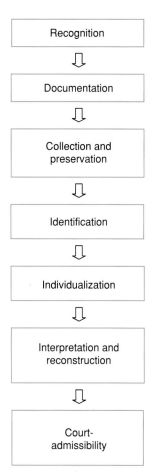

**Figure 2** Sequential schematic processing of evidence.

object as potentially possessing evidentiary value is dependent upon the case particulars and the experience and training of the crime-scene investigator. After recognition and before the evidence is touched or altered in any way, the evidence must be thoroughly documented. Documentation includes a variety of functions, such as note-taking, photographs, videotaping, and sketch preparation. After documentation is complete the evidence may be properly collected and preserved. The nature and method of collection and preservation will depend on the nature of the evidence, such as whether it is chemical, biological, or physical in nature. After documentation the identification of the evidence is the next logical step. This step may or may not require sophisticated laboratory analysis. Once the item is identified an examination scheme can be implemented to develop further class characteristics and proceed toward an individualizing methodology. Individualization of an object will require comparisons of the object to known standards or the source. For example, a paint chip located on the clothing of a hit-and-run victim may be compared to either known automobile paint databases

or to samples of paint obtained from the suspect's car. Once the examination process is complete scientists will need to evaluate and interpret the results in a scientifically reliable and objective manner.

In many instances, such as the example above, true individualization may not be possible. Rather, the correct conclusion is that the known and unknown samples were similar in all observed characteristics. This information can then be collated with other available information in a reconstruction process.

## Documentation

Documentation of physical evidence is best accomplished through a variety of means. The item should be photographed and videotaped in place, showing both overall perspectives and close-up photographs, some taken with scales or rulers in the photograph. In addition, the exact location where the item was located must be recorded. Usually, obtaining fixed measurements for each item of evidence and incorporating those measurements in a crime-scene sketch is the method of choice. Finally, notes should be maintained articulating every aspect of the process from discovery until the examination of the evidence is complete. Documentation functions should occur before, during, and after collection of the evidence. For a given piece of evidence there may be numerous photographs or documentations, some obtained at the crime scene and others during the examination process at the medical examiner's office or forensic science laboratory.

Proper documentation is required for many purposes – to document the crime scene for reconstruction or investigative purposes, to serve as demonstrative aids for legal proceedings, or to help establish and maintain a chain of custody for that particular piece of evidence.

## Collection

### General Considerations

The proper collection of evidence is determined by the nature of the evidence and potential uses or examination schemes to be employed. As a general proposition, evidence should be handled and packaged in a manner that minimizes the possibility of contamination, destruction, or spoilage. In addition, packaging and labeling must be sufficient to establish the authenticity and chain of custody in future proceedings.

The size and amount of sample to be collected will vary, but it is better to collect more samples than an amount so small that full analysis cannot be conducted. In addition to unknown or questioned samples it is important to collect known standards for comparison, such as a carpet sample from the room where the assault allegedly occurred. In addition, control samples may be beneficial for analysis and interpretation of the laboratory results. For example, in a suspected arson scene samples of the oak flooring apart from the suspected point of origin should be obtained. Known standards, such as blood, hair, and fingerprints, should be taken from the victim at autopsy or during medical evaluation and treatment.

### Biological Evidence

Biological evidence or items of evidence containing trace amounts of biological material requires special handling and packaging. Commonly encountered biological samples contain blood, semen, saliva, urine, feces, vomit, tissue, bone, and teeth. General precautions must be taken to preserve the biological evidence, preventing spoilage or bacterial growth that can negatively impact on subsequent testing.

Thus, items with biological stains must be air-dried before packaging and should be placed in nonairtight containers such as paper bags or envelopes. In addition, care must be used to avoid contaminating the samples either by the individual who is collecting or handling the samples or from cross-contamination between samples. Cross-contamination can occur if collection tools such as forceps or scalpels are not properly cleaned between each sample. Alternatively, disposable tweezers, pipettes, or other collection devices can be used. Contamination has always been an issue, but now more than ever it is a concern due to the increased sensitivity of DNA-typing methods. Mitochondrial DNA testing is particularly sensitive, thus even minute amounts of contamination will likely appear in the analysis. Minor components detected in case samples can be very problematic in interpretation and may subject one to claims of insufficient evidence-handling and preservation. Finally, by their very nature, biological materials may contain a wide variety of pathogens or harmful agents; therefore, anyone exposed to the evidence must employ universal precautions. Minimally this means handling the evidence with gloved hands, but may also require the examiner to don full protective wear, including a face mask and hairnet.

### Blood

Liquid blood can be collected on a sterilized cotton swab and allowed to air-dry. With large amounts of liquid blood the sample can be pipetted, placed in a purple-topped (with ethylenediaminetetraacetic acid) Vacutainer test-tube, and refrigerated. With dried blood stains there are a few options. First, if possible, the entire item with the dried blood stain

**Figure 3** Sterile swab.

can be collected or the area containing the blood may be cut and collected. Alternatively, the dried blood stain can be collected on a sterile swab moistened with saline solution or distilled water (**Figure 3**). Other less desirable options include scraping the stain or lifting the stain with adhesive lifters.

### Trace Evidence

A wide variety of trace evidence may be encountered at the crime scene, autopsy, or during the investigation. Trace evidence is essentially a small amount of material that may be either biological or chemical in nature. Many times this evidence is so small that it is not detected through macroscopic examination. Thus, evidence must be properly handled and preserved so as to maintain the possibility of locating trace evidence during subsequent microscopic or instrumental examination. Commonly encountered trace evidence includes hair, fibers, soil, glass particles, paint, gunshot residue, vegetative debris, organic and inorganic materials, and blood or other biological materials.

Collection methods will vary, but there are essentially three primary options.

1. Collect the item containing or believed to contain trace evidence and package it in a manner so as to prevent loss of trace material.
2. Macroscopically or microscopically examine the item and individually remove trace components, such as removing a hair from clothing with forceps. Once removed, place the trace item into a druggist fold, and place that druggist fold in a sealed envelope (**Figure 4**).
3. Utilize a collection method that will remove a majority of trace material from a surface, such as by vacuum methods, tape lifts, or scraping the item down over a piece of clean butcher paper.

**Figure 4**   Placing of trace item in a druggist fold.

## Hazardous Materials/Weapons of Mass Destruction

Evidence collection personnel, medical personnel, and laboratory examiners always need to be aware of potentially hazardous substances of a chemical, biological, radioactive, or explosive nature. However, with the possibility of exposure to weapons of mass destruction, individual precautions and refined procedures need to be developed and implemented. Only properly trained personnel, wearing the appropriate level of protection, should handle these types of hazardous materials. In addition, these materials should not be transported to a "normal" laboratory or facility unless they are conclusively determined to be a nonhazard, rendered safe, or brought to a facility that is designed to handle and store such materials safely. A potential dilemma is the need to conduct traditional forensic testing on an object that may be contaminated with a hazardous substance, such as anthrax (**Figure 5**). For example, it would be important to process a potentially tainted letter for trace evidence and latent fingerprints, and perform a questioned document examination on the written or printed material. These examinations will normally be done at a forensic laboratory that is not designed to handle pathogens safely. Therefore, the letter must be rendered or determined to be pathogen-free, or the forensic scientists will need to go to a facility where they can conduct their examinations safely.

## Electronic and Computer Evidence

In the present highly technological era it is common to encounter some form of electronic- or computer-based evidence at a crime scene or during the investigation. This type of evidence has unique challenges.

Since destruction or alteration of data or information can easily occur, it is highly recommended that

**Figure 5**   (A) Testing of a hazardous substance. (B) Traditional forensic testing.

only properly trained personnel collect and package this type of evidence. Preferably, a forensic data examiner or similar specialist will need to respond to a crime scene with computers or electronic evidence and assist in the system shutdown, dismantling, collection, and packaging. A "traditional" crime-scene technician, laboratory scientist, medical examiner, or investigator simply needs to be aware of the possibility of this type of evidence and the special handling techniques.

## Chain of Custody

### General Information

Regardless of how effectively a crime-scene search was conducted, resulting in the location and collection of relevant physical evidence, or the quality and breadth of laboratory testing, physical evidence is only as valuable as its ultimate use, such as admissibility in court. Rules of evidence dictate how evidence will or will not be used during the trial, but it is a fundamental rule that a general requirement for the chain of custody needs to be established, before that evidence may be admitted in the trial.

Underlying chain-of-custody rules are a necessity to identify the item of evidence being offered as the same evidence seized from the scene and ultimately presented in court, and to establish that the evidence is substantially unchanged. The process by which the identification and lack of spoilage are documented and substantiated is commonly referred to as the chain of custody.

A chain of custody begins once an item of evidence comes into the custody of government personnel or their agents. There is no requirement that a chain be established prior to the government seizure, regardless of how long the item of evidence has been in existence. Generally, once the item of evidence is presented in court, the stringent chain of custody is no longer required. However, depending upon the nature of the evidence and for what purpose it is being offered in trial, the relevant chain may terminate before trial. In several instances the critical chain is concluded once the item has been analyzed in a laboratory. For example, a package of white powder seized from the accused's clothing, subsequently tested at a reliable laboratory, and conclusively determined to be heroin, may require a stringent chain of custody only until the laboratory examination is complete. In contrast, consider a case where a stolen firearm will be admitted into trial as the tangible property upon which the offense is based. In this case a full chain of custody will need to be established all the way until the gun is offered into trial, and proven to be the same gun that law enforcement originally seized. Each of the links in this chain represents a period of time along the chain, and articulates specifically who was in custody of that item during that period of time. Each person, or link, may be called upon to establish that the item of evidence, while in his/her possession, was properly secured and preserved such as to assure its identity and prevent spoilage or alteration. It is not necessary to identify every individual that could potentially have access to that item, so long as each custodian or link can establish that he/she followed accepted protocols, ensuring the safe keeping and integrity of that evidence.

## How to Establish and Maintain an Effective Chain

Ultimately, a court must be convinced that the item of evidence being offered is in fact the same item originally seized during the crime-scene search, autopsy, or investigation. The goal is to make the item readily identifiable as the original item seized. Some items by their very nature are inherently identifiable, such as an original Claude Monet painting. These relatively identifiable pieces of evidence will require only a minimal chain of custody, generally limited to showing that the item is substantially unchanged.

Other items are quite fungible, such as one of dozens of dried blood stains swabbed from a crime scene. With fungible evidence the necessity for a detailed and strong chain of custody is even more essential.

One method for identifying fungible items at a later point is by uniquely marking the actual item. The practice of actually marking an item, often with the initials of the seizing individual, is effective, but may be detrimental to the evidence. Markings placed on the item of evidence may alter or destroy critical components or characteristics of the evidence that may be needed for laboratory analysis or comparison. Therefore, if an item of evidence is to be marked, extreme caution must be employed to place the markings in an area where they will not alter the evidentiary value. For example, a bullet recovered during autopsy should never be marked anywhere other than the base of the bullet, and only then when a preliminary macroscopic examination of the base reveals no signs or trace, transfer, or impression evidence in that area. With an item of clothing the markings should be placed in an area free of all stains, transfers, patterns, or defects in the material.

In many cases the item may be properly marked for future identification by sealing the item of evidence in an appropriate evidence container and placing markings on the packaging. This labeling should include the date and time of seizure, the location from where the item was seized, a description of the item, an investigative or case number, and the name of the seizing individual. In addition, the seizing officer should place his/her initials on this package, and any interior packaging such as a druggist fold. The sealing process will vary depending upon the packaging container. With paper bags, envelopes, and boxes, the container should be closed and any access point sealed with tamper-resistant tape. If tamper-resistant tape is not available, ordinary tape may be used and the seizing officer may inscribe his/her initials across the tape. It is preferable to use tape that will adhere to the packaging surface for an extended period of time, and also that can withstand extreme temperatures if the item needs to be refrigerated or frozen. Heat-sealed plastic bags are excellent for securing evidence. However, plastic or airtight bags are not appropriate for a variety of materials like those containing biological stains, such as blood or semen.

In addition to the label or information listed above, a bar-coded label may be adhered to the package. This barcode can be used to track and identify the item, thus establishing the requisite chain of custody. Barcodes can be purchased as commercially available generic products, or can be custom-designed and printed individually by the agency. Custom labels are advantageous in that additional information can

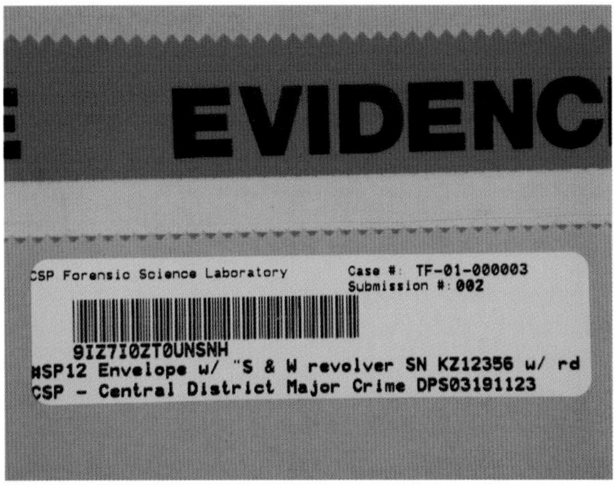

**Figure 6** Custom bar code label for physical evidence received at a forensic science laboratory.

be generated and printed on the actual barcode, such as case number, item, and brief description (**Figure 6**). However, this type of label cannot be prepared in advance, making it a difficult, though not impossible, option for field or crime-scene use.

Even with generic labels there are numerous evidence management programs that can capture the barcode and associate it with a particular case, or with an additional barcode printed back at the agency facility or forensic laboratory.

The chain of custody must be documented either in a written log or in an electronic medium that captures and maintains relevant data, or a combination of both the options. Chain-of-custody logs come in many varieties, but should minimally contain case or control number, individual exhibit number, brief description, location where originally seized, name of seizing individual, date and time of original seizure, and a series of entries for each and every occurrence if there was a change in custody. These transfers should include date and time of transfer, name of person to whom custody of the evidence is being given, and the new location where the evidence will be stored. These transfers should be verified by obtaining a signature from both the individual releasing the evidence and the individual receiving the evidence. Maintaining a chain of custody requires that an examination of the log will show where that evidence was stored for every moment since its original seizure, and who was responsible for that evidence during each of those time intervals.

These logs or forms may be separate forms, one for each piece of evidence, or a logbook that lists adequate chains for numerous pieces of evidence. In addition, some packaging material, such as a sex crimes evidence collection kit, may have a chain of custody form on the box itself. While the use of the form on

the packaging material is acceptable, it is recommended that an additional log be maintained and kept with the case file in case the packaging material is damaged, or the item or sections of the item are repackaged. If bar coding is utilized, then the evidence transfers can be recorded electronically with barcode readers and an appropriate database. However, these types of transfer can be unsecured transactions, thus leaving the integrity of the transfer in question. That is, it may be possible for anyone with access to the database to transfer any item of evidence under any individual's name, even without the listed individual authorizing the transfer. This problem can be alleviated by requiring secret PIN entries in conjunction with the transfer, or by incorporating an electronic signature.

One common dilemma is the situation where one piece of evidence is eventually segregated in several subitems. This separation process may occur at the laboratory once the examination process is commenced. When practical, items should be packaged separately such as to minimize this potential confusion. In order to achieve an effective chain of custody for the item of evidence in its entirety, each subitem must be properly logged and secured, and clearly associated with the piece of evidence upon which it was derived. For example, consider a loaded handgun that was recovered from an untimely death scene – all the potential evidence that may be derived from that one item, and all the potential necessary transfers for each of those subitems (**Figure 7**).

## Legal Requirements

The general legal requirements associated with a chain of custody are codified by Federal Rules of Evidence Rule 901(a): "The requirement of authentication or identification as a condition precedent to admissibility is satisfied by evidence sufficient to support a finding the matter in question is what its proponent claims." The burden of proof regarding this requirement rests on the party offering the item into evidence. Generally, the offering party only needs to make a *prima facie* showing of authenticity to gain admissibility. The offering party need not eliminate every possibility of substitution, alteration, or tampering, but rather show that there is a reasonable probability regarding the identity and substantially unchanged condition of the evidence. Once this burden of proof is established, evidence presented generally is admitted and any discrepancies or minor breaks in the chain of custody will go to the weight to be accorded by the jury. Since there are no "black-and-white" rules as to what constitutes a "minor" break in the chain going to the weight rather than

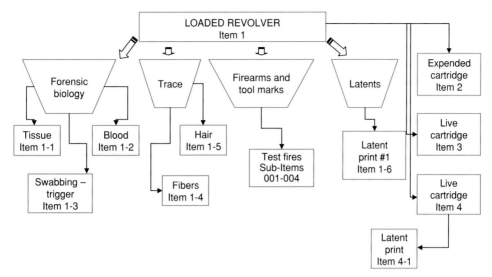

**Figure 7** Schematic segregation of evidence into sub-items.

admissibility of that piece of evidence, due diligence should be exercised to maintain an infallible chain.

Generally, the integrity of evidence is presumed to be preserved unless there is a showing of bad faith, ill will, or proof that the evidence has been tampered with. Even clerical errors relating to the chain are not necessarily fatal to the case so long as they occurred in good faith. Moreover, several courts have found that there is a presumption of regularity in the handling of evidence by officers, and that they presumably exercise due care in handling their duties. The state is only required to demonstrate that it took reasonable protective measures to maintain the evidence. However, these presumptions are predicated on an adequate foundation that reasonable evidence-handling procedures were in place and were followed. Yet, the standard may be elevated for fungible items of evidence where the identification of the item is not readily apparent.

The bottom line regarding chain of custody is that every effort should be made to handle and preserve a piece of evidence properly so that there is no doubt as to the authenticity or condition of that item from the time it is first collected until all potential uses are exhausted.

## See Also

**Computer Crime and Digital Evidence; Crime-scene Investigation and Examination:** Major Incident Scene Management; Recovery of Human Remains; Suspicious Deaths; **Evidence, Rules of**

## Further Reading

Federal Rules of Evidence, Article IX. Rule 901, Authentication and Identification.

Giannelli PC, Imwinkelried EJ (1993) *Scientific Evidence*, 2nd edn., pp. 193–214. Charlottesville, VA: Michie.
Lee HC, Harris HA (2000) *Physical Evidence in Forensic Science*. Tucson, AZ: Lawyer's and Judges Publishing.
Lee HC, Palmbach TM, Miller M (2001) *Henry Lee's Crime Scene Handbook*. London: Academic Press.
Moenssens AA, Inbau FE (1978) *Scientific Evidence in Criminal Cases*, 2nd edn. Mineola, NY: Foundation Press.
*Troxell v. State of Indiana* (2002) 778 N.E.2d 811, nd. Lexis 888.
*United States v. Briley* (2003) 319 F.3d 360, US App. Lexis 2713.
*United States v. Cardenas* (1989) 864 F.2d 1528, 491 US 909, 109 S. Ct. 3197.
*United States v. Gorman* (2002) 312 F.3d 1159, US App. Lexis 24485.

# Death-scene Investigation, United States of America

**M F Ernst**, St. Louis University School of Medicine, St. Louis, MO, USA

## Introduction

US death scene investigations were first mentioned by the Maryland Historical Society in the *Archives of Maryland* as early as 1635, when a coroner's inquest was held to determine the cause of death of an American colonist who died as a result of bodily weakness from fasting and cold. The US system originated from the English coroner system that had been brought to the New World by American colonists. Because the USA is composed of many states, each independently establishing its own type of medicolegal system (coroner or medical examiner) and reporting laws, training, resources, and personnel background prerequisites; the quality of death scene investigations varies greatly from state to state, and from county to county. In 1997, the US Department of Justice published the *Research Report: National Guidelines for Death Investigation*. These guidelines provide a structured, step-by-step process whereby investigators can achieve a thorough, scientific death scene investigation – every scene, every time.

## US Death Investigation Systems

The USA is composed of 50 states, the District of Columbia and four major territories (Puerto Rico, Guam, American Samoa, and the Virgin Islands). The estimated population is 290.3 million; life expectancy is 77.14 years and the annual death rate is 8.44 deaths/1000. Approximately 500 000 deaths are reported annually to medical examiner or coroner offices in 3137 counties, with 2185 death investigation jurisdictions. Ten states have coroner systems, 18 have statewide medical examiner systems, and 22 states have mixed systems. As a result, 48% of the US population is served by a medical examiner system, and 52% by a coroner system.

### Death-Reporting Systems

Without impinging on federal laws, each state and territory determines its own laws, system type (medical examiner or coroner), organizational structure (statewide or county-based), and the types of death reportable to the system. Commonly violent, suspicious, sudden, and unexpected deaths, death when no physician or practitioner treated recently, inmates in public institutions, in custody of law enforcement, during or immediately following therapeutic or diagnostic procedures, or deaths due to neglect are reportable to a medicolegal system. The medicolegal jurisdiction (medical examiner or coroner) is charged with determining the cause and manner of death of individuals whose demise is investigated.

### Military, Offshore, and Indian Jurisdiction

On military installations, the death investigation authority is determined by jurisdiction – exclusive federal, concurrent with state, partial, or mixed. On a military facility, such as an air force base, the armed forces medical examiner, the commanding officer, or the judge advocate may have authority to investigate a death. The county of first landfall has jurisdiction over offshore death scenes, such as airplane explosions over water. Native American Indians have jurisdiction to investigate deaths in Indian country, utilizing tribal coroners and tribal police, such as the Navajo nation in New Mexico. Smaller tribes, who do not have their own law enforcement agencies, often rely upon the Bureau of Indian Affairs to conduct their death investigations. Serious criminal matters, such as homicides, are under the jurisdiction of the Federal Bureau of Investigation.

### National Guidelines for Death Investigation

In 1997, the first *National Guidelines for Death Investigation* were established through a grant from the National Institutes of Justice, Office of Justice Programs, and the Centers for Disease Control and Prevention. The guidelines detail the 29 procedures that should be considered in every death investigation (every scene, every time) to achieve a thorough, scientific death inquiry. Although the guidelines are voluntary, they are slowly being implemented in most larger, heavily populated communities.

### First Responders

Personnel from emergency medical or law enforcement agencies are commonly the first responders, who determine that a death has occurred. An authorized individual, determined by state statute, then pronounces the person dead. State laws require that the medical examiner or coroner's office be immediately notified of the death. Death scene investigations are usually conducted on violent, suspicious, and unexpected deaths when the dead person has not been removed from the scene to a medical facility. All deaths of children involve a death scene investigation, even if the child is removed from the scene to a medical facility for evaluation. Based on an office's standard operating procedure (SOP) that will be determined by its resources, a medicolegal death investigator or a forensic pathologist responds to the death scene. Because of the severe shortage of forensic pathologists in the USA, few jurisdictions send forensic pathologists to death scenes. In jurisdictions with limited personnel or financial resources, no representative from the medicolegal office may be available to perform a death scene investigation. The scene investigation will then be conducted solely by the jurisdiction's law enforcement agency. This presents serious problems when a potential conflict of interest exists with the investigating agency, such as in a police shooting or a death occurring while in police custody.

### Multidisciplinary Team Approach

The US *National Guidelines for Death Investigation* state that a multidisciplinary team composed of representatives of the medical examiner/coroner office, law enforcement, and crime laboratory should respond to the death scene. The law enforcement agency has authority over the scene itself. The medical examiner/coroner has authority over the dead individual. Depending on the type of death, additional forensic scientists may respond to the death scene, that is, an anthropologist if skeletal remains are present, and an archeologist if a grave is suspected. Crime laboratory personnel are responsible for photographing and documenting the death scene, recognizing, and seizing evidence that is not adhering to the dead person, and transporting the evidence to the crime laboratory for analysis. Specialized federal and state investigative units respond to death scenes under their jurisdiction; for example, the National Transportation Safety Board (NTSB) will respond to deaths that occur as a result of a commercial airplane crash.

## Evidence

Trace evidence that is found at the scene and not attached to the decedent is photographed, documented, and collected by the crime laboratory investigator and conveyed to the crime laboratory for evaluation. Evidence that is on or attached to the deceased's body is documented, photographed, and retained on the victim who is conveyed to the morgue facility for examination.

## Scene Safety, Briefing, and Walk-Through

Upon arrival at the scene, first responders may call additional experts to evaluate the area to ensure a safe working environment for investigators. Scene boundaries are cordoned off by use of scene perimeter tape to restrict unauthorized persons from entry. Unofficial persons, such as family members, are immediately removed from the scene.

The scene commander, usually a member of law enforcement in nonmass casualty incidents, conducts a scene briefing and walk-through. Previously determined information and location of identified evidence are shared among investigators to avoid any damage or loss of items. Responsibilities and activities of each agency are defined, that is, law enforcement will interview witnesses and notify next of kin. The crime laboratory personnel will photographically document the scene. The medicolegal death investigator will identify and document marks or trauma, and evaluate time of death signs found on deceased. A scene walk-through is conducted to provide investigators with an overview of the scene, including the decedent, evidence, and other scene information.

## Chain of Custody

Following federal, state, and local laws, the chain of custody of evidence must be maintained to ensure that it is properly collected, packaged, transported, and transferred to the analyzing facility. Fragile and trace body evidence is identified by the medicolegal death investigator at the scene. The trace evidence on the decedent remains in place and is carefully protected from contamination or loss by enclosure in a clean, white sheet. Additional protection to hands and feet can be achieved by placing the body part into clean, unused paper bags. The dead person is then placed into a clean, sturdy body bag that is marked with identifying information on the outside for conveyance to the morgue facility. Fragile evidence found on the decedent is photographically documented, removed from its unsecured position, collected, and placed in an appropriate container for transfer with the deceased to the morgue.

## Scene Documentation

The death scene provides a wealth of information to investigators. A neat, clean, bedroom may suggest that a self-inflicted injury occurred instead of a homicidal gunshot wound to the victim's head. The death scene is photographically documented before anyone enters the area. If first responders have changed the death scene by moving the decedent or have left behind resuscitation items, the photographs should be taken as found. Investigators should not attempt to replace moved items. The death report should note what items first responders moved. The scene photographs provide a detailed picture that should include the decedent, evidence, and location references. Overall scene pictures, specific scene areas, full-body, and identification photographs should be taken from different angles. Items of interest, that is, weapons, notes, and ligatures, should also be photographed to corroborate investigative and medical findings of manner of death. Measurements should be taken of distances between the body and scene landmarks and weapons. Bloodspatter patterns should be photographed and measurements taken to develop data regarding points of convergence and size of spatter. A photographic record and written documentation of all information gathered at the scene should be made.

## Interview Witnesses

At least two people have valuable information as to the decedent's death: the person who last saw the deceased alive and the person who discovered him/her dead. The last person to see the decedent alive can describe whether the decedent had any medical problems, his/her mental state, topic of conversation, and upcoming plans. The person who discovered the decedent dead should be able to provide information as to the exact location of the body. The discoverer should also explain what set of circumstances caused him/her to discover the deceased. For example, the discoverer is the decedent's brother who telephoned earlier today and received no answer, so the brother came to the decedent's residence to check on his welfare. It is valuable to interview first responders at the scene. They can describe any movement of the deceased or scene items required to assess life signs.

### Actualization of Decedent

The decedent's body is the most important piece of physical evidence at a death scene. It can explain who the individual is, how long he/she has been at the scene, what or who caused death, where the decedent had been, and when the injury occurred. Documentation of the decedent's race, sex, approximate age, height, weight, and any unique features should be noted. Methodical evaluation of the deceased and his/her clothing can assist in determining the person's identification, time, cause, and manner of death. Following a preset pattern of evaluation, each body area should be closely inspected for injuries, color changes, or marks. Routinely beginning the actualization at the top of the body (head) and working downward (feet) will compel the investigator to assess all body parts and clothing thoroughly.

The position of the decedent when found should fit the scene precisely. The deceased's rigor and livor mortis should be congruent with the death scene environment. If it is not, suspicions that the decedent has been moved after death should be considered.

The scene environment temperature and the microenvironment of the decedent's body should be documented. Investigators should be suspicious if witness and scene information does not correlate with the decedent's postmortem indicators or state of decomposition. Dead people (and their bodies) have no reason to lie, but witnesses may.

Photographs and written documentation should be made of information collected during the actualization.

### Evidence on the Decedent

Trace evidence that is adhering to, attached to, or embedded in the dead person is the responsibility of the medicolegal death investigator. That evidence should be photographed, documented, preserved, and conveyed with the decedent to the morgue facility. If fragile evidence, such as a tiny rug fiber that may be lost, contaminated, or changed if not collected at the scene, is identified on the deceased, it should be photographed, documented, collected, packaged, and conveyed with the decedent for evaluation at time of examination and later analysis.

### Postmortem Changes

The decedent's body should be evaluated for signs of postmortem change. Gathering information regarding rigor mortis (stiffening of the body), livor mortis (settling of the blood in dependent body areas), algor mortis (body temperature), state of decomposition, insect activity, and scene time references (i.e., clocks, sales receipts) can allow the medicolegal death investigator to approximate the length of the postmortem interval. Inconsistencies between witness statements and postmortem changes should be recognized at the scene and discussed by investigators.

### Decedent's Clothing and Valuables

The victim's clothing and personal effects may assist the investigator to determine what the decedent had planned to do that day when he/she dressed. All clothing and personal effects should be photographed and described in report documentation as to item, size, color, and identifying characteristics. Clothing evaluation may help determine the subject's identification and actions before death. Personal effects may provide information that leads to the positive identification of the subject and identity of the next of kin. Clothing and personal effects are cataloged and safeguarded at the scene and at the receiving facility to ensure that all will be returned to the decedent's next of kin at the appropriate time.

### Identification of Deceased

Personal papers, jewelry, and personal effects found on the subject or at the scene can assist investigators to determine the subject's identity. Scientific identification is the best method of establishing the individual's identification. The decedent's fingerprints or DNA may be found at the scene. Samples can be collected from the scene to be used for analytical comparison. Identification of infants dying in the 1995 Oklahoma City bombing of the Murrah Federal Building was made by fingerprints and DNA samples taken from their residences. Teeth, dentures, and other orthodontic devices found at a death scene may be useful to odontologists in establishing the decedent's identification. Visual identification of a person who has died recently and whose body has not deteriorated is an acceptable form of identification if the person making the identification is trustworthy. Scientific identification is always preferred to visual identification or use of circumstantial evidence or personal property.

## Removal of Deceased from Death Scene

If it is determined that further examination is required, the deceased is placed in a clean body bag and conveyed to the morgue facility for radiographic and medical examination by a forensic pathologist. An identification tag is placed on the subject inside the body bag and on the body bag itself. The bag is secured so that the decedent, clothing, and physical evidence are safeguarded against contamination and/or loss.

## Scene Debriefing

After all scene investigative procedures have been completed (photography, collection of evidence, removal of decedent to morgue), investigators share information that they developed. This allows all parties to discuss issues and agree to postscene responsibilities such as notification of next of kin and follow-up interviews.

## Notification of Next of Kin

Next of kin may be present at the death scene or respond to the scene when notified of the death. If the identification and location of the next of kin have not occurred while at the death scene, a concerted effort between law enforcement and medical examiner/coroner office must begin to accomplish this task. Thorough and time-sensitive report documentation should include all notification efforts attempted by law enforcement and medicolegal personnel.

## Documentation of Medical, Psychological, Work, and Social History

The decedent's medical history is extremely important in determining if death was due to natural or other causes. Medical, psychological, and social history information can be found in scene documents, such as electronic day timers, medical bills, check registers, and notes as well as prescription and over-the-counter medications found at the scene. Documents can help determine the decedent's current and past health problems, medications, hospitalizations, and treating physicians. Tobacco products, alcoholic containers, and drug paraphernalia found at the scene can assist in developing the subject's health profile. Occupation-related materials found at the scene can assist the investigator to determine the subject's workplace or vocation.

The most important thing for investigators to remember when conducting a death scene investigation is that the scene is the final chapter in the decedent's book of life. If the decedent is aware that death is imminent, he/she may leave clues behind to assist investigators in determining what was happening at the time of death. A thorough death scene evaluation will provide investigators with the opportunity to identify those clues.

## American Board of Medicolegal Death Investigators

The American Board of Medicolegal Death Investigators (ABMDI) is a not-for-profit, independent, professional certification board that was established in 1998 to promote the highest standards of practice for medicolegal death investigators. The ABMDI was created, designed, and developed by veteran practicing medicolegal death investigators who were involved in the development of the *National Guidelines for Death Investigation*. More than 700 individuals have been awarded basic (registered medicolegal death investigator) certification and 40 people have been awarded advanced (board-certified medicolegal death investigator) certification.

The ABMDI certifies individuals who have the proven knowledge and skills necessary to perform medicolegal death investigations, as set forth in the publication *Death Investigation: A Guide for the Scene Investigator*, renamed and published in 1999 by the National Institutes of Justice. This is a voluntary certification program.

The purpose of the ABMDI is to:

- encourage adherence to the high standards of professional practice and ethical conduct when performing medicolegal death investigations
- recognize qualified individuals who have voluntarily applied for professional basic and advanced levels of professional certification
- grant and issue certificates to individuals who have demonstrated their mastery of investigational techniques and who have successfully completed rigorous examination of their knowledge and skills in the field of medicolegal death investigation, and to maintain a listing of individuals granted certification
- recertify individuals every 5 years according to established recertification criteria, including examination and continuing education requirements.

## Further Reading

Bevel T (1997) Documenting the reconstruction of a crime. In: Geberth VC (ed.) *Bloodstain Pattern Analysis*, pp. 197–229. Boca Raton, FL: CRC Press LLC.

Clark S (1996) *Medicolegal Death Investigator – A Systematic Training Program for the Professional Death Investigator*. Big Rapids, MI: Occupational Research and Assessment.

Dirkmaat D (1997) The role of archaeology in the recovery and interpretation of human remains from an outdoor forensic setting. In: Haglund WD, Sorg MH (eds.) *Forensic Taphonomy – The Postmortem Fate of Human Remains*, pp. 39–64. Boca Raton, FL: CRC Press LLC.

Ernst MF (1999) The death scene. In: Caplan YH, Frank RS (eds.) *Medicolegal Death Investigation, Treatises in the*

*Forensic Sciences*, 2nd edn., pp. 7–104. Colorado Springs, CO: Forensic Science Foundation Press.

Ernst MF (2003) Medicolegal death investigation and forensic procedures. In: Froede R (ed.) *Handbook of Forensic Pathology*, 2nd edn., pp. 1–10. Northfield, IL: College of American Pathologists.

Fisher BA (2000) Trace evidence and miscellaneous material. In: Fisher BAJ (ed.) *Techniques of Crime Scene Investigation*, 6th edn., pp. 161–215. Boca Raton, FL: CRC Press LLC.

Hochrein MJ and US Department of Justice (2003) A Bibliography Related to Crime Scene Interpretation with Emphasis in Forensic Geotaphonomic and Forensic Archaeological Field Techniques. In: *Federal Bureau of Investigation St. Louis MO Division*. Washington, DC: FBI Print Shop.

Humphry D (1991) *Final Exit – The Practicalities of Self-Deliverance and Assisted Suicide for the Dying*. Eugene, OR: Hemlock Society.

Institutes of Medicine of the National Academies (2003) *Medicolegal Death Investigation System: Workshop Summary*, pp. 7–29. Washington, DC: National Academies Press.

Jentzen J (1998) Developing medicolegal death investigator systems in forensic pathology. In: Clauser G (ed.) *Clinics in Laboratory Medicine*, pp. 279–322. Forensic Pathology II, 18. Philadelphia, PA: W.B. Saunders Company.

Miller M (2003) Crime scene investigation. In: James SH, Nordby JJ (eds.) *Forensic Science – An Introduction to Scientific and Investigative Techniques*, pp. 115–135. Boca Raton, FL: CRC Press LLC.

Saferstein R (2003) DNA and fingerprints. In: Mortimer K Jr. (ed.) *Criminalistics – An Introduction to Forensic Science*, 8th edn., pp. 361–426. Saddle River, New Jersey: Pearson Prentice Hall.

Shemonsky N (1993) Jurisdiction on military installations. *American Journal of Forensic Medicine and Pathology* 14: 39–42.

US Department of Justice (1997) *Research Report: National Guidelines for Death Investigation*. NCJ167568 Washington, DC: National Institutes of Justice.

# Major Incident Scene Management

**J Horswell**, Forensic Executives, Upper Mt. Gravatt, QLD, Australia

## Major Incident or Crime-Scene Investigation

The undertaking of a major incident or crime-scene investigation is no different from that of a minor crime-scene investigation. The same technical recording and recovery of potential evidentiary material must take place, as does an interpretation of what has occurred. The size and seriousness of the offense are of no consequence to the investigation sequence. What is of consequence in a comparison between the two is the size and type of incident being investigated and the application of resources to undertake the technical work and interpretation of the overall scene or scenes. The old adage "many hands make light work" applies when there is a large scene and the nature of the case will dictate the requirement for the presence or absence of other specialists, who may be required to attend the scene for their "expert" advice. For example, a break-and-enter into a dwelling with stealing can easily be undertaken by a crime-scene investigator carrying out the investigation on his/her own, whereas a major bombing scene with casualties and a wide distribution of building debris and bomb fragments will require several crime-scene investigators with a crime-scene manager (CSM). Depending upon the nature of the casualties and the recovery of explosive residues, other specialists may need to be involved. There is nothing prescriptive regarding the allocation of resources. Allocation of resources is a matter for the most senior crime-scene investigator such as the CSM or in relation to primary and secondary scenes, a crime-scene coordinator (CSC) to negotiate their application with the senior investigating officer (SIO).

It is the responsibility of the SIO to ensure that the crime scene is investigated by appropriately skilled and qualified crime-scene investigators and it is the responsibility of the relevant crime-scene unit head to ensure that he/she provides the appropriate resources. Resources should be based on the complexity and seriousness of the alleged incident and competence in their allocation in this regard only comes with considerable experience. It is invariably useful for the police to have a major incident response plan, which recognizes the crime scene as the principal responsibility of the forensic support group. It is vitally important that the crime-scene unit has a response plan that includes staff profiles with relevant backgrounds recorded so that appropriate crime-scene investigators can be dispatched to a particular or specialized crime scene when an incident occurs.

## What is a Crime Scene?

Crime-scene investigation is practiced differently in different jurisdictions worldwide, and the responsibility for crime-scene investigation may include a combination of the following types of incidents and examinations:

- accidental deaths, which include a multitude of circumstances, including misadventure
- suicidal deaths, which include a multitude of circumstances
- homicidal deaths, which include a multitude of circumstances
- sudden deaths, with or without suspicious circumstances
- forced entry on to premises, including houses, factories, shops, shopping malls, garages, and garden sheds
- forced entry into money containers, including safes and automatic teller machines
- theft, including the placement of thief traps
- fraud, including the scientific examination of documents but excluding handwriting identification
- sexual assault, which includes touching, penetration, and ejaculation, with or without violence
- assault with a weapon, such as a hammer, screwdriver, axe, knife, firearm, or piece of timber
- difficult victim identification, which includes mummification and putrefaction
- disaster victim identification dealing with multiple casualties
- fire-scene investigation
- explosion-scene investigation, which could include multiple casualties
- drug investigations, such as the importation of drugs, plantations, and clandestine laboratories
- firearms-scene examinations
- physical comparisons, including mechanical fit, footwear, tiretrack, and toolmark impression identification
- identification and recovery of micro- and macrophysical evidence, including the location, visualization, and recovery of fingerprints and other latent marks
- vehicle accidents, including car, bicycle, motorcycle, boat, or aircraft
- vehicle identification, including number falsification and restoration, vehicle parts identification, as well as headlight examination in vehicular accidents
- chemical and biological agents employed to kill numerous individuals.

The location or "locus" of an "incident" is usually called the crime scene. A crime scene could be anywhere, and it is usually a place where a crime or an incident that may end in legal proceedings has occurred.

In some "incidents," it may be readily apparent that a crime has indeed been committed and it is a "crime scene." However, in many situations one of the initial and primary tasks of the crime-scene investigator is to determine whether a crime has been committed. An obvious example is that of a deceased person. In many instances it will be obvious that death was not due to natural causes. In other instances it may be far from obvious; hence, the primary role of the crime-scene investigator is that of a key player in the overall forensic investigation.

## Australian Jurisdictional Differences in Crime-Scene Investigation

In the state and Northern Territory jurisdictions of Australia, relevant state and territory police have the responsibility for crime-scene investigation, which is usually confined to that jurisdiction or to other jurisdictions where suspects have traveled to avoid apprehension. In the federal jurisdiction there are no boundaries. This was recently seen with the Bali terrorist incident and less well-known crime-scene responses to Fiji, New Guinea, and Vanuatu. The skill and competency, education and training qualifications, and experiences vary considerably in Australia. Much has been done in the education and training arena to rectify this; however, there are still variations in approach, with some commonality. The differences are mainly structural and do not relate to the actual technical recording and recovery of potential evidential material.

### Primary Crime Scene

The primary crime scene is an area, place, or thing where the incident occurred or where the majority or a high concentration of physical evidence will be found, for example, where there has been a sudden suspicious death.

### Secondary Crime Scene(s)

Secondary crime scene(s) are areas, places, or things where physical evidence relating to the incident may be found. The potential physical evidence will usually be transported away from the primary crime scene. Some examples include:

- the deceased
- the get-away vehicle in crimes of armed robbery
- the suspect
- the suspect's environment
- the suspect's vehicle
- the weapon used in the crime.

## Approaches to Crime-Scene Investigation

The examination of a crime scene and subsequent collection of potential evidential material requires special skill, knowledge, aptitude, and attitude. The manner in which a crime-scene investigation is conducted may be a critical factor in determining the success of an investigation. The thorough examination of a crime scene requires a disciplined and systematic approach to recording the various observations made and collection of potential evidential material. This must be combined with the analysis of various observations and the interrelationship of potential evidentiary material with the dynamics of the crime. In order to undertake these investigations, the crime-scene investigator must have a well-developed understanding of the application of forensic science and how it can be applied to what is being observed, visualized, and recovered at the scene.

Examining a crime scene is often a demanding task, and in many instances, requires physical and mental stamina as well as team-member and team-leadership skills.

Forensic science has become a powerful aid to criminal investigation, with courts placing much emphasis on the results. Accordingly, the manner in which evidence is located, recorded, and collected, along with the observations and comparisons made, is vigorously examined by the courts in any subsequent proceedings.

Therefore, a systematic approach to crime-scene investigation will ensure:

- good coordination between investigation and crime-scene examination teams
- an efficient, effective, and thorough examination
- less fatigue
- orderly recording and collection of potential evidence
- correct observations and deductions.

## Crime-Scene Investigation Management

Crime-scene investigation management is a subject that encompasses:

- the management and coordination of human and physical resources
- the technical aspects of recording and recovery of potential evidentiary material
- the interpretation of what has occurred in the recent past as a recent archeological search, recovery, and interpretation.

The principles of professional investigation management apply equally to the overall investigation or to any part of the investigation, such as the forensic investigation, regardless of the enormity or political sensitivity of a particular major incident or crime scene. The principles are:

- Management decisions must focus on achieving specific outcomes.

- Forensic investigation, like any investigation, is subject to the realities of resource allocations.
- The investigation process must be open to administrative, operational, and judicial review.

There are three critical operational stages of a criminal investigation:

1. the control and coordination of the overall criminal investigation
2. the tracing, locating, and interviewing of witnesses and suspects
3. the forensic investigation.

Any investigation is dual, involving individuals and material items. Normally, the coordination of a major criminal investigation is delegated to an SIO. A senior investigator (SI) should also be appointed to coordinate the gathering of all oral evidence from witnesses and suspects (individuals). Likewise, a senior forensic investigator should be appointed to lead and coordinate the overall forensic investigation (material items), and this person should have the authority commensurate with the role as the CSC.

## Scene Control and Coordination

In relation to the management of major incidents or crime scenes, the two terms – CSM and CSC – can be interpreted as follows.

### Crime-Scene Manager

CSM is a term that applies to a senior crime-scene investigator who has been given the role of managing a large and complex single crime scene.

### Crime-Scene Coordinator

CSC is a term that applies to a senior crime-scene investigator who has been given the role of coordinating several single simple and/or complex scenes, all interlinked and interrelated, and who takes on the role of chairing case management committee meetings when both forensic personnel and senior investigating police come together for case management meetings.

The CSM must surround him/herself with competent, skilled, and qualified forensic investigators to carry out the task of conducting the crime-scene investigation.

In order to manage major incidents or crime scenes and multisited crime scenes successfully, both the SIO and the CSC must have a thorough knowledge and understanding of forensic science and criminal investigation.

## Scene Security and Control

The first officers attending the scene will make an initial assessment of the crime scene. They will secure the scene to an extent based on the information available at the time. This may include a perimeter cordon, which takes in areas not concerned with the primary crime scene, and then a further cordon closer to the primary crime scene. This enables crowd and press control and provides a buffer zone, which is useful in the identification of crime-scene tourists, which could include those members of the police service who do not have business at the crime scene.

The CSM, who will normally be a senior member of the crime-scene investigation staff, should attend the scene at the earliest possible opportunity to take charge of the management of the crime scene. A crime-scene investigator or a team of crime-scene investigators who will undertake the crime-scene investigation will normally accompany him/her. The size of the crime scene(s) will dictate the amount of resources allocated to the particular incident. It is imperative that the CSM has the authority to allocate the amount of resources required.

Once the crime scene is handed over to the CSM, a reassessment of the scene security should be made to ensure the scene security is adequate. A formal protocol should be used for the handing-over of a crime scene. This ensures control and the maintenance of the scene's chain of custody.

It is an essential element of any prosecution where forensic evidence is involved to prove the security of the scene and that it was maintained throughout the subsequent examination/investigation. Therefore, the objective of securing the crime scene is to:

- prevent evidence being destroyed or contaminated
- ensure security of information – generally only a media liaison officer or the SIO releases information to the media
- ensure that chain of custody of the scene is maintained, as is necessary with any item of potential evidence
- remove from the scene all unnecessary persons, including police officers and the media. It must be remembered that the more people present, the greater the potential for contamination and destruction of evidence. Large numbers of persons present will also inhibit the proper processing of a crime scene
- ensure that all evidence has been recorded and recovered. This may include securing the scene until the results of the postmortem or scientific analysis are to hand.

There are a variety of methods for securing the crime scene, including:

- posting guards
- rope or printed tape cordons
- the strategic placing of vehicles
- the use of markers, flags, and signs
- locking rooms or areas within buildings or using the external walls of a building as the barrier
- establishing safe walk areas (common-approach path with tape or purpose-built raised stepping plates).

The lack of appropriate control and coordination at the crime scene may lead to vital information not reaching the crime-scene investigator. This may render his/her efforts aimless and uncovered leads may never be passed on to investigators for follow-up action. This is most important when the crime scene is large and there are several crime-scene investigators present processing the scene or where there are secondary scenes away from the primary scene. There must be a flow of information back and forth between investigator and crime-scene investigator. This is one of the functions of the CSM.

## Management of Occupational Health and Safety Issues

The well-being of the crime-scene investigators is the primary responsibility of the CSM. He/she must be aware of fatigue and must cater for their comfort. Appropriate protective clothing and equipment should be made available. Breaks should be organized for the forensic investigators and refreshments should be on hand during those breaks. Scene guards should also be part of the crime-scene operation, regardless of the area they originate from. There should be a designated area where food and drink can be taken, equipment can be stored, and rubbish can be accumulated.

All personnel on site should be briefed regarding safety hazards, smoking and eating, the location of critical areas, and the use of telephones and toilets.

In relation to the investigation of fires, suitable safety equipment must be provided, including: hard hats fitted with battery torchlights, nonslip steel-plated boots, overalls, leather gloves, face shields, and gas and/or dust masks.

One of the most hazardous crime scenes that requires the adoption of specific crime-scene protective safety techniques, and one that is an emerging issue for the management of crime scenes in the twenty-first century, is the use of chemical, biological, and/or radiological materials. This has been experienced in recent years by the Japanese police in the sarin attack on the Tokyo underground and the experimentation that took place in outback Australia prior to these attacks, which were investigated by the Australian federal police. The recent anthrax and white-powder scares that were experienced by a number of police agencies in North America and Australia were indicators of the emerging protection required for crime-scene investigators in the current climate of terrorism.

Chemical, biological, and radiological crime-scene investigations require a specialist response with their own individual health and safety considerations, a subject in its own right to be dealt with separately.

## Management of Contamination Issues

In general terms, the greater the number of personnel present at a crime scene, the more likely it is that the scene and its evidence will be contaminated. As with any other personnel, crime-scene investigators who are required to be in attendance at the crime scene can deposit hairs, skin cells, and sweat, in addition to other trace evidence, such as fibers, or leave their own trace marks, such as shoemarks and fingerprints.

In light of recent advances in DNA technology and its sensitivity, there are increased risks of contamination. The addition of the crime-scene investigator's own DNA and/or the alteration of DNA recovered from the crime scene are issues for those who process crime scenes.

Crime-scene investigators and other specialists present at the scene should be equipped with the following protective clothing and adhere to their use: disposable overalls with hood, masks, shoe covers, and gloves.

These items should be changed as necessary and must be changed when dealing with secondary crime scenes, victims, and/or suspects. Gloves should automatically be changed when moving within a scene from one discrete area to another, particularly when dealing with different areas of body fluids, which can potentially come from a variety of sources.

The level of contamination risk to be expected is relative to the type of crime scene and the number of personnel required to have access to the scene. For example, the victim and the police officer taking the crime report may be the only individuals present at a burglary scene; therefore, the contamination risk is low. In contrast, at least the first responding police officer, ambulance officer(s), investigator(s), crime-scene investigator(s), and forensic pathologist would usually attend a typical suspicious death scene. In addition, the witness who discovered the deceased, family, friends and/or neighbors of the victim may also have visited or also be present at the crime scene. These individuals increase the potential for contamination.

Environmental conditions may also play a major role in the contamination of crime scenes and any potential evidence. Wind, sun, rain, snow, and temperature can play a key role in the contamination and degradation of potential evidence at a crime scene.

Protection measures should be considered and recovery of potential evidentiary material at risk should take priority over the recovery of any other potential evidence. The CSM or CSC should consider crime-scene protection tents, tarpaulins, and corrugated iron. These items can be used as covers to protect important evidence from any detrimental environmental conditions prevailing during the crime-scene search and potential evidence recovery stages.

Appropriate packaging and transportation have been discussed elsewhere in this encyclopedia.

## Management of Records

In order to conduct a thorough systematic crime-scene investigation, protocols should be developed for each activity. Each jurisdiction will have such protocols, with their own subtle differences. There should be pre-prepared forms, which will provide the crime-scene investigator with comprehensive notes taken during the examination, and these pro-forma records should be available for:

- crime-scene log – activities undertaken at the scene, including movements, who was at the scene on arrival, who arrived and who left the scene, and a summary of their activities whilst on-site
- formal "handover" and "takeover" of the crime scene from the first police at the scene to the crime-scene investigator to arrive or the CSM
- environmental conditions at the crime scene
- description of conditions within the premises and the surrounding area
- activities and observations at the crime scene
- exhibit list
- rough sketch of the crime scene
- photographs taken at the scene
- specialists attending the scene, with entry and exit times and detail of examinations undertaken
- initial findings from the crime-scene investigation and from all specialists attending the scene.

## Management of Quality Management Systems Records

Record management and the control of documents are integral parts of third-party quality management systems forensic science accreditation. Crime-scene investigation now forms part of both the American Society of Crime Laboratory Directors Laboratory Accreditation Board (ASCLD-LAB) and the National Association of Testing Authorities, Australia (NATA) and is likely to spread through the mutual recognition agreements (MRAs) with other international accreditation bodies. It is, therefore, desirable that crime-scene facilities have both "systems" and "technical" accreditation of their system conforming to the international standard ISO/IEC 17025.

The use of a computerized program to manage record management within a quality management system is the only systematic and comprehensive way to manage and control the quality management system documentation and thus control the quality system.

## Ongoing Case Management

Once the scene work is completed, the emphasis changes to the coordination of further examinations and the communication and flow of information and results from forensic analysis or examinations to investigating officers from forensic examiners, and from investigating officers to forensic examiners. If it is not practical for the CSC to chair further case management meetings, then another senior crime-scene investigator, who is already involved in the case, may be nominated to maintain that contact and coordinate the ongoing case management and chair case management meetings.

## Computerization of Case Management

There is only one effective way to manage all the information gathered at the crime scene and to ensure accountability and chain of custody of items using a specific case management system, which has either been developed in-house or is commercially available. There are several commercially available forensic laboratory information management systems. These will be employed to cater for the crime-scene investigation aspect of a forensic investigation after the key stakeholders come to the realization that the most critical aspect of forensic science is the crime scene and how it is examined. These systems manage the lodgment, tracking, and accounting for items in addition to the information gathered as a result of the crime-scene investigation as well as any subsequent laboratory examinations and/or analyses.

## The Future – Field Testing

Forensic science laboratories usually have backlogs of cases and there is usually a need to prioritize casework. This normally does not fit in with the urgent needs of investigators for results and leads to carry their investigation further and to assist in the identification of the suspect(s). Investigatory leads soon grow cold after a crime has been committed. Suspect(s) vanish, witnesses disperse, and potential physical evidence may only persist for a limited time or may be disturbed in some way, even by normal activities.

Although faster processing of potential evidentiary material in the forensic science laboratory is important, in many cases the ability to secure critical information by undertaking field testing at the crime scene could significantly enhance the likelihood of a successful resolution.

Field testing should not, and will not, replace laboratory testing; instead, it may enhance investigations conducted at the crime scene. For example, it could be used to identify the presence and type of flammable or combustible fuel at fire scenes and therefore provide investigators with lines of enquiry. It could also be used to screen potential DNA evidentiary items for those most likely to produce results and, through preliminary analysis conducted at the scene, to assist in developing investigative leads. Of course, confirmatory testing in the controlled laboratory environment should be continued to ensure absolute confidence in the results.

The role of preliminary analysis in the field is therefore elimination, arguably a more important role than incrimination in the early stages of any investigation.

There are many small gas chromatographs currently on the market and these would suffice in the preliminary testing of debris and residues from fire scenes. A portable microchip-based prototype DNA field-testing instrument has also been developed. The instrument, which produces findings within 30 min, is currently being trialed and improved, and will be made available commercially.

## The Future – Case Review

It is unfortunate that crime-scene sizes are constantly increasing; the terrorist attack in Bali is a case in point. There are issues that immediately come to mind with this type of major crime scene and they relate to control and access to the scene. In the early stages of the Bali scene, to an outside observer, it would seem that far too many people were allowed to move throughout the scene. Those in charge of such scenes are faced with gaining control and limiting access. It should be realized that in practice these are very challenging tasks.

The issue for the future with such large scenes with so much information and so many items with so many subsamples is to have everything that it is possible to have from such a scene. This is where a case review, which is an extension of case management, will play a more prominent role in crime-scene investigation in the future.

**What is a Review?**

The *Australian Macquarie Dictionary* (1988), second revision, defines a review as follows:

- critical article or report
- critique
- a viewing again
- a second or repeated view of something
- an inspection, or examining by viewing
- a viewing of past events, circumstances, or facts.

**Types of Review**

There are essentially three types of reviews:

1. constant informal reviews
2. independent formal reviews
3. quality assurance reviews.

**Constant informal review**   A constant informal review is the process that occurs in discussion with colleagues during an investigation and at case management meetings.

**Independent formal reviews conducted in-house** This is a formal procedure instituted in-house where nominated colleague(s) who are not involved in the case review and scrutinize the forensic investigation to ensure that nothing has been overlooked.

**Independent formal review**   This formal procedure is instituted as a means of scrutinizing a forensic investigation by another forensic science expertise provider. Although not the norm in Australia, this does happen in circumstances where second opinions are desired or where there are particular analyses required, as the primary investigating forensic science facility does not have the ability to conduct the examinations/analyses itself.

The primary reason for commissioning such reviews is to assist in achieving successful outcomes and ensuring that everything that needs to have been done has been done.

It is important to ensure, in an independent formal review, that:

- best practice in forensic science is being applied
- all reasonable avenues of examination and/or analysis are being considered and applied
- sufficient resources are available to complete the examinations/analysis

- the resources are being applied efficiently and effectively
- any health and safety issues arising from the forensic investigation requiring attention are dealt with
- lessons learned are shared with colleagues
- training, retraining, and/or remedial action that may be required
- an investigation carried out well is rewarded.

An independent formal review:

- should be conducted as soon as possible
- should appreciate the complexity and sensitivity of a forensic investigation
- should ensure the likelihood of reaching a conclusion in the near future
- should have adequate resources devoted to the forensic investigation
- should have benefits to be obtained from it.

Terms of reference of an independent formal review include:

- it must be written
- it must be clear and concise
- it must specify a timeframe
- it must specify the available resources
- it must include other relevant factors.

Conduct of an independent formal review consists of:

- detailed briefing
- review to minimize disruption and/or interference to the examinations and/or analyses being conducted
- review to add value to the forensic investigation
- prioritization of examinations and analyses.

**Other types of independent formal review**   These types of reviews are outside the control of the forensic expertise provider. If appropriate examinations and analyses have been conducted, covering all aspects of the case, then the likelihood of a case coming under the scrutiny and review of the following organizations is slim. Forensic practitioners, however, should be aware that every step they take could at some time in the future be subjected to the closest scrutiny by these organizations:

- the parent organization internal investigations department
- the ombudsman
- the defense council and their relevant specialists
- royal commissions
- commissions of inquiry
- parliamentary enquiries.

**Quality assurance reviews**  The work carried out by crime scene investigators, and for that matter laboratory examiners and analysts from a forensic science service, that has in place a quality management system, ensures, through regular reviews, or what are known as audits, that the examinations are conducted by appropriately educated and trained practitioners who are competent and proficient, the relevance of the methodology used in the examinations and/or analysis, and the equipment used is regularly maintained and calibrated. This is what is known as a quality management system which, when in place, underpins professional practice.

## The Future – Practitioners

Quality outcomes and systems in crime-scene investigation are dealt with elsewhere. The move by crime-scene investigation providers toward ensuring a quality product through embracing quality management systems should be applauded. One of the most significant issues in crime-scene investigation in the past has been the lack of formal externally assessed and validated standards. This is changing, as many crime-scene investigation organizations move to join their laboratory colleagues in putting in place an externally assessed forensic science quality management system by a third-party quality systems accreditation provider. This is not an issue for the fully integrated forensic science laboratory, as when laboratory services put in place a quality management system, it also includes the crime-scene investigation service.

Robertson put it succinctly when he stated "Strong leadership and management by the forensic science community will be required if appropriate standards are to be developed and maintained. It would help if more crime scene investigators had the confidence to view themselves as forensic scientists and if laboratory scientists would also recognise this self-evident fact."

Education and training of crime-scene investigators has come a long way since the 1980s. Historically, crime-scene investigators have been sworn police and only some have had the opportunity of a science education. During the early 1980s, programs were introduced to educate sworn police crime-scene investigators to raise their level of understanding and appreciation of the application of the "scientific method" so that their forensic investigations could be more objective. As history has shown, there has been a mixed degree of success. The author is now a proponent of science graduate recruitment into this unique field. Not all science graduates will be suitable for this type of career; however, many will be, and the present and future rest on having the appropriate selection processes in place and the appropriate professional training, which should be a recognized university qualification at an appropriate postgraduate level.

The forensic science community can ill afford to fall into the trap of a two-tier system of "volume" crime-scene investigators and "major" crime-scene investigators, as evidence will be lost through inexperience and we will return to the old days, with review of forensic science practice by royal commissioners again being a frequent occurrence. Crime-scene investigators need a cross-section of "crime types" and a considerable number of crime-scene attendances in order to maintain their expertise. As every crime scene is different, the challenges faced by the crime-scene investigator will also be different.

Robertson again put it succinctly when he stated: "Crime scene investigation is real science, and at least the more complex and major incidents demand a scientific approach requiring personnel with appropriate basic science and specialist training. It would be a tragedy for the future if this was to be lost in short-term 'fix it' solutions to deal with the challenges posed by volume crime."

## Summary

The management of major incidents and crime scenes, no matter what the size or seriousness of the crime, is a matter of gaining control of the crime scene and then managing the coordination and application of resources. What follows must be a systematic and thorough approach to processing the scene. Serious and major crime scenes will vary in size and complexity, some requiring many crime-scene investigators; others, which are smaller and less complicated, will require only one or two crime-scene investigators.

Overall scene management and the maintenance of a two-way flow of information and communication are the essential ingredients to successful crime-scene management. Regular case management meetings must be held to keep all stakeholders abreast of the latest available information. These should be recorded in the case notes as minutes of the meeting, as a record of what transpired and who is responsible for any ongoing action items.

Underpinning the crime-scene investigation facility should be quality systems that are technically assessed to conform to the international standard ISO/IEC 17025-1999, general requirements for the competence of testing and calibration laboratories.

The future is indeed bright for crime-scene investigation if the current trend of a willingness to be open and to review is applied at the early stages of a forensic investigation, rather than waiting until it is forced on practitioners by a royal commission.

## See Also

**Accreditation:** Crime Scene Investigators; **Crime-scene Investigation and Examination:** Collection and Chain of Evidence; Recovery of Human Remains; Suspicious Deaths

## Further Reading

Belgrader P, *et al.* (1998) Rapid PCR for identity testing using battery-powered miniature thermal cycler. *Journal of Forensic Sciences* 43: 315–319.

Fisher BAJ (2000) *Techniques of Crime Scene Investigation,* 6th edn. Boca Raton, FL: Chemical Rubber.

Gael Quality (2002) *Marketing Material for Q-PULSE*$^{TM}$ *Version 4.2*, Gael. East Kilbride, UK: Gael Quality.

Horswell J (2000) Major incident scene management. In: Siegal JA, Saukko PJ, Knupfer GC, *et al.* (eds.) *Encyclopaedia of Forensic Sciences*, pp. 428–432. London: Academic Press.

Horswell J (2004) Management of crime scene investigation. In: Horswell J (ed.) *The Practice of Crime Scene Investigation*, pp. 83–95. Boca Raton, FL: Chemical Rubber.

Horswell J, Edwards M (1997) Development of quality systems accreditation for crime scene investigators in Australia. *Science and Justice* 37: 3–8.

Ibrahim MS, *et al.* (1998) Real-time microchip PCR for detecting single differences in viral and human DNA. *Analytical Chemistry* 70: 2013–2017.

Kirk PL (1953) *Crime Investigation.* New York: Wiley.

Management Systems Designers (2003) *Marketing Material for FORENSIC LIMS*$^{TM}$. http://filmsmsdinc.com.

NATA, ISO/IEC 17025 (2000) *Application Document, Supplementary Requirements for Accreditation in the Field of Forensic Science*, Version 1. Sydney, Australia: National Association of Testing Authorities.

Robertson J (2004) Crime scene investigation: key issues for the future. In: Horswell J (ed.) *The Practice of Crime Scene Investigation*, pp. 399–406. Boca Raton, FL: Chemical Rubber.

Van Oorschot RAH, Jones MK (1997) DNA fingerprints from fingerprints. *Nature* 387: 767.

# Underwater Crime Scene

**R F Becker**, Chaminade University of Honolulu, Honolulu, HI, USA

## Introduction

More than 70% of the earth's surface is covered with water. Since earliest time human beings have worked, played, and committed crimes on, around, and in the water. It is not until recently that a new investigative specialty has evolved, that of the "underwater investigator."

Whenever a crime or disaster involves submerged material someone is charged with its retrieval. Historically attention was focused on locating and retrieving it. Little thought was given to the possibility of submerged items having evidentiary value. Most agencies today recognize that a crime scene may be inside, outside, or underwater. Once the police community was made aware of the potential of forensic evidence on submerged items it was not long before protocols were devised to preserve that potential forensic evidence.

## Underwater Crime Scenes

As waterway recreation and transportation expands so do crimes committed on those waterways. The first step in any underwater investigation is to locate the underwater crime scene. It is helpful to think of the recovery of underwater evidence as an extension of the overall investigation. By perceiving the recovery operation as an integral part of the overall investigation it is but one short step to viewing the underwater operation as the processing of a crime scene with depth as commuting time. If the offense suspected is such that it would precipitate a crime scene analysis then the underwater counterpart of that investigation should be conducted as meticulously.

Reconstructing a crime scene is accomplished by recording each piece of evidence in relation to other permanent nonevidentiary items at the scene. That reconstruction is the same regardless of the location of the crime scene. Indoor or outdoor evidence must be recovered with some record of its relationship to the environment from which it was removed. The inability to demonstrate that relationship at the time of trial may result in that evidence not being admitted. The underwater investigation begins with determining what is to be searched and where it is to be searched.

### The Underwater Search

The nature and scope of the search will be determined by the offense, existing current, tidal conditions, water depth, visibility, wind direction, and known bottom structure. It is the recovery team leader's responsibility to determine, based on the relevant variables, which search pattern to employ. Search patterns vary and have different attributes enabling them to address different search requirements but all search patterns should have certain basic attributes:

1. The pattern is to begin at a predetermined point and have predetermined midpoints and changes of direction, ending at a predetermined location or upon discovery of the item sought.

2. It includes communication from surface personnel to searchers through line signals or voice communication.
3. The pattern of search allows the searcher to deploy buoys to mark points of interest or evidence.
4. It is simple.
5. It effectively uses divers and resources.
6. It allows for safe support of the diver or divers.

Most searches involve a surface component (line tender) and a diver or divers. As a team the diver provides the labor and the tender provides the direction and support. The tender is the diver's eyes, ears, and lifeline.

### Temporal and Geographical Location of Evidence

After the team has located the evidence the usual procedure is to retrieve it. It is important to remember that the officer recovering the evidence will be responsible for testifying as to the method used in locating, marking, sketching, measuring, photographing, bagging, tagging, and maintaining the chain of custody.

All details pertaining to the dive site must be recorded prior to the recovery of any evidence. Failure to mark properly and record the location of the recovery site may result in the following:

1. losing it, in the event that more than one dive is necessary
2. inability to orient parts of a dismembered or dismantled auto, vessel, airplane, or body. In airline crashes body limbs, arms, hands, legs, and feet may be strewn over the site. Reconstruction of the bodies may require anthropological assistance. Often the fastest way to associate severed body parts with the torso is by recording the location of the body parts relative to each other or to the seat or seats to which the parts were closest. By referring to the seating chart body parts can be readily associated with the passenger who had been occupying the seat nearest to where the body parts were found
3. considerable expense in time and effort in relocating the site and the evidence at the site
4. having the evidence rendered inadmissible at the time of trial.

The most effective method of preserving a record is photography. Where visibility allows, the camera should be the first piece of equipment on the site.

### Photographing the Underwater Crime Scene

The method whereby the underwater crime scene is first recorded is through photographs and/or videograph. The video recorder is becoming a popular tool in recording the underwater crime scene. The film makes a permanent historical record of how the scene appeared when the film was exposed.

### Establishing a Reference Point

When evidence is recovered from a crime scene in a conventional crime, measurement is generally not a problem. There are fixed landmarks from which measurements can be taken. However, there may not be a readily available landmark for an underwater investigator to anchor measurements. After plotting the recovery area on the site chart it is generally necessary to establish a point of reference from which measurements can be made.

### Crime-Scene Measurements

Interior crime scenes utilize one of three basic measurement techniques: (1) rectangularization; (2) triangulation; and (3) baseline construction. Both triangulation and baseline construction work especially well outdoors where permanent landmarks are at a distance from the item to be measured, but none of these methods works very well when processing an underwater crime scene where measurement of items in the water to permanent objects on land is hampered by limited or zero visibility. Trilateration is a method of measurement in which the underwater investigator need not rely on sight for accuracy (**Figure 1**). Objects in the water are measured from two known locations on the shore. The end of the tape to be read is on shore at the prelocated position and the diver moves the tape to a point on the object being measured. The shore-based end of the tape is then moved from one known position to the other. It is important to note that this measurement will only give you the location of the object being measured, not the orientation. To orient the object two more measurements must be taken from a different point on the submerged item (**Figures 2 and 3**).

### The Underwater Crime-Scene Sketch

The data upon which the underwater crime scene sketch is based are gathered after the scene has been completely processed and photographed but before evidentiary items have been bagged, tagged, and transported. The sketch is a measured drawing showing the location of all important items, landmarks, permanent fixtures, and physical evidence.

## Handling Evidence

Physical evidence is usually handled according to a predetermined protocol. That protocol includes recording field information about all evidence discovered. That information may include but is not limited to:

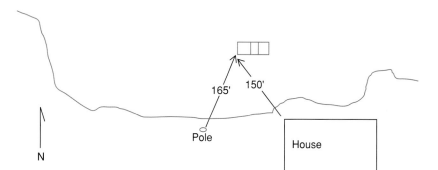

**Figure 1**   Trilateration. Measurements are read and recorded by the dive tender and on-scene intelligence officer. This measurement does not orient the vehicle, it could be anywhere 360 degrees around the established point.

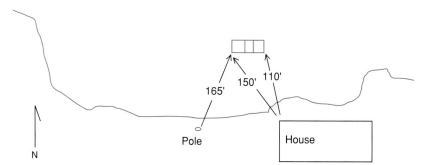

**Figure 2**   Trilateration (orientation). A third measurement is required to orient (lock in space) the vehicle.

**Figure 3**   Small grid orientation: in recoveries where small items are to be measured, it may be best to use an "orientation grid," first locating and orienting the grid then the objects within it.

1. identifying evidence by description in field notes and evidence tags
2. the location within the underwater crime scene at which the evidence was obtained
3. the name of the person who found the evidence
4. time and date of the finding of the evidence
5. a description of any special characteristics unique to a piece of evidence
6. the names of all participants in the search process.

## Firearms

Historically firearms have been treated in a cavalier way in recovery operations. It was understood that a firearm could not possess any important forensic information once submerged. A new perspective is being transmitted between agencies and jurisdictions. It is now recognized that water does not necessarily destroy forensic evidence and in some instances may even preserve it.

Weapons used in homicides may potentially contain a plethora of trace evidence. If a semiautomatic handgun was used to inflict a contact wound, a phenomenon known as "barrel blowback" creates a vacuum effect at the barrel of the pistol once the projectile has left. It may pull in fiber, tissue, and blood from the body of the victim. If that firearm is placed in a pocket, fibers may be ensnared by sights, clip, and safety releases. If the firearm is removed from the pocket of the assailant and placed under the seat of an automobile for transportation to a disposal location, again fiber evidence may be lodged in the metallic protuberances. Additionally, there are certain parts of the firearm that may retain a fingerprint, including the ammunition that was pushed into the clip by the suspect's thumb. The weapon is then transported to a waterway and thrown some distance where water enters the barrel creating, in effect, a water-block, trapping any materials within the barrel against the breach face. That equilibrium remains until a diver grabs the weapon by the barrel and carries it to the surface, emptying the barrel's contents as it clears the water's surface.

In an effort to preserve any prospective forensic information on the firearm it should be packaged in the water and in a watertight container (once photographed and measured). It should not be unloaded or handled unnecessarily. It should be presumed loaded, charged, and cocked, and handled accordingly.

## Automobiles

The traditional method of recovering autos was to wrap a chain around an axle and drag the vehicle to the surface. Although highly effective in removing the vehicle it may also destroy any forensic information on, around, or in the vehicle. Once the vehicle exits the water the pressure that was once equalized inside and outside the vehicle is drastically changed and the water now carries significant weight as the auto continues to clear the water. If the windshield had been shattered and the windows have not been rolled down, there is a good possibility that the windshield will be burst outward by the water pressure, flushing the contents of the interior through the front window. Most vehicles recovered by towing are damaged externally in the process. It is impossible to determine upon retrieval whether the damage occurred before the vehicle was submerged, during submersion, or as a result of the salvage operation.

Although most vehicle recovery is done by tow truck, floating (lifting) vehicles with airbags is a method that reduces internal disturbance, exterior damage, and unnecessary damage to the undercarriage.

If a vehicle has been stolen and used in the commission of a crime, fruits or instrumentalities of the crime may be lost during recovery. The license plate number and the vehicle identification number, if retrievable, may allow a computer check to determine the status of the vehicle. In water of limited visibility, license plate numbers and vehicle identification number (VIN) numbers can be read through a "water bath," which is a plastic bag filled with clear water. When pressed against a license plate, the water bath allows a diver to place his/her facemask against the bag and view the plate through clear water. Some stolen vehicles are not immediately reported, nor are some crimes that were committed with a stolen auto. The best policy is to treat each vehicle to be recovered as a possible tool in the commission of an offense and as a possible source of trace evidence.

If a vehicle has been involved in a vehicular accident or a hit and run, the investigating officers will probably subject it to a vigorous examination. If there are dents, scratches, fabric, or paint on the exterior that may have been transferred by another vehicle or body, all scuba and salvage equipment will have to be eliminated before any trace evidence can be considered useful. Therefore, the salvage operation should be done with the least adverse impact upon the vehicle, and all scuba and salvage equipment should be logged and specifically described to allow for exclusion of possible contamination by the dive and recovery team.

A considerable amount of information can be obtained from a submerged vehicle before efforts are made to raise it. If access into the vehicle is practicable and can be accomplished safely, an examination of the glove compartment can be made. All items in the glove compartment should be removed and placed in plastic bags, leaving water in the bags with the contents. The floors of the vehicle can be examined, photographed, and if anything is discovered, tagged and bagged. The most innocuous of items may prove to be useful. Inflatable and wooden toys may have been used to block the accelerator pedal.

Whenever practicable, occupant recovery should be conducted in the water. Much evidentiary information will be lost if the occupants are left in the vehicle during the recovery operation. Postmortem injuries to the body resulting from the contact with the interior of the vehicle during recovery will complicate the autopsy.

Items recovered in the water should be immersed in the medium from which they were retrieved, not just kept damp. Turning the items over to the lab wet transfers the responsibility for drying and preserving the items to the laboratory technicians.

An exterior examination of the vehicle should be performed that is similar to the preflight "walk-around" conducted by pilots of small aircraft.

During the swim-around, the diver, if s/he has an underwater slate, can record gross anomalies of the exterior of the vehicle (**Figure 4**). In black water where the diver cannot visually examine the exterior of the vehicle, s/he can conduct a tactile examination of a portion of the vehicle, surface, and verbally recount the findings to the tender and submerge and continue the swim-around. Many dive teams are investing in underwater communication systems that would allow a dive tender to direct and guide the diver in his/her tactile examination of the entire exterior of the vehicle by word of mouth.

It would also prove helpful to the investigation to know whether the lights were intact prior to recovery, because they too are often a casualty of the salvaging operation. If the light lenses are intact prior to raising the vehicle, no false assumptions will be drawn as to how the lenses were broken if they are broken during the salvaging of the auto. If the lenses are not intact prior to raising the auto, a bit of evidentiary information has been obtained. If there are pieces of the lens still in place, they will probably not be in place following the typical recovery. The pieces therefore, should be photographed, bagged, and tagged prior to lifting the vehicle.

The fact that the light switch is on or off is not always indicative of whether the lights were on or off at the time the vehicle entered the water. In salvage operations, the light switch will likely be struck by debris or bodies thrown forward as the vehicle is raised by its rear axle.

The light bulbs can often reveal whether the lights were "on" when the vehicle entered the water. A retrieval of the bulbs may prove to be useful as the investigation progresses.

Burning light filaments break in a characteristic fashion upon impact (their breakage differs from that of filaments that break when not lighted or after they have burnt out). It is important not to remove the bulbs from their housings when bulb comparisons may be necessary but instead to remove the entire light assembly so that damage to the bulbs and filaments will be kept to a minimum. The direction of an external impact can often be determined by the direction in which the hot filament was bent.

**Bodies**

Once a body has been located and measurements recorded, it must be raised to the surface. It is during

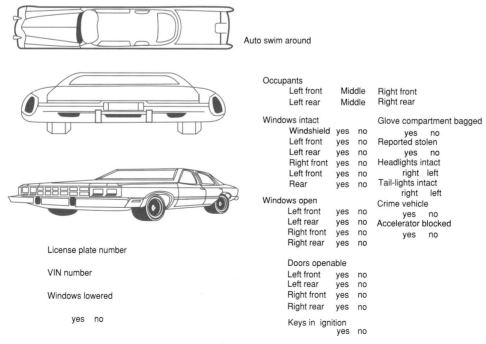

**Figure 4** Automobile swim-around checklist.

the recovery portion of the operation that evidence can be preserved or irredeemably destroyed or contaminated. All unattended drownings should be presumed homicide until proven otherwise.

All bodies should be bagged in the water. Any efforts to recover the body prior to bagging may result in the loss of transient evidence, such as hair, fiber, accelerants, residue, dirt, and glass. Hands should also be bagged to preserve any tissue, broken fingernails, or gunpowder that may be retrieved from the hands and fingers. Hands may also suffer postmortem damage during the recovery; if bagged, the nature of such damage is revealed in the damage to the material in which the hands are bagged.

Feet and shoes should be bagged while still on the body to preserve any trace evidence in the shoe soles. Footwear is often dislodged during traditional recovery procedures and along with it any trace evidence lodged in the soles of shoes may also be lost. Footwear evidence is especially important in recovery operations involving an unidentified body or body parts. All bags placed on hands and feet must be placed with due regard to the possibility of leaving postmortem ligature marks. The shod foot resists burning, decomposition, marine animal depredations, and water damage more consistently than do hands and especially fingers.

Personal effects, clothing, and gross anatomical features are the first items available for examination in attempting to determine the identification of a submerged body. In mass disasters (air crashes), descriptions of clothing and personal effects are provided by next of kin. Billfolds contain driver's licenses, credit cards, and personal papers. Jewelry is often unique and engraved. Keys are often distinctive in design and can be recognized as door keys, auto keys, briefcase keys, and suitcase keys. A successful unlocking provides a tentative identification.

## Postmortem Changes

After death physicochemical changes occur in submerged bodies just as they do in bodies on land; however postmortem intervals may be more difficult to determine based on salinity, bacteria, temperature, and depth. One of the first postmortem changes involves the eye. A thin corneal film may begin to develop within minutes of death. Corneal cloudiness develops within 3 h of death. If the eyes are closed, the appearance of corneal filming and clouding may be seriously delayed. Often a deceased has what is known as the "lazy eyelid," where the lack of muscle rigidity allows the eyelid to fall half over the eye. An examination of the eye will reveal that the lower exposed half has developed corneal filming while the upper half, still damp and protected from the air, has not. As the result of water immersion, the corneal filming that ordinarily occurs on dry land should not be evident in recent drowning victims and the existence of corneal filming in a drowning victim calls for an explanation.

Once the heart no longer circulates blood through the body, gravity causes blood to pool in the lower parts. The pooled blood imparts a purple color to the lower body parts and paleness to the upper body. This discoloration is known as postmortem lividity. In deaths that occur on land the location of lividity may reveal the body has been moved after death. Bodies in water should show little evidence of lividity because of the water's buoyancy. If lividity is prominent, death before submersion should be suspected. Lividity can be manufactured in fast-moving water where the current creates a gravitational pull independent of the earth's gravity on a stationary body, usually made stationary as a product of entanglement or entrapment. Lividity in those circumstances should appear in the downstream parts of the body.

Marine life feeds on the soft part of the victim's face. Often postmortem injuries to the eyelids, lips, nose, and ears are mistaken for traumatic antemortem injuries. A variety of algae may cover the exposed parts of the body, giving a green or black hue to those areas. A body may be so covered with algae that to make a determination of gender or race would be difficult.

Most police believe that all unencumbered submerged bodies float as a result of decomposition gases. The flotation of a submerged body is dependent upon the production of gases as decomposition progresses. Carbon dioxide, methane, sulfur dioxide, ammonium sulfide, and hydrogen sulfide make up the bulk of these gases, and they all have two characteristics that militate against postmortem flotation: they are water-soluble and easily compressed (water pressure increases 6.6 kg (14.7 lb) every 9.9 m (33 ft) of depth). At greater depths, where the water exceeds 33 m (100 ft) and the water temperature is less than 38 °F (3.33 °C), the body may never float. The depth impedes the production of decomposition gases sufficiently to let those that are created dissolve into the surrounding medium.

## Passenger Aircraft Crashes

### Large Aircraft

Aircraft crashes are especially visible because of the attention accorded them by the media, the great number of airports, the great number of aircraft, and the potential for large numbers of injured and dead.

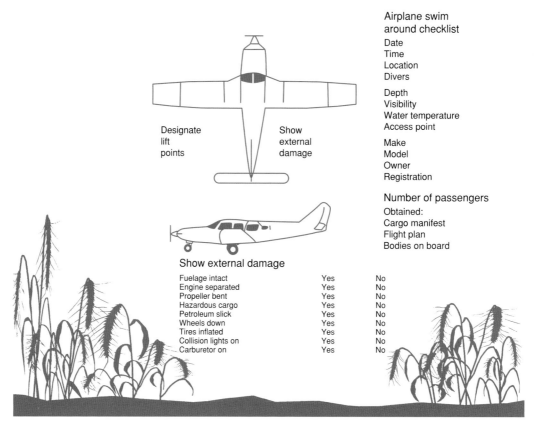

**Figure 5** Small aircraft swim-around checklist.

The primary objectives in an aircraft crash recovery operation are to:

1. recover the bodies
2. identify the bodies
3. reconstruct the events leading to the crash.

The recovery and identification of the passengers is generally the most time-consuming part of an air crash investigation, especially if that investigation is taking place underwater. Identification can be positive or presumptive. Positive identification is based on pre- and postmortem comparisons of dental records, fingerprints, palm prints, and footprints or DNA profiling. A positive identification is identification beyond reasonable doubt. A presumptive identification is an identification that is less than certain. A presumptive identification requires several points of inconclusive comparisons that cumulatively establish the legal identity of the body.

In all crashes, the specter of a human-caused explosion hovers. All clothing, personal effects, and body parts should be handled in the same fashion as for a known bombing. Any searches should include detonator components among the items sought. Aircraft parts should be recovered and documented, like any other evidence. Even in a crash where there is confirmation of accidental causes, those causes will be best discovered and corroborated by treating the recovery operation as a criminal investigation.

**Small Aircraft**

The crash of a small aircraft poses a different challenge to underwater investigations. Such aircraft are often intact. In the investigation of this type of crash, a preliminary swim-around should be conducted to ascertain gross features of the aircraft, passengers, and cargo. Occupants may still be strapped in their seats. In many instances, the entire aircraft and occupants can be lifted intact to the surface without disturbing the interior of the craft or destroying evidence (**Figure 5**).

## Conclusion

People flock to recreational waterways in vast numbers. As the number of people using such waterways increases, so too do the number of accidents, drownings, violent crimes, and homicides. Criminals often seek a watery repository for weapons and other evidence of wrongdoing. It has become an integral part of the police function to provide resources that can be deployed to retrieve this evidence. It is also becoming more common to find agencies with large bodies of water within their jurisdiction having underwater investigators with the specialized equipment and training necessary to process an underwater crime scene.

## See Also

**Crime-scene Investigation and Examination:** Collection and Chain of Evidence; Major Incident Scene Management; Recovery of Human Remains; Suspicious Deaths; **Odontology:** Overview

## Further Reading

Becker RF (1994) *Processing the Underwater Crime Scene.* Springfield, IL: Charles Thomas.

Becker RF (2001) *Criminal Investigation.* Gaithersburg: Aspen.

Fierro MF (1994) Identification of human remains. In: Spitz WU (ed.) *Medicolegal Investigation of Death,* 3rd edn., pp. 71–117. Springfield, IL: Charles Thomas.

Hendrick W, Zaferes A (2000) *Public Safety Diving.* Saddlebrook: PennWell.

Horton M (2001) *Public Safety Diver.* Miami Shores, FL: International Association of Nitrox and Technical Divers.

Perper JA (1994) Time of death and changes after death: anatomical considerations. In: Spitz WU (ed.) *Medicolegal Investigation of Death,* 3rd edn., pp. 14–49. Springfield, IL: Charles Thomas.

Spitz WU (1994) Drowning. In: Spitz WU (ed.) *Medicolegal Investigation of Death,* 3rd edn., pp. 498–515. Springfield, IL: Charles Thomas.

Teather RG (1983) *The Underwater Investigator.* Fort Collins: Concept Systems.

Teather RG (1994) *Encyclopedia of Underwater Investigations.* Best: Flagstaff.

# Recovery of Human Remains

**H B Baldwin**, Forensic Enterprises, Inc., Orland Park, IL, USA

**C P May**, Criminal Justice Institute, Little Rock, AR, USA

## Back to Basics

For the purpose of this article, the recovery of human remains is defined as the actual recovery of human remains from all crime scenes. This article focuses on the procedures that should be accomplished when removing human remains from death scenes and the safe deposition of these remains within a secure mortuary storage. Regardless of the type of death investigation, certain basic procedures should

be followed. Most crime scenes are secured prior to the arrival of the medical examiner/coroner official. The official will need to have proper identification so that he/she can identify him/herself to others at the crime scene. This will go a long way in allowing easy access to the crime scenes since most crime scenes are well secured by police officers. Once at the scene, the official will need to identify the lead investigator and other essential officials at the scene. The lead investigator will need to provide the official with all pertinent information about the case, essentially the who, what, where and when of the case.

Before the official enters the scene he/she must exercise good safety procedures. Hazards at crime scenes may include crowd control, building structure collapse, poisonous gases, and traffic. Environmental and physical threats must be removed in order to conduct a death investigation safely.

The lead investigator should conduct a walk-through with the official to provide an overview of the entire scene. This walk-through will help the official to understand the parameters of the scene and the dynamics of the scene. Potential evidence should be identified so that it is not destroyed or contaminated upon removal of the deceased.

The crime scene is the responsibility of the investigating law enforcement agency. The scene needs to be well documented by notes, photography, and sketching. Physical evidence at the crime scene must be protected from destruction and the scene must be protected from contamination. The official needs to work closely with the investigating agency to provide additional knowledge and support to the investigative process. Death investigations are a team effort. The medical examiner/coroner is a critical part of that team.

In any death investigation, all law enforcement officials involved have specific responsibilities; attempts to meet these responsibilities often impact the efforts of others. A crime scene can be handled in numerous ways and each case may dictate a different approach.

In processing a "normal" death scene the primary and secondary area of the scene must be identified. The primary represents that area where the body is located. The secondary area is the area leading to the primary death scene. For example, if a body is in the middle of a room, the primary area of the death scene is the room and is well defined by the walls, floors, and ceiling. The secondary area will represent all avenues to the room, including the outside yard. How did the suspect enter and leave the scene? Did he/she drive to the scene? These are all secondary areas of the crime scene.

A recommended protocol to be used by law enforcement to process a crime scene is as follows:

1. interview: gather and verify information
2. examine: examine and evaluate the crime scene
3. photograph: photograph the crime scene
4. sketch: sketch the crime scene
5. process: process the crime scene.

Before removing the deceased from the scene, several things must have already occurred. The scene must be both secured and safe for all those present. The scene needs to be well documented and evidence collected and secured properly. The documentation of the position of the body will play an important role when reconstructing or interpreting the scene. Blood stain patterns on the body or clothing are critical and need to be documented and protected for the pathologist. Other evidence associated with the body will also be important. This includes but is not limited to trace evidence such as hair and fibers, bodily fluid, including blood and seminal fluid, and impression evidence on the victim's skin or latent fingerprints on the skin. It will need to be determined at the scene what processing will need to be done before the body is removed. The potential for evidence is most critical in and around the body. Each death investigation is different and must be handled on an individual case basis. Only once these procedures have been accomplished should the body be removed from the scene.

Outdoor death scenes present unique situations because there are no physical barriers that tell us the size of the crime scene. The dimensions of the scene as well as the primary and secondary scenes need to be defined and secured. The potential for physical evidence in the outdoor scene is the same as indoor, with the additional potential of impression evidence such as footwear, tire impression, and possibly ridge detail on the ground or vegetation from the suspect. The medical examiner/coroner must be cognizant of this potential for evidence. The removal of the deceased could easily destroy or contaminate the evidence and crime scene.

Contamination of crime scenes is usually eliminated by the use of personal protective equipment (PPE). The PPE usually consists of a mask, jump suit, gloves, booties, and possible head cover. All of these items are disposable. Often the evidence unit may be seen wearing only booties, mask, and gloves in addition to their normal clothes. This is for their protection rather than a contamination issue.

Death investigations are normally classified as homicides, suicides, accidental, or natural. The potential exists that some deaths are not what they appear. That is the reason why all death investigations should be handled using the same procedures and methodologies. All deaths should be considered as potential homicides until proven otherwise.

## Additional Duties of the Medical Examiner/Coroner

At a death scene where law enforcement is present, the medical examiner/coroner's duties are limited to just the body. However, in deaths determined to be natural or accidental, law enforcement may not need to be present. Additional duties will need to be performed by the medical examiner/coroner in these situations. He/she will not have the luxury of having the "check and balance system" to work with; he/she will have to do the documentation, collection, and processing that law enforcement would normally do in these situations. This includes establishing a chain of custody for the evidence collected.

In all situations where a body is moved for transportation to a mortuary, the body should be properly recovered and transported. If the deceased is not handled properly, crucial evidence could be lost or destroyed. Documentation should further include observations such as fluid on the body as froth, purge, and bleeding from orifices. Additional considerations for evidence potential may include the fragile evidence of latent prints on the deceased's skin. The suspect may have touched, moved, or carried the deceased. This action leads to the potential of latent prints from the suspect left on the victim's skin or other clothing such as shoes.

Postmortem changes also need to be identified and documented. Some of these changes include livor, rigor, degree of decomposition, insect activity, scene temperature, and body temperature. This information will assist in establishing the time of death, corroborate witness statements, and indicate if the body has been moved after death. Complete photography and written documentation is required to document accurately the condition of the body when found and the condition of the scene.

Thoroughly securing the scene will prevent contamination and destruction of evidence. A command post concept should be used to have essential personnel, equipment, and communications limited to a specific area. A log listing the names, agency, and time entered/left of all individuals documents the personnel arriving and leaving the scene. An additional secured area should be identified and used to decontaminate those entering or leaving the scene to prevent additional cross-contamination of the scene or prevent the scene from cross-contaminating others and their equipment. Most death investigations have some form of biological fluids present and consequently create biohazard issues. Any potential biohazard must be decontaminated and detained within the secured area of the scene.

Every death investigation scene is different. No two are identical. This requires the medical examiner/coroner to think carefully about how the body is to be handled and moved without destroying evidence and contaminating the scene or body. The deceased body should be considered as a piece of evidence. Consequently, the body will need to be packaged and sealed, just like any piece of physical evidence. This can be accomplished by placing the body in a disposable body bag and then sealing and marking the bag, as with any evidence container. The date, incident number, and officer's initials should be included. A seal should be placed over the zipper of the bag to ensure the evidence bag is not tampered with between the scene and mortuary. However, before placing the body in a bag and sealing, the body should be laid on a white sheet. The sheet is then folded over the body and placed in the body bag. A backer board can be placed under the sheet to provide a rigid surface for easier removal and keeping the body in the same position as it was found. Wrapping the body in a white sheet and placing it in a body bag ensures that all trace evidence on the body is kept packaged within the white sheet. The medical examiner/coroner must maintain jurisdiction over the body. This action protects the chain of custody as the body is moved from the scene for an autopsy, specimen collection, or storage. Following packaging, the body should be transported directly to a mortuary where it is placed in a secured facility until the autopsy or specimen collection is completed.

Environmental conditions (i.e., rain, snow, wind, sun) can complicate the removal of a body from an outdoor scene. Geographic location and terrain should also be taken into consideration. Evidence potential is the same at outdoor and indoor scenes. However, latent prints and footwear impressions may be developed on the vegetation around the body in an outdoor scene.

If the death scene is a vehicle, additional complications may result because of the limited space for investigators to maneuver. Additional problems that may be encountered include the environmental conditions and any hazards. Vehicles present a unique problem in evidence recovery because of the different textures and surfaces present. The use of the backer board as described above will greatly assist in the removal process.

When removing a body from water or a fire, the same procedure as previously described should be followed. The body is wrapped in a sheet, then placed in a body bag, sealed, and transported. Documentation of the scene is the same. A sample of the water from which the body was found should be collected and analyzed for possible contaminates.

## Search Techniques for Human Remains

Because of the potential for scattering of the bones or hidden evidence, surface recovery of skeletal remains or the recovery of a buried body is different than most other scenes. The primary event in the recovery of the remains in these types of circumstances is finding the body. Most remains are found by accident. In the Midwest states of the USA a majority of the remains are found in the fall or spring by hunters, farmers, or others such as hikers in the woods and construction workers performing excavations at job sites. Once the remains are found the primary area of recovery is now defined. However, the secondary area of the scene should not be forgotten.

Remains can also be found incident to searching an area specified by investigative leads or informants. Before starting a search, the information received from informants or the result of investigative leads must be verified. Once the search area is defined and the information is verified, an evaluation, with respect to staffing levels and equipment needs should be conducted and a recovery team established. The team should consist of a team leader and searchers as well as crime-scene personnel for photography, sketching, collection of evidence, and the recovery of the remains. A detailed map of the area in question and aerial photos to show the layout of the search scene may be useful. Securing the assistance of someone who is familiar with the area can provide insight concerning the terrain and any unforeseen issues such as changes made to the area which have not been documented.

The team leader must also take comfort conditions into account. This might include weather conditions, food for the workers, bathroom facilities, plenty of liquids for drinking and water for cleaning up.

Once the area has been evaluated and a team is established, the team should be informed of the object of the search and how to look for it. Do not assume that they know what to do. Have a meeting before the search to explain in detail the objective of the search.

Search methods that can be useful for all outdoor crime scenes are circle, grid, strip, and zone. The method selected will depend entirely on the terrain to be searched and the amount of staff available. Always have the area searched twice, but not by the same person. Another person may find what the first person missed.

When using any of the search techniques, if one of the searchers finds an item the whole team stops until the item found can be photographed, its location sketched, then collected and marked for further examination later. After the item is marked or collected the searchers continue until another item is located. This process is continued until the entire area to be searched is covered.

Another search method to be considered is use of trained canines. Some dogs are trained specifically for recovering items of evidence in fields, while others are trained specifically for finding deceased bodies. If canines are to be used, they must be specifically trained for the search and recovery of human remains. Canines cross-trained for drugs, arsons, bombs, and other items of evidence are not as productive as canines specifically trained for recovery of human remains.

If you are looking for buried remains, use the same search methods as for surface recoveries but look for different search indicators, such as disturbances in vegetation, compacted soil, evidence of animal activity, and changes in soil coloration that may reflect a disturbance of the soil. In this type of search it is imperative that the searchers are educated in the different types of burial indicator that may be observed. Because of time of the year and weather elements, burial indicators may be difficult to find. These indicators will vary based on the type of terrain being searched. Remember, you may be looking for pieces of a body, which could mean multiple burial sites, rather than one large burial site.

Some special problem areas for visual indicators are sandy beaches, desert areas, and cultivated land. The visual indicators discussed above will not be useful in these areas. Locating a burial site in these areas requires a different approach to the problem. Several nondestructive methods, including infrared photography, methane detectors, and aerial photography, should be considered before using methods such as probing or large equipment such as a bulldozer, which may damage valuable evidence along with the body.

## Surface Recovery

Once the search is completed and the body is located on the surface, the recovery site should be defined. Keep in mind that there may be extreme scattering of the bones or body parts by animals. The area encompassing the scattered bones may be less than 1 m or several meters. Some of the bones may never be found because of vast scattering or consumption by animals. Vegetation, dead leaves, or fallen trees or branches may cover the bones. This covering of the deceased may be intentional by the suspect to camouflage the body.

Following the location of the remains and defining the recovery area, proceed as with any other crime scene. The area should be secured, examined, evaluated, photographed, sketched, and processed. An evidence-free access area to and from the site should also be established. An outer-perimeter search must be completed to locate other body parts or physical evidence. A command post should be set up, preferably away from the recovery site. A checkpoint should also be set up to check personnel and limit the number of people who are entering the site, just as would be done with any other crime scene. One way of limiting the difficulties caused by other people entering the scene is to take Polaroid or digital pictures of the site and leave them at the command post for viewing. Do not permit anyone to rush you. These scenes should be done right the first time. There are no second chances.

After photographing and sketching the scene, the primary area should be cleared of all vegetation and debris. This must be completed without disturbing the remains or any of the physical evidence that is present. Again, photos should be taken of the new "clean" site. A metal detector should be used prior to any further processing. Any items located with the detector should be marked with a wood or plastic stake for future reference. Using rope or string, a grid should be established for the purpose of locating the items by measurements and for ease in placing the items on a sketch. The grid should be measured so that the sides are square to each other. Plot all evidence and remains on the sketch. Close-up photographs should be taken of all evidence prior to removal. Of course the photographs should be taken with a scale to show the size of the item.

All evidence collected should be packaged separately. As a rule of thumb, each item of evidence should be packaged in a paper product unless it is liquid, in which case it should be placed in a glass vial. Paper product means paper fold, paper bag, or cardboard box. The remains of the deceased should be packaged separately if that is the way they were found. If the body is intact, use a wooden backer board, white sheet, and body bag.

Once the surface of the site has been cleared of all remains and evidence, recheck the area with a metal detector. If there are no further readings with the detector, then examine and excavate the top 15 cm (6 in.) of soil for any additional evidence or remains/bones. In some instances the remains have gone through a self-burial. Any object placed on the surface of the ground can work its way into the ground to some extent, depending on weight, ground density, and weather conditions. This will of course depend on the terrain of the area, the amount of time that has elapsed, and the weather conditions.

In removing the top centimeters of soil we have found that the best method is to cut the area into strips of about 15 cm (6 in.) wide and then to remove the soil from the strips a section at a time. This material should then be sifted with a fine sifter/screen. A sifter of 0.5 (1/4 in.) or 1 cm (1/8 in.) mesh should be used so that projectiles or teeth are not missed. Once this is completed one can be assured that the maximum amount of evidence and remains from this site have been collected. The one tooth that may be missed may be the tooth needed to make a positive identification of the deceased.

The possibility of contaminants in the soil beneath the remains should be considered. A sample of the soil should be collected for further analysis at a laboratory along with a standard of the soil from the general area.

Finally, all other evidence or body parts in the area outside the recovery site should be recovered. This recovery should be handled and processed as thoroughly as any other crime scene.

The length of time spent from the initial search to locating the remains to the completion of the processing of the site may be several days or weeks. Because of this time element, one must take into account the weather conditions and plan accordingly.

## Excavation Techniques

The same basic procedures that apply to surface recoveries also apply to excavations. The difference is that most of the evidence and the remains are below ground level.

Once the burial site is located and defined, an excavation method should be chosen. There are basically three methods of excavating the ground around the body: hole, trench, and table.

Because of the ease and comfort it provides personnel while removing the remains and evidence, many investigators prefer the table method. However, the time-consuming nature of some soils may make using this method time- and cost-prohibitive.

Regardless of the method chosen, the position of the body under the ground should be estimated before initiating the excavation. This is not as difficult as it sounds. Some portion of the body should already be visible because it has been determined that there is a body there. Based on what is seen, one can overestimate the position and dig around it.

As with any of these methods, the soil should be removed in strips approximately 30 cm (12 in.) wide and 15 cm (6 in.) in depth. The soil should be hand-checked and sifted as the different layers/strips are

removed. To accomplish these tasks it will be necessary to have one qualified person in the pit and at least four other people using the sifters.

What are you looking for in the soil? Anything that is not soil could be evidence or bones! Coins from victims' and/or suspects' pockets, wine bottle caps that can be physically matched to a wine bottle found in the suspect's vehicle, skin tissue with ridge detail that can identify the victim, soy beans and corn stalks that can provide a time element of the burial, magazines that can also provide a time element, and a whole host of other unusual items, not excluding weapons and projectiles, can be and have been found. Expect the unexpected and remember that any and all forms of evidence can be found in a gravesite.

The least cumbersome method of removing the body is to wrap it in a white sheet and place it on to a wooden backer board (all fire departments use them) before removing it from the grave. This will keep the body intact and make transportation easier. Once the body is removed, do not forget to check the ground under it for the suspect's footwear impressions in the soil. The soil beneath the body must also be removed for several centimeters and sifted again to locate evidence, bones, projectiles, and teeth.

Unfortunately, cases where the buried body is literally yanked out of the ground and taken away from the scene with no thought to evidence either in the grave or on the body are not uncommon. Just because a body is buried does not mean it cannot tell a story or point a finger at the murderer. If this was a fresh homicide scene and the body was in a parking lot, wouldn't one use everything available and do everything possible to process the scene? Then why is it that when a body is buried investigators often have a different attitude? Probably because it is something with which they are unfamiliar. One needs to take time in the recovery of the remains and try to plan for the welfare of coworkers, the changing weather conditions, equipment needs, and 24-h security at the scene.

## See Also

**Crime-scene Investigation and Examination:** Collection and Chain of Evidence; Major Incident Scene Management; Suspicious Deaths; **Crime-scene Management, Systems:** Continental Europe; United Kingdom; United States of America

## Further Reading

*Crime Scene Investigation: A Guide for Law Enforcement* (2000) Washington, DC: US Department of Justice.
Fisher BAJ (2004) *Techniques of Crime Scene Investigation*, 7th edn. New York: Elsevier Science.

Geberth VJ (2000) *Practical Homicide Investigation,* 3rd edn. New York: Elsevier Science.

Hawthorne MR (1999) *First Unit Responder.* Boca Raton, FL: CRC Press.

*Medicolegal Death Investigation Guidelines* (2001) Washington, DC: US Department of Justice.

Sansone SJ (1998) *Police Photography,* 4th edn. Cincinnati, OH: Anderson.

Siegel JA, Saukko PJ, Knupfer GC (2000) *Encyclopedia of Forensic Sciences.* Academic Press.

Spitz WV, Fisher RS (1993) *Medicolegal Investigation of Death,* 2nd edn. Springfield, IL: Charles C. Thomas.

Svenson A, Wendel O, Fisher BAJ (1993) *Techniques of Crime Scene Investigation,* 5th edn. New York: Elsevier Science.

# Suspicious Deaths

**J Horswell**, Forensic Executives, Upper Mt. Gravatt, QLD, Australia

## Background

To understand suspicious death investigation, police officers and specialist forensic scientists tasked with this type of investigation should understand the various mechanisms involved in suspicious deaths.

This would be second nature to a forensic pathologist; however, others who attend scenes of crime, such as senior investigating officers (SIOs), crime-scene investigators, and other more specialist forensic practitioners, should also be conversant with forensic medicine and forensic pathology. This is now certainly the case for crime-scene investigators; however it has not always been the case. With wider cross-training in these various forensic specialties, those specialists tasked with a suspicious death investigation where all participants will know where each other's specialist function begins and ends.

Kirk's view that any criminal investigation is a dual investigation, involving individuals and material items, is as true today as it was when he discussed these issues. Normally the coordination of a major criminal investigation involving a suspicious death scene certainly is a dual investigation, and it is normally delegated to a senior investigating office (SIO). A senior investigator (SI) should also be appointed to coordinate the gathering of all oral evidence from witnesses and suspects (individuals). Likewise, a senior forensic investigator (SFI) should coordinate the overall forensic investigation, gathering information and potential evidentiary material.

## Death as a Major Crime

In the community, the most serious crime is that of the intentional killing of one person by another and it is therefore necessary that each of these events be thoroughly investigated by a team of specialists, including SIOs, crime-scene investigators, fingerprint officers, a forensic photographer, and a forensic pathologist. In some jurisdictions the crime-scene investigator is also the photographer and a police medical officer may also visit the scene as opposed to a forensic pathologist, who may only become involved in the mortuary. If this is the case, the police medical officer should communicate with the forensic pathologist either before or during the preliminary stages of the postmortem examination.

The crime-scene investigator is the individual who is tasked with recording and processing the crime scene. He is also, in conjunction with his team colleagues, tasked with the interpretation of the crime scene. We often hear of forensic pathologists who attend crime scenes to gather information in relation to the cause and manner of death trying to take over the scene investigation: it is not their responsibility to usurp the legitimate role of the crime-scene investigator. The presence of a crime-scene manager at the scene will prevent this occurring as it will be the crime-scene manager who directs the application of all forensic resources.

## Overview of the Death Scene

All death scenes should be secured and recorded photographically and diagrammatically. If the information to hand, backed by the postmortem, suggests that the death was due to natural causes then the scene should not be processed any further. However, if there are signs at the scene, and other information suggests that the deceased died in suspicious circumstances, and this is reinforced by signs of a struggle or anything unusual, further processing for latent impressions and trace evidence should take place. If the results of the postmortem are not available and there are no obvious signs indicating how the deceased may have died then thorough processing of the scene should be undertaken. It is far easier to throw material away later if the postmortem reveals death was due to natural causes. What is not so easy is for crime-scene investigators to return to a scene that may no longer be in police possession, and which would have been contaminated, and then search for latent and/or trace material. Many jurisdictions conduct immediate postmortem examinations where sudden death has occurred and there are questions that remain unanswered. Of course some jurisdictions have backlogs and it may be several days before a postmortem takes place. When there are questions that require urgent answers then postmortem examinations should be carried out as soon as possible.

There are now two distinct tasks ahead of the crime-scene investigator. The first is the technical recording and retrieval of potential evidence from the scene. Just as important is the second, the reconstruction in the mind of the crime-scene investigator of the events surrounding the death. The technical issues will be discussed first, followed by the reconstruction issues.

## Crime-Scene Security

When a suspicious death is discovered, the death scene should be secured immediately so that no one has the opportunity to change it in any way.

Indoor scenes will be easy to secure and protect. Outdoor scenes present challenges. The more urban the outdoor scene, the more difficult it is to secure and there will be the need for several scene guards. The more remote the scene, the easier it is to secure. The weather and movement of animals through outdoor scenes add a dimension to the processing of a crime scene and the condition in which the deceased may be found.

## Observations

The crime-scene investigator should take photographs immediately, before anything is moved. Notes and a sketch should also be made at this time. The deceased's location relative to other objects and structures within the scene is very important. The position of the deceased is plotted: the head and groin of the deceased are good points on the body to use for plotting its position. Accurate measurements should be noted to place the items within the scene in the sketch in the same locations as they appear in the scene.

The deceased is the most valuable piece of potential evidence at any death scene. Hence, a systematic and thorough examination of the deceased should be undertaken at every death scene. Blood spillage or spatter should be noted and will remain after the removal of the body. Weather conditions, location, and poor lighting may mask some faint injuries and trace evidence on the body, therefore the crime-scene investigator should document in writing, by sketch, and by photography all information about the body that can be gathered at the scene. The remainder will have to wait until the postmortem examination, which is the role of the forensic pathologist.

The environment where the body was found will affect the rate of body cooling. The wind conditions, temperature, and the presence of any rain should be noted. The crime-scene investigator will need to develop a general description of the deceased, including gender, race, age, height, and weight.

One of the most important questions that needs answering is: did death occur at this location? The position in which the deceased was discovered is of particular importance as it will provide an indication as to whether the deceased was moved or not before being discovered. The presence or absence of rigor mortis or stiffness of the body, whether absent, minimal, moderate, advanced or complete, will help the crime-scene investigator determine if the person died at that locus in the position as found. Some crime-scene investigators with relevant training and experience may feel they are in a position to evaluate rigor mortis and hypostasis. A pink-purple discoloration is usually present at the lowest point of the body. This is due to the settling of the blood by gravitation and the location and state of fixation should be noted and photographed. For example, unfixed livor blanches white when moderate pressure is applied, as opposed to fixed livor mortis, which remains the same color when pressure is applied. If livor mortis is noted on the deceased in areas not consistent with forming in the lowest parts of the body then the crime-scene investigator should consider the possibility that the deceased was moved after death. However well trained a crime-scene investigator may feel he/she is, these observations should be discussed with the forensic pathologist. If the forensic pathologist was not in a position to attend the crime scene then photographs would assist in such discussions.

The blood flow and spatter patterns should match the position of the body. If the scene is one of apparent violence then the blood flow patterns may indicate the type of weapon and how it was used.

The crime-scene investigator must seek answers to the following questions: is trace evidence at the scene consistent with the death having occurred at this location? Does the body contain any trace evidence that is unusual for this location, for example, mud on soles of shoes, grass, or seed material embedded in or found on the clothing when the deceased was located inside a building? Is the death one that can be attributed to natural causes? Are there any external signs of violence? Is there anything amiss or out of the ordinary regarding the scene? Is there anything about the scene that arouses the crime-scene investigator's suspicions?

The crime-scene investigator should consider several hypotheses and then see if there is any evidence to disprove or support any of them. The physical evidence present, or absent, along with the known facts, should be sufficient to enable the crime-scene investigator to develop a reasonable hypothesis as to what has happened at the scene, however, this is not always possible. Suspicions may not be aroused until the postmortem reveals something that was not apparent at the scene. The forensic pathologist may, however, provide the investigator with a definitive suspicion of the cause of death. This gives investigators leads to start their lines of enquiry.

## Removal of the Deceased

The protocols for moving the deceased should be discussed with the forensic pathologist. Before the deceased is moved from the scene the crime-scene investigator should be available to assist the forensic pathologist in the examination of the deceased, systematically noting and photographing trauma and locating and removing potential trace evidence that may be lost on moving the deceased. Best practice suggests that the deceased's hands, feet, and head should be bagged using paper bags, as the use of plastic and any subsequent refrigeration will cause the bag to sweat. The bags should be large enough to be taped securely around the wrist, ankle, or neck and allow "ballooning" over the area to be protected. The body should then be rolled on to a clean white sheet and placed in a clean new body bag. This will then allow a thorough examination of the area that was previously covered by the deceased.

## Information-Gathering and Activities at the Death Scene

Forensic science is an information science and it is imperative to gain as much information from the scene and secondary scenes as possible. Forms should be designed in such a way that nothing is missed. These form the basis of the crime-scene investigator's notes made at the scene and his/her examinations. The following is a list of what should be recorded.

### Report to Crime-Scene Investigators: Receipt of Information

- Date and time of report
- Form of report (phone, fax, radio message)
- Crime-scene investigator receiving the report
- Crime-scene investigator(s) tasked with the case
- Summary of what has happened
- Officer at crime scene in charge of scene.

### Arrival by Crime-Scene Investigators at the Death Scene

- Time of arrival at scene
- Date of arrival at scene
- Scene address or location
- Weather conditions
- Temperature
- Street lighting if present and whether on, if dark
- Police officer in charge of the scene
- History of the incident as known by first officer
- Name and address of victim
- Names and addresses of relatives
- Determine the scope and ensure that adequate crime-scene protection and security is put in place
- Call for additional police for guard duty if required
- Post guards, barricade, rope or tape off crime-scene area
- Ensure that first officer is recording in a log all those who are there and have visited and all those who may visit the scene whilst the first officer is guarding the scene
- Identify a path that allows entry and exit to the critical area of the scene without disturbing potential evidentiary material
- Set aside an area for equipment and rubbish collection during crime-scene processing
- Ensure all specialists are briefed regarding eating, smoking, touching items, and using toilets
- Ensure briefings occur with SIO at regular intervals.

### Initial Death-Scene Assessment

- Location of the victim
- Enter death scene
- Ascertain and verify death – an absolute priority: this is sometimes very obvious and at other times less than obvious
- Note condition of deceased
- Implement procedures to protect any potential evidence and protect the critical areas from damage by weather or exposure or by the movement of specialist personnel in and out of the scene
- Commence death/crime-scene investigation.

### Death-Scene Investigation

- Identify the path that may have been used by the suspect to enter and exit the critical area of the scene: it is here that the crime-scene investigator should look for latent and trace evidence
- Allocate specialist resources to undertake a team-based approach to processing the death scene
- The death-scene search should not begin until all the photographs, sketches, measurements, fingerprint search, and narrative have been completed

- Ensure scene guard advises the crime-scene manager of the arrival of specialists
- Ensure records are kept of their names, specialty, and time of arrival and departure
- Record the death scene by photographs (video and stills), narrative, and sketch plan (observe, describe, and record)
- Record any alterations to the death scene that were made as a matter of investigative necessity or during the emergency response
- Record the following:
  - Lights: on or off?
  - Doors: open, closed, locked, or unlocked?
  - Deceased: moved or cut down?
  - Windows: open, closed, locked, or unlocked?
  - Names of all persons who moved the deceased before and during the death scene examination
  - Any furniture moved or anything touched?
  - Gas turned on or off at mains?
  - Gas on or off at appliances?
  - Electricity turned on or off at mains?
  - Electrical appliances on or off? Note televisions, radios, and clocks
  - If there is a vehicle involved, is the engine off or on? Is the motor cold or cool, warm or hot?
  - Ensure that the telephone within the death scene is not used
  - Does the telephone have an answering machine?
  - Check last number rung into the premises
  - Make a recording of any messages or take possession of any tape present
  - Check for mobile phones and/or pages and record messages and last numbers called, both incoming and outgoing
  - Check any computers present for messages or written texts
  - Check any cameras present and develop any film on camera.

### Death-Scene Photographs

- The entire location where the death took place should be photographed externally and internally, from the general to the specific
- Critical areas and their relationship to the deceased and other areas
- Close-up views of any observable evidence with ruler
- Date and time photographs were taken
- Use of a form to record views, location, and frame number
- Type of film and camera used
- Number of exposures

- Overall view of premises from all four sides
- Front entrance to the building
- Hallways, if any
- Entrance to the room where the deceased was found
- General view of the deceased
- Facial view of deceased
- Full-length view of deceased
- Views of any visible wounds
- View of any visible evidence
- View of entrance and exit routes considered to be used by the suspect
- View of any signs of forced entry
- Close-up views of any apparent evidence
- Area beneath deceased after removal
- Any additional evidence found.

### Death-Scene Sketch

- Make a simple line drawing of the death scene on a sheet of clean paper
- The following information should be included:
  - Measurements and distance
  - A title block consisting of:
    - North
    - Name and title of sketcher
    - Date and time the sketch was made
    - Nature of the incident
    - Relating the death of (victim's name)
    - Location of the sketch
  - A legend, to identify any objects or articles within the scene
  - A scale depicting measurements used.

### Death-Scene Search

After surveying the overall crime scene, it should be easy to recognize the sequence in which evidence is to be collected and areas to be searched and in what order. The collection and search should be systematic, ensuring absolutely nothing is overlooked.

Priority in collection should be given to:

- any items that are in danger of being removed or destroyed by wind, rain, vehicles, animals, tides, and the movement of individuals at the scene
- the collection of any evidence which will enable access to the deceased or any critical area of the crime scene, such as along entry and exit paths
- those critical areas of the crime scene which may render the most evidence, or once processed, enable the removal of a body, or the remainder of the examination to be carried out
- areas which may give a quick indication as to the identity of any suspect(s)

- areas which when processed will permit the release of scene guards and other resources
- the general examination of the remainder of the crime scene for potential evidence.

In establishing the manner and sequence of collecting potential evidence, consideration must be given to the possible destruction of evidence and which approach will yield the best result in terms of useful information. Consultation with other specialists such as the forensic pathologist as to the sequence and method of collection may be necessary to ensure the best result; however, at the scene this may not always be possible.

The following sequence provides some examples of the collection sequencing:

- Macroscopic evidence should be collected from an area before it is powdered for fingerprints.
- Blood stains and forensic evidence should be collected from an area before searching for fingerprints.
- Sweepings from the floor need to be collected before adding fingerprint powder to the scene.
- Polished floors need to be examined first with oblique lighting to locate latent shoemarks and/or any bare footprints.
- Visible fibers, hairs, and other trace material should be collected from an area before applying general collection techniques, such as tapelifts, sweeping and vacuuming.
- Tapelift areas of interest before removing deceased persons (for blood seepage), as handling and movement of the body can cause subsequent loss of trace evidence which may not be seen again at the mortuary.
- Larger objects should be examined before smaller objects and all items should be packaged and labeled at the time of collection.
- The last items to be recovered would be the pieces of bedding, such as sheets and blankets, that were on a bed in which the deceased was found.

Methods of searching critical areas include grids that are larger in less critical areas and smaller in critical areas, or searching in a clockwise or counterclockwise direction from a fixed point, or conducting a line strip search. All these form part of conducting a professional systematic search of a death scene.

A systematic approach to the searching of death scenes reduces stress and fatigue and ensures a more comprehensive search and recovery operation, minimizing the chance of losing potentially valuable evidentiary material.

## Postmortem Examination

The deceased should then be transported to the mortuary for a full external and three-cavity postmortem examination.

The postmortem examination is usually conducted by an experienced (in most cases) and qualified forensic pathologist. The crime-scene investigator should be present at the postmortem, as should be the investigating officer or delegate. If the scene was attended by a police medical officer, and not a forensic pathologist, then the medical officer should also be present to provide any medical information that is already known and a medical assessment of the crime scene.

## Summary

After all the information is to hand from the crime scene and the postmortem examination, those involved should, from the available facts, be able to work out the cause and manner of death. Although modern forensic investigation is advanced, there will be times when the crime scene does not provide information and the postmortem does not reveal a definitive cause of death. These cases are the difficult ones.

## See Also

**Accreditation:** Crime Scene Investigators; **Crime-scene Investigation and Examination:** Collection and Chain of Evidence; Major Incident Scene Management; Recovery of Human Remains

## Further Reading

Bevel T, Gardner RM (2002) *Bloodstain Pattern Analysis,* 2nd edn. Boca Raton, FL: Chemical Rubber.
Brooks PR (1996) Foreword. In: *Geberth's Practical Homicide Investigation.* Boca Raton, FL: Chemical Rubber.
Fisher BAJ (2000) *Techniques of Crime Scene Investigation,* 6th edn. Boca Raton, FL: Chemical Rubber.
Geberth VJ (1983) *Practical Homicide Investigation – Tactics, Procedures, and Forensic Techniques.* New York: Elsevier.
Geberth VJ (1996) *Practical Homicide Investigation – Tactics, Procedures, and Forensic Techniques,* 3rd edn. Boca Raton, FL: Chemical Rubber.
Horswell J (2000) Major incident scene management. In: Siegal JA, *et al.* (eds.) *Encyclopaedia of Forensic Sciences,* pp. 428–432. London: Academic Press.
Horswell J (2000) Suspicious deaths. In: Siegal JA, *et al.* (eds.) *Encyclopaedia of Forensic Sciences,* pp. 462–466. London: Academic Press.

Hunter J, Roberts C, Martin A (1996) *Studies in Crime: An Introduction to Forensic Archaeology*. BT Batsford.

Kirk PL (1953) Introduction. In: *Crime Investigation*. New York: John Wiley.

Lee H, Palmbach T, Miller MT (2001) *Henry Lee's Crime Scene Handbook*. London: Academic Press.

Lee K (2004) The role of the pathologist at the crime scene. In: Horswell J (ed.) *The Practice of Crime Scene Investigation*, pp. 195–240. Boca Raton, FL: Chemical Rubber.

Robertson J (2004) Crime scene investigation: key issues for the future. In: Horswell J (ed.) *The Practice of Crime Scene Investigation*, pp. 399–406. Boca Raton, FL: Chemical Rubber.

# CRIME-SCENE MANAGEMENT, SYSTEMS

Contents
**Continental Europe**
**United Kingdom**
**United States of America**

## Continental Europe

**Y Schuliar**, Institut de Recherche Criminelle de la Gendarmerie Nationale, Rosny-sous-Bois, France
**B Marc**, Compiegne Hospital, Compiegne, France

### Introduction

The term "continental system" of crime scene management suggests the possible existence of a system that is followed uniformly throughout continental Europe. Obviously, this is not the case.

In contrast to the Anglo-Saxon systems, it seems possible to identify some specific continental approaches to crime scene management. There is an international consensus about the important role of crime scene management in the initial inquiry and the need to utilize specialists at the crime scene.

Hearsay evidence or that provided by weak or antagonistic eye-witnesses does not constitute strong evidence – judicial systems increasingly consider scientific evidence as more acceptable. Detectives and prosecutors employ forensic physicians and scientists not only to collect various samples, including blood stains, at the crime scene but also to give their technical advice on crime scene management.

Significant changes have occurred in the way investigations are carried out. Conventional police investigators, who inquire into circumstances and collect, from the scene of crime, as many "proofs" as they can, should be contrasted with the "scientific police" – specialists working in closed-door laboratories. Contemporary procedures used to investigate suspicious deaths involve several experts in medicolegal investigations. A coherent collaboration between technical and scientific police is essential in order to establish clear connections between crime scenes and laboratories, including quality assurance requirements. Magistrates who direct the judicial procedure not only require a basic level of knowledge of criminalistics but must also be assisted by forensic physicians and forensic scientists as scientific advisors.

### A Short Definition of the Crime Scene

Some Anglo-Saxon definitions of the crime scene are rather broad. For example, "crime scenes" refers to different places that may have been linked to a homicide (e.g., place of attack, place of burial). The definition extends to places where accidental deaths occurred.

The law, mainly used in continental European countries, does not give a definition of the crime scene. In French penal and penal procedure codes, the term "crime scene" is not used as such but rather it is referred to as the scene of a crime or an offense.

The crime scene is the main focus of criminalistics. On the basis of observations, photographs, enquiries, and samples, the laboratory fulfills both a scientific and an operational role in allowing the magistrate to reconstruct the events leading to a crime. A possible definition of crime scene is that it represents all places and persons linked to a crime or an offense that needs a judicial inquiry. So, crime scene includes several places (e.g., of an attack, of a burial, a car used to carry a dead body) and victims, close witnesses, and suspects.

## The Judicial Framework

A large part of continental Europe has been influenced by the Napoleonic code, just as common law spread far beyond England. In spite of various similarities, the two systems differ significantly, and a unified system of continental law does not really exist. Differences exist, for example, between northern European countries (Sweden and Germany), countries with an inquisitorial system (France, Netherlands, Spain, Portugal), and other countries, such as Italy, that have turned their procedures to a more adversarial mode.

Consider the French, German, and Dutch judicial systems. In the continental system, rules are clearly established (by means of codes) that define the role of police investigators and the judicial procedures to be followed from the very beginning of the process. Magistrates appreciate the modes of police action. If needed, they can accompany detectives from the crime scene to the end of the initial inquiry procedure. In the Netherlands, the Public Ministry plays a prominent role in the treatment of penal affairs. The Queen's Prosecutor directs the penal inquiry.

In France, investigators and crime scene technicians from the police or gendarmerie are under the direct authority of the Public Prosecutor (Procureur de la République) and report directly to this authority. Some have considered that this link could sometimes allow some investigators to be overconfident. On the other hand, forensic physicians and court experts are considered to be justice auxiliaries, and do not have a hierarchic link with the Public Prosecutor or magistrates.

In France, different legal frameworks are used to investigate a crime scene. Briefly, investigators and crime scene technicians can work within the "preliminary inquiry," "obvious crime or offense," or the "search for the causes of death" procedures.

The crime scene is legally protected and any prosecutor can be assigned to the case. The existing laws place conservation of crime scenes under the authority of the police.

Although investigators and crime scene technicians are under the authority of the Public Prosecutor, they have real autonomy in conducting the initial inquiry. Investigators can require a qualified person

to give them advice, e.g., a crime scene technician or a forensic physician. A statement (technical or medical report) is prepared in a form that can be used as evidence.

If the case seems important enough, in the French system, the Public Prosecutor can open a judicial inquiry. Then another magistrate (juge d'instruction) takes charge of the inquiry and directs it, including the technical requirements. The magistrate orders court experts to complete further investigations and observations in order to finish the initial work of the crime scene technicians. The experts are required to produce their results in the form of statements which they can support in court.

In Germany, the first examinations carried out by crime scene technicians and further examinations by experts could indeed be quite different. In the Netherlands, only the crime scene technician and the doctor produce expert statements.

In the continental system, magistrates and investigators create all kinds of hypotheses. They study witness reports and ask crime scene technicians, scientists, and experts to study samples and provide medical reports to verify their hypotheses.

However, in France, the fact that suspects can only be kept in custody for short periods (48 hours, followed by two 24 hour extensions) limits the use of scientific methods in custody.

## Professionals on the Crime Scene

In the continental system, crime scene sampling and observation are managed by police technicians, whereas in the UK these specialists are often civilians. Police staff used as crime scene technicians take a special training course for a few weeks, during which they learn how to sample, observe, and manage a crime scene.

For example, in France, local police units are responsible for the first investigations at any crime scene. They ask crime scene technicians, belonging to special units of judicial police, to make precise observations and search and collect useful samples and stains. These technicians are familiar with the correct packaging of judicial seals and their dispatch to laboratories. They counsel the inquiry director and the magistrate about examinations required, validity of results and samples, and questions and analyses to be completed by experts or expert laboratories.

In France, for important crime scene investigations (e.g., Concorde air crash, sect mass suicide, Mont Blanc tunnel fire), some laboratories such as the Gendarmerie Criminal Research Institute (Institut de recherche criminelle de la gendarmerie nationale) can send in specially trained technicians to sample and use special materials and protocols. In Germany, the KTI (Kriminalteschnischesinstitut) Institute for Criminal Investigation Techniques from the centralized BKA (Bundeskriminalamt) works in a similar way. In the Netherlands, forensic technical researchers handle investigations at crime scenes. They can meet, if necessary, with the National Forensic Institute experts to discuss any further examinations, without referring to the magistrate.

In the continental system, especially in France, technical investigations and procedures are not directed by a crime scene manager, a crime scene coordinator, or a specialist adviser sent by a centralized laboratory. What is now being debated in France is how to create a reinforced body of specialists in criminalistics able to manage and direct the first steps of any crime scene investigation for crime scene technicians and police officers as well as to counsel magistrates in charge.

The first step of this process has been accomplished in France by the police force. If necessary, a crime scene investigation team, having followed a complete course and become familiar with the special techniques and equipment useful at the crime scene, can be provided to any investigator.

No suspicious-death scene can be correctly managed without the help of a qualified forensic physician. The doctor should visit the scene of the death before the body is removed, to relate it to the surroundings and obtain a general impression of the circumstances, including an estimation of time of death and an interpretation of postmortem changes. The physician can also provide initial advice about the possible cause of death and help make body identifications.

Advice on the collection of trace evidence and recording of external appearances by photographs is helpful to the multidisciplinary team in charge of judicial investigations.

The French Society of Forensic Medicine has recently stressed the need for close and permanent cooperation between all specialists in forensic sciences. In most countries, irrespective of their judicial system, there is a shortage of qualified forensic physicians. In France, emergency forensic units that can provide qualified physicians at any moment to investigators, only function in large urban areas. This leaves large parts of the country without qualified doctors able to attend scenes of death.

Owing to the lack of qualified personnel or facilities, crime scene investigators often use general physicians to examine a body or undertake for an external examination when the body has been carried to a city morgue. This can lead to unfortunate situations, as a poorly performed external examination of a decedent may be worse than no external examination at all.

In contrast, the forensic physician must be able to assist the crime scene team at the crime scene. Helping the crime scene technicians in their observations and samplings, the forensic physician can also carry out blood and urine samplings in some circumstances, helping to obtain accurate results in the shortest possible time.

When the body is removed from the crime scene, a complete examination must be carried out, with photographs at each step of clothing removal. Information obtained from the postmortem examination can guide investigators in their further observations and trace evidence collection. On the one hand, knowledge of criminalistics and forensic science is required for a forensic physician to be fully qualified, according to European Union requirements for all qualified physicians in Europe. On the other hand, specialists in forensic sciences and criminalistics must be able to follow the observations of the forensic pathologist and seek more precise details, before carrying out a medicolegal autopsy.

## Operational Methods at the Crime Scene

Although there are fewer specialists and coordinators in the continental system than in the Anglo-Saxon one, the operational methods employed at crime scenes appear to be similar. The best intervention schedule is the following one:

- securing and controlling the death scene
- taking account of the scene
- formulating hypotheses and searching for trace evidence
- sampling fragile stains and samples
- limiting access
- managing the body
- discussing hypotheses.

Trace evidence can be divided into two groups: fragile trace evidence (e.g., footprints, biological stains, microtraces, gunshot residues, toxicological samples) and nonfragile trace evidence (e.g., weapons, documents, explosives, fire materials, tools traces, visible traces and stains, insects).

Operating modes, samplings, and trace evidence search all follow certain protocols and checklists. In Germany, the police force have available a leaflet describing searching and collecting trace evidence. In France, crime scene technicians have a similar brochure.

It is necessary to maintain permanent links between investigators and crime scene technicians in order to direct sampling according to proposed hypotheses.

This helps to optimize the order of intervention at the scene and synthesizes the collection of data in the quickest way.

In the Anglo-Saxon system, continuity of proof and validity of the trace evidence are of prime importance. Therefore, any lack or failure in this procedure means that the trace evidence must be rejected.

In France, judicial procedure is not as strict and the magistrate may decide whether some trace evidence can be considered valid even if they have not been collected following a well-defined procedure. Police officers who present trace evidence are under oath to tell nothing but the truth. In contrast, packaging protocols for samples are strictly codified. Sealed trace evidence of any kind can be sent to different specialists and laboratories.

In Germany, protocols exist only for the sealing of some documents and samples (blood samples). The nature and quality of various seals depend on the authority which has collected the sample. In the Netherlands, collected trace evidence is not sealed but is listed on an inventory.

## The Use of Electronic Data (Databases)

The technology used in crime scene management is constantly improving. As soon as possible, the latest improvements must be taken up by investigators at crime scenes. The use of databases, including DNA databases, firearm characteristics, foot/shoeprints, drugs, and paints (especially car paints), is a powerful means of linking different activities and identifying suspects.

Concerning DNA, continental legislation is far more restrictive than in the UK, from the viewpoint of the criteria of file registration and file access. Investigators in the UK can directly consult DNA files. In France, investigators must refer to a magistrate, but the new law on interior security in place from March 18, 2003 has simplified the means of access to DNA files of past criminals and sexual offenders.

## Links to Laboratories and Central Organizations

The presence of the laboratory personnel at the crime scene is far less frequent in the continental system than in the UK. In France, technicians, investigators, and magistrates must be advised of advances in the technical capacity to treat any trace of evidence. For this purpose, a continuous-education program is necessary. In the Netherlands, a front-desk concept has been introduced by the Netherlands Forensic Institute (NFI). According to this concept, police technicians and investigators can come to NFI to discuss with laboratory experts technical possibilities relating to a specific case and samples.

Most countries have developed systems that can provide tools to manage the crime scene. If the British HOLMES system seems advanced, the French police can now work on similar ANACRIM software.

## Finances

In the UK, the police have an annual budget for technical and scientific police and pay laboratories for their analysis and results. In contrast, in most continental countries, laboratories dedicated to forensic science are often public laboratories, whose analyses are not directly paid for, since they receive an annual budget for their activity and staff. Some authors believe that the latter system ensures a better quality of forensic inquiry.

## European Collaboration

Working groups of the European Network of Forensic Sciences Institutes (ENFSI) and OISIN programs of the European Union have allowed scientific links between European countries and tend to unify the technical process.

Recommendations for good practice of crime scene management have been formulated. The role of crime scene manager has been defined and stressed. Recommendations for correct forensic medicine protocols have also been delineated.

## Criticisms, Conclusions, and Prospects

In criminalistics, scientific advances are rapid and sensitive techniques can be developed for fragile traces of evidence and samples. Software tools are also available that help with crime scene management.

How to observe, what and how to sample, which priorities to give to some samples, how to package the various samples, when and how to refer to the laboratory are questions that can be best answered if the scientist and the forensic physician are present at the crime scene. This is becoming quite common. Technology obviously has a prominent place, in contrast to those judicial aspects that were so significant in the past. This is more evident in the continental systems than in the Anglo-Saxon one, and is beginning to be translated to parts of continental Europe. The judicial continental systems are quietly moving from an inquisitorial system to an accusatorial one, following the enhanced use of scientific search for evidence.

## See Also

**Crime-scene Management, Systems:** United Kingdom; United States of America

## Further Reading

Crispino F (1997) *Modélisation de la gestion de la scène de crime, Mémoire de Diplôme Postgrade de Criminalistique Chimique*. Lausanne: Institut de Police Scientifique et de Criminologie.

European Crime Scene Management Good Practice Manual (2000) *OISIN Funded Project to Develop Standards of Performance for Crime Scene Management*. Brussels: CEE.

Fisher BAJ (2000) *Techniques of Crime Scene Investigation*, 6th edn. Boca Raton, FL: CRC Press.

Geberth VJ (1997) *Practical Homicide Investigation. Checklist and Field Guide*. Boca Raton, FL: CRC Press.

Kirk P (1974) *Crime Investigation*, 2nd edn. New York: Wiley.

Lahri N (2003) *La gestion de la scène de crime: l'exemple anglo-saxon. Mémoire*. Paris: Centre de Prospective de la Gendarmerie Nationale, Direction Générale de la Gendarmerie Nationale.

Lee HC, Palmbach T, Miller MT (2001) *Henry Lee's Crime Scene Handbook*. London: Academic Press.

Nijboer JF, Sprangers WJJM (2000) *Harmonization in Forensic Expertise: An Inquiry into the Desirability of and Opportunities for International Standards*. Amsterdam: Thela Thesis.

Peter A (2000) *The Manual of the Standard Operating Procedures for Scientific Support Personnel at Major Incident Scenes*. Durham, UK: ACPO Crime Committee, National Training Center.

Schuliar Y (2002) Role of forensic pathologists at the crime scene: a collaboration with crime scene technicians. *Journal de Médecine Légale, Droit Médical, Victimologie, Dommage Corporel* 45: 4–5.

Standards of Performance for Crime Scene Management (2000) *OISIN Funded Project to Develop Standards of Performance for Crime Scene Management*. Brussels: EEC.

Weston PB, Wells KM (1990) *Criminal Investigation, Basic Perspectives*, 5th edn. New York: Prentice Hall.

# United Kingdom

**J Fraser**, University of Strathclyde, Glasgow, UK
**C Ratcliff**, Thames Valley Police, UK

## Introduction

The purpose of crime-scene management is similar throughout the world, irrespective of the crime or jurisdiction. Despite the enormous range of incident types, from homicide to terrorist offenses, the aims in most cases are to ensure that the best intelligence and evidence is obtained from the scene. It is also essential that the process by which this is achieved meets the standards of the particular jurisdiction. However, differences in legal systems, police procedures, and scientific methodologies all mean that there are large variations in the detail of the approach.

In the UK there are over 50 police organizations with varying responsibilities and powers. These organizations operate within a number of distinct common-law jurisdictions and therefore there is no single agreed upon system of crime-scene management. Despite this, there is a great deal of consistency in terminology, practice, and standards throughout the UK. This article provides an overview of crime-scene management in serious and major crime in the UK and some of the background to how it has developed.

For the sake of simplicity, the terminology and illustrations used derive mainly from the English legal system.

## Particular Aspects of Crime-Scene Management in the UK

There are a number of particular factors that have resulted in distinctive approaches to crime-scene management in the UK. Many of these relate to England and Wales but their influence generally extends beyond this jurisdiction, often to the entire UK.

The increase in importance of forensic evidence in police investigations and a desire on the part of the courts to have more objective and probative evidence is a growing trend. This is partly due to increased expectations of police investigators and the courts due to major scientific developments. Good examples of such technological developments are the intelligence databases in the UK, which are of significance to crime-scene management. The largest of these is the national fingerprint identification system (NAFIS), which has over 5 million sets of fingerprints from individuals. DNA databases are the next most significant. In England and Wales the national DNA database has over 2 million samples from individuals and 200 000 samples from crime scenes. Both these databases are linked to the police national computer that retains all criminal records and other relevant intelligence. Legislation in England and Wales allows the retention of all legally taken DNA samples and fingerprints from individuals, irrespective of whether they have been convicted. This is not the case in Scotland and Northern Ireland. There is little doubt that the huge growth in the national DNA databases is a consequence of the funding provided by central government specifically for this purpose. The most recent addition to intelligence databases is the national firearms forensic intelligence database, which is still in its early stages of use.

In recent years, there has been a concerted drive to set and improve standards in many aspects of forensic work including crime-scene management. The bulk of training in crime-scene management is carried out by Centrex, which is the national police training organization in England and Wales. There are also a number of other organizations involved in setting standards, including the Police Skills and Standards Organization and the Forensic Science Society. In addition, the Council for Registration of Forensic Practitioners (CRFP) was created in response to miscarriages of justice caused in part by poor standards of forensic work. The aim of CRFP is to develop a register of competent experts in order to improve standards and public confidence. This includes all forensic practitioners "from crime scene to court."

The National Crime and Operations Faculty (NCOF), part of Centrex, provides expert advice and assistance to all UK police forces in investigative and forensic matters. The NCOF maintains the National Injuries Database and a directory of experts from a wide range of highly specialist fields such as behavioral profiling. NCOF has extensive experience in investigative and forensic reviews of homicides and serial offenses. The NCOF, together with the Association of Chief Police Officers (ACPO), has also been involved with other parts of Centrex in publishing standards and guidance in relation to investigation and crime-scene management. The *Murder Investigation Manual* (1998) was the first publication of its type in the UK and it is intended to be a manual of good practice that is regularly updated. The manual includes chapters of particular relevance to crime-scene management including forensic awareness, forensic strategies, and the use of expert witnesses. Another key ACPO publication is the *Manual of Standard Operating Procedures for Scientific Support Personnel at Major Incident Scenes*. This was first published in 2000 and includes detailed guidance on the principles and practice of crime-scene management. There are also specific chapters on the management of bomb scenes, shooting incidents, deaths in police custody, and major disasters.

Traditionally, fingerprints and forensic science are dealt with separately in the UK. Police organizations, for the most part, carry out fingerprint examinations whereas scientific analysis is predominantly done outside the police service in professional laboratories. In Scotland, all of the forensic laboratories are in police organizations but in England and Wales most of these laboratories are, or soon will be, private organizations.

## The Roles of Crime-Scene Manager and Coordinator

In the UK a system has been developed to provide professional management to support forensic science investigations using the designations crime-scene manager (CSM) and crime-scene coordinator (CSC). In most UK police forces these roles are carried out by police staff rather than sworn police officers, although in the Metropolitan police, for instance, the CSC is often an experienced detective. The CSM is normally a senior scene investigator supported by a team of crime-scene investigators (formerly scenes of crime officers or SOCOs). In many police forces the CSC is a principal CSI or head of department. Most UK forces have a scientific support manager (SSM) whose role varies greatly with the size of the force. In smaller forces this person will sometimes perform the functions of CSC. This is less common in larger forces, where the SSM role is usually managerial rather than operational. Although there is variation in terminology, it is important to stress that the individuals who carry out the roles of CSM and CSC do so on the basis of expertise and knowledge.

The senior investigating officer (SIO) has overall responsibility for the conduct of the investigation, including crime-scene management, but this is normally delegated to the CSM. The SIO leads a team of experienced detectives and other specialists working together as part of an incident room.

## Crime-Scene Manager

A CSM is always appointed to the main scene in any major inquiry and will be supported by a CSC in cases involving multiple scenes or scenes that are complex or high profile. In the case of multiple scenes, a CSM is often appointed to each scene or aspect of the investigation. As an additional guideline to the level of response in any particular case there are nationally agreed categories of investigation:

- category AA: major crime of grave public concern, such as the murder of a child, multiple homicide, or the murder of a police officer
- category B: major crime where the offender is not known
- category CA: major crime where the identity of the offender(s) is known.

A CSM is responsible for:

- assessment of, planning, and agreeing on the forensic approach, including the specific sequence of examinations in individual scenes
- determining and allocating appropriate numbers of suitably trained personnel to individual aspects of the scene examination
- managing welfare of staff
- health and safety risk assessments and implementation of control measures
- planning and managing the forensic aspects of postmortem examinations
- briefing scene personnel and communicating findings from scene to investigation team
- advising the SIO on the investigative potential of different forensic evidence types generally and specifically
- advising the SIO on the value of using experts in particular fields such as ballistics, blood patterns, and fire investigation
- coordination of individual experts within the overall scene examination
- agreeing on the forensic strategy with the SIO
- maintaining ongoing communication between forensic laboratories, individual experts, and the investigation team.

A CSC will usually be appointed in the following circumstances:

- multiple scenes or complex/high-profile investigations
- serial offenses
- mass disasters.

The CSC is appointed to oversee and control the forensic investigation of a case in liaison with the SIO.

## The Scene

If there are casualties present they must take priority and if there are fatalities then death must be certified as soon as possible. The initial function of a CSM is to ensure the integrity and preservation of a crime scene. This is achieved by ensuring that scene cordons and logs are in place and that access to the scene is limited to those with a need to attend. A common approach path is implemented and used by all personnel entering the scene. This should be positioned, if possible, away from any route used by a suspect. Active scene preservation may be needed should inclement weather or other factors require evidence to be protected or recovered quickly.

Following an assessment of the scene, the CSM defines the extent of the scene to be examined and sets search and examination parameters. In some instances there may be conflicting forensic opportunities at the scene that require specialist knowledge to evaluate. In these circumstances, decisions are made based on the recovery of evidence that is likely to be of most value to the investigation. The examination strategy is also based upon any intelligence or information known.

The CSC works closely with the SIO as part of the senior management team of the investigation. This creates an effective communication link between the SIO and the forensic specialists, including CSIs, the CSM, and any other experts or advisers. Both the CSC and CSM attend daily briefings and form part of the SIO's forensic management team that may also include a specialist adviser from a forensic laboratory and an exhibits officer. The exhibits officer is responsible for managing all exhibits and ensuring chain of custody. The CSC also monitors the submission of exhibits to external forensic science laboratories. Police experts would normally deal with fingerprints. The CSC is the main communication link between the incident room, the SIO, and all other forensic agencies involved. Routine systems are used to avoid cross-contamination between scenes, victims, and suspects. The CSC or CSM keeps records to show what actions have been taken to prevent this possibility.

## Forensic Strategy and the Forensic Management Team

CSMs and CSCs are trained and qualified practitioners in their field and act as advisers to the investigating officer who retains overall responsibility. The benefits of this approach are that specialist skills of the CSM can be brought to bear on investigative problems using an array of approaches and techniques with which the CSM will be familiar. The main drawback of this approach is that more individuals are involved in an already complex process and there is the possibility of a fragmented approach or poor communication. The purpose of the forensic management team (FMT) and the forensic strategy is to ensure that the problems outlined above do not occur. The aim of the forensic strategy is to ensure that

- all forensic opportunities are brought to the attention of the FMT for their consideration
- forensic opportunities are considered in the light of investigative requirements
- all relevant expertise is engaged in developing a forensic strategy
- time scales for forensic outcomes such as DNA results are adhered to
- financial matters are considered
- information regarding forensic and investigative issues is communicated

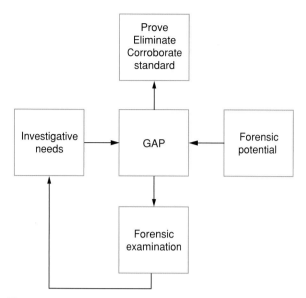

**Figure 1** Schematic diagram of gap analysis.

- the forensic strategy is agreed upon, recorded, and regularly reviewed
- a team-based, problem-solving approach is used.

The FMT should consist of all of the relevant individuals and expertise to ensure that the forensic strategy fulfills its objectives. The composition of the FMT typically includes the SIO, deputy SIO, CSC, CSMs, exhibits officer, and one or more scientific advisers. These advisers may be individual experts such as pathologists or may represent larger laboratories and advise on a wide range of forensic matters.

**Figure 1** provides an illustration of how gap analysis can be used to develop a forensic strategy. This approach is as follows. Given the current context of the investigation (witness information, intelligence, and evidence), what is the gap between what is known (or can be proved) and what is required? Defining the investigative needs can be achieved by addressing the following questions:

- What do I need to prove?
- What do I need to eliminate?
- What do I need to corroborate?
- What standard of proof is required for each of the above?

Having addressed the investigative needs, the forensic potential (DNA, fingerprints, etc.) from the crime scene is then considered. This can be explored in conjunction with the investigative requirements in order to close the gap by the quickest, most cost-effective, and lowest-risk options.

Examples of the types of questions the forensic management team would consider when setting a strategy are:

- Is there any material at any of the scenes that may lead directly to identifying the offender, such as body fluids of any type or fingerprints?
- Is there any material that could potentially connect the offender with the scene, such as shoemarks, fibers, or other trace evidence?
- In cases where it is known that the offender was at the scene, are there any materials that are incriminating due to their particular location in the scene?
- How were premises entered – is there an identifiable point of entry?
- Can a sequence of events at the scene be identified using forensic evidence such as blood patterns?
- Is there information available at the scene to support or refute hypotheses considered by the investigation team (hypothesis testing)?
- What type of search is required at the scene – is documentation from bank accounts, telephone records, and vehicles needed urgently?
- How should the information be relayed to those who need to know? Should the examination be stopped for briefing purposes or is the examination more urgent?
- What staffing levels are required to carry out the strategy in a realistic timescale?

## Resources and Priorities

In all crime investigations time and resources are limited. During the Stephen Lawrence Inquiry in the UK, Sir Paul Condon, Metropolitan Police Commissioner at the time, commented: "In any given scenario, there is potentially an enormous number of items that could be seized for forensic examination. Difficult choices have to be made and this calls for judgment, experience, and expertise. The advent of increasingly complex and expensive scientific tests increases the number of ways items can potentially be tested for forensic evidence. However, it must be acknowledged that the law of diminishing returns means that some tests will not justify the expense incurred, and sound judgment is required to target resources effectively in the search for forensic evidence."

It follows therefore that sometimes difficult decisions need to be made that balance the use of public money against an effective and appropriate investigation.

The order in which forensic examinations are carried out will often create conflicts between different searches, for example, using chemical enhancement techniques for fingerprinting may well damage or destroy any DNA present. It is important therefore that examinations are conducted in the optimum order in an effort to gather the most effective evidence for that investigation. These priorities may also change, for instance, in cases such as kidnapping, where the priority is to locate the victim as soon as possible. The strategy in such cases may be to carry out a search for documentation that could provide lines of urgent enquiry before more conventional forensic techniques are brought to bear on a scene.

It is vital that control of a scene examination rests with one person. Implementation of a strategy requires consistency and planning. Handovers from more than one CSM to another are to be avoided if possible to prevent mistakes or gaps in the examination. Communication of all aspects of the investigation is vital. There is little point in setting a forensic strategy if it is based on incomplete information or if those involved in laboratory examinations are unaware of the relevant circumstances of the case and the significance of the examinations they have been requested to conduct. Evidence from a forensic science expert is invariably based upon some element of interpretation given the particular circumstances of the case. If any information on which the examination is based changes, the interpretation of the findings may be affected. All those involved in the forensic examination will work to an agreed hypothesis, constantly monitoring and updating their approach in relation to changing circumstances, new information or intelligence. This methodology does not stop once the scene examination is concluded and is a continuing process throughout the course of an investigation up to and including the presentation of evidence in court.

With the creation of the roles of CSM and CSC the professional management of crime scenes continues to improve. Training and continued professional development are becoming an expected requirement of the role, together with registration with CRFP. Membership of a relevant professional body is likely to be the next step in developing the profession.

## Use of Forensic Experts

A key element of crime-scene management in the UK is dealing with forensic experts from a wide range of disciplines. Whilst the SIO in major inquiries has ultimate responsibility for this issue, the CSM generally has wider knowledge of the potential expertise available and more experience in the use of experts. The key issues for a CSM with respect to forensic experts are:

- From an initial scene assessment, is there a need to call experts to the scene?
- What experts are required and at what stage should they be contacted?
- What information will the expert need before and after the scene examination?
- Should the expert be part of the forensic management team?
- How should items be selected and prioritized for examination?
- What costs, if any, are involved in the use of particular experts or laboratories?

The CSM generally acts as the link between the investigation team and individual experts and forensic laboratories. This includes ensuring that the expert is fully briefed on the case circumstances, that items for examination are submitted for analysis promptly, and the priority examinations are clearly identified. Consultation between the CSM and the relevant expert establishes any particular needs that the expert has in order to carry out the examination. This may include scene measurements, plans, photographs, and witness statements. Typically in the UK, most forensic examinations are sent to a single laboratory that provides a wide range of specialist expertise. In such instances there is normally a formal process of submission that is fully documented and recorded. In England and Wales all such analyses are paid for by individual police forces.

In an article of this nature it is not possible to deal with the extensive range of experts that may be used, therefore we will confine ourselves to a single example of the type of case which requires a number of experts. When firearms have been used in a suspected murder or unlawful killing it is recommended practice in England and Wales for a pathologist, a ballistics expert, and often a blood-pattern expert to attend the scene. Each expert has a different contribution to make. Examination of the bodies *in situ*, establishing the trajectory of bullets, and interpretation of blood patterns are likely to provide the best opportunity for accurate reconstruction of the incident. Failure to take this approach is likely to compromise the investigation significantly. It is the role of the CSM to coordinate this process, to provide each expert with the relevant briefing, and integrate the outcomes of each specialist examination with the overall investigation. This process can be time-consuming and requires the CSM to maintain a constant focus on the needs of the experts and the needs of the investigation.

## See Also

**Crime-scene Investigation and Examination:** Collection and Chain of Evidence; Major Incident Scene

Management; Recovery of Human Remains; Suspicious Deaths

## Further Reading

*European Crime-scene Management Good Practice Manual*. Derbyshire Police, UK.
Fraser JG (1999) Not science ... not support: forensic solutions to investigative problems. *Science and Justice* 40.
*Murder Investigation Manual* (2000) Association of Chief Police Officers.
Sir W (1999) *The Stephen Lawrence Inquiry*. MacPherson.
*The Manual of Standard Operating Procedures for Scientific Support Personnel at Major Incident Scenes* (2000) Association of Chief Police Officers.

# United States of America

**J J Nordby**, Final Analysis Forensics, Tacoma, WA, USA

## Introduction

### Importance

However "crime scene" is defined, it remains that only the crime scene provides physical evidence to establish the commission of a crime. Both witness statements and confessions remain mere hearsay accounts, which demand either support or refutation through some type of physical evidence. Without such physical evidence, whether direct or circumstantial, police investigators, medical examiners, forensic scientists, prosecutors, defense attorneys, and ultimately, the courts, would be left with little if any professional work to accomplish in criminal cases. For this reason alone, a systematic approach to any crime scene remains the most vital of all tasks facing criminal investigators in their sworn pursuit of justice, both for the victims of crime, and for those accused of its commission. Indeed, processing the crime scene remains the essential link between crime and science, giving both crime laboratories and medical examiners the necessary grist for their scientific mills.

### Definition

Attempts to define crime scene often become mere enumerations of different types of crime scene by simple illustration. Such enumerations, while useful to help us classify different types of crime scenes, fail to provide a robust definition. Many have argued that "crime scene" represents a necessarily elastic notion with myriad instances and plural nuances, even some, perhaps, as yet unimagined. But some lexical definition, capturing both its essential link to physical evidence and its necessarily metamorphic nature, can be useful to help focus the roles of forensic science and forensic medicine in the investigation of physical evidence.

In the USA, the words "crime scene" are used to mean any identifiable physical location potentially supplying physical evidence relevant for adjudicating hypotheses concerning a given crime. While perhaps overly inclusive, this usage entails that appropriate crime scenes may include the entire forested area where a homicide victim's body lies; any roads or trails providing access to the area; the body itself; the site where the victim met the perpetrator such as a vehicle, an apartment, a truck stop, or a bar; any site where the initial assault took place; and the site where the victim died: anything, in short, which supplies a location for existing physical evidence documenting the contact between victim and perpetrator. In common use, this may include the body, and items located near it – each being a mini crime scene unto itself.

This definition leaves the exact scope of the crime scene itself, that is, how much of the forested area, which roads, and which other sites, entirely to the individual investigator's professional discretion. In the USA, the exact nature and scope of specific crime scenes depend upon informed human judgments rather than upon lexical rigidity for both their physical and conceptual boundaries.

### Scope

The definition entails that we may find crime scenes within crime scenes: each macroscopic crime scene contains multiple microscopic crime scenes, ranging from a bedroom to the victim's clothing to the microscopic traces on the clothing. While this may at times invite confusion by calling some strange locations crime scenes, it rests upon the most basic postulate of forensic science, Edmund Locard's principle of exchange – that every contact between two distinct items transfers part of one on to the other. In this manner, Locard's principle justifies the expectation of physical evidence at crime scenes and explains its potential significance.

## Processing Crime Scenes

### The Practical Preservation of Evidence

Before any physical evidence can be examined by forensic scientists, it must be recognized as potential evidence and, where relevant, collected and preserved in an uncontaminated state. This must occur during the initial crime-scene investigation since many such locations cannot be maintained under official control for indefinite periods. Crime scenes may involve public places, roadways, apartment buildings, or private homes, which exist to serve ongoing purposes precluding any sustained control by investigators.

They may be outdoors and subject to weather or other deleterious environmental effects, or they may involve temporally dependent evidence such as footprints in melting snow, muddy tire tracks in a rainstorm, or even odiferous vapor clouds which exist only fleetingly. Nor do shrinking budgets and limited personnel resources permit the additional drains involved in the perpetual control of most typical crime scenes. This underscores the importance of documenting the crime scene to ensure its continued existence and thereby enable its continued investigation – representative notes, films, drawings, and collected evidence remain held under rigid protection in perpetuity.

## Crime-Scene Processing Personnel

Practical problems and limitations also affect crime-scene processing among the many independent jurisdictions in the USA. A paucity of trained personnel provides a potential roadblock in the movement of evidence from the crime scene to the forensic laboratory or medical examiner's office. The lack of trained crime-scene personnel may even prevent the very recognition that a crime has been committed in the first place. Regardless of the scientific prowess of crime laboratory or medical personnel, if they fail to visit the crime scene to collect their own evidence, then they must depend upon the skills of the assigned crime-scene personnel for all the evidence that they examine. If crime-scene personnel fail to recognize the evidence, fail to collect it, or fail to collect it properly, then the operations of forensic science and forensic medicine, and the integrity of the justice system itself, suffer immeasurable damage.

As a remedy, crime-scene technicians, who are not trained forensic scientists or experienced forensic medical investigators, function simply to document the crime scene as thoroughly and completely as possible and to collect items of potential evidence according to one of many well-developed crime-scene processing protocols. Documentation protocols provide guidelines for measuring, drawing, photographing, and videotaping scenes while collection protocols provide guidelines to help uncover potential evidence, and, for example, to lift latent fingerprints and retrieve weapons, projectiles, cartridge cases, or blood and other biological evidence. They also teach the proper packaging and transporting of these items of physical evidence to the appropriate agencies, while preserving legal chain-of-evidence requirements, guaranteeing that the evidence remains protected and uncompromised.

## Processing Protocols

In theory, with such protocols adopted, potential evidence has a better chance of being preserved. Of course one merit of the approach remains that only after considerable study does the scientist begin to distinguish significant from insignificant data. The practical merit allegedly remains the preservation of scarce budgetary and personnel resources by training lower-paid technicians to handle crime-scene processing. Advocates of this approach assume that the chance of significant data being both documented and collected outweighs the chance that data will be missed entirely, or even partially compromised by oversight or omission.

The practical effects of this overall management method remain an ongoing concern in the scientific investigation of crime and in the rigorous assessment of its evidence in courts of law. Many forensic professionals believe that quality crime-scene processing must be done by personnel more extensively trained in both the natural sciences and scene investigation. Given the multijurisdictional nature of investigative agencies processing crime scenes in the USA, the debate over alternative models of crime-scene management will not resolve soon. Nor will one particular approach emerge as "the standard" to be embraced by all jurisdictions regardless of size, location, or financial resources.

## Basic, General Stepwise Protocols

**First responders and securing the scene** The protection of a crime scene becomes law enforcement's first priority. The goal remains to prevent any accidental transfer of items to the scene, which may confuse or compromise the "slice in time" that the scene represents. Steps must be taken to keep unnecessary visitors away from the crime scene. Police establish physical barriers of some type to block entrance and to segregate the area from the public. Usually one officer becomes the scene security officer responsible for maintaining scene security.

No crime scene remains pristine – neither relatively protected indoor crime scenes, nor relatively exposed outdoor crime scenes. Seldom are crime-scene personnel the first to discover the scene. Even before the crime's discovery, proper first responders may include emergency medical technicians, firefighters, residents, relatives, hikers, construction workers, or even nonhuman visitors such as dogs, cats, mice, rats, birds, local fauna, and of course insects. Each visitor, regardless of scene, leaves some mark of his/her presence.

The official duty of securing the scene includes documenting who or what visited the scene as a so-called "first responder." (The documentation continues beyond first responders to include a visitor's sheet, recording the date and time that anyone, including crime-scene technicians, medical personnel, and detectives, enters or leaves the scene.) For many scenes, documenting first responders is handled by collecting ambulance or firefighter run sheets, and by asking first responders to report their movements at the scene. If necessary, shoe prints, hair, clothing samples, blood, and even DNA may be collected for later laboratory elimination purposes.

The task becomes more complex when securing outdoor scenes. A scene involving a hiker's discovery of disarticulated skeletal remains, which has enjoyed varied company over some period of time, falls beyond the scope of such simple documentation. The hiker's movements must still be documented, but documenting the activities of other first responders requires the expertise of forensic anthropologists, forensic entomologists, and even forensic botanists.

As the data at crime scenes become more scientifically diverse, many processing protocols in the form of activity lists exhibit inherent shortcomings. Many scientific disciplines have a narrow focus, which remains unfamiliar to crime-scene technicians. The lack of specific scientific knowledge and experience can result in missing data otherwise available at such scenes, thereby inducing hardships upon investigators working the case.

Many crime-scene technician training programs cover the recognition, collection, and preservation of entomological and botanical data as well as information about the habits of indigenous birds, mammals, and fish. Some jurisdictions hire outside consultants to help with cases requiring specific and narrow expertise. Depending upon budget and cases, coroner's or medical examiner's offices may employ a forensic anthropologist to assist in the identification and recovery of human skeletal remains as well as to help law enforcement and the public distinguish human from nonhuman artifacts.

**Human bodies as evidence**   In virtually all jurisdictions, the body of any deceased person and its scientific inspection remains the sole province of the coroner or the medical examiner. Human remains exist outside the crime-scene technician's province, despite popular television portrayals to the contrary. For this reason, the crime-scene technician is joined by a deputy coroner, medical examiner's representative, or a trained medical investigator. This representative may perform the duty of evidence recognition, documentation, and collection with respect to a human decedent. This evidence is then evaluated by the forensic pathologist to identify the decedent, and to establish both the cause and manner of death. Each official must work together closely and cooperatively for such a team effort to be both scientifically productive and legally successful.

Limitations to this medical version of the crime-scene technician become obvious when cases demand more of the medical technician than his/her lack of knowledge and experience can supply. Jurisdictions unable to afford trained medical investigators may simply function as a removal service, waiting until detectives release the body from the scene, and then merely transporting it to some preestablished location for analysis. The only personnel requirements for such positions appear to be a strong back and an equally strong stomach.

The legal and scientific prowess of such systems when faced with challenging cases remains at best questionable. As with crime-scene processing models, the best model to adopt for scientific death investigation remains a much-discussed topic among forensic professionals. However, in both areas, continuing education and robust educational requirements have led to promising certification programs designed to teach practitioners to seek help from those with more training and experience in relevant areas.

**Survey the scene**   Once secured, with appropriate personnel in place, the next step involves some type of reconnoitering, or a "walk-through" to establish the scene's potential scope and peculiar working requirements. This involves both crime-scene and medical personnel who work together at the scene with detectives. The walk-through should establish basic parameters by noting each avenue of entry and exit, while specifically noting any hazards requiring supplemental measures, ranging from additional protective equipment to a call for additional security. The walk-through should provide a clear understanding of the equipment, personnel, and time required for the tasks at hand, and an initial prioritization of those tasks.

**Document the scene**   Priorities for crime-scene processing depend both on the scene's peculiar circumstances and on the specific methods of various sciences. The general principle becomes to arrange the evidence-processing and collection activities from the least invasive or destructive to the most invasive or disruptive of the scene's current protected status. The most benign task becomes providing an accurate documentation of the entire scene as it initially presents itself to investigators.

This remains the most important step to aid future analysis of the scene's elements when various investigative hypotheses are formed and tested. Usually elements not believed to be relevant at the scene may become supremely relevant later on as further information develops. Thus the proper, complete, and orderly documentation of the crime scene becomes the primary task for the crime-scene technician.

*The forms of documentation* This documentation assumes several forms. Notes cover data from listing personnel, notification, and arrival times to a thorough description of key scene elements ranging from the victim to the surrounding environs, including the structure, its furniture, and even the contents of ashtrays, refrigerators, and dressers. The notes must follow a clear, logical order, usually moving from descriptions of the larger toward details of the smaller; or from the overall to the specific depending upon the scene. The same logical principles apply regardless of whether the crime scene is in the woods, or in a housing project.

Measurements and both rough and scale drawings are developed to map the scene, giving detailed numerical distance relationships among items in three-dimensional space. A crime scene is not flat: coordinate systems with $x$-, $y$-, and $z$-axes are most practically used to locate items in space and capture their essential features. While not commonly used, three-dimensional coordinate systems are powerful tools in the analysis and documentation of, for example, blood stains or bullet holes which necessarily occur at some height as well as at some two-dimensionally fixed location.

Three basic measurement methods for locating items two-dimensionally include triangulation (locating an object by measuring its distance from two fixed points), baseline (locating an object by measuring its distance at 90° from a straight line between two fixed points), and polar coordinate methods (locating an object using a transit or compass by determining its north–south–east–west angle and distance from a fixed point). The choice depends upon the nature of the scene and the ease with which items can be relocated in the same space years after the scene has been abandoned. Each method identifies two fixed starting points judged to be relatively permanent in both nature and location, and develops the corresponding locations of all evidence in specific relation to these two fixed points.

Videotape photography also captures the scene according to these logical principles, for example, noting roads, orienting north–south–east–west directions, the weather, time, temperature, and other physical phenomena. No detail at the scene can be considered inconsequential or unworthy of inclusion in the taped record. The videotape of a crime scene does not include an audio track. Such a track might inadvertently record irrelevant comments by investigators, not properly a record of the scene itself. Exceptions might include the need to record unusual noises or sounds, which are an integral part of its nature, and therefore must be included for a complete understanding of its varied elements.

Still photography must capture the entire scene, again moving from overall shots showing the orientation of various items toward specific, examination-quality photos documenting each element. Standard practice captures items first without identifying numbers or measuring devices, then with such identifiers and scales present. A consistent numbering or lettering system identifies the items in both photos and drawings. Systems usually come as "tents," like triangular signboards, with numbers or letters in black script on a white or yellow background. Long after items of evidence are collected, these numbers, visible in the photos, provide an orientation of the item along with other items of evidence similarly documented at the scene.

**Evidence discovery and collection** Disciplined scene searches help ensure that no items of potential significance are missed as the crime-scene processing progresses. Different search techniques, such as establishing a logical linkage among items, line searches, zone searches, and wheel, spiral, or grid searches, can be applied, depending upon the type of location being processed. In many cases, logical linkages among items provide the most useful approach. For example, if six spent cartridge cases appear at a scene, the linkage search technique implies that investigators search for evidence of six bullets and their associated trajectories at the scene. Even if six bullets cannot be accounted for, this too provides useful information about the crime which must be considered in any eventual reconstruction of events leaving these effects.

Other search patterns are based upon geometric patterns: some, such as the line search, may apply more usefully to larger outdoor scenes. Often some combinations of these search techniques develop as a reasoned response to the peculiarities of the specific situation under investigation. The choice of technique remains part of a thoughtful response to the uniqueness of the specific scene and there is no single search pattern that can be applied blindly in all circumstances. Search techniques as basic tools of crime-scene processing are chosen by investigators to best attain the objectives dictated by the case at hand.

Once the scene has been revealed as completely as possible, evidence collection and preservation techniques remove items of evidence for further analyses, to be completed by specialists, usually in the crime laboratory. While there is no rigid order for the collection of evidence, usually the most fragile, easily lost, and transient items are first collected. This ensures that such items remain uncontaminated. Different types of evidence require different collection and packaging techniques.

Collection principles are based upon the logic mirrored in search patterns. For example, fingerprints are lifted from various surfaces which are chosen based on logical linkages – one might ask, for instance, which surfaces would be touched by anyone gaining entry to the scene and producing the effects observed during the scene's investigation? These locations, then, provide the most logical places to attempt latent fingerprint lifts. If all surfaces at a crime scene were blindly dusted for prints, little else would be accomplished. Sound evidence collection depends vitally upon the logical sagacity of the crime-scene technician working the scene.

Once collected, evidence must be consistently marked, packaged, and sealed to avoid contamination and to preserve the chain of custody. Usually one person is assigned evidence collection and packaging responsibilities. This ensures uniformity and consistency, while preventing needless duplication of effort if each investigator collected evidence independently. Packaging is chosen to best preserve the evidence. For example, bloody evidence is sealed in paper bags to allow the items to dry and to prevent deterioration of the evidence by condensation, or biological activity, which would be encouraged if such items were sealed in plastic. In appropriate packaging, the items are sealed with evidence tape, documented in the evidence log with their number and a brief description, and then signed and dated by the collection technician.

Whenever packaged evidence is opened and examined by laboratory or other personnel, the item is resealed using the identical protocol – it is resealed with evidence tape, resigned, and redated by the new analyst. This ensures that the chain of custody is preserved by providing a record of the item's disposition at all times, under all circumstances. While much of this scientific analysis occurs away from the actual crime scene, some types of evidence may require that the forensic scientist conduct his/her analyses at the crime scene itself.

### Scientific Evidence Analysis at Crime Scenes

In most cases, crime-scene personnel are thought to have the training needed to document all scene data, if not to provide the scientific analysis and interpretation of its significance. However some data at crime scenes may demand that trained scientists (with expertise beyond that of the crime-scene technician) visit the scene in order to provide a scientific analysis of data, which cannot easily be separated from the location. In these cases, trained forensic scientists or forensic pathologists must visit the crime scene in order to provide their analyses and interpretations and to release crime-scene technicians from difficult, if not impossible, documentations needlessly risking the inadvertent distortion of valuable data.

## Crime-Scene or Event Reconstruction

### Characterization

An anecdotal recitation of personal opinion, regardless of source, is not a crime-scene reconstruction. A properly developed crime-scene reconstruction links a series of scientific explanations to illuminate the events leaving physical evidence. This process involves proposing, testing, and evaluating explanatory connections among the physical evidence related to these events. The purpose of the analysis is to determine their best explanation.

### Example

Upon entering a room, one sees a yellowish-fluid puddle on the white linoleum floor. A small puppy wiggles submissively as it runs up to greet you at the room's entrance. The logic relevant to crime-scene reconstruction also licenses an explanation of the puddle on the floor. The scientific process involves discovering evidence to support or refute your proposed claim. The same logical process justifies more scientifically complex crime-scene reconstructions. While no reconstruction can explain every element of a scene, the explanations must minimally withstand sustained logical and scientific scrutiny.

## Conclusions

As important as the crime scene remains in the investigation of crime, often scant attention is paid in the USA to the need for a systematic approach to crime-scene management, processing, and documentation. No better evidence can be supplied than to examine the miniscule budgets for training crime-scene technicians, crime laboratory personnel, medical examiner's personnel, or especially, for training police officers both in the basics of crime-scene protocols, and in the scope and limit of current forensic science and forensic medical practice. Much misinformation exists among law enforcement personnel concerning forensic enterprises ranging from fingerprints and their significance to DNA and its limitations. Improved training provides the best remedy.

Often the quality of equipment available to actors playing forensic scientists on television far exceeds the equipment available to real scientists and technicians charged with processing and documenting actual crime scenes. Until these matters change significantly, crime-scene processing will continue to lack substantial uniformity and will remain of varying quality among the many jurisdictions charged with this vital task in the USA.

## See Also

**Crime-scene Management, Systems:** Continental Europe; United Kingdom

## Further Reading

Adelson L (1974) *The Pathology of Homicide.* Springfield, IL: Charles C. Thomas.

Association for Crime Scene Reconstruction. http://www.acsr.com.

Doyle AC (1930) *The Complete Sherlock Holmes.* Garden City, NY: Doubleday & Co., Inc.

Fisher BJ (1999) *Basic Crime Scene Investigation.* Boca Raton, FL: CRC Press.

Gebreth V (2000) *Basic Homicide Investigations.* Boca Raton, FL: CRC Press.

James S (2000) *Bloodstain Patterns at the Crime Scene.* Boca Raton, FL: CRC Press.

James S, Nordby JJ (2003) *Forensic Science: An Introduction to Scientific and Investigative Techniques.* Boca Raton, FL: CRC Press.

Kirk P (1953) *Crime Investigation: Physical Evidence and the Police Laboratory.* New York: Interscience Publishers, Inc.

Lee H, Palmbach T, Miller M, *et al.* (2001) *Henry Lee's Crime Scene Handbook.* San Diego, CA: Academic Press.

National Medicolegal Review Panel (1999) *Death Investigation: A Guide for the Scene Investigator.* Washington, DC: US Department of Justice, Office of Justice Programs.

Nordby JJ (1999) *Dead Reckoning: The Art of Forensic Detection.* Boca Raton, FL: CRC Press.

Technical Working Group on Crime Scene Investigation (2000) *Crime Scene Investigation: A Guide for Law Enforcement.* Washington, DC: US Department of Justice, Office of Justice Programs.

Thorwald J (1965) *The Century of the Detective.* New York: Harcourt, Brace & World, Inc.

Thorwald J (1967) *Crime and Science.* New York: Harcourt, Brace & World, Inc.

United States Army Criminal Investigation Division (1997) *Field Manual 19–20.* Washington, DC: Headquarters, Department of the Army.

# CRIMINAL PROFILING

**R J Morton and W D Lord**, Serial Killer Unit, FBI Academy, Quantico, VA, USA

Published by Elsevier Ltd.

## Introduction

Dr. James A. Brussel, a New York psychiatrist, was one of the first practitioners of criminal profiling. For a 16-year period during the 1940s and 1950s, New York City was terrorized by the "Mad Bomber," who set off 37 bombs in the New York area. The police contacted Dr. Brussel for an analysis of the case. Dr. Brussel concluded that the individual would be a heavy-set man, foreign-born, a Roman Catholic, and living with a sibling. He further stated that when the police located the man, he would be wearing a buttoned double-breasted suit. In 1957, George Metesky was arrested by the police for the bombings. Metesky was a heavy-set, foreign-born, Roman Catholic, who lived with his sister. When he answered the door, he was wearing a double-breasted suit, buttoned.

In the 1970s, the Federal Bureau of Investigation (FBI) began providing criminal profiling based upon a multidisciplinary approach of investigative experience, psychology, crime scene expertise, and forensics. Special Agent Howard Teten was a member of the FBI's Behavioral Science Unit (BSU), who developed and taught a course titled Applied Criminology (profiling). Teten co-taught this course with a fellow agent, Pat Mullany, who was also an instructor at BSU. Together, they began to receive requests from police investigators to review and conduct profiles on current, ongoing cases. Their analyses met with many positive results. The success of Teten and Mullany led to the creation of the FBI's National Center for the Analysis of Violent Crime (NCAVC) and put the process of criminal profiling into common practice.

The process of criminal profiling continues to evolve, and the purpose of this article is to provide a historical view of the process, outline the changes that have occurred, and to present the process as it now exists.

## History

The process of profiling has its origins in "psychological profiling" and criminal case-study descriptions originally published by forensically inclined psychologists and psychiatrists seeking to further the understanding of the criminal mind. Early profiling work also involved the psychiatric and psychological assessments of individuals for strategic purposes, such as the psychiatric assessment of Aldof Hiltler during World War II. Historically, psychiatrists and psychologists wrote psychological profiles of criminals as diagnostic formulations. Early profiling efforts were disseminated among mental-health professionals to foster discussion and debate on a broad diversity of theoretical issues. These "profiling" orientations practiced by mental-health professionals often lacked overt practical law-enforcement application.

In the 1970s, "psychological profiling," sometimes referred to as "criminal or behavioral profiling," was systematically implemented as an investigative technique by the BSU. The FBI's approach to profiling differed markedly from the methodology employed by mental-health professionals. Rather than conducting a clinically based construct of a known offender as a means of gaining insight, detailed examinations of the behavior(s) evidenced in the interactions between offenders and victims, and displayed at the scenes of crimes served as the basis of analysis and prediction. The FBI approach to criminal profiling was predicated on the belief that criminal behavior, as evidenced in victim–offender interactions and crime scene activities, reflected offender personality traits and that such traits could be identified and categorized. FBI profiling began as an informal analysis, but gradually transitioned into a formal service as the practical law-enforcement value of behaviorally based crime analyses became evident. With time, research involving the interviews of incarcerated offenders, coupled with the standardization of analytical protocols and training methodologies, served to formalize the profiling process.

Early FBI criminal profiling efforts focused primarily on ascribing behavioral and personality characteristics to unknown offenders in serious violent crimes and serial offenses. Central to this approach was the concept of an organized/disorganized behavioral dichotomy. This continuum was based on recognized differences in a spectrum of behavioral characteristics indicative of varying degrees of criminal sophistication. Organized offenders planned their offenses, would target a victim who was a stranger, and were very evidence-conscious. Disorganized offenders tended to commit spontaneous offenses, were acquainted with the victim, and left physical evidence at the crime scene.

Through analysis of the crime scene, profilers could utilize crime scene characteristics to ascertain personality traits of either organized or disorganized offenders. Organized offenders were described as very intelligent, with better than average IQ scores, high birth-order status in their family, socially and sexually competent, worked in a skilled profession, were in a controlled mood during the commission of their crime, used alcohol during the crime, were very mobile, and followed the crime in the news media. Disorganized offenders were described as of average intelligence, had minimal birth-order status, were socially immature, sexually incompetent, had poor work history, were in an anxious mood during the crime, did not consume alcohol during the crime, lived near the crime scene, and had minimal interest in the news media.

This system was limited, however, because of the inherent problems of a simple two-category classification model. Human behavior is much more variable than an "either/or" choice of organized behavior/disorganized behavior. Behavior falls along a continuum between the two poles and usually displays descriptive characteristics of both organized and disorganized offenders.

## Criminal Profiling

Criminal profiling analysis has evolved, with time, into a broader investigative adaptation of applied clinical psychology, psychiatry, and behavioral science. This process is defined by the FBI as criminal investigative analysis (CIA). CIA is an investigative, forensic, and behaviorally based investigative tool utilized to assist law enforcement in the solution of unsolved crimes. It employs psychological concepts and principles in the assessment of offender behavior and personality characteristics. Case analyses are routinely conducted by teams of behaviorally trained, experienced violent-crime investigators in consort with a cadre of expert consultants including psychologists, psychiatrists, forensic pathologists, crime laboratory scientists, linguists, and other specialists.

CIA is a comprehensive method of reviewing and assessing the facts of a criminal act, or series of criminal acts, by personnel who have extensive investigative experience, specialized academic training, and have participated in research involving violent offenders. CIA entails an in-depth, multidisciplinary review of submitted case materials from investigative, forensic, and behavioral perspectives and often includes an analysis of the offender's behavior and interaction with his/her victim(s), as exhibited during the commission of a crime, or as evidenced in the crime scene. The goal of CIA is to narrow the investigative focus thereby enhancing investigative resource management, and timely case resolution. Additionally, CIA seeks to provide information of lead value to criminal investigators and to offer analyses and explanations of violent criminal behavior that exceed the ordinary professional and life experiences of investigators, attorneys, mental-health practitioners, and the courts. CIA should be viewed as a process of reviewing crime(s) from behavioral, investigative, and forensic perspectives.

## The Process of CIA

CIA involves both deductive and inductive logic based on a detailed knowledge of case facts, behavioral and criminological research, empirical analyses, clinical psychology, and criminal investigative experience. The CIA process is, in many respects, comparable to the process of clinical diagnosis. Both involve the gathering of objective facts, reliance on previously tested data, a combination of inductive and deductive reasoning, and the practical experience and insight of professional practitioners.

Deductive reasoning is defined by Webster's Dictionary as a learning process where a conclusion logically follows from a stated premise. Deduction can be described as inferring a conclusion based upon general information and applying it to a specific incident. The use of deductive reasoning in the CIA process consists of utilizing empirical studies identifying the characteristics of certain populations of violent offenders to make predictions relevant to the specific case being reviewed.

Inductive reasoning was first put forth in the seventeenth century by Bacon, who defined it as reasoning that moved from the specific to the general. Inductive reasoning is the process by which specific information is utilized to make predictions concerning general trends or populations. The use of inductive reasoning in the CIA process consists of identifying factors in a specific case and applying those factors to an entire population of violent offenders to explain common behavior.

It is a common myth that CIA can only be conducted using either inductive or deductive reasoning; however, it is the practice of the FBI's NCAVC to utilize both, as well as other processes in the consultative process.

Case facts represent the single most important element utilized in CIA. These include crime scene characteristics, crime scene interaction between the victim and the offender, neighborhood demographics, neighborhood crime rates, neighborhood criminal activity trends, media coverage of the crime(s), victimology, forensic results, and investigative results.

Research through interviews with incarcerated violent offenders provides glimpses into the offender's method of operation (MO), victim selection criteria, potential pool of victims, offender view of law enforcement efforts, and possible offender motivation.

Research utilizing empirical studies provides statistical models of offender behavior by examining large populations of violent offenders to identify common characteristics or behaviors, including MO, victim selection criteria, disposal scenarios, and postoffense behavior.

Clinical psychology provides insight into the mental disorders that are common to violent offenders including psychopathy, psychosis, and paraphilias which encompass a variety of sexual deviations. Knowledge of these disorders can be beneficial in explaining apparent bizarre behavior exhibited at a crime scene.

Extensive case experience in violent crime investigations, and in particular experience in CIA, exposes the agent/investigator to a plethora of repetitive, unusual, and bizarre cases, and provides a broad base of knowledge concerning these types of crimes. Experience in criminal investigations is also essential in the CIA process as it is an investigative tool. It is extremely important to be able to apply the results of CIA investigatively, to generate leads or focus an investigation towards a certain type of offender.

## Present Status of CIA

CIA is increasing in its popularity and utilization within the law enforcement and criminal justice community in the USA and elsewhere. This is due, in part, to its continuing success as an investigative tool and also to the zealous attention it receives in the news and entertainment media and the popular press.

CIA currently encompasses a broad array of behaviorally based services provided to law enforcement and criminal justice professionals. Utilization of the CIA process allows a variety of analyses to be conducted, including crime analysis, behavioral characteristics of unknown offenders, personality assessment, interview techniques, investigative and media strategies, search warrant assistance, prosecutorial and trial strategies, and expert testimony.

## Crime Analysis

Crime analysis is the interpretation and opinion resulting from the assessment of a crime and/or crime scene, generally incorporating information relating to the offender's motivation, sophistication, and actions, as well as the sequence of events and their relationship to other criminal acts.

## Behavioral Characteristics

Behavioral characteristics of an unknown offender can be determined by analyzing the way a crime was committed. Criminal investigative analysts can often identify the major personality and behavioral characteristics of an individual. Generally, the person's basic patterns of behavior, exhibited in the commission of a crime, will also be present in that person's lifestyle. Thus, a criminal investigative analyst may be able to determine the type of person who committed the crime and his/her possible motive(s). Some, but not necessarily all, of the following areas may be addressed in a typical "profile": age, gender, race, intelligence level, lifestyle, work habits, marital status, social adjustment, personality characteristics, location of residence in relation to the crime, sexual adjustment, and perversions. Ascribing behavioral and personality characteristics to unknown offenders, inherent in classical criminal profiling, represents only one facet of the current CIA process.

## Personality Assessment

Personality assessment evaluations are done to identify an individual's strengths, weaknesses, and vulnerabilities from a law enforcement viewpoint. Because each request is unique, the assessment process requires detailed submission of data about the person targeted and demands extensive review and consultation by the analyst. The availability of this material is considered essential in constructing appropriate interview strategies. This type of assessment is appropriate in lieu of a "profile" when a suspect has been identified.

## Interview Techniques

Interview techniques combine a general assessment of a person with an analysis of the crime and the behavior exhibited therein. Suggestions are made as how best to interview an individual, particularly when the investigating agency may only have one opportunity for a successful interview. Suggestions on the most appropriate type of interviewer, desired approach, and/or the best environment in which to conduct the interview may be included.

## Investigative Strategy

Certain investigative suggestions and strategies may be offered, based on a review of the entire case, focusing particularly on an evaluation of the crime scene and an assessment of the offender. These proactive suggestions are based upon years of experience in reviewing these types of cases and expertise in crime scenes, forensic techniques, and investigations.

## Media Strategy

Media strategies are carefully crafted, with attention given to how information can be delivered to the public in an effort to gain cooperation and address issues that impact the investigative process. Extreme care in the use of language and text must be considered to avoid challenging an offender to commit another offense.

## Search Warrant Assistance

Search warrant assistance can be particularly beneficial to support affidavits. Research and experience have shown that specific types of offenders commonly possess certain behavioral and personality traits, and based upon these behaviors, may retain specific instrumentalities of the crime. This articulable information is proffered to the court to support the affidavit. A list of specific items that offenders may possess or keep from victims is provided.

## Prosecutive/Trial Strategy

At the request of the investigative agency or prosecuting attorney, recommendations may be offered concerning crime analysis, crime motivation, overall prosecution theme development, possible cross-examination techniques for offenders and/or witnesses, and considerations regarding jury selection.

## Expert Testimony

Criminal investigative analysts have qualified and provided testimony as experts in the areas of crime scene analysis, violent criminal behavior, and assessment of dangerousness. Each of these services, however, is targeted at enhancing the court's and jury's understanding of offenders, their MO, motivation for committing offenses, and future dangerousness to the public.

# Future of CIA

CIA continues to evolve, particularly in its incorporation of empirical research and scientifically sound hypothesis testing. While recent research points to the reliability and validity of the CIA process, empirically based studies remain scant. Rigorous statistical testing of well-defined, scientifically sound hypotheses could significantly enhance the predictive value and reliability of the criminal investigative process. Additionally, empirical studies would provide a clearer estimation of behavioral variability and methodological errors rates, and ultimately assist in refinement of the process.

The continued union of research-based actuarial information and seasoned investigative experience will serve to increase the future accuracy and applicability of CIA. Alternative offender and offense classification systems, based on differing diagnostic, motivational, and definitional criteria, have been developed by criminologists, sociologists, and clinical psychologists in an effort to advance the value and applicability of the profiling process. The multitude of potential classification schemes underscores the complexity of human criminal behavior, the lack of uniformity in definitions, and the need for empirically based research.

## Geographic Profiling

Another application of behavioral science and technology to the law enforcement arena is geographic profiling. Geographic profiling examines the spatial behavior of offenders and seeks to identify significant locations (places of work, residences, etc.) based on the spatial patterns evident in serial and repetitive crimes. Geographic profiling serves as an adjunct to classical behavioral profiling and the CIA process. Geographic profiling is centered in the behavioral theory of psychological comfort zones and the ecological construct of home range. Each posits that offenders will initially commit their crimes in close proximity to areas of familiarity and perceived safety, namely, near residences or places of work, recreation, and entertainment. With experience and success, offenders expand their geographic sphere of criminal activity. Geographic profiling theory also considers both physical and psychological barriers as factors in an offender's decision-making process.

Geographic profiling may serve to narrow investigative focus and enhance law-enforcement resource management by identifying potential areas of offender familiarity and victim encounter. Geographic profiling can provide valuable insights in repetitive offense mapping, and the development of crime prevention strategies. Geographic profiling, however, is limited in scope due to the need for a large number of repetitive offenses in order to make accurate assessments.

## Further Reading

Ankrom LG (2002) *Criminal Investigative Analysis*. Miscellaneous publication of the FBI's National Center for the Analysis of Violent Crime. Washington, DC: Department of Justice.

Ault RL, Reese JT (1980) A psychological assessment of criminal profiling. *FBI Law Enforcement Bulletin* 49: 22–25.

Davies A (1994) Offender profiling. *Medicine, Science and the Law* 34: 185–186.

Depue RL (1986) An American response to an era of violence. *FBI Law Enforcement Bulletin* 55: 1–8.

Dietz PE (1985) Sex offender profiling by the FBI: a preliminary conceptual model. In: Ben-Aron MH, Hucker SJ, Webster CD (eds.) *Clinical Criminology: The Assessment and Treatment of Criminal Behavior*, pp. 207–219. Toronto: Clarke Institute of Psychiatry.

Douglas JE, Ressler RK, Burgess AW, Hartman CR (1986) Criminal profiling and crime scene analysis. *Behavioral Sciences and the Law* 4: 401–421.

Geberth VK (1996) *Practical Homicide Investigation: Tactics, Procedures, and Forensic Techniques*, 3rd edn. Boca Raton, FL: CRC Press.

Holmes RM, Holmes ST (1996) *Profiling Violent Crimes: An Investigative Tool*. Thousand Oaks, CA: Sage Publications.

Homant RJ, Kennedy DB (1998) Psychological aspects of criminal profiling: validity research. *Criminal Justice and Behavior* 25: 319–343.

Ressler RK, Burgess AW, Douglas JE (1988) *Sexual Homicide: Patterns and Motives*. New York: Lexington Books.

Rossmo DK (1997) Geographic profiling. In: Jackson JL, Bekerian DA (eds.) *Offender Profiling: Theory, Research and Practice*, pp. 159–175. New York: John Wiley.

Schlesinger LB (2000) *Serial Offenders: Current Thoughts, Recent Findings*. Boca Raton, FL: CRC Press.

Vorpagel RE (1982) Painting psychological profiles: charlatanism, coincidence, charisma or new science. *Police Chief* 3: 156–159.

Wilson P, Lincoln R, Kocsis R (1997) Validity, utility, and ethics of profiling for serial violent and sexual offenders. *Psychiatry, Psychology and the Law* 4: 1–12.

Witte G (2000) *A Comparative Analysis of Serial Homicide and Single Homicide Event Characteristics*. Philadelphia, PA: MCP Hahnemann University.

# CUSTODY

Contents
**Death in, United Kingdom and Continental Europe**
**Death in, United States of America**

## Death in, United Kingdom and Continental Europe

**J Payne-James**, Forensic Healthcare Services Ltd, London, UK
**J Carter**, Sussex Forensic Medical Services, Brighton, UK

### Introduction

This article makes reference to deaths in police and prison custody in the UK and continental Europe, and illustrates in detail the causes of deaths in police custody within England and Wales and the mechanisms in place to investigate such deaths. The evolution of the process from the previous system of police forces investigating deaths in neighboring forces to the current independence of inquiry will be referred to. Additionally the processes by which attempts are made to reduce the frequency of such deaths will be reviewed. Generally the term "death in police custody" is used to refer to deaths whilst individuals are being held in, or are in transit to or from, the police station whilst being investigated or held prior to court proceedings. The broad principles can be applied to deaths in all types of custody including deaths in long-term detention such as in prison.

### Deaths in Prison Custody in Europe

The majority of potentially preventable deaths in prison relate to self-harm. As a result most data referring to prison custody refer to issues of self-harm and suicide.

A recent review of suicide by prisoners in prison custody in the UK showed that almost half were remand (nonconvicted) prisoners, and 32% died within 7 days of arrival in prison. A total of 92% committed suicide by hanging or self-strangulation. The profile of these individuals showed that 72% had a history of mental disorder, 62% a history of drug misuse, 53% a history of self-harm, and 31% a history of alcohol misuse. This profile is very similar to the profile and range of problems of those prisoners arrested and detained short-term in police custody in the UK.

A study of the characteristics and management of inmates of Scottish prisons showed that 4.5% of the total prison population were identified as being at risk of suicidal behavior at the time of reception while 1.9% were at risk at some other time in their detention.

Studies in Switzerland from 1995 to 1998 have identified that suicide rates in custodial institutions are higher than in the general population; however, they are decreased in proportion when compared to the 1970s, and it has been suggested that strategies of concentrating prisoners guilty of serious crimes together may intensify feelings of hopelessness and helplessness. Similar studies in Spain have shown that most violent deaths in a high-security prison psychiatric hospital were suicides. Of these, two-thirds suffered from schizophrenia and one-third had self-harmed previously.

German data show that the suicide rate for people on remand and offenders classified as mentally ill was 231 per million versus 191 per million – eight times the suicide rate in the general population. The suicide rate for sentenced offenders was 80 per million. Data from Italy suggest that the suicide rate in a prison population was of the order of 100 per million, and the risk factors included mental disorder, drug addiction, previous prison sentence, and failure to assess potential risk factors appropriately.

Similar figures in Austria resulted in the recommendations that screening instruments should be applied to assist in the appropriate management of inmates at higher risk.

Studies from the Netherlands suggest that suicidal inmates reported increased episodes of sexual abuse, physical abuse, emotional abuse, and previous suicide attempts.

An interesting statistical assessment attempted: (1) to predict the potential numbers of suicides in UK prisons; and (2) to advise on when an alert should be issued if the number of deaths – which it is accepted are not all preventable – exceeded predefined levels. For Scotland this was suggested to be 12, and 28 in England and Wales. An Austrian study identified the three different most significant periods of high suicide risk as being immediately after admission, and 2 months thereafter for prisoners on remand. For long-term prisoners the risk increases with the length of the sentence.

A Swedish study over a 4-year period reviewed 74 deaths, of which almost 30% were either lawfully or unlawfully out of prison custody. There were 34 suicides, 22 accidents, three homicides, and 15 cases of natural death. Of 15 natural deaths, 14 were associated with substantial drug or alcohol misuse. The accidental deaths were predominantly related to alcohol or other drugs and advice is given that drug-dependent inmates should be informed about reduced tolerance to drugs prior to leave or release.

Thus the spectrum of deaths in prison custody is particularly weighted toward incidents of self-harm, and these incidents are associated with a number of factors, of which previous self-harm, mental health issues, and drug and alcohol dependence are key factors. These factors are also the same ones with which death in police (short-term) custody are also noted.

## Historical Aspects of Investigation of Deaths in Police Custody in England and Wales

In the UK, a number of deaths related to police intervention in the 1970s highlighted the vulnerability of ordinary people when the police chose to use aggressive tactics when enforcing the law. These deaths also identified apparent inadequacies of the internal police inquiry, the coronial system, and public inquiry to address the issues. As a result certain changes in the review of cases were set in motion and in the Administration of Justice Act in 1982 juries were made mandatory where there was reason to suspect "that the death occurred while the deceased was in police custody, or resulted from an injury caused by a police officer in the purported execution of his duty."

One landmark case was the death of Jim Kelly in 1979 aged 53 following being arrested as "drunk and disorderly" in Merseyside, UK. It appeared that the Home Office pathologist was not given information of any struggle: he noted some bruising but recorded heart failure as the cause of death. However, Jim Kelly's brother noted bruising to his head and wrists and also that his tobacco tin from his pocket was badly dented and the lighter inside it smashed. A police investigation was started and the inquest opened and adjourned. The family made a formal complaint to the police. Witnesses at the scene told the family that four officers had given him a beating and dumped him semiconscious in the police van. The

family instructed a pathologist who found over 30 injuries, including a double jaw fracture not found by the original pathologist. The second pathologist also gave "heart failure" as the cause of death, stating that Kelly could have died suddenly at any time, but was more likely to die during severe emotional stress or physical exertion. In the conclusion of his report he said that Jim Kelly suffered more injury than can be reasonably expected in a man who resists arrest. Subsequent investigations found eye-witnesses who described police hitting Kelly repeatedly and using a hard weapon and that Jim Kelly had been thrown into the back of the van as though he were an "old bag of bones." Requests for a public inquiry were refused by the Home Secretary William Whitelaw whilst awaiting the outcome of the inquest.

At the coroner's inquest a verdict of "misadventure" was brought in after the coroner had emphasized that the pathologists had given the cause of death as heart failure and that Jim Kelly was drunk and had exerted himself. The question of negligence was not raised. The Home Secretary was satisfied by the inquest and did not think a public inquiry with a wider remit appropriate. The police view was that the officers had been exonerated. It remains true however that if the police had left Jim Kelly to walk home he was unlikely to have died that evening.

The coroner's court was perceived by the public as being an inadequate inquiry as it was selective in the evidence presented and its interpretation. It was not a forum for the role of the arresting officers to be examined critically in order for recommendations to be made about arrests in the future. The general public, having seen the newspaper and television reports, could not feel it was a thorough and adequate legal explanation of the death.

A Home Affairs Select Committee investigation of Deaths in Police Custody in 1980 recommended that the contents of police investigations should be disclosed, but they continued not to be. In 1984 the Police and Criminal Evidence Act set up the Police Complaints Authority (PCA) to replace the Police Complaints Board to improve the investigative procedure.

The PCA developed a role in monitoring deaths in custody. It has successfully used the information collected to steer the police forces to change their policies and training practices to reduce the likelihood of individual deaths. In 2004 the Police Reform Act replaced the PCA with a new body, the Independent Police Complaints Commission (IPCC), further distancing investigation of complaints against the police from the police themselves and further increasing public confidence in independence and objectivity (**Table 1**). The IPCC can investigate independently any complaint or matter referred to it – a role for

**Table 1**  Independent Police Complaints Commission (IPCC): changes in new system of investigation of police complaints compared with Police Complaints Authority (PCA)

- Most complaints will still be investigated by the local police. However, local police will be required to meet strict IPCC standards
- In certain circumstances a number of investigations will be run by the IPCC's own investigators (e.g., death in custody, police shooting)
- In certain circumstances IPCC investigators will have full police powers and rights of access to premises, documents, and other evidence when requested
- Individuals making a complaint will be able to appeal to the IPCC if they feel they have not been given sufficient information by the police or if they are unhappy with the outcome of an investigation by the police
- People other than victims will be able to make a complaint. Anybody who has been "adversely affected" by the incident – which could include a witness – can register a complaint
- There will be a legal obligation to keep complainants informed of the progress of an investigation; this may include giving complainants a copy of the investigating officer's report

which the PCA had neither the statutory power nor the resources.

In its almost two decades of existence, the PCA, by collecting and analyzing the statistics of deaths, has raised awareness of predictable factors and preventive measures: *Lessons From Tragedies* analyzed deaths in the Metropolitan District from 1986 to 1995 and *Deaths in Police Custody; Learning the Lessons* looked at the deaths in England and Wales where data were available from January 1990 to December 1996. Recent publications from the PCA include *The Role of Alcohol in Police Related Deaths, Safer Restraint,* and *Drug-Related Deaths in Police Custody.*

Together with the transition from the PCA to IPCC, a new categorization of deaths of members of the public from police contact was defined in order to differentiate between deaths where there was some real or potential control by the police resulting from the person's contact with them and those where there was not. The latter group will no longer be defined as a "death in custody." The four categories now used for statistical purpose are:

1. category 1: fatal road traffic accidents involving the police ($n = 25$ in 2002–2003)
2. category 2: fatal shootings involving the police (only those who died as a result of being shot by police) ($n = 3$ in 2002–2003)
3. category 3: deaths in custody are one of a group which generally require an inquest with a jury and interested parties, e.g. families, police and prisoners; other appropriate persons or bodies may contribute to the proceedings.
4. category 4: deaths during or following other types of contact with the police that did not amount to detention, and where there is a link between that contact and a death, and that may have occurred in a public place or in the person's home.

Generally this article relates to category 3 deaths.

In addition to the investigation of deaths by the IPCC, all deaths in custody will undergo jurisdictional investigation in England and Wales via a coroner's inquest. Deaths in custody inquests are one of a group, which generally require an inquest with a jury and interested parties, e.g., families, police, prisons. Other appropriate persons or bodies, may contribute to the proceedings. An inquest does not have the power to address issues of criminal or civil liability but is there to confirm who has died and the circumstances of how and when they died. The inquest verdict can result in recommendations to authorities and issues of concern may be raised. Decisions to refer to criminal prosecution services may also be made. In Scotland, such deaths are investigated by means of a fatal accident inquiry.

## Deaths in Custody, Causes and Statistics – England and Wales

A large retrospective study was carried out by the Police Research Group (PRG) of the Home Office. A total of 277 deaths over the 6-year period between January 1990 and December 1996 in England and Wales were studied where there was sufficient information available to confirm that the deaths fell within the criteria. The Home Office had received notification of 380 deaths in that period. The coroner's records reveal the causes given at the inquests. The PRG calculated the rate in proportion to notifiable offences for England and Wales, which does not include all who pass through the custody blocks, as 3.2 deaths per 100 000 arrests for notifiable offences. The PRG paper categorized the 277 deaths into three groups according to causal factors. In 63% the deceased's own actions were causal; this group included deliberate self-harm (DSH) and substance misuse. In another 29% their medical condition was causal and in 8% another person's actions may have been associated.

**Table 2** Analysis of deaths in, or following, custody[a] in 2002–2003

|  | Cell or police station | Public place | Police vehicle, not having been in cell | Home | Other | Total |
|---|---|---|---|---|---|---|
| Medical | 5 | 1 | 1 | 0 | 2 | 9 |
| Alcohol/and or drugs | 5 | 1 | 1 | 0 | 4 | 11 |
| Self-harm | 2 | 2 | 0 | 0 | 0 | 4 |
| Other | 2 | 2 | 0 | 0 | 2 | 6 |
| Total | 14 | 6 | 2 | 0 | 8 | 30 |

[a]These deaths represent category 3 of the Police Complaints Authority *Guidelines for the Reporting of Deaths of Members of the Public During, or Following, Police Contact.* Category 3 is defined as "deaths in police custody: includes people who died following arrest or detention by police, and deaths that occur while a person is being arrested or taken into custody."

The most recent analysis of deaths in or following custody is shown in **Table 2**. This categorization is probably the most helpful in attempting to determine the highest risk areas and means of risk reduction. Each year DSH, alcohol and drug intoxication make up 50% or so of deaths, and it is these that are most likely to be preventable through adequate training and education.

## Deliberate Self-Harm

The figures found in the studies for DSH must be taken into the broader context within England and Wales of an increased suicide rate of young males in the general population. The risk factors include low social class, depression, conduct disorders, and substance misuse. Some or all of these factors apply to many young detainees.

The DSH group in the PRG paper included 17 deliberate overdoses taken before arrest and 73 self-hangings in custody. A recent study has shown that one-third of suicides (in prison) occur within a week of entry into prison and 11% occurred within 24 h; suicide is most common by hanging, using bedclothes and window bars; and there is a high rate of mental disorder and drug dependence in this group. Much work has been undertaken to reduce (by careful cell design) the means by which individuals can self-suspend but those with a desire to harm themselves can be very resourceful. It is important for all involved in the healthcare of prisoners (whether short- or long-term) to realize that death by ligature suspension can occur within just a few minutes or even seconds. Older designs of cells, whereby blankets could be attached to the viewing windows (the "wicket"), are now less common (**Figure 1A** and **B**).

However, even recessed lighting can be broken and a suspension point identified (**Figure 2**). Attempts have been made to manufacture bedding and clothing that are not capable of being used as ligatures.

For each self-harm attempt that ends in death there are calculated to be 200 nonfatal attempts. These can cause significant morbidity. **Figure 3A** and **3B** shows

a police cell where a prisoner was able to conceal himself by the toilet and (nonfatally) severely self-harm by cutting wrists.

Attempts to reduce self-harm from implements such as knives and forks used for food have been addressed by using rubberized eating implements. **Figure 4A** shows rubberized knives and forks, which prevent self-harm from cutting; however, **Figure 4B** shows a rubberized knife which a prisoner chewed and then thrust down into his throat, causing airway obstruction (serious harm was prevented as the incident was observed on a closed-circuit television (CCTV) monitor).

Additional safety measures, for example, the avoidance of standard crockery and the provision of meals in plastic containers, may also be helpful. However, even microwave containers can be fashioned into implements of self-harm and an incident has been documented when part of the plastic container shown in **Figure 5** was torn off and its sharp edge used to create cuts that required suturing.

It is important to recognize and take into account a variety of warning signs for risk of self-harm. Those who have previously been arrested may have a "risk of suicide" marker on the Police National Computer (PNC) and information on the "exceptional risk" transfer forms that are completed. These data however tend to ensure closer observation of those with warnings, at the expense of those without. Expressions of intent, hopelessness, and signs of previous attempts can give warning but in the vast majority this may not be present or identified. In one-third of the in-custody DSH episodes a forensic physician (forensic medical examiner/police surgeon) had seen the detainee and in eight cases warning signs were apparent. Review by a doctor cannot guarantee safety. In one study a doctor was called to assess half of the cases: one died before his arrival, four were assessed as "fit to detain," and one was evaluated as needing admission to a psychiatric hospital.

In response, methods for trying to identify and reduce the risk can be applied. Use of trained civilian staff for the custody care role is appropriate; a

**Figure 1** (A) The view of the "wicket," which had previously been left open for a prisoner. The blue is a blanket that has been wrapped around the wicket, which was then pulled shut from within the cell. (B) The view from within the cell, demonstrating how the prisoner had used the cell blanket in an attempt to self-harm, by twisting it around his neck, and allowing suspension from the wicket.

friendly supportive attitude by people unconnected to the arrest helps detainees to calm down and feel less isolated. Allowing the permitted phone calls and giving drinks, food, magazines, and (untearable) bedding may tip the balance and prevent a suicide bid. Not all police forces or all stations within police forces have the financial resources to do this. If prisoners indicate that they will self-harm or they have suicidal thoughts, constant surveillance may be needed. A medical assessment may be carried out, if necessary followed by a full mental health assessment. The medical consultation may be therapeutic in itself; medication may be given or sometimes a mental illness diagnosis may lead to psychiatric hospital admission or arrangement for outpatient care.

Within the Metropolitan Police Service (London, UK) and some other UK forces all detainees in police custody are now specifically asked on arrival at the police station whether they have ever self-harmed. This allows identification (of some, but not all) of potential higher-risk detainees. The use of CCTV monitoring of some police cells for detainees who are at higher risk is another development to assist care, but CCTV monitors need to be placed so they are not obscured from view and are constantly in an observer's sight line (**Figure 6**).

## Alcohol and Drug Misuse

The PRG paper refers to deaths due to substance abuse (drugs and alcohol) under the category of "the deceased's own actions," these deaths being thought to be directly related to consumption of a substance (alcohol, drugs, or both) prior to arrest. Medical conditions not due to the consumption of substances prior to death were classified as "medical conditions." Sixty-nine (25%) of the deaths were attributable to substance misuse. In 45 cases the deceased had consumed alcohol alone; in 16 drugs were thought to be the cause, whether an overdose, the mixing of drugs, or connected to the withdrawal from drugs. In a further eight cases, the combination of drugs and alcohol was the given cause of death. This total does not include the relevant contribution made to the other causes of death by the longer-term use of substances, for example, heart damage (alcohol and cocaine in particular). Also it was known that two-thirds of the detainees included in the study had

**Figure 2** Broken recessed lighting panel; the sharp edges were used to cut the cell blanket into strips, and the light surround was used as a suspension point.

consumed some alcohol before they died, but the alcohol was not thought to be a direct cause of death.

The massive and explosive increase in drug misuse, particularly heroin and cocaine (as crack), and to a lesser degree, other substances such as ecstasy and $\gamma$-hydroxybutyrate, has in recent years brought a new problem to custodial situations. Since 1992 the number of police detainees with significant drug problems has increased threefold from 11%. Many of the users have codependencies. In addition to drug intake for drug effects, the dangers of drug concealment (e.g., swallowing rocks of crack to avoid being charged with possession or supply of drugs) are great. There have now been a number of deaths in custody due to drug swallowing. The Metropolitan Police Service has issued orders to all officers that, if drug swallowing is witnessed or suspected, the prisoner must be taken immediately to hospital for assessment, as the absorption of crack from even one rock that leaks into the gastrointestinal tract can be enough to cause death.

Excited delirium is recognized as a potential cause of death and police and healthcare professionals assessing prisoners have been made increasingly aware of this syndrome in those who may have ingested stimulants and who may have been involved in chases, been violent, required restraint, or otherwise have behavior patterns of concern.

Drug intoxication can be mistaken for drunkenness. The study revealed that nearly half of those dying from drug abuse were arrested for being "drunk," despite most of them not having consumed

**Figure 3** (A) View from the door of the cell; the toilet is obscured for privacy behind a low wall. (B) View of the toilet in the same cell showing blood following a successful (and hidden) self-harm attempt; there had been no warnings or previous history.

alcohol. The physical appearance and behavior characteristics of "drunkenness" in these cases are due to a dangerous effect of drugs.

A recent review of the role of alcohol in police-related deaths (a total of 58 in 2000–2001) concluded that those with gross alcohol intoxication are not adequately cared for in police custody, and when medical crises occur in this population, police officers do not have the support, resources, skills, or training to provide the emergency interventions required.

*Lessons from Tragedies* recommended three main measures: (1) the use of CCTV for those known to be at risk in the cells and also in vehicles used to transport high-risk detainees; (2) that under no circumstance should a person arrested for being "drunk and disorderly" or "drunk and incapable" be placed in a cell with another person; and (3) that custody in a police cell is clearly not an appropriate place for someone who has had to be detained on account of "drunkenness."

## Medical Conditions (Including Head Injury)

Of those separately categorized in the PRG study as deceased due to severe or chronic medical conditions, 81 (29%) were recorded. The average age of this group was the oldest; many had been transferred to hospital before they died. The commonest five causes of death were: (1) heart problems (39%); (2) head injury (33%); (3) lung problems (10%); (4) epilepsy (5%); and (5) liver problems (4%). The head-injury group were often not recognized as such at booking in. Often the term "head injury" is misunderstood and it needs to be emphasized that any blow to any part of the head with any implement is technically a head injury. Alcohol predisposes to falls and may

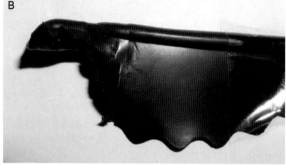

**Figure 4**   (A) Rubberized knife (blade is flexible and will not cut skin). (B) Close-up of rubberized knife blade after chewing.

**Figure 5**   Microwave meal container documented as having been used as a cutting implement by tearing a strip of the plastic container.

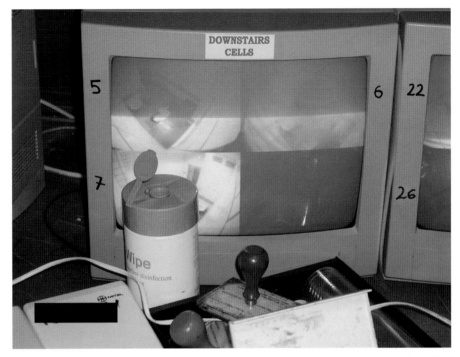

**Figure 6**    Closed-circuit television monitor with screen for a cell under observation has been obscured by a plastic container.

prevent the person giving an account, but also head injury alone may cause behavior that is like alcohol intoxication. The National Institute for Clinical Excellence (NICE) has issued guidelines for medical care, stating that the presence of all but a superficial (undefined) head injury in the presence of alcohol and/or drugs requires hospital assessment. It must be accepted that care given during detention may not always affect outcome. However, in the preventive sense, establishing the correct diagnosis and management can save some individuals sent to hospital appropriately, for example, head-injury victims who are hospitalized in time for life-saving treatment. Failure to recognize or act on problems once identified are areas which rightly cause the public much concern.

## Deaths Associated with Other People's Actions, Including Police Restraint

Arrests, of necessity, sometimes involve force but it should be the minimum. A definition of "excessive force" is any force that a police officer of the highest skill might find a way to avoid. No figure is available for the restraint rate at arrest of all arrestees. In the PRG study, 16 deaths were associated with restraint at arrest or in the custody block, giving an estimated figure of 1.4 deaths for every million people arrested

for notifiable offences. Of these 16, in three cases coroner's verdicts of "unlawful killing" were returned. In others substance misuse or medical factors contributed to the deaths. Key features common to many of the 16 where restraint was a factor included: resisting arrest and "struggling"; physical restraint and equipment combined; and generally a quick reaction to the deterioration in condition of the arrestee, with attempts at resuscitation and calling for an ambulance. But three were "carried" into the custody block, indicating a failure to recognize the severity of the problem at this stage.

The risks associated with neck holds, that may be used in an attempt to restrain, or to prevent swallowing of drugs, are now widely recognized, and basic training emphasizes to police officers the dangers inherent in such practices.

## Minimizing the Risks

Protocols for custody care have changed in response to the recognition of risk factors for suicide, whereas previously cell hatches were often deliberately opened for distressed individuals, they are now kept shut to reduce the risk of hangings. New cell designs attempt to minimize obvious suspension points. Other measures used include more frequent cell checks, CCTV, nontear blankets, and clothing removal.

A risk assessment booking-in form is completed by custody officers, in which specific questions are asked about both medical conditions and self-harm, and this forms part of the custody record. A new prisoner escort record (PER) and improved standards of information transfer are currently being introduced. The PNC is being used for basic health information and is routinely checked in custody.

Training must be a high priority for all those involved in the care of prisoners – gaolers, custody officers (those tasked by the police with the welfare of prisoners), forensic physicians, and custody nurses. Likewise, arresting officers must be trained to recognize medical emergencies. This training must be undertaken at a high level and reinforced on a regular basis and applicable to local needs.

It is important to emphasize that, although many deaths in custody are potentially preventable, a number are not. As well as unpredictable deaths from illness, a determined self-harmer may achieve success despite the best efforts of those responsible for his/her care and an individual may conceal drugs, use the drugs in a cell, or suffer the effects of hidden drugs leaking from wrapping within the body and subsequently die. All such deaths are tragic. It is perhaps important to remember that the spectrum of individuals passing through police custody are those that are most vulnerable. Many have multiple problems encompassing drugs, mental health issues, social isolation, and deprivation. Deaths are inevitable, but it is up to those tasked with aspects of their care to try and ensure that deaths are not due to ignorance, omission, or negligence. It is surely the responsibility of any state to have systems by which such deaths can be independently investigated. The system in England and Wales is far from perfect, but at least a system is in place, and one that continues to evolve.

## See Also

**Custody:** Death in, United States of America; **Detainees:** Care in Police Custody, United Kingdom; Care in Prison Custody, United Kingdom; **Restraint Techniques, Injuries and Death**

## Further Reading

Benezech M, Abdelfattah M-P, Loo P, et al. (1999) Suicide and its prevention in French prisons. Annals of Medicine and Psychology 157: 561–567.

Best D, Kefas A (2004) The Role of Alcohol in Police-Related Deaths: Analysis of Deaths in Custody (Category 3) Between 2000 and 2001. London: Police Complaints Authority.

Christiansen WF, et al. (1999) Deaths among inmates in the institutions of the prison service. Ugeskr-Laeger 61: 1410–1414.

Frottier P, Eher R, et al. (2002) Jailhouse blues revisited. Society of Psychiatry and Psychiatric Epidemiology 37: 68–73.

Fruhwald S, Rutter K, et al. (2000) Assessment of custodial suicide risk – jail and prison suicides in Austria 1975–1996. Psychiatric Praxis 27: 195–200.

Gore SM (1999) Suicide in prisons. Reflection of the communities served, or exacerbated risk? British Journal of Psychiatry 174: 50–55.

Havis S, Best D (2003) Drug-related Deaths in Police Custody. London: Police Complaints Authority.

Konrad N (2002) Prison suicide – European developments including the situation in Switzerland. Schweizerische Archiv für Neurologische Psychiatrie 153: 131–136.

Leigh A, Johnson G, and Ingram A (1999) Deaths in Police Custody; Learning the Lessons. Police Research Series paper 26. London: Home Office Police Research Group.

National Council for Civil Liberties (1980a) Southall 23 April 1979. The Report of the Unofficial Committee of Inquiry into the Disturbances in Southall. London: National Council for Civil Liberties.

National Council for Civil Liberties (1980b) The Supplementary Report of the Unofficial Committee of Inquiry. London: National Council for Civil Liberties.

Norfolk GA (1998) Death in police custody during 1994: a retrospective analysis. Journal of Clinical Forensic Medicine 5: 49–54.

Perez-Carceles MD, Higo C, Luna A, et al. (2001) Mortality in maximum security psychiatric hospital patients. Forensic Science International 119: 279–283.

Police Complaints Authority (1998) Custody Officer Training: Investing in Safety. London: Police Complaints Authority.

Police Complaints Authority (1999a) Deaths in Police Custody: Reducing the Risks. London: Police Complaints Authority.

Police Complaints Authority (1999b) One Year On Deaths in Police Custody: The Risks Reduced. London: Police Complaints Authority.

Police Complaints Authority (2002) Safer Restraint. London: Police Complaints Authority.

Power KG, Nordik E (1997) Characteristics and management of prisoners at risk of suicide behaviour. Archives of Suicide Research 32: 109–123.

Shaw J, et al. (2004) Suicide by prisoners. National clinical survey. British Journal of Psychiatry 184: 263–267.

Tatarelli R, Mancinelli I, Taggi F, et al. (1999) Suicide in Italian prisons in 1996 and 1997: a descriptive epidemiological study. International Journal of Offender Therapy and Comprehensive Criminology 43: 438–447.

Ward T (1986) Death and Disorder. London: Inquest.

Young JG, Chiasson DA, Cairns JT, Payne-James JJ, Carter EJ (2002) Custody and restraint deaths. In: Payne-James JJ, Busuttil A, Smock W (eds.) Forensic Medicine: Clinical and Pathological Aspects. Greenwich, UK: Medical Media.

# Death in, United States of America

**C V Wetli**, Suffolk County Department of Health Services, Hauppauge, NY, USA
**G A Natarajan**, Chief Medical Examiner's Office, Perth Amboy, NJ, USA

## Introduction

Changing social norms and innovative technologies determine current law-enforcement tactics and policies of arrest, incarceration, and interrogation. The serve-and-protect role of the police requires them to ensure the safety and well-being of those in their custody. A death in police custody, therefore, initiates a public inquiry into the adequacy, appropriateness, and safety of any established policies and procedures. This public inquiry is most intense when the death is accompanied by violence, particularly when there is the application of lethal force. A death in custody is always "high-profile," regardless of any attention afforded by the news media.

The term "in-custody death" may include a wide variety of cases, such as death within 24 h of being released from police custody, or death in state-run long-term care or mental health facility. For the purposes of this discussion, "in-custody death" in the USA refers to any individual who dies while incarcerated, or who dies during the attempt to arrest, transport, or interrogate the subject. Deaths in custody may be divided into three groups: (1) nonviolent (e.g., from natural disease, drug overdose, or drug withdrawal); (2) controlled violence (e.g., suicide, judicial electrocution); and (3) uncontrolled violence, when police attempt to restrain an agitated or violent subject and progress through a use of force continuum up to and including the application of lethal force (e.g., police use of chemical sprays, electrical stun devices, neck holds, and firearm discharge). However, for purposes of this discussion, "police" refers to all law-enforcement and correctional officers.

## General Consideration for In-Custody Deaths

In-custody deaths almost invariably raise questions and allegations that can only be addressed by a complete autopsy, including toxicologic analysis, appropriate chemical studies, and histologic confirmation. No matter how obvious the cause of death, questions and allegations often concern other issues such as maltreatment of the prisoner, the role of alcohol and drugs, and timely attention to medical needs. Some

community groups have a deep mistrust of the police and an in-custody death automatically heightens suspicion of "police brutality." A government pathologist is frequently considered to be a part of the law-enforcement establishment and therefore viewed as someone prone to "cover up" for the police. Hence, the necessity of good photographic documentation of not only what is present but also what is not found at autopsy (e.g., presence or absence of neck injury, conjunctival petechiae, rib fractures). Although somewhat controversial, having another pathologist (representing the family or a segment of the community) witness the autopsy may go far towards alleviating suspicions of a cover-up. Police and prosecutors are often reluctant to allow an outside pathologist, particularly if chosen by the family, to witness this autopsy. However, it should be realized that a pathologist hired by the family would do a second autopsy (often in a funeral home) where misinterpretation of postmortem and postautopsy artifact is quite possible or even likely. In general, it may be wiser to have the second pathologist observe the first autopsy rather than misinterpret postautopsy artifact. It is nonetheless acknowledged that some circumstances may prohibit any first-hand observation by an outside pathologist.

Formal guidelines for the investigation and postmortem examination of in-custody deaths have not been established in the USA. Nonetheless, special consideration should be given to certain dissection techniques (**Figures 1–3**) that are generally not performed in routine autopsies. Every death in police custody should include a layerwise anterior neck dissection (after organ evisceration to eliminate artifacts), and a back dissection (to demonstrate contusions). Consideration should be given to a posterior neck dissection, facial dissection, and stripping of the parietal pleura to identify or exclude rib fractures. Examination of the scrotal sac for testicular contusion and paratesticular hematoma should not be overlooked. Consideration should also be given to examining the entire spinal cord whenever the terminal event was of a violent nature. Hemoglobin electrophoresis should be requested to identify or exclude a sickle-cell hemoglobinopathy if the subject is of African descent.

When the terminal event required an escalation of the "use of force continuum," up to and including the use of maximum restraint ("hog-tying"), or the application of lethal force, two subsequent procedures are quite useful. One is a scene reenactment, preferably with the involved police officer(s). Both videographic and photographic documentation should be done. The second procedure involves a conference with all those involved in the death investigation:

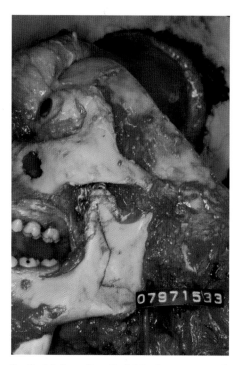

**Figure 1** Facial dissection. Facial fractures may not be visualized by radiologic imaging techniques. In this case it was important to document or exclude blunt facial trauma. Reflecting the face revealed a fracture of the mandibular ramus not related to the gunshot wound of the maxilla. Note also that the projectile (anterior and deep to the mandibular ramus) is easily accessible with this approach. (The dissection technique allows for easy facial reconstruction and subsequent viewing of the body at the funeral home.)

homicide detectives, officers from internal review, crime-scene personnel, appropriate crime/laboratory personnel, toxicologist, and pathologist. The meeting is generally held about 2 weeks after the death, and each discusses the case from his/her perspective. The purpose is to share information, identify areas for further testing and investigation, and to ensure the proper preservation and disposal of evidence. Often with in-custody deaths, the investigation is equally important as the autopsy findings.

When the custody death is, or is perceived to be, the consequence of police action, there will likely be judicial proceedings in the not too distant future. There may be an inquest, grand jury inquiry, criminal trial, or civil litigation. In addition, in the USA, there may also be federal civil rights charges against the police. Therefore, it is imperative that all notes, meetings, and proceedings be carefully and completely documented. To help ensure quality, it is recommended that the autopsy report also be proofread by another pathologist for clarity and accuracy. In deaths where there are multiple injuries, attaching a clarification diagram will greatly assist the reader of the autopsy

report to understand the location of the injuries and pathways of projectiles (in cases of police shootings). Because of the scrutiny associated with in-custody deaths, it is important to preserve all original notes and drafts.

When a prisoner is found dead in a jail cell, the question of time of death invariably arises. Although determinations of time of death are hazardous, a reasonable estimate may be given provided close observation of the body at the scene is followed up several hours later. Hence, observing rigor in the jaw, little lividity, and cutis anserina, with more pronounced rigor and lividity 5 h later, could suggest death occurred 1–3 h before the body was discovered. Alternatively, the detection of fully developed rigor mortis would not be compatible with a guard's statement that the subject was asleep and breathing 1 h before being found dead.

## Nonviolent In-Custody Death

### Expected Natural Death

Prisoners dying outside the conventional hospital setting from acquired immunodeficiency syndrome (AIDS), cancer, or other previously diagnosed terminal illness are generally the least problematic of the in-custody deaths. Nonetheless, there may be allegations of the timeliness or adequacy of treatment. Since these questions or concerns may not surface for some time, and since an in-custody death is always the subject of official and public scrutiny, an autopsy should be considered in anticipation of these potential concerns. Documentation of the extent of the disease process as well as the lack of any evidence of maltreatment will prevent much needless speculation. The same reasoning applies to toxicologic testing in that the presence of appropriate drugs in sufficient concentrations is documented. Likewise, the detection or absence of contraband drugs such as heroin or cocaine is of great significance.

### Sudden Unexpected Natural Death

When sudden in-custody death occurs from natural causes in the absence of any medical history, allegations frequently emerge that the police ignored signs, symptoms, or other indicia of medical distress. Furthermore, it will be alleged that this failure deprived the subject of adequate and life-saving medical treatment. Autopsy and toxicologic studies are of obvious benefit in addressing these issues. Also, documentation of lack of injuries (or their presence) is of crucial importance. When a medical condition is known to the police and sudden death occurs, there is invariably the allegation that police failed to administer the drugs appropriately.

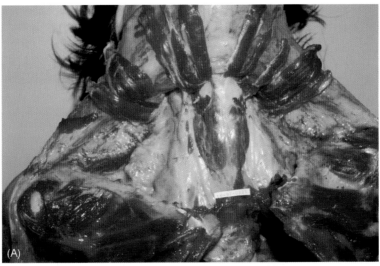

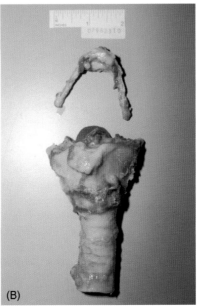

**Figure 2** Layerwise neck dissection. This technique provides clear documentation of the location, or absence, of any neck injury. (A) The strap muscles are reflected to demonstrate the absence of any injury; (B) the hyoid bone and laryngeal cartilages (including the cricoid cartilage) are exposed and demonstrated to be free of injury.

However, since a subject may refuse treatment, a genuine conundrum develops when the subject refuses medication (e.g., insulin) or medical treatment (e.g., dialysis for chronic renal failure). Although criminal charges are unlikely in such a circumstance, civil litigation should be anticipated.

## Death from Drug Overdose

Surreptitious ingestion of drugs shortly before police apprehension may take one of three forms: (1) a suicidal ingestion of drugs (or a poison) followed by some behavior that attracts the police; (2) swallowing of a drug or drug packet to elude police detection

("minipackers"); and (3) delayed death from having swallowed drug packets for smuggling purposes ("body packers"). In any of these categories there will be questions as to whether the police knew or should have known about the ingestion. In some cases subjects may actually tell the police about their suicidal ingestion. Ignoring the statement by assuming it was made to manipulate the system may have obvious dire consequences.

Both drug dealers and drug users may swallow a drug or drug packet to hide the contraband from police, thinking they will not die of a drug overdose. At autopsy, there may be no evidence for this ingestion unless remnants of the packet are found, usually

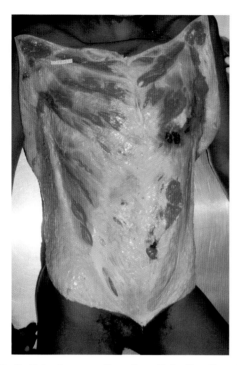

**Figure 3** Subcutaneous dissection. Reflecting the skin of both the front and the back provides for ready identification and localization of contusions. This is particularly important since many contusions may not be externally evident, especially in dark-skinned individuals.

in the stomach (or, rarely, obstructing the upper airway). Body packers usually ingest many large packets, which can be seen on an abdominal radiograph and may be found throughout the gastrointestinal tract. Also, it may be that all but one packet was passed before arrest and incarceration. At autopsy, fragments of the packaging material will be found in the colon, particularly the cecum (which is larger, contains more water, and is less muscular than the left side of the colon). Sudden unexpected death in police custody shortly after arrest or incarceration should always prompt consideration of drug ingestion, and the intestinal contents should be carefully searched for drug packets and packaging material.

It is important to remember that drugs may be purchased in jail from corrupt guards or others with direct or indirect access to prisoners. Loss of drug tolerance during incarceration may well predispose heroin addicts to a fatal narcotic overdose. Individuals with hypertensive or arteriosclerotic cardiovascular disease may succumb to stimulant drugs such as cocaine or methamphetamine.

Finally, it is important to note that death may occur from narcotic withdrawal. Today, this is rare and highly unlikely because of access to medical care in the jail setting. Nonetheless, the possibility must be given consideration.

Toxicological sampling should include blood, urine, bile, and vitreous fluid as well as liver and brain to evaluate levels of drugs and medications in tissues and fluids, and perhaps to estimate the approximate time of ingestion.

## Controlled Violence

### Suicide

Most jail suicides result from hanging. The usual ligature is a belt, or item of clothing, shoelace, or bed linen. If prisoners are perceived as a suicide risk, the clothing is taken from them and they are checked frequently (e.g., every 15 min). Without anything to fashion a ligature and nothing sharp available (toilets are stainless steel) the likelihood for a successful suicide is greatly diminished. Nonetheless, other methods such as jumping, prescription drug overdose, and even suicidal drowning in a toilet bowl have successfully occurred.

The investigation will attempt to assess how the person could have actually committed suicide with other prisoners and guards nearby. The autopsy is needed to confirm the cause of death (i.e., that hanging was indeed the cause of death), that there is no evidence for it being a homicide made to look like a suicide, and the role of drugs or alcohol. Neck compression in a kneeling or sitting position, as well as partial suspension, results in atypical findings that are not characteristic for classic hanging. Hence it is crucial to compare injuries with body position.

### Capital Punishment

Judicial executions, at least in the USA, are witnessed by a number of public officials, often a victim's family, and representatives of the news media. Despite all the preparations and the witnesses, and an obvious cause and manner of death, an autopsy is required to ensure the procedure was effective and humane, and that the prisoner was not drugged or mistreated prior to the execution itself. A judicial hanging, for example, should result in a clear hangman's fracture of the high cervical spine to cause instantaneous death. Likewise, death by firing squad or electrocution should have evidence of near instantaneous death as demonstrated by the autopsy.

Medical ethics dictates that physicians must not participate in an execution. It has further been alleged that performance of an autopsy and certification of death is unethical because it makes the pathologist a participant in capital punishment. However, the executed prisoner is not the patient of the forensic pathologist – society is, and the autopsy is the last quality-control check on the handling of that prisoner. To avoid the allegation or appearance of impropriety, the physician should not pronounce death, and the autopsy should be done some hours after the execution and at a site removed from the facility where the execution took place.

### Torture

Lethal injuries may occur during interrogation accompanied by beatings or other physical trauma. When a fatal injury is obvious (e.g., closed-head trauma, lacerated spleen), it must be correlated with the terminal event. Also, the body must be carefully examined for other, often subtle, evidence of injury, which may be associated with severe pain but is far from lethal. There could be small punctate lesions from repeated application of a stun gun, inflamed paranasal sinus membranes from aspiration of carbonated beverages, irregular patellar scars or abrasions from forced crawling on gravel, and anogenital injury from sexual assault. Pathologists should be familiar with pattern injuries resulting from the use of batons, flashlights, and other objects commonly carried by law-enforcement personnel. The possibilities are endless, and the pathologist is left to document the injuries and scars with the hope of correlating these at some future date when and if the interrogation methods are revealed. Death certification in such cases may be problematic if the medical examiner is pressurized to accept a terminal scenario that does not easily correlate with the lethal injury or other injuries observed on the body. At worst, the medical examiner deliberately falsifies the cause and manner of death and covers up the evidence of torture.

## Uncontrolled Violence

Violent subjects always pose a very real threat to themselves and others. Consequently, police must utilize techniques to control and contain the subject while simultaneously protecting innocent people and preventing injuries to the responding police officers. Ideally, the subject is quickly controlled and removed from the scene uninjured and before any harm has come to others. Various techniques and instruments have been devised to incapacitate a subject safely for a brief period that will allow the police to handcuff and hobble the subject safely. The methods are regarded as nonlethal when properly utilized. That assumption comes under question when death occurs during or shortly after the struggle (*post hoc ergo propter hoc*). Methods, techniques, and instruments often change for a variety of reasons. The methods more commonly used today that provoke controversy and stimulate lawsuits include the lateral vascular neck restraint (also referred to as LVNR, carotid sleeper hold, or upper-body control hold), electrical stun device (stun guns, tasers), pepper spray, and maximal restraint ("hog-tying").

### Lateral Vascular Neck Restraint

This technique, when properly applied, is supposed to render the subject unconscious for a few seconds to allow the police officer to place handcuffs on the subject. The basic technique consists of standing behind the subject and placing the upper extremity around the subject's neck with the elbow pointing forward in the midline. The arm compresses one side of the neck, the forearm compresses the other side, and the larynx is protected by the flexion of the elbow. Since only the sides of the neck are compressed, this is not a "choke hold," and the airway is not compressed or injured. The theory is that the carotid arteries are compressed, thereby causing cerebral hypoxia, and the carotid bodies are stimulated and reduce the heart rate. However, the mechanism is probably more complex since the carotid arteries are probably not completely occluded and the jugular veins are obstructed. Prevention of blood flow from the brain while blood is still flowing to the brain via the vertebral arteries (at least) rapidly increases cerebral blood volume and results in hyperacute cerebral swelling, which also results in a rapid loss of consciousness. Release of the pressure allows for rapid recovery. Most police agencies require the hold to be released after 30 s. The obvious physical danger of this technique is that during the struggle the LVNR could turn into a forearm bar-hold (forearm going across to the front of the neck), which will compress the airway.

Use of the LVNR is very controversial. Although some agree it is effective and safe when properly applied with appropriate safeguards, its use is banned by many police departments and in many countries, because of the perception that it is a choke hold, and because it will be the alleged cause of death should the subject die during or shortly after the struggle. In the absence of other findings it would be very difficult to disprove.

### Electrical Stun Guns

These devices are designed to deliver many thousands of volts of electricity at very low amperage. The subject becomes incapacitated from pain and localized muscular contraction. One device requires the electrodes of the unit (about the size of a standard deck of playing cards) be placed against the subject's body. Another, referred to as a taser (an acronym for "Thomas A. Swift's electric rifle"), shoots darts attached to wires. Both leave small red marks on the skin. These devices are uniformly regarded as safe and effective, and they do not cause cardiac rhythm disturbances. It must be noted that these electrical stun devices may be used as a torture instrument.

## Pepper Spray

The active ingredient is an extract of pepper, oleoresin capsicum (OC), a severe mucosal irritant that creates a burning sensation of the eyes and mucous membranes of the mouth. It may also irritate the upper airway and cause some coughing. It is not known to cause any life-threatening incapacitation or lasting harm. Only one death has been reported where pepper spray probably contributed to the death and this occurred in a person with an inflammatory lung disease. Other deaths temporally related to the use of OC spray have been shown to be due to other causes, despite plaintiff allegations to the contrary. It should be noted that pepper-spray canisters are designed to release short bursts, not a continuous stream. At autopsy, no objective signs (such as redness or swelling of oropharyngeal mucosa) have been observed except, perhaps, for scleral injection. Aside from specious allegations that it was the cause of death, the major concern about pepper spray is that it caused incapacitation and yet the police continued to act. That, of course, is to be determined by investigation, not the autopsy. However, it is not infrequent that, although OC spray was discharged, it failed to hit the subject. Therefore, if OC spray has been used, swabs of the clothes, face, nose, eyes, and mouth should be taken to confirm its presence, or provide some evidence that it did not reach the intended target. Since the substance is highly volatile, the swab should be taken and analyzed as soon as possible.

## Maximum Restraint ("Hog-Tying")

Violent individuals who continue to kick and thrash about before being handcuffed behind their back may be further secured by hobble restraints placed on their ankles, and these in turn are then connected to the handcuffs by another strap or cord. It has been hypothesized that the bowed position, particularly while prone (and obese), interferes with the bellows action of the chest and diaphragm and causes death by asphyxiation. The term "positional asphyxia" or "restraint asphyxia" has been applied to this proposed phenomenon. Thus far, there is no direct evidence to fully support this hypothesis of positional or restraint asphyxia, and recent studies indicate these cases of sudden death are primarily cardiac and associated with a severe metabolic acidosis.

Additional experiments on healthy volunteers reveal there is no significant compromise of respiration from being restrained in this fashion after physical exertion. The postmortem examination should, nonetheless, specifically mention the presence or absence of petechiae in the conjunctivae, upper airway (epiglottis), lining membrane of the sphenoid sinus, and lingual tonsils. Documentation of rib, chest, and back injuries, or their absence, is also of paramount importance.

When maximum restraint is necessary, police are instructed to place the subject on his/her side and continually monitor vital signs until the subject is taken to a medical facility or jail.

## Police Shootings

The police are the only civilian segment of US society authorized to use lethal force. When such force is used, there is invariably an intense investigation as to whether the use of lethal force was, in fact, justified. Frequently, the autopsy contributes important information to this investigation by documenting projectile pathways and providing evidence of range of fire.

One characteristic of police shootings is that there are frequently multiple shooters. Knowing where they were located and what type of ammunition was being fired frequently allows for a reconstruction of the movements and position of the subject. All projectile pathways must be accurately traced and recorded. In addition, more important perhaps than all the photographs taken are clarification diagrams which reveal projectile pathways and allow for good correlation of the scene and the terminal events. The following is illustrative.

A man was shot 11 times by four police officers. The police fired when the subject was about to strike one of the officers with a hammer. The plaintiff allegation was that the subject was incapacitated with pepper spray and he was unnecessarily executed by the police. Evaluation of the bullet pathways supported the police scenario. In the clarification diagram (**Figure 4**), note bullet wounds #9 and #2. The photographs revealed that this is one projectile pathway #9, entering the right arm laterally, exiting medially, and re-entering the body at #2. The only way this could align is if the arm is raised above the head, consistent with swinging a hammer as the police indicated. Knowing the position of the shooting officers further indicated, with the use of this diagram, that the subject continued to move his arm down and twist toward the left before dropping the hammer and taking a few steps until he collapsed.

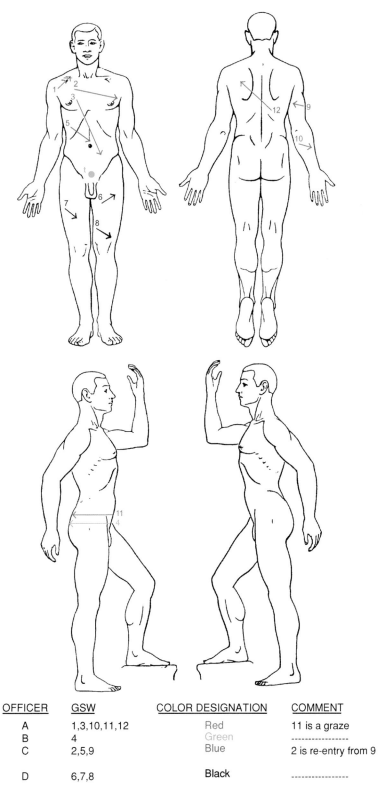

| OFFICER | GSW | COLOR DESIGNATION | COMMENT |
|---------|-----|-------------------|---------|
| A | 1,3,10,11,12 | Red | 11 is a graze |
| B | 4 | Green | ---------------- |
| C | 2,5,9 | Blue | 2 is re-entry from 9 |
| D | 6,7,8 | Black | ---------------- |

**Figure 4** Clarification diagram. Delineation of the pathways greatly aids in determining the likely sequence of shots. In this case, #9 and #2 are one wound that could only occur if the arm is raised, consistent with attacking, with a hammer. As the subject swung the hammer down and twisted towards the left, he sustained wounds #9/#2, #1, #4 and #11, then #3 and #5 as he twisted left and bends forward, and finally sustained #10 and #12. It is uncertain in the scenario when the lower-extremity wounds occurred.

When confronted by police, a subject may attempt suicide in such a way as to precipitate a barrage of police fire. Two scenarios are likely. One is where the subject shoots him/herself. The police, thinking they were the targets, open ("return") fire. The autopsy will reveal the suicidal gunshot wound and that the police actually shot a dead or dying person. The other scenario is termed "suicide by cop" whereby the subject forces the police to shoot him/herself fatally. One example is where a subject threatens police or a hostage with a realistic-appearing toy gun, forcing the police to shoot and kill the subject.

### Excited Delirium

Agitated or excited delirium is an acute confusional state marked by intense paranoia, hallucinations, and violence toward objects and people. The most common causes seen today are toxicity from stimulant drugs, especially cocaine and methamphetamine, and psychiatric patients who stop taking their medication. The bizarre and threatening behavior of these individuals invariably leads to a police response. The subject violently resists any attempts at being restrained by the police and displays a surprising amount of strength. Several police officers are needed to handcuff and ankle-cuff the individual. Sudden death occurs within a very short time of being restrained in most cases.

The violent nature of this syndrome often results in the police application of a variety of techniques to restrain the subject. These include baton strikes, LVNR, OC spray, stun guns, and maximum restraint. The effects of all these techniques must be carefully evaluated by both investigation and autopsy. Thus far, available evidence indicates that there are sudden cardiac deaths associated with a severe metabolic (lactic) acidosis. Nonetheless, civil litigation nearly always alleges so-called positional or restraint asphyxia as a cause of death, with or without the contribution of the other instruments used by the police (i.e., pepper spray, LVNR, stun gun).

### Summary

Deaths in police custody invite intense scrutiny. The autopsy and related studies (such as toxicology) must be complete and thorough, anticipating questions that will eventually arise. Dissection must demonstrate both what is present and what is not present. Thorough documentation by photographs and diagrams is of paramount importance. Finally, the medical examiner must observe the reenactments and be included in sharing information with other investigative agencies. Since in-custody deaths frequently involve physiologic processes, or chemical

and drug reactions, there may well remain legitimate differences in interpreting the objective findings.

## See Also

**Custody:** Death in, United Kingdom and Continental Europe; **Detainees:** Care in Police Custody, United Kingdom; Care in Prison Custody, United Kingdom; **Excited Delirium**; **Injuries and Deaths During Police Operations:** Shootings During Police Stops and Arrests; Special Weapons and Training Teams

## Further Reading

Anders S, Junga M, Schutz F, Püschel K (2003) Cutaneous current marks due to a stun gun injury. *Journal of Forensic Science* 48: 640–642.

Bhana BD (2003) Custody-related deaths in Durban, South Africa. 1998–2000. *American Journal of Forensic Medicine and Pathology* 24: 202–207.

British Medical Association (2000) *Medicine Betrayed. The Participation of Doctors in Human Rights Abuses*, pp. 116–117. London: Zed Books.

Chan TC, Vilke GM, Neuman T, Clausen JL (1997) Restraint position and positional asphyxia. *American Journal of Emergency Medicine* 30: 578–586.

Chan TC, Vilke GM, Clarsen J, *et al.* (2002) The effect of oleoresin capsicum "pepper" spray inhalation on respiratory function. *Journal of Forensic Science* 47: 299–304.

Council on Ethical and Judicial Affairs of the American Medical Association (1993) Physician participation in capital punishment. *Journal of the American Medical Association* 270: 365–368.

Gutstadt JP, Sathyavagiswaran L, Stephens B (2003) *Drowning in a Toilet Bowl: A Rare Form of Suicide in Adults*, abstract 69. San Jose, CA: National Association of Medical Examiners Annual Meeting.

He X-Y, Felthons AP, Holzer CE, Nathan P, Veesey S (2001) Factors in prison suicide: one year study in Texas. *Journal of Forensic Science* 46: 896–901.

Hick JL, Smith SW, Lynch MT (1999) Metabolic acidosis in restraint – associated cardiac arrest: a case series. *Academic Emergency Medicine* 6: 239–243.

Ikeda N, Harada A, Suzuki T (1991) Homicidal manual strangulation and multiple stun-gun injuries. *American Journal of Forensic Medicine and Pathology* 13: 320–323.

Introna F, Smialek JE (1989) The "mini-packer" syndrome: fatal digestion of drug containers in Baltimore, MD. *American Journal of Forensic Medicine and Pathology* 12: 43–48.

Khan A, Leventhal RM (2002) Medical aspects of capital punishment executions. *Journal of Forensic Science* 47: 847–851.

Koiwai EK (1987) Death allegedly caused by the use of "choke holds" (shime-waza). *Journal of Forensic Science* 37: 419–432.

Kornblum RN (1986) Medical analysis of police choke holds and general neck trauma. *Trauma* 27: 7–60 (part I); 28: 13–64 (part II).

Kornblum RN, Reddy SK (1991) Effects on the Taser® in fatalities involving police confrontation. *Journal of Forensic Science* 36: 434–448.

Luke JL, Reay DT (1992) The perils of investigating and certifying deaths in police custody. *American Journal of Forensic Medicine and Pathology* 13: 98–100.

Natarajan GA, Fonseca CA (1997) Beyond nose jobs and face lifts: an illustrated technique of facial dissection. *American Society of Clinical Pathology Check Sample* FP97-8 39: 111–125.

Norman ES, Winston DC (2001) Neuroleptic malignant syndrome, psychotropic medications, police custody, and sudden death. *American Society of Clinical Pathology Check Sample* FP01-9 43: 105–116.

O'Halloran RL, Frank JG (2000) Asphyxial death during prone restraint revised – a report of 21 cases. *American Journal of Forensic Medicine and Pathology* 21: 39–52.

Ordog GJ (1982) Electronic gun (Taser®) injuries. *Annals of Emergency Medicine* 73: 103–108.

Parkes JM (2000) Sudden death during restraint: a study to measure the effect of restraint positions on the rate of recovery from exercise. *Medicine, Science and the Law* 40: 39–43.

Reay DT (1998) Death in custody. *Clinics in Laboratory Medicine* 18: 1–23.

Reay DT (1999) Judicial hanging. *American Society of Clinical Pathology Check Sample* FP99-5: 61–73.

Reay DT, Eisek JW (1982) Death from law enforcement neck holds. *American Journal of Forensic Medicine and Pathology* 3: 253–258.

Ross DL (1998) Factors associated with excited delirium deaths in police custody. *Modern Pathology* 11: 1127–1137.

Segest E (1987) Police custody: deaths and medical attention. *Journal of Forensic Science* 32: 1694–1703.

Steffee CH, Lantz PE, Flannahan LM, Thompson RC, Jason DR (1992) Oleoresin capsicum (pepper spray) and "in-custody" deaths. *American Journal of Forensic Medicine and Pathology* 16: 185–192.

Stephens CL, Wallace WA (2002) A death in the jail: in-custody death. *American Society of Clinical Pathology Check Sample* FP02-9 44: 115–126.

Stratton ST, Rogers C, Brickett K, Fruzinski (2001) Factors associated with sudden death of individuals requiring restraint for excited delirium. *American Journal of Emergency Medicine* 19: 187–191.

Truog RD, Brennan TA (1993) Participation of physicians in capital punishment. *New England Journal of Medicine* 329: 1346–1350.

Watson WA, Stremer KR, Westdrop EJ (1996) Oleoresin capsicum (Cap-Stun) toxicity from aerosol exposure. *Ann Pharmacotherapy* 30: 733–735.

Wetli CV, Davis JH (1994) Participation of physicians in capital punishment (letter to the editor). *New England Journal of Medicine* 330: 936.

Wetli CV, Mittleman RE (1981) The body packer syndrome: toxicity following ingestion of illicit drugs packaged for transportation. *Journal of Forensic Science* 26: 492–500.

# D

**Death, Post-mortem Changes** *See* **Postmortem Changes:** Overview

**Death, Post-mortem Electrolyte Disturbances** *See* **Postmortem Changes:** Electrolyte Disturbances

# DEATHS

Contents

**Trauma, Head and Spine**
**Trauma, Thorax**
**Trauma, Abdominal Cavity**
**Trauma, Musculo-skeletal System**
**Trauma, Vascular System**
**Perioperative and Postoperative**
**Sports**

## Trauma, Head and Spine

**P Marks**, The General Infirmary at Leeds, Leeds, UK

### Introduction

Trauma to the head and cervical spine is a well-recognized cause of death. The management of traumatic brain injury continues to challenge clinicians throughout the world. It has been conclusively shown that the overall mortality for patients who suffer trauma is three times higher in patients with a head injury than those who have not suffered such damage. In patients who have sustained head injuries, the cause of death is attributable to brain injury in 68% of cases, extracranial injuries in 7%, and to both intracranial and extracranial trauma in the remainder. The severity of a head injury remains the strongest predictor of overall outcome in individuals who have sustained polytrauma. In addition to head injury, acute injuries of the spine and spinal cord are amongst the most common causes of severe disability and death following trauma.

The neuropathology and clinical features of traumatic brain injury have been covered extensively elsewhere in this encyclopedia, but certain points need to be emphasized, particularly the type and pattern of injuries that tend to prove immediately fatal or are refractory to therapy of whatever sort.

### Patterns of Fatal Head Injuries

The two forms of primary brain injuries that are recognized (i.e., contusions and lacerations of the brain on the one hand and diffuse axonal injury on the other) have been extensively described elsewhere. Multiple contusions which are associated with overspill of blood through the leptomeninges into the subdural space, so-called "burst lobes," may prove rapidly fatal and the victim may not survive sufficiently long to reach hospital. Similarly, severe cases of diffuse axonal injury where there is disruption of the brainstem and interference with the central pathways that control respiration and other vital autonomic functions may again prove rapidly fatal. Generally, the main predictor of a poor outcome is a low score on the Glasgow Coma Scale. Thus, if the observed coma scale at the time the victim is first found is 3 and the pupils are fixed and dilated, the outlook is essentially hopeless. Periods of apnea resulting in hypoxia will compound primary brain damage of whatever form and lead to an ineluctably fatal outcome.

Rapidly expanding mass lesions such as extradural (**Figure 1**) and subdural hematomas or generalized brain swelling can all prove to be rapidly fatal (**Figures 2** and **3**).

## Direct Brainstem Trauma

Contusions and lacerations of the brainstem occur most commonly in association with traumatic lesions in other topographical regions of the brain, yet they may occur as apparently isolated lesions. Although direct brainstem injuries are most commonly seen in forensic medical practice, there are significant numbers of patients who survive for some time and indeed case reports exist of patients surviving for several weeks following pontomedullary tears after a road traffic accident. At autopsy, well-defined partial tears were observed in these cases with associated reactive changes, refuting the hypothesis that they were produced at the time of brain removal at postmortem. As is implicit in the name, a pontomedullary tear or rent occurs at the junction of the pons and medulla and in extreme cases may represent a complete transaction. Many cases have been reported, and in over 95% there is evidence of a skull fracture, in particular a ring fracture at the skull base and/or a fracture of the upper cervical spine, especially of the atlas or axis. The mechanism of traumatic disruption is most often due to hyperextension of the head on the neck, often with force being applied to the forehead with the trunk and legs bending forward over the temporarily immobile head. Tears at the pontomesencephalic junction may also occur as isolated injuries of the brainstem, but are far less common than rents at the pontomedullary junction. Similarly, tears or complete transections can arise at the junction of the caudal medulla and the upper cervical cord. This type of injury tends to be instantaneously fatal, most often being due to separation of the atlas from the occiput (**Figure 4**).

## Total Destruction of the Skull

Such overwhelming and obviouslyinstantaneously fatal injuries may be seen following falls from heights, high-velocity gunshot wounds, injuries due to

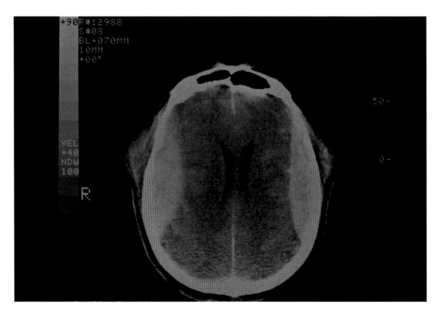

**Figure 1**  This man fell off a stepladder while painting a ceiling. His computed tomography scan shows bilateral extradural hematomas. His Glasgow Coma Scale was 3 on arrival to hospital and he suffered a cardiorespiratory arrest 40 min after the injury and died.

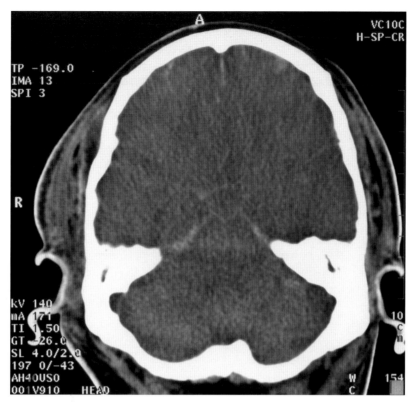

**Figure 2** This computed tomography scan shows complete effacement of the basal cisterns in a patient who sustained a severe closed-head injury. Diffuse brain swelling was present and was refractory to all therapy. This man died 24 h after the accident.

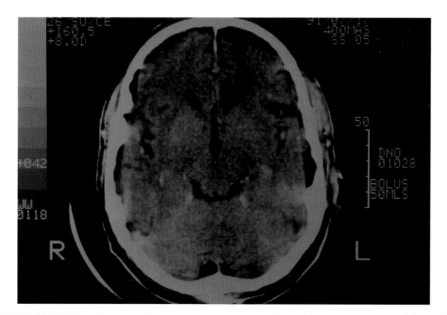

**Figure 3** By contrast, this computed tomography scan shows a normal pattern of basal cisterns around the midbrain (perimesencephalic cisterns). These comprise the interpeduncular cistern anteriorly, the quadrigeminal cistern posteriorly, and the ambient cisterns laterally.

explosions (**Figures 5** and **6**), including suicide bombers, and certain forms of high-speed deceleration injuries such as plane crashes. Identification may be problematic and remains may be an over optimistic term, particularly when they are widely scattered.

## Fatal Injuries Resulting from Trauma to the Cervical Spine

Spinal cord injuries tend to occur in young individuals in the second or third decade, although a secondary

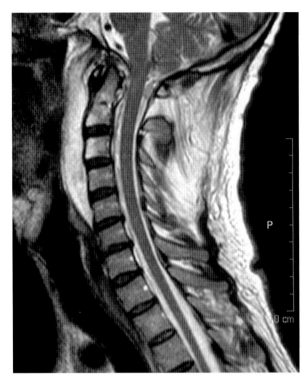

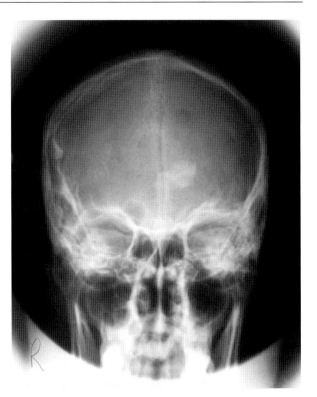

**Figure 4**   This magnetic resonance imaging scan shows a patient who had a traumatic dislocation of the atlantooccipital joint after being thrown from a motorcycle through a hedge. Note the increased distance between the skull base and the upper cervical vertebrae and the widened upper prevertebral space.

**Figure 5**   This lateral skull radiograph shows the effects of a blast injury to the head. Fragments of the skull vault have been driven into the brain. At autopsy, the brain was severely disrupted and pulped.

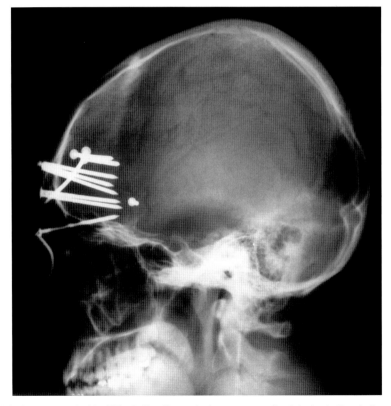

**Figure 6**   Some blast injuries are survivable. This skull radiograph shows penetrating injuries to the skull caused by a nail bomb. The frontal lobes were disrupted but, following lobectomy, the patient survived, albeit rather disinhibited.

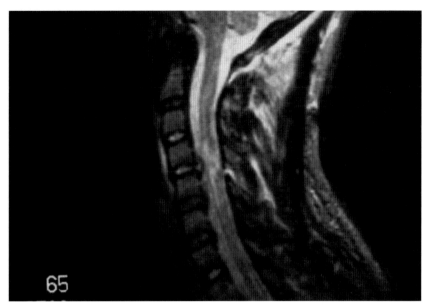

**Figure 7** This magnetic resonance imaging scan shows an acute cervical disk protrusion that is causing spinal cord compression. Abnormal signal change is seen within the cord, indicating edema. This injury was sustained by acute forward flexion of the cervical spine in a rugby scrum. The patient suffered diaphragmatic paralysis and required ventilatory support.

peak exists in the elderly population. Males are affected at least 10, if not 20, times more frequently than females, although in those over the age of 80 years, the male-to-female preponderance is equal. In the USA about 14 000 people sustain a spinal cord injury each year and, of these, 4200 die before reaching hospital. Of those who survive initially, 1500 will die during their admission. Cervical spine fractures represent up to 30% of all spinal injuries and 50% of all injuries affecting the spinal cord. Interestingly, only 10–30% of spinal trauma results in cord injury. Road traffic accidents cause between 35% and 45% of all spinal cord injuries and the cervical region is the segment of the spine that is most frequently injured. Other causes of spinal trauma include assaults, industrial accidents, and recreational pursuits, including equestrian injury, accidents resulting from the use of jet skis, snow mobiles, snow boarding, and parachuting. Penetrating injuries to the spine resulting from gunshots or stab wounds should not be forgotten and may result in complete or total transection of the spinal cord.

## Biomechanics

Consider a road traffic accident in which the occupant of a vehicle is wearing a seatbelt. As impact or deceleration occurs, the head moves forward with a higher amount of angular velocity and is then jerked back, when the head hits an object such as the dashboard or windscreen or the neck is unable to flex any further. It is these rapid changes in the angular momentum of the head that produce fractures in various parts of the spine and cause disruption of the ligaments and associated structures (**Figure 7**). The degree of injury is variable and ranges from minor whiplash injuries which rapidly settle to tetraplegia and death. Such injuries are also noted after fatal aircrashes where there is a 25% incidence of cervical spine fracture. In general, the higher the level of cord injury, the more likely it is to be fatal. Thus, the mortality of atlantooccipital dislocation ranges from 71% to 100%, whereas there is a 17% incidence of death from C1 injuries and only a 3.7% mortality from injuries at C4.

It should be remembered that, in pediatric practice, 60% of cervical spine injuries result in a fracture without neurological deficit, but on the other hand, spinal cord injury can occur without radiological abnormality. This condition is given the acronym SCIWORA. SCIWORA is usually associated with a complete lesion in 75% of cases and has a poor prognosis. In pediatric practice the high incidence of high cervical spine injury is thought to be due to the fact that young children have a relatively larger head when compared with the rest of their body. In addition, the unossified synchrondrosis of the dens and less complete ossification of the other vertebral bones result in an alteration in the center of gravity of the head and neck which can, under conditions of trauma, produce increased strain on the upper cervical ligaments. It has recently been recognized that in road traffic accidents involving children there may be a high incidence of fatal atlantooccipital dislocation. It is thought that airbags may contribute to this problem if an expanding airbag comes directly into contact with the head rather than the head and chest.

## Mechanisms of Death in Cervical Spine Injuries

Death may result from high cervical spine injuries in which the spinal cord is transected with immediate loss of cord function and paralysis of respiratory function. Spinal shock occurs with bradycardia and concomitant hypotension. Acute disk protrusion with cord compression and edema is another mechanism by which cervical spine injury may prove fatal.

## Patterns of Injury within the Cervical Spine

There is no universally accepted classification for fractures involving the cervical spine; some classifications are based on the pattern of bony injury whereas others focus on whether neurological injury is present or not. There are, however, some well-recognized patterns of bony injury which it is important to recognize.

## Atlantoaxial Injuries

These are potentially the most serious of spinal injuries and may result in complete transaction of the cord at C1 or C2 with resultant diaphragmatic paralysis and death. A burst fracture of the atlas is often referred to as a Jefferson fracture and typically arises from axial compression of the C1 ring. This results in bilateral spreading of the lateral masses with resultant failure of the anterior and posterior arches of the atlas (**Figure 8**). As the involved fragments tend to spread away from the neural canal, neurological damage is not usual, but the fractures are unstable and injudicious movement can result in cord damage with a fatal result. Jefferson fractures (41%) are associated with a fracture of C2.

### Fracture of the Odontoid Peg

These are usually caused by high-velocity injuries and are often fatal. They are classified into three types:

1. Type I, which is the rarest and involves the apex of the dens and is caused by avulsion of the apical ligament. The dens is largely intact and the spine is stable.
2. Type II is the most common form of odontoid fracture and is unstable. The fracture line passes through the base of the dens and, as this may result in disruption of the blood supply, avascular necrosis and nonunion are common sequelae in those who survive.

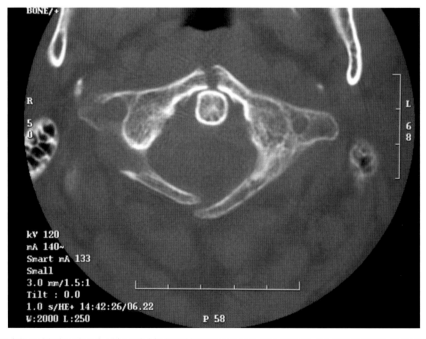

**Figure 8**   This man fell on his head and, although his head injury was not very severe, he complained of neck pain. This computed tomography scan shows a Jefferson fracture – note the fracture lines involving the anterior and posterior arches of the atlas.

3. Type III fractures involve the cancellous bone of the body of the axis which is well vascularized and usually united following a period of immobilization in a halo jacket (**Figure 9**).

## Traumatic Spondylolisthesis

This is the so-called hangman's fracture and is a common pattern of injury affecting the axis. With this type of injury fracture lines pass bilaterally through the pars interarticularis or pedicles. Typically subluxation of C2 on C3 occurs with associated disruption of the ligaments. These injuries are unstable and radiologically four patterns are recognized; where displacement is minimal, neurological injury may not occur, but if there is gross dislocation and angulation, cord injury is likely and is usually fatal because of respiratory paralysis.

Hangman's fractures are of course so called because they are produced by judicial hanging where the "long-drop" technique is employed. Death is attributable to high-cord or brainstem injury and it should be noted that fracture of the skull base may be an accompanying feature. If the drop is greater than 4 m, decapitation may occur.

In fatal cases where cervical spine injury is suspected, radiographic evaluation of the spine before the dissection of the body can add valuable information to the gross findings at autopsy.

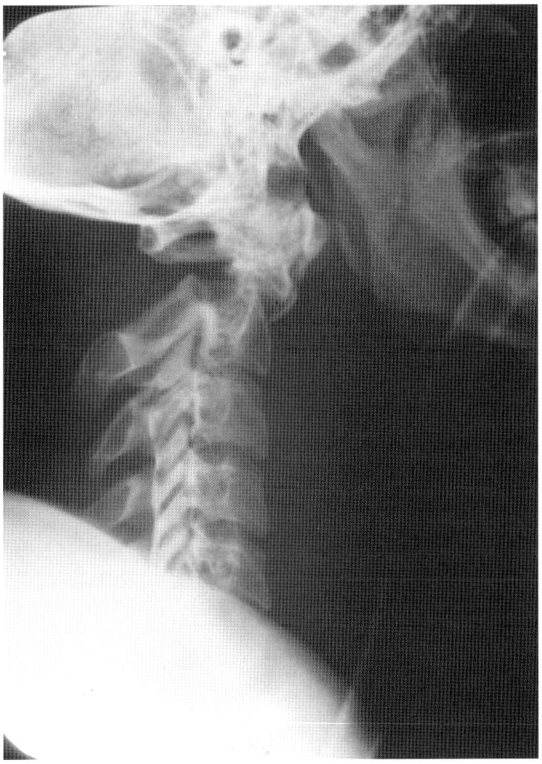

## See Also

**Head Trauma:** Pediatric and Adult, Clinical Aspects; Neuropathology

## Further Reading

Houghton GR (1989) *Spine Injuries*. Philadelphia: JP Lippincott.
Winn HR (ed.) (2004) *Youman's Neurological Surgery*, vol. 4, 5th edn.

# Trauma, Thorax

**A W Fegan-Earl**, Forensic Pathology Services, London, UK

## Introduction

The thorax represents a significant proportion of the surface area of the body, and is thus potentially subjected to a wide variety of trauma that may result in death. It is not just the surface area of the thorax that is important but also the contents of the thorax when considering the high chances of death that may follow thoracic trauma. If the importance of the structures for sustaining life contained within the confines of the thorax is considered, it is immediately obvious why injury to the thorax may be life-threatening. Furthermore, the thorax and its contents are frequently injured in combat between individuals. The purpose of this article is to review the nature of trauma to the thorax using an anatomical and trauma-type basis, and set it in a forensic perspective.

## Anatomy

The thorax is a complex anatomical area, bounded superiorly by the thoracic inlet, inferiorly by the diaphragm, anterolaterally by the ribs and posteriorly by the vertebral column. Reference should be made to anatomical texts for the detailed anatomy. For the consideration of trauma to the thorax of a severity that may cause death, the thorax may be divided into a number of sections:

**Figure 9** This patient was brought into hospital in extremis after a high-velocity road traffic accident. This lateral radiograph of the cervical spine shows a fracture of the odontoid peg with marked anterior translocation of C1 on C2. At autopsy, complete transection of the spinal cord was noted.

1. the heart
2. the great vessels
3. the chest wall
4. the lungs.

## The Heart

The heart occupies the middle part of the mediastinum. As the central component of the cardiovascular system, it has a constant and unremitting throughput of blood. Injuries to the heart may therefore result in profound and rapid blood loss with significant compromise of the circulation. Once the pump function of the heart is compromised, hypovolemic or cardiogenic shock will become an inevitable consequence. Such compromise may occur as a result of a number of mechanisms.

Sharp-force trauma   In the UK, the commonest method of homicide is by stabbing. A significant proportion of these homicides occur as a result of stab wounds to the thorax, frequently involving the heart. The heart is contained within the pericardial sac that affords it a degree of support and lubrication. However, the enclosing and protective nature of the sac may become a hazard following a stab wound to the heart that penetrates both the pericardium and heart. In this situation, following withdrawal of the knife, blood issues from whichever chamber is breached, initially under normal blood pressure, if not a degree of hypertension owing to the adrenergically induced elevation in pressure that accompanies any serious physical engagement. This blood accumulates around the heart under a number of different conditions, e.g., if the stab wound is not too large, or the sheer volume of blood issuing from a wound outpaces the degree of drainage that can occur. Furthermore, as blood clots, the defect to the pericardium may be sealed, with similar effects. The accumulation of blood imposes an ever-increasing compressive effect around the ventricles, leading to a progressive deterioration in cardiac output. Thus, even though the heart continues to attempt to maintain an output, the ever-increasing blood clot prevents such output. In such cases if an individual reaches hospital, then the monitor may show pulseless electrical activity confirming such an action of the heart. Death from hemopericardium is not immediate, however, and, contrary to popular action films, survival is possible for some time with purposeful movement. This is because of the well-designed adrenergic response that is so intrinsic to a physical engagement, leading to maintenance of cardiovascular stability for a significant period of time. Similarly, in terms of stabbing, the forensic population often tends to be young, with added intrinsic reserve as a benefit of youth. Anecdotal stories abound of otherwise young and fit individuals who receive a mortal wound to the heart but are capable of pursuing their assailant for a considerable distance prior to inevitable collapse.

A hemopericardium is a useful finding in cases where multiple stab wounds to the body are present as it may allow the pathologist to ascribe some order to the attack. As stated, a blood pressure, and therefore a beating heart, is required for the development of a hemopericardium. Thus, it is reasonable to suggest that if a hemopericardium is found together with other stab wounds, often with a paucity of bleeding, then the knife wound to the heart occurred earlier in the assault. The author recently encountered a case of over 80 stab wounds, many in the back, but with only a few to the front. Many of the back wounds had penetrated the internal viscera, but with minimal bleeding. However, a tense hemopericardium was present, indicating that this wound had occurred early in the attack.

Comparatively superficial wounds to the surface of the heart may result in death if part of the epicardial coronary vasculature is transected, leading to myocardial ischemia and infarction, and the attendant risks of a fatal arrhythmia. Blood loss from a breach of an epicardial vessel may also lead to a slowly accumulating hemopericardium.

It is sometimes speculated as to which of a stab wound to the right or left ventricle would be more dangerous. Some proponents would say that the right ventricle is thin-walled, and bleeds torrentially following a wound to this area, and that the thin muscle cannot seal the defect, such as may occur following contraction of the thicker left ventricle. The opposing view indicates that the blood within the left ventricle is under greater pressure and thus leads to a more rapid hemorrhage through the wound. In practice, stab wounds to any chamber of the heart are life-threatening and require immediate medical attention if death is not to supervene.

It is true that many stab wounds to the heart may bleed out into the mediastinum through the imposed pericardial defect, leading to hypovolemic shock rather than cardiac tamponade due to hemopericardium.

Stab wounds elsewhere on the body may cause death as a result of heart problems. Incised wounds to the neck may allow ingress of air into the jugular vessels. This may then give rise to air embolism, with large volumes of blood frothing up within the cardiac chambers and preventing effective cardiac output. The condition is best considered early in the autopsy when radiography of the chest may demonstrate air within the ventricles. At autopsy, upon sectioning the heart, frothy blood may spill out of the ventricles.

**Blunt-force trauma** The heart is a comparatively robust structure, but in the context of high-velocity, high-energy trauma, rupture and laceration may occur. Thus, it is not unusual to find rupture of the heart following high-speed road traffic accidents or falls from heights. Often in such cases, the thinner and weaker atria may rupture preferentially over the ventricles. Severe stamping injuries may also lead to rupture of the heart, although this will frequently occur in association with multiple rib fractures. Indeed, the heart may be penetrated by splintered fragments of bone following such injury to the chest wall.

Passage of a gunshot wound through the heart results in gross laceration of the heart and immediate loss of purposeful cardiac function. The same is true of an explosion that involves the thorax.

One form of death following blunt trauma to the heart is that of commotio cordis. In this phenomenon, a hard blow to the praecordium may result in the development of an arrhythmia inconsistent with maintenance of a cardiac output. This is perhaps not such an unusual phenomenon if one thinks about the administration of a praecordial thump following a witnessed cardiac arrest.

It is, however, a difficult forensic diagnosis to make, and one is reliant upon a witnessed collapse immediately following a blow to the chest. If one is lucky, a bruise may be seen upon the chest wall.

## The Great Vessels

The chest contains large-volume vessels such as the aorta, venae cavae, and pulmonary vessels. Such structures may be injured both by sharp- and blunt-force trauma with the consequent risks of profound intrathoracic hemorrhage.

**Sharp-force trauma** Stab wounds that breach the chest cavity may put the great vessels at risk of penetration. The great arteries and veins run an intrapericardial course and, thus, if breached, may lead to the development of a hemopericardium.

In the extrapericardial course, torrential hemorrhage may occur into the mediastinal or pleural spaces. Such hemorrhage is internal with very little, if any, external hemorrhage, and this may belie the gravity of the situation following any stab wound to the chest. Given the large volume of blood that courses through such vessels, cardiac compromise soon follows such injuries. Stab wounds that involve the veins result in a slower bleed as a result of the lower pressure therein. Owing to the thinner structure of veins that collapse following death, identification of such injuries may be on occasion notoriously difficult to identify at autopsy.

**Blunt-force trauma** High-energy incidents may result in trauma to the great vessels, including falls from heights and road traffic accidents. In such cases, partial-thickness or even complete transection of the aorta may be encountered. The appearance of such injury may be remarkably linear, even in appearance, with complete transection resulting in a perfectly and symmetrically divided aorta. The site of such a transection is often located at the junction of the aortic arch and the descending aorta. It is thought that in cases of sudden deceleration, as occurs in the aforementioned scenarios, the heart may be thrown anteriorly. The aorta is relatively tethered at the junction of the arch and the descending aorta, and thus the heart is thrown forward in a pendulum fashion, exerting great force at the point of aortic adherence, causing circumferential tearing. The heart may on occasion be found lying severed and loose within the thorax. Less severe trauma may result in partial-thickness endothelial tears of the aorta, in a so-called ladder configuration. The veins may also be injured in such high-energy trauma.

## The Chest Wall

Comprised anteriorly by the sternum, anterolaterally by the ribs, and posteriorly by the vertebral column, the chest wall serves to afford the intrathoracic organs a degree of protection, and also attaches the muscles of respiration, leading to efficient respiratory in- and outflow.

**Sharp-force trauma** Stab wounds to the chest wall frequently penetrate the thoracic cavity, not just by the 50/50 chance of the blade contacting an intercostal space, but also by the knife rolling over the convexity of the rib before following the path of least resistance into the chest cavity.

A rib or even the sternum may be penetrated by the passage of a knife. This is helpful in generally indicating the level of force employed during the course of the assault: clearly, significant force is required to cause such bony breach. Unless one of the intercostal vessels that skirt the inferior aspect of each rib is breached, transection of a rib or penetration of the sternum is unlikely to have deleterious effects; instead, there may be greater consequences for those organs that are penetrated by the passage of a swiftly moving weapon.

Examination of the transected rib may give some detail of the responsible knife. When examining skeletal remains, knife tooling upon the ribs may be an important positive finding of and an aid to interpretation of the cause of death.

A more serious consequence of penetration of the chest wall may be the development of a pneumothorax.

Two types of pneumothorax may be encountered commonly. In the first the pleura is breached by a weapon, but the defect is sealed following removal of the weapon. The ingress of air causes the pneumothorax with concomitant collapse of the lung, partial or otherwise. The clinical effects of such an injury will depend on the respiratory reserve of the injured person. In most cases, relief and removal of the pneumothorax may be effected by inserting chest drains through thoracostomy incisions.

The more important and life-threatening type is that of a tension pneumothorax. In this case, the penetrating injury leads to a situation in which during the inspiratory phase air is drawn into the chest cavity, with compressive effects upon the lung. However, as a result of a small flap of tissue that hinges during the phases of inspiration and expiration, air is not released. Thus, over only a few breaths, massively increased intrathoracic pressure leads to both respiratory and cardiac compromise, unless air collection is rapidly relived by medical intervention. When conducting an autopsy in which there has been penetration of the chest wall, suspicion of a pneumothorax should be considered early, and demonstrated before opening of the thoracic cage, either by passing a part water-filled syringe and needle into the suspected hemithorax, and observing for bubbles entering the barrel of the syringe, or by reflecting the skin and musculature of the chest wall from the ribs, resulting in a pocket that may be filled with water. The pleura may then be breached by passage of a blunt instrument and once again the release of air bubbles sought.

**Blunt-force trauma**   Rib fractures may be extremely painful, as anyone who has suffered a single cracked rib will attest. It is not difficult then to appreciate the effects of multiple rib fractures that may occur following blunt trauma, whether in crush injuries, road traffic accidents, or stamping assaults. In such cases, the integrity of the chest wall is compromised and the normal actions of respiration are prevented.

If a number of ribs are fractured in two locations then a flail segment will result. This represents a segment of the chest wall that is virtually floating free compared to the majority of the thoracic cage and paradoxical movement occurs during both inspiratory and expiratory phases, with obvious respiratory embarrassment. Such a finding is commonly encountered clinically during road traffic accidents, in which part of the chest wall is crushed by intruding parts of the car following a crash.

In stamping injuries multiple rib fractures may be found in the same plane, often bilaterally, and inconsistent with providing any form of efficient respiratory movement.

A serious complication of a rib fracture may be the production of one or more jagged ends that may be displaced inwards into the thoracic cavity with the risk of penetration of the pleurae and lungs or even the heart and great vessels with serious sequelae.

The site of the fracture may help in elucidating the cause. Rib fractures close to the sternum and overlying the heart may have occurred during the course of vigorous attempted resuscitation, particularly in the elderly and those suffering from osteoporosis. Further signs of resuscitation may be present, such as intravenous cannulae, or defibrillator-type burns upon the anterior chest wall. Clearly the history will be important together with perusal of the hospital notes.

Falls on to the sides may result in fractures within either the anterior or posterior axillary lines.

The situation of pediatric deaths is dealt with elsewhere; suffice to say that squeezing a small infant may be associated with posterior rib fractures, close to the costovertebral junctions. These fractures may be very difficult to identify, and this highlights the appropriate use of ancillary techniques such as radiography before examination. Similarly, a useful autopsy technique is to incise the pleura lining the posterior chest wall close to the costovertebral junction. It is then comparatively easy to peel off the parietal pleura from within the chest cavity, preventing small fractures being missed.

In the young, the ribs are cartilaginous and frequently pliable, thus riding out compressive force to the chest wall without injury. In such cases, however, deep organ injury may lie underneath what appears to be an uninjured chest.

Blunt trauma to the chest and diaphragm may result in rupture of one or both leaflets of the diaphragm with the attendant risk of herniation of the intestines into the thoracic cavity with resultant respiratory compromise.

One form of asphyxia may relate to chest compression and that is the phenomenon of crush or traumatic asphyxia. In this situation the chest is compressed, either by other individuals such as in a stampede situation, e.g., the Hillsborough (UK) disaster in which a stampede occurred during the course of a football match when fans attempted to gain access to an already full ground. As a result, 94 individuals died from crush asphyxia either from pinioning against strong security fences isolating the field or crushing by body upon body. In other situations the chest may be compressed by solid objects that may act like liquids, e.g., soil, grain, and thus an occupational cause may frequently coexist, such as in the agricultural or food industries. Effectively, while the structures of the chest wall are intact the compression and fixation of the chest wall prevent the normal movements of respiration, leading to suffocation or asphyxia. Typical asphyxial signs may be present such as petechial hemorrhages in the lax tissues of the head, together with facial congestion and cyanosis. Again the history is of paramount importance.

An interesting historical aside to the subject is the phenomenon of "burking." This relates to the infamous Burke and Hare, who operated in the eighteenth century in Scotland, procuring bodies for the purposes of anatomical dissection at a time in which it was effectively outlawed. Not content with digging up the freshly interred for such purposes, it is said that they proceeded to suffocate a victim: Mr Burke would sit on and compress the chest of a live victim, leaving no apparent marks of violence. Positional asphyxia also has relevance to restraint by police. Great caution is now paid to the position of an individual who is being actively restrained and police are aware of the dangers of respiratory embarrassment that may occur if an individual is held face-down with the arms pinioned.

### The Lungs

The lungs are protected by the ribs. A number of injuries have already been described, such as penetration by a fractured rib and collapse following pneumothorax. The following additional injuries may also be encountered.

**Sharp-force trauma**  The soft parenchyma of the lungs may be readily injured by stab wounds and may bleed profusely and collapse as a result. Following a stab wound the lung will collapse. When considering the track followed by a knife such collapse will have to be taken into account when trying to estimate the wound track length if a falsely increased length of putative weapon is not to be submitted to investigating authorities. Estimates are therefore best given, allowing for aforementioned dynamism of engagement during a struggle and movement of intrathoracic structures.

**Blunt-force trauma**  Blunt trauma may give rise to extensive laceration of the lung parenchyma, sometimes with avulsion of the lung from the relatively more robust hilum. Less violent injuries may result in extensive intraparenchymal hemorrhage.

Barotrauma as a result of diving accidents may result in extensive intraparenchymal hemorrhage, together with alveolar rupture and consequent emphysematous changes and subcutaneous emphysema.

Those involved with explosion deaths will be familiar with blast lungs. During the course of an explosion, a blast wave is produced. Where the wave of energy contacts an air–solid interface, as is the case between alveolae and inspired air, then extensive disruption may occur, and significant intraparenchymal and subpleural hemorrhage with tense hemorrhagic bullae are often seen. These features make up the blast lung. Often the ribs may provide a shielding effect and following evisceration, paler bands can be seen on the surface of the lung, representing protection afforded by the ribs, alternating with the deeply hemorrhagic intervening tissue.

## Causes of Death in the Thorax Related to Trauma Elsewhere

Owing to the vital nature of the heart and lungs, not infrequently trauma elsewhere may cause death as a result of complications involving the intrathoracic organs.

### Coronary Heart Disease

Coronary heart disease is common in the western world, and accounts for a significant proportion of sudden natural deaths. It is however well established that emotional and physical excitation, both of which are common attendants of altercation and assault, are associated with increased adverse cardiac events such as arrhythmias and myocardial infarction. Such issues may be of vital relevance during the course of restraint by law enforcement agencies. It may therefore become the task of the pathologist to unravel the link between an assault and a subsequent cardiac death. This may be straightforward if the temporal link is short, but as the time interval between assault and cardiac events lengthens then such a link is more difficult to prove. Furthermore, the chances of the death occurring had the assault not occurred may need to be taken into account.

### Pulmonary Thromboembolism

Assault may be followed by periods of enforced immobilization and hospitalization and it is in this setting that the risk of pulmonary thromboembolism consequent upon deep-vein thrombosis may occur. Again, consideration must be given towards the link between event and embolism, especially as up to 20% of thromboembolic phenomena may occur in the ambulant individual.

## Summary

Injuries to the thorax are common and serious, causing death by a number of different mechanisms upon the underlying organs and structures. An understanding of the basis of this trauma is vital to the practice of forensic pathology.

## See Also

**Deaths:** Trauma, Head and Spine; Trauma, Abdominal Cavity; Trauma, Vascular System; **Injuries and Deaths During Police Operations:** Shootings During Police Stops and Arrests; Special Weapons and Training Teams

# Trauma, Abdominal Cavity

**J A Prahlow**, South Bend Medical Foundation and Indiana University of Medicine – South Bend Center for Medical Education at the University of Notre Dame, South Bend, IN, USA

## Introduction/Overview

Then Joab took Amasa by the beard with his right hand to kiss him. Amasa was not on his guard against the dagger in Joab's hand, and Joab plunged it into his belly, and his intestines spilled out on the ground. Without being stabbed again, Amasa died.

2 Samuel 20: 9–10

This article deals specifically with abdominal trauma. Depending on one's definition of "abdomen," a variety of tissues and organs might be included. However, since other portions of this encyclopedia specifically deal with the spinal cord, the vasculature, the musculoskeletal system, and the genitourinary system, this will be limited to the following organs and tissues: stomach, small intestine, large intestine, liver, biliary tree, pancreas, spleen, adrenal glands, mesentery, omentum, the peritoneal cavity, and the diaphragm. A section dealing with specific anatomic sites will be followed by a section addressing specific types of trauma.

## Sites of Injury – Abdomen

### Abdominal Wall

Many of the injuries described in this section have associated abdominal wall trauma, including injuries of the skin, subcutaneous tissues, musculature, and peritoneal lining. Occasional cases of self-mutilation involve inserting objects through the abdominal wall and into the peritoneal cavity or abdominal organs. Self-mutilation is typically associated with various psychiatric disorders, intoxication, or certain disorders characterized by mental disability (Lesch–Nyhan syndrome).

### Gastrointestinal Tract

The abdominal gastrointestinal tract (including stomach, small intestine, and large intestine) typically contains foreign material (food), along with various microorganisms. As such, gastrointestinal injury of a variety of types predisposes to peritoneal inflammation and infection. In fact, injuries that might be considered "minor" elsewhere in the body (such as a focal contusion) may lead to necrotic bowel, peritonitis, sepsis, and death in the gastrointestinal tract. Although infection represents a significant risk when gastrointestinal injury occurs, other mechanisms of injury may also occur, not the least of which involves vascular disruption with acute hemorrhage. Traumatic rupture of hollow viscera can occur in a variety of settings; compression against the vertebral column, shearing type of injuries, and bursting secondary to a rapid increase in intraluminal pressure are known to occur. Shearing injuries tend to occur at points of fixation (first portion of jejunum, terminal ileum). Traumatic injuries are frequently transmural (full-thickness); however, non-transmural injuries can occur, with injury confined to the mucosal side or the serosal side of the organ. Traumatic seromuscular rupture of the intestine is an example of the latter, occurring as a result of blunt-force injury. With some of these injuries, onset of signs and symptoms may be delayed for hours or even days. Duodenal injuries may be associated with retroperitoneal hemorrhage. Gastrointestinal ischemic damage related to the lack of blood flow that frequently accompanies major body trauma (in any location) is not infrequent. "Stress ulcers" or erosions may affect the gastric or duodenal mucosa in association with various types of trauma (burns, head injuries, hypothermia). Gastric acid adds an additional potentially destructive force should gastric wall injury or breakdown occur. Certain genetic conditions are known to predispose to gastrointestinal rupture, with or without preceding trauma. Ehlers–Danlos syndrome type IV is an example of such a condition. Insertion of objects into the rectum can lead to lacerations, peritonitis, sepsis, and other complications. Gastrointestinal complications such as volvulus, intussusception, and herniation may also occur in association with various forms of abdominal trauma.

### Hepatobiliary System

As a relatively large abdominal organ, the liver is frequently injured in cases of abdominal trauma. The liver is particularly vulnerable when external forces compress the liver between the abdominal wall anteriorly and the vertebral column posteriorly. Right-sided rib fractures may be associated with underlying liver trauma. Depending on the mechanism

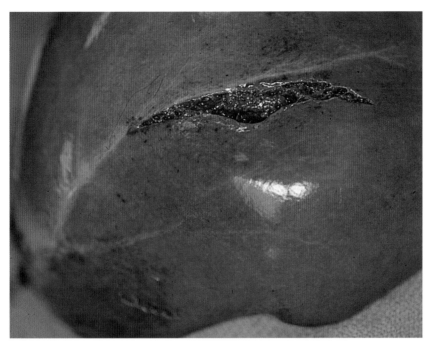

**Figure 1** Superficial liver laceration related to blunt-force abdominal impact in a motor vehicle collision.

**Figure 2** Fragmentation injury of liver related to a suicidal jump from a 10-story building.

of trauma, hepatic injuries can range from superficial lacerations (**Figure 1**), to deep, penetrating trauma, to total fragmentation (**Figure 2**). Bleeding is the primary result with such injuries. Secondary infection may occur. Certain natural conditions and diseases may be associated with "spontaneous" rupture or hemorrhage of the liver. These include pregnancy, malaria, syphilis, and blood vessel tumors/malformations. Certain infectious processes, such as hepatitis C, may be associated with traumatic exposure to infected blood. Biliary tree damage can lead to peritonitis and other complications.

## Pancreas

While the pancreas is relatively protected from external trauma, due to its location, it can nevertheless be directly injured, when significant abdominal trauma or penetrating/perforating trauma occurs. Rarely is the pancreas the sole site of traumatic injury. In general, the pancreas does not tolerate injury well; digestive enzymes from the injured organ tend to "autodigest" the pancreas and surrounding tissues. Hemorrhagic pancreatitis may ensue, with a lethal outcome. Pseudocysts and abscesses can occur as chronic complications following pancreatic trauma. In addition, metabolic/physiologic injury can occur secondary to a variety of injurious stimuli, including various toxins, including ethanol. Pancreatitis is a known complication of severe trauma, even if it occurs outside the abdominal cavity. Elevated amylase levels are a laboratory indicator of pancreatitis.

## Spleen

Splenic lacerations are relatively common in the setting of abdominal blunt-force trauma (**Figure 3**). Left-sided rib fractures are a frequent associated finding. Life-threatening splenic injuries can occur with little or no evidence of external injury. Delayed splenic rupture can occur following abdominal trauma. Most cases occur within 2 weeks of the injury. Certain natural disease processes increase the chances of splenic injury, secondary to increased size or increased fragility. So-called "spontaneous splenic rupture" typically occurs in the setting of one of these disorders, such as mononucleosis, leukemia, or malaria. Minor trauma may theoretically play at least a contributory role in the splenic rupture in these cases. Persons who survive after having undergone splenectomy secondary to trauma are at increased risk for a variety of bacterial infections; subsequent infection, sepsis, and death can be considered a complication of the original trauma.

## Adrenal Glands

The adrenal glands, like the pancreas, are relatively protected from minor to moderate abdominal trauma; however, severe trauma, as well as penetrating or perforating injuries, may injure the adrenals (**Figure 4**). Frequently, the underlying kidney is also affected. Isolated adrenal hemorrhage should raise the concern of bacteremia/sepsis, as occurs in the Waterhouse–Friderichsen syndrome, particularly in association with *Neisseria meningitidis* infection.

## Mesentery and Omentum

The mesentery is a very vascular tissue. Mesenteric injuries can produce significant amounts of bleeding (**Figure 5**). Frequently, mesenteric injuries are

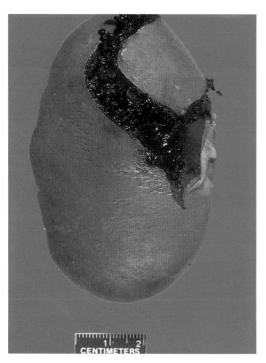

**Figure 3**   Splenic laceration due to blunt-force abdominal impact in a motor vehicle collision.

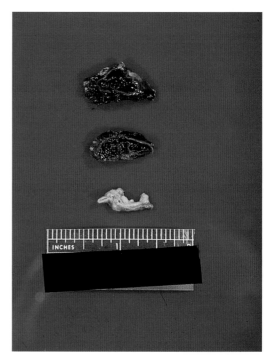

**Figure 4**   Two cross-sections of the injured right adrenal gland (above), with a cross-section of the uninjured left adrenal gland (below) for comparison. The adrenal gland injury was one of several deep abdominal injuries in a 6-month-old victim of child abuse.

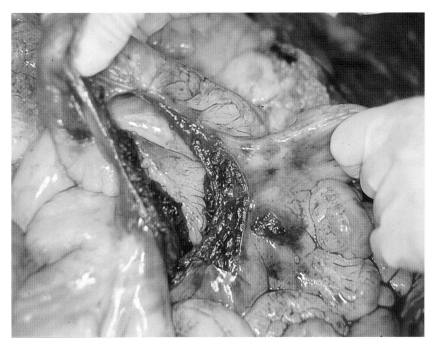

**Figure 5**  Mesenteric laceration sustained in a motor vehicle collision.

associated with bowel injuries, predisposing to peritonitis. Omentum injuries can also lead to hemorrhagic complications.

## Peritoneal Cavity

Two peritoneal cavity processes that have already been addressed are of prime concern with regard to traumatic abdominal deaths. The first is hemorrhage. Hemoperitoneum is ultimately part of the mechanism of death in many abdominal trauma cases (**Figure 6**). The second is infection. Peritonitis can result from many injuries involving the abdominal organs, especially the bowel. Spontaneous bacterial peritonitis occurs in certain situations, most notably in the setting of chronic alcoholism. Self-mutilating behavior characterized by inserting objects into the peritoneal cavity was previously described.

## Retroperitoneum

Involvement of the retroperitoneum by trauma is typically manifest as retroperitoneal hemorrhage. Significant amounts of retroperitoneal hemorrhage (retroperitoneal hematomas) can result in shock and death. Relatively large amounts of retroperitoneal hemorrhage can remain hidden clinically. In addition, such bleeding can occur slowly, over time, before becoming symptomatic. Retroperitoneal hemorrhage frequently occurs with pelvic or spinal fractures, but may also occur with injuries of the pancreas, duodenum, and urinary tract, including the kidneys.

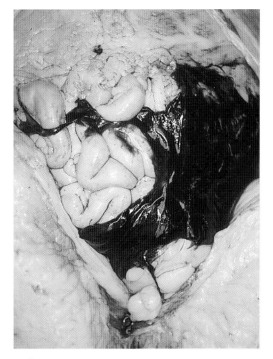

**Figure 6**  Example of hemoperitoneum as seen at autopsy.

## Diaphragm

While not necessarily considered a part of the abdominal cavity, since it actually separates the abdomen from the thorax, a few comments regarding diaphragm injury are in order. The diaphragm is an essential component of the respiratory process. As such, injuries of the diaphragm can significantly compromise respiratory function. In cases of positional or traumatic asphyxia, increased abdominal pressure can be transferred to the thoracic cavity via an intact diaphragm, resulting in respiratory compromise. Traumatic lacerations of the diaphragm can result in abdominal organ herniation into the thorax, with resultant pulmonary and/or cardiac compromise. Particularly with regard to penetrating and perforating injuries, such as occur with gunshot wounds, the diaphragm can provide "communication" between thoracic and abdominal cavities, with blood (or air) traveling from chest to abdomen and vice versa. Finally, with regard to toxicology concerns, it should be remembered that "blind," transcutaneous, cardiac puncture for blood sample collection in trauma cases that are not autopsied should be avoided, because left hemidiaphragm lacerations can allow for gastric contents to intermix with chest blood, with possible erroneous toxicology results (e.g., a markedly elevated ethanol level). In a similar fashion, a left-sided diaphragmatic laceration can allow the intact stomach to herniate into the left chest cavity, such that blind cardiac puncture for toxicology fluid may result in aspiration of gastric contents (**Figure 7**).

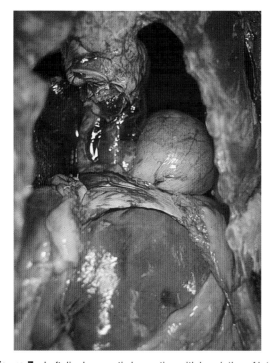

**Figure 7** Left diaphragmatic laceration with herniation of intact stomach into the left pleural cavity, demonstrating why "blind" transcutaneous attempts at cardiac puncture for toxicology specimen collection are not recommended.

## Types of Trauma – Abdominal Cavity

### General Comments

With any of the injury types described, overall body injury may be limited primarily to the abdomen or more widespread, involving other body regions. The comments herein will be limited to the abdominal cavity as previously defined. For injuries specifically involving vasculature, spinal cord, musculoskeletal system, or the genitourinary systems, the reader is referred to other articles in this encyclopedia.

### Blunt-Force Trauma

Blunt-force abdominal trauma is relatively common. It can range in severity from minor cutaneous injuries to deep internal injuries, and even complete body transection (**Figure 8**). Frequently, blunt-force trauma is related to sudden deceleration mechanisms in addition to impact forces. Factors influencing the severity of abdominal blunt trauma, as well as many other types of trauma, include the size of the striking object, the site and force of impact, the strength of the abdominal wall, the underlying condition of the viscera, the extent of hemorrhage, and the level of consciousness of the victim prior to impact. Severe trauma is more likely if the blow is forceful and sudden. A relaxed abdominal wall tends to provide little protection against external forces; if the victim recognizes that an abdominal blow is imminent, contraction of the abdominal muscles can lessen the transfer of force to internal organs, thus lessening the severity of the injuries. Common blunt-force abdominal injuries include liver and spleen lacerations, bowel contusions and lacerations, mesenteric lacerations, and various skeletal and vascular injuries. Abdominal organs may be crushed against the vertebral column or torn by shearing forces. Hollow organs may burst due to rapidly increased intraluminal pressure. Even seemingly "minor" abdominal trauma, such as a small-bowel contusion, should really be considered a potentially lethal injury, since such injuries may progress to bowel wall necrosis, with secondary hemorrhage and/or peritonitis, sepsis, and death. Abdominal blunt-force injuries related to falls from great heights are frequently spectacular, with possible complete fragmentation of the liver. Traumatic seromuscular rupture of the intestine results when blunt abdominal trauma causes partial tearing of the intestine wall, such that the innermost (mucosal) layer remains intact; various levels of injury are possible. The injury may have various manifestations, including intramural hematoma, "degloving"-type changes, or diverticulum formation. Traumatic seromuscular rupture of the intestine frequently presents as an acute

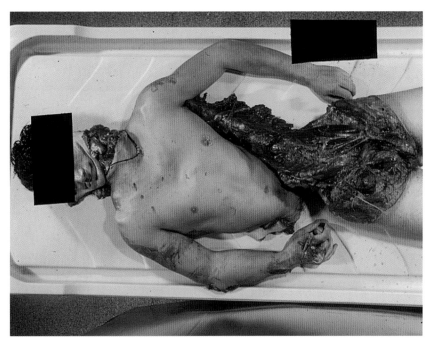

**Figure 8**  Complete body transection, across abdomen, sustained in a motorcycle accident.

injury; however, chronic forms of the injury can occur in cases where the acute injury is not recognized clinically. The injury is frequently considered to be a seatbelt-associated injury; however, other mechanisms of blunt abdominal trauma can cause the injury. The "seatbelt syndrome" refers to abdominal injuries caused by the sudden deceleration and focal compression forces applied to the abdomen by a seatbelt when a motor vehicular collision occurs. Muscular rupture, possible diaphragm rupture, gastrointestinal tract rupture or shearing injuries, and injuries of various solid organs, such as the spleen, liver, and pancreas, may occur. Occasionally, preexisting natural disease (abdominal aortic aneurysm, liver cell adenoma) may predispose a person to hemorrhagic injury.

### Sharp and Cutting-Edge Injury

As elsewhere, the severity of sharp and cutting-edge injuries involving the abdomen depends entirely on the location of the wounds (**Figure 9**). Massive cutting injuries of the abdominal skin may look horrific, but have no underlying internal injuries. In contrast, a single, small, abdominal stab wound might not appear so bad externally, but if it perforates the liver and inferior vena cava, it could be the cause of death. As with blunt injuries, sharp injuries of the gastrointestinal tract can cause bleeding, infection, or inflammatory complications, possibly leading to death. Another mechanism of injury with certain sharp injuries of the abdomen involves air embolism. This most

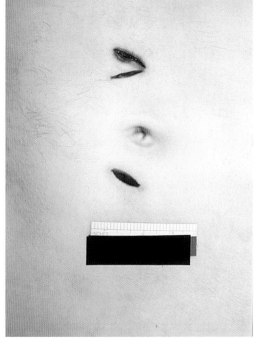

**Figure 9**  Multiple, suicidal, stab wounds of the abdomen.

frequently occurs in the setting of laparoscopic surgery, when a blood vessel is injured.

### Firearm Injury

Deaths related to abdominal firearm injuries usually occur as a result of tissue injury and its associated blood loss (**Figures 10** and **11**). Differences in injury type and severity occur when comparing handguns or other low-velocity guns, high-velocity weapons, and shotguns. Low-velocity weapons tend not to produce as much tissue damage as high-velocity weapons. Shotgun pellets produce widespread injury, related to pellet size and number, while shotgun slugs tend to produce massive tissue destruction. While tissue injury and hemorrhage are common mechanisms of death in abdominal firearms injuries, other mechanisms of death are not uncommon. In fact, a relatively common scenario involves isolated gunshot wounds of the abdomen (with no lethal firearms injuries elsewhere on the body), where surgical repair is performed, but the victim eventually dies related to postinjury/postoperative complications, frequently with infection, and/or the systemic inflammatory response syndrome.

**Asphyxial Injury**

The abdomen can be involved in three types of asphyxial injury. The first is positional (or postural) asphyxia, where a body is typically inverted (upside down), and the weight of the abdominal contents presses against the diaphragm, thus compressing the thoracic organs and leading to cardiorespiratory compromise and death. The second is a variant of what is typically referred to as traumatic or compressive asphyxia. In the typical case of compressive asphyxia, direct chest compression prevents cardiorespiratory function. In the abdominal variant, massive external compression of the abdomen (by external force) causes severe upward force on the diaphragm, with thoracic organ compromise and subsequent death. Finally, the abdomen can have findings that help to support a diagnosis of drowning.

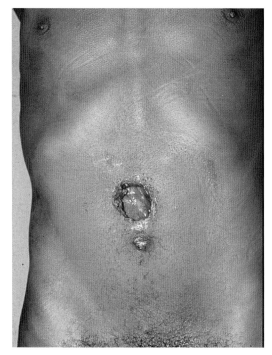

**Figure 10**   Homicidal shotgun wound of the abdomen.

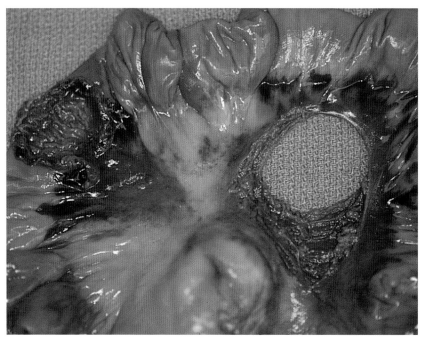

**Figure 11**   Perforating gunshot wound injuries of the small intestine and mesentery.

Finding fluid within the stomach and upper gastrointestinal tract that is similar to the fluid in which a person has reportedly drowned can be a valuable finding in making a determination that the person did, in fact, drown. Such fluid is present as a result of the person swallowing during the drowning process. Air can also be found in the upper gastrointestinal tract of drowning victims.

## Temperature-Related Injury

External (and sometimes internal) thermal injuries typically seen in fire deaths may involve the abdomen. Bright-red discoloration of lividity and internal organs associated with elevated carboxyhemoglobin levels is also a common abdominal finding in fire deaths. While soot is typically confined to the upper airway, larynx, and esophagus, it is possible for soot to be seen in the stomach. Scalding injuries primarily affect the skin surface, and may involve the abdomen. Chemical and/or caustic burns can also affect the skin, but may also involve the upper gastrointestinal tract if ingested, or the lower gastrointestinal tract if inserted via the rectum. In certain cases of hyperthermia, the liver may demonstrate centrilobular necrosis microscopically. In hypothermia, numerous, regularly spaced, superficial, punctate, hemorrhagic gastrointestinal mucosal erosions or ulcers (Wischnewski ulcers) may be evident, particularly in the stomach (**Figure 12**). The shallow erosions typically measure 0.1–0.5 cm in diameter. Mucosal erosions, or "stress ulcers," may also be seen in persons who have sustained head injuries (Cushing's ulcers), thermal injuries (Curling's ulcers), or other severe, life-threatening conditions. Hemorrhagic pancreatitis may also occur in hypothermia. All organs and tissues, including those of the abdomen, tend to be well preserved histologically in hypothermia deaths.

## Explosive Injury

Explosions may produce abdominal injuries related to thermal, chemical, pressure (blast), or shrapnel effects. Hollow organs, such as those of the gastrointestinal tract, are at increased risk for injury related to blast effects, because they contain air (gases) and thus are not a uniform tissue media for transmission of the shock waves. Typical injuries include hemorrhagic foci, although rupture can occur. The cecum and colon are at greatest risk for injury. In contrast, solid organs, such as the liver, more readily transmit the shock waves without causing tissue injury. Blast injuries of the gastrointestinal tract tend to be more common and more severe in underwater explosions (in a submerged person, when an underwater explosion occurs).

## Electrical Injury

External electrical injuries of the abdomen have skin characteristics similar to electrical injuries elsewhere on the body. The reader is referred to other articles in this encyclopedia that deal specifically with electrical injury. Internal abdominal trauma related to

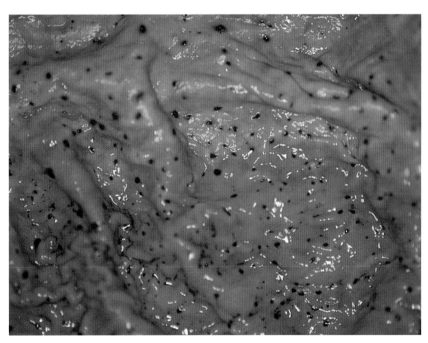

**Figure 12**  Gastric mucosal erosions (Wischnewski ulcers), characteristic of hypothermia.

electrical injury is limited to electrothermal effects (thermal damage in high-voltage electrocutions). Some have reported microscopic changes consistent with electrical injury in the aorta of certain victims of electrical injury.

### Drug/Toxin-Induced Injury

Many drugs, whether therapeutic or illicit, can result in cellular/tissue injury. It is beyond the scope of this article to provide extensive details regarding every drug that can produce abdominal organ injury. It is generally well known that many drugs and toxins can produce injury to the liver. Examples include ethanol, aspirin, acetaminophen (paracetamol), tetracycline, halothane, methotrexate, isoniazid, oral contraceptives, carbon tetrachloride, and lead. *Amanita* mushrooms can induce fatal, hemorrhagic, hepatocellular necrosis, in association with steatosis. Pancreatitis is a known complication of ethanol abuse. Other drugs can cause damage to gastrointestinal organs. A common example is antiinflammatory agent induction of gastric ulceration. Another common example is acute gastritis associated with ethanol consumption. Widespread gastric mucosal hemorrhage is known to occur with cyanide ingestion. Collection and analysis of gastric contents can be very useful in suspected drug/toxin overdose cases. In addition, microscopic analysis of gastric contents may reveal abundant polarizable material in certain drug overdose cases.

### Nutritional Disorders

Starvation can induce macrovesicular steatosis within the liver, as well as mucosal atrophy within the gastrointestinal tract. Bulimia (binge-eating followed by induced vomiting) predisposes to electrolyte imbalance (hypokalemia) and possible gastroesophageal rupture. Various vitamin deficiencies may have manifestations that affect abdominal organs. Vitamin K deficiency results in a lack of vitamin-K-dependent clotting factors that are normally produced in the liver. One of the classic features of niacin deficiency (pellagra) is diarrhea. Diarrhea may also be a finding in zinc deficiency. Obesity is generally considered a risk factor for many common diseases, including hypertension and atherosclerotic cardiovascular disease. The abdominal organs play a participatory role in the development of obesity.

### Infections/Foodborne Illness

This topic is beyond the scope of this article, but brief mention is in order. A variety of bacterial, parasitic, and viral organisms, as well as various chemical agents, are known to produce foodborne or waterborne disease.

Most cases are self-limited; however, death can occur. Examples of microorganisms that may cause "food poisoning" include *Clostridium botulinum*, *Escherichia coli*, *Salmonella*, *Shigella*, *Vibrio cholerae*, *Giardia lamblia*, and Norwalk agent. Certain forms of seafood consumption can lead to infectious or toxic syndromes. Examples include ciguatera, scombroid, neurotoxic shellfish poisoning, paralytic shellfish poisoning, and tetrodotoxin fish poisoning. In each of these disorders, the pathologic effects or route of entry of the microorganism or toxin involve the gastrointestinal system.

### Childhood Abdominal Trauma

Childhood abdominal trauma is similar to that seen in adults; however, because of children's relatively small size, certain differences may exist. For example, while an abdominal blow of a certain amount of force might not cause internal injury in an adult, because of abdominal fat and/or muscle, the same blow to a child might be lethal. Liver lacerations and intestinal/mesenteric injuries are relatively frequent injuries in lethal child abuse cases (**Figures 13** and **14**). Traumatic seromuscular rupture of the intestine (as described above under "Blunt-force trauma," where injury does not extend all the way through to involve the mucosa) is a subtype of intestinal injury that can occur in children. Clinically, unrecognized cases can result in various complications, including peritonitis and death. Such chronic forms of traumatic seromuscular rupture of the intestine may be mistaken for a natural-disease-associated process.

### Therapy-Related Injuries

Therapeutic procedures have associated risks and benefits. The goal is to maximize the benefits, while reducing the risks. Unfortunately, unintended injury and death may occasionally occur with various therapies. Hemorrhagic and infectious complications following abdominal surgery or other procedures are known to occur. Fatal air embolism may result from intraabdominal vascular damage occurring during laparoscopic surgery. Gastrointestinal endoscopy procedures can also result in lethal complications, including traumatic rupture, hemorrhage, and infection. Drug-related complications have previously been discussed.

### Natural Diseases Exacerbated by Trauma

Numerous natural disease processes involving the abdomen can be exacerbated by trauma. Many of these have already been mentioned; a few examples will be provided. Gastroesophageal bleeding/rupture can occur in chronic alcoholism. Splenic rupture can

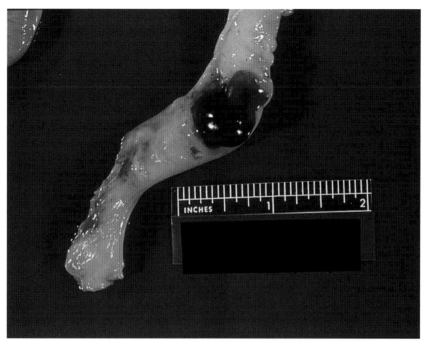

**Figure 13** Sigmoid colon hematoma in a 19-month-old victim of child abuse.

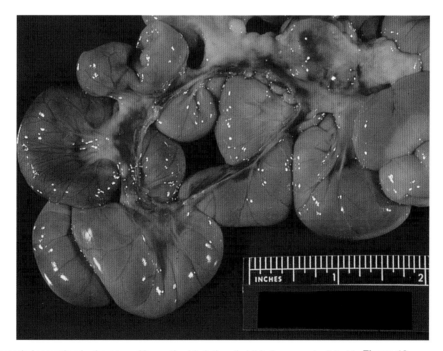

**Figure 14** Mesenteric laceration in the same 19-month-old victim of child abuse as depicted in **Figure 13**.

occur in various situations, including infectious mononucleosis, leukemia, and lymphoma. Abdominal vascular or gastrointestinal tract rupture can complicate Ehlers–Danlos syndrome type IV. Colonic necrosis or rupture can occur following trauma in the setting of "toxic megacolon" in Hirschsprung's disease. Ruptured hepatic hemangiomas may lead to massive hemoperitoneum following abdominal trauma.

**Postmortem Injury**

Abdominal trauma is usually antemortem, i.e., it occurred prior to death. However, it is important to

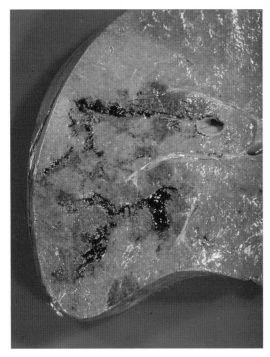

**Figure 15** Internal lacerations in the right lobe of the liver, caused by inappropriately excessive force applied to the abdomen during cardiopulmonary resuscitation.

remember that certain abdominal injuries may actually be postmortem in nature. Postmortem liver lacerations can be related to improperly performed cardiopulmonary resuscitation (CPR), in which the liver is compressed between the vertebral column and the anterior abdominal wall, or between the ribs and the diaphragm (**Figure 15**). Other injuries that can be related to resuscitation include splenic rupture, gastric rupture, and omentum hemorrhage. Most information regarding such CPR-related injuries focuses on adult patients. The likelihood of CPR-related primary abdominal trauma should be considered low. Another postmortem phenomenon is referred to as "postmortem gastromalacia." It is characterized by an extremely soft, friable gastric wall, with or without associated rupture. The esophagus may also be involved. There is no evidence of inflammation microscopically. The condition appears to be more common in debilitated persons or in individuals who die after a prolonged coma.

## Summary

The abdomen represents a portion of the anatomy that contains wide-ranging organs and tissues. As elsewhere, abdominal injuries may involve a variety of mechanisms. Two characteristics make certain abdominal injuries different from injuries that occur elsewhere in the body. First, because of the presence of abundant commensal microorganisms which exist within the gastrointestinal system, abdominal injuries are particularly prone to result in infectious complications. As such, delayed deaths following significant abdominal trauma are not infrequent. Second, the gastrointestinal tract provides a route for foodborne microorganism disease, drug absorption, and toxin exposure, thus playing a significant role in disorders that are not necessarily considered "physical injuries."

## See Also

**Deaths:** Trauma, Head and Spine; Trauma, Thorax; Trauma, Musculo-skeletal System; Trauma, Vascular System; **Electric Shocks and Electrocution, Clinical Effects and Pathology**

## Further Reading

Ackroyd FW (1977) The liver, pancreas, spleen and gallbladder. In: Tedeschi CG, Eckert WG, Tedeschi LG (eds.) *Forensic Medicine – A Study in Trauma and Environmental Hazards,* pp. 210–215. Philadelphia, PA: WB Saunders.

DiMaio VJ, DiMaio D (2001) *Forensic Pathology,* 2nd edn. Boca Raton, FL: CRC Press.

Dix J, Graham M, Hanzlick R (2000) *Asphyxia and Drowning – An Atlas.* Boca Raton, FL: CRC Press.

Fatteh A (1973) *Handbook of Forensic Pathology.* Philadelphia, PA: JB Lippincott.

Fisher RS (1977) Postmortem changes and artifacts. In: Fisher RS, Petty CS (eds.) *Forensic Pathology – A Handbook for Pathologists,* pp. 56–63. Washington, DC: National Institute of Law Enforcement and Criminal Justice Law Enforcement Assistance Administration, US Department of Justice.

Froede RC (ed.) (2003) *Handbook of Forensic Pathology,* 2nd edn. Chicago, IL: College of American Pathologists.

Hechtman HB (1977) Gastrointestinal tract. In: Tedeschi CG, Eckert WG, Tedeschi LG (eds.) *Forensic Medicine – A Study in Trauma and Environmental Hazards,* pp. 215–221. Philadelphia, PA: WB Saunders.

Knight B (1996) *Forensic Pathology,* 2nd edn. London: Oxford University Press.

Pepin M, Schwarze U, Superti-Furga A, Byers PH (2000) Clinical and genetic features of Ehlers–Danlos syndrome type IV, the vascular type. *New England Journal of Medicine* 342: 673–680.

Simpson K (1964) *Forensic Medicine,* 5th edn. London: Edward Arnold.

Spitz WU (1993) *Medicolegal Investigation of Death,* 3rd edn. Springfield, IL: Charles C. Thomas.

Wecht CH (ed.) (1981) *Forensic Sciences.* Albany, NY: Matthew Bender.

# Trauma, Musculo-skeletal System

**P S L Beh**, The University of Hong Kong, Hong Kong, China

## Introduction

Traumatic deaths often involve many parts of the body and as a rule are rarely isolated to particular organ systems, the head and brain being perhaps the notable exception. There are occasions, however, when the forensic pathologist will encounter a case where there are no apparent injuries in other organ systems except that of the musculoskeletal system.

The cause of death following musculoskeletal injuries is often complications associated with injuries in general such as hemorrhage, embolic phenomena, particularly fat emboli, acute renal failure associated with rhabdomyolysis and myoglobinuria, and of course infection.

## Background

Traumatic deaths from multiple injuries including musculoskeletal injuries are common occurrences in high-speed transportation fatalities, and in falls from heights, whether accidental, suicidal, or homicidal.

The causes of deaths under such circumstances are rarely difficult to establish. Traumatic deaths as a result of predominantly musculoskeletal system injuries will, however, still be associated with hypovolemic shock with associated complications. Such deaths may be encountered in the following situations:

1. crush injury
2. crowd stampede
3. beatings
4. Asian gang fights.

### Crush Injury

Crush injury was first described in victims pulled alive from bomb-raid shelters during the Second World War, only to die later from complications of their injury. Such scenarios will of course still occur in armed conflicts but the usual scenarios of such deaths encountered by the average pathologist are more likely to be those of major natural disasters such as earthquakes, landslides, and mudslides. Other more common disasters created by humans include collapsing structures and buildings either during construction or even during demolition of buildings. Deaths in these situations include those due to traumatic asphyxia, or head injuries, and where death is not immediate as a result of complications of injuries to the musculoskeletal systems. The complications of fat embolism and rhabdomyolysis will be discussed further in later.

### Crowd Stampede

Common situations where there have been crowd stampedes in recent years include a panicked crowd attempting to escape from a riot in a football stadium or a fire in a nightclub or discotheque. The potential for such a tragedy always exists in any heavily crowded situations such as rallies and festivities. Again, most deaths are a result of traumatic asphyxia, but the forensic pathologist should not be over-complacent. The possibility of complications from injuries to the musculoskeletal system should be considered and the pathologist should not be overly liberal in attributing deaths to traumatic asphyxia. Crowd stampedes were particularly bad in the 1990s, when tragedies occurred following clashes between soccer fans. Fortunately, these incidents are now on the decline thanks to a combination of measures aimed at improving crowd segregation and stadium design. This has been aided by intelligence and cooperation between law enforcement agencies in identifying soccer hooligans and restricting their ability to travel to attend games.

### Beatings

Beatings are the everyday work of most forensic practitioners. Most do not result in death but the potential for fatalities exists. Conditions that are likely to lead to death are those where several attackers impose their weight on a fallen victim, and where weapons such as baseball bats, chairs, or water pipes are used. Even when weapons are not used, the heavy jackboots favored by some sections of society can be lethal in the amount and extent of injury they can cause when used to kick and to stamp on a fallen victim. Typical injuries would be fractured ribs with associated lung injuries as well as abdominal visceral injuries, particularly of the liver, spleen, and kidneys. The hollow organs are less commonly injured, probably due to their ability to move away from blunt impacts. Where injuries occur, they are likely to be at junctions between a relatively fixed portion and that of a more mobile segment, namely, duodenal–jejunal junctions, ileocecal junctions, and sigmoid–rectal junctions.

### Asian Gang Fights

Unlike gang fights in the movies where bullets fly everywhere, many Asian gangs, and particularly street gangs, still settle their differences or their territorial disputes with a show of force of their followers or members, often culminating in a running street battle between opposing gangs. The common weapons used in such clashes are long-bladed knives and choppers. It often surprises accident and emergency doctors that many of these victims do not die, despite their many wounds. An occasional fatality occurs when a participant is cornered or has fallen and is then set upon by several attackers.

## External Pattern of Injuries

Where victims are pulled from mudslides or collapsing structures, the bodies are invariably covered with debris, masonry, sand, or mud. There are often bruises and abrasions. Fractures of limbs are also commonly found. In fatal cases or potentially fatal cases, body parts are often severely crushed and amputations are often required to remove crushed and/or gangrenous limbs.

Victims of crowd stampede often show very little external injuries. In those where traumatic asphyxia has occurred, there may be the characteristic congested face, neck, and upper chest with deep cyanosis of the lips and fingernail beds. Imprinted abrasions or intradermal bruises may help identify the surface that such victims were lying on or were trapped against.

Beatings will often reveal an extensive distribution of bruises, often abrasions over the face, trunk, and upper limbs, particularly when the victim had at least tried to put up a fight. Where rod-like objects are used, it is not uncommon to find criss-crossing or overlapping tramline bruises or rectangular-shaped bruises. Kicking and stamping may sometimes leave imprints of patterns of the sole or parts of the shoes on the victim. Such marks can be extremely useful in identifying the culprit(s) involved. Unusual external markings should be carefully documented, as they may help confirm subsequent confessions or accounts of events.

At the autopsy of a 27-year-old man, multiple small $1.5 \times 1$ cm rectangular-shaped bruises and bruised abrasions were seen over the back (**Figure 1**). Individually these did not cause much external bleeding and did not appear to be important. Subsequent police investigation revealed that he was "disciplined" by members of his gang and had been subjected to a prolonged period of beating with wooden poles and folding chairs (**Figure 2**). The metal legs of the folding chair are secured to the wooden seat by rectangular-shaped brackets, which were causing the marks. Further dissection revealed extensive rib fractures with internal hemorrhages.

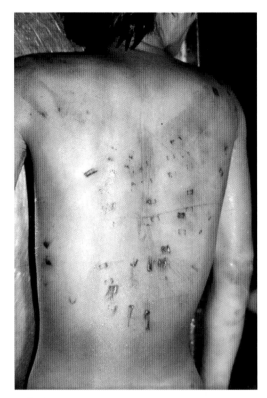

**Figure 1** Multiple rectangular-shaped abrasions over the entire back of a young male victim beaten by members of his own gang, allegedly for a breach of "gang rules."

**Figure 2** A typical and common folding chair with a wooden seat and metal legs.

Typically, however staff at an accident and emergency department will be presented with a victim in a critical state and, whilst the trauma team is preoccupied with resuscitating the victim, the persons accompanying the victim disappear without leaving any particulars of the victim or of themselves. Occasionally, when asked by nursing staff the typical response is that they were "good Samaritans" who saw the victim and helped them to the hospital and they did not know the victim at all. Even when the victims are initially conscious, they are generally not very communicative and often do not reveal

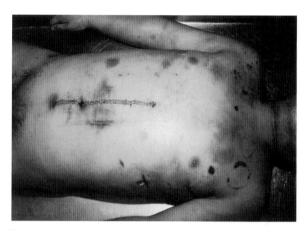

**Figure 3** External bruises over the body of a young male victim who was involved in a fight. Notice the extensive distribution of bruises. The body also shows fresh surgical wounds that are found when there are active and aggressive resuscitative interventions.

the cause of their injuries or the identity of their attackers.

In a recent case, a 30-year-old man admitted himself to a local accident and emergency department alleging head injury sustained in a fight. Whilst under observation and awaiting a computed tomography scan, he disappeared from the ward, only to return 12 h later, demanding to be discharged.

He reappeared 2 days later, supported by two males and requiring immediate attention. His blood pressure was unrecordable and immediate aggressive resuscitation by the trauma team was required, with initial success. However, he died without regaining consciousness 2 days later.

Enquiries made of the two accompanying men by the nursing staff at the accident and emergency department drew the typical response of "we are casual acquaintances and we found him collapsed." Before the police could be notified they had disappeared.

The subsequent autopsy findings were of extensive soft-tissue hemorrhages involving the trunk and limbs associated with multiple bilateral fractured ribs with extensive hemothoraces (**Figures 3** and **4**).

Fatal victims of Asian gang fights will often be found collapsed on the street or at a playground where there has been a report of a gang fight. Such victims may be unconscious in a large pool of blood with obvious multiple cut and chop wounds. Classically there will be the typical "defensive" injuries (**Figure 5**), as toward the end, they would have tried to ward off the attacking blows. Most of the wounds are to be found over the upper parts of the body and

**Figure 4** Multiple extensive fractures of the ribcage revealed at postmortem examination of the victim shown in **Figure 3**. Hemothoraces and laceration of the lungs are common and expected findings.

the upper limbs, and show features of a downward swinging slash or cut typically sustained whilst the victim was still on his feet.

## Autopsy Procedures

The general autopsy procedures for investigations of fatalities should apply. However, several areas should be considered, to enable the pathologist to establish as full a picture of the musculoskeletal injuries as possible. Postmortem radiology should be arranged

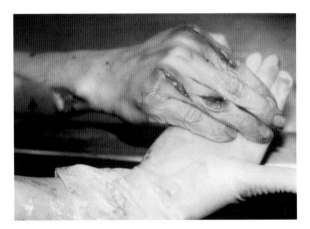

**Figure 5** Defensive wounds, often found in victims of Asian gang fights. Such cut wounds are suggestive of perhaps an aggressive defense such as would be expected in a combatant. Contrast these with the more common cuts found over the palms of victims grappling with an attacker's knife.

if it is not routine. This not only helps the pathologist visualize fractures, old and new; it can also guide the dissection and display of such injuries for autopsy documentation and photography.

Another procedure seldom performed in routine autopsies is that of dissecting the skin away from the underlying fat and muscle fascia. This is a tedious and time-consuming procedure for an adult but is the only way to visualize the extent of bruising and injury to the underlying soft tissues and muscles. It is also a good way of documenting and demonstrating to jury members at subsequent trials the severity of injuries sustained (**Figures 6** and **7**). There is, however, no simple or accurate way of estimating the amount of blood loss into soft-tissues; some authors have recommended measuring the size of a hematoma, but even such measurements are far from accurate. It is perhaps often best to rely on the circumstances surrounding the death or the clinical findings recorded before death, particularly the fact that there was no or very low blood pressure recordings and the extent of blood at the scene of crime.

During an autopsy under such circumstances, particular note should be made of the amount of blood remaining in internal cavities such as the chest and abdomen. Interpretation of these will, however, be dependent on the nature of the resuscitative efforts and the amount of blood transfused. Histological samples of all organs should be routine in all autopsies and, in such cases in particular, histological sections of the kidneys and lungs must be taken.

**Figure 6** Autopsy dissection of the skin to expose the extent of subcutaneous and muscular injuries in a case of musculoskeletal injuries. This photo shows the findings revealed in the victim shown in **Figure 3**.

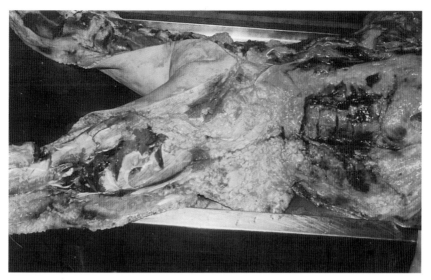

**Figure 7** Similar dissection revealing extensive injuries over the back, flanks, and lower limbs. Such a dissection technique provides a clearer picture of the sites and likely severity of blunt impacts sustained by the victim.

Extensive muscle injury will lead to rhabdomyolysis and myoglobinuria. Microscopic sections of the kidneys may reveal the presence of myoglobin casts in the renal tubules in all autopsies on traumatic deaths; it should be routine to collect frozen sections of tissues to look for fat emboli. Microscopic examination of the lungs in particular may show the presence of fat and/or marrow emboli. In many cases, some fat emboli will be detectable in other organs, such as the brain and kidneys.

## Causes of Death

The cause or causes of death in trauma to the musculoskeletal system in general will be attributable to hemorrhagic shock and/or complications of irreversible shock. The findings of rhabdomyolysis, myoglobinuria, and fat embolism are more likely to be found following aggressive resuscitation and a period of survival before death. This is particularly true in the context of modern medical advances with dialysis and ventilator care.

## Rhabdomyolysis

This is a condition where cells of the skeletal muscles become damaged and macromolecules, particularly myoglobin and enzymes such as lactate dehydrogenase and creatinine phosphokinase, are found in the plasma. There are many possible causes of such damage to the skeletal muscles. Some of these are shown in **Table 1**. It is unlikely that myoglobin itself is toxic and its damaging effects arise specifically as a

**Table 1** Causes of rhabdomyolysis*

Physical conditions
  Strenous exercise
  Status epilepticus
  Heat stroke
Traumatic conditions
  Crush injuries
  Severe burns
  Extensive blunt trauma particularly involving muscles
Substances of abuse
  Depressants
    Alcohol poisoning
    Heroin
    Methadone
  Stimulants
    Cocaine
    Phencyclidine
    LSD
    Amphetamines
    MDMA
    Ecstasy
Therapeutic substances
  Salicylates
  Neuroleptics
  Cyclic antidepressants
  Anesthetic and paralytic agents
  Statins
Infections
  Septicemia
    Bacteria, viral or fungal
Others
  Myositis
  Myopathies
  Severe metabolic disorders, e.g. diabetic ketoacidosis, thyrotoxicosis, etc.

*Note: This is not an exhaustive list but gives an idea of the possible causes of rhabdomyolysis.

result of its obstruction of the renal tubules leading to acute renal failure.

A recent event has been deaths from rhabdomyolysis associated with the introduction of a new group of cholesterol-lowering drugs known as statins. These reports eventually led to the voluntary withdrawal of the drug in 2001 from the market by the pharmaceutical company, despite initial approval by the Food and Drug Administration (FDA) in 1997.

## Myoglobinuria and Acute Renal Failure

Myoglobin is a relatively large molecule (molecular weight 17 800 Da) which will result in physical blockage of the renal glomeruli and tubules. Plasma myoglobin levels rise even before the elevation of creatinine phosphokinase. However they disappear rapidly after the cessation of injury due to rapid renal excretion. When present in large quantities, they can result in acute renal failure. Thankfully modern dialyses have meant that such occurrences are now rarely fatal.

## Fat and Marrow Embolism

Damage to adipose tissues and to long bones will release fat globules into the circulatory system. Fat is normally transported bound to proteins in plasma and is soluble. In fat embolism, fat globules are freely circulating and these can result in physical obstruction of small capillaries. The lungs are frequently the most common organs where such emboli are detected. When there is a large enough load, fat will escape into the systemic circulation where it can cause local infarction and necrosis of the areas of supply and can be potentially fatal when the brain is involved. The pathologist must however be aware that a small amount of fat emboli is not uncommonly found and death should not be attributed to fat embolism unless there is evidence of necrosis of vital organs such as the brain and lungs as well as correlation with clinical symptoms. In particular, it would be a rare situation for fat embolism to be attributable as the sole cause of death in situations of traumatic deaths where death was likely to have been rapid. The available literature is quite varied in describing the presence or absence of fat emboli in traumatic deaths; perhaps it is as suggested by Knight, that its presence is a function of how thorough or how hard they were looked for.

## Liposuction

Since the 1990s there has been an ever-increasing demand to exploit the advances in medical and surgical techniques to enhance body shapes to fit self-perceived ideals of body image. Rather than adopting measures like diet control and physical exercise, the technique of liposuction was introduced. The procedure involves the introduction of a suction apparatus into subcutaneous sites of adipose tissue deposition to remove fat cells. Such procedures are associated with fatalities reported at 19.1/100 000. In a study conducted by Grazer and de Jong in 2000, fat embolism was the cause of death reported in 11 out of 130 deaths following such procedures.

## Rib Fractures

Single rib fracture is rarely of any clinical significance except for the pain, the need for pain relief, and reassurance of the victims. Rib fractures associated with more serious consequences are however commonly seen in assaults, falls, and traffic accidents. Extensive rib fractures can result in hemothoraces, pneumothoraces, or hemopneumothoraces. Multiple extensive fractures of the ribcage give rise to a "flail chest" where paradoxical movements of the "flail segments" will cause further compromise to an already embarrassed respiration.

## Pelvic Fractures

Fractures of the pelvis are seen in conjunction with other extensive skeletal injuries in victims of high-speed transportation injuries and in falls from heights. In such circumstances they form but part of a myriad of other injuries.

Fracture of the pelvis occurs in victims of traffic accidents and also in falls from heights. Most orthopedic textbooks will provide the reader with the different types and description, together with the appropriate treatment. It is commonly forgotten that such fractures are the result of major force and can result in massive blood loss into the retroperitoneal space and such blood loss can cause death if proper clinical attention is not paid to victims admitted to hospital with such injuries. To complicate matters, it is not uncommon that there is oozing from the fractured bony surfaces; damage to blood vessels, particularly veins, is never easy to identify, even during exploratory surgery. Angiography and embolization techniques have proven useful and helpful in hemostasis in such circumstances.

## See Also

**Deaths:** Trauma, Head and Spine; Trauma, Thorax; Sports; **Postmortem Changes:** Overview

## Further Reading

Bernard K (1998) *Forensic Pathology,* 2nd edn. London: Arnold.

Grazer FM, deJong RH (2000) Fatalities from liposuction – census survey of cosmetic surgeons. *Plastic and Reconstructive Surgery* 105: 436–446.

Mason JK, Purdue BN (eds.) (2000) *The Pathology of Trauma,* 3rd edn. London: Arnold.

McMurtry RY, McLellan BA (eds.) (1990) *Management of Blunt Trauma.* Baltimore, MD: Williams and Wilkins.

Steven BK (2002) *Karch's Pathology of Drug Abuse,* 3rd edn. Boca Raton, FL: CRC Press.

US Food and Drug Administration (2001) Bayer voluntarily withdrawals Baycol. FDA Talk Paper Aug 8 2001. Available at: www.fda.gov/bbs/topics/ANSWERS/2001/ANS01095.html.

# Trauma, Vascular System

**N Hunt**, Forensic Pathology Services, Abingdon, UK

## Introduction

The chief consequence of vascular injury is hemorrhage, the volume of which depends on the extent and nature of the tissue damage and the caliber and type of the blood vessels injured.

All classes of injury may be associated with a degree of hemorrhage, with the exception of the most superficial of abrasions in which the dermal blood vessels are not disrupted. The consequences of hemorrhage may be of pathophysiological or forensic significance or both.

In this article it is intended to provide an overview of the mechanisms by which blood vessels may be injured; the pathophysiology of hypovolemic shock; the management of hypovolemic shock; implications for survival; special categories of vascular trauma; and the forensic implications of vascular trauma.

## Mechanisms of Vascular Injury

All types of injury may be associated with vascular damage, including blunt-force injuries (with the exception of classical abrasions), sharp-force injuries, gunshot wounds, and explosions.

Vascular trauma and its complications is the most common cause of death in respect of stab and incised wounds caused by sharp weapons, although clearly if a structure such as the upper cervical cord or brainstem is severed in the course of a sharp-weapon

assault then death may occur well before hypovolemia becomes relevant. Of the lower-limb vessels, one of the more commonly seen vascular injuries is to the vessels within the femoral canal. Certainly damage to these vessels may be associated with death. With respect to the upper-limb vessels the subclavian vessels are sometimes the source of fatal hemorrhage. Cases have been documented within the literature in which isolated vascular injury to the radial or ulnar artery has been the sole cause of death. Such cases provide the clearest challenge to the oft-repeated medical dogma that complete transection of an otherwise healthy peripheral artery is harmless. The injuries are usually the result of self-harm and one assumes that the deceased takes active measures to interrupt hemostasis either by massaging the limb to remove clots or achieving a similar effect, immersing the arm in water. More typically, damage to these vessels is a contributory factor to death where other injuries have been inflicted, the decedent has underlying, usually coronary arterial disease, and/or there has been drug ingestion (**Table 1**).

Whilst sharp-weapon injuries may relatively cleanly divide blood vessels, gunshot wounds tend to lead to irregular lacerations, providing potentially large defects within blood vessels, particularly in the case of bullets fired from high-velocity rifled weapons. Such injuries make it difficult for the body to mount its local hemostatic responses. Whilst the major complications seen with stab wounds in forensic practice are hypovolemic shock and death as the result of damage to the heart or great vessels, injury to lesser vessels may also be significant in causing or contributing to death.

The nature of the vascular injuries seen in gunshot wounds means that the mortality figures published in the major series comparing gunshot wounds with stab wounds are worse for the former than the latter. In the case of explosions, the vascular injury may be as the result of projected missile injuries directly lacerating blood vessels. It may also typify primary blast injury due to the propagation across the body of the blast wave with disruption, in particular, of alveolar

**Table 1** Factors affecting the outcome of vascular trauma

- Mechanism of injury
- Size and nature of vessel(s)
- Anatomical compartments
- Nature and extent of associated injuries
- Underlying natural disease
- Drugs (including alcohol)
- Efficacy of hemostasis
- First aid/medical intervention

capillary beds. This causes the lungs to be flooded with blood, impairing both ventilation and perfusion. This is a good example of where injury to smaller blood vessels, when on a large scale, may prove fatal. Vascular trauma may also occur as a result of blunt force impacts. Indeed, one of the more common injuries resulting in deaths in motor vehicle collisions is laceration, or even complete transection of the descending thoracic aorta at the level of the ligamentum arteriosum. This injury frequently results in internal exsanguinations.

Whilst vascular trauma and hypovolemic shock may be relevant to many deaths involving firearms or explosion, also relevant in these cases is tissue destruction, which may be massive. Again, death may supervene before hypovolemia becomes relevant.

Hypovolemia as a result of severe bruising may sometimes be relevant to the cause of death; however, it should be remembered that other factors may play a role in death in persons with severe bruising including, of course, hematoma formation within restricted compartments as well as precipitating decompensation in otherwise compensated liver failure.

The volume of blood lost from fractures should never be underestimated and indeed fractures of large long bones such as the femur may be associated with a liter or more of blood loss and hematoma formation. Disruption of the bony pelvis may also be associated with significant hemorrhage, particularly if there is disruption of the major venous plexus in the presacral region. The bleeding occasioned by such an injury may be very difficult to control surgically.

## Hemorrhage and the Pathophysiology of Hypovolemic Shock

Hemorrhage may be divided into primary, reactionary, and secondary hemorrhage. Primary hemorrhage occurs at the time of the original injury. This may be the only mechanism by which bleeding occurs. Reactionary hemorrhage is a term sometimes used to refer to hemorrhage occurring within 24 h of the primary injury (and usually within 4–6 h) and may be due to clot or ligature displacement. A secondary hemorrhage refers to hemorrhage after 7–14 days. It may be due to local complications such as delayed dissection, aneurysm formation, or infection.

In pathophysiological terms, "shock" may be defined as a clinical syndrome resulting from inadequate tissue perfusion. One of the features that defines hypovolemic shock is that it is a state of low cardiac output in the face of high systemic vascular resistance. Hypovolemic shock has a number of causes, the one pertinent to the present discussion being hemorrhage. As with other forms of shock,

hypovolemic shock may be divided in a number of ways, but one of the more useful may be the division into nonprogressive (compensated), progressive (decompensated), and irreversible shock.

Hypovolemic shock may also be divided on the basis of the percentage of blood volume lost. Whilst it is often said that the average adult circulating blood volume is of the order of 5 l, surgically, calculations based on the patient's weight may be used on the assumption that for adults the blood volume is of the order of 65–75 ml kg$^{-1}$ and, for infants, 80–85 ml kg$^{-1}$. Practically speaking it is, however, difficult to estimate blood loss accurately, particularly in the relatively uncontrolled environment of a crime scene where blood may be soaked into garments, the ground, or bandages.

Using volume-based criteria, hypovolemic shock may be divided into mild (less than 20% of blood-volume loss), moderate (20–40% of blood-volume loss), and severe (greater than 40% of blood-volume loss).

Whilst there may be some utility in subdividing types of shock clinically, it should be remembered that the effects of particular percentage losses of blood volume on the whole person may be significantly modified by other factors, including underlying natural disease (especially cardiovascular disease), intoxication, and environment. It also needs to be remembered that subdivisions for the purposes of classification are essentially artificial and that the development of shock is a progression rather than a series of quantum events.

In the early stages of this process (nonprogressive or compensated shock) the body has a number of physiological mechanisms, which help to limit the effects of blood-volume loss. These include vasoconstriction, tachycardia, increased secretion of antidiuretic hormone, activation of the renin–angiotensin system, and increased adrenocorticotrophic hormone secretion. Vasoconstriction includes constriction of arteries and also of the venous capacitance vessels. The arterial supplies to the heart and the brain exhibit the physiological characteristic of autoregulation which helps ensure continued perfusion of these vital organs at the expense of other tissues, at least until mean arterial pressure falls below about 60 mmHg.

In addition to the systemic responses to volume loss, there are, of course, the local regulatory mechanisms of primary and secondary hemostasis. Primary hemostasis includes the processes of vasoconstriction, and platelet plug formation. The phenomenon of secondary hemostasis is the result of fibrin deposition following activation of the coagulation system. If there is failure of the primary and secondary hemostatic mechanisms, as a result of either natural disease or circumstances particular to the case, then significant hemorrhage may occur even from relatively small vessels.

With up to 10–15% of circulating blood volume lost, the blood pressure is maintained by a combination of tachycardia, vasoconstriction, and the other mechanisms mentioned above. Once the blood loss starts to exceed these sorts of levels then the regulatory mechanisms may become overwhelmed and hypotension develops. The patient then enters the phase of decompensated shock.

As the blood volume is lowered venous return falls and this may be added to by progressive cardiac dysfunction. The overall result is a lowering of the systemic blood pressure.

Once blood pressure starts to fall then one of the results is tissue hypoxia leading to lactic acidosis. Hydrogen ions, lactate, and other anaerobic metabolites may be formed that can override vasomotor tone. The lactic acidosis may also impair cardiac function. If there is concomitant severe tissue injury and hypothermia then this may further impair myocardial contractility. Further reductions in tissue perfusion lead to ischemia, which may end, ultimately, in frank infarction. In persons with preexisting arterial narrowing this may be a relatively early event.

With continued bleeding there is also consumption of platelets and coagulation factors leading to impaired hemostasis. The use of massive transfusions of packed red blood cells may also have a dilutional effect upon platelets and clotting factors as neither are present in standard red-cell preparations. Another consequence of tissue hypoxia is the pathological activation of the coagulation system leading to disseminated intravascular coagulation (DIC) and further consumption of platelets and clotting factors, including factors V and VIII. In addition, the formation of microthrombi within tissues leads to further local tissue hypoxia.

The overall effects of these changes in the decompensated phase of hypovolemic shock is to initiate an essentially self-perpetuating mechanism by which further tissue damage occurs unless interrupted by therapeutic intervention. Eventually, however, the victim then passes into a state in which no further intervention will succeed in reversing the state of shock and this is known as the irreversible phase of shock, which essentially occurs as the result of irreversible injury at the cellular level.

## Other Complications of Vascular Trauma

The complications of trauma to blood vessels may be divided into early complications and late complications. The nature and importance of the complications will depend upon the blood vessel injured and the anatomical location of those blood vessels.

The most obvious early complication of vascular trauma is, of course, hypovolemic shock of whatever degree. Another potentially fatal complication may be the development of air embolism if a significant quantity of air manages to enter the vascular system (greater than 100 ml is usually quoted). In the context of this discussion it is almost exclusively venous embolism that is relevant and in this circumstance the system usually becomes interrupted by way of cardiac pump failure with the air trapped within the right heart and great veins. The autopsy detection of air embolism depends upon having an index of suspicion for the phenomenon having occurred and some authors consider chest radiography to be the gold standard for diagnosis. The use of an aspirometer to remove gas from the cardiac ventricles has also been recommended. Upon dissection the relevant finding is frothy blood within the great veins and the right side of the heart. The heart may be opened under water in order to assist in demonstrating the presence of air.

The release of blood within particular compartments may be associated with specific complications. Within the cranial vault vascular trauma such as extradural/subdural hematoma may cause a space-occupying lesion leading to raised intracranial pressure. Sudden bathing of the brainstem with blood, as occurs in traumatic basal subarachnoid hemorrhage, may lead to virtually instantaneous cardiac and respiratory arrest and death.

Injuries to the mid-face and nose may cause significant hemorrhage with a potential for aspiration of blood in the obtunded victim. Bleeding within the neck may cause sufficient hemorrhage to compromise the airway and in one case, seen by the author, rapid escape of arterial blood within the carotid sheath from a single stab wound to the neck, leading to "reflex" cardiac inhibition, has been the only conceivable explanation for the rapid death of a man with minimal exsanguination.

Within the chest significant hemorrhage may cause either cardiac tamponade or hemothorax and their attendant complications.

Late complications of vascular injury sometimes come to the attention of forensic pathologists. Whilst the development of posttraumatic aneurysms or pseudoaneurysms is well documented in the clinical literature, these relatively rarely present to the forensic pathologist.

There are a number of cases documented in the forensic pathological literature (and the author has experience of a further case) in which there has been injury to the vertebral arterial system with delayed rupture of a subsequent aneurysm. Other late complications of vascular trauma include dissection, secondary hemorrhage, and loss of function.

## Autopsy Findings in Hypovolemic Shock

The autopsy findings will vary with the rate of blood loss and other factors, including the presence or otherwise of underlying natural disease and intoxication. In a fully developed state of shock, following a prolonged bleed, one may see multiple internal petechiae and small hemorrhages in major organs. The brain and heart may be particularly affected with hypoxic/ischemic changes seen in the brain, especially at so-called "watershed" areas lying between arterial territories (clinically there may be a state of hypoxic encephalopathy which may be mistaken for intoxication).

Within the heart there may be subepicardial and subendocardial hemorrhages as well as evidence of early infarction. The kidney may show acute tubular necrosis and the liver central lobular necrosis and the accumulation of intracellular fat within hepatocytes. The adrenal glands may show evidence of lipid depletion within their cortices. The gastrointestinal mucosa may show evidence of hemorrhage and necrosis (hemorrhagic enteropathy).

## Trends in the Clinical Management of Hemorrhage

Until relatively recently the clinical management of hemorrhage depended upon stopping bleeding and what may be called normotensive or hypertensive resuscitation with the use of aggressive fluid therapy. There has been a long-standing debate as to the relative merits of crystalloid or colloid.

Recently, there has been a growing body of medical opinion advocating less aggressive fluid management of patients with hypovolemic shock whereby the aim of resuscitative therapy is to raise blood pressure sufficiently to obtain a palpable radial pulse. This has been referred to as hypotensive resuscitation. The advocates of such therapy would argue that there is less risk of clot disruption and reactive hemorrhage and that the overall outcome may be improved.

Another recent development is the advent of hypertonic saline fluid resuscitation. There has been considerable drive for this in military medicine where the use of 7% saline and 6% hyperoncotic colloid dextran has been promulgated. This is available in 250-ml bags and it has been suggested that a single 250-ml bag of hypertonic saline/dextran may

provide the same plasma volume expansion as three 1-l bags of normal saline. The effects of such a solution are to cause a shift of water from the intracellular fluid compartment to the extracellular fluid compartment, leading to an increase in plasma volume and a rapid cardiovascular response with improvements in mean arterial pressure and cardiac output. The other obvious advantage is the considerable saving in space and weight offered by using one fluid as opposed to the other; however, there are also suggested clinical advantages in damping down other aspects of the systemic response which may impact upon morbidity and mortality. What remains to be determined is whether or not the use of such fluids causes any histologically demonstrable injury that may be relevant to the clinical outcome. Thus an awareness of the use of such fluids and detailed pathological investigations are of importance in monitoring and potentially refining such therapies.

Whilst both the nature of fluids and the administration regimens are changing, surgical practices are also beginning to change with the concept of so-called damage limitation surgery being advocated by a growing number of trauma surgeons. The aim in damage limitation surgery is to control hemorrhages as rapidly as possible and to correct physiological parameters before undertaking definitive surgical repair on the stabilized patient.

The ethos behind damage-control surgery is that of trying to break, or avoid, the cycle of events in decompensated shock in which hypothermia, acidosis, and coagulopathy play such an important part.

Hypotensive resuscitation aims to achieve a balance between preserving vital organ function and reducing the risk of further bleeding.

## Factors Affecting Outcome of Vascular Trauma

Larger outcome studies of patients receiving emergency medical intervention for vascular injuries of the abdomen emphasize the importance of both size and nature of the injured vessel and also the number of injured vessels in influencing mortality. Thus whilst there may be 45% overall mortality with one vessel injured; this may rise to 100% if more than four vessels are injured. Although one might expect the outcome to be poor with isolated injuries to the aorta or inferior vena cava, significant mortality is also seen in injuries to the portal and superior mesenteric veins as well as the superior mesenteric artery, iliac artery, and splenic artery. Even if one considers the same vessel, that is the inferior vena cava, then the survival for retrohepatic caval injuries appears to be worse than for other intraabdominal injuries to this vessel. Such studies indicate that the most significant risk factor for death include a low initial systolic blood pressure (below 70 mmHg in the emergency department), hypothermia, and high-unit blood transfusion.

Another important factor, which may influence the outcome after vascular trauma, is the integrity of the person's coagulation system. This may be affected as a result of therapy, including warfarin, heparin, and aspirin, but may also be affected by underlying deficiencies in the proteins involved in coagulation or indeed in platelet number or function. Whilst these may be of relevance in influencing the outcome, the general principle in English law is that an attacker "takes his victim as he finds them" and therefore the forensic significance of such underlying conditions, whilst important to document and comment upon, may be more limited than the clinical implications. However, one cannot assume anything and this is not a decision for the pathologist to make; rather it is the duty of the pathologist to present the court with all the information relevant to the case as well as his/her opinion regarding the cause of death.

## Survival Time and Acting Capacity

This may be of great significance within the forensic context and is frequently a question asked of the forensic pathologist by barristers within the English courts. As with so many other areas of forensic practice, there is no room for dogma and unjustifiable certainty in one's conclusions for the vast majority of vascular injuries. Both personal experience and reading of the published literature lead to the inevitable conclusion that there is great interindividual variation in survival time and acting capacity for what may be ostensibly similar injuries. In arriving at an estimate, one has to consider all relevant factors, including the nature and caliber of the injured vessel, the demonstrable amount of blood loss, the nature and extent of any associated trauma, such as burns, soft-tissue injury, the mechanism of injury, the existence of comorbidity (at both macroscopic and microscopic levels), and the toxicological findings.

## Weapon Assessment

Abrasions and intradermal bruises are good examples of where apparently trivial vascular trauma may be of great forensic significance. These types of injury may hold clear impressions of an inflicting object such as the sole of a shoe, a ligature, or a tool. Due to the nature of arterial walls, even if there is destruction of skin, there may still be the impression of an inflicting

weapon, such as a knife, left within the aorta for example, following a stabbing in which either decomposition or burning has obscured the external features of the wound.

## Blood Pattern Analysis

Whilst not the expert province of the forensic pathologist in England, it is important that the pathologist is able to communicate meaningfully with scene-going biologists who are ordinarily tasked with the role. The accurate description of vessels injured, and communication of these findings to the biologist, may be very helpful in optimizing the interpretation of the blood pattern at a scene of crime and assisting in the reconstruction of events. The judicious use of enhancement techniques such as Luminol by forensic biologists may play a significant part in reconstructing crime scenes which have either been cleaned or in which there has been a significant passage of time since the event.

The utility of such techniques may be greatly increased in the light of detailed and accurate descriptions of vascular injury.

## See Also

**Deaths:** Trauma, Head and Spine; Trauma, Thorax; Trauma, Abdominal Cavity; Trauma, Musculo-skeletal System; **Injury, Fatal and Nonfatal:** Blunt Injury

## Further Reading

Di Maio VJ, Di Maio D (2001) *Forensic Pathology*, 2nd edn. New York: CRC Press.
Froede RC (ed.) (2003) *Handbook of Forensic Pathology*, 2nd edn. Northfield, IL: College of American Pathologists.
Knight B (1991) *Forensic Pathology*. New York: Oxford University Press.

# Perioperative and Postoperative

**P N Cooper**, University of Newcastle upon Tyne, Newcastle upon Tyne, UK

## Introduction

Perioperative death means any death occurring around the time of an operative procedure and includes those occurring between admission and the operation (preoperative), those occurring during the operation and the immediate recovery period (operative), and those occurring after the operative period (postoperative). It is not possible to define the incidence of perioperative death, as there is no single definition of what constitutes the postoperative period. Many studies use a period of 30 days after the operation. Others define it using a shorter time period. In one study of over one million anesthetics given, there were six deaths per thousand within 6 days of the procedure. Whatever the definition, death is most likely to occur on the day of the operation or the following day, with the incidence then gradually declining. Although many of these deaths are caused or contributed to by natural disease, many will have been at least contributed to by the operative procedure. Therefore this is one of the commonest deaths investigated by autopsy pathologists.

## The Role of the Pathologist

The investigation of a perioperative death aims to answer the following questions:

- Was the death caused or contributed to by the medical procedure and its aftermath, and, if so, how?
- Was the death caused or contributed to by natural disease or other preexisting factors and, if so, how?
- Was the preoperative assessment of the patient accurate in terms particularly of operative risk and the nature and extent of the disease for which the procedure was being performed?
- Was the standard of medical treatment before, during, and after the operation adequate?

The autopsy pathologist plays an important role in the first three of these. The pathologist's main role and responsibility are to perform a careful detailed postmortem examination, carefully document the findings, interpret them within the limits of his/her expertise, and prepare a report for whoever commissioned the postmortem examination. A less obvious role, but an important one, is to assist clinicians and nursing staff in establishing protocols within the hospital in defining how such deaths should be dealt with. Specifically hospitals, or more particularly their operating theaters, need to have a policy in place as to whether endotracheal (ET) tubes and other medical paraphernalia are left in place after a perioperative death. From the viewpoint of the pathologist it is best if all tubes are left in place in all cases coming to autopsy but this causes problems for medical and particularly nursing staff who wish to make the deceased as presentable as possible for relatives. Unfortunately, the ET tube is the most relevant in this respect but also the most intrusive. A sensible compromise should be reached.

If there is a possibility that the anesthetic agents have caused death, all open drug ampoules should be kept in case later analysis is required to check whether the drug was present in the appropriate concentration.

Pathologists should be available to provide advice to clinicians as to how individual postprocedure deaths should be dealt with. The enthusiastic autopsy pathologist will promote the value of the autopsy to his/her clinical colleagues, present such deaths at clinicopathological conferences, mortality meetings, and audit meetings, and make the results of the examination available promptly and in a clinically relevant form.

## The Postmortem Examination

A detailed postmortem examination is an essential part of the investigation of a perioperative death, frequently revealing an unexpected cause of death or diagnostic error. In one study postmortem revealed an unsuspected cause of death in 31% of postthoracic surgery deaths. In a general-surgery population major diagnostic errors are revealed at postmortem in about 30% of cases and errors whose appreciation would have resulted in a change of therapy which might have improved survival in 10% of cases or more. The majority of these latter findings are infections (30–40%), pulmonary (10–20%), or cardiovascular pathology (10–20%). Patients who spend prolonged periods in intensive care postoperatively are particularly likely to have undiagnosed infections found at postmortem examination.

However, a perioperative death will not invariably be followed by a postmortem examination. Whether it does varies between countries, hospitals, clinicians, and, in England and Wales, between coroners. In England and Wales most postoperative death postmortem examinations are performed at the request of the coroner and only a few are "consented" or "hospital autopsies." Under the coronial system any death where the operative procedure may have "caused, contributed to, or accelerated death" should be referred to and investigated by the coroner. This system, however, relies upon a clinician referring the case to the coroner in the first place and then on the coroner deciding that the case falls within his/her jurisdiction. Generally, hospital doctors have a poor understanding of which cases require referral to the coroner and there is considerable variation between coroners as to which cases they will investigate. Many coroners are happy to accept a "recognized complication" of an operative procedure as a natural part of the disease process and will only investigate the death if there is potential negligence. Whatever the inconsistencies, the coroner's system in England and Wales does at least mean that a relatively high proportion of post-procedure deaths come to postmortem examination. However, the quality of such postmortem examinations and the reports they generate is at best variable. With the implementation of clinical governance and in light of the General Medical Council inquiry into deaths after surgery in a pediatric center in England, it is likely that the results of surgical procedures, particularly death, will be more closely monitored in the future.

The individual pathologist should have the time, inclination, and experience to be able to perform the examination to a high standard, particularly as the dissection is often difficult, the findings may be minimal, and interpretation may be problematic. If there is any allegation of negligence it is advisable for the pathologist to be independent of the institution concerned.

The actual examination is best thought of in four stages: (1) clinical history; (2) external examination; (3) internal examination; and (4) further investigations. Each will be considered in turn.

### Clinical History

The full hospital notes, including the operation notes and preferably the X-rays, should be available and further information is often gained by speaking to the surgeon and/or anesthetist prior to the examination. Most useful of all is to have the surgeon(s) and/or anesthetist(s) present at the examination. Such consultation is essential in complex or controversial cases. Some pathologists feel threatened by this but their presence can only be advantageous. Clinical events and surgical procedures can be explained; the findings can be viewed firsthand by the clinicians, and in most cases a mutually acceptable explanation for the death can be arrived at.

### External Examination

The usual thorough external examination should be performed with particular reference to the presence and position of any lines, catheters, drains, other tubes, and surgical incisions (in line with the Royal College of Pathology guidelines).

### Internal Examination

The way in which the internal examination proceeds must be tailored to the individual case. The use of postmortem radiography to establish the presence of air embolism, pneumothorax, and the position of the ET tube should be considered beforehand where relevant.

If the ET tube is still *in situ* its position should be checked first. Some authorities recommend pre-autopsy radiography to establish its position. The position of the tube is equally well established by careful dissection and direct inspection. The skin of the neck should be incised with a V-shaped incision and reflected back as far as the jaw line. The trachea can be palpated and sometimes the tube can be felt within it. A careful incision through the midline of the anterior wall of the larynx and trachea will confirm its position. (If its position is contentious it should then be photographed before the dissection proceeds.) If the ET tube is in the esophagus, the length which protrudes into the esophagus should be measured.

If the ET tube has already been removed there may be a residual ring of edematous esophageal mucosa or bruising, laceration, or even perforation. In esophageal intubation the stomach is often distended by anesthetic gas. In theory, analysis of a sample of this gas should reveal the presence of the anesthetic agent.

The skin of the trunk should then be reflected using the usual midline incision but avoiding any surgical wounds or drains. Before opening the chest, consideration should be given to testing for pneumothorax in the usual way. If air embolism is a possibility, for example, in a death following laparoscopic surgery, this should be checked for. Techniques recommended include radiography and careful dissection.

The operative site must be carefully examined, particularly for evidence of infection or hemorrhage. The volume of any blood present should be measured.

As the evisceration proceeds, surgical anastomoses should be checked gently *in situ* as soon as they become visible. Intestinal anastomoses should be checked before the intestines are removed. Even then it may be difficult or impossible to distinguish antemortem breakdown from postmortem autolysis. Of value in this distinction is the presence or absence of evidence of leakage from anastomoses in the form of local reaction, abscess formation, or frank peritonitis.

In cases where the routine autopsy procedure does not expose the operation site, usually following musculoskeletal or spinal surgery, it is important to remember to examine the operative site specifically for hemorrhage, infection, and other local effects of surgery.

Any perioperative death autopsy should also check whether the trauma or natural disease for which the procedure was performed was actually present and if so, to what extent and how "successful" the operation has been. For example, in the case of a surgical resection of a carcinoma it is important not only to confirm the clinical diagnosis but also to assess evidence of residual local tumor or metastatic disease.

All the major organs should be checked in the normal way, in particular those organs that are likely to have contributed to perioperative death, especially the cardiac and respiratory systems.

The postmortem findings should be carefully documented and photographed. It may be of value, particularly if the surgeon is not present at the autopsy, to retain larger specimens, organs, or parts of organs for later examination and dissection. Whether this is legal depends upon the nature of the authority or consent given for the postmortem examination, which must of course be complied with.

### Further Investigations

Histological examination of tissues is of use in the majority of perioperative death postmortems and in a large minority is absolutely essential to define the pathology present. Histology from the operation site helps in the diagnosis of infection, to identify predisposing causes for hemorrhage or infection and to determine if there is, for example, residual tumor. Histological sampling of distant organs is aimed first at specific naked-eye pathology to confirm its nature and to date it (for example, a presumed perioperative myocardial infarct) and is of use in identifying systemic complications such as disseminated intravascular coagulation (DIC), ischemia, and septicemia, and in confirming the presence of preexisting disease.

Samples from possible areas of infection should be sent for microbiological examination. Blood collected from the heart or else a piece of spleen is of most use in identifying septicemia. Microbiological samples should be taken as early in the examination as possible so as to minimize contamination and using techniques which are as sterile as possible.

Samples of blood and urine should be kept if there is any possibility of overdosage or reaction to a drug or anesthetic agent. If there is any possibility of malignant hyperthermia or transfusion reaction the hospital laboratory should be asked to retain any antemortem blood or urine samples if still available. Techniques for taking postmortem samples can be found in Forrest.

### The Report

The best and most detailed postmortem examination is of little use unless the results are communicated to the clinicians and/or the medicolegal authority requesting the examination. The postmortem report should be set out according to the Royal College of Pathology or similar guidelines and should end with a detailed clinicopathological correlation. The exact extent to which a pathologist should interpret postmortem findings is open to debate. At one end of the spectrum there is a school of thought that believes that the pathologist's role is simply to document the findings at postmortem carefully but not to interpret them in the light of the clinical evidence. It is certainly important for the pathologist to realize the limitations of his/her expertise. Many postoperative autopsies are essentially negative from a pathological point of view and establishing the cause of death rests on interpretation of the clinical findings. This is a task best undertaken by a clinician. It is, however, quite in order for a pathologist to interpret simple clinical findings as long as he/she makes the limits of his/her expertise plain. In the most extreme case where all rests on clinical interpretation it is not only acceptable but also sensible for the pathologist not to commit him/herself to a cause of death when submitting a report.

## Interpretation of Findings

For the pathologist to make a sensible clinicopathological correlation it is important that he/she has a basic understanding of the pathology of perioperative death. Often such deaths involve a complicated interaction of factors which predate the operative procedure such as natural disease or trauma, the direct and indirect complications of the procedure, and often events which occur after the operation on the ward, for example aspiration of vomit.

It is convenient to divide the effects of a surgical operation into those related to the anesthetic and those related to the procedure itself, albeit this is often a rather artificial division. The effects of anesthesia and the procedure are summarized in **Table 1**.

### Anesthetic-Related Factors

Only about 1 in 10 000 patients undergoing surgical operation dies solely as a consequence of the anesthetic and related procedures but it has been calculated that anesthesia contributes to death in closer to 1 in 1700 patients. Many of these deaths are potentially avoidable. The autopsy in such cases often has few positive findings.

Cardiac arrest is the most common mode of anesthetic-related death and acute cardiovascular failure is the most common cause of death. Such deaths are often associated with the start or finish of the surgical procedure in the lightly anesthetized patient and may be precipitated by laryngoscopy or intubation.

**Table 1** Summary of the effects of anesthesia and of the surgical procedure

*Anesthetic-related*
Acute cardiovascular failure
Respiratory failure
   Airway obstruction
   Equipment failure
   Respiratory depression
   Dose-related
   Idiosyncratic
*Procedure-related*
Cardiac death
   Arrhythmic
   Ischemic
   Pump failure
Hemorrhage
Local infection
Chest infection
Leg-vein thrombosis
Pulmonary thromboembolism
Systemic thromboembolism
Procedure-specific damage

Induction of anesthesia is commonly accompanied by lowering of the blood pressure and heart rate, which may cause cardiac arrest as a result of decreased myocardial perfusion, particularly in patients with preexisting coronary artery disease. On the other hand, blood pressure often rises during intubation and laryngoscopy. This carries risks of its own. Cardiac arrest may also be caused by vasoconstrictors such as norepinephrine (noradrenaline) used in local anesthesia, particularly if given in excess.

Respiratory failure is the second commonest anesthetic mode of death. It can be due to airway obstruction, respiratory depression, or occasionally from a fault in the anesthetic equipment or gas supply. In the case of gas supply, expert examination of the equipment is required. Airway obstruction may be caused by malintubation or, more commonly, aspiration of blood or vomit. Postmortem findings in such cases are rarely clear-cut as they are distorted by vigorous resuscitation and, not infrequently, a considerable period of survival after the event. The clinical history, as so often, is absolutely vital in such cases. Vomit found in the main airways at postmortem with no clinical suggestion of significant aspiration is almost always a postmortem artifact and not relevant to the death.

Anesthetic agents predispose to respiratory failure in a dose-related fashion and one study shows that overdose of anesthetic agent contributed to death in a quarter of all anesthetic-related cases. Anesthetics, including local anesthetics, also occasionally cause idiosyncratic reactions such as posthalothane hepatic failure, malignant hyperpyrexia (usually precipitated by succinylcholine and halogenated anesthetic agents such as halothane), and anaphylaxis. Anaphylaxis produces sudden collapse, classically with a clinical syndrome including bronchospasm, laryngeal edema, peripheral vasodilatation, and hypotension. However, the actual symptoms produced are variable; sudden collapse due to shock without any difficulty in breathing occurs in most fatal drug reactions. Postmortem findings are similarly variable and may have been drastically modified by attempts at resuscitation and a period of survival. For example, laryngeal edema was only present in seven of 21 cases of fatal drug-related anaphylactic reactions reported by Pumphrey and Roberts, with the only relatively constant postmortem finding being the nonspecific presence of pulmonary congestion and/or edema. If anaphylaxis is suspected it is essential to retain a sample of peripheral blood obtained as soon after the collapse as possible. Specialized regional laboratories can measure mast-cell tryptase, which will be high in a true anaphylactic reaction and can also look for immunoglobulin E specific to the suspected allergen. Both immunoglobulin E and mast-cell tryptase are stable in serum for several days and can be measured in postmortem samples.

Respiratory arrest is also a specific complication of epidural anesthesia if the agent is allowed to diffuse upwards to the cervical level or is given in excessive dose. In such cases the dura should be examined carefully for an inadvertent puncture site and a sample of cerebrospinal fluid retained.

## Procedure-Related Factors

Periprocedure deaths are more frequently the result of the procedure itself rather than the anesthesia. Complications may be local to the operation site or systemic. **Table 1** includes a classification of procedure-related causes of death.

**Cardiac death** Cardiac complications account for more than half of perioperative deaths and can be classified as arrhythmic, ischemic, or due to pump failure. A proportion of perioperative deaths occur suddenly after an arrhythmia with no episode of ischemia documented clinically or evident at postmortem. Fatal and nonfatal arrhythmias are a common complication of both anesthesia and surgery.

Electrocardiogram monitoring suggests that perioperative myocardial ischemia is usually subendocardial as a result of factors such as tachycardia, hypotension, and increased cardiac output rather than due to coronary artery occlusion. Drugs used for induction and maintenance of anesthesia may also cause myocardial depression, vasodilatation, and potentially hypotension but a clinically documented perioperative hypotensive episode is, however, the exception rather than the rule. Most significant episodes of cardiac ischemia occur after, rather than during, the operation, with the majority of myocardial infarcts occurring some days later.

Perioperative myocardial infarction is predisposed to by preexisting coronary artery atheroma or cardiac failure and is more likely to occur if there is a history of recent myocardial infarct.

Pump failure is a common cause of peri- and postoperative death but is a problematic diagnosis for the pathologist to make. It is also difficult from the conceptual viewpoint, as in the absence of documented myocardial infarction the cause is often ill-defined and death is not sudden.

**Hemorrhage** Whenever vascularized tissue is cut there will be bleeding. Clinically important hemorrhage usually occurs either during the operation and immediate postoperative period (primary) or around a week or 10 days later (secondary). A delay in the onset of hemorrhage on occasion simply reflects the fact that bleeding from a vessel may not become apparent until the blood pressure returns to normal in the postoperative period.

These two peaks of incidence have different causes. Intraoperative or primary hemorrhage is due to division or damage to blood vessels caused either intentionally, when it is often the result of a general ooze rather than one focal hemorrhage, or else unintentionally, when the damage may be to an organ or a large vessel. Secondary hemorrhage is usually a complication of infection at the operation site. In such cases appropriate microbiological samples should be taken. In the majority of both types of hemorrhage the surgeon has a considerable advantage over the pathologist when it comes to identifying the source of hemorrhage in that first, he/she may see the hemorrhage as it occurs, and second, by the time of the postmortem the source of the hemorrhage has usually been obscured by further surgical intervention.

On occasion, however, particularly after sudden unexpected death, a specific source of hemorrhage may be identified at postmortem examination. For example, damage to the inferior vena cava or aorta complicates laparoscopic abdominal operations in around 0.25% of cases; the liver may be damaged during a paracentesis, the thoracic aorta during coronary angiography, or a liver biopsy track may pass into a hemangioma.

Histological confirmation of such findings is essential and histology may reveal a predisposition to hemorrhage not visible to the naked eye, such as infiltration by tumor or myxoid degeneration in

**Table 2** Factors predisposing to hemorrhage

| |
|---|
| Obesity |
| Steroid therapy |
| Coagulation/disorders |
| Liver disease |
| Blood transfusion |
| Other medications |
| Advanced age |
| Sepsis |

a large artery or infection in a case of secondary hemorrhage.

The need for careful examination of suture lines is self-evident. Truly unexpected hemorrhage occurring in the day or two after surgery may be due to a surgical suture slipping or "cutting out" or occasionally a suture breaks. Any apparent suture-related problem must be discussed with the surgeon before any conclusion is reached.

As well as any local operative-site reasons for hemorrhage, the patient may suffer from a systemic bleeding tendency (**Table 2**). This may be evident from the patient's clinical notes or at the postmortem in the form of liver disease such as cirrhosis or bone marrow disease such as a myeloproliferative disorder. DIC is a factor in some postoperative deaths. In the context of postprocedure hemorrhage, DIC usually follows substantial blood loss and equally substantial blood and fluid replacement. The condition is usually suspected clinically and may well have been confirmed in life by laboratory tests. At postmortem it is suggested by the presence of hemorrhages away from the operation site, especially in the form of petechial hemorrhages in multiple organs. It may be confirmed histologically by the presence of fibrin microthrombi in small vessels in multiple organs.

The significance of blood loss after operation requires careful interpretation. In some cases, such as cardiac tamponade or a massive unexpected hemorrhage, there can be no question that the bleeding has been significant. Quite considerable blood loss may however be essentially irrelevant to the death in the context of adequate fluid and blood replacement by the clinical team. Consultation with the clinician as to the relevance of hemorrhage in such cases is essential.

The body is generally able to compensate and maintain perfusion when blood loss is less than about 15% of the total volume. If there is substantial further blood loss, however, the blood pressure falls and if there is a reasonable period of survival a characteristic pattern of hypotensive organ damage is seen. At postmortem the kidneys may show acute tubular necrosis and the lungs adult respiratory distress syndrome. Hypotension is also suggested by watershed infarcts in the brain and intestine and subendocardial rather than regional infarction in the heart. The postmortem examination should seek other potential causes of ischemic damage such as sources of emboli and evidence of local thrombosis. Histologically an attempt should be made to age any ischemic damage for correlation with clinical episodes of hypotension.

A final source of hemorrhage is stress ulceration of the gastric mucosa, which occurs perioperatively as a consequence of local ischemia.

Blood loss, of course, is not the only cause of hypotension. The effects of anesthetic agents have already been mentioned. Postoperatively analgesia, particularly opiates, may contribute.

**Local infection** Any surgical incision which breaches an epithelial surface can lead directly to local infection at the site of the procedure. The presence of a foreign body after surgery, such as a hip replacement, makes postoperative infection more likely. In some postoperative deaths, such as surgery for a ruptured colonic diverticulum, infection will have been present before the surgical operation and in a third group will only commence some time after the operation as a result of, for example, an anastomotic breakdown or delayed perforation, as in laparoscopic surgery, where unsuspected electrosurgical burns to the intestine are a frequent mechanism of unrecognized bowel injury. If infection is present at the operation site at the time of postmortem examination, it is important to determine which of these three possibilities applies and to attempt to identify the organism concerned by taking appropriate samples for culture.

The principal potentially fatal consequences of local infection are secondary hemorrhage and septicemia. Histological evidence of septicemia may be found in distant organs, including the heart and liver. Common systemic factors which may contribute to the development of infection include diabetes mellitus, steroid therapy, and immunosuppression. Factors predisposing to infection may be evident in the clinical history or at the postmortem (**Table 3**).

**Chest infection** Chest infection is a common postoperative complication particularly in the elderly. Factors which predispose to it in the postoperative patient are: (1) inhalation of gastric contents during anesthesia; (2) prolonged ventilation; and (3) pain when coughing or breathing deeply. If inhalation is suspected the airway contents should be inspected particularly carefully and microscopic sections of lung examined for the presence of vegetable and meat in small airways. The presence of vomit in major airways may, however, simply be a postmortem

**Table 3** Factors predisposing to leg-vein thrombosis

*Preexisting*
Obesity
Age over 40
Malignancy
Hypercoagulable disorders
Contraceptive pill and hormone replacement therapy
Past history of thrombosis
Pregnancy
Heart failure
*Perioperative*
Lack of prophylactic measures
Long operation (>30 min)
Leg and pelvis operations
Local vessel damage
Postoperative increase in blood coagulopathy
Immobility

phenomenon and is seen in about 25% of coroner's autopsies.

Abdominal and thoracic operations are particularly prone to postoperative bronchopneumonia partly because of the pain produced by coughing but also because of temporary paralysis of the diaphragm. The prevalence in such surgery is around 20%.

In the presence of a postoperative bronchopneumonia the role of other natural disease such as heart failure, emphysema, obesity, general debility, smoking, or pulmonary fibrosis has to be assessed.

**Leg vein thrombosis and pulmonary thromboembolism** Without antithrombotic prophylaxis between 8% and 15% of patients develop leg vein thrombosis after major surgery and a much larger proportion after major surgery to the leg. As with any other possible complication of operation risk factors may be evident in the clinical history or at postmortem (**Table 3**).

Three factors predispose to vessel thrombosis after operation: (1) local vessel damage; (2) increased levels of clotting factors; and (3) platelets and immobility. Immobility is the principal predisposing factor to postoperative leg-vein thrombosis. However, both acute stress and tissue trauma of any type have a prothrombotic effect. In the days after surgery the platelet count rises, occasionally to levels in excess of $1000 \times 10^9$ per liter. The concentration of fibrinogen reaches a peak at around 3 days, and remains high for over 7 days. There is also a fall in the fibrinolytic activity of plasma.

Local vessel damage may be relevant when it comes to venous thrombosis, particularly in pelvic operations, but is more often relevant in the field of vascular surgery where a blood vessel has been damaged in some way, for example, by a cannula passed into it, by angioplasty, or during surgical removal of a thrombus or embolus.

Pulmonary thromboembolism is the cause of death in about 1 in every 500 postoperative patients each year. The peak incidence of thromboembolism is around a fortnight after the surgical operation but a significant proportion occur on the same day and the risk is still increased many weeks or even months after the operation. On the balance of probability, in the absence of other major predisposing causes, these are still true complications of the procedure. There is always the possibility that the patient already had leg-vein thrombosis before the operation and it may be of medicolegal value to date the embolus or thrombus.

The value of searching for residual thrombi in leg veins, for example, is sometimes questioned. It is, however, important to locate residual thrombi. It does not prove that the fatal embolus came from this site but it is very likely that it did. Occasionally thrombus is found in an area directly damaged by surgery, such as in the pelvic veins after a gynecological operation. In the case of leg surgery it is useful to establish whether the leg-vein thrombosis is on the same side as the operation, strengthening the causal link.

**Systemic thromboembolism (stroke)** Thromboemboli originating in the systemic system may end up in any organ, causing intestinal, renal, splenic, or cerebral infarcts, as well as gangrene. Stroke is the most often clinically relevant end result of such embolism.

In the general surgical population strokes usually occur some days after the operation. Perioperative stroke is more likely to occur in patients who are elderly, hypertensive, who have evidence of atheromatous disease, and after certain types of surgery.

Most postoperative strokes are related to systemic thromboembolism; the heart is the commonest source of emboli and perioperative atrial fibrillation is a significant factor in a large proportion of cases. It is only a minority of postoperative strokes that are related to hypotension. A further small proportion occurs as a result of either local thrombosis or a hypertensive bleed. Paradoxical thromboembolism should always be considered if systemic and pulmonary thrombi are found at the same autopsy.

**Procedure-specific damage** Any invasive procedure has an associated list of specific recognized and potentially fatal complications. Prior to postmortem examination the pathologist should be aware of this list. During the examination each should be sought and the presence or absence of each noted in the report. Examples include: atheromatous emboli dislodged by angiography or cardiac surgery; fat embolism occurring as a complication of hip replacement; air embolism arising after open surgery to the neck and head; talc embolism following talc pleurodesis; acute pancreatitis and bile leakage as a result of endoscopic retrograde cholangiopancreatography (ERCP); damage to the ureters during hysterectomy; rupture of the esophagus during dilatation; pneumothorax as a result of bronchial biopsy or mechanical ventilation; colonic perforation during sigmoidoscopy; rejection after heart transplantation; and ileus and acute gastric dilatation after abdominal surgery.

## Conclusion

Postmortem examination of a perioperative death is often technically difficult and the postmortem findings are not infrequently minimal or alternatively complex. Such postmortems often turn up unexpected and clinically relevant findings that are of great value to relatives and medical staff when it comes to understanding why death occurred and useful for audit and medical education. The postmortem should address the presence of preexisting conditions both in relation to the reason for surgery and to assess nonoperative factors that may have caused or contributed to death. Findings must be accurately documented and photographed. It is essential that the pathologist has a basic understanding of the pathology of procedure-related complications, including the deleterious effects of anesthetics and the potential relevance of hemorrhage, infection, embolism, and cardiac death. For any particular procedure the pathologist should be aware of and check for specific complications. Any postoperative complications should be interpreted in the light of the clinical history and the preoperative state of the patient. In no other group of postmortem examinations is clinicopathological correlation more important.

## See Also

**Autopsy:** Medico-legal Considerations; **Complaints Against Doctors, Healthcare Workers and Institutions**; **Medical Malpractice:** Anesthesiology; Colorectal Surgery; Facio-maxillary Surgery; Neurosurgery; Oral Surgery; Plastic and Cosmetic Surgery; Vascular Surgery

## Further Reading

Campos JRM, Werebe EC, Vargas FS, Jatene FB, Light RW (1997) Respiratory failure due to insufflated talc. *Lancet* 349: 251–252.

Deziel DJ, Millikan KW, Economou SG, *et al.* (1993) Complications of laparoscopic cholecystectomy: a national survey of 4292 hospitals and an analysis of 77 604 cases. *American Journal of Surgery* 165: 9–14.

Dingle HR (1996) Antihypertensive drugs and anaesthesia. *Anaesthesia* 21: 151.

Doty JR, Willentz RE, Salazar JD, Hruban RH, Cameron DE (2003) Atheroemboli in cardiac surgery. *Annals of Thoracic Surgery* 75: 1221–1226.

Forrest ARW (1993) Toxicological and biochemical analysis. In: Cotton DWK, Cross SS (eds.) *The Hospital Autopsy*, pp. 134–143. Oxford, UK: Butterworth-Heinemann.

Gray AJG, Hoile RW, Ingram GS, Sherry KM (1998) *The Report of the National Confidential Enquiry into Perioperative Deaths 1996/1997*. London: HMSO.

Hofmann S, Hopf R, Mayr G, Schlag G, Salzer M (1999) In vivo femoral intramedullary pressure during uncemented hip arthroplasty. *Clinical Orthopaedics and Related Research* 360: 136–146.

James DS, Leadbeatter S (1997) The use of personal health information in the coroner's inquiry. *Journal of the Royal College of Physicians of London* 31: 509–511.

Kam PCA, Calcroft RM (1997) Peri-operative stroke in general surgical patients. *Anaesthesia* 52: 879–883.

Keogh BE, Dussek J, Watson D, Magee P, Wheatley D (1998) Public confidence and cardiac surgical outcome. *British Medical Journal* 316: 1759–1760.

Landesberg G, Luria MH, Cotev S, et al. (1993) Importance of long-duration postoperative ST-segment depression I cardiac morbidity after vascular surgery. *Lancet* 341: 715–719.

Larsen SF, Zaric D, Boysen G (1988) Post-operative cerebrovascular accidents in general surgery. *Acta Anaesthesiologica Scandinavica* 32: 698–701.

Lee AHS, Gallagher PJ (1998) Post-mortem examination after cardiac surgery. *Histopathology* 33: 399–405.

Lunn JN, Mushin WW (1982) *Mortality Associated with Anaesthesia*. Oxford, UK: Nuffield Provisional Hospital Trust.

Mangano DT (1990) Perioperative cardiac morbidity. *Anesthesiology* 72: 153–184.

Mort TC, Yeston NS (1999) The relationship of pre mortem diagnoses and post mortem findings in a surgical intensive care unit. *Critical Care Medicine* 27: 299–303.

Ooi A, Goodwin AT, Goddard M, Ritchie AJ (2003) Clinical outcome versus post-mortem finings in thoracic surgery: a 10 year experience. *European Journal of Cardiothoracic Surgery* 23: 878–881.

Pumphrey RSH, Roberts ISD (2000) Post-mortem findings after fatal anaphylactic reactions. *Journal of Clinical Pathology* 53: 273–276.

Roberts ISD, Gorodkin LM, Benbow EW (2000) What is a natural cause of death? A survey of how coroners in England and Wales approach borderline cases. *Journal of Clinical Pathology* 53: 367–373.

Roberts ISD, Gorodkin LM, Benbow EW (2000) When should a coroner's inquest be held? The Manchester guidelines for pathologists. *Journal of Clinical Pathology* 53: 340–343.

Simon SR, Powell LH, Bartzokis TC, Hoch DH (1995) A new system for classification of cardiac death as arrhythmic, ischaemic or due to myocardial pump failure. *American Journal of Cardiology* 76: 896–898.

Spencer RC (1993) The microbiology of the autopsy. In: Cotton DWK, Cross SS (eds.) *The Hospital Autopsy*, pp. 144–157. Oxford, UK: Butterworth-Heinemann.

Sprung J, Lesitsky MA, Jagetia A, et al. (1996) Cardiac arrest caused by coronary spasm in two patients during recovery from epidural anaesthesia. *Regional Anesthesia* 21: 353–360.

Start RD, Cross SS (1999) Pathological investigation of deaths following surgery, anaesthesia and medical procedures. *Journal of Clinical Pathology* 52: 640–652.

Start RD, Delargy-Aziz Y, Dorries CP, Silcocks PB, Cotton DWK (1993) Clinicians and the coronial system: ability of clinicians to recognise reportable deaths. *British Medical Journal* 306: 1038–1041.

Start RD, Usherwood TP, Carter N, Dorries CP, Cotton DWK (1995) General practitioners' knowledge of when to refer deaths to a coroner. *British Journal of General Practice* 45: 191–193.

Stöllberger C, Slany J, Schuster I, et al. (1993) The prevalence of deep venous thrombosis in patients with suspected paradoxical embolism. *Annals of Internal Medicine* 119: 461–465.

*The Royal College of Pathologists Guidelines for Post-Mortem Reports* (1993) London: The Royal College of Pathologists.

Verstraete M (1997) Prophylaxis of venous thromboembolism. *British Medical Journal* 314: 123–125.

Warden JC, Horan BF (1996) Deaths attributed to anaesthesia in New South Wales 1984–1990. *Anaesthesia and Intensive Care* 24: 66–73.

Yaffe MB, Fink MP (1997) Hospital-acquired pneumonia in the postoperative setting. *Seminars in Respiratory Critical Care Medicine* 18: 121–132.

# Sports

**L M Shapiro**, Papworth Hospital, Cambridge, UK

## Introduction

The first recorded death of an athlete occurred in 490 BC. Pheidippides was a renowned Athenian long-distance runner. In two days he ran 240 km without difficulty and then he returned from Marathon to Athens, running a distance of 35 km. He reportedly shouted, "Rejoice, we conquer!" He then died.

The highly conditioned competitive athlete epitomizes the healthiest component of society. Young athletes, in the prime of youth, with their unique lifestyle and exploits, seem to epitomize health and invulnerability. They are often thought to be capable of extraordinary physical achievements. Sudden cardiac death continues to occur, usually unheralded, and in the absence of prior warning, and often leads to considerable emotional and social impact on both medical and lay public. These findings are now more widely featured by the media but more than a century ago similar concerns were apparent and are beautifully described in a poem by A E Housman (1885):

> "To An Athlete Dying Young"
> "The time you won your town the race.
> We chaired you through the market-place;
> Man and boy stood cheering by,
> And home we brought you shoulder-high.
> Today, the road all runners come,
> Shoulder high, we bring you home,
> And set you at your threshold down,
> Townsman of a stiller town."

The subject of sudden death amongst athletes remains a topic of continuing interest amongst physicians. More than 80% of nontraumatic sudden unexpected deaths in athletes are caused by cardiovascular abnormalities. These are usually inherited, congenital, functional, and structural abnormalities. The precise incidence of sudden-death occurrences in young athletes is unknown. Sudden cardiac death, however, is thought to be uncommon. Estimates in the USA suggest that 1 in 200 000 competitors may be affected. Such data are limited and the true incidence may be substantially higher. A number of conditions, such as the ion channelopathies, which may predispose to fatal arrhythmias, are not associated with structural heart disease. In addition, autopsies in young athletes are often performed by pathologists who rarely see such cases and subtle examples may well be missed. There is no national registry for sudden cardiac death in athletes and this may lead to an underestimate of the incidence of the condition. Sudden death is investigated by a coroner whose priority is to exclude foul play rather than to reach a precise cardiac diagnosis.

## Definitions

For the purposes of this article an athlete is defined as an individual who participates in an organized team or individual sport in which competition is a regular component. In such individuals a high priority is placed on vigorous training, excellence, and achievement. Competitive participation can occur in all age groups but for the purpose of definition, "young" will be below the age of 35.

## Sudden Death in Young Athletes

While the incidence of sudden death in athletes is low, a number of clinically unsuspected cardiac diseases have been found in young athletes. Hypertrophic cardiomyopathy has been consistently noted to be the most common cause of sudden death in autopsy series. This often accounts for one-third of the total events. Hypertrophic cardiomyopathy is defined as a hypertrophied nondilated ventricle that is asymmetrically thickened. It is a relatively frequently found genetically based cardiac disease with an incidence of about 1 in 500 of the general population. There is a heterogeneous, clinical, morphological, and genetic expression. Histologically disorganized myocardial architecture may be demonstrated. Sudden death usually relates to electrical instability with reentry ventricular tachyarrhythmias.

Congenital anomalies of the coronary arteries are the second most frequent cause of sudden death in athletes. These abnormalities are unrelated to coronary artery atherosclerosis. As most anomalies are asymptomatic, a diagnosis in life is rarely made, except if a young athlete complains of exertional chest pain or syncope. The commonest abnormality is where the artery arises from the wrong aortic sinus. Most frequently this is the left main stem artery arising from the right sinus of Valsalva. The mechanism of ischemia is probably kinking of the origin of the artery or compression of the vessel between the aorta and the pulmonary artery during strenuous exertion.

Echocardiography or magnetic resonance imaging may allow a diagnosis to be made. Usually coronary arteriography will need to be performed to define the anomaly accurately. The anomaly of the right coronary artery arising from the left sinus of Valsalva may also be a risk factor for sudden death. In this situation there is an acute bend of the right coronary artery as it lies between the aorta and the pulmonary artery. There are a number of other variants of coronary anatomy that could be responsible for sudden death in athletes. These include single coronary artery with the whole coronary blood supply from the right coronary artery. Possibly, myocardial bridging may be responsible for sudden death. In such abnormalities usually the left anterior descending coronary artery is completely surrounded by myocardium in a tunnel for at least a portion of its course. It is possible that in such individuals the artery may become critically constricted during a systole and this may lead to myocardial ischemia.

Aortic rupture may occur as a cause of sudden death in athletes. The weakening of the aortic wall by a decreased number of elastic fibers in the aortic media is commonly called cystic medial necrosis. Some athletes may manifest features of Marfan's syndrome. This may be particularly the case in sports where height is a competitive advantage, such as basketball.

Valvular heart disease such as aortic valve stenosis and mitral prolapse, or degenerative mitral valve regurgitation, may be found. Myocarditis is difficult to diagnose but is possibly the cause of death.

A small proportion of athletes (approximately 2%) have a structurally normal heart at autopsy. These are thought to be due to ion channel disorders, including the long QT syndrome, Brugada syndrome, and Wolff–Parkinson–White syndrome. Structural abnormalities of the conducting system and a variety of other disorders have been implicated.

Local variation in disease prevalence may affect causes of death in athletes. In the Veneto region of Italy, arrhythmogenic right ventricular cardiomyopathy is common and is the most frequent cause of death on the athletic field. This is due to the particular genetic predisposition of the population in this area.

## Sudden Death in Older Athletes

Older individuals are now participating in active sport. This may involve rigorous physical training and competition. As seen in young athletes, more mature individuals may not be protected against sudden cardiac death despite a lifetime of training. However, a high degree of physical fitness is a positive factor in preventing degenerative heart disease. As in the young, the frequency of sudden cardiac death amongst well-conditioned individuals is low. The causes of sudden death for young athletes described above may also apply to the older age group. However, the predominant cause of sudden death in older age groups is degenerative, especially due to coronary heart disease. Such individuals usually have significant (>75%) narrowing by atherosclerotic plaque of one or more extramural coronary arteries.

Deaths in young athletes are usually unexpected and the majority do not experience cardiac symptoms before death. In contrast, older athletes with coronary heart disease more frequently have prodromal symptoms of chest pain, breathlessness, or syncope, or have a known history of coronary disease.

## Comparison of Sport and Nonsport-Related Causes of Sudden Cardiac Death

Up to 50% of all cardiovascular deaths are classified as sudden. Comparison of sport-related and nonsport-related sudden death in Maryland from 1991 to 1998 revealed 34 in the former group and 656 in the latter. In the former group hypertrophic cardiomyopathy and the other rarer congenital diseases described above were the predominant form. In the nonsport-related sudden deaths, coronary heart disease was much more frequent (**Table 1**).

## Sudden Death Unrelated to Cardiovascular Disease

Sudden death may occur in individuals undertaking sport who do not have heart disease. There are a number of causes of this. The commonest is *commotio cordis*. This is due to a blow to the chest producing ventricular fibrillation. This is not associated with structural injury to the ribs or sternum, or even the heart. The blow is blunt, nonpenetrating, and usually due to a projectile such as a baseball or hockey puck, but also a karate blow or collision. This is most commonly found in adolescents and children as their chest walls are more compliant and allow the transmission of energy from the blow to the myocardium. Deaths may not only occur in competition but also during informal sporting activities. Criminal intent has been initially considered in some cases.

**Table 1** Cardiovascular causes of sudden death in 387 young athletes

| Cause | No. of athletes | Percent |
|---|---|---|
| Hypertrophic cardiomyopathy | 102 | 26.4 |
| *Commotio cordis* | 77 | 19.9 |
| Coronary artery anomalies | 53 | 13.7 |
| Left ventricular hypertrophy of indeterminate causation | 29 | 7.5 |
| Myocarditis | 20 | 5.2 |
| Ruptured aortic aneurysm (Marfan's syndrome) | 12 | 3.1 |
| Arrhythmogenic right ventricular cardiomyopathy | 11 | 2.8 |
| Tunneled (bridged) coronary artery | 11 | 2.8 |
| Aortic valve stenosis | 10 | 2.6 |
| Atherosclerotic coronary artery disease | 10 | 2.6 |
| Dilated cardiomyopathy | 9 | 2.3 |
| Myxomatous mitral valve degeneration | 9 | 2.3 |
| Asthma (or other pulmonary condition) | 8 | 2.1 |
| Heat stroke | 6 | 1.6 |
| Drug abuse | 4 | 1.0 |
| Other cardiovascular cause | 4 | 1.0 |
| Long QT syndromes | 3 | 0.8 |
| Cardiac sarcoidosis | 3 | 0.8 |
| Trauma involving structural cardiac injury | 3 | 0.8 |
| Ruptured cerebral artery | 3 | 0.8 |

Adapted from Maron BJ (2003) Sudden death in young athletes. *New England Journal of Medicine* 349: 1064–1075.

Survival is poor following such events, except where cardiopulmonary resuscitation and defibrillation are available. An animal model in swine shows that the ventricular fibrillation may be provoked by blows directly over the heart. The blow has to occur 15–30 ms after the T-wave peak. This is the vulnerable phase of depolarization.

A number of other causes of sudden death, not of cardiac origin, have been described. This may include hyperthermia and heat stroke, head and spine injury, bronchial asthma, ruptured intracranial aneurysm, and subarachnoid hemorrhage. The role of prescription and recreational drugs is unknown.

## Athlete's Heart

The enlarged heart of the athlete was initially described, in the nineteenth century, by Henschen. He noted that all parts of the heart were enlarged and attributed this to the physiological adaptation of athletes undertaking long-distance skiing events. He identified this with clinical examination and simple investigation techniques.

In subsequent decades there were many conflicting views, particularly as to the nature of athletic adaptation of the heart. At times it was considered to be pathological and not a physiological process. This misunderstanding can be understood because of the interpretation of the tests that were available at the time. The physical signs include a sinus bradycardia, quiet systolic murmurs, and added heart sounds, particularly third and fourth. The chest radiograph may show cardiac enlargement and the electrocardiogram may be quite abnormal. This may show evidence of left ventricular hypertrophy and also repolarization changes. The heart of the athlete has adapted to prolonged training. This is observed as an increase in ventricular volume and heart weight. The resting heart rate declines.

The development of echocardiography in the 1970s allowed an understanding of the physiological consequences of prolonged exercise training. All forms of exercise lead to an increase in cardiac output. Endurance sports such as swimming, running, and cycling demand prolonged elevation of cardiac output. This is maintained by increases in stroke volume. Growth occurs in the normal heart muscle to match the workload imposed upon it. To retain the normal relationship between systolic cavity pressure and wall thickness to ventricular cavity radius there needs to be hypertrophy. However, if the stimulus to hypertrophy is predominantly isometric, as in power sports, an increase in cardiac mass may be the predominant feature in some

athletes. The physiological increase in cardiac mass will vary according to the sport engaged in. The most marked changes in cavity size and wall thickness have been noted in rowing, cross-country skiing, cycling, and swimming. Ultra endurance sports tend to have rather less adaptation, possibly because the requirement of cardiac output has a lower magnitude but a more prolonged duration. Angiotensin-converting enzyme genotypes have been associated with a degree of left ventricular hypertrophy during training. This suggests that genetic factors may have an important role in this process.

The electrocardiogram may be quite abnormal in highly trained athletes. These abnormalities, that occur in more than a third of athletes, may resemble those seen in cardiac disease. Abnormalities such as increased QRS voltages, Q waves, and repolarization are common. Abnormal rhythm, such as atrial and ventricular premature beats, bradyarrhythmias, junctional rhythms, and heart block (first-degree, Wenckebach and Mobitz type II) are not uncommon.

The training adaptations that occur within the heart usually lead to an increase in left ventricular cavity size and wall thickness of 10–20%. In most athletes hypertrophy is not severe and usually does not lead to measurements that are outside the normal limits. However, the left ventricular hypertrophy can be quite pronounced and, in a study of 900 elite athletes, 2% had wall thickness greater than 13 mm. Although uncommon, this minority with increased wall thickness makes it difficult to differentiate athletic adaptation from hypertrophic cardiomyopathy. This is important, as hypertrophic cardiomyopathy is a disqualification from competition. In the majority with lesser hypertrophy, the differentiation is not difficult as in general hypertrophic cardiomyopathy has localized hypertrophy with small cavity dimensions, in contrast to athletes who tend to have generalized hypertrophy with slightly increased cavity dimensions. Hypertrophic cardiomyopathy has abnormal diastolic function and in athletes it is normal. Athletes tend to have metabolic exercise indices such as peak $Vo_2$ that are above normal, in comparison to patients with hypertrophic cardiomyopathy who have reduced values. Genetic examination may aid diagnosis.

## Athletes with a Known Diagnosis of Cardiac Disease

Athletes with an identified cardiovascular abnormality were discussed at the 26th Bethesda Conference in 1994. This recommended that athletes with unequivocal hypertrophic cardiomyopathy should not participate in competitive sport with anything other than the lowest degree of intensity. Older athletes without established risk factors for sudden death (nonsustained ventricular tachycardia, family history of premature sudden death, syncope or abnormal blood pressure responses to exercise, severe left ventricular hypertrophy, and outflow tract gradient) could be allowed to continue. Athletes with possible cardiac disease should be examined for potential risk of sudden death as well as those thought to be at high risk.

## Screening

The identification of asymptomatic individuals with congenital and genetic cardiac disorders could be considered in an attempt to prevent sudden death. There are major difficulties with preparticipation screening. The number of athletes involved is very large and sudden death is rare. History-taking and physical examination are insufficient to detect significant cardiac abnormalities with any reliability. For the last 30 years the Italian government has mandated national preparticipation screening. They require medical clearance of all young athletes who wish to participate in sporting activities. Their program has excluded a number of individuals with significant heart disease. The English Football Association has performed preparticipation screening in all 15–16-year-old football players. Some 4000 youths have been screened by physical examination, 12-lead electrocardiography, and two-dimensional echocardiography. So far only one individual has been diagnosed with hypertrophic cardiomyopathy and there have been a small number of nonlethal abnormalities, none of which required cessation of sporting activities. These studies show that it is difficult and expensive to screen a large number of athletes and there is a very low yield of significant abnormalities.

## See Also

**Sudden Natural Death:** Cardiovascular

## Further Reading

Brugada P (1992) Right bundle branch block, persistent ST segment elevation and sudden cardiac death: a distinct clinical and electrocardiographic syndrome. A multicenter report. *Journal of the American College of Cardiology* 20: 1391–1396.

Burke AP, Farb A, Virmani R, Goodin J, Smialek JE (1991) Sports related and non-sports-related sudden cardiac death in young adults. *American Heart Journal* 121: 568–575.

Firoozi S, Sharma S, McKenna WJ (2003) Risk of competitive sport in young athletes with heart disease. *British Heart Journal* 89: 710–714.

Huston TP, Puffer JC, Rodney WM (1985) The athletic heart syndrome. *New England Journal of Medicine* 313: 24–32.

Kenny A, Shapiro LM (1992) Sudden cardiac death in athletes. *British Medical Bulletin* 48(3): 534–545.

Maron BJ, Epstein SE, Roberts WC (1986) Causes of sudden death in competitive athletes. *Journal of the American College of Cardiology* 7: 204–214.

Maron BJ, Isner JM, McKenna WJ (1994) 26th Bethesda Conference: recommendations for determining eligibility for competition in athletes with cardiovascular abnormalities. Task Force 3: hypertrophic cardiomyopathy, myocarditis and other myopericardial diseases and mitral valve prolapse. *Journal of the American College of Cardiology* 24: 880–885.

Maron BJ, Shirani J, Poliac LC, et al. (1996) Sudden death in young competitive athletes. Clinical, demographic and pathological profiles. *Journal of the American Medical Association* 276: 199–204.

Opie LH (1975) Sudden death and sport. *Lancet* i: 263–266.

Pelliccina A, Maron BJ, Spataro A, et al. (1991) The upper limit of physiological cardiac hypertrophy in highly trained elite athletes. *New England Journal of Medicine* 324: 295–301.

# DEATH INVESTIGATION SYSTEMS

## Contents
**China**
**Japan**
**Nordic Countries**
**Certification of Death and the United Kingdom System**
**United States of America**

## China

**P S L Beh**, University of Hong Kong, Hong Kong, China
**B Luo**, Sun Yat Sen Medical School, Gungzhou, China

### Introduction

The ancient Chinese forensic manual, translated as *Washing Away of Wrongs*, written by Song Ci in 1247 AD, is widely accepted as the first systematic manual on medicolegal death investigation. The topics covered are varied and some of the recommendations made, although crude, will still work today, although others are quite incomprehensible. It is important to point out that a thorough reading of the manual will reveal that the body examination referred to was merely an external examination. Postmortem dissection was not described and thus was not practiced. However, the manual did detail how deaths should be investigated at the scene and noted the signs an examiner should be looking for.

To appreciate fully the death investigation processes in modern-day China, the reader should understand that the legal framework is still undergoing rapid changes, and it would be prudent for practitioners to keep abreast of developments which could be at local, county, state, or national levels. To give a broad picture, the modern Chinese death investigation process is similar to the continental system, where the examining magistrate makes the decision as to how far to pursue an investigation.

### Death-Reporting Procedures

When a person dies, the death needs to be reported to the authorities. In urban cities, this would generally mean an office of the Public Security Bureau (PSB). In rural areas, the relevant authorities may well be the village elder or a party cadre charged with maintaining the population roll-call for the community. Where death is believed to be due to natural causes, no further investigation is required and a death certificate can be issued. In urban areas, the death certificate would most likely be issued by a doctor, where available. In the absence of a doctor, a local official would issue the death certificate.

Where the circumstances of death are unnatural, the scene of death will be examined by PSB officials who may or may not be medically qualified. It is not uncommon for the scene to be attended by a large contingent of officers from the PSB, each performing a different task, such as fingerprinting.

The forensic doctor will often be a PSB officer required to attend the scene of death. The forensic doctor will often be involved in a scene of death assessment as well as performing a detailed external examination of the deceased person(s). In a large number of instances a conclusion is made, a cause of death is given, the case is closed, and a death certificate is subsequently issued.

An autopsy examination can be required under the following circumstances:

1. a cause of death is uncertain but it is believed that the death is suspicious
2. a cause of death is certain, but the family disagrees with the conclusion and requests the procurator to order an autopsy
3. death in hospital where there is a dispute as to the cause of death between the doctor and the next of kin.

A diagrammatic representation is shown in **Figure 1**.

### Autopsy Examination

Autopsy examination will be performed in mortuaries belonging to the PSB or in hospitals with autopsy facilities. Autopsies are performed by medically qualified doctors who are employed by the PSB, judiciary, or university (where there is a forensic medicine department/staff). It is a fact that autopsy examination is still widely viewed as taboo in China and unacceptable by the next of kin.

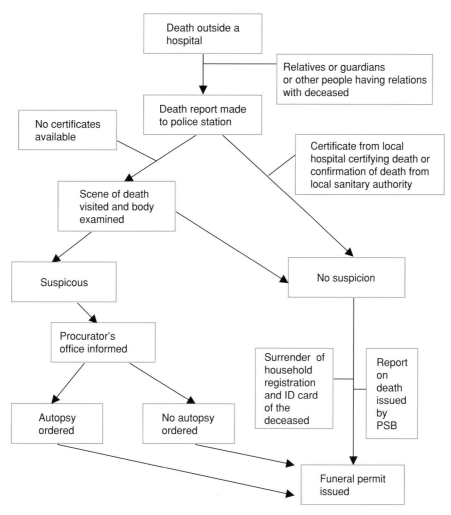

**Figure 1**   Schematic of death investigation.

## Organization of Forensic Medical Staff

Most forensic doctors are employed by the PSB. They are tasked with the bulk of the front-line contact forensic work, which covers a wide spectrum of forensic pathology, clinical forensic medicine, and many aspects of forensic science as well. The scope of coverage of each individual outfit depends on the size of the population it serves and also on whether it is an urban or rural unit. Large centers in major cities such as Beijing, Shanghai, and Guangzhou have departments with well-equipped mortuaries and laboratories.

The judiciary/procurator's office also employs forensic medical personnel who are required to review the reports submitted by the PSB doctors. They can, and often do, ask for clarification or further investigation and are charged with deciding whether there is sufficient evidence to recommend or support further legal proceedings.

## The Academic Forensic Departments

There are currently 13 recognized centers of forensic teaching in China. These are listed in **Table 1**. These institutions are tasked with training all forensic scientific and medical personnel. They offer the equivalent of undergraduate levels, such as a bachelors degree in forensic science and forensic medicine, and also masters and doctorate levels. The different institutions can be roughly divided into those that had their origins in the late 1950s and early 1960s and the newer ones, established in the mid-1980s. They have generally been strategically situated across China to cater to the needs of the surrounding regions. Despite an obvious shortage of trained forensic staff and a clear demand for these academic departments, they, too, are handicapped in their ability to compete for funding, particularly for setting up modern facilities. Most modern facilities are now found in the large cities and are under the umbrella of the PSB.

**Table 1**   Death investigation in People's Republic of China: the 13 recognized centers of forensic teaching

| Name | Location | Period established |
|---|---|---|
| Faculty of Forensic Medicine, Sun Yat Sen Medical College, Sun Yat Sen University | Guangzhou | 1953 |
| School of Basic and Forensic Medicine, Sichuan University | Chengdu | 1953 |
| School of Forensic Medicine, China Medical University | Shenyang | 1952 |
| Faculty of Forensic Medicine, Tongji Medical College, Huazhong University of Science and Technology | Wuhan | 1957 |
| Faculty of Forensic Medicine, Medical Center of Fudan University | Shanghai | 1953 |
| Faculty of Forensic Medicine, Xi'an Medical College, Xi'an University | Xi'an | 1953 |
| Department of Forensic Medicine, Shanxi Medical University | Taiyuan | 1980 |
| Department of Forensic Medicine, China Criminal Police Medical College | Shenyang | 1960 |
| Department of Forensic Medicine, Wan Nan Medical College | Wuhu | 1984 |
| Faculty of Forensic Medicine, Luoyang Medical College, Henan University of Science and Technology | Luoyang | 1984 |
| Faculty of Forensic Medicine, Kunming Medical College | Kunming | 1984 |
| Faculty of Forensic Medicine, Hebei Medical University | Shijazhuang | 1984 |
| Department of Forensic Medicine, South-West China University | Chongjing | 1957 |

Despite this, academic staff are still highly regarded by the profession and play important roles in the Chinese Academy of Forensic Sciences and in the dissemination of academic literature in the field. Academic staff here are often called in as independent experts to resolve disagreements or conflicts between the reports from the PSB and the judiciary. In some areas, these academic staff are also involved in a small number of front-line forensic work.

Academic staff are of course responsible for training the forensic doctors of the future. The medical degree in China is a five-year course with a one-year internship. Since 2001, all medical undergraduates are required to sit for a common national licensing exam. The forensic doctors' medical degree is also a five-year course. However, one and a half years of this course are focused on forensic subjects and topics. There is also a required attachment period with PSB units.

There is still an extreme shortage of forensically trained doctors to meet the requirements of the current system of practice. It is estimated that at least 12 000 full-time forensic doctors are required for China just to meet the current level of service provision and coverage.

## Postgraduate Training in Forensic Medicine/Pathology

There is currently no organized and structured postgraduate training in forensic pathology or any other branch of forensics in the sense that is familiar to those working in the British Commonwealth situation. Experience is gained on the job and professional recognition is gained from seniority and publication. Membership of the Chinese Academy of Forensic Sciences is also an accepted professional recognition. There are also many state-level professional societies. Formal postgraduate training is available but is organized in a similar way to research-based disciplines, i.e., in the form of research degrees such as MPhil and PhD, and such qualifications may have little relevance to practical forensic work.

## Hong Kong and Macau

Hong Kong and Macau are now Special Administrative Regions of China. A brief description of the death investigation processes in these two regions is described.

Hong Kong continues to work under the common-law system, and deaths are investigated under the provisions of the coroners' ordinance. Unlike UK coroners, Hong Kong coroners are full-time appointed magistrates who are legally qualified. In fact only legally qualified individuals can be coroners. Doctors in Hong Kong are required to report deaths to the coroner under 20 circumstances of death (**Table 2**). The family of the deceased will be interviewed by pathologists and/or forensic pathologists before the autopsy examination. Police are responsible for the investigation of the deaths, as directed by the coroners' office. Inquests with a jury are mandatory in deaths under official custody and are public. They are often held where it is deemed that there is public interest. Such inquests may or may not be in front of a jury.

The training of forensic pathologists requires six years post medical school and is overseen by the Hong Kong Academy of Medicine through its constituent Hong Kong College of Pathologists.

Death investigations in Macau follow the continental system and are similar to that as practiced in Portugal. Investigations are directed and decided upon by the prosecuting magistrate. This system too is currently retained in Macau. There are no medical

**Table 2** List of reportable deaths under the coroners' ordinance, laws of Hong Kong Special Administrative Region, China

1. Any death where a registered doctor is unable to state accurately the medical cause of death
2. Any death of a person who has not been seen by a doctor during his/her last illness within 14 days of the death (excluding terminal illness)
3. Any death where an accident or injury caused death
4. Any death where a crime or suspected crime caused the death
5. Any death of a person where:
   a. an anesthetic caused the death
   b. the person was under the influence of general anesthesia at the time of death or
   c. death occurred within 24 h of the administration of general anesthesia
6. Any death of a person where:
   a. an operation caused the death
   b. the death occurred within 48 h of a major operation
7. Any death of a person where:
   a. an occupational disease caused the death
   b. death may be connected directly or indirectly with such occupation
8. Any stillbirth where:
   a. there is doubt whether the fetus was born alive or dead
   b. there is suspicion that the stillbirth might not have been a stillbirth
9. Any death of a woman where death occurred within 30 days of:
   a. birth of a child
   b. abortion
   c. miscarriage
10. Any death of a deceased where:
    a. septicemia is the cause of death and
    b. the primary cause of the septicemia is not known
11. Any death of a person where there is a suspicion that death was caused by suicide
12. Any death whilst in official custody
13. Any death of a person where death occurred during the course of the discharge of his/her duty by a person having powers of arrest or detention
14. Any death in the premises of a government department
15. Any death of a person where:
    a. a patient dies within a mental hospital under the Mental Health Ordinance
    b. a patient is subject to a detention order under the Mental Health Ordinance
16. Any death of a person in a premise where care of the person is carried out for reward or other financial consideration
17. Any death caused by homicide
18. Any death caused by administration of drug or poison
19. Any death due to ill treatment, starvation, or neglect
20. Any death of a person outside Hong Kong but where the body is brought into Hong Kong

schools in Macau and very little postgraduate training activities.

## Conclusion

In summary, the situation of forensic medical training in China is a "growth area" but is still different from that in the West. The characteristics of death investigation in China are also quite varied and only time will tell how the system will evolve.

## See Also

**Court Systems:** Law, China; Law, United Kingdom; Law, United States of America

## Further Reading

Peng Z, Pounder DJ (1998) Forensic medicine in China. *American Journal of Forensic Medicine Pathology* 19(4): 368–371.

# Japan

**K-I Yoshida**, University of Tokyo, Tokyo, Japan

## Report of Unusual Deaths and the Postmortem Inspection System

In Japan, a doctor must report a death to the local police station within 24 h when he/she inspects a cadaver and finds it "unusual," according to the Doctor's Law (Article 21). The Japanese Society of Legal Medicine (JSLM) has defined "unusual death" as "all deaths except those for whom clinicians have found the solid diagnostic evidence for natural death at the death scene." In 1994 the JSLM published detailed guidelines of reportable unusual death, including: (1) deaths from external causes; (2) deaths from the complications or sequelae of injuries; (3) deaths suspected to be extrinsic or from injury complications; (4) unexpected or suspected deaths associated with medical practice; and (5) death of unknown cause.

In the local police station receiving the report, the Traffic Department investigates traffic deaths, while the Robust Crime Investigation Department inspects the cause and manner (whether homicide, suicide, accident, natural, or unknown) of other deaths. The police classify the reported cases into: (1) noncriminal deaths; (2) criminal deaths; and (3) "unnatural deaths" that cannot be determined as either noncriminal or criminal by external examination. However, many concerned parties do not realize the difficulty of assessing criminality by external examination: there are many cadavers without surface injury or evidence of crime but with serious internal injuries, concealed intoxication, or other forms of crime involvement. Notably, the autopsy results that reveal the cause of death point to the crime or responsibility of a suspect, but before autopsy the inspector's professional attitude and awareness of the possibility of crime do not always reveal that a crime was committed. Sufficient experience in death investigation and autopsy attendance in addition to forensic training and education are required for such crime disclosure and a judgment of the need for autopsy – apparently most Japanese investigators are not sufficiently experienced in these matters.

Note the difference between "unusual deaths," in which natural deaths are excluded from a medical (medicolegal) viewpoint, and "unnatural deaths," in which potentially criminal deaths are examined from a crime investigation viewpoint.

The postmortem inspection of unnatural deaths looking for criminality must be performed by the district prosecutor, according to the Criminal Procedure Act, but qualified police officers (or prosecuting officers, nominally) substitute for the prosecutors in most investigations. Obvious crime victims immediately undergo crime investigation. The preliminary reports of postmortem inspections are sent to the police headquarters where superintendent inspectors judge the necessity of on-the-scene investigation and criminal autopsy. There are 2–3 such senior inspectors in averagely populated prefectures with 1–2 million inhabitants, and several inspectors in Tokyo and large prefectures. The superintendent inspectors, who are very experienced in crime investigation, have only had a 2-month course of lectures and practice at the scene-of-death investigation and in autopsy rooms and thus may be inexperienced. Although they devote themselves to death investigation day and night, they usually leave the position after 2–3 years before they gain enough experience for proper judgment. Additionally, they can only investigate at the scene 10–15% of selected cases among all unusual deaths.

In Japan, police detectives who are not death investigation specialists perform death inspection for unusual deaths. The police require forensic pathologists to carry out crime autopsies. In contrast, in Tokyo metropolitan districts, it is the prosecutors who demand crime autopsies according to the Crime Procedure Act. Many inexperienced lay prosecutors are in charge of a death investigation. By contrast, by law in Scotland and in common practice in Munich, Germany, specialist prosecutors are in charge of autopsies or other death investigation processes as their only or principal practice, and often attend the autopsy.

It is a major drawback of the Japanese death investigation system that there is no experienced and responsible death investigation specialist, comparable to the US medical examiner or coroner in England and Wales, who takes charge of the entire process of death investigation.

Generally, death inspection doctors submit their inquest report to the bereaved. The format of the inquest report is the same as the death certificate. The death inspection doctors are usually general practitioners or salaried doctors serving voluntarily as police surgeons, while emergency hospital doctors who reported the death to the police often inspect at the request of police. Death inspection doctors have usually not experienced forensic practice and their primary duty is the medical care of individuals in police custody. Recently, the JSLM has begun submitting accreditations for death inspection doctors. However, the requirements for education and training are not enough because of the lack of human and financial resources. The Ministry of Health, Welfare and Labor is now preparing to provide a short intensive training course for police surgeons and death inspection doctors, in collaboration with the JSLM. It should also be borne in mind that there is neither a systematic review system on the death certificate or inquest report nor a correction system after finding the true cause of death on autopsy or other examinations. Thus, in Japan, an unusual cause and manner of death are not subjected to specialist review.

## Criminal Autopsy System in Japan

During the Meiji era of Japanese modernization, a German doctor, Wilhelm Doenitz, first gave a lecture in forensic medicine at the current University of Tokyo in 1875. In 1888, Kuniyoshi Katayama founded the first Department of Forensic Medicine at the same university and started criminal autopsies in Japan. The Japanese government of the time decided to introduce the German legal system of death investigation as well as medicine in general. Somehow that legal death investigation system has been modified into the present system, although the autopsy rate is much lower in Japan. After World War II, the ME system was also introduced under the guidance of the USA.

With the exception of administrative autopsies performed in a few densely populated ME areas and many other sparsely populated districts, most forensic autopsies are crime (legal) autopsies for the purpose of crime investigation of suspected persons, even in medical accident cases where the doctor's criminality is often not evident. As such, there are difficulties in investigating medical accidents and deaths in jail or police custody.

In Japan, the autopsy rate is very low: about 1.3% for forensic (legal and administrative) autopsies, and about 3.0% for pathological autopsies (in the year 2000), though about one in four unusual deaths are subjected to administrative autopsy following the ME's judgment in Tokyo metropolitan districts and Osaka city. Although the autopsy rate is not as high in the USA (e.g., 8–9% in Los Angeles and Florida), the MEs themselves investigate and determine whether to perform autopsy and the requirements for each autopsy. In Japan, forensic pathologists perform criminal autopsies at the request of the police or prosecutor with the court's permission. Crime autopsies are performed at Departments of Legal (Forensic) Medicine in the medical schools. There are more than 80 medical schools in Japan, with at least one school in a prefecture. Annual autopsy numbers vary greatly for each institution, from 20 to 200 per year, and many institutions perform many criminal and few administrative autopsies. In Japan, the Departments of Forensic Medicine suffer from human and financial resource deficit. In many national medical schools, that will be independent administrative corporations in 2004, there are 3–4 specialists (usually 1–2 medical doctors) and a parttimer with poor financial support from the government. It is also of concern that there are few young successors.

In Japan, no particular legal qualification is required to carry out a criminal autopsy. However, since 1999 the JSLM has submitted accreditations for qualified forensic pathologists. These requirements are 200 autopsies or death investigations, including more than 60 legal autopsies, affiliation to the forensic institution for more than 4 years and to the JSLM for more than 5 years, and more than five published original articles. Applicants also have to pass a written examination. This qualification will be required for promotion. In contrast, the requirement for an ME in the Tokyo Metropolitan Department of Medical Examiner is more than 100 death investigations at the scene and more than 50 administrative autopsies under the guidance and approval of experienced MEs and finally, with the governor's permission.

In the USA, forensic pathologists are required to fulfill 3 years' residency as general pathologists and a 1-year course as a forensic pathology specialist. A short forensic practice course is required for general pathologists. Although expert opinions must be submitted in Tokyo and other districts, there are many areas where expert opinions are not routinely submitted. In such districts, the police's attendant reports for autopsy are used for prosecution or litigation. Forensic pathologists are only occasionally summoned in the court as witnesses. There is no formal peer-review system for medicolegal expert opinion. However, prosecutors try to find a cooperative forensic pathologist if the original expert opinion does not meet the burden of proof on the part of the police or prosecutor.

## Medical Examiner System and Administrative Autopsy

In Japan, the ME system was introduced by the USA in 1946, after World War II, to elucidate the cause of unusual death in eight large cities under the Corpse Dissection and Preservation Law. Today in Tokyo metropolitan district, Osaka city, and Kobe city (and suburban area) districts, the ME organizations are substantially supported by provincial government, despite a financial deficit. All unusual deaths are investigated by MEs, except for traffic deaths in Oaska. MEs occasionally uncover murder or accident cases in which the police had overlooked criminality; this reinforces the need for the ME system and the involvement of forensic pathologists in screening unusual deaths.

In the 23 special Tokyo metropolitan districts (8 219 622 inhabitants), 2386 administrative autopsies (23.8% of unusual deaths) were performed at Tokyo Metropolitan Department of Medical Examiner, whereas 213 criminal autopsies were performed at five medical schools in 2001. The rate of unusual deaths to total deaths is about 16.7% (about 12% all over Japan), with a gradual increase due to an increase in homicide, suicide, and death of the elderly living alone. There are 10 fulltime MEs and 42 parttimers (predominantly forensic pathologists from medical schools). In Los Angeles county, USA (9 653 900 inhabitants), the rate of unusual deaths was almost twice that in Tokyo (30.6%), and MEs undertook 5094 forensic autopsies (27.3% of unusual deaths, July 2000–June 2001). The forensic (administrative and criminal) autopsy rate in Tokyo (4.3%) is much higher than the overall rate in Japan (1.3%), although it is still lower than the rate in Los Angeles and England and Wales, 8.5% and 24%, respectively. The death rates for accident, suicide, and homicide were 10.9%, 18.5%, and 1.4%, respectively, in Tokyo metropolitan district, while those in Los Angeles were 28.9%, 8.0%, and 10.9%, respectively. The homicide rate was much lower in Tokyo than in Los Angeles. However, homicide has increased due to the increase in shtarkers and illegal immigrants in Tokyo and other large cities. In Japan, the suicide rate of middle-aged workers has greatly increased (>30 000 annually), reflecting the economic depression.

In the disaster after the earthquake around Kobe districts in 1995, Kobe's MEs and voluntary forensic pathologists from other districts performed more than 6000 death inspections with police in conditions of fire, destruction, poor transport conditions, and malnutrition, while some attendant forensic pathologists lost their homes.

A few prefectures collaborate with local doctors' associations to support the administrative autopsy. In many other prefectures, 10–20 administrative autopsies annually are financially supported by prefectures, while the police support communication with the bereaved, transportation, and documentation. These administrative autopsies base their legal grounds on the Corpse Dissection and Preservation Law, and so require the consent of the bereaved, as do pathological autopsies. Although many more administrative autopsies should be performed, the financial deficit does not allow it. Further attempts are required to advocate the importance of administrative autopsy to the public.

## Medical Accidents and their Death Investigation

In Japan, controversy has arisen about the reporting of medical accidents since litigation in 1999 for an accident as a result of injection of an antiseptic instead of heparin. The hospital principal did not report the accident to the police according to the Doctor's Law, and he advised the attendant doctor to describe the cause of death as natural on the certificate.

In 2001, there were 18 criminal autopsies for medical accidents with a few doctor's voluntary reports in Tokyo metropolitan districts, and similar numbers supposedly underwent administrative autopsy. In Los Angeles, which has a similar population background, about 450 medical accident cases are reported annually to MEs and 33 were autopsied (July 2001–June 2002). Although the number of criminal autopsies on medical accidents has increased in our department, there are still many unreported medical accidents that require report and forensic investigation according to US standards. **Table 1** gives a comparison of medical accident investigations in the USA and Japan.

The guideline on reportable unusual death from the JSLM states that sudden unexpected deaths and deaths of unknown cause during or shortly after any medical practice, irrespective of error, should be reported to the police. This is because the judgment by the concerned party is misjudged as a concealment of doctor's error. In Japan, all reported medical accidents are examined by criminal autopsy to investigate for involuntary manslaughter due to malpractice by the medical practitioner, although there are many cases where autopsy is unnecessary or ineffective, but investigation by clinical specialists is required. According to the Japanese Criminal Procedure Act, the purpose of the report is to initiate the crime investigation. However, the purpose should be the fair determination of the cause of death, as in the USA and UK, particularly for medical accident cases.

The importance of the fair elucidation of the cause of medical accident and death by forensic autopsy following the report is not well appreciated by many doctors, the bereaved, and other concerned parties in Japan. As a result, autopsies are rarely performed in such cases.

In Japan, many doctors appear to hesitate to report because they fear unjustified criticism as a result of the police investigation, despite not knowing that the report ensures the credit on the doctor's side. There are many misconceptions on the part of the bereaved, despite the doctor's honest and sincere explanations. Thus, although a report is mandatory for the fair determination and legal or administrative management of medical accidents, many doctors and citizens do not properly understand the significance of the report and autopsy in Japan. This is largely because of the death investigation system in Japan.

Appropriate disclosure of the cause of unexpected death, which can be ensured by forensic autopsy and medicolegal investigation by a specialist such as an ME, is another important aspect of disclosure of

**Table 1**   Comparison of US and Japanese systems for dealing with medical accidents

|  | Japan | Los Angeles, CA, USA |
| --- | --- | --- |
| Unusual death | 12% (of total death) | 30.6% |
| Forensic autopsy | 1.3% | 8.5% |
| Reported by doctors | Rare | Many (450 annually) |
| To whom | Police | Medical examiner (ME) |
| Purpose | Crime investigation | Death-cause investigation |
| Audit | Police | ME, ME investigation |
| Who demands the autopsy | Police, prosecutor | ME |
| Institution | Medical school | Department of ME (administrative) |
| Check for certificate | No | ME, registrar |
| Autopsy results | Not disclosed | Disclosed |
| Accident prevention | Not available | Available |

medical information, which the bereaved and public strongly demand from doctors. In fact, our preliminary investigation of citizens demonstrated that, unlike doctors, they could not discriminate between malpractice and an inevitable mishap in a model study. Additionally, it has been shown that low-tech autopsies disclose misdiagnoses in nearly half of clinical diagnoses. Moreover, autopsies were shown to be of benefit for doctors, even in malpractice cases diagnosed by autopsy, in an analysis of 99 appeal court cases in the USA. As stated, our experience clearly shows that autopsy can prevent dispute and litigation. Taken together, medicolegal death investigations following the report of a medical accident as an unnatural death are beneficial for all parties concerned, given that all accidents are properly investigated. However, this situation is far from the case in Japan.

Although autopsy and independent investigation are required for the fair determination of the causes of death and medical accident, there are many drawbacks in the criminal autopsy system in Japan. Many doctors feel that the police attitude to investigating crime impairs the social credibility and pride of doctors, though few doctors understand the necessity for the investigation. Pathologists often autopsy medical accident cases, but pathological autopsies are frequently not taken as fair processes because of the poor preservation of evidence and lack of neutrality of the autopsy operator. However, many clinical associations have encouraged pathological autopsy for medical accidents.

We can point out many difficulties in the criminal autopsy procedure for medical accidents in Japan. It is not doctors (forensic pathologists) but police detectives who audit the medical practitioners concerned in the accident. To maintain the confidentiality of the investigation, an autopsy operator cannot explain the results of the autopsy and examinations to the bereaved, and the feedback of information to the hospital is also prohibited. However, many bereaved family members have asked for the autopsy information. Additionally, forensic pathologists cannot always provide evidence in medical accident cases as expert opinion because of their inadequate clinical experience and cooperation with clinicians who tend to be reluctant to peer-review colleagues. Thus, the result of a criminal autopsy can only be used for prosecution or litigation, although the purpose of the death investigation is to reveal the truth, judge responsibility for the concerned parties, and improve medical practices. Additionally, there is no administrative alternative dispute resolution system for malpractice claims.

In conclusion, although medical accidents are a part of unusual deaths, it is urgent for reform of the Japanese death investigation system for medical accidents aiming at disclosure of the cause of death. This innovation will increase the voluntary reporting of medical accidents and improve the correctness of the diagnosis, quality, transparency, and credibility of medical practice.

Recently, there have been movements toward reformation of the death investigation of medical accident cases in Japan. On April 2, 2004, the Japanese Society of Medicine, Surgery, Pathology, and Legal Medicine together announced on a new death investigation organization for potentially therapeutic deaths, which ceased the dispute and launched for the set up of the organization. On April 13, 2004, the Supreme Court judged that the attendant doctor must report such therapeutic deaths as the wrong injection as mentioned above. On September 30, 2004, 19 major medical academic societies including the aforementioned four societies extended the April announcement to accelerate setting up of the organization. Shortly afterwards, the Ministry of Health, Labor, and Welfare opened a budget for a pilot study in which about 200 "medical administrative autopsies" and medical appraisals will be performed by clinicians, pathologists, and forensic pathologists, as a team in 2005. This project will open a window to the reformation of Japanese death investigation system.

## See Also

**Court Systems:** Law, Japan

## Further Reading

Berigan TR, Deagle EA III (1998) Low-tech autopsies in the era of high-tech medicine. Continued value for quality assurance and patient safety. *Journal of the American Medical Association* 280: 1273–1274.

Bove KE, *et al.* (2002) The role of autopsy in medical malpractice cases, 1. A review of 99 appellate court decisions. *Archives of Pathology and Laboratory Medicine* 126: 1023–1031.

Guideline of reportable unusual death of Japanese Society of Legal (1994) *Medical Japanese Journal of Legal Medicine* (in Japanese) 48: 357–358. Available on the home page of JSLM (http://web.sapmed.ac.jp/JSLM/about.en.html).

Yoshida K (2001) *Case-Oriented Textbook of Legal Medicine* (in Japanese), pp. 34–35. Tokyo: Yuhikaku.

Yoshida K, Takeichi H, Kawai K (2002) Is medical accident unnatural death? (in Japanese). *Japan Medical Journal* 4069: 57–62.

Yoshida K, Kuroki H, Takeichi H, Kawai K (2002) Death during surgery in Japan. *Lancet* 360: 805.

Yoshida K, Takeichi H, Kawai K, *et al.* (2002) Proposal of new investigation system for medical accident on the basis of the UK and USA systems (in Japanese). *Japan Medical Journal* 4086: 57–61.

Yoshida K, Segami K, Takeichi H, Kawai K (2003) A report on Los Angeles County Department of Medical Examiner (in Japanese). *Japan Medical Journal* 4150: 59–64.

Yoshida K, Kuroki H, Takeichi H, Kawai K, Kikuchi Y (2003) Investigation of death in prison in Japan. *Lancet* 362: 921–922.

# Nordic Countries

**M Thid and A Eriksson**, Umeå University, Umeå, Sweden
**T O Rognum**, University of Oslo, Oslo, Norway

## The Nordic Countries

The Nordic countries include the Scandinavian peninsula – Sweden and Norway – as well as Denmark, Finland, and Iceland. The Faroe Islands and Greenland belong to Denmark, whereas Spits Bergen is under Norwegian jurisdiction. Total population is approximately 25 million people. The Nordic countries have a common history and the borders between the countries have changed considerably over the centuries. The Viking age, from 700 to 1100 AD, was a period of external aggression and expansion. Moreover, Sweden also had an imperialistic period in the seventeenth century. In 1380, Sweden, Denmark, and Norway (including Iceland) were joined in a union. However, in the early 1500s, Sweden broke away from the union while Norway was under Danish political control until 1814. Finland was ruled by Sweden for a long period and under Russia from 1809. In 1814 the Vienna Congress gave Norway to the Swedish king to compensate for the loss of Finland and for Swedish support against Napoleon. The union between Sweden and Norway was terminated in 1905. Finland became independent from Russia in 1918. In 1943, Iceland gained its independence from Denmark.

Although Sweden, Norway, and Denmark have their own languages, the linguistic differences are relatively small. The Icelandic language is different, it is similar to the written language of Norway in the Viking age. In contrast, Finland has a completely different language, belonging to the same linguistic family as Hungarian (Finno-Ugric).

Socially, the Nordic countries are fairly similar. They are all among the richest countries in the world with very high standards of living. The Nordic countries are welfare states, with "free" health care and education.

Norway, Sweden, and Denmark are kingdoms, whereas Finland and Iceland are republics. They are all western democracies with a relatively large number of political parties.

## Forensic Medicine in the Nordic Countries

Although the Nordic countries are relatively homogeneous with regard to their social organization, they vary in the regulation and organization of forensic medicine. It may be claimed that in all Nordic countries forensic medicine is organized following the Continental European university-based system, but no Nordic country adheres strictly to this tradition. The legislation may differ, but in terms of the practical organization of forensic medicine, all Nordic countries have a government connection. In Sweden and Finland, forensic medicine organizations are government-controlled: by the National Board of Forensic Medicine (*Rättsmedicinalverket*) in Sweden and through a less centralized model in Finland. In Denmark, the government connection is confined to the formal approval of the state forensic pathologist (*statsobducent*).

Legislation is sparse in Norway but complicated in Sweden. In Finland and Denmark legislation is unified, structured, and lucid. Sweden and Finland have a separate forensic medicine specialty. Denmark, Iceland, and Norway lack such a specialty, and in these countries, forensic medicine is more of a subspecialty of clinical pathology. In Finland, Sweden, and Denmark, experts in forensic medicine are involved in autopsies as well as in clinical forensic medicine (examining living persons at the request of legal authorities). The only common feature of all Nordic forensic medical systems is the fact that the police decide when a forensic autopsy should be performed.

In this article, the medicolegal systems in the Nordic countries are described with regard to regulations, medicolegal organization, criteria for medicolegal investigations, the different types of medicolegal death investigations, and training of specialists in forensic medicine.

### Denmark

In Denmark, the provisions on death are regulated in one law, the Postmortem Examination and Transplantation Act (*Lov om ligsyn, obduktion og transplantation m.v. LOV nr* 402 *af* 13/06/1990). There are a number of guidelines relating to this law that help practitioners and the police to understand their responsibilities. Two guidelines are of special interest for medicolegal investigation. The first is the Circular on Legal Postmortem Examinations and Autopsies (*Cirkulære om foretagelse af retslægelige ligsyn og obduktioner m.v.*, CIR nr 11631 af 21/11/1995), which gives practical advice on medicolegal examination. This guideline is directed at forensic pathologists. The second relevant document is the Police Guideline on Postmortem Examinations and Transplantations (*Vejledning til politiet om ligsyn, obduktion og transplantation m.v.*, VEJ 60305 af 08/02/1993), which gives practical advice for the police.

The Danish medicolegal organization has two parts: (1) the governmental *Embedslægevæsendet*; and (2) the institutes of forensic medicine. The *Embedslægevæsendet* employs *embedslægen*, doctors who have legal duties. One such duty is to perform a *retslægelig ligsyn*, which is a thorough external examination of the deceased, performed together with the police. After this examination, the police will decide whether to order a medicolegal autopsy. Such autopsies are performed at one of the institutes of forensic medicine, located at the universities of Copenhagen, Århus, and Odense. Only certain professionals are permitted to perform a forensic autopsy: these include the *statsobducent* and the *vicestatsobducent*, both of whom are employed at the institute as professor or assistant professor.

Death must always be pronounced by a practitioner – in principle any doctor – and the practitioner is then required to report certain deaths to the police.

A medicolegal death investigation, performed as a *retslægelig ligsyn* by the *embedslæge* and the police, is carried out after the practitioner has filed a report to the police declaring a person dead. The following deaths are to be reported: all unnatural deaths, persons found dead, sudden or unexpected deaths, work-related deaths, deaths associated with medical malpractice, deaths within the penal system, and when any of these criteria cannot be excluded.

If a death is caused by a crime, or when this cannot be excluded, or to allay suspicions of foul play, a medicolegal autopsy must be performed. The same applies for cases when a *retslægelig ligsyn* is insufficient to determine the cause of death with reasonable certainty. It is also possible to perform a medicolegal investigation whenever it is in the interest of the police.

In Denmark there are two types of medicolegal death investigation: medicolegal external examination (*retslægelig ligsyn*) and medicolegal autopsy (*retslægelig obduktion*).

Danish experts in forensic medicine are clinical pathologists who have specialized in forensic pathology. The Danish Society of Forensic Science has established a program of training and required knowledge for candidates in forensic medicine, leading to certification in forensic medicine. At the time of writing, 11 pathologists have been certified.

## Finland

All rules relating to death are combined in one law, the Determination of Cause of Death Act (*Laki kuolemansyyn selvittämisestä* 459/1973 – *Lag om utredande av dödsorsak* Nr 459/1973) and one statute, The Determination of Cause of Death Statute (*Asetus kuolemansyyn selvittämisestä* 948/1973 – *Förordning om utredande av dödsorsak* Nr 948/1973). Guidelines also provide interpretations and recommendations regarding the legislation. The regulation defines different parties' responsibilities and what should be done when a death has occurred.

In Finland, regional authorities (*länsstyrelsema*) are responsible for medicolegal investigations. Autopsies are performed by a forensic pathologist who is employed by the regional authority. In turn the regional authorities can make an agreement with one of the four university departments of forensic medicine (Helsinki, Turku, Tampere, and Oulo) to conduct medicolegal autopsies in a specified geographic area. The forensic pathologist employed by a regional authority also scrutinizes all death certificates issued by other physicians. Moreover, in Finland all deaths initially have to be pronounced by a medical doctor.

When a death may be unnatural, and when the deceased during his/her last illness was not treated by a physician, the police have to initiate a medicolegal investigation. A medicolegal investigation must be performed if the death was caused, or may have been caused, by crime, suicide, accident, poisoning, work-related disease, or medical malpractice. In Finland there is only one category of medicolegal death investigation, the medicolegal autopsy.

Finland has a formal education and a medical specialty in forensic medicine, requiring at least 5 years of training. Candidates work in forensic medical centers and departments of clinical pathology, take courses, and finally have to pass an examination or an evaluation, before becoming a specialist.

## Iceland

There are three laws concerning death in Iceland: (1) the Human Death Act (*Lög um ákvörðun dauða nr. 15. mars* 1991); (2) the Transplantation Act (*Lög um brottnám vefja nr. 16, 6. mars* 1991); and (3) the Certificate of Death and Autopsy Act (*Lög um dánarvottorð, krufningar o.fl. nr. 61 12. júní* 1998). The Certificate of Death and Autopsy Act regulates the medicolegal investigation of death.

Most forensic autopsies are performed at the Department of Pathology at the University Hospital of Reykjavík, but some are performed in the town of Akureyri. There are only two experts practicing forensic medicine in Iceland, and together they perform almost all the forensic autopsies in the country. Very few medicolegal autopsies are performed by clinical pathologists.

The practitioner who declares a person dead must report to the police any death caused by crime, suicide, or accident. Furthermore, it is compulsory to report when a person is found dead, unexpected deaths, deaths associated with medical malpractice, and deaths within the penal system. In Iceland, permission from the next of kin is required to perform a medicolegal autopsy. If they refuse to give permission, a court can order an autopsy.

There are two types of medicolegal death investigation in Iceland: medicolegal external examination and medicolegal autopsy.

In Iceland, the experts in forensic medicine are clinical pathologists who have specialized in forensic pathology. Forensic medicine is not a recognized medical specialty in Iceland.

## Norway

Norway has four laws concerning death. These are: (1) the Transplantation, Clinical Autopsy, and Donation of Corpses Act (LOV 1973-02-09 nr 06: *Lov om transplantasjon, sykehusobduksjon og avgivelse av lik m.m*); (2) the Treatment of Corpses Act (LOV 1898-06-04: *Lov inneholdende visse Bestemmelser om Behandlingen av lig*); (3) the Health Care Workers Act (LOV 1999-07-02 nr 64: *Lov om helsepersonell m.v.*); and (4) the Criminal Trial Act (LOV 1981-05-22 nr 25: *Lov om rettergangsmåten i straffesaker*). The first two laws regulate how to decide that death has occurred, while the last two dictate when a practitioner has to report a death to the police and when a medicolegal investigation has to be, or can be, performed. In Norway, there are guidelines for the different parties involved in the investigation of deaths.

There are four forensic medicolegal units connected to the universities in Oslo, Bergen, Trondheim, and Tromsø. These units perform about 85% of the forensic autopsies in Norway. The remaining 15% are performed by clinical pathologists at departments of pathology in regional hospitals.

A physician has to report all unnatural deaths to the police. Unnatural deaths are defined as deaths inflicted by murder or other physical assault, suicide or other self-inflicted actions, accidents, industrial disease, medical malpractice, drug abuse, sudden or unexpected death, deaths within a penal institution, and unidentified bodies. The police will then decide whether a medicolegal investigation should take place. The medicolegal investigation can be made based on the same criteria that apply to the obligation to report to the police.

In Norway there are two types of medicolegal death investigation (*sakkyndig likundersøkelse*): medicolegal external examination (*likskue*) and medicolegal autopsy (*likåpning*).

There is no specialty in forensic medicine in Norway and no specified requirements for medical doctors who practice in forensic medicine; however, to obtain a permanent position in forensic medicine at one of the four universities, a doctoral degree is necessary. For several years, the Norwegian Society of Legal Medicine has been arguing for a training program and a specialty in forensic medicine. There has been great resistance from the health authorities which do not want too many specialties, and from clinical pathologists who do not want to lose the possibility of working for the police. The Norwegian Society of Legal Medicine has proposed a training program for specialist candidates and an official report (NOU 2001:12) has recommended that forensic medicine should become a separate specialty. This report suggests that all medical doctors and dentists should have some training in forensic medicine (level A), whereas doctors and biologists who work for the court regularly should have a level B qualification. Finally, full-time specialists in forensic medicine (pathologists, toxicologists, and geneticists) should be qualified to level C. In 2004, the first training course for B-level experts was held in Trondheim, arranged by the Commission of Legal Medicine. Forty candidates attended this course, which consisted of lectures and practical training in simulated court trials.

## Sweden

The regulations on how to handle a death are detailed in several laws and statutes. The Criteria for Determination of Human Death Act (*Lag 1987:269 om kriterier för bestämmande av människans död*) regulate the definition of a person's death. The Burial Act and the Burial Statute (*Begravningslagen* 1990:1144 and *Begravningsförordningen* 1990:1147) regulate how the practitioner reports to the police and how to write the death certificate. The Autopsy Act (*Lag 1995:832 om obduktion m.m.*) outlines the criteria for when to conduct a medicolegal investigation. Sweden also has several guidelines for these laws.

A governmental authority organized under the Ministry of Justice, the Board of Forensic Medicine or *Rättsmedicinalverket,* is responsible for medicolegal death investigations in Sweden. This authority, which also organizes forensic toxicology, forensic genetics, and forensic psychiatry, is responsible for the six departments of forensic medicine located in Umeå, Uppsala, Stockholm, Linköping, Göteborg, and Lund, together with the university departments of forensic medicine. Physicians are employed by *Rättsmedicinalverket,* but a few are also employed by the universities as teachers and researchers. All forensic autopsies in Sweden are performed at these six departments.

Sweden is the only Nordic country where there is no definition of when a medicolegal death investigation must be performed. Instead, Swedish law details when a medicolegal death investigation may be performed. In short, it is possible to perform a medicolegal death investigation on the same grounds as in Denmark and Norway.

In Sweden *Rättsmedicinalverket* has made a request to the Ministry of Justice to simplify the complicated regulations on medicolegal death investigations. Among several requests, some are of particular interest. One is that all deaths that are required to be reported to the police should be medicolegally investigated. Another is that the Board would like a governmental mandate to act preventively, as an "early-warning system."

Furthermore, a discussion was recently initiated regarding all Swedish forensic laboratory facilities merging into one authority – not just medical departments, but also the central crime laboratory.

Sweden has three types of investigation: (1) medicolegal external examination (*rättsmedicinsk likbesiktning*); (2) medicolegal autopsy (*rättsmedicinsk obduktion*); and (3) extended medicolegal autopsy (*utvidgad rättsmedicinsk obduktion*).

Sweden has a formal education and a medical specialty in forensic medicine, requiring at least 5 years of training. Candidates work in departments of forensic medicine (and departments of clinical pathology), take courses, and finally have to pass an evaluation.

## The Workload of Forensic Pathologists

The autopsy rate differs significantly between the Nordic countries, with Finland in a leading position (**Figure 1**). The numbers of practicing forensic pathologists in each country are shown in **Table 1**.

## Comparison of Medicolegal Death Investigations and Organization

There are significant differences in how the Nordic countries legislate for and structure their medicolegal systems. Some Nordic countries have full government control while other systems are based more on the Continental European/generic criminal investigation and judicial tradition.

The Swedish system is controlled by the government through the National Board of Forensic Medicine (*Rättsmedicinalverket*), which employs all specialists and trainees in forensic medicine. This highly centralized system has had a positive effect on the implementation of national guidelines. However, the Swedish legislation concerning medicolegal autopsies is complex and in need of simplification.

Finland also has a government-based system, but is less centralized than that of Sweden. Many specialists are employed by regional authorities, and this has the advantage of a fairly widespread geographic distribution of specialists. Furthermore, the forensic pathologists employed by a regional authority scrutinize all death certificates issued by other physicians, a practice that enhances the quality and standardization of death certificates in general. The Finnish legislation is unified.

Denmark has a partly government-based system. The official external death examination (*retslægelig ligsyn*) is a thorough external examination of the deceased made by a government doctor (*embedslægen*). The medicolegal autopsy is performed by the state forensic pathologist (*statsobducent*), which reflects some governmental control; appointments must be approved by the government but there is no specific connection to a governmental body. Like Finland, Denmark has unified, clear, and well-structured legislation.

Norway's approach is unique compared to the other Nordic countries with respect to legal regulation and organization. Medicolegal autopsies are regulated in the Code of Criminal Procedure (*straffeprosessloven*), which is not the case in the other Nordic countries. The sparse legislation in Norway leaves some important areas uncovered, e.g., there is no certification of medical doctors who are qualified to perform medicolegal autopsies, and no certification of where these autopsies may be performed. This lack of regulation explains why about 15% of forensic autopsies are performed by clinical pathologists at hospital departments. Nevertheless, Norway is the only Nordic country with a system of comprehensive external quality control by the Commission

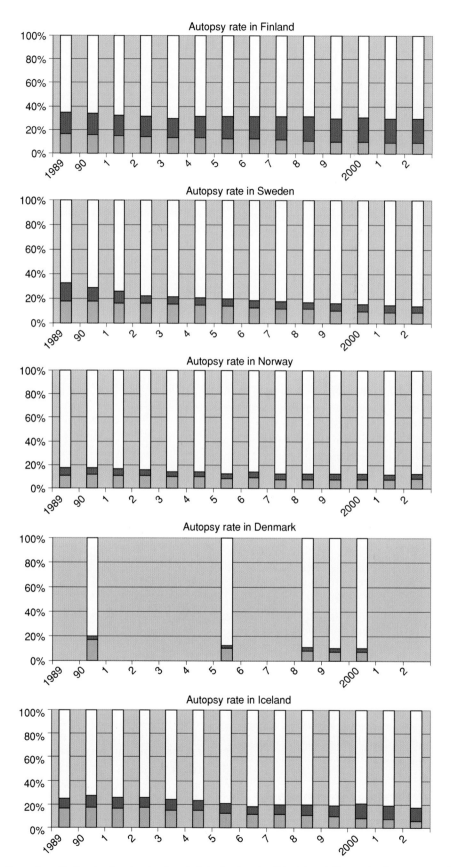

**Figure 1**   Proportions of medicolegal autopsies (red) and clinical autopsies (blue) in relation to deaths not autopsied (yellow) in the Nordic countries.

**Table 1** Status and number of forensic pathologists and trainees, and number of deaths in the Nordic countries

| Country | Specialty | Forensic pathologists in year 2004 (n) | Trainees in year 2004 (n) | Number of annual deaths (n) |
|---|---|---|---|---|
| Finland | Yes | 28 | 5 | 49 000 |
| Sweden | Yes | 21 | 14 | 94 000 |
| Denmark | No | 18 | 6[a] | 58 000 |
| Norway | No | 8 | 3[a] | 45 000 |
| Iceland | No | 2 | – | 1800 |

[a]These countries do not have forensic medicine as a specialty and the trainees are often doctoral candidates and similar, working at a forensic medicine unit.

of Forensic Medicine (*den Rettsmedisinske Kommisjon*). This commission was established in 1900, and has a separate expert group which analyzes all autopsy reports and all clinical forensic medicine reports.

## Conclusion

Nordic medicolegal systems have a range of regulation and structure, dependent on country. In the authors' opinions the Swedish system is more difficult to understand than those of Finland and Denmark. The Danish system appears to be the best regulated and structured.

It may be claimed that the organization of forensic medicine in the Nordic countries is influenced by the generic criminal investigation and judicial system. In our opinion, however, none of these countries belongs strictly to this tradition, but to some extent they all have a government connection when it comes to their practical organization. The only common denominator is the fact that the police decide when a medicolegal autopsy is to be performed. In spite of this, Denmark has a markedly lower proportion of medicolegal autopsies than the other Nordic countries, perhaps as a result of more effective selection through *embedslægen*.

## Further Reading

This article draws heavily upon an earlier publication by the authors [Thid M, Rognum T, Eriksson A. Forensic Pathology in the Nordic Countries. *Scand. J. Forens. Sci.* 10:1, 4–7. 2004], with permission of the publishers.

*Asetus kuolemansyyn selvittämisestä 948/1973 – Förordning om utredande av dödsorsak Nr 948/1973.*

*Begravningsförordningen 1990:1147.*

*Begravningslagen 1990:1144.*

*Lag 1987:269 om kriterier för bestämmande av människans död.*

*Lag 1995:832 om obduktion m.m.*

*Laki kuolemansyyn selvittämisestä 459/1973 – Lag om utredande av dödsorsak Nr 459/1973.*

*Lov inneholdende visse Bestemmelser om Behandlingen av lig, LOV 1999-07-02 nr 64.*

*Lov om helsepersonell m.v., and LOV 1981-05-22 nr 25.*

*Lov om ligsyn, obduktion og transplantation m.v. LOV nr 402 af 13/06/1990.*

*Lov om rettergangsmåten i straffesaker.*

*Lov om transplantasjon, sykehusobduksjon og avgivelse av lik m.m, LOV 1898-06-04.*

*Lög um ákvörðun dauða nr. 15. mars 1991.*

*Lög um brottnám vefja nr. 16, 6. mars 1991.*

*Lög um dánarvottorð, krufningar o.fl. nr. 61 12. júní 1998.*

Thid M, Rognum T, Eriksson A (2004) Forensic pathology in the Nordic countries. *Scandinavian Journal of Forensic Science* 10(1): 4–7.

## Certification of Death and the United Kingdom System

**P Dean**, Rochford Police Station, Rochford, UK

### Background and History

In England, Wales, and Northern Ireland, a coroner system is in operation for the detailed investigation of all sudden, violent, or unnatural deaths, and this operates alongside a system for the certification of the medical cause of all other deaths, from which many of the referrals to the coroner system, in fact, also originate. The system for death investigation differs in Scotland, where another system operates, based upon the procurator fiscal system, which will also be discussed in this article.

It is clearly in the general interests of any community that all sudden, unnatural, or otherwise unexplained deaths should be investigated properly, and therefore, the role of the coroner has adapted over many centuries from being a form of medieval tax-gatherer to an independent judicial officer charged with the investigation of sudden, violent, or unnatural death.

At the present time, coroners respond to and investigate those deaths that have been referred to them for a wide variety of reasons (just over one-third of all deaths in England and Wales), rather than proactively examining all community or hospital deaths that occur and then deciding which ones should be subjected to further scrutiny.

The latter approach is not allowed for by the law as it stands at the present time. However, in the wake of the activities of Dr. Shipman, a general medical practitioner who was convicted of the murder of 15 of his patients but is believed to have murdered 700 more over a long period of time, much attention has been paid to the fact that he was able to certify the deaths as natural himself, and thereby avoid referral to and scrutiny by the coroner service. At present the coroner service can only legally respond to referrals and does not have the legal powers to screen all deaths.

Since the trial and conviction of Dr. Shipman, there have been three separate inquiries into different aspects of the investigation and certification of sudden death, and it is likely that there will ultimately be new legislation and changes to the way in which all deaths are investigated and, as a consequence, the manner in which coroners carry out their duties. Some of these proposals will be discussed below, but initially, we will look briefly at how the office of coroner developed and the current processes of death certification and investigation.

Sudden death in the community had always been considered important and was the subject of investigation, although for very different reasons to those of today. After the Norman Conquest of England in 1066, to deter the indigenous population from a continuing habit of killing Normans after hostilities had ceased, a heavy fine was levied on any village where a dead body was discovered, on the assumption that it was presumed to be Norman unless it could be proved by the local population to be English.

The fine was known as the "murdrum," from which the word "murder" is derived and, as the system developed, many of the early coroners' inquests dealt with the "presumption of body's Normanry," which could only be rebutted by the local community (and a fine thus avoided) by the "presentment of body's Englishry."

The duties of the early coroners were entirely fiscal (rather than to further the cause of justice itself) and astonishingly varied, including the investigation of almost any aspect of medieval life that had the potential benefit of revenue for the crown. Medieval coroners investigated suicides, on the grounds that the goods and chattels of those found guilty of the crime of "self-murder" would then be forfeit to the crown, and also investigated fires, wrecks at sea, the catching of "royal fish" such as sturgeon and whales, and the discovery of buried treasure, a function still performed by coroners in England and Wales today, originally as "treasure trove" but now broadened by a recent Act of Parliament.

The coroner system continued to adapt to social and legal changes over the following centuries, but in the nineteenth century major developments relating to the investigation of death in the community occurred. In 1836, the first Births and Deaths Registration Act was passed, prompted by the public concern and panic caused by the inaccurate "parochial" recording of the actual numbers of deaths arising from epidemics of cholera and other diseases. There were also growing concerns that, given the combination of uncontrolled access to numerous poisons at that time and inadequate medical investigation of the actual cause of death, many homicides were not being detected.

The coroner's fiscal responsibility gradually diminished, and the Coroners Act of 1887 made significant changes, repealing much of the earlier legislation. Coroners then became more concerned with determining the circumstances and the actual medical causes of sudden, violent, and unnatural deaths for the benefit of the community as a whole, rather than to benefit the royal coffers.

## Death Certification and Referral to the Coroner

At the present time, in England and Wales, Section 22 of the Births and Deaths Registration Act of 1953 provides that "In the case of the death of any person who has been attended during his last illness by a registered medical practitioner, that practitioner shall sign a certificate in the prescribed form stating to the best of his knowledge and belief the cause of death and shall forthwith deliver that certificate to the registrar."

The registrar of births and deaths, a post created by the first Births and Deaths Registration Act in 1836, scrutinizes all medical certificates of cause of death, and has a statutory duty under Section 41(1) of the Registration of Births and Deaths Regulations 1987 to report the death to the coroner if it is one of the following:

1. in respect of which the deceased was not attended during his last illness by a registered medical practitioner; or
2. in respect of which the registrar
   a. has been unable to obtain a duly completed certificate of the cause of death; or
   b. has received such a certificate with respect to which it appears to him, from the particulars contained in the certificate or otherwise, that the deceased was not seen by the certifying medical practitioner either after death or within 14 days before death; or
3. the cause of which appears to be unknown; or

4. which the registrar has reason to believe to have been unnatural or to have been caused by violence or neglect or by abortion, or to have been attended by suspicious circumstances; or

5. which appears to the registrar to have occurred during an operation or before recovery from the effect of an anesthetic; or

6. which appears to the registrar from the contents of any medical certificate of cause of death to have been due to industrial disease or industrial poisoning.

Local arrangements often exist for notifying deaths that occur within 24 h of admission to hospital. This is not a statutory requirement, but the registrar may otherwise question a certificate if it appears that the patient may not have been in hospital long enough for the cause of death to be fully established, or if it appears that the patient was not attended during the last illness by a registered medical practitioner other than treatment given *in extremis* by hospital staff.

Section 41(1) of the Registration of Births and Deaths Regulations defines most of the instances when a death must be reported to the coroner. It does not cover absolutely every case; however, an exception is those deaths in custody which, rather than being notified by the registrar, will be reported directly to the coroner by the appropriate prison or police authority.

A thorough investigation into the circumstances of every death in prison or police custody, and a full public exploration of the facts in the subsequent coroner's inquest, together with the opportunity to learn lessons from any tragedy or avoidable death that has occurred, is clearly a vital function of the service. Its role and responsibilities here have been further emphasized by cases arising following passage of the Human Rights Act into English law, such as the recent decisions of the House of Lords in the Middleton and Sacker cases.

## The Management of Deaths Not Referred to the Coroner

At the present time, in England and Wales, as stated above, Section 22 of the Births and Deaths Registration Act 1953 provides for the completion of a medical certificate of cause of death by the doctor in attendance for the final illness, which is then subsequently delivered to the registrar of births and deaths.

Where the death is entirely natural and does not fall into any of the above categories of referral to a coroner, then to ensure that the medical certificate of cause of death is acceptable to the registrar of births and deaths, care must always be taken to ensure that the certificate is completed correctly. Much unnecessary additional distress to grieving relatives waiting to register a death, and a great deal of subsequent anger directed at the individual doctor by those bereaved, can easily be avoided by care in the completion of the medical certificate of cause of death.

In the first instance, this involves a knowledge and recognition of those deaths that must be reported to the coroner, as outlined previously. Sadly, not all doctors recognized these deaths that must be reported; therefore, useful advice on correct certification of death was given in a letter to doctors from the Office of Population Censuses and Surveys in 1990. This letter reminded doctors that the certificates served both legal and statistical purposes, and pointed out some of the common errors that occur. It specifically mentioned that there is no need to record the mode of dying, as this does not assist in deriving mortality statistics, and stressed that it is even more important not to complete a certificate where the mode of dying, e.g., shock, uremia, or asphyxia, is the only entry.

It also emphasized the need to avoid the use of abbreviations at all times, which can clearly be a source of ambiguity and confusion, particularly where abbreviations are shared, such as "MI" (which might mean mitral incompetence or myocardial infarction), or "MS" (which might mean mitral stenosis or multiple sclerosis). Advice was also provided on the correct inclusion and positioning of any relevant antecedent diseases or conditions, to ensure that causes were filled in correctly and in a logical sequence.

At the present time, as stated previously, just over one-third of all deaths in England and Wales are reported to coroners. The rest are dealt with by medical certification alone, and in those cases, once the registrar has scrutinized the medical certificate of cause of death, if the case is not one deemed to require referral to a coroner, then the death is registered by the registrar and a disposal certificate is issued to allow for arrangements to be made to dispose of the body. There are additional procedures and safeguards before cremation in these "noncoroner" cases, requiring further examination of the body by a second doctor, who must also discuss the cause of death with the original certifying doctor before countersigning a form authorizing the cremation. Finally, this form must also be scrutinized and signed off by a further independent doctor at the crematorium. Sadly, these extra procedures failed to detect Dr. Shipman's activities until a great many deaths had occurred, and they were not initially considered suspicious or referred to a coroner until concerns arose much later. As stated above, reviews of the systems in place for the investigation and certification of sudden death have taken place following the Shipman murders.

The outcome of cases referred to coroners in the normal course of events is examined in the following.

## Natural Deaths

In those circumstances where further enquiry by coroners and their officers indicates that a reported death is due to natural causes and does not require a postmortem examination, the coroner will issue a form (100A), notifying the registrar that the death was due to natural causes, and the attending doctor will be advised to complete a medical certificate of the cause of death in the usual manner. In the majority of cases reported to coroners, however, a postmortem examination is still required to ascertain the cause of death, although the proportion of cases requiring this has been declining slowly over the years. If the cause of death is found to be natural at autopsy, the coroner will issue a form (100B), which notifies the registrar of the cause of death and that no further action is to be taken. Upon receipt of either the medical certificate of the cause of death from the attending doctor, or form 100B from the coroner, the registrar is able to register the death and issue a disposal certificate to allow for arrangements to be made to dispose of the body.

In 2002, postmortem examinations were conducted on 117 700 of the cases reported to coroners, representing just over 58% of the 201 389 reported deaths and continuing a steady downward trend in the UK. There has, however, been a steady increase in the number of cases where neither a postmortem examination nor an inquest has been required.

## Unnatural Deaths and Inquests

In cases where the cause of death is found not to be natural, the coroner has a statutory duty to conduct an inquest under Section 8(1) of the Coroners Act 1988, which provides that:

> Where a coroner is informed that a body of a person ("the deceased") is lying within his district and there is reasonable cause to suspect that the deceased (a) has died a violent or unnatural death; (b) has died a sudden death of which the cause is unknown; or (c) has died in prison, or in such a place or in such circumstances as to require an inquest under any other Act, then, whether the cause of death arose within his district or not, the coroner shall as soon as practicable hold an inquest into the death of the deceased either with or, subject to subsection (3), without a jury.

The issue of what constituted an "unnatural death" for the purposes of an inquest was explored by the Court of Appeal in *R. (Touche)* v. *Inner North London Coroner* [2001] QB 1206, CA. Here a woman had died from severe hypertension and cerebral hemorrhage following the delivery of twins by cesarean section, and there was medical evidence that the death would probably have been avoided had her blood pressure been monitored postoperatively. The Court of Appeal ruled that, even if a death arose from what was essentially a recognized natural cause, it should be considered as potentially "unnatural" for the purposes of an inquest if there was evidence that negligence could have contributed to the death.

Other cases in recent years have demonstrated the impact of the Human Rights Act 1998, particularly Article 2 dealing with the right to life, and have emphasized the importance of a thorough inquest in the investigation of deaths such as those in prison or police custody and the role of the coroner's inquest in fulfilling the obligation of the state to ensure that there has been a suitable inquiry into all such deaths. Practice is evolving as the case law in this area develops.

## Juries

Prior to 1926, every inquest had to be held with a jury, but nowadays, in the majority of inquests, the coroner sits alone. Section 8(3) of the Coroners Act 1988 provides that:

> If it appears to a coroner, either before he proceeds to hold an inquest or in the course of an inquest begun without a jury, that there is reason to suspect–
>
> a. that the death occurred in prison or in such a place or in such circumstances as to require an inquest under any other Act;
> b. that the death occurred while the deceased was in police custody, or resulted from an injury caused by a police officer in the purported execution of his duty;
> c. that the death was caused by an accident, poisoning or disease notice of which is required to be given under any Act to a government department, to any inspector or other officer of a government department or to an inspector appointed under Section 19 of the Health and Safety at Work etc. Act 1974; or
> d. that the death occurred in circumstances the continuance or possible recurrence of which is prejudicial to the health or safety of the public or any section of the public,
>
> he shall proceed to summon a jury in the manner required by subsection (2).

## Procedures at an Inquest

The conduct of an inquest is governed by the Coroners Rules 1984, and the function and ambit of an inquest were usefully examined and clearly reaffirmed by the Court of Appeal in *R* v. *North Humberside Coroner, ex parte* Jamieson [1994] 3 WLR 82 CA.

Rule 36 (Matters to be Ascertained at Inquest) provides that:

1. The proceedings and evidence at inquest shall be directed solely to ascertaining the following matters, namely–
   a. who the deceased was;
   b. how, when and where the deceased came by his death;
   c. the particulars for the time being required by the Registration Acts to be registered concerning the death.
2. Neither the coroner nor the jury shall express any opinion on any other matters.
   and Rule 42 (Verdict) provides that:
   No verdict shall be framed in such a way as to appear to determine any question of–
   a. criminal liability on the part of a named person, or
   b. civil liability.

It is important to appreciate that an inquest is a fact-finding inquiry rather than a fault-finding trial, and the proceedings are inquisitorial rather than adversarial in nature, but, as the Master of the Rolls indicated giving the judgment of the court in R v. North Humberside Coroner, ex parte Jamieson, it is the duty of the coroner to "ensure that the relevant facts were fully, fairly and fearlessly investigated." The restriction in Rule 42 applies solely to the verdict, however, and to ensure that a thorough enquiry has been conducted, there are occasions when exploration of the evidence itself must unavoidably involve matters bearing on liability.

The coroner will initially examine a witness under oath, after which relevant questions may be put to the witness by any of those with a proper interest in the proceedings, either in person or by counsel or solicitor. Those people who have this entitlement to examine witnesses are defined in Rule 20 of the Coroners Rules.

Evidence given under oath before a coroner may subsequently be used in proceedings in other courts but, as in any other court, there is a right against self-incrimination. Rule 22 provides that:

1. no witness at an inquest shall be obliged to answer any question tending to incriminate himself, and
2. where it appears to the coroner that a witness has been asked such a question, the coroner shall inform the witness that he may refuse to answer.

This privilege does not allow a witness to refuse to enter the witness box, and the protection against self-incrimination that it offers applies only to criminal offenses, and not to possible civil or disciplinary proceedings.

Inquests were held on 26 430, or just over 13%, of deaths reported to coroners in 2002, continuing a reversal of the decline in inquests which had been taking place until the early 1990s. The most common verdicts were death by accident or misadventure, which was recorded in 40% of cases; natural causes, recorded in 19% of cases and suicide, recorded in 14%. Verdicts of death from industrial diseases almost doubled in 10 years – from 5% in 1984 to 10% in 1994. This verdict was recorded in 11% of cases in 2002, largely reflecting the long latent period between contact with asbestos, usually acquired through employment, and the subsequent development of malignant mesothelioma, a very significant problem at this time.

Since the Coroners (Amendment) Act of 1926, coroners have had to be barristers, solicitors, or doctors of no less than five years' standing. Coroner's officers themselves have no statutory definition or requirement for any specified qualifications, but in practice, many of them are former police officers or have similar investigative experience.

## Treasure Trove

Apart from those duties relating to unnatural death that are provided by Section 8(1) of the Coroners Act 1988, one last vestige of the coroner's medieval duties remains. Section 30 of the Coroners Act 1988 provides that a coroner shall continue to have jurisdiction to inquire into any treasure which is found in his/her district, although in modern times this has more to do with the preservation of antiquities rather than for any financial benefit to the crown. The Treasure Act of 1996 has introduced new requirements for reporting and dealing with finds.

## Northern Ireland

The coroner system in Northern Ireland is similar to that in England and Wales, although there are some significant differences. Coroners in Northern Ireland are appointed by the Lord Chancellor, unlike those in England and Wales, who are appointed by local authorities, that appointment then being subject to the approval of the Home Secretary. In Northern Ireland, only barristers and solicitors are eligible to become coroners, whereas in England and Wales doctors are also eligible.

In Northern Ireland, the medical practitioner is required to issue a medical certificate of cause of death if he/she has attended and treated the deceased within the last 28 days and is satisfied that the cause of death was natural, rather than the current 14-day limit before referral to the coroner in England and Wales. The medical practitioner in Northern Ireland also has a statutory duty to refer reportable deaths to the coroner, in addition to the registrar, and a statutory obligation not to issue a certificate in those cases.

In England and Wales, the doctor who has attended the deceased in the final illness has a statutory duty to issue a certificate in every case, and it is only the registrar in England and Wales who has the statutory duty to report deaths to the coroner at the present time. It is, of course, appropriate practice for doctors in England and Wales to report relevant deaths to the coroner themselves at the earliest opportunity, despite the lack of a statutory obligation to do so, although all of these areas are likely to change in any new system.

In Northern Ireland, the relevant statute, the Coroners Act (Northern Ireland) 1959 (as amended), states that the coroner "may" hold an inquest, thus introducing an element of discretion, whereas, when a death is reported in England and Wales, the coroner "shall" (i.e., must) hold an inquest if the death falls within Section 8(1) of the Coroners Act 1988, as discussed earlier.

The jurisdiction of the coroner in England and Wales arises from the presence of a body within his/her district, irrespective of where the death occurred, and therefore also covers deaths that occur abroad if the body is returned to the district. In Northern Ireland, however, the coroner only has jurisdiction if the death takes place, or the body is discovered, within the district itself.

## Scotland

In Scotland, Section 24 of the Registration of Births, Deaths and Marriages (Scotland) Act 1965 places a duty on a registered medical practitioner who has attended the deceased during the last illness to complete a medical certificate of cause of death. If no doctor has attended the deceased during the final illness, then any other doctor who knows the cause may complete the certificate.

In Scotland, there is no coroner system, and the law officer responsible for inquiring into all sudden and unexpected or unnatural deaths is the procurator fiscal, who has a statutory duty to investigate the following categories of death:

- deaths where the cause is uncertain
- deaths from accidents caused by any vehicle, airplane, or train
- deaths from employment, whether from accident, industrial disease, or industrial poisoning
- deaths due to poisoning
- deaths where suicide is a possibility
- deaths occurring under anesthetic
- deaths resulting from an accident
- deaths following an abortion or attempted abortion
- deaths appearing to arise from neglect
- deaths in prison or police custody

- death of a newborn child whose body is found
- deaths occurring not in a house, and where the residence of the deceased is unknown
- deaths caused by drowning
- death of a child from suffocation, including overlying
- deaths from food poisoning or infectious disease
- deaths from burning or scalding, fire, or explosion
- deaths of foster children
- deaths possibly arising from defects in medicinal products
- any other violent, suspicious, sudden or unexplained deaths.

The medical practitioner in Scotland has a duty to report deaths in these categories to the procurator fiscal, as does any citizen under a general duty, and the registrar of births, deaths, and marriages also has a specific statutory duty to inform the procurator fiscal of these deaths under the Registration of Births, Deaths and Marriages (Scotland) Act 1965.

The jurisdiction of the procurator fiscal is the same as the civil jurisdiction of the sheriff in whose court he/she appears, although, where the death is criminal and the body has been moved from one jurisdiction to another, the area where the crime was originally committed will determine which procurator fiscal supervises the investigation.

The procurator fiscal's inquiries are made in private, regardless of how the death was caused, although a public inquiry may be held if the relatives persuade the fiscal of the need for this. In practice, much of the investigation will be conducted by the police, but further opinion may also be sought from medical practitioners involved in the care of the deceased, from pathologists, and from independent experts on other technical matters if relevant.

The procurator fiscal has a common-law power to order a postmortem examination, but may apply for a warrant in suspicious cases granting authority to two named pathologists to conduct the examination. In nonsuspicious cases, the procurator fiscal will only instruct a postmortem examination if the circumstances justify it, and the postmortem rate for "natural" deaths is significantly lower than in England and Wales. If a death is expected to be natural and the deceased's general practitioner cannot issue a certificate, another doctor may be asked to undertake an external examination and report the results of this to the procurator fiscal, who may then decide to accept a certificate from that doctor.

If a death occurred in custody or was caused by an accident in the course of employment, then, under the Fatal Accidents and Sudden Deaths Inquiry (Scotland) Act 1976, the procurator fiscal must hold a fatal accident inquiry in public before a sheriff. Such an inquiry may also be held in some discretionary circumstances where it appears to the Lord Advocate that it would be in the public interest, and this will include some sudden, suspicious, or unexplained deaths or where there was significant public concern.

## Proposals for Reform

The constraints of space do not allow for anything other than a very brief overview of some of the proposals from the inquiries set up in the aftermath of the Dr. Shipman's conviction, and cannot, therefore, do justice to the considerable time and effort that has been spent in examining current systems for death investigation. It is highly recommended that those with a particular interest in these matters read the original reports.

Both the Fundamental Review into Death Certification and Investigation and the Third Report of The Shipman Inquiry (Death Certification and Investigation of Deaths by Coroners) have recommended an increased level of medical input into the process of death investigation, coupled with organizational and structural reform to the service itself.

The Fundamental Review recommended that there should be a statutory medical assessor in each coroner's area who would appoint a panel of doctors to provide all community second certifications, and has recommended a regional structure to the coronership among other proposed changes.

The Third Report of the Shipman Inquiry proposes an alternative structural change, creating both judicial coroners and medical coroners for each region and a radically reformed coronership which will seek to establish the cause of all deaths, supported by trained investigators.

The Home Office, having received both reports, produced a position paper in March 2004 entitled *Reforming the Coroner and Death Certification Service*, which represents the government's response to the previous reviews and expresses the intention to introduce a new system combining an independent check on all deaths with professional oversight of death patterns which would be based on one national jurisdiction for England and Wales, divided administratively into local coroners' areas with one local coroner and deputies, coroner's officers with a more clearly defined and consistent investigative role, and a medical team to support each office.

There are still details to be established, funding issues to be resolved, and legislative changes that would need to be enacted before any new system could be put in place. It clearly remains in the general interest of the public that deaths are investigated in a way that it is independent and thorough for the benefit of the community as a whole, and remains sensitive to the feelings, needs, and beliefs of those bereaved families most closely affected by the death itself.

## See Also

**Death Investigation Systems:** China; Nordic Countries; United States of America

## Further Reading

*Death Certification and Investigation in England, Wales and Northern Ireland.* The Report of a Fundamental Review 2003. Cm 5831.

*Jervis on Coroners*, 12th edn. (2002) Sweet and Maxwell.

Office of Population Censuses and Surveys (1990) *Completion of Medical Certificates of Cause of Death.* London: Office of Population Censuses and Surveys.

*R. v. Her Majesty's Coroner for the Western District of Somerset ex parte* Middleton (2004) HL 10.

*R. v. Her Majesty's Coroner for the County of West Yorkshire ex parte* Sacker (2004) H 11.

*Reforming the Coroner and Death Certification Service*, a Position Paper. Cm 6159.

Statistics of Deaths Reported to Coroners: England and Wales 2002.

The Shipman Inquiry, Third Report. *Death Certification and Investigation of Deaths by Coroners.* Cm 5854.

# United States of America

**C H Wecht** and **S A Koehler**, Alleghency County Coroner, Pittsburgh, PA, USA

## Introduction

This article outlines the chronology of the development and history of the coroner and medical examiner systems in the USA. The institutional and postgraduate specialty requirements for a forensic pathology training program are described.

## The Early Development of Forensic Investigation

The written record indicates that the development of the field of forensic pathology began in Europe in 1507, in a volume known as the *Bamberg Code*. In 1530, a more extensive penal code, known as the *Constitutio Criminalis Carolina*, was issued by Emperor Charles V for all the lands included in his empire. These two documents portrayed the importance of forensic pathology by requiring that medical testimony be an integral part of the proof and trials involving decisions about whether the manner of death was infanticide, homicide, abortion, or poisoning.

## The Coroner System in England and Wales

The present-day coroner system in the USA developed in England. The Charter of Privileges included a grant of the coroner's office by King Athelstane to an English noble, identified as St. John of Beverly, in the year 925. The office of the coroner was formally described in September 1194; the justices in Eyre were required to provide that three knights and one clerk were elected in every county as "keepers of the pleas of the crown." The appointment then listed the coroner's duties. The term coroner is derived from the Latin word for crowner (appointed by the King or Crown). The justices in Eyre, who were comparable to the traveling circuit court judges of modern day, could order the coroner to perform duties of an administrative or inquisitorial nature within the region for which he had been appointed. These duties were carried out either alone or with the sheriff. Among these were conducting inquests over dead bodies and appeals (inspection of an individual's wounds, recording the accusation against another individual, and, if the wounds appeared likely to be fatal, arresting the accused individual). The coroner was also authorized by the county courts to attach or arrest witnesses or suspects and to appraise and safeguard any lands or goods that might later be forfeited by reason of guilt of the accused. An 1194 ordinance established the coroner as a permanent office in England. The coroner was elected by all of the freeholders in the county court. He was elected for life, or at least as long as he acted in good behavior, and was able to perform the duties of the office.

There was little change in the role of the duty and function of the coroner until the middle of the nineteenth century. In 1860, the fee system was abolished and salaries were established for the county coroners. In 1877, a law was enacted requiring the inquest to be conducted whenever the coroner had reasonable cause to suspect violent or unnatural death or when the cause of death was unknown. This change had the effect of granting the coroner the widest authority to investigate cases. Over time the coroner system developed as a broad-spectrum investigative agency concerned with a large proportion of all deaths, including many nonviolent deaths. In 1888 the election of the coroner was abolished and replaced with an appointive system in which the head of the local governmental unit appointed the coroner. The minimum qualifications for the office were established in 1926, when a law was enacted requiring five

years; experience as a medical practitioner, barrister, or solicitor if the individual was to qualify as coroner.

In 1807, the University of Edinburgh established the first chair of legal medicine in the English-speaking world, occupied by Andrew Duncan Jr. The keystone textbook on medical jurisprudence *The Principles and Practice of Medical Jurisprudence* was published in 1836, and even today remains a standard. The British Association of Forensic Medicine was established in the twentieth century.

## The Coroner/Medical Examiners System in Early USA

The early American colonists from England brought the coroner system, as it existed in the early 1600s, to the new continent. There are records of a coroner's inquest in the colony of New Plymouth, New England, in 1635; in summary, the inquiry found that John Deacon died as a result of bodily weakness caused by fasting and extreme cold. At that time the coroner's office was one and the same as the sheriff's office, and while it did not carry any fixed stipend, it provided a substantial income because the sheriff was responsible for the collection of property taxes, poll taxes, and other levies, and he usually received 10% of his collection. A 1640 definition of the duties of the coroner included:

> Upon notice or suspicion of any person that hath or shall come to his or her death entirely within the limits of that hundred to warn as many inhabitants of the said hundred as you conveniently may to view the dead body and to charge the said persons with an oath truly to inquire and true verdict to grant how the person viewed came upon his or her death according to the evidence.

Autopsy examinations of bodies were recorded in Massachusetts as early as 1647. The medicolegal application of an autopsy was recorded in Maryland on March 21, 1665, when Mr. Francis Carpenter was brought before the Talbot county court on suspicion of murdering one Samuell Yeoungman, a servant of his. The report stated that there were bruises about the head and body, and two depressions in the skull with blood between the dura and pia mater. The autopsy clearly revealed that the cause of the injuries was the result of the impact of a club and that the injuries were the cause of the demise of Samuell Yeoungman. However, the verdict that was handed down by the coroner and six lay jurors was that the servant had died because he had not gone to a doctor.

The earliest teaching of jurisprudence in the New World appeared to be by Benjamin Rush of Philadelphia, who presented lectures with titles such as *On the Study of Medical Jurisprudence*. The first formal use of physicians in connection with the workings of the coroner's office was in 1860 in Maryland, where the code of Public General Laws authorized the coroner or his jury to require the attendance of a physician in cases of violent death. In 1877, the Commonwealth of Massachusetts adopted a statewide system requiring that the coroner be supplanted by a physician known as a medical examiner. At that time, the jurisdiction of the medical examiner was confined to "dead bodies of such persons only as are supposed to have come to their death by violence."

The science of pathology as a subspecialty of medicine involved with the investigation of deaths began in the latter part of the nineteenth century. In 1890, a city ordinance authorized the Board of Health in Baltimore, Maryland, to appoint two physicians with the title of medical examiner and assign them the duty of performing all autopsies requested by the coroner or the state's attorney. In 1915, New York City eliminated the coroner's office and created a medical examiner system, authorizing investigation of deaths resulting from criminal violence, casualties or suicide, or sudden death while in apparent health, or when not attended by a physician or imprisoned or in any suspicious or unusual manner. The medical examiner had the authority to make a decision as to the necessity of an autopsy. The first chief medical examiner, Dr. Charles Norris, was given the authority to order an autopsy when in his judgment it was necessary, thus establishing the essential responsibility and necessary authority of an effective medical examiner's system.

## The Death Investigation Systems in Modern USA

Each year approximately 20% of the 2 million deaths undergo a postmortem examination. This examination will take place in either a coroner's office or at a medical examiner's office dictated by the jurisdiction in which the office has been established. The type of system varies from municipality to municipality and from state to state. The USA is divided into over 2000 separate jurisdictions with responsibility for investigating unnatural deaths. State laws dictate when and how examinations should occur in 21 states, while local or regional rules take precedence in 29 states.

A 2002 survey of the medicolegal investigative system in the USA found that 22 states had a medical examiner system: 19 of these states have a state medical examiner, two have county medical examiners, and one state has district medical examiners. A total of 18 states have a mixed medical examiner and coroner system: 11 states have a mix of a county medical examiner and a coroner system, while seven

states have a mix of a state medical examiner and county medical examiner or coroners. A total of 11 states have a coroner system: nine of those states had county coroners and two had district coroners. In this century, medical examiner systems have gradually replaced coroner systems, but such change has slowed in recent years, with medical examiner systems now serving about 48% of the national population. Few states or counties have implemented medical examiner systems since 1990. A complete list of the type of death investigations system state by state is available at www.cdc.gov/epo/dphsi/mecisp/death_investigation.htm.

## The Coroner's Death Investigation Systems

Today, in states and counties utilizing a coroner as the medicolegal investigator, the coroner is elected for a four-year term. In addition, the coroner has to be 18 years of age or older, a US citizen, and a resident of the county while holding office and for at least one year prior to election. The coroner may appoint one or more deputies. This person is responsible for making rulings on the cause and manner of death in those cases that warrant investigation, including violent deaths, sudden and/or unexpected deaths, suspicious deaths, deaths involving drugs and toxic substances, deaths during medical treatment, deaths during employment, deaths during interaction with law enforcement agencies, and those cases in which a physician is not present at the time of death.

The coroner may or may not consult a physician, may or may not order an autopsy, and may or may not rule in agreement with the autopsy findings. In fact, the training that a coroner receives may range from absolutely none to a few weeks. A forensic pathologist, in contrast, must complete four years of undergraduate college. The coroner is responsible for determining the cause and manner of death that may have significant civil and criminal consequences. There is great variation as to the qualifications of the elected coroner. For example, in Pennsylvania the elected coroner of Allegheny County has medical and law degrees; board certified in anatomic, clinical, and forensic pathology; and is a nationally recognized forensic pathologist. In contrast, the surrounding counties have elected coroners who are primarily employed as funeral directors and are parttime coroners. The Cuyahoga County Coroner in Ohio is board-certified in anatomy, clinical, and forensic pathology. In a number of counties, such as in California, the coroner system is set up to combine the offices of both the sheriff and coroner. In some cases the same person is investigating death and arresting suspects at the same time. The sheriff also investigates the deaths of inmates in his/her own jail. The counties that are smallest by population have the elected prosecuting attorney also serve as coroner. The requirements for the coroner vary from state to state.

## The Coroner's Inquest Systems

The coroner's office, unlike the medical examiner's office, is empowered to conduct a coroner's inquest. An inquest is generally used to describe the coroner's formal procedure for inquiry into the cause and manner of death, and circumstances of any death resulting from violence or occurring under conditions which give reason to suspect that the death may have been due to a criminal act or criminal negligence. Reasons to hold an inquest may also include cases in which an individual died during some interaction with law enforcement officers, and deaths during incarceration or in a mental hospital. A coroner may also hold inquests into the cause of fires where life or property has been lost or endangered or at the direction of the attorney general. The procedure is governed as a part of the coroner's general duties for the investigation of death. During the inquest the coroner has the power to examine persons under oath, subpoena witnesses, and require them to present papers and documents relevant to the investigation. At the conclusion of the inquest, the coroner must prepare a formal determination of the cause and manner of death and provide a written report for further legal proceedings and for public inspection.

There are two types of inquest: closed and open. Closed inquests, which are preliminary hearings, are initiated by the district attorney or a police officer. Normally, the process begins with the arraignment of the suspect(s) at the coroner's office, at which time formal charges are made and the propriety of bond is addressed. A date for the inquest is then set, usually within 3–10 days of the arraignment.

An open inquest is conducted by the coroner's solicitor. Evidence is presented by witnesses, law enforcement personnel, and medical experts. The hearings are fact-finding in nature and are open to the public. When a coroner's jury is empaneled at an open inquest, it is selected from the regular jury panel summoned by the jury commissioner in the Criminal Division of the Court of Common Pleas. At the conclusion of the hearing, the coroner's jury is instructed as to the law by the solicitor. The jury then retires to deliberate on the evidence presented and returns its own findings in the matter. These findings consist of a formal determination of the cause and manner of death. When there are identifiable persons determined to be criminally responsible for the death, such persons are held for further court proceedings.

A court reporter is in attendance at all inquests, during which the proceedings are transcribed. The coroner retains the original and a copy is forwarded to the Office of the District Attorney. If the coroner decides that a *prima facie* case exists against any person for an indictable offence, he/she can commit a person to trial in the District or Supreme Court.

Under state law, the coroner has the power of subpoena and attachment, and may compel the attendance of any witness at an open inquest into any death in the coroner's jurisdiction. The coroner is not bound by the strict rules of evidence and can summon witnesses to be questioned about relevant matters. In addition to establishing the cause and manner of death, and whether one is held criminally liable, the coroner may use the open inquest as a forum to bring about changes in laws and regulations and to create public awareness of health and safety issues.

The power of the open inquest to bring about changes which directly affect the health, safety, and welfare of the citizens of the county in which that coroner's office serves is one of the great strengths of this traditional system. Inquests have resulted in regulations controlling the safety of backyard swimming pools, and changes in safety features at sporting stadiums, transportation systems, nursing homes, hospitals, and playgrounds.

## The Medical Examiner's Death Investigation Systems

The medical examiner system was first introduced in the USA in 1877 in Massachusetts. The public was dissatisfied with lay coroners and the system changed to one of appointed physicians. One medical doctor was appointed in each district (similar to a county jurisdiction) to be the public official responsible for the investigation of sudden and unnatural deaths. Medical examinations were a part of the investigation and the term medical examiner has been in use ever since. The state was divided into a number of sectors in which a designated physician functioned as a medical examiner and determined the cause and manner of death. At that time the medical examiner did not have the right to order an autopsy of the deceased. This right did not appear in the state until the 1940s. The first true medical examiner system came into existence in New York City in 1918. An individual was designated as the Chief Medical Examiner and was a physician who was experienced in the field of pathology (forensic pathology did not become a board-certified subspecialty until 1959) with statutory authority to investigate death. He was provided with a dedicated facility, support staff, and toxicology laboratory. In the last several decades, the medical examiner system has slowly replaced the coroner system in the USA.

For example, in the state of West Virginia the state Chief Medical Examiner is appointed by the Director of the Division of Health for a five-year term and appoints the County Medical Examiner for a three-year term. The state Chief Medical Examiner must be a licensed physician and a diplomat of the American Board of Pathology (ABP) in anatomic and forensic pathology with experience in forensic medicine and pathology. The Deputy Chief Medical Examiner must also be a licensed physician and have completed an ABP-approved fellowship in forensic pathology. The County Medical Examiner must be qualified to practice in the field of medicine as a duly licensed physician, registered nurse, physician's assistant, paramedic, or other licensed emergency medical technician, who has received training in the field of medicolegal death investigation and who holds certification from the American Board of Medicolegal Death Investigation. A statewide medical examiner system increased the quality of death investigation and forensic pathology services with presumed independence from population size, county budget variation, and politics. A statewide system theoretically creates uniformity, designed to insure credentialing, training, and continuing education of medical examiners, death investigative procedures, and the coding of deaths. These features enhance not only death investigation, but also public health, epidemiology, and overall community medical surveillance.

## The Forensic Pathologist

Forensic pathology is a specific branch of medicine that applies the principles and knowledge of medicine and related sciences to problems that concern the general public and related legal issues. A forensic pathologist is a physician with specialized medical and forensic science training and knowledge. In practice, forensic pathologists concentrate closely on the understanding of types and causation of injuries and causes of sudden and unnatural death. The ABP was established in 1936 and recognized forensic pathology as a formal subspecialty in 1958. Forensic pathologists are commonly involved in death scene investigations, the performance of forensic autopsies (forensic autopsies have a different focus than that of hospital autopsies conducted in cases of natural death), review of medical records, interpretation of toxicology and other laboratory studies, certification of sudden and unnatural deaths, and court testimony in criminal and civil law proceedings.

Since 1959, there have been 1172 pathologists in the USA certified in forensic pathology by the ABP.

The ABP requires the incorporation of forensic pathology training in all pathology programs, and 80% of medical school pathology courses offer an average of three hours of instruction in this discipline. Most forensic pathologists are members of the American Academy of Forensic Sciences (AAFS) and the National Association of Medical Examiners (NAME). The three main publications focused on forensics are the *Journal of Forensic Science,* started in 1956, the *American Journal of Forensic Medicine and Pathology* (1980), and *Forensic Science International,* which commenced publication in 1972.

### Training and Certification in Forensic Pathology

Training programs in forensic pathology are monitored by the Accreditation Council for Graduate Medical Education (ACGME), which confers accreditation of residency programs. ACGME carries out its functions through residency review committees, one of which is devoted to pathology. There are 41 forensic pathology training programs with full accreditation in the USA. Programs are conducted in larger metropolitan coroner or medical examiner offices.

**The institution**  The coroner's or medical examiner's office participating in a residency training program in forensic pathology must have the following institutional resources:

1. Approximately 500 medicolegal autopsies should be conducted each year. Of these, 100 or more should be in cases in which death is due to the immediate and direct effects of physical or chemical injury.
2. The office should conduct about 300 additional autopsies for each additional resident position requested.
3. Facilities and competent personnel shall be available and properly unitized for the conduction of all bacteriological, biochemical, toxicological, firearms, trace evidence, physical anthropology, odontology, and other scientific studies as may be needed to ensure complete postmortem investigation.
4. If the resident is to spend parts of the training program at other laboratories or institutions, such training must be adequately supervised by qualified personnel.

**Residency program in forensic pathology**  The program is one year and must be directed by a pathologist who is certified by the ABP in forensic pathology. The Residency Review Committee (RRC) for pathology is responsible for certification and accreditation of graduate medical education programs in pathology. The ABP is responsible for certification of individual physicians in pathology.

The requirements are as follows:

1. The resident should perform 250–350 autopsies in a year and should have experience in scene investigations, including examination of the body before it has been disturbed.
2. The resident should have responsibility for the performance of autopsies in cases that are likely to result in criminal prosecution or civil litigation, and it is desirable for residents to have opportunities to participate in the legal follow-up of cases if such occurs during the course of their year of training.
3. The resident should accompany staff pathologists when they testify in courts and give depositions.
4. During the year of approved training, the resident must have a period of four to eight weeks devoted exclusively to laboratory experience in toxicology, physical anthropology, and components of the crime laboratory, such as firearms, serology, and trace evidence.

## Professional Associations for Medical Examiners and Coroners

There are a number of professional associations for coroners, medical examiners, and forensic pathologists. These include the AAFS, NAME, and the American College of Legal Medicine (ACLM).

The AAFS, a nonprofit professional society organized in 1948, is devoted to the improvement, administration, and achievement of justice through the application of science to the process of law. The AAFS consists of 10 sections representing a wide range of forensic specialties with over 5000 members. The members are physicians, attorneys, dentists, toxicologists, physical anthropologists, document examiners, psychiatrists, engineers, criminalists, educators, and others who practice, study, and perform research in the forensic sciences. They represent all 50 states in the USA, Canada, and 50 other countries worldwide. As a professional society dedicated to the application of science to the law, the AAFS is committed to the promotion of education and the elevation of accuracy, precision, and specificity in the forensic sciences. It does so via the *Journal of Forensic Sciences*, newsletters, annual meetings, conducting seminars and meetings, and the initiation of actions and reactions to various issues of concern.

NAME, founded in 1966, is the national professional organization of physician medical examiners, medical death investigators, and death investigation system administrators who perform the official duties of the medicolegal investigation of deaths of public interest in the USA. NAME's purpose is to foster the professional growth of physician death investigators and to disseminate the professional and technical information vital to the continuing improvement of the medical investigation of violent, suspicious, and unusual deaths. NAME has expanded its scope to include physician medical examiners and coroners, medical death investigators, and medicolegal system administrators throughout the USA and other countries. NAME members provide the expertise for medicolegal death investigation that is essential to the effective functioning of the civil and criminal justice systems. NAME is now the national forum for the interchange of professional and technical information in this important segment of public administration. NAME serves as a resource to individuals and jurisdictions seeking to improve medicolegal death investigation by continually working to develop and upgrade national standards for death investigation. The published NAME *Standards for a Modern Medicolegal Investigative System* provides a model for jurisdictions seeking to improve death investigation. NAME aims to involve competent professional medicolegal death investigators in every jurisdiction in the USA. Membership of the National Association of Medical Examiners is open to all physicians, investigators, and administrators who are active in medicolegal death investigation.

Founded in 1960, the ACLM is the official organization for professionals who focus on the important issues where law and medicine converge. The ACLM is a professional community of physicians, attorneys, dentists, healthcare professionals, administrators, scientists, and others with a sustained interest in medicolegal affairs. The ACLM is the organization of healthcare and legal professionals whose diverse education, training, and experience enable the College to promote interdisciplinary cooperation and an understanding of issues where law and medicine converge. Through its medicolegal resources, the College educates and assists healthcare and legal professionals, advances the administration of justice, influences health policy and improves healthcare, promotes research and scholarship, and facilitates peer group interaction.

### Training and Certification in Death Investigation

The origin of lay examiners who work for medical examiners can be traced back to the 1950s. Over time the training improved. In 1974, the first formal one-week training course was offered by St. Louis University. Seven states now mandate minimal training requirements for death investigators. The basic week-long course for death investigators includes death investigation, examination of the decedents at the scene, estimation of time of death, evidence recognition, notification of the next of kin, legal issues, mass-casualty instant response, organ and tissue donation, and testifying in court. There are lectures on the ancillary forensic sciences, such as anthropology, odontology, toxicology, and forensic psychiatry. Credentialing of individual death investigators has advanced to the point that death investigators are recognized as affiliate members of NAME or members of the AAFS.

In 1995, the National Institute of Justice held the first technical working group to develop national guidelines, which were released in 1998, specifying 29 essential components of a thorough death scene investigation. Also in 1998, the American Board of Medicolegal Death Investigators was created to certify death investigators. It confers two levels of certification – registry and board certification.

## Who Can Pronounce a Death?

Only the coroner/medical examiner or a physician may pronounce an individual death. A registered nurse or licensed practical nurse may contact a doctor and advise him/her of the lack of vital signs and probable death. The physician may assume the responsibility of pronouncing death by telephone. No other medical personnel may give this information to a doctor. A physician can only complete death certificates where the manner of death is natural. A coroner may only make a pronouncement (via telephone) when notification of the lack of vital signs and probable death is received from a registered nurse or a physician. In the absence of either a registered nurse or a physician, the coroner must go to the scene of the death, examine the scene and the deceased, and make an on-scene pronouncement. In general, law enforcement personnel usually make the request, but EMTs (Emergency Medical Technicians), other caregivers, and family members can request that a coroner proceed to a death scene in the absence of police, a registered nurse, or a physician.

## The Death Certificate

After a thorough review of the death scene investigation reports, results of the postmortem examination, and the results of toxicological analysis of the body fluids, the certificate of death is completed by a forensic pathologist and reviewed by either the coroner or the medical examiner. The death certificate is a public record intended to inform the public and be utilized by a variety of agencies, but does not mandate, prevent, or preclude any other type of action by any other individual, agency, or public office. In other words, a death certificate is a legal statement of the cause and manner of death, but is not otherwise legally binding for any other agency or any other individual. Guidelines for the completion of the death certification have been established by the National Center for Health Statistics of the Centers for Disease Control and Prevention (CDC). The coroner/medical examiner considers the CDC and state guidelines when certifying death. The National Center for Health Statistics has published statements regarding the "precision of knowledge required to complete death certificate items," which include: "the cause-of-death section in the medical–legal officer's certification is always an opinion; it represents the best effort of the medical–legal officer to reduce to a few words a synthesis of the cause of death; and a best estimate of the manner of death and the time and date of injury may also be required when neither investigation nor examination of the deceased provides definitive information." The coroner/medical examiner should use reasonable medical probability in the formulation of opinions and in the certification of death in the same way that clinicians make diagnoses and plans for treatment. Published operational criteria for determination of suicide are considered in the designation of manner of death.

The death certificate is a civil law document, not a medical science document, and is specific to each state, but based on a national standard form. The standard death certificate is composed of three main sections: Section I (a), "the Immediate Cause and (b) the morbid conditions, giving rise to the immediate cause"; Section II, "Other Significant conditions contributing to death, but not related to the disease or condition causing it, and the Manner of Death. There are six manners of death: Natural, Accident, Suicide, Homicide, Pending Investigation, and Can Not Be Determined. Modes or mechanisms of death should not be entered on the death certificate. Conditions that existed, but that did not contribute to death, should not be entered." All deaths of an unnatural cause fall under the jurisdiction of the coroner/medical examiner and are to be certified by the coroner/medical examiner. It is proper for "natural" deaths to be certified by one of the decedent's attending physicians.

The death certificate must be issued within 72 h, even if the cause of death is unknown. If the cause of death is not established with reasonable certainty within 72 h, the coroner shall file a certificate of death, with the cause of death designated as "deferred or pending further action" or simply "pending." As soon as the determination of the cause of death is made, the coroner shall file a supplemental or replacement death certificate indicating the cause of death.

**Definition: Medicolegal**

The term "medicolegal" includes very general and quite broad forensic issues, which include any interaction between medical health concerns and the law, claims of misdiagnosis, malpractice, wrongful injury or death, settlements of wills and estates, issues of paternity and custody, insurance claims, worker's compensation issues, directives to physicians, living wills, defining brain death, and organ harvesting. Many individuals, private groups, corporations, government agencies, public officers, and attorneys are involved in dealing with medicolegal issues.

A potential civil law action, somehow related to a death, does not serve as sufficient reason by itself for the coroner/medical examiner to assume jurisdiction in a particular death case. The question still remains: is a death "unnatural" or of specific "general public" concern? It is not within the authority or the responsibility of the coroner/medical examiner's office to investigate or be involved with all medicolegal issues. State law very narrowly defines the jurisdiction and authority of the medical examiner. It is clear that within the narrow spectrum of medical examiner cases, such deaths, due to their "sudden" or "violent" nature, will have many related criminal and/or civil legal ramifications. The work of the coroner/medical examiner's office must remain focused on identifying and investigating deaths that are of immediate concern to the public as a whole.

No coroner/medical examiner case is ever considered to be irrevocably closed. New or additional information can be presented to the coroner/medical examiner's office at any time for their consideration and evaluation. This new or additional information may or may not change the preponderance of evidence and previously arrived at conclusions and classifications. Opinions and classifications, however, can change if the new information does significantly alter the preponderance of evidence for a given case. The coroner/medical examiner's office as a whole and each of its staff members must keep an open mind in all cases.

## Summary

Whether a coroner or medical examiner system is being utilized, both systems must continue to evolve and keep up with the advancing technology of forensic science. Failure to do so would greatly hamper their primary function of accurately determining the cause and manner of death. The field of forensic science has made rapid advances since the 1980s. The method of grouping blood evidence into the four ABO blood types has given way to DNA fingerprinting. What is science fiction today will be standard practice tomorrow.

## See Also

**Death Investigation Systems:** China; Nordic Countries; Certification of Death and the United Kingdom System

## Further Reading

Combs HR (1998) Medical examiner and coroner systems: history and trends. *Journal of the American Medical Association* 18: 870–874.

Criteria for Reportable Cases to the Coroner's Office. Available at www.co.rock.wi.us/departments/Coroner/report_cases.htm.

DiMaio VJ (2001) *Forensic Pathology.* Boca Raton, FL: CRC Press.

Hanzlick R (1995) History of the National Association of Medical Examiners and its meeting, 1966–93. *American Journal of Forensic Medicine and Pathology* 16: 278–313.

Hanzlick R, Combs D (1998) Medical examiner and coroner systems: history and trends. *Journal of the American Medical Association* 279: 870–874.

History of Forensic Medicine. Available at www.autopsy-md.com/History.html.

Howard J Pierce County Medical Examiner. Available at www.co.pierce.wa.us/pa/abtus/ourorg/me/guide.htm.

Knight B (1999) *History of the Medieval English Coroner System.* Available at www.britannia.com/history/coroner1.html.

*Medicolegal Death Investigation System: Workshop Summary* (2003) Washington, DC: National Academies Press.

Simpson K, Knight B (1985) *Forensic Medicine.* London: Edward Arnold.

Spitz WU (1980) *Medicolegal Investigation of Death.* Springfield, IL: Charles C.Thomas.

The Office of the Coroner. Available at www.state.in.us/ctb/pdf.

US Department of Justice. *Death Investigation: A Guide for the Scene Investigator* (1999) US Department of Justice. Washington, DC: US Department of Justice Office of Justice Program.

Wadee SA (1994) Forensic pathology – a different perspective: investigative medicolegal systems in the United States. *Medical Law* 13: 519–530.

Wecht CH (1999) *Forensic Science.* New York: Matthew Bender.

**Death, Legal Definitions of**  *See* Legal Definitions of Death

**Death, Medical Definitions of**  *See* Medical Definitions of Death

**Death, Post-mortem findings: Asphyxia**  *See* Asphyxia

**Death, Post-mortem Findings: Acute and Chronic Alcohol Use**  *See* Alcohol: Acute and Chronic Use, Postmortem Findings

**Death, Post-mortem Findings, Carbon Monoxide Poisoning**  *See* Carbon Monoxide Poisoning: Incidence and Findings at Postmortem

**Death, Post-mortem Findings, Drowning**  *See* Autopsy, Findings: Drowning

**Death: Post-mortem Findings - Falls from Height, Adult**  *See* Falls from Height, Physical Findings: In Adults

**Death: Post-mortem Findings - Falls from Height, Pediatric**  *See* Falls from Height, Physical Findings: In Children

**Death, Post-mortem Findings: Sudden Infant Death Syndrome**  *See* Autopsy, Findings: Sudden Infant Death Syndrome

# DECOMPOSITION, PATTERNS AND RATES

**M K Marks and M A Tersigni**, University of
Tennessee, Knoxville, TN, USA

## Introduction

Forensic pathologists spend the majority of their careers examining the fresh, or recently expired, decedent rendering expert opinion on cause and manner of death, identity, and time since death. Estimations of time since death in the recently deceased follow a traditional, time-honored understanding of algor, livor, and rigor mortis that substantiate a "ballpark," but legally defensible, estimation for the legal community they serve. Exposure to bodies subjected to extended postmortem time prior to discovery comes from years of practical experience appropriate for understanding those events even more vague than the highly variable mortis occurrences. In fact, most expertise in understanding the postmortem processes of human soft-tissue decomposition is primarily acquired by rare case-based examples, reinforced by similar cases, unfortunately, sometimes only through memory long after the remains have left the facility.

Pathologists venture estimations of time since death into the bloat stage of decomposition and even after perforation of the thoracoabdominal wall. However, once viscera and tissues have liquefied or desiccated, they become hard-pressed to discern any meaningful histological evidence or pathological processes and are unable to rule on cause of death. Keeping in mind that temperature primarily guides the postmortem decomposition process, most routine forensic pathological protocol can become abbreviated in as little as 1 week after death.

At the other extreme of postmortem time, the biological anthropologist traditionally examines museum collections of prehistoric and historic skeletons that are long devoid of the moist soft-tissue envelope so important to forensic pathology. Their examination involves the odontoskeletal system only and, while they may be able to venture a manner of death, provided there are perimortem traumatic signatures, little else is possible.

This is not to imply that pathologists are not astute in the examination of bone or that anthropologists know nothing about soft tissue. By virtue of the research facility, forensic anthropology is now developing a legally defensible battery of expertise to collaborate with forensic pathologists in understanding the complex processes between fresh remains and skeletal remains.

## Anthropological Research Facility

There has been remarkable progress in our understanding of the complexities of the later postmortem process of soft-tissue decomposition since the late 1970s. Much of this knowledge stems not only from the burgeoning development of forensic anthropology as a discipline within the American Academy of Forensic Sciences and a resource for forensic pathological inquiry, but from the formation and maintenance of an outdoor research facility at the University of Tennessee, USA, where these processes of human soft-tissue decomposition have been studied. William M. Bass envisioned firsthand witnessing of these processes in a natural setting with bodies donated to scientific research. Presently, 600 donations have been received at the research facility. The facility is a wooded 4-acre tract protected by a chain link fence with razor wire and a privacy fence and under constant surveillance. While carnivores are inhibited from inside access, rodents often gain access.

The facility provides the unique opportunity to study longitudinally the accumulated effects of decomposition of soft tissues under a wide range of variables, including temperature and humidity, clothing, burial, water submersion, effects of sun exposure, and body posture/gravity. Also examined are biochemical soil change, odor, and burial/grave testing using ground-penetrating radar technology. Finally, the lion's share of forensic entomology is derived from facility research. Most of this research has been fueled by collaboration with law enforcement and our attempts to stage research that answers specific problems relating to time since death.

This natural laboratory holds a colossal advantage over the cross-sectional exposure provided by isolated decomposition cases introduced to the forensic pathologist. No matter how accurate the assessment of postmortem time may be, after identification the remains are removed for burial/cremation without any opportunity to study the progression of the events. So, the pathologist gains expertise in soft-tissue decomposition after a career of exposure gaining confidence for testimony. No one doubts the time since death testimony afforded by the senior forensic pathologist armed with a career of cases. However, the resident or new pathologist has little recourse as a result of limited exposure to decomposed bodies and therefore is poorly equipped to render expert opinion.

The facility allows examination and appreciation of decomposition daily, weekly, monthly, and even, annually. In a sense, the research facility is one giant validation study.

Besides a laboratory to study decomposition, the research facility provides an outdoor classroom for training graduate students in forensic anthropology. The bulk of the research conducted has been formulated through their interests as associated with particular crime-scene events. Also, local, regional, state, and national law enforcement agencies, members of the medicolegal community into whose service the forensic anthropologist is called, as well as canine search and rescue teams, are afforded the training opportunity in clandestine grave discovery and excavation techniques at the research facility.

The anthropological research facility contributes to forensic science by enumerating the changes that occur during decomposition of human remains related to temperature and other previously described variables. Through this type of longitudinal study, researchers have determined the sequence of stages through which human remains move to reach the skeletal state. Some of these stages are better correlated with time since death than others, but nonetheless, each body, if allowed to decompose naturally, will eventually undergo each of the following stages.

## Stages of Decomposition

The biochemical process of internal decomposition begins immediately at clinical death with a process called autolysis. Autolysis is the irreversible cascade of cell death that destroys structural integrity and the cell-to-cell junction. Besides leading to widespread tissue necrosis, autolysis triggers three events that produce the three familiar externally visible manifestations: algor, livor, and rigor mortis. Algor mortis is internal cooling of the body to ambient temperature. Livor mortis is the gravitational pooling of blood in the capillary beds of dependent body parts. Initially, livor mortis is "unfixed" and gentle pressure on a livor area will blanch. After 8–12 h, livor becomes "fixed" as capillary blood begins clotting. Rigor mortis is stiffening of muscles fibers after death, resulting from the flood of calcium ions into the sarcomere (contractile units of the muscle fiber). During life, this calcium is pushed back into the sarcoplasmic reticulum by adenosine triphosphate (ATP), but with little or no ATP production at death, increased calcium causes muscle contraction. Rigor starts 2–6 h after death, typically manifested by stiffness in the jaw and neck, and then spreading to the rest of the body over the next 4–6 h and lasting from 24–48 h after onset. These temporal estimates are just that, estimates, and pathologists have

long recognized situations of delayed onset or abbreviated duration based primarily upon temperature. Similarly, temperature controls the onset, tempo, and duration of the remaining postmortem processes of decomposition.

One of the externally visible signs of autolysis is skin slippage. During autolysis, the junction of the epidermis and dermis is weakened by the release of hydrolytic enzymes. This loosening allows the epidermal layer to slip off the dermal layer, giving rise to the term skin slippage (**Figure 1**).

The products liberated by autolysis fuel the next process of decomposition: putrefaction. Putrefaction is the consumption of soft tissues through the exponential proliferation of endogenous enteric bacteria. It is caused by release of acidic autolyzed cellular contents that, along with an almost completely anaerobic environment, creates a perfect environment for bacterial proliferation. This first occurs in the cecum where the largest population of endogenous bacteria is found (**Figure 2**).

Hydrogen sulfide ($H_2S$) gas is a byproduct of this bacterial growth from the interaction with the iron in hemoglobin to form a black precipitate, ferrous sulfide (FeS). This darkening is the agent that discolors the body's circulatory architecture as intravascular hemolysis/marbling (**Figure 3**).

Initially, other cecal discoloration is caused by the hydrolytic enzymes attacking the biliary system to release biliverdin, bilirubin, and urobilin pigments into the abdominal tissues. The bloating stage results from the release of vast amounts of hydrogen sulfide within the body's organs and cavities from bacterial growth in the anaerobic environment. This gas diffuses with ease through body tissue due to its

**Figure 1** Skin slippage on the plantar portion of the foot associated with early decomposition. This phenomenon occurs due to the weakening of the junction between the dermis and epidermis during decomposition, causing the epidermis to slip away from the dermis.

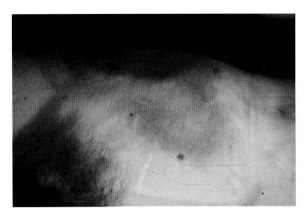

**Figure 2** Purplish-green discoloration in the cecal region of the lower right abdominal quadrant associated with early decomposition caused by the proliferation of endogenous bacteria producing hydrogen sulfide in a now anerobic environment.

**Figure 4** An adult male in full bloat 2 weeks postmortem during late spring. Note the extreme expansion of the abdominal cavity causing splitting of the soft tissue of the lateral chest wall. Also note the elevated posture of the pelvic limbs.

**Figure 3** The marbling pattern (intravascular hemolysis) of the circulatory system that appears in early decomposition, caused by the invasion of the circulatory system by hydrogen sulfide gas, producing bacteria. This same process of gas production results in the bloating that is characteristic of the middle stages of decomposition.

small molecular structure. Gas accumulation within the body causes distension of the abdomen and swelling of limbs and facial structures (**Figure 4**).

## Insect Activity

It is during the bloat phase that insects become a major factor in the modification of tissues. Forensic entomologists learned that insect growth, feeding, and migration are generally genus-specific and are as driven by temperature, daily and seasonally, as the events of internal biochemical decomposition. Sarcophagic insects and their activity are the litmus test for soft-tissue reactions during decomposition.

Insect interest in a dead body is instantaneous upon placement at the Anthropological Research Facility.

Blowflies are usually first to arrive, ovipositing in any natural or traumatically created shaded orifice. These include the ears, nostrils, mouth, eyes, hair, and the shaded regions of the genital region and the ground–body interface. At the crime scene, detection of differential decomposition of soft tissues and insect activity in areas other than these regions signals peri- or postmortem trauma that has provided an artificial segue for ovipositing (and subsequent feeding).

It is important to realize that, while numerous arthropods habituate the host off and on during the entire decomposition tenure, blowfly larvae (maggots) are responsible for ingesting 95% of the body mass. After eggs hatch, larvae develop through three distinct stages of growth that are termed instars. After the final stage, third-instar maggots migrate away from the body, seeking a dark, cool, subterranean location (or clothing) to generate a pupal casing where they remain until emerging as adult blowflies.

The entomologist, using a strategy of collecting a representative sample of maggot sizes on the body to capture growth variation, and looking away from the body for pupal casings, can estimate with confidence the length of time the body has been colonized and thus narrow a postmortem interval. At the beginning of the drying phase, other arthropod species become more interested in the tissues and sites of fluid runoff. These include, but are not exclusive to, dermestid beetles, ants, wasps, and other types of beetle that continue to ingest the drying skin and remaining cartilaginous regions. By determining species, one can identify the most reliable postmortem interval, as some species, for example, will not colonize when the remains are too moist or too dry (see **Decomposition, Patterns and Rates**).

As bloat subsides, deflation of the abdomen occurs, with drying of the skin. Drying begins at exposed tissue margins, that is, lips, nose, eyelids, and wounds, besides hands and feet. Generally, on the level of the entire body, drying follows bloat, but specific regions dry more quickly (tissue margins) than the rest of the body. The drying stage refers to the drying of the entire body or large portions of it, not these focal areas. Coincident with drying is rib head and cervical bone exposure. It is not uncommon for the stages of bloat and drying to coincide.

If the soft tissues (including skin) have not been destroyed or decomposed by bacteria or arthropods, there are two avenues in which decomposition can proceed in order to reach a skeletonized state: adipocere formation and/or mummification. Adipocere is a white or cream-colored waxy, homogeneous substance derived from body fat that may form during the decomposition of remains in a moist environment, that is, water submersion, damp grave. The chemical process is termed saponification and used interchangeably with adipocere formation. Adipocere formation appears to benefit from a catalyst of alkaline, such as formaldehyde, which is commonly used in embalming fluid. Yet, certain soils are highly alkaline, which also contributes to adipocere formation. Alkaline will hydrolyze the fat, turning it into this soap-like substance.

Mummification is the drying of soft tissues to take on a hard, leathery appearance. This is most common in arid areas with low humidity or little precipitation. However, it is the terminal stage in soft-tissue decomposition processes at the anthropological research facility, even though mummification happens more quickly in dry arid environments. The speed with which moisture and fluids evacuate the body is much quicker in an arid environment, though no time estimates can be given due to lack of a research facility in that climate. Complete mummification often occurs in individuals with little body fat since fat can have enough moisture content to prevent complete mummification (**Figure 5**).

## Estimation of Time Since Death (TSD)

Accumulated degree days (ADD) are defined as the total number of degrees accumulated in a given time period, represented by the highest temperature for each period. Thus, the ADD for a week is the highest temperature for each day, added to that of the following day. So, if the temperature is $20\,^{\circ}\text{C}$ each day, the ADD for the week is $140\,^{\circ}\text{C}$ ($7 \times 20 = 140$). Vass used this measure to track the degree of decomposition, thereby linking temperature with time. Essentially, if a body was in $x$ state of decomposition,

**Figure 5** An adult male in mummified stage of decomposition (2 months after death) prior to skeletonization.

based on the chemical breakdown of certain lipids, Vass could backtrack the length of time the body had been exposed by adding up the temperatures for the preceding days and comparing that to actualistic studies performed at the facility. This provided a standard for chemical values versus the ADD to be set. This standard would be compared to the chemical values found at a crime scene and the corresponding ADD value could be used to determine the length of time since death. With the ADD value, the TSD (time since death) estimate is calculated by removing the temperatures from the preceding days until this equals 0. This would give an estimate of the number of days the body had been decomposing in that area.

Marks and colleagues used ADD but compared them to stages of decomposition. The ADD was not consistent across decomposition stages and the researchers were hard-pressed to get narrowed ADD estimates to fall within single decomposition stages for every body. Instead, there was an overlap of overlap upon different stages of decomposition. The problem may be that ADD is not representative of the "amount" of accumulated temperature and does not take into account the 24-h temperature fluctuations. Vass also recognized this and attempted to correct it by adjusting ADD to cumulative degree hours (CDH). This measure represents an average value of each 12-h period (the high + the low/2). Thus, if temperature is $10\,^{\circ}\text{C}$ at 12 P.M. and $0\,^{\circ}\text{C}$ at 12 A.M., the CDH would be 5. For one day, there are two calculations of CDH (one for each 12-h period).

We have found that this procedure does not adequately characterize the temperature fluctuations in a 24-h period either, and, if a body decomposition scene is not covered by a temperature gauge, then it is virtually unusable. These problems are currently being resolved through ongoing facility experimentation.

**Figure 6** A woman in differential decomposition. Note the advanced state of decomposition of the head, which has been completely blackened, while the rest of the body retains a near-natural skin color.

This plethora of research in determining time since death implies that there are many circumstances and variables that affect postmortem interval estimation. It is by no means an exact science but rather an approximation. One major result of this longitudinal study affords the researcher the luxury of seeing commonality between the decomposition processes of each body, and more importantly, the ability to discern where the normal process of decomposition has been compromised or altered. Nowhere is this more applicable than in forensic cases that display differential decomposition. Differential decomposition is the term used to describe a situation where one body exhibits different stages of decomposition in different parts of the body. It is paramount for a forensic anthropologist to determine what caused this differentiation. For example, **Figure 6** depicts a forensic case where the body of a woman was found in a wooded area. It is clear that her head is in a more advanced state of decomposition than the rest of her body. The goal is to determine why the head has moved more quickly through the decomposition phases, or perhaps, why the decomposition of the rest of the body has been retarded.

## Conclusion

We realize that the process of decomposition is regionally variable: temperatures and humidity that guide decomposition in the southeast will probably not apply to other regions of the USA. However, all bodies will go through the same itemized changes. Decomposition will not skip stages, but the specific chronology of change will vary slightly from victim to victim based on other variables.

It is important to realize that, regardless of location in postmortem time, decipherment of human decomposition will never be an exact science. Like growth and development, decomposition is a biological continuum that cannot be easily quantified and qualified. Hence, understanding the deterioration of multiple criteria is necessary to best satisfy our curiosity. The anthropological research facility provides a unique opportunity to understand the processes of human soft-tissue decomposition and the research agenda is partially fueled by collaboration and consultation within the medicolegal community. The research potential of the facility, not unlike a crime scene, provides a crossroads where the perspectives of many forensic investigators intersect and flourish.

## See Also

**Anthropology:** Morphological Age Estimation; Sex Determination; **Back-tracking Calculations**; **Entomology**; **Postmortem Changes:** Overview; Postmortem Interval

## Further Reading

Bass WM, Jefferson J (2003) *Death's Acre: inside the legendary forensic lab the Body Farm where the dead do tell tales.* New York: G.P. Putnam's Sons.

Byrd JH, Castner JL (eds.) (2001) *Forensic Entomology – The Utility of Arthropods in Legal Investigations.* Boca Raton, FL: CRC Press.

Catts EP, Haskell NH (1990) *Entomology and Death – A Procedural Guide.* Clemson, SC: Joyce's Print Shop.

Love JC (2001) Evaluation of decay odor as a time since death indicator/Jennifer Cheryl Love. University of Tennessee Dissertation: Hodges Library/Thesis/ Dissertation.

Love JC, Marks MK (2003) Taphonomy and time: estimating the postmortem interval. In: Steadman DE (ed.) *Hard Evidence: Case Studies in Physical Anthropology.* Upper Saddle River, NJ: Prentice-Hall.

O'Brien TG (1994) Human soft-tissue decomposition in an aquatic environment and its transformation into adipocere/Tyler G. O'Brien—Haglund 1.

Marks MK, Love JC, Elkins SK (2000) Time since death: A practical guide to physical postmortem events. *American Journal of Forensic Science Proceedings.*

Miller ML (2002) Coupling ground penetrating radar applications with continually changing decomposing human targets: an effort to enhance search strategies of buried human remains. Michelle Lee Miller. University of Tennessee Thesis: Hodges Library/Electronic Thesis.

Miller RA (2002) The affects of clothing on human decomposition: implications for estimating time since death. Robyn Ann Miller. University of Tennessee Thesis: Hodges Library/Thesis/Dissertation.

Srnka CF (2003) The effects of sun and shade on the early stages of human decomposition. Carrie F Srnka. University of Tennessee Thesis. Hodges Library/Thesis/Dissertation.

Vass AA (1992) Time since death determinations of human cadavers utilizing soil solution. Arpad Alexander Vass. University of Tennessee Dissertation Hodges Library/ Thesis.

# DELIBERATE SELF-HARM, PATTERNS

**J Payne-James**, Forensic Healthcare Services Ltd, London, UK

## Introduction

Individuals may harm themselves in many ways and for many different reasons. These factors may themselves be influenced by a variety of personal and cultural factors. In many cases, the method of self-harm is clear and unambiguous. An individual who survives an attempt at self-harm will generally be able to give an account as to the reasons for the attempt. In fatal self-harm, the circumstances may not clearly indicate self-harm and thus investigation will be required to determine the circumstances surrounding the death. The stigma associated with self-harm in some societies means that it is important to establish clearly whether suicide was intended. In some jurisdictions (e.g., England and Wales), a coroner will give a verdict of suicide only when strict criteria have been applied to the circumstances. A belief that a suicide attempt was intended may be a misinterpretation in other circumstances, e.g., autoerotic asphyxia. An attempt at hiding criminal activity may result in the staging of a death to look like suicide. It is thus clear that the investigation of puzzling or unusual deaths should be rigorous and extensive. This article will focus predominantly on the range of physical patterns of injury where the question of deliberate self-harm may be obscured, misinterpreted, or misleading.

## Range of Self-Harm

In the living individual attempts at self-harm or self-multilation may indeed be deliberate acts, but can occasionally mask other activities. One example is the need to try and differentiate between injuries in torture cases, where it may be extremely difficult to determine whether an injury is self-inflicted or accidental by evaluating solely the distribution of traumatic lesions or scars on the patient's body. **Table 1** gives further examples of the potential motives for self-harm, over and above an intent to commit suicide because of depression.

It is important to realize that patterns of deliberate self-harm vary from country to country, from culture to culture and also depend on the occupation and characteristics of the self-harmer. Reviews of studies from around the world indicate variations in incidence and methods of self-harm that may result in death or injury. In Oman, most cases involve females, students, or the unemployed, with a high incidence of family, marital, and psychiatric or social problems. The methods used most often are the use of analgesics (e.g., paracetamol) and nonpharmaceutical medications. Self-burning is rare in Europe, but a study from Iran showed a high incidence, with an average age of 27 years, 83% of them being female. Most were married homemakers with high-school education; 62% had had an impulsive suicidal intention and the major motive was marital conflict. The mortality rate was 79%. A similar study on cases of self-inflicted burns in Australia showed the presence of schizophrenia, depression, and personality disorder in 71%, with the majority of the remainder showing evidence of intoxication. These cases were divided into attempted suicides almost all of which involved males, and 60% had a major psychiatric illness, and "self mutilations," where the self-harmers suffered much less serious burns and all survived. In the UK, a recent study found that self-harm in 15–16-year-old schoolchildren was more common in females than males (11.2% vs. 3.2%). For females, the factors associated with self-harm included: self-harm by friends, self-harm by family members, drug misuse, depression, anxiety, impulsivity, and low self-esteem. For males, the associated factors were suicidal behavior in friends and family members, drug use, and low self-esteem. Other diagnoses with strong links with potential for self-harm include bulimia (almost 25% reporting suicide attempts), and this increased to about 50% where there is a dual diagnosis of alcoholism. A recent review of the epidemiology of parasuicide (defined as suicide attempts and deliberate self-harm inflicted with no intent to die) from the USA showed an annual rate of parasuicide within the last three decades as ranging from 2.56 to 11 000 per 100 000 and lifetime prevalence rates ranging from 720 to

**Table 1** Examples of reasons why individuals may self-harm

Psychiatric and associated disorders
Malice (attempting to give the impression that the individual has been assaulted by another)
Allegations of sexual assault
To avoid work (prevented by the injury)
To "reinforce" or "re-emphasize" an injury that already exists
Attention-seeking behavior
Insurance fraud
Benefits fraud
Factitious injury – to imply a medical problem (e.g., a slow-healing skin ulcer)

**Table 2**   Characteristics that may be associated with self-harm injury

| Characteristic | Additional comments |
| --- | --- |
| On an area of the body that the individual can access themselves | Sites less accessible (e.g., the middle of the back) are less likely |
| Superficial or minor injury (see **Figures 2, 4, 5, 6** and **9**) | More severe injury may be caused, particularly in those with a psychiatric disorder |
| If there is more than one cut, the cuts are of similar appearance, style, and orientation (see **Figures 5** and **6**) | Typically self-inflicted cutting injuries are more superficial, numerous, and similar than those sustained in an assault from another, where the natural reaction of the injured person is to avoid repeated injury |
| Other types of injuries (e.g., scratches, cigarette burns) are of similar appearance, style, and orientation (see **Figures 2, 4, 8** and **9**) | As above; more than one similar injury should raise an index of suspicion as to the possibility of self-infliction |
| Multiple similar injuries (see **Figures 2, 4, 5, 6** and **8**) | Raise a high index of suspicion as to the possibility of self-infliction |
| Parallel injuries (see **Figures 4, 5** and **9**) | As above |
| Injuries are grouped in a single anatomical region (see **Figures 2, 4, 5** and **6**) | As above |
| Injuries are grouped on the contralateral side to the patient's handedness (see **Figures 1, 2, 5** and **6**) | Right-handed person will tend to inflict harm on the left-hand side of the body and vice-versa |
| Tentative injuries (see **Figure 1**) | Smaller or lesser injuries grouped with the main injuries suggest initial "tentative" attempts at self-harm |
| Old healed scars in similar sites (see **Figures 4** and **6**) | May indicate previous attempts at self-harm |
| Scars of different ages in similar sites (see **Figures 5** and **6**) | May indicate repeated previous attempts at self-harm |
| Slow-healing injuries (see **Figure 7**) | Persistence of wounds that would otherwise have been expected to heal in the absence of any other factors |
| Psychiatric and related issues – such as eating disorders, drug or alcohol misuse | |

5930 per 100 000. The most important risk factors were younger age and female gender. Other important factors included being single or divorced, being unemployed, having a recent change in living situation, and having a previous parasuicide incident.

## Identification and Interpretation of Self-Harm Injury

Individuals injure themselves for a number of reasons, including psychiatric illness or motives of gain. Self-inflicted injuries have a number of characteristics, which are not diagnostic, but which together may give an indication of self-inflicted. In many cases, the individual will admit to having self-harmed. The role that is most relevant to that of the forensic practitioner is to be able to assist with the determination of whether an injury is self-inflicted, particularly if the injured person denies it or gives an account that conflicts with the appearance of the wound or the accounts of witnesses. If the self-inflicted fits the type and pattern of wounds it should be compared with the various characteristics referred to in **Table 2**. **Table 2** and **Figures 1–9** identify and illustrate characteristics of injury that suggest self-infliction. Some or all of these characteristics, commonly inflicted by some object (e.g., a knife or a nail), may be present but it is important to reinforce that only some and

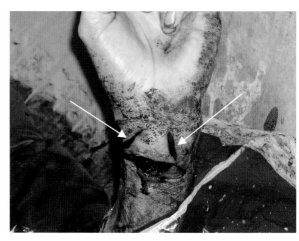

**Figure 1**   The left wrist of a right-handed male who had left a note indicating his intention to commit suicide. Death was caused by exsanguination following cutting with a sharp knife from the main wound seen running transversely across the wrist – both ulnar and radial arteries were severed. The two arrows show two lesser cuts – tentative injuries which are characteristic of self-harm.

rarely all may be present. The absence of a particular characteristic does not preclude self-infliction nor does the presence necessarily imply self-infliction. Of course, it also may be possible that despite an injury being associated with all the relevant characteristics it may not be self-inflicted.

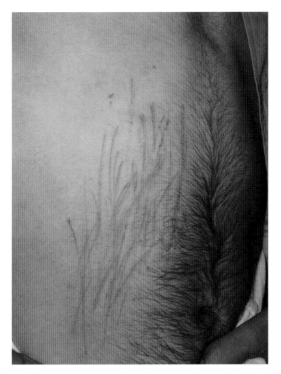

**Figure 2** Multiple superficial minor scratches to the right-hand side of the abdomen in a young male who was left-handed. He presented to a police station alleging he had been robbed of his wallet and wristwatch and had been stabbed by his assailant with broken glass, which had caused these injuries. He had been wearing a T-shirt, which was undamaged. Confronted with the suggestion that the lesions were self-inflicted, he admitted this. His motive appeared to be to make an insurance claim for his wallet and wristwatch, and the injuries were created to reinforce his story. Reproduced with permission from J Payne-James, "Assault and Injury in the Living", from Jason Payne-James, Anthony Busuttil, William Smock, *Forensic Medicine: Clinical and Pathological Aspects*, 2003. Greenwich Medical Media, now published by Cambridge University Press.

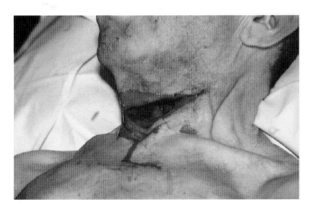

**Figure 3** A serious attempt at self-harm by a male with chronic schizophrenia. This 60-year-old psychotic male took a kitchen knife to his neck transecting deep structures including trachea and oesophagus. He survived following surgery and remained well after reassessment and reinstigation of his antipsychotic medication. Reproduced with permission from J Payne-James, "Assault and Injury in the Living", from Jason Payne-James, Anthony Busuttil, William Smock, *Forensic Medicine: Clinical and Pathological Aspects*, 2003. Greenwich Medical Media, now published by Cambridge University Press.

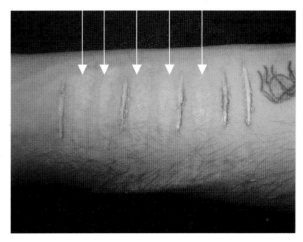

**Figure 4** Multiple linear parallel fresh injuries to the volar aspect of the forearm. These injuries were created by the self-application of a knife heated over a gas stove. This 24-year-old Asian male had been self-harming in this manner since the age of 15, and closer observation shows the healed scars of previous similar attempts (arrows). Reproduced with permission from J Payne-James, "Assault and Injury in the Living", from Jason Payne-James, Anthony Busuttil, William Smock, *Forensic Medicine: Clinical and Pathological Aspects*, 2003. Greenwich Medical Media, now published by Cambridge University Press.

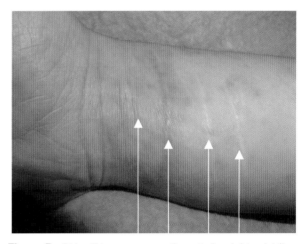

**Figure 5** Old self-harm scars on the anterior right wrist (in a left-handed person; arrows) – with no fresh injuries – in a male arrested for a driving offence and brought into police custody. The male denied episodes of previous self-harm. He had in fact a long history of self-cutting – the image here shows scars of different ages – and significant overdoses. The image shows pale, barely visible pink and white scars of previous attempts at self-harm. Such scars can easily be missed and should be specifically sought, where concerns of self-harm are evident.

## Examples of Deliberate Self-Harm

Many examples of self-harm may be subtle and only detectable on close examination. The importance of detecting current or previous self-harm in the living is related to the need to care or treat that individual. For example, a young female given a prison sentence may be at particular risk of self-harming, and if the risk factors have been identified then processes can be put

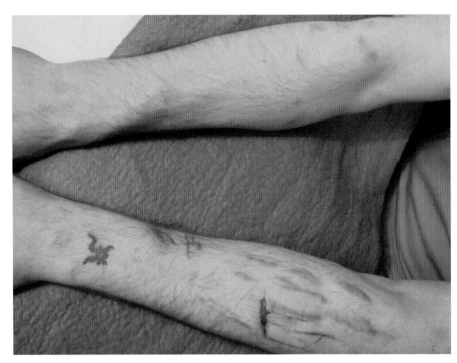

**Figure 6** Arms of a male who had self-harmed for many years. His motivation was to get doctors to provide medication that he wanted (benzodiazepines). Failure to accede to his demands would result in a nonfatal attempt at self-harm. The photograph illustrates many of the features of self-harm – multiple, similar appearance, relatively superficial or minor, of different ages, sited contralaterally to handedness (he was right-handed).

in place to attempt to reduce the risk of self-harm occurring. Equally, recognition of patterns of self-harm seen in the community may permit arrangements to be made for assessment and review with mental health or related services to attempt to treat any of the predisposing factors for self-harm. Early recognition of nonfatal attempts at self-harm may prevent a successful attempt at suicide in the future. This is an area of great significance, for instance, for prison officials where the profile of those incarcerated may be exactly those of individuals more likely to self-harm. The examples below illustrate some of the important characteristics when attempting to determine whether self-harm is a factor in injury.

There are also instances where injuries may be due to self-harm but the individual may be self-harming without deliberate intent – but perhaps due to alcohol and drug misuse or psychiatric illness.

Deliberate self-harm is a common occurrence around the world, although the nature of such self-harm may vary widely according to the country and culture. Many incidences of self-harm whether non-fatal or fatal are obvious and admitted to by the person self-harming. Injuries caused by self-harm may be indistinguishable from injuries caused by other agents or individuals, but there are certain characteristics which may assist in determining whether or not self-harm is involved. As with any

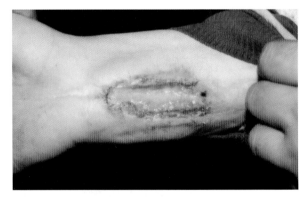

**Figure 7** Right forearm of a male alcoholic with a personality disorder. At the time of the photograph, this unhealed ulcer had been of similar appearance for about 4 years. Healing would only take place when the patient was admitted to hospital and treated with close monitoring and occlusive dressings. There were no other causative factors. This factitious injury was used as a means of eliciting sympathy when begging. Reproduced with permission from J Payne-James, ''Assault and Injury in the Living'', from Jason Payne-James, Anthony Busuttil, William Smock, *Forensic Medicine: Clinical and Pathological Aspects*, 2003. Greenwich Medical Media, now published by Cambridge University Press.

injury, appropriate history, from the individual and others and appropriate examination of the injuries will assist considerably in attempting to answer the questions about causation of injury, how and by whom.

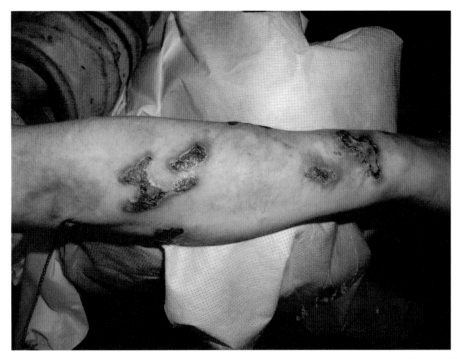

**Figure 8** An example of a female crack addict who would scratch herself repeatedly when under the influence of crack, creating a mass of open excoriated sores all over her body that failed to heal. The lesions, although unusual, are of similar shape and style and the scars of healed similar lesions (which healed at the times she was in prison and drug-free) are evident between the current active lesions.

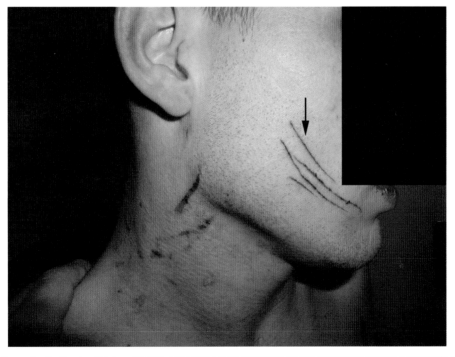

**Figure 9** A mixture of actual assault injury (in this case fingernail scratches to the right neck during a domestic dispute) and self-inflicted injury to the right cheek area (shown with an arrow) where the ''victim'' had attempted to make the injuries look more extensive and more impressive for the purpose of a criminal trial. The neck scratches were abrasions totally consistent with nail scratches, but the cheek injuries (which were each of a similar nature – superficial, parallel, and multiple) were subsequently admitted after discussion to have been caused by the ''victim'' with a metal nail.

## See Also

**Asphyxia**; **Autoerotic Death**; **Custody:** Death in, United Kingdom and Continental Europe; Death in, United States of America; **Injury, Fatal and Nonfatal:** Sharp and Cutting-Edge Wounds; **Suicide:** Etiology, Methods and Statistics; Parasuicide; Youth Suicide

## Further Reading

Bragg WD, Hoover EL, Turner EA, *et al.* (1992) Profile of trauma due to violence in a statewide prison population. *Southern Medical Journal* 85: 365–369.

Cameron DR, Pegg SP, Muller M, *et al.* (1997) Self-inflicted burns. *Burns* 23: 519–521.

Hawton K, Rodham K, Evans E, *et al.* (2002) Deliberate self-harm in adolescents and the factors associated with it. *British Medical Journal* 325: 1207–1211.

Kirschner R, Peel M (2002) Physical examination for late signs of torture. In: Peel M, Iacopino V (eds.) *The Medical Documentation of Torture.* London: Greenwich Medical Media.

Knight B (ed.) (1996) *Forensic Pathology,* 2nd edn. London: Edward Arnold.

Ohshima T, Kondo T (1997) Eight cases of suicide by self-cutting or stabbing: consideration from medicolegal viewpoints of differentiation between suicide and homicide. *Journal of Clinical Forensic Medicine* 4: 127–132.

Ozkalipci O (2002) Physical examination following allegations of recent torture. In: Peel M, Iacopino V (eds.) *The Medical Documentation of Torture.* London: Greenwich Medical Media.

Purdue BN (2000) Cutting and piercing wounds. In: Mason JK, Purdue BN (eds.) *The Pathology of Trauma,* 3rd edn. London: Edward Arnold.

Sansone RA, Levitt JL (2002) Self-harm behaviors among those with eating disorders: an overview. *Eating Disorders* 10: 205–213.

Welch SS (2001) A review of the literature on the epidemiology of parasuicide in the general population. *Psychiatric Services* 52: 368–375.

Zaidan ZAJ, Burke DT, Dorvlo ASS, *et al.* (2002) Deliberate self-poisoning in Oman. *Tropical Medicine and International Health* 7: 549–556.

Zarghami M, Khalilian A (2002) Deliberate self-burning in Mazandaran, Iran. *Burns* 28: 115–119.

# DETAINEES

## Contents

Care in Police Custody, United Kingdom
Care in Prison Custody, United Kingdom
Fitness to be Interviewed

## Care in Police Custody, United Kingdom

**J Payne-James**, Forensic Healthcare Services Ltd, London, UK
**S Robinson**, Altrincham, UK

### Introduction

The term detainee in police custody is used generally in this setting in most cases to indicate an individual who has been arrested and brought to the police station for investigation of an alleged crime. It will also include those who have been brought to a police station for questioning about an offense, or who have been charged with an offense and are awaiting transfer to court, or who have been lodged in a police station by other authorities (e.g., customs and excise, immigration) whilst undergoing investigation or awaiting transfer. In general such detainees will remain for only a short time – rarely more than 48 h if charged for court, although in exceptional cases (e.g., prevention of terrorism) certain detainees may remain in a police station rather than being transferred to longer-term prison custody.

### Roles of a Healthcare Professional

The health, safety, and welfare of any person detained in police custody are important to both the individual and to the body responsible for health and welfare. A doctor or any other healthcare professional may be given the responsibility of assessing an individual and determining whether or not he/she is fit (physically and mentally) to remain in the custody of the police, and if so, whether any particular measures may be required to ensure that his/her health, safety, and welfare are maintained. This may put certain pressures on the healthcare professional as his/her professional duties may conflict with his/her roles for police in matters of police procedure or forensic interpretation. The term "three-faced" doctor has been used to draw attention to the therapeutic, police, and forensic roles that may all interact when an individual is seen in police custody for whatever reason.

Table 1 lists a range of purposes for which a doctor may be required by the police to see a detainee in police custody. Doctors in particular have clearly defined duties of confidentiality to detainees who require therapeutic intervention – although there are certain situations where duty to the public may override the duty to the individual – specifically with regard to serious crime and harm to others. Certain detainees may not be able to provide consent for examination (for example, some with mental health issues, or intoxicated through drugs or alcohol). Doctors are advised that they should place the individual's welfare first and then proceed to assess someone without consent, although the reasons why the decision was made should be very clearly documented in contemporaneous medical records. The need for consent, for example, when taking forensic samples, is the same as in the general medical setting. Police procedure and statute sometimes conflict with this duty, but medical defense organizations reinforce the need for consent strongly and any practitioner who feels coerced into undertaking procedures without consent should seek advice immediately from his/her medical defense organization.

Within England and Wales the Police and Criminal Evidence Act 1984 (PACE) guides police in matters involving those persons detained in police custody (detainees). In particular, the Codes of Practice advise specifically on when an appropriate healthcare professional (generally a doctor but also possibly a nurse or paramedic) should be called to assess detainees. These guidelines are shown in Table 2 and Table 3. These guidelines reflect the increased awareness of the need to identify those who are at risk of death or harm in custody. Although of different jurisdictions, Scotland and Northern Ireland have broadly similar approaches to the care of detainees. The British Medical Association and the Association of Forensic Physicians (formerly the Association of Police Surgeons) have specifically addressed the special circumstances of detainees in police custody in the publication *Health Care of Detainees in Police Stations.*

On arrival at the detention area within the police station, the doctor should determine exactly who had

**Table 1**  Examples of reasons for assessment of detainees in police custody

Fitness to detain
Fitness to interview
Fitness to charge
Fitness to release
Fitness to transfer
Mental health assessment
Assault and injury
Road traffic offenses (blood samples/driving under influence/ failure to provide samples)
Obtaining forensic samples

**Table 2**  Police and Criminal Evidence Act 1984 – Codes of Practice (April 2003): guidelines to assist police on care of detainees and need for appropriate healthcare professional

Para 9.3
Detainees should be visited every hour
Those suspected of being intoxicated through drink or drugs or whose level of consciousness causes concern must, subject to any clinical directions given by the appropriate healthcare professional
– be visited and roused at least every half-hour
– have their condition assessed as in Annex H
– and clinical treatment arranged if appropriate
Para 9.5
Custody office must make sure a detainee receives appropriate clinical attention as soon as reasonably practical if the person:
(a) appears to be suffering from physical illness; or
(b) is injured; or
(c) appears to be suffering from a mental disorder; or
(d) appears to need clinical attention
If the need for attention appears urgent, e.g., when indicated as in Annex H, the nearest available healthcare professional or ambulance must be called immediately
[A healthcare professional is defined as a clinically qualified person working within the scope of practice as determined by his/her relevant professional body]
Para 9C
A detainee who appears drunk or behaves abnormally may be suffering from illness, the effects of drugs, or may have sustained injury ... a detainee needing or dependent on certain drugs, including alcohol may experience harmful effects within a short time of being deprived of their supply ... when there is any doubt, police should always act urgently to call an appropriate healthcare professional or an ambulance

**Table 3**  Annex H of Codes of Practice – Police and Criminal Evidence Act 1984

[if a detainee] ... fails to meet any of the following criteria, an appropriate healthcare professional or an ambulance must be called:
Rousability – go into the cell, call their name, shake gently
Response to questions – what's your name? where do you live? where do you think you are?
Response to commands – open your eyes, lift one arm, now the other arms
Remember to take into account the possibility ... of other conditions

requested his/her presence, and for what reason. As has been mentioned, there may be a dual role, such as assessing the detainee for fitness for interview as well as determining any health needs. The doctor should be aware of this, not only because of the differing assessment demands but also with regard to the issue of patient consent. In addition to the requirements of the examination, the police may have medically relevant information which could be a useful adjunct to the medical history. The police officers may have previous knowledge of the patient, his/her domestic background, recent social behavior, and the circumstances surrounding the arrest of the individual.

For many of the 43 police forces in the UK, custody officers (those police officers who are responsible for the care of detainees whilst in custody) may have specific proforma that give specific direct questions to be asked of each detainee to assist in the risk and health assessment. Part of this risk assessment proforma explores medical issues while another part explores mental health issues, in particular with respect to the need for an appropriate adult – an individual separate from the police – who is there to assist those who may be vulnerable, for example, due to mental disorder or learning difficulties. These proformas act as an additional safeguard over and above the statutory requirements of PACE.

## Spectrum of Disease and Illness

Individuals taken into police custody and seen by a doctor have a broad spectrum of disease which may be different from that normally seen in primary care. Various surveys of detainees have been undertaken and suggest that there is a high proportion of risk factors for harm and death in custody. Such factors do not just include standard pathologies such as diabetes, asthma, epilepsy, and myocardial disease, which themselves will require assessment and appropriate management, but also those that are more specific to the detainee in police custody.

A recent survey has shown that in central London 18% of detainees seen by a doctor will have significant mental health issues and 15% will have significant alcohol misuse problems. Thirty percent will be dependent on heroin or crack cocaine; of those, 93% will be using heroin and 87% crack. Many will also be prescribed methadone and many will be using substantial quantities of benzodiazepines. In addition, almost 30% will not be registered with a primary care physician and so may not have access to regular medical or healthcare advice. Many with general medical problems may not have current supplies of medication that they should be receiving

and it may be necessary to confirm the medication requirements with the individual's ordinary medical practitioner if the detainee is registered. The incidence of noncompliance or poor compliance with medication, e.g., antihypertensive or antiepileptic therapy, appears to be high in this group and thus particular care should be taken for monitoring such detainees.

Of those with drug misuse problems, 21% may have or have had significant medical complications of such misuse, including hepatitis B and C, human immunodeficiency virus (HIV), abscess, or deep-vein thrombosis.

## Facilities for and Practicalities of Assessment

The availability of high-quality examination rooms is rare. Generally spartan and clean (but not sterile) medical examination rooms are available which allow a history and medical examination to be undertaken in appropriately private conditions (with the presence of a chaperone in the case of opposite-sex examinations). Purely clinical disorders, such as infections, should be handled in a manner that is appropriate for the community setting. The management chosen should take into consideration the aspect that police officers, or others handling the care in custody, are generally untrained in any medical, nursing, or paramedical skills, and should not be expected to practice a medical or nursing level of competence.

A police medical examination room is generally not an appropriate place for anything more than first-aid dressing of wounds, infections, or injury prior to referral to an appropriate setting such as an emergency department, if necessary with a police escort. Certain prisoners will try to evade custody by indicating that they have a medical problem, which may appear to be a substantial problem to the nonmedical eye (Figures 1–3). A medical opinion can reassure the custody team that such a problem is chronic and does not require an acute assessment or direct referral to hospital for appropriate treatment.

Police officers and others in contact with prisoners have health and safety and occupational health concerns about the risk of developing infections such as hepatitis, tuberculosis, and HIV. With regard to viral infection, particularly hepatitis B, C, and HIV, there is a high incidence of risk factors in the detainee population and it is appropriate that all individuals seen in clinical forensic practice should be treated as if at high risk of HIV. It still seems sensible to extend this to consider any detainee as being at risk for viral disease. This assumption also overcomes the need to disclose medically confidential details to police. However

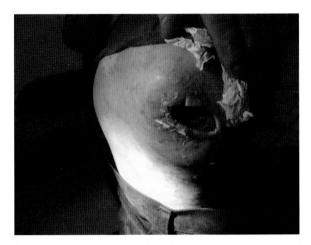

**Figure 1**  A chronic neuropathic ulcer of the left buttock secondary to a stab wound to the spinal cord in a drug user who had failed to pay his drug dealer. The ulcer had been present about 4 years and was used as an excuse to avoid detention in custody.

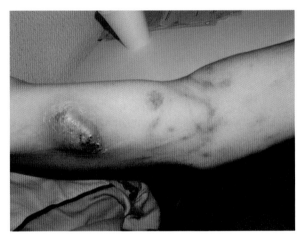

**Figure 2**  Multiple intravenous puncture sites in a drug misuser. Large abscess on the upper arm which necessitates transfer to hospital for incision and drainage.

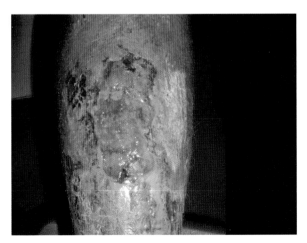

**Figure 3**  Chronic venous ulceration of leg secondary to deep-vein thrombosis secondary to intravenous injection of drugs to the groin.

there are some conditions, often minor, such as scabies, that could be transmitted by simple contact between the detainee and the custodian, which are of no great consequence but which may require treatment. Withholding such information from the custodian due to lack of consenting disclosure by the detained person would be unfair, and as it is so easily treatable disclosure would be generally of no disadvantage to the patient.

## Undertaking an Examination

Ideally the examination should occur in the medical examination room reserved for clinical purposes. It is possible that due to the morbidity of a detainee, for example, a severe degree of intoxication, or due to an aggressive individual, transfer from a cell or holding room to the medical room is not appropriate or possible. The doctor should perform any urgent assessment or try to establish a rapport with the patient, wherever the patient may be, aiming to perform a fuller assessment, unless urgent hospital transfer is indicated, in a more appropriate setting as soon as possible (**Table 4**). The police may undertake certain screening questions to establish whether medical or mental health problems exist (**Table 5**).

Consent should be obtained for the examination and the provision of a subsequent medical report or statement for court purposes. The detainee should be advised that all notes could eventually be disclosed if

**Table 4**  Examples of situations that may require urgent/immediate assessment/discussion

| |
|---|
| Unrousable detainee (no recognizable verbal response) |
| Breathing difficulties |
| Chest pain (in the absence of trauma) |
| Collapse |
| Reduced/reducing conscious level |
| Head injury + alcohol/drugs |
| Obvious injuries needing hospital |
| Possible positional asphyxia |
| Possible excited delirium |
| Specific expressions of intention to self-harm |

**Table 5**  Screening questionnaire to establish current problems

**Medical screening**

Are you suffering any illness, injury, or other medical or mental health condition?

Are you receiving treatment for your illness, injury, or condition?

Are you taking any medicine or any other sort of medication?

Have you ever tried to harm yourself?

Have you ever harmed or tried to harm yourself?

(If the answer is yes to any of these questions, medical assessment may be required)

so directed by the court. Some disclosure of medical information may be necessary to enable the custody officer to maximize the safety and good care of the patient. This disclosure can be discussed at the beginning of the meeting with the patient when consent for the examination is obtained. Adopting a polite, considerate, and professional approach may well allow a rapport to be developed with even the most violent of detainees. However, the adage that it should never be assumed that there is no risk of violence is a sound one, and the doctor should be aware of the surroundings and of ways to preserve his/her own safety without communicating either apprehension or a defensive approach to the patient. It should be remembered that the mentally disordered patient is not alone in being unpredictable.

There have been repeated discussions about the presence of chaperones and the police officer's role. Ideally all medical consultations should have a chaperone of the same sex as the patient. This is often impractical in the custodial setting unless that chaperone is a police officer. The presence of a member of the constabulary in the examination room may produce various responses. It must be remembered that the ethical restraints on a police officer with regard to disclosure are not those that are followed by the physician. Appropriate measures should be taken to encourage free discussion with the patient or ensure that the patient fully realizes the consequences of anything disclosed within earshot of a law enforcement officer. Serious violence against forensic clinicians is rare but not unknown and the doctor should seek to maximize the validity of the dialog with the patient whilst preserving the dignity of the patient and protecting the practitioner's own safety. This task is not always simple. An open, explanatory approach to the detainee is useful, but ultimately, if the detainee is in a position to consent, his/her wishes must be respected. If the medical practitioner's presence is not welcome and the detainee indicates verbally or physically that he/she is not going to cooperate with an examination, the doctor still has a duty to consider the health and welfare of the patient. The doctor should attempt to determine whether the lack of cooperation is an appropriate response in someone who is fit to make a decision or whether the patient is suffering from a medical condition which has affected reason. Head injury (with or without the presence of alcohol and drugs), hypoglycemia, and intoxication are all well-recognized examples of conditions that could result in abnormal behavior, altered insight, and an uncertain outcome.

In order to undertake an assessment a history must be taken appropriate to the detainee's situation and then an examination based on that history. The history and examination will permit a diagnosis (or diagnoses) to be made, and at-risk patients to be identified. Full contemporaneous notes must be made indicating the means by which the diagnosis and subsequent management plan were achieved. The police custody team must be clearly advised on the instructions for management, in particular any medication required, any risk factors, and the type of monitoring required (e.g., rousing to speech every 15 min), and what to do if the situation changes. There must be a low threshold for transferring out to an appropriate assessment unit (e.g., emergency department) for further investigation and treatment. It is important to be aware that a police cell is not an appropriate place to monitor any individual where there are concerns about his/her present or future well-being.

## Specific Conditions

Detainees seen in police custody may have any of the conditions that present in any other setting, and the role of the forensic physician is very much that of a primary care physician in a community setting. However, because of the overrepresentation of certain conditions, described above, the examining forensic physician must have a lower threshold of diagnosis than he/she might otherwise have in a better-equipped or less stressful setting. The management of illness is exactly the same as it would be in any other setting; if detainees are prescribed and are taking complex medical therapies then they should be provided with the same therapy as they would if they were not in custody. For some common conditions particular aspects may have relevance in a police custodial setting, although the treatment is otherwise the same. A good basic rule for custodial care is that if the patient was at home and the general practitioner would choose for him/her to be hospitalized, then the same should apply for the detainee.

Table 6 identifies some of the special issues that may arise in relation to specific medical issues. The list is not exhaustive but is intended to indicate the possible areas of concern. Many detainees may have more than one significant pathology, each of which may either impact on other pathologies or influence police procedure (e.g., fitness to interview).

## Summary

The prime aim is for the examining forensic physician to try to prevent death or harm caused by medical or health-related issues. The police procedural and forensic aspects of the role are always secondary to the prime aim. This will be best achieved by taking an

**Table 6** Examples of specific issues with medical problems in detainees (in addition to standard care)

| | |
|---|---|
| Alcohol misuse | Be aware of risks of alcohol withdrawal (fits, delirium tremens) in addition to dangers of acute intoxication – ensure that the condition is solely alcohol-related. Many chronic alcoholics may have dual pathology |
| Asthma | It is appropriate for asthma sufferers to have appropriate medications in the cell with them. Inhalers should be checked for tampering before being allowed in a cell |
| Benzodiazepine use | Benzodiazepines are in widespread use amongst alcoholics and drug misusers. There is a high incidence of prescription in the community, and a risk of withdrawal fits |
| Claustrophobia | A common complaint. It is important to explore the degree of claustrophobia, as there is an associated risk of self-harm |
| Deliberate self-harm | Frequent occurrence in the custodial population. There are many different patterns: self-cutting and self-suspension are most frequent in police custody. Practitioners should be particularly aware of those who make specific threats |
| Diabetes | The level of diabetic control is of great significance with regard to fitness to interview. Hyperglycemia may render an individual unfit for interview. Hypoglycemia may be mistaken for intoxication |
| Drug misuse | Very significant in terms of fitness to interview. Withdrawal and intoxication may render a person unfit to be interviewed. A full and detailed history of intake is required. Use substance misuse guidelines to assist management |
| Epilepsy | Ensure appropriate medication is supplied if medication is known and the detainee is known to be compliant. Epilepsy may be secondary and frequently is associated with alcohol or benzodiazepine withdrawal |
| Head injury | Low threshold for transfer to hospital. New National Institute for Clinical Excellence guidelines indicate that head injury ± drug or alcohol intoxication requires hospital assessment |
| Heart disease | Low threshold for assuming pain of cardiac origin. Permit presence of glyceryl trinitrate inhaler spray in cell, once the spray has been assessed for tampering |
| Infectious disease | Ensure police personnel are aware of true risks of conditions with which they may come into contact. Have readily available protocols to address issues such as blood spill, bites, needlestick injuries, or exposure to tuberculosis |
| Injury | Distinguish between those needing forensic documentation for evidence and those that require treatment (e.g., in hospital) |
| Mental health issues | Full knowledge of mental health law and how to get appropriate access to full assessment is required |
| Pregnancy | Be aware of those females with higher-risk pregnancies, e.g., withdrawing opiate users |
| Smoking | A number of police stations are now nonsmoking. Alcohol and drug misusers are prescribed medication to stop withdrawal symptoms. Failure to address concerns of smokers has resulted in threats and actual deliberate self-harm |

appropriate history and appropriately examining the detainee; by making a diagnosis (or diagnoses); by identifying at-risk patients; by advising police clearly and appropriately on management; by transferring out for review/treatment if there are any concerns; and by having a low threshold for diagnosis of problems.

Finally it is important to realize that a police cell is not an appropriate place to monitor any individual where there are concerns about his/her present or future well-being, and that for every detainee seen the examining physician should consider how he/she would justify his/her actions in court. This is greatly assisted by maintaining full and detailed contemporaneous notes that also document relevant negative, as well as positive, findings.

## See Also

**Custody:** Death in, United Kingdom and Continental Europe; Death in, United States of America; **Detainees:** Fitness to be Interviewed; **Occupational Health:** Police; **Professional Bodies:** United Kingdom; **Substance Misuse:** Crime

## Further Reading

British Medical Association, Association of Police Surgeons (1994) *Health Care of Detainees in Police Stations.* London: British Medical Association.

British Medical Association, Association of Police Surgeons (1999) *Guidelines for Doctors Asked to Perform Intimate Body Searches.* London: British Medical Association.

Editorial (1993) Three-faced practice: doctors and police custody. *Lancet* 341: 1245–1247.

Evand V, Howitt J (1997) *The Safety and Security of the Administration of Medication in Police Custody.* Harrogate, UK: Education and Research Sub-Committee of the Association of Police Surgeons.

Johns A, Clarke S, Stark MM (1997) Management of potentially violent detainees. *Journal of Clinical Forensic Medicine* 4: 139–144.

National Institute of Clinical Excellence (2003) *Head Injury: Triage, Assessment, and Investigation and Early Management of Head Injury in Infants, Children and Adults.* CG4. London: National Institute of Clinical Excellence.

Norfolk G, Stark MM (2000) Care of detainees. In: Stark MM (ed.) *A Physician's Guide to Clinical Forensic Medicine.* Boca Raton, FL: Humana Press.

Payne-James JJ (1992) Work patterns of a Metropolitan Police forensic medical examiner. *Police Surgeon* 42: 21–24.

Payne-James JJ (1997) Alcohol misuse in clinical forensic medicine. In: Bonner A (ed.) *Alcohol: The Facts*. London: Wiley.

Payne-James JJ, Smith J (2004) Professional bodies. In: Payne-James JJ, Wall I, Dean P (eds.) *Medicolegal Essentials of Healthcare*. London: Greenwich Medical Media.

Payne-James JJ, Keys D, Dean P (1994) Drug misusers in police custody: a prospective survey. *Journal of the Royal Society of Medicine* 87: 13–14.

Payne-James JJ, Keys DW, Wall I, Dean P (1994) Prevalence of HIV risk factors in clinical forensic medicine. *Journal of Clinical Forensic Medicine* 1: 93–96.

Payne-James JJ, Wall IJ, Bailey C (2004) Drug misusers in police custody: a prospective survey. *Journal of Clinical Forensic Medicine* (in press).

Royal College of Psychiatrists (2001) *Substance Misuse Detainees in Police Custody*, 2nd edn. London: Chitem Press.

Schnieden V, Stark M, Payne-James JJ (1995) Violence in clinical forensic medicine. *Medicine, Science and the Law* 35: 333–335.

# Care in Prison Custody, United Kingdom

**V Evans**, Ilkley, UK

## Introduction

Her Majesty's Prison Service (HMPS) is an executive agency of the Home Office (there are similar provisions in Scotland and Northern Ireland), which works in partnership with others in the Criminal Justice System to deliver the Home Office aim of effective execution of the Court's Orders so as to reduce reoffending and protect the public.

As of February 2004, there were 137 prison service establishments within England and Wales, which include high-security prisons, local prisons, closed and open training prisons, young offender institutions (for sentenced prisoners under the age of 21), and remand centers. All adult male prisoners are placed in one of the four security categories: A (dispersal), B, C, or D. Dispersal prisoners are those whose escape would be highly dangerous to the public or to the security of the state. Category B prisoners do not demand the highest level of security but still pose a risk. Category A–C prisoners are held in closed prisons. Category D or open prisons hold prisoners who are not deemed a risk to the public and who are unlikely to escape. Women and young offenders may be placed in category A establishments but are not otherwise categorized and may be held in open or closed prisons dependent on risk.

The prison population in England and Wales continues to increase and now exceeds 75 000 for the first time. This has brought with it problems of overcrowding as increases in the prison establishment have not kept pace and, from time to time, prisoners have had to be temporarily housed in police cells until a space in the establishment became available.

Doctors who work in the prison service in the UK may be employed directly by the service, or by contractors running prison establishments for the service, or by the National Health Service (NHS).

There is an independent prison inspectorate that is responsible for the inspection of all prison establishments in England and Wales, whether directly managed by HMPS or contracted out. The inspectorate also undertakes, by invitation, inspection of Immigration Service detention centers, prison service establishments in Northern Ireland, and prisons in the Channel Islands and the Isle of Man, and overseas. The Chief Inspector is concerned with the major issues of the treatment of prisoners rather than with individual prisoners' grievances, which are dealt with by the prisons Ombudsman. The Chief Inspector sends a written report to the Home Secretary with recommendations for improvement after each inspection.

## General Issues

Prison healthcare is not yet a specialty in its own right, although doctors practicing in the field should receive additional training in the health needs of the prison population, and in the forensic aspects of their work. Prisoners are often from marginalized groups in society and bring with them social and behavioral problems and an increased risk of medical morbidity.

Prisoners should receive the same quality of healthcare as they would if they were in the community and have the same access to specialist intervention as appropriate: in reality there are many barriers to this. Prisons have never been regarded as a priority for healthcare. There is poor support for prison doctors, and, there is often, sadly, a reluctance on the part of other health professionals to offer treatment to prisoners. This reduces the opportunity an individual prisoner may have for diagnosis and treatment.

Prison medicine is not for the fainthearted. It requires that the doctor is aware of and can apply ethical principles on a daily basis, often with little support. The doctor may be the only independent person with access to a prisoner and must act as the patient's advocate, with the patient's consent, remembering that where abuse is concerned the prisoner may be at risk of reprisal from other prisoners, prison staff, and the state. Political and societal attitudes outside prison may effectively increase tolerance of unacceptable behavior toward prisoners and lead to the demonization of certain groups of prisoners, e.g., sex offenders.

The primacy of security in the ethos of the prison service may lead to conflict between the prison authorities and the doctor when the doctor believes that admission of a prisoner to a public hospital for investigation and treatment is in that prisoner's best interest. Cost limitations may be placed on the doctor's ability to prescribe or refer a prisoner, which may conflict with the doctor's responsibilities. The doctor must guard against collusion with prison staff and the state in covering up abuse of a prisoner or contributing to medical inaction or neglect.

## Problems Specific to the Prison Environment

In England and Wales all prisoners should be seen by a healthcare professional when they are admitted to a prison establishment so that an assessment of their health needs can be made and, if necessary, a referral to a doctor made. This should allow for the identification of, for example, drug and alcohol dependence and an increased risk of self-harm. Effective communication with forensic physicians who may have been caring for a prisoner whilst in police custody and with a prisoner's general practitioner is an essential part of continuity of care. A healthcare plan should be made and each prisoner made aware how to access healthcare. Ideally a medical examination should also occur at the end of a period of detention and this is particularly important for vulnerable groups, e.g., those held under terrorism and immigration legislation.

All prisoners are particularly vulnerable at the time that they enter the prison system. They face an unknown environment, are often frightened, may have been separated from their family for the first time, and almost certainly will have unresolved social and medical problems. Young offenders are at particular risk in this regard and may also be vulnerable to bullying and physical and sexual abuse by older inmates. It is salutary to realize that in 1999 in the UK, 26% of all prisoners and 38% of those under 21 years of age had been in the care of a local authority at some time, compared with just 2% of the general population.

Women are also a vulnerable group for whom issues around child care are often paramount. The problem of childbirth whilst in custody was recently highlighted when a complaint was made about a woman who was handcuffed to the bed during labor and delivery, highlighting the conflict between the need for security and human rights issues.

Despite the provision of some places for mothers and babies in units within the prison establishment, there are not enough places available, leading to the separation of mothers and infants. There remain issues as to what happens if either a mother or baby is taken ill – unhappily this is usually still resolved by their separation.

Whilst sexual assault and harassment of women prisoners are not often reported in UK prison establishments, the risk is still a real one.

The importance of the need to assist prisoners in maintaining contact with their families whilst they are in custody has been increasingly recognized as this has a positive effect in reducing reoffending and successfully rehabilitating prisoners back into the community. Placement of a prisoner in an establishment away from his/her family can be very disruptive and increase a prisoner's vulnerability. This is an increasing problem with prison overcrowding.

Common to all prison establishments is the unofficial power structure amongst the prisoners, with the professional criminals and "bosses" at the top, followed by the nonprofessional criminals, and, as "outcasts" at the bottom, the collaborators ("grasses"), sex offenders, and those whose offenses involve children. This unofficial caste system can be a real barrier to the provision of care and may, for example, lead to bullying, the inappropriate request for medication by prisoners, and the internal trading of medication amongst prisoners.

## Specific Medical Problems

The goal of the prison medical service should be to provide adequate and appropriate healthcare to the prisoner over the long term. The same standards should be applied to the provision of prevention and treatment for acute and chronic conditions as would be applied in general practice in the community. Certain conditions, however, need special consideration in a prison setting, either because of their increased prevalence or because of the difficulty in delivering care on an ongoing basis. This latter is often complicated by the prisoner being moved unexpectedly without notice from one establishment to another, by the limitations a regime may place on the time available for healthcare, and by the need for healthcare appointments to compete with legal or family visits or court appearances.

When prescribing in a prison setting the doctor needs to ensure that he/she does not fall into the trap of either underprescribing or overprescribing. For example, the widespread use of a "chemical cosh" to control prisoners' behavior, sometimes in collusion with disciplinary staff, is unacceptable.

The doctor must be aware that prisoners may use drugs as a form of internal currency within the prison. They may conceal drugs in body orifices or may abuse everyday drugs with an inventiveness that may have unexpected and tragic consequences. Finally doctors should recognize that prison conditions are emotionally traumatic for some vulnerable prisoners and well-intentioned pharmaceutical help in alleviating this can easily lead to addiction.

### Drugs and Alcohol

In the UK a majority of those admitted to prison admit to the current abuse of illicit drugs, pharmaceuticals, and/or alcohol. Many establishments now have protocols that may involve the prisoner going to a detoxification center or being admitted to the prison hospital, where detoxification can be supervised safely. Such prisoners may also have an increased risk of drug- and alcohol-related pathology, including infectious disease, and are more likely to have come from an unstable environment, e.g., living rough, before coming into custody. In complex cases admission to an outside hospital facility may be needed.

Specialist treatment may be needed both to manage the prisoner whilst in custody and to treat both the substance abuse behavior and any associated mental health problems. Comorbidity is common.

Whilst in the past detoxification (with or without supervision) has been the only option offered to the prisoner, the prison service is now being asked to consider whether maintenance treatment, for example, on methadone, might be appropriate, especially where prisoners are on remand or serving only short sentences, and they are already stabilized in the community. It is hoped in this way to reduce the potential for drug-related deaths soon after release from custody when tolerance has been lost. There are many problems to overcome with this approach, not least the issue of ensuring a prisoner's clinical safety in a situation where he/she is vulnerable and locked up alone, unsupervised, for many hours.

Over the last few years the prison service has successfully introduced a pathway which, having identified a prisoner with a substance abuse problem, can be used to track that prisoner through the criminal justice system and put in place a care plan tailored to that individual's needs, embracing follow-up treatment and housing on discharge.

Issues of harm reduction cannot be ignored in the prison setting. Education initiatives, which give drug users information about preventing infectious disease and harm reduction, are to be commended. With respect to needle sharing in prison, historically there has been a reliance on prohibition of drug use in prison, rather than consideration of alternative strategies such as the provision of needle-exchange schemes.

### Infectious Disease, Including Sexually Transmitted Disease

Prisons are large institutions with a constant exchange of prisoners with the community. It is therefore not just an issue for individual prisoners that there should be available the means to diagnose and treat infectious disease, but also a public health issue.

Consent to testing and confidentiality should not be compromised in the prison setting and robust protocols need to be in place to protect individual prisoners. One way of doing this is to buy this service in from a specialist provider outside the prison healthcare service. This has the added advantage that follow-up in the community and contact tracing should be seamless. Training of all prison staff with regard to basic hygiene and modes of transmission of the commoner infestations and infectious diseases, such as hepatitis, human immunodeficiency virus (HIV), and tuberculosis, is essential to dispel the myths that have grown up around these disorders.

The promotion of harm reduction strategies in respect of both substance abuse and sexual activity is essential. The recognition that sexual activity does occur in prisons and the provision of condoms has been a step forward in this respect.

### Epilepsy

This is a surprisingly common condition within the prison population. A clear diagnosis is the first prerequisite to compliance with effective treatment, but this is often surprisingly difficult to achieve for a prisoner in the prison system. Systems for regular monitoring of treatment should also be in place.

### Diabetes, Asthma, and Coronary Heart Disease

Whilst the principles of care in prison are the same as those in the community, supervision and monitoring can be particularly difficult in a prison setting, even when there are specialist clinics set up to facilitate this. It is important that all staff are taught to recognize and respond to signs and symptoms of deterioration in these conditions, so that appropriate assessment and treatment are sought from appropriate healthcare staff rather than being dismissed as feigned for some secondary gain. The increasing prevalence of cocaine use in young adults has made acute stroke and coronary events more common in this age group.

### The Management of Chronic Pain

This is a particular problem within a prison setting where drugs such as opiates are commonly abused.

Each establishment should have a policy agreed by the medical staff with respect to the prescription of analgesics for new complaints and to the continuation of medication prescribed in the community. A documented continuing clinical need, individualized prescribing, and the need to verify what was being prescribed in the community and why are essential prerequisites for success. It would be unethical to deny a prisoner analgesia when a need for such had been identified.

## Psychiatric Problems

Mental illness is a source of major morbidity and, sadly, of mortality within the prison establishment. There is much unmet need, with a high proportion of those suffering from depression and even major affective disorders remaining undiagnosed in the prison population.

Recently, within England and Wales there has been a drive to improve psychiatric and allied services, with increased provision of general psychiatric services, services dedicated to those with dual diagnosis (coexisting mental health and substance abuse problems), and the reversion of forensic psychiatric services to the provision of more specialized assessment and care.

An important initiative has focused around the identification of suicide risk with respect to any particular prisoner. All staff who have contact with a prisoner receive training about identification of risk factors and are encouraged to share concerns in a planned and consistent way. Once suicide risk is identified by any member of staff, a medical assessment is carried out and an appropriate care plan drawn up which always involves regular review. This may lead to a change of location within the establishment, the involvement of a "listener" or "buddy" (a volunteer prisoner specially trained to support a distressed prisoner) or admission to a healthcare facility. Such excellent schemes risk being compromised by the current state of overcrowding in the prison establishment, which restricts choice as to where a prisoner can be placed within the establishment.

Part of the role played by the psychiatric services within the criminal justice system is advising the courts as to the risks an individual poses to the public and, at the stage of sentencing, what might be the most appropriate disposal for that individual, possibly under the Mental Health Act 1983. Despite efforts to increase the number of beds available for the transfer of prisoners, both on remand and after sentence, for treatment in secure accommodation, resources continue to be inadequate to meet demand.

There is a unique facility within the prison service at Grendon, which is run as a therapeutic environment for the treatment of sex offenders. There is a rigorous selection procedure for admission and, once there, prisoners are expected to address their behavior according to a demanding and structured program. There is a recognition that cure is not usually possible; rather the offender should recognize the nature of his/her behavior and its cues so that the behavior does not lead to reoffending.

## Special Issues

Doctors who work in the prison system have a dual obligation, which can lead to conflict between their medical and ethical responsibilities to an individual patient and their perceived responsibility to their employer, who controls and directs their work. A doctor may be faced with a lack of cooperation or active opposition from the prison administration and in the past this has led doctors in the UK to complain about unacceptable restrictions imposed by prison governors on their clinical independence and their ability to do what is best for their patients.

In England and Wales the Prison Rules state that the prison medical service is responsible for the "care of health, physical and mental" within a prison. The doctor, however, as patient advocate, also has an ethical responsibility to ensure that the circumstances of incarceration for an individual are not having a deleterious effect on physical or mental health, as stated in the United Nations Principles of Medical Ethics.

Medical ethical responsibility also places a specific ban on the use of medical skills or knowledge in any way that might contravene a prisoner's basic human rights.

### Inhuman and Degrading Treatment and Torture

The European Convention on Human Rights was formally ratified in the UK in the Human Rights Act 1988 and is now in force. There is an absolute ban on doctors participating in torture.

There needs to be a recognition by doctors working in the criminal justice system that most torture and inhuman and degrading treatment takes place soon after arrest or while a prisoner is held incommunicado without access to lawyers or family members, a situation which may arise under legislation to combat terrorism in the UK. Ethical values and legal principles will usually be complementary but where there is conflict, ethical obligations will be paramount and take precedence – a stance that is supported by the doctors' professional organization in the UK, the British Medical Association, and by the General Medical Council.

Where a doctor in the UK believes a prisoner's human rights have been violated the issue of documenting and reporting any maltreatment should be decided in partnership with the prisoner concerned wherever possible, remembering that to report such treatment may lead to reprisal against the prisoner and the doctor. In the UK, in theory, a "whistle-blower" may have some legal protection from the Public Interest Disclosure Act 1998.

## Intimate Searches

Forcible examination or treatment of a prisoner by medical staff is unacceptable on ethical grounds, except in very special circumstances.

The principles of consent and confidentiality are the same in prison and the community. Prisoners must be provided with relevant information in respect of any diagnosis, prognosis, or treatment concerning them in a manner which they can understand (where appropriate, this may involve the use of an interpreter). Every competent adult can accept or refuse treatment. The only exceptions to this would be compulsory treatment of a mental illness to prevent harm to themselves or others (under the provisions of the Mental Health Act 1983) or, rarely, where there is a risk of serious harm to others, for example, to prevent the spread of infectious disease.

Doctors should not undertake intimate body searches without a prisoner's valid and informed consent. Where such a search is undertaken for concealed drugs, it should be carried out in a setting where there are adequate facilities for immediate resuscitation and ongoing care of the prisoner. The doctor should be aware that the use of inappropriate and routine strip-searching of prisoners by prison staff may be used as a means of intimidation.

## Hunger Strikes

Hunger strikes can be an important form of protest by prisoners, especially where conditions in prison fall well below an acceptable international standard. In the UK, competent patients who refuse food and/or fluid would not be forcibly fed, even if this resulted in their death. This being the case, when a prisoner first goes on hunger strike, the prisoner should be seen and assessed as to competency by an independent doctor who should make it unambiguously clear what the medical response to the prisoner's actions will be, that is, nonintervention, even if the prisoner lapses into coma and death ultimately supervenes.

## Punishment and the Death Penalty

The death penalty has been abolished in the UK, except for treason. It is ethically unacceptable for any doctor to participate in any way in carrying out the death penalty.

In the UK, a doctor is much more likely to be involved in the use of restraints with respect to a prisoner. There is sometimes an assumption on the part of the prison authorities that a doctor should be in attendance to advise whether a particular form of restraint should be used. A doctor should only participate in this way if there is clarity as to his/her role, that is, that the doctor is not just a witness, but has real authority to intervene and stop the procedure being used. The prison authorities should keep accurate records as to which restraints are used, when, for how long, how often, and by whom, and the records should be open to inspection.

The use of restraints, for example, shackles, during medical treatment is also contentious. There needs to be a recognition of security risk but in each individual case there should be negotiation as to how these risks can be managed taking into account the medical need for flexibility in provision of treatment and a duty to respect the patient's dignity. Where there is a serious risk of escape or violence, safeguards will be required but these should be commensurate with actual risk and should respect the privacy of the doctor–patient relationship.

Doctors should not be the arbiters of punishment, nor should they be asked to examine prisoners to assess their fitness for such.

Solitary confinement could be regarded as being inhuman and degrading treatment if it is unnecessarily prolonged and/or indeterminate. Where it is considered necessary for therapeutic reasons or for a prisoner's own protection, solitary confinement may be acceptable, provided that it is done for as short a time as possible and is monitored and documented. Whilst a doctor should not certify a patient as fit to withstand solitary confinement as punishment or for disciplinary purposes, he/she should remain responsible for attending to the patient's health needs. Where a doctor considers that continued solitary confinement would endanger the health of an individual, he/she has a duty to speak out and inform the appropriate authorities.

## Research and Prisoners

Whilst prisoners should not be used as a convenient pool of research subjects for the general population or for research on conditions that are not relevant to themselves, they are entitled to the same innovative treatments available to those in the community and should receive the same information as to possible risks and benefits. Where any research is proposed that involves prisoners, such risks and benefits should be made explicit when approval is sought from local ethical committees.

## Deaths in Custody

In the UK, all deaths in custody are investigated by the coroner (or procurator fiscal in Scotland), who must hold an inquest with a jury. This is an independent fact-finding inquiry to establish the identity of the deceased, the place of death, the time of death, and how the deceased came to die. It is not the function of the coroner or jury to determine any question of criminal or civil liability, to apportion guilt, or to attribute blame.

It is essential that when a death in custody occurs, any doctor called to the scene treats it as a crime scene, confirming the fact of death and otherwise disturbing as little as possible according to forensic principles. The doctor should be assiduous in documenting contemporaneously his/her observations and actions.

## Conclusion

The provision of high-quality medical care of prisoners is challenging to those who are charged with delivering it. Where doctors are adequately trained and supported to meet these challenges it can be rewarding for both prisoner and doctor. The ability of a society to provide high-quality medical care sustained over a period of time is a reflection of its commitment (or otherwise) to all its constituent members, and their human rights.

## See Also

**Custody:** Death in, United Kingdom and Continental Europe; Death in, United States of America; **Detainees:** Care in Police Custody, United Kingdom; Fitness to be Interviewed

# Fitness to be Interviewed

**G H Gudjonsson**, Institute of Psychiatry, London, UK

© 2005, Elsevier Ltd. All Rights Reserved.

## Introduction

In some countries, when the police interview mentally disordered persons and juveniles, special legal provisions are available to ensure that their statements to the police are reliable and obtained properly and fairly. For example, in England and Wales, the current legal provisions are detailed in the Codes to Practice that accompany the supplement the Police and Criminal Evidence Act 1984 (PACE). Even when the police adhere to all the legal provisions, a judge may on occasions consider it unsafe or unfair to allow the statement to go before the jury. Here the crucial issue may be whether or not the defendant was "mentally fit" when interviewed by the police (i.e., whether the suspect was sufficiently mentally well to cope with the questioning and give reliable answers). In cases concerning fitness to plead and fitness to stand trial, clear operational criteria are available to guide mental health professionals and the court. In contrast, until recently there were no established criteria for determining fitness for interview which could be applied by forensic physicians (also known as police surgeons), psychiatrists, and psychologists when assessing suspects at police stations. Indeed, "fitness for interview" is not a term that appears within PACE, and it was first introduced formally into legal terminology in the current Codes of Practice, which became effective on April 1, 2003.

In this article the author discusses the current legal framework relating to fitness to be interviewed, reviews the development of the concept, and provides a framework for the assessment of cases. This is a unique development in England and Wales and the principles, conceptual framework, and practice should be applicable to criminal justice systems worldwide.

## The Legal Framework

The legal significance of confession evidence in England and Wales is regulated by PACE and became effective in January 1986. The Act is supplemented by five Codes of Practice, referred to as Codes A (stop and search), B (entry and searches of premises), C (detention and questioning of suspects), D (identification parades), and E (tape recording of interviews). The Codes act as guidance to police officers about procedures and the appropriate treatment of suspects. Code C is particularly relevant to issues surrounding "fitness to be interviewed," because it provides guidance "on practice for the detention, treatment, and questioning of persons by police officers."

The most important interview procedures set out in PACE and its Codes of Practice are as follows:

1. A person suspected of a criminal offense must be cautioned before being questioned about it. The caution shall be read in the following terms: "You do not have to say anything. But it may harm your defense if you do not mention when questioned something which you later rely on in court. Anything you say may be given in evidence."

2. Persons detained at a police station must be informed of their legal rights; this includes that they are entitled to free legal advice at any time, that they can have somebody notified of their detention, and that they have the right to consult the Codes of Practice.

3. In any 24-h period the detainee must be allowed a continuous period of rest of at least 8 h. There should be a break from questioning for at least 15 min every 2 h. Meal breaks should normally last for at least 45 min.

4. There are special provisions for detainees who are vulnerable in terms of their age or mental problems relating to access to a responsible adult (known as an "appropriate adult"). Their function is to give advice and further communication, and ensure that the interview is conducted properly and fairly.

5. All interviews shall be tape-recorded (there are some exceptional circumstances when tape recording is not required, as in the case of terrorist offenses).

The Codes only have legislative power in as far as breaches may result in evidence, including confession evidence, being ruled inadmissible by a trial judge during a *voir dire*. Serious breach may lead to disciplinary action against police officers, but this does not often happen.

## Fitness for Interview: The Background

Prior to the implementation of PACE, forensic physicians commonly only addressed issues relevant to fitness for detention (i.e., whether the suspect was physically or mentally fit enough to be detained in custody). Recently, they increasingly also specifically assess fitness for interview and the need for an appropriate adult, although great regional variations have been found in England. Fitness for detention is undoubtedly easier to assess and determine than fitness for interview. The former relies principally on physical signs and symptoms and possible referral to hospital, whereas the latter is typically concerned with the effects of mental factors on the suspect's functioning whilst in police custody, and these may be difficult to detect on the basis of a short interview.

In 1995, Gudjonsson discussed a conceptual framework for assessing fitness for interview when mentally disordered suspects are detained in police custody. The framework was developed from a court case involving a mentally disordered man, who had been arrested on suspicion of murder and interviewed by the police in the presence of a solicitor and an appropriate adult. Even though all legal provisions in accordance with PACE were adhered to in the case by the police and the interviews were conducted in "an impeccably fair and considerate way," the interviews were ruled inadmissible by the trial judge. This judgment was given in spite of the fact that two doctors, both of whom testified at the trial during a *voir dire*, had found the detainee fit to be interviewed by the police. The case illustrated the legal, psychiatric, and psychological issues involved and provided a conceptual framework for assessing fitness for interview in cases of mental disorder. Following this case, improved criteria for evaluating fitness for interview have been developed for forensic physicians. Gall and Freckelton have discussed fitness for interview in Australia, presented empirical data, and reviewed the relevant legal cases and judgments. Their article is important, because little work has been done on fitness for interview outside England. In Australia, as in England, important safeguards have been developed and implemented for persons detained for interview at police stations.

## A Conceptual Framework

Mr. S was 34 years of age and had a 10-year history of schizophrenia. His principal symptoms were extreme social and emotional withdrawal. He also complained of hearing voices that were making derogatory comments against him. After his fourth admission to hospital his care was transferred to a general practitioner.

Whilst being treated in the community, Mr. S was arrested on the suspicion of having battered a woman to death. The murder weapon was apparently a champagne bottle and had been found in the vicinity of the murder victim. Mr. S's fingerprint was on the bottle and a small trace of blood was found on the bottle that could have come from the victim, but this was not conclusive. Mr. S had no previous criminal convictions.

Before he was interviewed, the police knew that Mr. S had a psychiatric history and obtained the services of a psychiatric social worker, who acted in the capacity of an appropriate adult. Mr. S was seen by an FME, who considered that he was "fit to be interviewed," but in view of the seriousness of the case and concerns raised by the solicitor, the FME recommended that Mr. S should be assessed by a psychiatrist. A consultant psychiatrist assessed Mr. S and concluded: "He is calm and coherent; he has no overt psychotic symptoms but some evidence of thought block. He seems to understand why he has been brought to the police station. In my opinion he is fit to be interviewed."

The appropriate adult was also of the view that Mr. S was fit to be interviewed.

Mr. S was interviewed on five occasions over a 36-h period. The interviews were all fairly short. The longest interview lasted 40 min and the five interviews lasted in total less than 2 h. A solicitor and an appropriate adult were present during all the interviews. It was evident from the audiotape recording of the interviews that Mr. S was interviewed very carefully by the police officers. They asked him simple and nonleading questions and clearly avoided placing him under pressure.

Mr. S did not confess to the murder during any of the interviews, but he made some incriminating comments that were used against him at his trial. First, he had made apparently untrue denials (e.g., not having been out of his house for 3 weeks, which was contradicted by witnesses), which the prosecution relied on as incriminating evidence. Second, there was, according to the prosecution, an indication of special knowledge, which involved his acknowledging during the third interview that the woman had been hit on the head with a bottle (i.e., "I didn't hit her over the head at all with it. Well, she was hit over the head by the bottle, was she?"). This reply was in response to the officer telling him, "I have a bottle and on that bottle is the blood of Miss... and also on it is your fingerprint. Can you tell me how that can be?"

The author was commissioned by the defense to evaluate whether or not Mr. S had been fit for interview whilst in police detention. This involved focusing on the mental state of Mr. S at the time and the content of his answers to police questioning during the five interviews with a view to assessing their reliability. All the police interviews had been recorded on audiotapes and transcripts made. The author listened to the tapes of the interviews and studied the transcripts.

Mr. S was difficult to assess, because he was very agitated and absorbed in his immediate needs (i.e., smoking cigarettes, wanting to go and watch television). An intellectual assessment indicated an IQ of 62, which was very much lower than the score of 83 that he had obtained when assessed during his first admission to hospital 10 years previously. His memory and concentration were very poor on testing. It was not possible to have a meaningful conversation with him and his answers were very concrete.

Custody record indicated that Mr. S's solicitor had been unsuccessful in explaining the "old" police caution to him. (He was arrested and interviewed before the new and more complicated caution was introduced in 1995.) The solicitor informed the custody officer that he did not think that his client was fit for interview. The police did not accept the solicitor's views and continued to interview Mr. S. They had the benefit of the opinion of two doctors and a

psychiatric social worker, all of whom had considered at the time that Mr. S was fit for interview.

Mr. S's answers and comments during the police interviews were interesting, because they showed that Mr. S was not functioning well mentally. For example, first, at the beginning of the second interview, Mr. S said he could not recall anything about the previous interview that had been conducted a few hours previously. Second, the taped interviews showed that Mr. S was preoccupied with being released from custody. Third, some of Mr. S's statements were incoherent (referred to as "gibberish" by the trial judge). Fourth, there was an indication from two of the tapes that Mr. S confused the identity of his solicitor and the appropriate adult with the police officers (e.g., at one point he turned to his solicitor and said, "Are you the Chief Inspector?").

The psychological assessment showed that Mr. S had not been functioning well mentally during the police interviews and it was unsafe to rely on his answers. Mr. S had not been fit for interview, which was indicated by his confusion, disorientation, and concrete thinking during the police interviews.

The first legal issue addressed at trial was Mr. S's fitness to plead. He was found unfit to plead by a jury empaneled for that purpose. A second jury was then sworn in to try the issue of whether he had committed the criminal act he was charged with (i.e., murder or manslaughter). Prior to the trial proper, there was an application by the defense under PACE to exclude the five police interviews. The basis for the submission was Mr. S's mental state at the time of the police interviews. The defense argued that he had been unfit to be interviewed by the police and it would therefore be unfair, in accordance with section 78 of PACE, to allow his statements to go before the jury.

The prosecution called the two medical witnesses who assessed him at the police station prior to the interviews. They gave evidence during the *voir dire*.

The forensic physician testified that:

> his views were that the question that he had to ask himself in the context were whether or not when he asked general questions about how he came to be there, and what he had been doing, and matters of that kind by way of general discussion, if his answers were given rationally and no incongruity was found ... he regarded him as fit for interview.

The consultant psychiatrist testified that Mr. S had been fit to be interviewed by the police.

Gudjonsson testified for the defense and argued on the basis of the psychological assessment that Mr. S had not been fit to be interviewed whilst in police custody. This was based on Mr. S's poor mental functioning whilst in police custody and his answers and comments during the police interviews.

The judge ruled that the police interview statements were inadmissible under section 78 of PACE:

> it would be unfair, and that the fair conduct of these proceedings would be adversely affected by the admission of these interviews.

This judgment was in spite of the fact that the judge clearly thought that the police had dealt with Mr. S "in an impeccably fair and considerate way." Thus:

> In the course of the interviews these officers were, in my judgment, extremely careful to avoid long, oppressive, complicated, or leading questions and they, as far as I can tell, did their utmost to avoid asking questions which were suggestive of the answers that they wished to be heard.

The main basis of the judge's ruling was as follows:

1. The two doctors, at the time of their assessment, had failed to approach "the question of fitness on the basis of considering whether or not any answers given by Mr. S ... to any questions asked of him by the police officers were necessarily reliable." Instead, the two doctors had "considered that the ordeal and stress and strain of being interviewed, particularly on such a serious charge as this, was something that in their judgment the suspect could sustain without suffering any consequential harm to either his physical or mental health."
2. The judge discussed the psychological evidence and it formed the basis on which the judge ruled the police interview statements inadmissible.
3. The judge accepted that Mr. S was incapable of appreciating or understanding the full impact of the caution properly administered at the outset and beginning of each interview.
4. The judge concluded that the jury would find it impossible, even if they had the benefit of expert evidence and the appropriate warning that he would otherwise have given, to make sense of Mr. S's comments in the interviews.

The case provided a potential conceptual framework for the assessment of fitness for interview. The case suggested that the criteria used by judges in the future to determine fitness for interview are likely to be very stringent. The trial judge came to the firm conclusion that the term "fitness for interview" does not mean that "a person must be shown to be capable of understanding or dealing properly and accurately with questions put to him," because this is adequately dealt with by various provisions within PACE and its Codes of Practice for special groups considered to be vulnerable or at risk during interviewing. This includes the presence of an appropriate adult during

interviews and a warning to the jury by the judge about the defendant's vulnerabilities.

The additional vulnerabilities considered important by the trial judge for unfitness for interview are mental factors that substantially impair the detainee's ability to: (1) understand his/her basic legal rights, such as the police caution; and (2) give a reliable statement to the police during questioning.

Using the present case as a yardstick, there appeared to be at least three broad criteria for fitness for interview, although all three may not necessarily be required in every case.

First, does the detainee understand the police caution after it has been carefully explained to him/her? If, for example, a solicitor finds it impossible to explain the police caution to his/her client after making several attempts, this would be a good indicator that the detainee may be unfit for interview. This was the case with Mr. S.

Second, is the detainee fully oriented in time, place, and person, and does he/she recognize the key persons present during the police interview (e.g., can he/she differentiate between the police, the solicitor, and the appropriate adult)? In the case of Mr. S, he confused both the solicitor and the appropriate adult with the police. This suggested a serious mental disturbance.

Third, is the detainee likely to give answers that can be misconstrued by the court? In the case of Mr. S, the normal assumption that lies during a police interview indicate a sense of criminal guilt was possibly unfounded, because of his obsession with his immediate needs, concrete thinking, and inability to foresee the likely consequences of his answers. In exceptional cases involving confessions, detainees may be so mentally disturbed that they will incriminate themselves in order to fulfill their immediate needs (e.g., being released from custody, going to hospital).

The three basic criteria proposed above involve the functional abilities of the detainees and require a functional assessment (i.e., an assessment that directly addresses the relevant areas of the detainee's functioning, such as his/her understanding of what is happening).

Within the conceptual framework provided above, and based on the findings of the studies by Gudjonsson and coworkers, it is rare for suspects detained at a police station to be found to fulfill the criteria set out above as being unfit for interview. However, the case suggested a worrying possibility of this happening, even if rare, and FMEs must learn to address issues relevant to reliability rather than focusing principally or exclusively on factors that relate to possible consequential harm from the interview to the detainee's physical and mental health.

## The Home Office Working Group

The Report of the Home Office Working Group on Police Surgeons in 2001 provided a review of the current situation in England with regard to fitness for interview. The Group's recommendation was that judgment about fitness for interview required the consideration of the following three factors:

1. The assessment of the person to be interviewed – the forensic medical examiner (FME – a term used in some settings for forensic physicians) will consider the physical and mental state of the detainee and the emphasis is on the functional ability of the detainee rather than relying on a medical diagnosis.
2. The likely demand characteristics of the police interview – long and complex interviews require a greater physical and mental capacity than short and straightforward interviews.
3. The impact of the physical or mental disorder on the interview process and the reliability of any statements made – the FME will consider all the relevant aspects and circumstances in the case, including the nature of the arrest, detention, and police interview. It is essential to establish how the physical or mental condition will affect the capacity of the detainee to function in the police interview. The presence of mental illness does not automatically render a detainee unfit for interview. It is the effects of the mental illness on cognitive and emotional processes that are crucial, not the illness *per se*. It is also important to note that, in the absence of mental disorder, a detainee who is disoriented, has severe concentration problems, or is intoxicated or withdrawing from illicit substances while in police custody, is likely to be considered temporarily unfit for interview. Here the impaired physical and mental condition is likely to be considered temporary and the FME will probably reexamine the detainee within a few hours to ascertain if he/she is now fit for interview.

The Home Office Working Group advised that a detained person may be unfit for interview: (1) if the interview is likely to have significant adverse effects on the physical or mental illness that is already present, and (2) when the detainee's statements may be considered unreliable in subsequent court proceedings, because of the impaired physical or mental condition.

The FME may quantify the risk of such unreliability into one of the four categories:

1. Definite risk: here the detainee is unlikely to be fit for interview in the foreseeable future.
2. Major risk: the detainee is unfit for interview at the time of the assessment, but a further evaluation is required at a later time to ascertain fitness.
3. Some risk: precautions are advised, which may include a recommendation for the presence of an appropriate adult or a referral to other medical or psychiatric advice.
4. No discernible risk: the interview can take place without the presence of an appropriate adult or a further medical or psychiatric intervention.

Whilst an individual is being detained at a police station, there are other important issues to be addressed, apart from fitness for interview, such as fitness for detention, charge, transfer, or release, and detainees being able to give informed consent about the provision of intimate samples (e.g., blood specimen) and attending identification parades.

## Conclusion

The introduction of the concept of fitness to be interviewed into legal practice in the current Codes of Practice in England and Wales is a significant step toward a safer and fairer criminal justice system. It builds on the work that has previously been carried out into the psychological vulnerabilities of persons detained at police stations for interviewing and cases of miscarriage of justice. A similar framework has been introduced in Australia. It is important that other countries follow these new legal provisions and ensure that their vulnerable police detainees are adequately protected to ensure reliability, fairness, and safety of self-incriminating admissions and confessions.

## See Also

**Detainees:** Care in Police Custody, United Kingdom; Care in Prison Custody, United Kingdom; **Forensic Psychiatry and Forensic Psychology:** Mental Handicap and Learning Disability; Personality Disorder; Multiple Personality Disorder; Criminal Responsibility

## Further Reading

Gall JA, Freckelton I (1999) Fitness for interview: current trends, views and an approach to the assessment procedure. *Journal of Clinical Forensic Medicine* 6: 213–223.

Gudjonsson GH (1995) "Fitness for interview" during police detention: a conceptual framework for the forensic assessment. *Journal of Forensic Psychiatry* 6: 185–197.

Gudjonsson GH (2003) *The Psychology of Interrogations and Confessions. A Handbook.* Chichester, UK: Wiley.

Gudjonsson GH, Clare ICH, Rutter S, Pearse J (1993) *Persons at Risk During Interviews in Police Custody: The Identification of Vulnerabilities.* Royal Commission on Criminal Justice. London: HMSO.

Gudjonsson GH, Hayes GD, Rowlands P (2000) Fitness to be interviewed and psychological vulnerability: the view of doctors, lawyers and police officers. *Journal of Forensic Psychiatry* 11: 74–92.

Home Office (1985) *Police and Criminal Evidence Act 1984*. London: HMSO.

Home Office (2001) *Report of the Home Office Working Group on Police Surgeons*. Police Leadership and Powers Unit. London: Home Office.

Home Office (2003) *Police and Criminal Evidence Act 1984. Codes of Practice A-E*, revised edition. London: HMSO.

Norfork GA (1997) Fit to be interviewed – a proposed scheme of examination. *Medicine, Science and the Law* 37: 228–234.

Norfork GA (1999) Physiological illnesses and their potential for influencing testimony. *Medicine, Science and the Law* 39: 105–112.

Norfork G (2001) Fit to be interviewed by the police – an aid to assessment. *Medicine, Science and the Law* 41: 5–12.

Robertson G (1992) *The Role of Police. Royal Commission on Criminal Justice*. London: HMSO.

---

**Digital Evidence** *See* **Computer Crime and Digital Evidence**

---

# DNA

## Contents
**Basic Principles**
**Ethics of Forensic Applications and Databanks**
**Statistical Analysis**
**Risk of Contamination**
**Mitochondrial**
**Postmortem Analysis for Heritable Channelopathies and Selected Cardiomyopathies**
**Hair Analysis**

## Basic Principles

**B Ludes and C Keyser-Tracqui**, Institut de Médecine Légale, Strasbourg, France

Deoxyribonucleic acid (DNA) is a macromolecule with a helical structure harbored in cell organelles such as the nucleus and mitochondria. DNA is built up of nucleotides that are formed by three biochemically distinct molecules, which are nucleobases, sugars, and phosphates. Sugar molecules and phosphates form the backbone of the DNA molecule and the succession of the four nucleobases, adenine (A), thymine (T), cytosine (C), and guanine (G), represents the genetic code. This structure codes for all genetically determined traits in a living organism, from metabolism to phenotypic characteristics. The helical DNA molecule is organized as a double-stranded helix that is maintained together by hydrogen bonds built between complementary bases. There are two bonds between adenine and thymine and three bonds between cytosine and guanine; the forces keeping cytosine and guanine held together are stronger.

Each strand of DNA is a polymer of nucleotide subunits, consisting of a phosphate group, a deoxyribose sugar, and a nitrogenous base that form a purine or pyrimidine ring structure. The nitrogenous bases are linked to the sugar by a glycosidic bond and the nucleotide monomers are linked in succession by phosphodiester bonds. These bonds occur between the 3′-carbon of one sugar residue and the 5′-carbon of the next, so that the linear chain of nucleotide subunits has a polarity, that is, a 5′ and a 3′ end. The two strands of the helix run with opposite polarity, and the planar nitrogenous bases from each strand point inward to form hydrogen-bonded pairs, like steps on a spiral staircase. The base pairing always involves one pyrimidine (C = cytosine or T = thymine) and one purine (A = adenine or G = guanine); adenine pairs with thymine and cytosine pairs with guanine. The linear sequence of bases in DNA constitutes its informational content. DNA

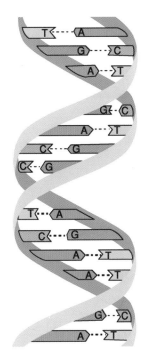

temperature, low ionic strength, high pH, or the presence of chemical denaturants such as urea or formamide. Once denatured, the single strands of DNA will reanneal if conditions permitting hydrogen bonding are restored, and in solution, single-stranded DNA will diffuse and hybridize to its complementary opposite strand. This sequence-specific reassociation is the basis for techniques that utilize hybridization probes which recognize specific genetic sequences. During probe hybridization, the degree of specificity required for annealing can be determined by adjusting temperature and ionic strength. During DNA replication in the cell, the two strands of DNA are transiently separated, so that each may serve as a template for replication of a new opposite strand, complementary to the original. Replication of DNA in nature takes place by linkage of the 5' phosphate of an unincorporated nucleotide to the 3'-hydroxyl group on the elongating strand. *In vitro* enzymatic replication of DNA also occurs in this manner, and is the basis for the polymerase chain reaction (PCR) (**Figure 1**).

## Chromosomal DNA (Nuclear DNA)

### Generality

The vast majority of DNA is located in the cell nucleus, densely packed together with histones, very stable proteins, and divided into chromosomes. The human genome consists of 46 chromosomes in the diploid status. A double set of 23 homologous chromosomes is present and each set is inherited through the haploid gametes from either parent according to Mendelian inheritance. This kind of transmission of genetic information to the next generation leads to a unique recombination in each individual, with the exception of homozygotic twins. Each oocyte or sperm cell receives a random haploid set combination derived from the 23 pairs of chromosomes, so that $2^{23}$ different combinations result just from meiosis. Through union with the opposite gamete, more than seventy trillion possible combinations are possible and in addition there is the possibility of exchanges of sequence regions between chromosomes in the course of mitosis: this is called crossing-over events.

Only 5% of the human genome is made up of protein-coding genes; the other 95% comprises noncoding sequences. Some of these noncoding sequences are the basis of genetic identification methods since they reveal considerable individual variability. The potential of these polymorphisms in terms of human identification was first discovered by Jeffreys and coworkers, who in 1985 published the observation that total human DNA digested by enzymes reveals random patterns for different individuals.

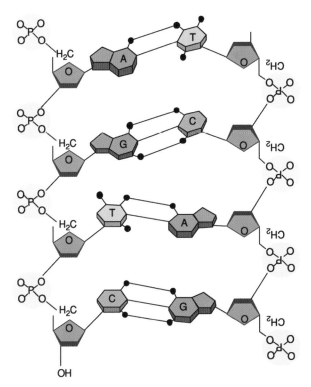

**Figure 1**  The DNA molecule.

determines the amino acid sequences of proteins using a triplet base code.

The two strands of the double helix can be separated in a process called denaturation. This is affected by any conditions that destabilize the hydrogen bonding between base pairs, such as increased

The patterns proved empirically to be unique to each individual and the term genetic fingerprint was conferred on this method. It was based on the analysis of sequence polymorphisms using the restriction fragment length polymorphism technique that needs large amounts of high-molecular-weight DNA. These conditions are rarely found in forensic evidence material.

With the development of PCR technology it was possible to amplify polymorphic tandem repeat structures that were perfectly suitable for typing minute amounts of degraded DNA. First, the so-called minisatellites or variable number of tandem repeats (VNTR) were applied to forensic evidence material. These are regions of tandemly repeated sequences 20–70 bp long: their degree of polymorphism was defined by the number of alleles that were found in a population.

Second, the microsatellites (STRs; short tandem repeats) were developed and designed as better targets for the amplification of polymorphic small regions in cases of degraded DNA. For VNTRs and STRs, the basis of the power of discrimination is the length polymorphism that is found in human populations. Due to the short length of their tandemly repeated core units, which are only 2–6 bp, the STRs are more suited in cases of rare or degraded DNA. These properties of the STRs allow the analyses of ancient DNA in anthropological and archeological applications to identify and assign skeletal elements in destroyed grave fields and to reconstruct historic genealogies and population genetics. The multiplex analysis of STRs allows one rapidly to profile genetically a sample at the individual level that gives a very special value in validating DNA amplification results.

Other chromosomal markers have been described, such as a particular locus of the X- and Y-chromosomal amelogenin gene used for sex determination, but other STRs located on the X and Y chromosomes were indicated to improve the determination of sex, and family lineages were identified in population genetics by means of Y-chromosomal STRs.

## Amelogenin

The amelogenin gene is a gene coding for a protein of tooth enamel, located on Yp11.2 of the Y chromosome and the homologous region Xp22.31–p22.1 of the X chromosome. It was discovered that a region on intron 1 of the gene reveals a 6-bp deletion on the X chromosome. Amplifying this region with the published primer sets leads to a single amplification product of 106 bp for females and two amplification products of 106 and 112 bp for males.

## Autosomal STRs

The microsatellites or STRs are present in noncoding regions of the human genome and represent about 20% of it. They are found in all 22 different autosomes and on both sex chromosomes. Genetic typing of an individual is based on the characterization of these STRs. They comprise tandemly repeated sequences of 2–6 core units; the most common are dinucleotide (CA)n repeats and the second largest group is tetranucleotide repeats. These second repeats are not a uniform group: some always reveal the same core unit throughout the entire repeat structure (e.g., (AGAT)n), while others reveal combinations (e.g., (AGAT)n(ACAT)m). Futhermore, many tetranucleotide repeats reveal so-called interalleles, which do not even consist of four bases (e.g., (AGAT)n(AT)m(AGAT)l(AGA)k). The nomenclature of STR alleles is based on the number of repeat units that are present. Interalleles are termed fractions, e.g., ".2" or ".3" (**Figure 2**).

To identify individuals genetically, the STRs of choice should reveal a high level of polymorphism and must be independent from other STRs under investigation. A suitable STR must not be linked to genes that may underlie different selective pressures in different environmental conditions. The suitability of a particular STR can be roughly deduced from the heterozygosity rate and its chromosomal location. The heterozygosity rate is determined by the number of alleles and their frequency; and the allele frequency gives an impression of whether the no-gene-linkage criterion is fulfilled. This is mostly the case in all Gaussian distributions, and this is interpreted as an indication that there is no selective pressure against one or more allele. This condition ensures a stable intra- and interpopulation power of discrimination of the respective STR locus. The calculation of the power of discrimination ($P_d$) of combined STR analysis is only possible if the STRs are not linked to each other. This is the case if they are located on different chromosomes. The systematic nomenclature of STRs gives their chromosomal location: for example, in the case of D18S51: D (=DNA) 18 (=chromosome 18), S (=single copy sequence), and 51 (=51st locus described on chromosome 18).

AGAT   AGAT   AGAT

Allele 3

AGAT   AGAT   AGAT   ACA   AGAT

Allele 4.3

**Figure 2**  Structure and nomenclature of short tandem repeats (STRs).

All these essential criteria for autosomal STR typing have been fulfilled in the commercially available kits, which allow simultaneous analysis of several STRs, by so-called multiplex analysis.

The $P_d$ value of autosomal STRs depends on heterozygosity and typically ranges from 0.6 to 0.9. It is a measure of the average probability that two individuals will show different genotypes. In fact, STR databases (http:///www.cstl.nist.gov./div831/strbase/index.htm) give population-related and population-specific data for many common autosomal and gonosomal STRs that are in forensic use.

Another value often used in STR identification is matching probability ($P_m$). The $P_m$ value is inverse to $P_d$, it indicates the statistical probability that two unrelated individuals will reveal the same genotype in an STR analysis ($P_m = 1 - P_d$). If the average overall $P_m$ of multiple STRs ($P_{m\text{total}}$) is indicated, the average $P_m$ values of all STRs must simply be multiplied ($P_{m\text{ total}} = P_{m\text{ STR1}} \times P_{m\text{ STR2}} \times \ldots \times \text{Pm}_{\text{STR}n}$). Commercially available kits for human DNA typing consist of 5–16 STR loci, with average $P_m$ values ranging from $10^{-6}$ to $10^{-18}$. With values up to $10^{-11}$, we can assume that no two humans share their STR-based DNA profile, providing they are not identical twins or members of a strongly inbreeding group. Allele distributions and heterozygosity have been found to be very similar in even genetically isolated populations compared to other European populations. Those parameters can be tested by using respective allele frequency data on the population or the group.

### Y-chromosomal STRs

Y-chromosomal STRs have the same structure as autosomal STRs, but, in contrast to autosomal STRs, present a haplotype because there are no homologs on the X chromosome. This haplotype is passed from father to son as a set and therefore Y-chromosome STRs permit paternal lineages to be followed up, analogous to mitochondrial DNA HVR (hypervariable region)-haplotyping that supports the recognition of maternal lineages. The most important application of the Y-chromosome STRs is in population genetics. In fact, these markers, showing regional variation in Y-chromosome haplotype frequencies, are a valuable tool for migration research.

### X-chromosomal STRs

The structure of X-chromosome STRs is the same as for autosomal STRs and males reveal single amplification products from one allele only. However this does not represent a true haplotype due to the possible crossing-over of maternal X-chromosomal sequence fragments during mitosis. Female subjects reveal two alleles with comparatively high heterozygosity rates of 0.6–0.8 for the X-chromosomal STR markers.

## Conclusion

The chemical structure of the DNA molecule is the same in every individual but the difference between people is in the order of the base pairs. The millions of base pairs constituting each person's DNA allow every person to have a different sequence.

## See Also

**Anthropology:** Role of DNA; **DNA:** Mitochondrial

## Further Reading

Brenner CH (1993) A note on paternity computation in cases lacking a mother. *Transfusion* 33: 51–54.

Chakraborty R, Stivers DN, Su B, Zhong Y, Budowle B (1999) The utility of short tandem repeat loci beyond human identification: implications for development of new DNA typing systems. *Electrophoresis* 20: 1682–1696.

Edwards A, Hammond HA, Jin L, Caskey CT, Chakraborty R (1992) Genetic variation at five trimeric and tetrameric tandem repeat loci in four human population groups. *Genomics* 12: 241–253.

Elliott JC, Fourney RM, Budowle B, Aubin RA (1993) Quantitative reproduction of DNA typing minisatellites resolved on ultrathin silver-stained polyacrylamide gels with X-ray duplicating film. *BioTechniques* 14: 702–704.

Gill P, Jeffreys AJ, Werrett DJ (1985) Forensic application of DNA "fingerprints." *Nature* 318: 577–579.

Horn GT, Richards B, Klinger KW (1989) Amplification of a highly polymorphic VNTR segment by the polymerase chain reaction. *Nucleic Acids Research* 17: 2140.

Hummel S (2003) *Ancient DNA Typing. Methods, Strategies and Applications.* Berlin: Springer.

Jeffreys AJ, Wilson V, Thein SL (1985) Individual-specific "fingerprints" of human DNA. *Nature* 316: 76–79.

Keyser-Tracqui C, Crubezy E, Ludes B (2003) Nuclear and mitochondrial DNA analysis of a 2000 year old necropolis in the Egyin Gol Valley of Mongolia. *American Journal of Human Genetics* 73: 247–260.

Mannucci A, Sullivan KM, Ivanov PL, Gill P (1994) Forensic application of a rapid and quantitative DNA sex test by amplification of the X–Y homologous gene amelogenin. *International Journal of Legal Medicine* 106: 190–193.

Moretti TR, Baumstark AL, Defenbaugh DA, *et al.* (2001) Validation of short tandem repeats (STRs) for forensic usage: performance testing of fluorescent multiplex STR systems and analysis of authentic and stimulated forensic samples. *Journal of Forensic Science* 46: 647–660.

Seielstad M, Bekele E, Ibrahim M, Toure A, Traore M (1999) A view of modern human origins from Y chromosome microsatellite variation. *Genome Research* 9: 558–567.

Sullivan KM, Mannucci A, Kimpton CP, Gill P (1993) A rapid and quantitative DNA gender test: fluorescence-based PCR-analysis of X–Y homologous gene amelogenin. *BioTechniques* 15: 636–641.

Wilson JF, Weiss DA, Richards M, *et al.* (2001) Genetic evidence for different male and female roles during cultural transitions in the British Isles. *Proceedings of the National Academy of Science of the USA* 98: 5078–5083.

# Ethics of Forensic Applications and Databanks

**S Cordner**, Victorian Institute of Forensic Medicine, Southbank, VIC, Australia

## Introduction

There is no question that DNA profiling is now the single most powerful tool possessed by forensic science. Reevaluation of numerous convictions for capital offenses in the USA using DNA techniques has led to the release of many dozens of innocent people. Such is the discriminating ability of DNA profiling that, if samples are collected correctly, processed, and analyzed, one can be confident that the DNA originates from the individual with the matching profile; however, mistakes can, and do, occur. The National DNA Database in the UK has transformed policing in that country. It has helped to clear up volume crime in the UK as well as performing its well-known role in violent offenses. In 2002, the UK database materially assisted the investigation of 21 000 crimes and linked suspects, on average, to 15 murders, 31 rapes, and 770 car crimes per month.

The ability of DNA to withstand degradation by environments too toxic for proteins (such as blood group substances and serum proteins) contributes to its powerful role in the investigation of crime. Numbers of old offenses have been cleared up by analyzing old crime-scene samples and comparing the DNA profiles with those held in current databases. This resilience is also the basis for DNA's substantial contribution to the identification of decomposed or even skeletalized human remains of considerable antiquity. In addition, the very small size of the sample required for analysis, which dwarfs that required for blood group and serum protein analyses, represents another powerful characteristic of the tool. For example, manual contact with a telephone or a steering wheel can leave sufficient DNA for analysis. (However, reliance on these minute samples has its own problems.)

The power of the technique, in the particular social and political milieu of our times, is being used to challenge firmly held ethical beliefs about the balance between civil liberties and the "fight" against crime, and more recently, the "war" against terrorism. The issues are most conveniently discussed in two contexts: the domestic and the international. A comprehensive evaluation of all the issues is beyond the scope of this article, and the emphasis here will be to identify the issues and to discuss briefly what is at stake.

## The Domestic Context

### Background

As is obvious, the current basis of the contribution of DNA profiling in any forensic context is the comparison of the profile of the DNA extracted from a sample taken from a place (e.g., a crime scene) or a person (e.g., a victim) with the profile of the DNA from another person or with many profiles housed in a database. The practical steps involved in DNA analysis in a domestic forensic science context include the following:

- Ensuring the samples are taken only from those people permitted by law.
- Obtaining the sample (e.g., blood, saliva, or hair) usually with "consent." If there is no "consent," then the threat or use of force, subject to procedural safeguards, is required. In some jurisdictions, as an alternative to the threat or use of force, there is provision for allowing an adverse inference to be drawn, from the refusal to provide a sample, at later court proceedings.
- Analyzing the DNA from a fraction of the sample (the subsample).
- Preserving and storing the remaining part of the sample.
- Analyzing only a minute portion of the genetic information in the subsample and producing the DNA profile – a "bar code" that is also expressible as a series of numbers.
- Entering these numbers into a database linked to other personal or contextual details.
- Comparing the profile (the "bar code" expressed as a series of numbers) found in a sample from a crime scene or a victim, which represents the DNA of a potential suspect, with those in the database. In the event of a match, recomparing the DNA profiles extracted from samples from the crime scene or victim with the DNA profile extracted from a sample freshly taken from the suspect. (The existence of such a step is tacit acceptance that results from the preceding steps can be mistaken.)

The applicability of these steps varies slightly between jurisdictions. However, one can begin to see the ethical issues taking shape. They can be grouped as follows: (1) obtaining the sample; (2) testing the sample/using the results; and (3) retaining the sample.

## Obtaining the Sample

**Who will be required to provide a sample?** There are two issues here. First, who is required to provide a sample in relation to the investigation of an offense? Second, who is required to provide a sample, the profile from which will be stored in the database? In relation to the first, in Victoria, Australia, for example, samples are obtained from individuals where there are reasonable grounds for suspecting that the person has committed an offense for which the penalty is more than 5 years' imprisonment. The suspect's sample and profile must be destroyed after 12 months if charges are not laid, the prosecution is abandoned, or the defendant is acquitted. In relation to the second, only the results of those convicted and imprisoned for offenses for which the possible penalty is more than 5 years' imprisonment are retained on the database. For the purposes of the UK National DNA Database, samples (e.g., of saliva/buccal swab) are obtained from all those arrested for offenses which carry possible jail terms upon conviction. This includes many road traffic offenses. The US national database (CODIS – Combined DNA Index System) holds the DNA profiles from 1 400 000 individuals convicted of a felony. In the Netherlands, only those profiles from cases where DNA profiling has been used in obtaining a conviction are housed in a database. In France, the database is limited to sexual offenses.

It is unclear what independent audit arrangements are in place to ensure that only authorized profiles are held in the various DNA databases. In healthcare contexts, there is increasing discussion about the concept of "GeneTrustees," a third-party intermediary independent of the subjects and the database custodians who have responsibilities related to the protection of privacy and confidentiality. Such a person could also have responsibility for the integrity of the database. The author is not aware of any such system in existence in relation to forensic DNA databases. Such a system would obviously enhance public confidence. In Victoria, Australia, external audit by another government agency, the Auditor-General's Office, is currently being considered.

**What "consent" regime will apply to those from whom samples are required?** The notion of "consent" in these circumstances is arguably an example of Orwellian doublespeak. Consent is the free and voluntary agreement to a proposal, in this context, a proposal about one's self. In circumstances of detention or investigation by police, the consequences of not agreeing to provide a sample might include: a court being invited to draw an adverse inference from the refusal, that is, the court can infer that the person has something to hide; or the threat or application of force to obtain the sample.

Clearly these are circumstances where the notion of consent is a false one. This is particularly so if it is compared to its usage in healthcare, a plausible comparison, given that we are considering consent to the taking of a biological sample with important ramifications for the individual. It is a wrong use of the notion of consent because coercion is inherent in the circumstances surrounding the decision. Many would say that the coercion is justified. The power of the techniques and the consequent benefit to the public interest, so the argument would go, more than justifies the minimal nature of the infringements to individual rights. Really, the response would continue, it is not much different to requiring a suspect to provide a fingerprint, and why would anyone refuse that if they have nothing to hide?

But if the coercion is justified, then falsely claiming that the sample was obtained with consent is to obscure the real nature of what is happening: the state has decided that clearing up crimes requires biological samples from those suspected of committing them, therefore including those who are innocent. This need, the state asserts, overrides the right of individuals to bodily integrity and the right not to incriminate themselves. The counterview is that the state ought not to have access to so much that is personal on the chance that a person might have committed an offense. In addition, a fundamental bulwark against the power of the state is the right of people not to incriminate themselves. The state must prove its case in front of an independent tribunal without requiring, as opposed to the accused volunteering, self-incrimination. It is still the case in many jurisdictions that accused persons are not required to answer questions if they do not wish to. In some of those jurisdictions, the court is not allowed to draw any adverse inference from that refusal. If one is not required to answer questions, why should one be required to provide samples for DNA analysis? It is hard to imagine anything tangible that is more the essence of self than his/her DNA. Requiring this to be provided on the grounds that it might exculpate the accused, but also might incriminate him/her, is clearly the pinnacle of self-incrimination. Providing the sample should, arguably, be at the complete discretion of the person suspected or accused of the offense.

None of the above even begins to address the particularly problematic situation, common in the criminal justice system, of incapacity by reason of intellectual, psychiatric, or drug-induced impairment.

**Is obtaining the sample a "medical procedure"?** If the answer to this question is yes, certain consequences flow. Some jurisdictions have regarded the taking of intimate samples (e.g., vaginal swabs, blood samples) as the province of healthcare professionals. Healthcare professionals, even those employed by police, are bound in various ways to act in the best interests of the patients. However, the police-minded doctor might say: "The suspect is not a patient, and certainly not my patient, as I am seeing him/her for nonhealthcare reasons; therefore the rules of the doctor–patient relationships do not apply." The response to this is that the suspect, knowing that the person taking the sample is a doctor, and that taking biological samples is the sort of thing doctors do, could quite reasonably suppose that the ordinary rules do apply. The police-minded doctor counters by saying: "Before I took the blood sample, I specifically cautioned the suspect that I was acting on behalf of the authorities and I was not concerned with his/her interests but simply carrying out a task requiring skills that I possess."

Many doctors would take the view that exercising medical skills outside a "healthcare" context to the detriment of the individual is not something they would wish to do. Such doctors would say that everything they do is as doctors. This view could be expressed as follows: upon entering a healthcare profession, of which medicine is the exemplar, one cannot simply ordain that in a particular context one is not acting as a member of that profession.

This issue is further complicated by increasing reliance upon samples such as buccal swabs or saliva which are being taken by police officers. Would a procedure which is a medical procedure, if performed by a doctor, be protected by the same rules if it is performed by someone else for nonhealthcare purposes? In practice, it would seem not, but this is a serious issue for policy-makers to address.

### Testing the Sample/Using the Results

In the normal course of events, it is only DNA which has no known specific function which is analyzed to produce a DNA profile. This profile has no meaning on its own, except to compare with another profile. In the current state of knowledge, it does not identify any characteristics of the individual.

Samples in the USA are routinely analyzed for 13 loci for its national database CODIS. The nine loci relied upon in Australia are all represented in these 13. The Interpol standard set of loci, identical with the European standard set recommended by the European Network of Forensic Science Institutes, has seven loci, all of which are represented in the 13 loci used in the USA, plus an optional eighth, amelogenin, which is not.

This means that there is a high level of international comparability: test results in one country can be compared with databases in another. However, discussing the regulatory regimes for such comparisons is beyond the scope of this article. The possibility for comparisons with databases in other jurisdictions could undermine the principles upon which sample and data collection and storage are based in the first country.

As indicated earlier, correct sample collection, processing, and analysis, as well as high-quality database management, are all preconditions for having a high level of confidence that a reported match means that the sample came from the nominated individual. There are cases where contamination by exogenous DNA has implicated individuals who have subsequently been able to establish conclusively that they were far removed from the scene at the time of the offense. (A theoretical alternative explanation may be an adventitious match.) Such contaminations can occur in a number of ways, which evidence handlers and laboratories must guard against. The problem of contamination is a strong basis for ensuring that high levels of quality control and assurance are in place.

Other laboratory errors leading to mismatches have been reported. As of September 2003 in the USA, only three states – New York, Oklahoma, and Texas – require accreditation to specified standards. This is despite several cases where laboratories have mishandled DNA evidence. Suggestions have been made that the probability of an error occurring, such as contamination, should be built into the probability calculations of the match. Estimates of error are crucial. It is clear that there is not a zero probability of error and scientists are certainly not infallible. To try and put it simply, if a scientist (or a laboratory director) was invited to estimate his/her error rate and stated that it was low (say, one in 1000 cases, over several years), it would be more correct to cite the one in 1000, and not the one in millions, probability that the nominated person is not the source of the sample. There is also argument over whether performance in quality assurance programs, and other evidence of the laboratory's general performance, should be available to a court wishing to investigate the reliability of the laboratory's performance.

The power of DNA techniques also raises whether or not any duty exists – an ethical one, not a legal one – for legal systems to revisit as many cases as possible where any doubt is harbored about the conviction, samples still exist, and DNA testing would resolve that doubt. The UK has established a quasiadministrative approach for reviewing such convictions, among others (e.g., where there is doubt over the quality of expert evidence). This eases the process for reviewing convictions after all formal appeal processes have been exhausted. After evaluation the Criminal Case Review Commission can refer suitable cases to the Court of Appeal for formal judicial review.

It is likely in the future that instrumentation will be developed which will enable on-site analysis of samples (e.g., at a crime scene) and speedy identification of matches via links to national databases. In the laboratory itself, improvements in miniaturization and automation will dramatically improve throughput, minimizing the technical impediments to analyzing samples from the entire population. In some countries, such samples already exist in routinely maintained stores of neonatal heelprick blood samples (so-called Guthrie spots) for testing for metabolic diseases such as phenylketonuria.

### Retaining the Sample

On July 15 2003, Home Office Minister Hazel Blear loaded the two-millionth DNA profile into the UK National DNA Database. (At the same time she also donated a sample of her own DNA for inclusion in the database as an indication of there being nothing to fear from it.) From March 2003, UK police have had the power to retain samples in all cases where they are collected, whether or not the person is even charged. The UK database had been previously established as the Criminal Justice DNA Database on the basis that it would contain profiles (and that samples would be retained) only from those convicted of offenses punishable by imprisonment. The recent change of name, dropping the phrase "criminal justice," surprisingly does not seem to have elicited much comment, let alone public concern, that it may herald major shifts in the database's underlying philosophy.

In the USA, states vary in their requirements to destroy the sample after conviction, or after the conviction is overturned. The US National Institute of Justice's Commission on the future of DNA evidence regards the currently used 13 loci as robustly in place, well understood, and unlikely to change in the foreseeable future. The argument, therefore, for retaining the sample once it has been analyzed is weak and has to be measured against bolstering public confidence in the system and removing the temptation to use the sample for purposes other than those stated or intended at the time of collection.

A *Lancet* editorial has claimed that "police scientists are already investigating the correlation of DNA markers with physical characteristics." This will include things like facial features, skin, hair, and eye color, propensities for genetic disease, and ranges of height and weight. This is but one demonstration of what can happen when samples are retained. The samples might also reveal a history of illness (e.g., infectious diseases identified by remnants of viral nucleic acids). This sort of information will put pressure on other databases (e.g., those of medical records) to provide information to assist police. A citizen may be entitled to wonder if privacy is on the way to becoming a fiction, or historical curiosity.

## The International Context

Human genetic data have a special status on account of their sensitive nature since they can be predictive of genetic predispositions concerning individuals and … the power of predictability can be stronger than assessed at the time of deriving the data; they may have a significant impact on the family, including off-spring, extending over generations, and in some instances, on the whole group; they may contain information the significance of which is not necessarily known at the time of the collection of biological samples; and they may have cultural significance for persons or groups … the collection, processing, use and storage of human genetic data have potential risks for the exercise and observance of human rights and fundamental freedoms and respect for human dignity (preamble to the International Declaration on Human Genetic Data, United Nations Educational, Scientific, and Cultural Organization, 2003)

The provisions of the declaration "apply to the collection, processing, use and storage of human genetic data, human proteomic data, and biological samples, except in the investigation, detection, and prosecution of criminal offenses and in parentage testing that are subject to domestic law that is consistent with the international law of human rights." Thus, it would seem the International Declaration applies both in the international context and where domestic law is absent.

This is important, because, contrary to common expectation, regulation of activities of many sorts in international contexts is weak compared with domestic contexts. This is even more so, obviously, in situations of war, internal violence, or breakdown of civil society. What, the reader might say, has such extreme situations got to do with forensic applications of DNA technology and databanks? The answer begins with the fact that samples for DNA profiling are being collected from detainees in the Middle East and Guantanamo Bay.

> The purpose of collecting Personal Identification Data is to create a better database for identifying potential enemy threats and to screen those individuals to determine if they meet the criteria to be treated as detainees. If an individual meets the specified criteria, they are taken into custody in a detainee status and secured for further processing . . . Personal Identification Data (PID) packets consisting of names, fingerprints, DNA and digital photographs, has become a key tool in America's "War on Terrorism" (Hughbank RJ and Curry JL. Detainee personal identification data collection processing Afghanistan. Available online at: http://call.army.mil/homepage/trngqtr.htm (accessed September 23, 2003).

As an indication that the process is not being taken lightly, the article referred to above outlines the components of a "PID collection operation." This consists of eight different teams:

1.  command and control team
2.  perimeter security team
3.  staging area security team
4.  PID collection team
5.  mobile interrogation team
6.  medical team
7.  holding area team
8.  detainee security team.

At the time the article was written, "PID operations have been conducted in over five different areas throughout Afghanistan, collecting data on over 3500 potential members of terrorist organizations."

It is clearly beyond the scope of this article to discuss the defense of necessity which would be raised to counter any assertion that this collection of DNA was unethical or even unlawful. As far as the latter is concerned, there are almost certainly no specific rules of international law regulating the practice because the science and technology are so new. Some articles of the Geneva Conventions could be argued to apply in a more general sense: e.g., Article 3(1)c (which is common to all four Geneva Conventions), prohibits outrages upon personal dignity. One is probably never going to be in a position to discover the full facts about the obtaining of DNA samples in the circumstances outlined above. It would be reasonable to conclude, however, that:

- if there is not transparency about the whole process, especially with regard to the criteria determining who provides samples and the use to which the results both individually and collectively will be put; or
- if there is not a clear legal framework within which the DNA samples are being taken, analyzed, and

retained, and authorizing the results being kept in a database; or
- if the samples are being taken without the provision of comprehensive information about the process and/or taken against the wishes of the person; or
- if the technical and ethical standards being applied are not compatible with best practice at the national level of the country responsible for taking the samples; or
- if there is no compliance with best practices regarding privacy and confidentiality,

then there has been an outrage upon the personal dignity of those from whom the samples have been taken.

The other new application of DNA technology in international contexts has been its use in the identification of mass deaths following war or internal violence.

Using DNA to identify, or contribute to the identification of, human remains in these circumstances requires:

- retrieval of the remains
- removal of a sample from the remains
- retrieving DNA from the sample
- collection of samples for DNA extraction from
    a.  if identity of the remains is suspected
        - likely relatives of the deceased
        - the missing person's effects (e.g., hair from a comb) or past surgical samples
    b.  if identity is uncertain or unknown
        - large numbers of individuals with relatives missing who are presumably/probably/possibly dead.

It will then be necessary to match the profiles from the remains with the profiles from the relatives, the population of sample donors, or the missing person's effects.

The exemplar in this area has been the Balkans where the International Commission on Missing Persons has been championing a DNA-led strategy for the identification of the tens of thousands of dead, many of whom were buried in mass graves. The International Committee of the Red Cross (ICRC), as part of its project to create a comprehensive and systematic approach to the problem of those "missing" as a result of war or internal violence, has considered the contribution of DNA to the identification of human remains in these international contexts. Much of what follows is taken from the ICRC's work:

- DNA analysis must not preclude the use of other objective means of identification.
- DNA analysis must not be considered as the sole method available for making a positive

identification (additional practical methods are needed to confirm an identification; it is not always feasible operationally; it may put relatives under duress to provide samples; laboratory errors cannot be ruled out).
- The decision to use DNA analysis should be based on sound scientific and practical considerations within an overall identification strategy defined for the context.
- The decision to use DNA analysis should not be based only on requests generated by individuals, families, communities, organizations, or governments.
- Laws must not be enacted requiring mandatory DNA analysis for the purpose of identification.
- In the preinvestigation phase (e.g., in defining the overall strategy) the social, religious, and cultural characteristics of the community concerned must be taken into consideration. The families and the community will accept the outcome more readily if they have confidence in the investigation.
- When DNA analysis is deemed necessary for identification, it must be performed in laboratories that: work to accredited standards of quality; handle remains, data, and samples in accordance with internationally accepted norms; do not operate on the basis of maximum profit; minimize commercial considerations; and whose accounts are externally audited.

Following war or internal violence there is a real possibility that expectations could be raised in the minds of vulnerable or traumatized populations of rapid identifications of deceased individuals using DNA technology. If these expectations are not met, further trauma may be inflicted. Such expectations need to be reduced since there are major impediments to the implementation of DNA-based programs in such circumstances:

- the identification of graves (e.g., graves from the recent conflicts in the Balkans are still being found)
- exhuming the remains (this is a resource-intensive process and therefore a major limiting step. As of May 2003, 8 years following the peace in Bosnia, about 50% of the 30 000 missing and presumed dead in that country have been exhumed)
- individualizing the sets of remains (i.e., dealing with the problem of commingled remains)
- obtaining samples from the remains and extracting DNA
- obtaining samples from the population of those who believe their missing relative may be dead and extracting DNA from those samples
- developing in-country laboratories and skills to avoid the potentially catastrophic political, social,

and other consequences of taking the samples and their analytical results out of the country
- developing the information technology systems to house and manage the data
- applying the results to individual cases and involving surviving relatives in an identification process that is meaningful to them.

The enormity of these tasks is no reason not to undertake them, although it may mean that funding them is difficult. It is a reason, however, to be conservative, cautious, and humble when thinking of applying them in a particular context. Populations may need to be well warned that even with the assistance of DNA technology:

- many remains may never be found
- depending on the number involved and the resources available, it may take years and even decades to exhume all the known remains
- logistical considerations may mean that some remains will never be exhumed
- it may not be possible to extract DNA from all remains
- not all relatives will wish to provide samples for DNA analysis
- it will take time (amongst other things) to develop in-country expertise and laboratories.

For all these reasons and others, expectations will need to be kept at reasonable levels.

Finally, obtaining mass samples of particular populations means that the genetic parameters of the population, and of groups within the population, can be defined. Now that the specter has been raised, within credible circles, of biological agents which could target genetic characteristics of certain human groups, people will have to be consulted, well informed, and confident about proposals to collect samples on a wide scale for whatever purpose. It goes without saying that the probity, regulation, and oversight of the organizations and laboratories involved should be of the highest order.

## Conclusion: Scientists and Human Rights

DNA technology throws into sharp relief a less well-appreciated ethical issue in science generally as well as forensic science in particular. Science is not the value-free pursuit of knowledge for the benefit of humanity. As the particular issue of DNA demonstrates, there is real capacity to use the technology to breach fundamental rights of individuals, whether by accident or intentionally. Scientists must understand what it is they are doing. The professional obligations of scientists will become blurred or ambiguous when they are employed by agencies whose primary functions are not the pursuit of knowledge for its own sake; e.g., police forces and armies. Loyalties to the ideals of science may be further stretched by a degree of isolation or even ostracism associated with working within police or security agencies. Scientists generally are poorly prepared or trained to identify potentials for abuse in what they are doing and what to do if they feel that this might be happening. In relation to well-known abuses by the medical profession in South Africa during the era of apartheid, the South African Truth and Reconciliation Commission had this to say:

> Health professionals who are employed in situations in which they have dual loyalties are, because they do not enjoy full independence in making or implementing decisions, at risk of becoming involved in overt or covert abuses of the human rights of their patients. It is all too easy for health professionals who are not particularly vigilant or well informed to assume the culture of the organization for which they work, rather than maintaining independence and putting the needs and rights of patients above those of the organization. Appropriate measures are needed to prevent or pre-empt the moral and ethical dilemmas that may arise for health professionals faced with the (often conflicting) needs of their patients and expectations of their employers (*Report of the Truth and Reconciliation Commission*, vol. 4, chapter 5, para 21, Macmillan Reference, London, 1999).

Insert "scientists" and "society" for "health professionals" and "patients" respectively, and that is the message.

## See Also

**DNA:** Basic Principles; Statistical Analysis; Risk of Contamination; Mitochondrial; Postmortem Analysis for Heritable Channelopathies and Selected Cardiomyopathies

## Further Reading

*Forensic Sampling and DNA Databases in Criminal Investigations* (2004) Victorian Parliament Law Reform Committee. Victoria, Australia: Government Printer.

Kellenberger J (2002) An appeal to governments and scientists. *International Herald Tribune* September 27, p. 8.

Taitz J (2001) *Exploring the Use of DNA Testing for Family Reunification*. Geneva, Switzerland: International Organisation for Migration.

The Future of DNA Testing (2000) Research and Development Working Group of the US National Commission on the Future of DNA Evidence. Washington, DC: National Institute of Justice.

The Missing and their Families. International Committee of the Red Cross (2003) Available online at: www.icrc.org/Web/eng/siteeng0.nsf/html/themissing.

*Universal Declaration on the Human Genome and Human Rights* (1997) and *International Declaration on Human Genetic Data* (2003) UNESCO. Available online at: http://www.unesco.org/shs/humanrights/hrbc.htm.

# Statistical Analysis

**W K Fung and Y-Q Hu**, University of Hong Kong, Hong Kong, China

## Introduction

Nuclear deoxyribonucleic acid (DNA) profiling or DNA fingerprinting has become a very powerful method for forensic human identification since its inception in 1985. It is regarded as one of the most important discoveries in forensic science since the introduction of dermal fingerprinting. Two reports about the use of this technique have been released by the US National Research Council (NRC) in 1992 and 1996. The method is now widely employed in courtrooms, though warnings have been sounded about using it carefully. DNA can be found in blood, semen, hair/hair root, bone, and body fluids, such as saliva and sweat. In theory, no two persons, except for identical twins, have the same DNA sequence. However, with the DNA markers that are currently in use, a unique identification cannot be assured. Statistics play an important role in assessing the uncertainty in identification and evaluating the weight of DNA evidence.

## Single-Source Specimen

Consider a case where a crime has been committed, the perpetrator has left a blood specimen at the crime scene, and a suspect has been identified. The blood stain and the blood specimen of the suspect are typed genetically, often at nine loci or more (the loci are usually located at different chromosomes). If the two DNA types/alleles match with each other, the suspect would not be excluded as a possible contributor to the blood stain. Under the current legal system, the match probability or the (relative) frequency of the alleles has to be calculated and reported in the courtroom.

## Product Rule

Suppose that, at a particular locus, the alleles found in the crime scene and typed from the suspect are in common, say, $A_i A_j$. The match probability at this particular locus can be obtained using the product rule as follows:

$$A_i A_j: 2p_i p_j, \qquad i \neq j,$$
$$A_i A_i: p_i^2, \qquad i = j,$$

where $p_i$ and $p_j$ are the frequencies of alleles $i$ and $j$ respectively. The factor 2 appears because there are two ways that a person can inherit alleles $A_i$ and $A_j$, $i \neq j$ from his/her parent. The match probability may also be interpreted as the frequency estimate of the genotype $A_i A_j$ at that particular locus. The overall match probability can be obtained by multiplying individual probabilities over all loci. In practice, it is common to find match probabilities such as 1 in a million or 1 in a billion.

It may sometimes be argued that the blood stain was left behind by a relative of the suspect. The match probability may then be evaluated using the formulae:

$$A_i A_j: 2p_i p_j + 2(p_i + p_j - 4p_i p_j)F,$$
$$A_i A_i: p_i^2 + 4p_i(1 - p_i)F,$$

with the kinship coefficient $F = 1/4$ for parent and offspring; $F = 1/8$ for half-siblings or for uncle and nephew, and $F = 1/16$ for first cousins. For unrelated persons, $F = 0$; this set of formulae reduces to the previous set obtained by the product rule. For full siblings, being bilineal rather than unilineal, different formulae are required:

$$A_i A_j: (1 + p_i + p_j + 2p_i p_j)/4,$$
$$A_i A_i: (1 + 2p_i + p_i^2)/4.$$

The effect that a relative of the suspect is the perpetrator on the match probability is demonstrated in **Table 1** with $p_i = 0.1$ and $p_j = 0.2$. It is noticed that the match probability increases substantially when a close relative such as a cousin or a full sibling of the suspect is the perpetrator.

**Table 1** The match probability for a genotype $A_i A_j$ when a relative (measured by the kinship $F$-value) or a full sibling of the suspect is the perpetrator, with $p_i = 0.1$ and $p_j = 0.2$

| $F$ | 0 | 1/16 | 1/8 | 1/4 | Full sibling |
|---|---|---|---|---|---|
| Match probability | 0.04 | 0.0675 | 0.095 | 0.15 | 0.335 |

## Hardy–Weinberg and Linkage Equilibrium

The above match probability assessment uses the product rule in which the alleles are taken to be independent statistically, or in Hardy–Weinberg (HW) and linkage equilibrium genetically. Two broad classes of tests have been constructed for testing for HW (independence of alleles within loci): (1) the goodness-of-fit ($\chi^2$) test; and (2) the exact test, which is often more powerful than the former one. Although there have been opposite views of whether HW is satisfied or not, most recent studies seem to suggest that there is generally no strong violation of HW. Tests for linkage equilibrium (independence of alleles across loci) have been suggested, but their statistical power may not be high due to the high dimensionality of data.

In genetics, it is well known that the HW law is seldom exactly certain or correct. Nevertheless, testing for HW is still useful because it can possibly indicate anomaly in the process of data collection. However, statistical insignificance does not imply that the HW law is absolutely correct. In fact, the corresponding population is often subdivided and a coefficient $\theta$ is empirically determined to measure the degree of population subdivision. This fact was also acknowledged by the NRC II report and modifications to the product rule taking $\theta$ into account in the calculation were suggested. Some laboratories prefer to use the following adjustment formulae:

$$A_i A_j: 2p_i p_j,$$
$$A_i A_i: p_i^2 + p_i(1 - p_i)\theta,$$

to account for the increase in frequency of homozygous alleles due to population subdivision. The value of $\theta$ may also be interpreted genetically (NRC II) and it measures the variation of allele frequencies between subpopulations. A (conservative) value of $\theta = 0.01$ is recommended for most populations, while for some small, isolated populations, a value of 0.03 may be appropriate. This is one of the recommendations (recommendation 4.1) of the USA NRC II report.

In some European countries and laboratories, the theory of subdivided population and the conditional match probability argument are adopted. Under this circumstance, the match probability is evaluated conditionally and is given as follows:

$$A_i A_j: 2[\theta + (1 - \theta)p_i][\theta + (1 - \theta)p_j]/[(1 + \theta)(1 + 2\theta)]$$
$$A_i A_i: [2\theta + (1 - \theta)p_i][3\theta + (1 - \theta)p_i]/[(1 + \theta)(1 + 2\theta)].$$

The derivation for this set of formulae can be interpreted statistically as well as genetically.

In practice, both sets of adjustment formulae often only have a small effect on the numerical value of the match probability.

## Paternity Determination

DNA profiling can also be used for paternity testing and kinship determination. Consider the standard trio case in paternity testing. Let M, C, and AF be the genotypes of the mother, her child, and the alleged father, respectively. The following set of explanations or hypotheses is often of interest.

$H_p$: Alleged father is the true father (TF) of the child
$H_d$: The TF of the child is a random unrelated man.

The idea of likelihood ratio (LR) in statistics is commonly used to assess the weight of forensic evidence, including paternity testing. The ratio is often evaluated under two explanations or hypotheses ($H_p$ and $H_d$) from the prosecution and defense, in the form as follows:

$$LR = P(\text{evidence}|H_p)/P(\text{evidence}|H_d)$$

which is a ratio of the probability of observing the (genetic) evidence given $H_p$ to that of given $H_d$. In a standard trio paternity testing setting, the evidence comprises the genotypes of the mother, her child, and the alleged father, i.e., M, C, and AF. Thus, the LR is evaluated as

$$LR = PI = P(M, C, AF|H_p)/P(M, C, AF|H_d),$$

which is termed the paternity index (PI) in paternity testing. Using some results on conditional probability, the index can be simplified to:

$$PI = P(C|M, AF, H_p)/P(C|M, H_d).$$

Suppose the genotypes at a particular locus are obtained as $C = A_1A_2$, $M = A_1A_3$, and $AF = A_2A_4$. The numerator of the PI is $(1/2)$ $(1/2)$, since there is a 1/2 chance that the mother passes the allele $A_1$ to

the child, and a 1/2 chance for the alleged father (who is the father of the child under $H_p$). The denominator can similarly be obtained as $p_2/2$, thus giving $PI = 1/(2p_2)$. **Table 2** gives the PIs for various genotype combinations for standard trio cases.

If the alleged father argues that he is not the TF but his relative, say his brother, is, the resultant hypotheses become:

$H_p$: Alleged father is TF of the child
$H_d$: A relative (brother) of the alleged father is the TF of the child.

The PI can still be obtained easily using the formula $PI = 1/[2F + 2(1 - 2F)p_2]$, where $F = 1/4$ is the kinship coefficient between the alleged father and his relative, in this case his brother. The PIs or LRs for other situations can be referred to the last column of **Table 2**.

Sometimes the mother is unavailable. Instead, some of her relatives can provide the genetic information. The calculations are generally nontrivial, and there exist only a few paternity calculation programs for such a purpose. **Table 3** gives an example where the genotypes of some of the possible relatives are available. The corresponding allele frequencies at D5S818 are taken as $p_7 = 0.035$, $p_8 = 0.025$, $p_9 = 0.072$, and $p_{10} = 0.252$.

**Table 4** gives the PIs, with various combinations of possible relatives, under:

$H_p$: Alleged father is TF of the child versus two different alternative hypotheses:

$H_d$: TF of C is a random man or
$H_d$: TF of C is a brother of AF.

**Table 2** Paternity index (PI) for a standard trio case. The LR is evaluated under $H_d$: A relative of the alleged father is the TF of the child. $F$ is the kinship coefficient of the alleged father and his relative

| M | C | AF | PI | LR |
|---|---|---|---|---|
| $A_iA_i$ | $A_iA_i$ | $A_iA_i$ | $1/p_i$ | $1/[p_i(1 - 2F) + 2F]$ |
| | | $A_iA_j^*$ | $1/(2p_i)$ | $1/\{2[p_i(1 - 2F) + F]\}$ |
| | $A_iA_j^*$ | $A_iA_i$ | $1/p_i$ | $1/[p_i(1 - 2F) + 2F]$ |
| | | $A_iA_k^{**}$ | $1/(2p_i)$ | $1/\{2[p_i(1 - 2F) + F]\}$ |
| $A_iA_j^*$ | $A_iA_i$ | $A_iA_j$ | $1/p_j$ | $1/[p_j(1 - 2F) + 2F]$ |
| | | $A_jA_k^@$ | $1/(2p_j)$ | $1/\{2[p_j(1 - 2F) + F]\}$ |
| | $A_iA_j^*$ | $A_iA_i$ | $1/(p_i + p_j)$ | $1/[(p_i + p_j)(1 - 2F) + 2F]$ |
| | | $A_iA_j^*$ | $1/(p_i + p_j)$ | $1/[(p_i + p_j)(1 - 2F) + 2F]$ |
| | | $A_iA_k^#$ | $1/[2(p_i + p_j)]$ | $1/\{2[(p_i + p_j)(1 - 2F) + F]\}$ |
| | $A_iA_k^#$ | $A_iA_j$ | $1/p_j$ | $1/[p_j(1 - 2F) + 2F]$ |
| | | $A_jA_l^+$ | $1/(2p_j)$ | $1/\{2[p_j(1 - 2F) + F]\}$ |

$^*j \neq i.$
$^{**}k \neq i.$
$^@k \neq j.$
$^#k \neq i, j.$
$^+l \neq k.$

These PIs were obtained from some existing general algorithm for kinship determinations. It is observed that the PI reduces substantially when the alternative hypothesis is changed to $H_d$: TF of C is a brother of the alleged father. This indicates that DNA profiling performs less well in distinguishing paternity among relatives.

Another concept that some laboratories like to use is: random man not excluded (RMNE). Consider a simple case in which the child and the mother have genotypes $C = A_i A_i$ and $M = A_i A_j$. A random man without the allele $A_i$ (i.e., in whom both alleles are not $A_i$) will then be excluded. Thus, there is the probability that a RMNE is $1 - (1 - p_i)^2$. Table 5 gives the RMNE probabilities for other situations. The RMNE method has the appeal that it is easy to understand by a jury, but it ignores the genotypes of the alleged father and so some scientists do not recommend it. The method, however, is used in some countries, such as the USA.

## DNA Mixture

The above consideration is given to a single-source specimen of evidence or sample. It is not unusual that, for a large variety of crimes, the samples contain material from more than one person. This is especially common in rape cases. In such cases, the sample may contain material from the victim, her consensual sexual partners, and/or the perpetrator(s). The assessment and interpretation of mixed DNA samples in some particular cases were discussed in terms of LRs of match probabilities. However, the general mixed-samples problem is complex, as shown by the comments in the NRC II report.

A simple mixture problem is considered as follows. Suppose that at a particular locus the mixture sample $M$ has alleles $A_1 A_2 A_3$, i.e., $M = \{A_1 A_2 A_3\}$, the victim's sample has heterozygous alleles $A_1 A_2$, i.e., $V = A_1 A_2$, and the suspect's sample has homozygous alleles $A_3 A_3$, i.e., $S = A_3 A_3$. Additionally, suppose that the mixture sample is known to have been contributed by the victim and perpetrator. To judge whether the suspect is the perpetrator, two alternative explanations are considered as follows:

$H_p$: Contributors of the mixture sample were the victim and the suspect
$H_d$: Contributors of the mixture sample were the victim and an unknown person.

Now consider the likelihood ratio $LR = P(\text{Evidence}|H_p)/P(\text{Evidence}|H_d)$ which, after simplification, can be expressed as $P(M|H_p, V, S)/P(M|H_d, V, S)$. As before, LR measures the weight of evidence if $H_p$ is correct to that if $H_d$ is correct. An LR of over, say, 1000 or 10 000 may provide a strong support for $H_p$ over $H_d$. In this particular example, we have seen four alleles of known sources, $\{A_1 A_2 A_3 A_3\}$, i.e., $A_1 A_2$ from the victim and $A_3 A_3$ from the suspect under $H_p$ or $H_d$. Under $H_p$, the mixture $M$ was contributed by the victim and the suspect; therefore $P(M|H_p, V, S) = 1$. Under $H_d$, the unknown person must have at least one $A_3$ allele but cannot have alleles not found in the mixture sample $M = \{A_1 A_2 A_3\}$. Since every person has two alleles (not necessarily distinct), there are three possible sets of alleles for the unknown person here (ignore the orderings of the alleles pairs): $A_3 A_1$, $A_3 A_2$, and $A_3 A_3$. So we have

$$LR = 1/[2P(A_3 A_1 | A_1 A_2 A_3 A_3)$$
$$+ 2P(A_3 A_2 | A_1 A_2 A_3 A_3)$$
$$+ P(A_3 A_3 | A_1 A_2 A_3 A_3)]$$

**Table 3** Genotypes corresponding to a paternity case at locus D5S818

| C | M | AF | FoM | S1oM | S2oM |
|---|---|----|-----|------|------|
| 7, 8 | 7, 9 | 8, 10 | 7, 10 | 7, 8 | 7, 10 |

C, child; M, mother; AF, alleged father, FoM, father of the (missing) mother; S1oM, sibling 1 of the (missing) mother; S2oM, sibling 2 of the (missing) mother.

**Table 4** Paternity index with $H_p$: true father (TF) of child (C) is alleged father (AF) versus $H_d$

| $H_d$: TF of C is | C-M-AF | C-AF | C-FoM-AF | C-FoM-S1oM-AF | C-FoM-S1oM-S2oM-AF |
|---|---|---|---|---|---|
| A random man | 20.0 | 10.0 | 18.8 | 8.38 | 8.90 |
| A brother of AF | 1.90 | 1.82 | 1.90 | 1.79 | 1.80 |

M, mother; FoM, father of the (missing) mother; S1oM, sibling 1 of the (missing) mother; S2oM, sibling 2 of the (missing) mother.

**Table 5** Probabilities of random man not excluded (RMNE)

| C | M | RMNE probabilities |
|---|---|---|
| $A_i A_i$ | $A_i A_j$ | $1 - (1 - p_i)^2$ |
| $A_i A_j^{\#}$ | $A_i A_k^{*}$ | $1 - (1 - p_j)^2$ |
| $A_i A_j^{\#}$ | $A_i A_j^{\#}$ | $1 - (1 - p_i - p_j)^2$ |

$^{\#}j \neq i$.
$^{*}k \neq j$.
C, child; M, mother.

where the factor 2 appears because of the two possible ways of inheritance. Under the HW equilibrium, the LR can be obtained as

$$LR = 1/(2p_3p_1 + 2p_3p_2 + p_3^2).$$

As mentioned earlier, the HW law is seldom exactly certain or correct. Based on genetic and statistical justification, it can be shown that, in a structured population, if there are $y$ alleles of $A_i$ observed among $n$ alleles, then the probability that the next allele is an $A_i$ is:

$$P(A_i|y\ A_i \text{ among } n \text{ alleles}) = [y\theta + (1-\theta)p_i]/$$
$$[1 + (n-1)\theta]$$

This recursive formula can also be obtained if a state of evolutionary equilibrium has been established. Based on the recursive relationship, the LR can be expressed, under a subdivided population, as:

$$LR = \frac{(1+3\theta)(1+4\theta)}{[2\theta + (1-\theta)p_3][7\theta + (1-\theta)p_3 + 2(1-\theta)(p_1+p_2)]}.$$

This simple example demonstrates the evaluation of conditional (match) probability for mixture calculations. However, in that particular example, there are only three possible sets of genotypes for the only unknown person. Suppose we consider a more general alternative hypothesis:

$H_d$: Contributors of the mixture sample were the victim and $x$ unknown individuals.

For $x = 2$, the number of possible sets of genotypes of the two unknowns is 27. It is cumbersome to list all these combinations and a general formula and software have been developed in the literature to deal with such complicated problems; see the first author's home page http://www.hku.hk/statistics/staff/wingfung/for the freeware. The applicability of the software is illustrated below.

## Example

We analyze the well-known case of *People* v. *Simpson*, where a three-band restriction fragment length polymorphism (RFLP) mixed profile $A_1A_2A_3$ at the locus D2S44 was recovered from the center console of an automobile owned by the defendant. The profiles of the defendant OJ Simpson and a victim RG were found to be $A_1A_2$ and $A_1A_3$, respectively. The allele proportions for the Afro-Americans were taken as $p_1 = 0.0316$, $p_2 = 0.0842$, and $p_3 = 0.0926$, which are quite small. In this case, the court ordered that the

number of contributors ($n$) to the mixed samples evidence be set to 2, 3, or 4. The two alternative explanations are:

$H_p$: Contributors were the victim, suspect and $m$ unknowns
$H_d$: Contributors were $n$ unknowns.

**Table 6** shows the effect of $\theta$ on the LRs under different combinations of $m$ and $n$. The single-banded alleles are taken as true homozygotes. In all cases, taking $\theta \neq 0$ is more conservative than $\theta = 0$. Take, for example, the extreme case where $n = 4$ and $m = 0$; the LR with $\theta = 0.02$ is about 26 times the LR with $\theta = 0$. The strength of the evidence (LR) is dramatically reduced if $\theta = 0.02$ is taken. When the "'more reasonable'" scenario $n = 2$, $m = 0$, is considered, the LR drops from 1623 to 424 (one-fourth) when $\theta = 0.02$. The value of $\theta$ can have a substantial effect on the LR in this RFLP example where the allele frequencies $p_1$, $p_2$, and $p_3$ are small.

The contributors of the DNA mixture in this example are regarded as belonging to the same ethnic or

**Table 6** Likelihood ratios for the Simpson case

| n, number of unknowns under H$_d$ | $\theta$ | Likelihood ratios for the following values of m, number of unknowns under H$_p$ | |
|---|---|---|---|
| | | 0 | 1 |
| 2 | 0.00 | 1623 | 70 |
| | 0.02 | 424 | 32 |
| 4 | 0.00 | 396 495 | 17 220 |
| | 0.02 | 15 426 | 1165 |

**Table 7** Likelihood ratios for the Simpson case. Scenarios 1 and 2 correspond to the hypothesis $H_p$: the contributors were the victim, the suspect and $m$ unknowns. Scenario 1, $m = 0$; scenario 2, $m = 1$ unknown of Afro-American origin

| Under H$_d$, the number of unknowns belong to group | | | Scenario | | | |
|---|---|---|---|---|---|---|
| | | | 1 | | 2 | |
| AA | CA | CH | $\theta = 0$ | 0.02 | 0 | 0.02 |
| 2 | 0 | 0 | 1623 | 702 | 70 | 43 |
| 0 | 2 | 0 | 403 | 262 | 17 | 16 |
| 0 | 0 | 2 | 1817 | 1637 | 79 | 100 |
| 1 | 1 | 0 | 736 | 419 | 32 | 26 |
| 1 | 0 | 1 | 1530 | 911 | 66 | 55 |
| 0 | 1 | 1 | 611 | 476 | 27 | 29 |

AA, Afro-American; CA, Caucasian; CH, Chinese.

racial group: Afro-American. In practice, this may not be always the case. Actually, in this case, the defendant OJ is an Afro-American, and the two victims are Caucasians. It is sensible to take the ethnicity into account.

The ethnicity of the defendant and the victim are known in this case. For the unknown persons, we regard them as being Afro-American (AA), Caucasian (CA), and/or Chinese (CH). The following frequencies are taken for the three alleles $A_1, A_2, A_3$, respectively, AA: 0.0316, 0.0842, 0.0926, CA: 0.0843, 0.0821, 0.1087, and CH: 0.0165, 0.0746, 0.1528. For brevity, only some of the results for $n = 2$, $m = 0$ and 1 are listed in **Table 7**. We can see that the effect of different ethnic groups can be large. For example, looking at scenario 1 ($m = 0$) with $\theta = 0.02$, the LR at row 3 (1637) is about 6 times the LR at row 2 (262). A similar phenomenon is also found in the other scenarios with $m = 1$.

The interpretation of DNA mixture with the presence of relatives is also discussed in the literature.

## See Also

**DNA:** Basic Principles; Ethics of Forensic Applications and Databanks; Risk of Contamination; Mitochondrial; Postmortem Analysis for Heritable Channelopathies and Selected Cardiomyopathies

## Further Reading

Aitken CGG (1995) *Statistics and the Evaluation of Evidence for Forensic Scientists.* New York: Wiley.

Balding DJ, Nichols RA (1994) DNA profile match probability calculation: how to allow for population stratification, relatedness, database selection and single bands. *Forensic Science International* 64: 125–140.

Brenner C (1997) Symbolic kinship program. *Genetics* 145: 535–542.

Egeland T, Mostad PF, Mevåg B, Stenersen M (2000) Beyond traditional paternity and identification cases: selecting the most probable pedigree. *Forensic Science International* 110: 47–59.

Evett IW (1992) Evaluating DNA profiles in case where the defense is "It is my brother". *Journal of Forensic Science Society* 32: 5–14.

Evett IW, Weir BS (1998) *Interpreting DNA Evidence.* Sunderland, MA: Sinauer Associates.

Fukshansky N, Bär W (2000) Biostatistics for mixed stain: the case of tested relatives of a non-tested suspect. *International Journal of Legal Medicine* 114: 78–82.

Weir BS, Triggs CM, Starling L, *et al.* (1997) Interpreting DNA mixtures. *Journal of Forensic Science* 42: 213–222.

# Risk of Contamination

**G N Rutty**, Forensic Pathology Unit, Leicester, UK
**E A M Graham**, University of Leicester, Leicester, UK

## Introduction

Ever since the recognition by Jeffreys in 1985 of the use of DNA as a forensic tool for, initially, the investigation into the identification of an offender (living) and, latterly, for the identification of the deceased, those utilizing this analytical tool rapidly became aware, as with many other areas of forensic investigations, of its restrictions and complications due to the problem of contamination. Over the last 18 years the methodology used in DNA identification has significantly changed, becoming ever more sensitive to the extent that, today, forensic investigators contemplate identifying offenders or the deceased from DNA amplified from degraded partial cells. However, as the techniques have become more sensitive the issues related to contamination, equally, continue to raise their ugly head and, in fact, potentially negate the use of this significant tool in forensic investigations. It is with this in mind that the issue of DNA contamination is considered within this article.

The article is presented in five sections related to areas where contamination may occur during the entire process used in DNA identification. A summary flow diagram of this process is shown in **Figure 1**. From this figure it can be seen that the corresponding principal areas where contamination may occur are on the body/material itself, at the scene of the crime, during movement of a body from the scene to the mortuary, at the mortuary where the autopsy investigation is undertaken, and at the laboratory during the extraction, amplification, and profiling of the samples. Areas of proven and theoretical contamination are discussed along with measures that could be considered to try and reduce, but not entirely remove, contamination from the overall process.

## History of DNA Contamination

All those working in the field of crime investigation should be aware of the issue of DNA contamination. If you are not, one thing is for certain: that the lawyers instructed for the accused will be, and will have an "expert" to highlight the potential areas where contamination may have occurred to try and negate the DNA evidence from the trial.

As with any analytical method, the issue of contamination will have first been realized during the

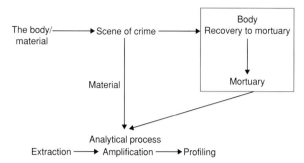

**Figure 1** Flow diagram of the principal theoretical areas of DNA contamination from the source of the DNA sample to the production of a profile.

discovery and development of the techniques used in the method. Thus, during the very first use of DNA identification in the Pitchfork murder (1986), the possibility of contamination within the laboratory analytical method will have been considered. However, the possibility that the contamination could have arisen by secondary transfer at the scene of crime or in the mortuary where the body is examined is a relatively recent consideration and is reflected by a paucity of publications on the subject. All of these areas are considered within the following sections of this article.

## The Body/Material

DNA evidence can theoretically be collected from the surface of any animate or inanimate body/object/material assuming the following are met. The DNA has been deposited on to the surface in the first place, that it has remained on the surface until the time of sampling, that the surface is such that it allows for DNA sampling/recovery, that the environment in which the DNA is left allows for its preservation, and that the period of time between deposition and sampling has not led to the degradation of the DNA beyond that where it can be used for profiling. Despite these limitations, sampling for DNA evidence is at the forefront of all crime-scene investigations whether one investigates, for example, volume crime (e.g., burglary, vehicle crime) or crimes against the person. The principles for contamination of either a body (living or dead) or an inanimate material are the same, although for simplicity and considering the publications in this area, the issues pertaining to the problem of contamination will be restricted to the living and the dead.

### Living and Dead

In 1923, a French police officer named Locard published a set of observations related to the interaction of an offender, the victim, and the scene, which highlighted the potential for the recovery of trace evidence

from them. Locard's principle, as it has become known, can be summarized as follows:

- The perpetrator will take away traces of the victim and the scene.
- The perpetrator will leave traces of him/herself at the scene.
- The victim will retain traces of the perpetrator.
- The victim may leave traces of him/herself on the perpetrator.

At the time of Locard's observations "traces" would have referred principally to fingerprints, footprints, and fiber evidence. However, this principle is still in existence today and can be expanded to include DNA. Thus, using Locard's principle one can hypothesize that DNA from the offender will be transferred on to the victim and vice versa from the victim to the offender.

This hypothesis, as applied to DNA, was originally reported by Wiegand and Kleiber in 1997, during their experimental observations related to manual strangulation. These observations were later verified and expanded upon by van Oorschot and Jones, Ladd and colleagues, Wickenheiser, Banaschak and colleagues, and Rutty. It has been shown that, in the case of manual strangulation, at the site of contact on the victim's neck where the offender had placed his/her fingers one could recover, for up to at least 48 h after the event, DNA from the offender. Equally, upon the fingerpads of the offender one could recover the DNA from the victim. These observations are equally applicable to both the living and the dead, to any area of exposed skin on the body, and for both adults and children, although in the case of children no published data exist to date.

However, van Oorschot, Ladd, Banaschak, and Rutty all identified a potential problem in relation to their observations. Rutty identified in his experiments that not only was the offender's DNA found upon the neck of the victim but there was also found the DNA of a number of unidentified third parties. Third-party DNA was also identified on the fingerpads of the offender. All four authors came to the same independent conclusion that this DNA had arisen during the normal day-to-day activities of the victim and the offender. It was considered that this third-party DNA had arisen from weapons, door handles, computer key pads, telephones, and any other surface or person with which the offender had been in contact. Banaschak found that the DNA from one person could be introduced to another by the innocent action of kissing. A summary of the possible sources of transference is shown in **Figure 2**.

This area for potential contamination of the evidence has become more apparent since the technology related to the amplification and profiling

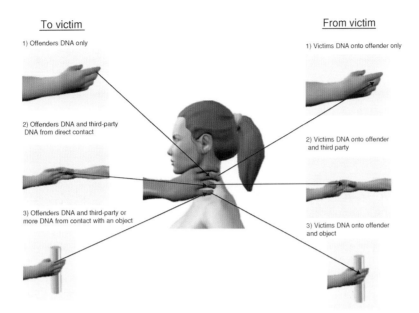

**Figure 2**   A summary diagram of the possible sources of DNA on the fingers of an offender and the neck of a victim during the process of manual strangulation. Reproduced with permission from Rutty GN (2002) An investigation into the transference and survivability of human DNA following simulated manual strangulations with consideration of the problem of third party contamination. *International Journal of Legal Medicine* 116: 170–173. Copyright Springer-Verlag GmbII and Co KG.

of DNA has become increasingly more sensitive. Partially degraded single nucleated or nonnucleated epithelial cells or free DNA, possibly liberated within sweat that can be found on the exposed surface of the body, can be readily transferred from one individual to another. The ability to do this is in part related to the shedder status of the individual. As ultimately the DNA of the offender will be in extremely small quantities, it could be that equally small amounts of DNA are identified from exogenous third parties and, in fact, whole profiles may be subsequently generated. Thus, when the profiles are considered to identify a potential offender a number of individuals may now fall into this category. Although Ladd and coworkers argued that this was in fact not a significant problem, as all of the profiles will originate, with the exception of the offender's, from innocent third parties who have nothing to do with the crime, this will cause three problems: (1) the increase in complexity of the interpretation of the DNA results, especially as the techniques become ever more sensitive; (2) the elimination of unknowns; and (3) the potential for the arrest and conviction of an innocent. Thus, if, in due course, all humans are placed on to a national or global DNA database, it is inevitable that those not involved in a crime will be investigated as potentially being involved with a crime due to the transference of third-party DNA.

DNA contamination from handling or being bitten by an animal is not a problem unless one is unfortunate enough to be in contact with a primate, as primates are known to share up to 98% of our DNA. The principal source of contamination to most individuals would be from household pets, that is, cats and dogs whose DNA profiles are far removed from that of humans and thus the problem does not arise. If required, amplification/profiling kits specifically for household pets are now commercially available.

## The Scene of Crime

The scene of crime is a high-risk environment for third-party contamination. Again, although the observations made within this section are equally applicable to both the inanimate and animate, to reflect the published literature on the subject the scene of a murder is considered in order to discuss the issues.

When one considers a murder scene, it is highly unlikely that the first person to discover the body will be a trained scene of crime officer or forensic pathologist wearing appropriate scene of crime protective clothing. The more realistic scenario is that a number of individuals will have already entered the scene and talked over or handled the body before the arrival of the forensic investigative team and, thus, potentially contaminated it prior to DNA sampling. A summary of potential people involved at a scene is shown in **Figure 3**.

The first person to discover the body is usually a relative or friend of the deceased or, in the UK it may be the "man walking his dog." Rather than realizing that they have found a dead body and then seeking appropriate help they may handle it, try to feel for a

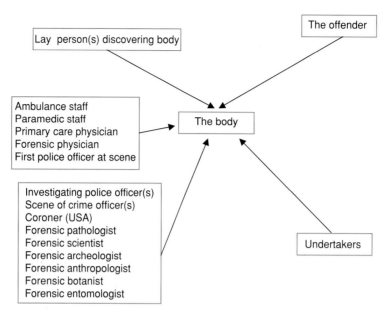

**Figure 3**   Summary diagram of those parties that may come into contact with a dead body at a scene of crime.

pulse, roll it over, or try to resuscitate it. Any of these actions will potentially transfer the finder's DNA on to the body along with any third-party DNA that is already present to the exposed surfaces of the finder.

The next thing that the finder may do is call for assistance. This may be from police officers but often may be from members of the general public. Thus, it is not uncommon to have several members of the general public coming to view a body and, thus, potentially contaminating it in a manner similar to the original finder. Police officers will then attend, followed or preceded by paramedic or ambulance crews. In the UK, unless the body is decomposed or decapitated, the crew is obliged to seek signs of life, and in so doing will contaminate the body. It has been the experience of the principal author that paramedic crews may call other paramedic crews to see the body, purely from professional curiosity, hence more parties arrive on the scene. Finally, a local general practitioner or a police surgeon will attend the scene to examine the body and pronounce life extinct. Thus, a minimum of four personnel (the finder, the police officer, the paramedic, and the doctor) may examine the body following its discovery and all of these persons along with any third-party DNA that they are carrying on their clothing or exposed skin surfaces may further add to contamination of the body.

Ultimately the scene will be secured and the investigative team will attend. Examples of personnel who may attend are shown in **Figure 3**. Each of these individuals may be a source of contamination.

The older textbooks are full of photographs of investigators at scenes of crime standing in their work suits and long overcoats. There should be nowhere in the world where this practice continues today, if only from health and safety grounds. Those entering into a scene of crime should do so with DNA awareness training and wearing appropriate scene clothing, which, although originally designed to protect the investigator from the environment of the scene, these days protects the scene from the investigator. Rutty and coworkers demonstrated through a series of experiments the necessity to wear a full-body scene suit, hood, mask, gloves, and overshoes at scenes of crime. It was demonstrated that unless a person stood completely still, did not speak, and did not breathe over the body then it was impossible not to deposit DNA contamination on to the body and surfaces at the scene. Of course, if this is true for the investigator, then it is also true for the offender and any of the people listed above, hence the need to consider where to sample for DNA evidence at the scene, which may not necessarily be confined to the body itself but may extend to the immediate surrounding surfaces.

Rutty hypothesized that the principal source for the contamination was epithelial cells within the clothing of the investigators. These were thought to be shed through body movement. The next hypothesized area of cell shedding came from exposed areas of skin, not covered by the scene suit. Breathing, speaking, and coughing led to projection of oral DNA. Although aerosol contamination is reduced by wearing a facemask (but not a visor), this may depend on the type of mask worn and how long it is worn for. Wearing masks and suits at hot scenes may lead to profuse sweating and it may be hypothesized that this will cause a bigger problem than not wearing the protective clothing at all. Finally, if a communal box of gloves is used, every time someone dips an ungloved hand into the box, the external surface of adjacent gloves may become contaminated. Thus, two pairs of gloves from two separate boxes should be considered.

The awareness of the potential for DNA contamination has led to a change of scene management. In the past, the scene examination related to the body may have been relatively short with rapid movement of the body to the mortuary. This has changed. These days as many of the external and internal orifice exhibits as possible should be taken at the scene before moving the body. To reduce alteration of bloodspatter patterns on clothing, clothing is now removed at the scene rather than at the mortuary, although the deceased's clothing could be a source of exogenous DNA depending upon where and with whom the person worked and lived. Thus in the event that an unknown DNA profile is identified from the scene examination, one knows that it has arisen at the scene and not during the movement or autopsy examination of the body. All those who work at scenes of crime should have their DNA profile on an exclusion database for elimination if a scene-recovered profile is identified.

## Movement of the Body

In the case of a crime involving all or part of a body then at some point the human remains must be transferred from the scene of crime to a mortuary for examination. As highlighted above, most, if not all, of the exhibits should have been removed from the body at the scene. However, under some circumstances this may not be possible or may not be the policy of those investigating the crime. Thus, in those cases where specific DNA sampling has not occurred before moving the body then consideration must be given to the potential for contamination of any DNA material during movement of the body. This can occur due to the causes described below.

### Undertakers

As shown in **Figure 3**, those attending the scene will include an undertaker. Those at the scene may be reluctant to move the body themselves. They may not be trained in appropriate lifting techniques or the body may be in such a position that it may pose difficulties in movement. Thus, the option to employ the skills of the attending undertaker may be considered. However, if the undertaker enters the scene, he/she may contaminate it. This may be from clothing, contact with ungloved hands, and from talking or breathing on an exposed body surface. Although the body should be within a body bag or plastic sheeting by the time the undertaker arrives the undertaker's passage can still contaminate the general environment of the scene.

Thus, wherever possible undertakers should not enter scenes of crime: rather, the body, already within the body bag, should be taken to the undertakers. If it is necessary for undertakers to enter the scene then they must put on the same protective clothing as those already working within the scene, that is, a hooded scene suit, mask, two pairs of gloves, and overshoes, and consideration must be given as to whether to take a DNA buccal swab sample from them.

### Body Bag

Until recently it was not unheard of for undertakers or other personnel to reuse body bags. There are 90 different types of body bag in use within the UK which vary in make, size, strength, and purpose of use. In general it can be stated that the more robust the bag, the more expensive it is; as a result, it has been tempting to clean out and reuse more expensive bags. If a body is placed into a bag that has been used before then contamination can occur due to persistence of second-party DNA present within the body bag. To avoid this, a brand new, sterile body bag or plastic sheeting must be used in each case with the bag being exhibited after use and not used again.

### The Body in the Bag

The body in the bag may itself be a significant cause of contamination. If DNA material has not been retrieved from the exposed surfaces or clothing before placement in the bag then this material can be lost during transportation. Bodies with penetrating wounds will bleed extensively within the body bag. This causes two problems. First, the deceased's blood will potentially cover the areas of exposed skin, rendering sampling of these areas for exogenous DNA difficult, if not impossible. Second, blood leakage will alter bloodspatter patterns or fiber evidence, fingerprints, or shoe marks, and trace evidence on clothing, thus altering the appearance of the clothing and potentially rendering it extremely difficult to interpret. Thus, wherever possible, clothing must be removed from the body before it is placed in a body bag.

### Hospital Staff

The victim of the crime may be taken to a hospital in an attempt to save his/her life, or in the case of a nonlife-threatening assault, to seek treatment. During the examination or resuscitation process the victim will come into contact with paramedic/medical personnel as well as hospital staff who will all try and save the victim's life or offer assistance. The crime victim will come into contact with a number of surfaces, including a stretcher and hospital beds or tables. Instruments may be used to cut away clothing and equipment may be used, for example, DC paddles, electrocardiogram leads, and other medical equipment. Direct contact from the hands of those attending the patient may also lead to significant DNA contamination of exposed surfaces. Serious consideration must be given to the appropriateness and usefulness of any DNA sampling under such circumstances, as it may be impossible to isolate an offender's DNA from that of attending medical personnel, none of whom are likely to have their DNA on any form of exclusion database.

A separate problem related to hospital treatment is that of secondary DNA introduced into a person through blood transfusion. Although blood used in trauma circumstances is usually packed red blood cells and should not theoretically contain nucleated cells, free DNA may still be present within the blood. However, studies of blood of those who have received multitransfusions show no evidence of second person DNA in the sample. Thus post transfusion blood does not have a contamination problem. A problem can arise however due to fraternal (dizygotic) twins, maternal "trafficking," i.e., where maternal cells enter the foetal circulation, organ transplantation, etc. and following bone marrow transfusions.

## The Mortuary

Mortuaries come in many shapes and sizes, from temporary tents in fields, to the back of converted vans, to purpose-built forensic institutions. The principal risk to those working within the mortuary environment from the aspect of communicable disease is that of aerosols created during the autopsy procedure. Toledano and coworkers were the first to discuss the potential problem of airborne DNA contamination in mortuaries. They undertook two 5-week studies evaluating this problem and drew attention to the fact that DNA could be found on the structural surfaces of the mortuary but concluded that, from a criminal investigative viewpoint, airborne DNA contamination was not an apparent problem. It was not until 2000 that Rutty and coworkers and Grass and Hidding, in a series of articles, drew attention to the real source of contamination within the mortuary – the instruments.

In the UK in 1999 an unknown DNA profile was identified from the body of a murdered female. The DNA sample had been recovered from the body at a mortuary. After a search, the DNA profile was matched to that of another murdered female who had been autopsied in the same mortuary several weeks earlier. Following this revelation a national edict was sent out instructing that only disposable instruments should be used in mortuaries for criminal work. As it was unknown whether this was a national problem or a single, dirty mortuary, Rutty and coworkers undertook a study for the presence of DNA on "clean" mortuary instruments and surfaces at 20 mortuaries. They identified that 50% of those mortuaries sampled had one or more people's quantifiable DNA on the instruments and surfaces tested. Partial profiles were found on most test samples. They also considered the methods of sterilization undertaken in the mortuaries, showing that the common practice of autoclaving instruments did not remove DNA contamination.

The contamination can come from a number of sources. Brand new instruments could have been handled at the manufacturing factory before packaging. When the instrument is removed from the package, it is assumed to be clean and thus the mortician may handle it whilst not wearing gloves. It is placed on to a work surface, which may have been contaminated by aerosols. The instrument may then be used at other autopsies and subject to a variety of cleaning methods from being under a running tap, to the use of antiviral agents, or the use of an autoclave, which may or may not be effective against DNA. When it comes to sampling, the operator may not be wearing gloves, masks, or a scene suit. The sample must then be placed into a DNA-free container.

To date, in the UK there have been several repetitions of this occurrence, although this should not happen due to the adoption of a number of practices. First, DNA samples from skin should be taken at the scene, not the mortuary, using the sterile double-swab technique. Swabs can be used for body orifices, again before moving the body, although flossing teeth with sterile dental floss is an alternative for oral samples. Fingernails should be cut with ultraviolet (UV)-irradiated nail clippers or scissors. If samples are taken in the mortuary, and irradiated instruments are not available, then the instruments should be swabbed with a moistened swab before use so that the swab acts to clean the instrument and as a control sample.

Mortuary surfaces should be kept as clean as possible. The use of UV lights overnight to sterilize work surfaces should be considered, although they must not be used whilst personnel are within the mortuary. Finally, if DNA samples are to be retrieved from the body at the mortuary, then the same clothing and masks must be worn in the mortuary as at the scene of crime to avoid contamination from the same sources as discussed above. All those working within the mortuary should be on a DNA exclusion database.

## Analytical Methods

In order to understand why contamination is such a significant problem in DNA profiling we must look at the analytical methods involved in the process. In order for any given piece of DNA to be visualized it must first be amplified. At present all DNA profiling methods used in forensic investigations are based around an amplification technique invented by Kary Mullis in 1986 and known as the polymerase chain reaction (PCR). This technique mimics the processes used by all living things to replicate DNA within the nucleus of the cell. The driving force behind the reaction is a thermostable enzyme known as a polymerase; specifically Taq polymerase derived from the bacterium *Thermus aquaticus* in the case of DNA profiling. The reaction involves a heat-dependent cyclic process consisting of three stages: (1) denaturation of template DNA; (2) annealing of a "primer"; and (3) extension of DNA by the action of the polymerase. In terms of sensitivity, a PCR can theoretically be initiated from a single copy of DNA and proceeds in an exponential manner, doubling the number of DNA templates within the reaction with each cycle, although in practice amplification from a single template molecule is rarely successful. Mainly the aforementioned primer controls the specific nature of the PCR. A primer is a short, typically 15–30 sequence of single-stranded DNA, known as an oligonucleotide. As DNA consists of a sequence of units (nucleotides), only capable of binding in pairs (adenine to thymine, guanine to cytosine), under the correct conditions, a 20-nucleotide sequence of DNA will only find a complementary sequence to which to bind on average once every 2 billion basepairs. Additionally, before use in a reaction the chosen primer sequence will be checked against a database (e.g., National Center for Biotechnology Information) to ensure that it will only bind once, in the desired position of the human genome, and is not complementary to a region of DNA in any other species.

### Types of Evidence

A wide variety of evidentiary materials may be collected from the crime scene to be submitted for DNA profiling, ranging from discarded beer bottles, bloodstained material, or buccal swabs, to bones and teeth. When considering the problem of contamination, materials can be broadly placed into one of two categories: discrete or nondiscrete. The first category includes all physically stable materials, where DNA is to be extracted from within the sample, e.g., hairs,

bones, and teeth. Contamination with exogenous DNA can be considered less of a problem with discrete evidence types as the external surface can be washed or mechanically removed in the case of bone before analysis. Most evidence types fall into the nondiscrete category and include materials submitted to the laboratory such as cigarette butts, drinking containers, internal swabs (buccal or vaginal), and external swabs (skin or object surface). In all cases, DNA must be recovered from a bodily fluid (blood, semen, sweat, saliva) or from cells deposited on an item, so no washing stage can be attempted before extraction.

### Low-Copy-Number DNA

A number of PCR kits are commercially available. For example, the kit used for forensic casework in the UK is the AmpF*l*STR Second Generation Multiplex Plus (SGM Plus) from Applied Biosystems (Foster City, CA, USA). It consists of 11 primer sets, designed to amplify 10 short tandem repeats (STR) loci and a region of the amelogenin gene, used for sex-typing DNA. Kits of this type are optimized to amplify DNA from a starting quantity of 1 ng, equivalent to about 160 diploid cells. In 1997 Findaly and co-workers reported successful profiling from a single buccal cell using the SGM+ STR kit, a starting quantity of only 6 pg DNA: however, this is not a routinely successful practice. The increased levels of detection undoubtedly make it much more difficult for an individual to walk away from a crime scene without leaving some form of trace DNA evidence but also greatly increase the risk of contamination of the scene by persons discovering or investigating the crime. For purposes of simplicity low-copy-number (LCN) DNA includes all materials from which less than 100 pg is recovered for profiling. To understand the nature of problems connected to LCN DNA evidence we must once again look at the amplification method employed. As the PCR can be initiated from a single template molecule and proceeds in an exponential manner, it follows that DNA replicated in early stages of a reaction will be present in high quantities in the final product. If contaminating DNA is preferentially amplified during these important early cycles the end-product will consequently contain a far greater proportion of alleles unrelated to the crime scene in the final profile. An additional consideration is the quality of DNA recovered, as typically materials classified as "LCN" consist of collections of cells or free DNA deposited on surfaces such as drinking containers or from fingerprints. In such situations, it is likely that the DNA will also be degraded to some extent. In such situations, if there is contamination from a contemporary source it may not be in great quantity but will most likely be of better quality than that of the sample. This higher-quality DNA will again be preferentially amplified in the PCR.

## DNA Degradation

Next we must consider the quality of DNA obtained from any given sample. The breakdown or degradation of DNA begins immediately after death via the action of endogenous nucleases, cellular enzymes that catalyze the hydrolysis of (phosphodiester) bonds in the "backbone" of the DNA molecule. The observation that recovered ancient and forensic DNA molecules are usually between 100 and 200 bp in length has led to the suggestion that this enzymatic cleavage occurs at vulnerable linker regions, situated between nucleosomes of the DNA tertiary structure. It logically follows that, for any DNA to survive, the action of these biological enzymes must be slowed or halted before complete degradation is achieved. Unfortunately, the action of endogenous nucleases is not the only factor affecting DNA preservation. Water-induced hydrolysis has two main effects on the DNA molecule, as discussed by Lindahl in 1993. First, acid-catalyzed hydrolysis can cause the loss of primary sequence information, which may result in the loss of the PCR primer-binding site. The organic bases themselves are susceptible to hydrolytic damage causing instability in the DNA molecule as a whole. Damage induced by oxidation is another important consideration in preservation as its effects have been shown to alter the chemical structure of the DNA, resulting in the formation of altered nucleotides that are unrecognized by Taq polymerase and are therefore unable to participate in a PCR. Some other factors that must also be taken into account include the presence of bacteria and fungi. These microorganisms contribute to the degradation of DNA not only by digestion but also by increasing the risk of contamination by extraneous DNA. The effect of UV radiation damage is another important consideration, as UV radiation is known to form cross-links between pyrimidine residues, which are another inhibitor of PCR.

## Sources of Contamination

### The Laboratory

Before moving on to the individual techniques involved, it should be stated that the single largest danger posed throughout the whole process is that of amplified DNA. The exponential amplification of DNA during PCR results in the production of billions of copies of the template molecule. This excess of DNA will be present not only on the machines used but also in the surrounding environment, including all work surfaces and the air itself. For this reason it is

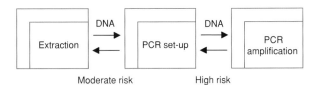

**Figure 4** Diagram to show single direction movement of DNA during profiling.

necessary to perform PCR in a physically separated laboratory. It is critically important to ensure that no post-PCR material is ever taken into areas of the laboratory where pre-PCR work is to be undertaken. Dedicated reagents, equipment, and clothing should be used and must never be transferred to pre-PCR areas. Whenever possible, each stage of the profiling process should be carried out in a dedicated area, as shown in **Figure 4**.

Amplified DNA may present a significant threat but it is not the only consideration during processing: physical separation of workstations alone will not eliminate the risk of contamination. Each laboratory must be regularly disinfected to prevent the build-up of DNA from processed samples on work surfaces and equipment. Solutions commonly used for this purpose include commercial bleach, sodium hypochlorite, isopropanol, and microsol 3. The use of UV light, which acts to form cross-links between neighboring pyrimidine bases (thymine or adenine), rendering the DNA incapable of participating in the PCR, is also commonly encountered.

When discussing potential sources of evidence contamination within the laboratory we must once again consider the "human factor." All personnel involved in the process have the potential to shed and possibly contaminate the sample with their own DNA. In order to prevent this possibility similar measures are taken to that of the pathologist or scene of crime officer. Protective clothing, consisting of laboratory coat, facemask, goggles, hair net, and disposable latex gloves, which must be changed regularly, should be worn as standard before any work is initiated. Many laboratories undertaking forensic DNA profiling will take the additional step of wearing completely disposable full-body suits, including disposable booties and masks that are discarded after each period of time spent within the laboratory.

It is important to consider the consequences of laboratory-induced contamination. In major forensic investigations such as murder inquiries, material submitted to the laboratory may be in limited supply, for example, a single hair found on the body of the victim could provide the only physical link between the victim and the perpetrator. In cases such as this contamination within the laboratory may prove devastating to the investigation. Wherever possible it is advisable to process only half of the submitted material so that in the event of contamination occurring, a second profiling procedure can be undertaken. It is equally important to consider the possibility of cross-sample contamination. In order to be of use at trial the exact context of DNA evidence must be proven. For example, if blood is recovered from a crime scene that is believed to belong to a suspect who is later taken into custody, both the fluid from the scene and a buccal swab taken from the suspect may be submitted for DNA profiling in order to prove the connection. If both samples are processed at the same time, within the same laboratory, it could be argued that at some stage of the procedure the DNA extracted from the buccal swab had contaminated the blood sample or vice versa, diminishing the value of the evidence. To protect against this possibility it is critical that each individual item is processed individually and the laboratory is thoroughly cleaned before and after each use. The next area to consider involves the materials and reagents used at each stage of the laboratory process.

## DNA Extraction

To obtain DNA in a condition compatible with the critical amplification reaction it must be extracted and purified from the material received. Due to the wide range of evidentiary samples submitted for DNA profiling, a number of techniques are available to ensure an optimal amount from each sample type is obtained for use in subsequent techniques. The details of each method are beyond the scope of this article and as such a general overview of the equipment, reagents, and materials used at this stage will be discussed.

The first consideration must be the reagents and plastic ware used in the process. Great care must be taken to ensure all reagents and disposables are received sealed and are guaranteed "DNA-free" by the manufacturer. If any component is purchased without this guarantee it must be autoclaved and treated with UV light before use in experiments. A second important consideration is the method of liquid transfer during any given technique. Liquids are transferred by use of a pipette with disposable tips. The tip must be changed after every single transfer to reduce the risk of cross-contamination between samples. Additionally the action of the pipette itself results in the creation of aerosols that may contain DNA, and can accumulate within the shaft and on the surfaces of the pipette. To combat this problem the use of plugged pipette tips is recommended, designed to provide a physical barrier between aerosols and the internal parts of the pipette. Additionally the surface of the pipette should be washed with a weak bleach

solution (or equivalent) before and after each experiment. A negative control should always be processed in parallel to each batch of extractions, whereby the whole process is carried out identically with the omission of sample material. This allows the investigator to monitor the introduction of laboratory-derived contamination and may also allow the source of said contamination to be elucidated.

## DNA Amplification

The same factors affecting the extraction phase are applicable to the amplification stage of the profiling process. Again, all reagents and plastic ware must be either guaranteed DNA-free from the supplier or autoclaved and UV-treated before use. In addition to these criteria, as the sample will now be transferred to the PCR area, it is essential at this stage to ensure all reaction tubes are firmly sealed to contain the mixture and, more importantly, to prevent amplified DNA entering the reaction. As with the extraction procedure, a negative control must always be included, where template DNA is replaced by sterile water. If a negative control is found to contain any DNA after analysis, all samples processed in parallel must be discarded. The inclusion of a positive control, consisting of contemporary DNA of known profile, is advised when performing a PCR, as an internal control designed to diagnose reaction failure due to human error or out-of-date reagents, as opposed to insufficient template addition. The use of a positive control should be carefully considered in forensic investigation as, when evidentiary DNA is of LCN or in a degraded state, the manipulation of high-quality material in the close vicinity of such samples poses a great risk of contamination.

## Postamplification/Analysis

At this stage of an investigation all of the proven and theoretical problems discussed above are no longer applicable: we must now concentrate on how contamination, if encountered, is recognized. Due to the biparental nature of DNA acquisition, whereby all children inherit one chromosome from their biological mother and one from their biological father to form each pair, all individuals have a unique combination, except in the case of monozygotic twins, of two STR loci at each site targeted by PCR. It is therefore expected that each individual will have two alleles at each STR loci, with the notable exception of genetic diseases, such as Down syndrome, in which trisomy of chromosome 21 will result in three alleles being amplified. In all other cases, the amplification of more than two alleles indicates that more than one person's DNA has been amplified during PCR. When processing material of a degraded nature or of low quantity, all results should be repeated independently and results should concur 100% in order to be accepted, as it is highly unlikely that the same "mistake" of amplification will be encountered twice. Having fulfilled these criteria the mixed profile must now be interpreted. The primary concern raised throughout this article is that of contamination by persons involved in the investigation. It is advisable for all personnel who have been in contact with the evidentiary material to have their own profiles held on an exclusion database. Under these circumstances any result showing the profile of a member of the investigative team will be recognized and discounted, saving a search being launched for a person unrelated to the crime. Under certain conditions a mixed profile is inevitable, such as when vaginal swabs are collected after a rape, and as such cannot be avoided. In the event that a mixed profile is generated that is unexpected and cannot be attributed to any known member, a number of theories must be considered in order to establish the source of the DNA.

1. The profile has components of that of the victim and the perpetrator(s).
2. The profile has components of that of the victim and an individual(s) unrelated to the crime.
3. The profile has components of the perpetrator(s) and an individual(s) unrelated to the crime.

It is at this point that, if the source of contamination cannot be identified the information generated must be accepted as true and be passed on to the investigating authority for consideration.

## See Also

**DNA:** Basic Principles; Ethics of Forensic Applications and Databanks; Statistical Analysis; Mitochondrial

## Further Reading

Banaschak S, Moller K, Pfeiffer H (1998) Potential DNA mixtures introduced through kissing. *International Journal of Legal Medicine* 111: 284–285.
Davidson AK, Lee LD (1999) Unusual results due to transfused blood. *Science and Justice* 39: 179–180.
Grass H, Hidding M (2000) DNA contamination by examination instruments. *Archiv für Kriminologie* 205: 177–181.
Ladd C, Adamowicz MS, Bourke MT, Scherczinger CA, Lee HC (1999) A systematic analysis of secondary DNA transfer. *Journal of Forensic Science* 44: 1270–1274.
Lowe A, Murray C, Whitacker J, Tully G, Gill P (2002) The propensity of individuals to deposit DNA and secondary transfer of low level DNA from individuals to inert surfaces. *Forensic Science International* 129: 25–34.

Rubocki RJ, McCue BJ, Duffy KJ, Shepherd SJ, Wisec JL (2001) Natural DNA mixtures generated in fraternal twins in utero. *Journal of Forensic Science* 46: 120–125.
Rutty GN (2000) Human DNA contamination of mortuaries; does it matter? Invited editorial. *Journal of Pathology* 190: 410–411.
Rutty GN (2001) DNA contamination at scenes of crime and in mortuaries. An editorial to provoke thought. *Internet Journal of Forensic Medicine and Toxicology* 2: January. Available online at: http://anil299.tripod.com/vol_002_no_001/editorial.html.
Rutty GN, Watson S, Davison J (2000) Contamination of mortuary instruments and work surfaces by human DNA; a significant problem in forensic practice? *International Journal of Legal Medicine* 114: 56–60.
Rutty GN, Hopwood A, Tucker V (2003) The effectiveness of protective clothing in the reduction of potential DNA contamination of the scene of crime. *International Journal of Legal Medicine* 117: 143–148.
Sweet D, Lorente M, Lorente JA, Valenzuela A, Villanueva E (1997) An improved method to recover saliva from human skin: the double swab technique. *Journal of Forensic Science* 42: 320–322.
Toledano T, Quarino L, Leung S, et al. (1997) An assessment of DNA contamination risks in New York City medical examiner facilities. *Journal of Forensic Science* 42: 721–724.
van Oorschot R, Jones M (1997) DNA fingerprints from fingerprints. *Nature* 387: 767.
Wickenheiser RA (2002) Trace DNA: a review, discussion of theory, and application of transfer of trace quantities of DNA through skin contact. *Journal of Forensic Science* 47: 442–450.
Wiegand P, Kleiber M (1997) DNA typing of epithelial cells after strangulation. *International Journal of Legal Medicine* 110: 181–183.

# Mitochondrial

**W Goodwin**, University of Central Lancashire, Preston, UK

## Introduction

Since its advent in 1985, the development of deoxyribonucleic acid (DNA) profiling methodology has had an explosive impact on forensic science. The majority of forensic casework utilizes DNA markers that are found in the nuclear genome; short tandem repeats are the favored marker of the forensic geneticist. However, there are some scenarios in which the analysis of nuclear DNA markers is impossible or impractical; mitochondrial DNA (mtDNA) analysis has proven to be a valuable tool in a number of these cases.

## Forensic Applications of mtDNA Profiling

Three main features of the mtDNA genome make it a valuable forensic marker. First, it contains relatively high levels of polymorphisms, which allow individuals to be differentiated. Second, there are multiple copies of the mtDNA genome in each cell, increasing the probability of recovering mtDNA from forensic samples. Third, it is maternally inherited, which increases the scope for finding a suitable reference sample, for the purpose of human identification.

mtDNA profiling is mainly of use in human identification and in the analysis of crime scene samples that contain very small amounts of DNA, including hair shafts (with no attached root) and fecal samples. A common feature of all these sample types is that they normally contain low amounts of DNA, making conventional DNA analysis difficult. mtDNA profiling also has an advantage when DNA-profiling human remains. In some cases, it may be possible to obtain large amounts of DNA suitable for nuclear DNA profiling; however, there may be no suitable relative with whom to compare the profile. In these cases, the maternal inheritance of mtDNA can prove to be a valuable trait.

This article examines the critical features of the mtDNA genome that make it a valuable forensic DNA marker and provides an overview of the procedure that is followed to generate, analyze, and evaluate a mtDNA profile for the purpose of matching crime scene evidence to a suspect or matching human remains to living relatives. Finally, there are also features of the mtDNA genome that make it attractive for other forensic applications, including inferring ethnicity and species identification. Both of these areas are briefly discussed.

## Mitochondrial DNA

The mitochondria are organelles that exist in the cytoplasm of eukaryote cells. They carry out the vital job of producing approximately 90% of the cells' energy; this is achieved through the process of oxidative phosphorylation. The mitochondria contain their own genomes: this fact was discovered in the 1950s after unusual patterns of inheritance of certain phenotypes were explained by the existence of extranuclear genomes that did not obey Mendel's laws of inheritance. The mtDNA genome only encodes for a subset of the proteins that are required for a fully functioning organelle; most mitochondrial proteins are encoded by the nuclear genome.

## Structure of the mtDNA Genome

In 1981 the sequence of the human mtDNA genome was published, this was 20 years before the draft human nuclear genome was released to the public. The sequencing of the mtDNA genome, however was a much simpler task; the circular genome is only 16 569 base pairs (bp) long. The size and complexity of mtDNA genomes vary widely between different species. The human genome size is typical of complex eukaryotes, whereas simpler eukaryotes, such as yeast, and flowering plants have much larger genomes.

Analysis of the human mtDNA genome has revealed a very economic use of the DNA. There are very few noncoding bases within the genome, except in a region called the D-loop region. The genome encodes for 22 transfer RNAs (tRNAs), 13 proteins, and two ribosomal RNAs (12S and 16S rRNA). The D-loop is a region of approximately 1100 bp between two tRNAs; it has no open reading frames and is involved in the replication of the mtDNA genome. The regulatory role of the D-loop has led to its other name – the control region. **Figure 1** shows the main features of the mtDNA that are of interest to forensic geneticists.

Compared to the nuclear genome, the mtDNA is very small (<0.001% of the size of the nuclear

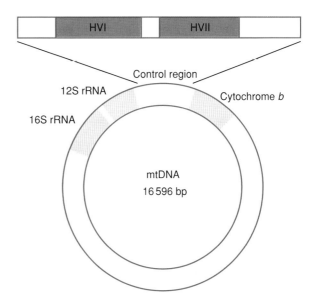

**Figure 1**  Schematic representation of the mitochondrial DNA (mtDNA) genome. The mitochondrial genome is circular and 16 569 base pairs long. It encodes for 13 proteins, 22 transfer RNAs, and two ribosomal RNAs. The regions that are most commonly used for forensic analysis are the hypervariable regions I and II, which are located within the control region. Other regions of the genome that are utilized in forensic casework are the coding regions for the 12S and 16S ribosomal RNAs and cytochrome b gene; mutations in the noncoding regions, identified here as single nucleotide polymorphisms (SNPs), can also be useful.

genome), but it represents approximately 1% of total cellular DNA. The mtDNA genome is present in multiple copies. A human mitochondrion contains between 1 and 10 identical copies of the genome; with approximately 1000 mitochondria per cell: this results in up to 10 000 copies of a single genome within a single cell. The high copy number is a valuable trait with regard to forensic applications, increasing the probability of successfully extracting DNA, particularly from degraded remains.

## Polymorphisms in mtDNA

The mtDNA genome evolves relatively rapidly, at about 10 times the rate of the nuclear genome. This high rate of change does not affect all regions of the mtDNA genome equally. Several regions show much slower levels of change, and this reflects their functional importance, whereas other areas show accumulations of mutations at much higher frequencies. The relatively high mutation rate is due in part to the exposure of the mtDNA to reactive oxygen species produced as byproducts in oxidative phosphorylation, coupled with the lack of histone proteins, closely associated with the double helix in the nuclear genome. These proteins provide the nuclear DNA with some protection from reactive oxygen species.

### Hypervariable Regions

In most forensic cases, the aim of DNA profiling is to differentiate between individuals; therefore, areas of DNA that display the highest levels of difference between individuals are the regions of choice for analysis. The other consideration is the relative ease of analysis; forensic analysis cannot be prohibitively expensive.

Following sequencing of the human mtDNA genome, it was apparent that the D-loop was not under the same functional constraints as the rest of the genome. Some blocks within the control region are highly conserved but large parts are not. Two main regions are the focus of most forensic studies. These are known as hypervariable regions I and II (HVI and HVII) and they contain the highest levels of variation within the mtDNA genome. Both of the hypervariable blocks are approximately 350 bp long. The level of mutation is not constant throughout the hypervariable regions: some sites are hot spots for mutation while others show much lower levels of alteration. (Note that mutations in the hypervariable regions are normally referred to as base substitutions because they do not have an effect on any of the products encoded by the mtDNA. However, for simplicity, the term mutation is used throughout this article.)

The rate at which bases in the hypervariable region mutate has been estimated by studying human pedigrees. Taking the average of the pedigree studies that have dealt with mutations in HVI and HVII, mutations occur in approximately 1 in 100 transmission events. In most cases, when a mutation is detected there is only one base change between the mother and child; rarely is more than one mutation transmitted.

## mtDNA Diversity

The value of any genetic locus as a forensic marker depends in part on the level of diversity that the marker displays. The diversity within any particular population of interest is the most significant factor; this will reflect the power of the marker to link a forensic sample to a reference sample.

Caucasian and Asian populations show similar levels of mtDNA diversity, whereas African populations show considerably more variation. The differences in diversity are explained by the ages of the different populations. Modern genetics in combination with archaeology have estimated that modern humans were in Africa approximately 150 000 years ago, whereas Asia and Europe were populated 60 000 and 35 000 years ago, respectively. African populations have therefore had more time to accumulate variation within their gene pool. Pairwise comparisons of 300 Caucasians, 300 East Asians, and 300 sub-Saharan Africans found average pairwise differences in the HVI to be $5.28 \pm 2.24$, $6.27 \pm 2.29$, and $8.36 \pm 3.2$, respectively.

By examining the frequencies of the different profiles present within a population, it is possible to estimate the probability that two individuals selected at random from a population will have the same profile. This is the probability of two individuals' profiles matching coincidentally, and it is a good measure of the power of a forensic DNA marker. In Caucasian populations, the value is normally approximately 0.02–0.04 for the HVI, 0.04–0.05 for HVII, and 0.01–0.02 when both HVI and HVII are used. Asian populations have very similar values, whereas African populations have slightly lower probabilities, again reflecting the higher levels of mtDNA diversity found in African populations. The greater degree of variability in HVI has made it the most popular region of the mtDNA to analyze.

## Inheritance of the mtDNA Genome

The mtDNA genome is inherited through the maternal lineage. During fertilization of an ovum, only the sperm head penetrates. The sperm head does contain a few mitochondria, but these are not retained after fertilization.

Maternal inheritance is a useful feature in some circumstances, particularly when identifying human remains, because any maternal relative can be used as a reference. Maternal inheritance is also one of the weak points of mtDNA in a forensic context: all members of a maternal lineage, in the absence of any mutation event, contain identical mtDNA genomes.

## Homoplasmy

When all of the mtDNA genomes are identical, this is referred to as homoplasmy. There has been much debate on how homoplasmy is maintained from generation to generation. Because mutations will inevitably occur within the mtDNA of an individual, why are these mutations not passed on to future generations? The process is not precisely understood. What is accepted is that a genetic bottleneck occurs at some point before the formation of the mature oocytes and this helps to maintain homoplasmy. The bottleneck means that only a limited number of mtDNA molecules pass on from the mother to the child; estimates of exactly how many maternal mtDNA molecules contribute to the mtDNA genome of a given oocyte range from approximately 10 to 200. Passing on a limited number of mtDNA genomes reduces the possibility of passing on a mixture of wild-type and mutant genomes.

## Heteroplasmy

When more than one type of mtDNA genome exists within a cell, this is known as heteroplasmy. Heteroplasmy results when a mother passes on a normal version of her mtDNA genome (wild-type) and also a version of the genome that contains a mutation. The degree of heteroplasmy depends on how much of each mtDNA genome is passed on to the offspring. Work on inherited genetic disorders, which are frequently heteroplasmic, has shown that the segregation, even with deleterious mutations, is normally a random event. Genetic drift seems to determine which species of molecule eventually prevails in future generations. In some cases, heteroplasmy will be eliminated in the offspring of a heteroplasmic individual, whereas in other maternal lineages the heteroplasmy may persist for several generations. A heteroplasmic individual retains the same level of heteroplasmy throughout life. An example of heteroplasmic sequence is shown in **Figure 2**.

## Producing an mtDNA Profile

### DNA Extraction

After the collection of any evidence for which a mtDNA profile will be generated, the first step is to extract DNA from the sample. The samples that are provided for mtDNA profiling include bone, teeth, hair shafts, feces, blood, and saliva.

The processes used to extract mtDNA are the same as those used for nuclear DNA extraction; the protocols do not differentiate between mtDNA and nuclear DNA. Well-established methods that have been used in the forensic community include phenol:chloroform and Chelex resin-based extractions. In addition to these, there are numerous commercial-kit-based methods.

When dealing with degraded remains that contain very low levels of DNA, the sensitivity of mtDNA detection makes contamination more likely. For this reason, strict precautions must be taken to limit the possibility of introducing exogenous DNA.

### Polymerase Chain Reaction Amplification

The amplification of mtDNA is relatively straightforward; however, there are a number of points that need to be considered. For relatively high-quality samples the process is simple because primers that amplify the entire HVI and, if necessary, HVII can be employed. When dealing with highly degraded remains, the choice of primers is more problematic. In order to amplify the mtDNA, HVI or HVII primers approximately 400 bp apart are required. In many forensic cases in which mtDNA is being employed, there are no molecules of this length in the DNA extract.

In this case, at least one of the primers has to be within the hypervariable region. Because of the hypervariable nature of the template sequence, primers have to be carefully designed so that they will amplify, as far as possible, all samples. Regions within the hypervariable region that show limited polymorphisms are selected for this purpose. This maximizes the probability that they will amplify any given individual mtDNA. Different primer sets may be used for populations of different ethnic origin to minimize the possibility of nonamplification through mismatching of primer and target sequences.

Due to the low amount of DNA that is often analyzed using mtDNA, a single round of amplification may not produce enough product to analyze. In such cases, it is necessary to perform a second round of polymerase chain reaction (PCR) amplification.

### DNA Sequencing

After the hypervariable regions have been amplified, the PCR amplicons are directly sequenced without any subcloning using standard techniques. Most laboratories use fluorescent dye terminator sequencing technology followed by analysis on a platform

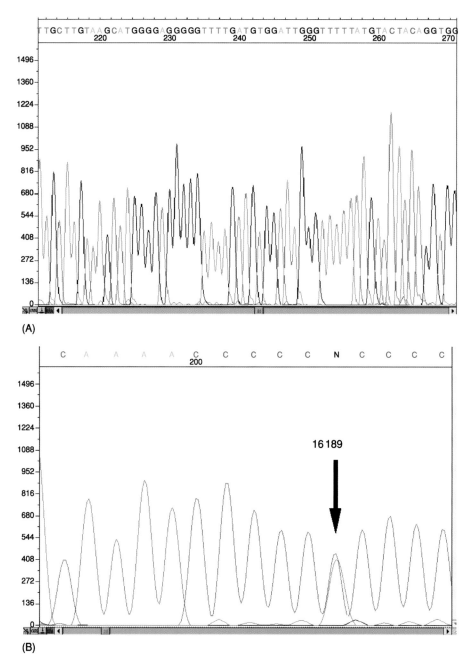

**Figure 2**   (A) Example of DNA sequence data. The sequence is a region of the mitochondrial DNA (mtDNA) hypervariable region I. The software interprets the sequence data and ''calls'' the bases; this information is provided above the sequencing peaks. It is vital that the forensic analyst check the sequence manually for artifacts and the possible presence of heteroplasmy. If the sequence is of poor quality at any position, an N is shown to indicate that the sequence cannot be interpreted. (B) Example of DNA sequence data displaying heteroplasmy. The sequence shows the presence of heteroplasmy at position 16 189; two bases, a C and an A, are present in approximately equal amounts.

that can separate DNA by size and detect at least four different fluorescent spectra.

In **Figure 2A,** a region of sequenced HVI is shown. This was generated using the ABI Big Dye Terminator kit, followed by analysis on an ABI 377 sequencer. The software interprets the sequence and "calls" the bases. If areas of the sequence are of poor quality and

the sequence is unclear, the software records an N, which is an indication that it has not called the base and that any one of four bases may be present at that position. In all cases, the sequence must also be checked manually for any discrepancies. **Figure 2B** shows a region of the HVI that contains a heteroplasmic base.

# Interpretation of mtDNA Profiles

mtDNA is used both to associate crime scene samples with individuals and to identify human remains. In both cases, the profile generated has to be compared to a reference profile. In the case of a crime scene, this is a sample from a suspect, and in the case of human identification it is a maternal relative of the individual or a personal artifact, such as a toothbrush or clothing, that is very likely to carry the profile of the individual.

The first step is to turn the information into a more manageable form. After the sequencing data have been checked manually to ensure that the quality is sufficient, the sequence is compared to the Cambridge reference sequence (also referred to as the Anderson reference sequence; the reference, published in 1981, is the first complete sequence of the mtDNA genome). Differences between the questioned sequence and the Cambridge reference sequence are noted. Caucasians differ from the reference sequence on average in three to five positions; more differences are commonly found in Southeast Asians and especially sub-Saharan Africans, who commonly differ from the reference sequence by up to seven or eight positions. Caucasians differ less than East Asians and sub-Saharan Africans because the original reference sequence was of a Caucasian individual and, therefore, other Caucasians on average diverge less from the reference sequence. Table 1 shows an example in which a profile generated from a set of human remains is compared to profiles generated from three reference samples, one of which matches while the other two can be excluded.

## Evidential Value of mtDNA Profiling

After interpreting the sequence data and comparing the questioned and reference samples, the forensic scientist has to assess whether definitive matches or exclusions can be declared. In the example shown in **Table 1**, this task would be relatively simple: reference 1 can be declared to be a match, whereas references 2 and 3 can be classified as exclusions. Declaring a match is usually straightforward. Declaring an exclusion can be more problematic: if a questioned sample and a reference sample differ at only one position, the likelihood of that difference occurring through a mutation rather than as a result of the two mtDNAs being different maternal lineages has to be assessed. Mutations over HVI and HVII are transmitted approximately once in every 100 cases.

If a match is declared, the statistical significance of the match has to be assessed. The mtDNA genome is inherited as a single locus; this limits the evidential value of the marker in forensic cases. The sequence of

**Table 1** The representation of mitochondrial DNA (mtDNA) sequence data

| Sample | HVI sequence | | | |
|---|---|---|---|---|
| Right femur | 16 189C | 16 223T | 16 271C | 16 278T |
| Left femur | 16 189C | 16 223T | 16 271C | 16 278T |
| Right pelvis | 16 189C | 16 223T | 16 271C | 16 278T |
| Left ulna | 16 189C | 16 223T | 16 271C | 16 278T |
| Left tibia | 16 189C | 16 223T | 16 271C | 16 278T |
| Maternal reference 1 | 16 189C | 16 223T | 16 271C | 16 278T |
| Maternal reference 2 | Same as Cambridge reference sequence | | | |
| Maternal reference 3 | 16 278T | 16 293G | 16 311C | |

In order to simplify comparisons between questioned and reference mtDNA the sequences are compared against the Cambridge reference sequence (CRS); differences from the CRS are noted, and the position and the nature of the mutation are shown. **Table 1** shows an example where an mtDNA profile has been generated from the hypervariable region I (HVI) of five bones that were found close to one another. The mtDNA profiles of three women who were maternal relatives of different people who have gone missing are also shown. Maternal reference 1 clearly matches the femur profile, while maternal reference 2 and 3 can be excluded as potential maternal relatives. In this particular case the mtDNA profiling helped to establish the identification of the human remains, and that the remains all came from the same person.

the hypervariable regions (this can be the sequence of one or both regions) is called the haplotype. Haplotype frequencies have to be measured directly by counting the occurrence of a particular haplotype in a database. When databases are relatively small (e.g., 100), many of the less common haplotypes that are within a population will not be represented.

There are mechanisms that allow smaller databases to be used. One method commonly employed when calculating DNA profiles using databases is called the Balding and Nichols correction. Using this method to estimate the significance of a match between a crime scene sample and a suspect using a reference database containing 100 profiles, before the frequency of the questioned samples is calculated, both the crime scene and the suspect's profile would be added to the database. This assumes that the samples are not from the same biological source (favoring the suspect). The reference database will now contain a total of 102 reference profiles. If there was one matching haplotype in the database before the correction was made, then before the correction the frequency of the mtDNA haplotype within the population would have been given as 1/100; after the correction the frequency would be given as 3/102. This ensures that in criminal cases the evidential value of the mtDNA is not overstated. In cases involving human identification, less conservative methods may be used, such as adding the reference samples to the database. To maximize the evidential power of mtDNA evidence, larger databases have been constructed containing more than 1000 sequences.

## Ethnic Inference Using mtDNA Profiles

Base substitutions other than those in the hypervariable region do occur around the genome. Many of these are represented at high frequencies within a particular population and can be useful makers of ethnicity.

Much of the work undertaken on the mtDNA molecule has involved tracing its evolutionary history (this is called molecular phylogenetics). The results of phylogenetic analysis can be displayed either as a tree or as a network. When dealing with intraspecies variation, a network approach has been found to be the most powerful technique. Using established methods, the mtDNA sequences can be grouped into related sequences that are known as haplogroups. Haplogroups can contain a large number of haplotypes, but these will all be related by one or more common mutations. **Figure 3** shows a simple network analysis that illustrates the relationship between major mtDNA haplogroups and some of the major world populations. The numbers on the branches of the network refer to the nucleotides around the genome that define the separation of different haplogroups.

The technique is restricted to differentiating between broad ethnic groups, and even then there are limitations to the usefulness of the technique. One limitation is the fact that admixture (mixing of different populations) occurs between all ethnic groups, and therefore a person identifying self-ethnically as Caucasian may have, as the result of admixture, possibly several generations ago, a mtDNA haplogroup associated with Southeast Asia or sub-Saharan Africa, which would lead to the incorrect inference of ethnicity.

Notwithstanding the limitations, there are situations in both human identification and the analysis of crime scene samples in which the inferred ethnicity of a questioned sample may provide the investigators with some valuable information.

## Species Identification

To this point, this article has been concerned with the identification of human material. It is worth covering another application of mtDNA profiling. As previously discussed, mtDNA accumulates mutations relatively rapidly. When the mtDNA from different species is compared, this feature is reflected in the degree of sequence divergence, which is assessed using phylogenetic methods.

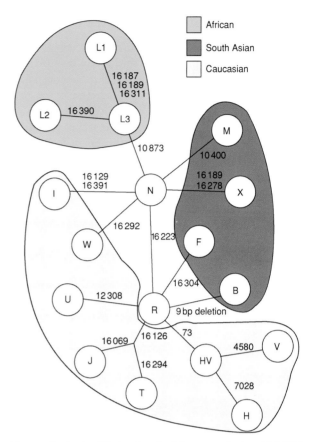

**Figure 3**  A simplified network of human mitochondrial DNA (mtDNA) haplogroups. The network shows the relationship between major haplogroups. The number next to the line that joins any two haplogroups indicates the position of a nucleotide that is polymorphic; the status of these key nucleotides allows mtDNA genomes to be assigned to a specific haplogroup. For example, regarding position 7028, if an mtDNA genome has a cytosine base at this position, then it is classified as haplogroup H; if it has a thymine, it can be deduced to be anything but H. The one exception to this is haplogroup B, where a 9-bp deletion is the diagnostic feature. The shaded zones indicate the ethnic groups that are associated with different haplogroups.

When using DNA for species identification, the hypervariable regions are not normally analyzed. Regions that evolve more slowly, particularly the cytochrome *b*, 12S, and the 16S ribosomal RNA genes, are routinely analyzed.

There are several applications in which identification of a species can be useful from a forensic standpoint. In cases in which animal remains, or sometimes the complete animal, have been recovered, the identification of the species is vital before a judgment can be made on whether, for example, poaching or trading of a protected species has occurred.

Animals can also deposit material, particularly hairs, that can act as trace evidence. If a hair from a nonhuman source is found on a suspect, it may be of value to identify the species from which the hair derived. Several studies have taken further the potential use of animal DNA as evidence by also examining the hypervariable region of the animal DNA; databases exist that allow the evidential value of cat and dog hairs to be assessed by measuring the frequency of different haplotypes.

## Case Study

### The Identification of the Romanov Royal Family

The identification of the deposed Russian royal family was more a matter of resolving historical questions than bringing the perpetrators of the killing to justice. It does, however, illustrate some of the advantages that mtDNA provides.

It is believed that, after the overthrow of the ruling tsar in 1917, the tsar, his wife and four children, their doctor, and three of their servants were shot and disposed of in a shallow pit. Sulfuric acid was thrown on to the bodies and a truck was repeatedly driven over the bodies, once in the pit, to hinder any attempts to identify them. In 1991, the grave site was found and nine bodies were recovered. Classical anthropological investigation tentatively identified the bodies; however, genetic confirmation was sought.

DNA was successfully extracted from the nine bodies, and both nuclear and mtDNA analyses were successful. The nuclear DNA was used to identify the family grouping within the recovered bodies, and it

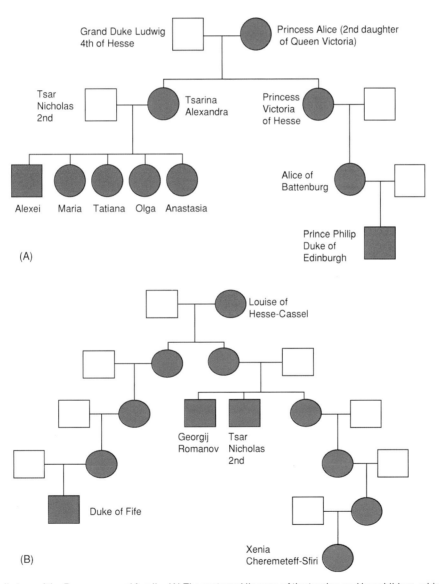

**Figure 4** The family tree of the Romanov royal family. (A) The maternal lineage of the tsarina and her children, which provides a direct link to Prince Philip Duke of Edinburgh. (B) The maternal lineage of Tsar Nicholas, linking him to two living maternal relatives, the Duke of Fife and Xenia Cheremeteff-Sfiri. The squares represent males and the circles represent females; the transmission of the relevant mitochondrial DNA type is indicated by shading.

also helped to conclude that one of the tsar's daughters and his son were missing from the grave. The mtDNA profiles generated from four of the bodies that were identified as the tsarina and three of her daughters were matched to the profile of Prince Philip Duke of Edinburgh, who was maternally related (**Figure 4**). The tsar's mtDNA profile was compared to two living relatives and their profiles matched, except at the 16 169 position; detailed examination of this revealed that the tsar's sequence was heteroplasmic at this position. Subsequent analysis of the tsar's brother also revealed heteroplasmy at this position, providing strong evidence that the remains were those of the tsar.

A further twist from the identifications involved the identification of Anna Anderson Manahan. She claimed that she was the Duchess Anastasia, the missing royal daughter, and was supported by a number of people in this claim. A sample of bowel tissue that had been removed during an operation in 1979 and fixed in formaldehyde and preserved in paraffin wax was used to investigate possible genetic links to the Romanovs. Nuclear and mtDNA were extracted from this sample and analyzed. The results were inconsistent with Anna Anderson Manahan being a daughter of the tsar and tsarina. Franziska Schanzkowska was a German woman and many suspected that this was the true identity of Anna Anderson Manahan. A maternal relative of Franzisca Schanzkowska donated a DNA sample and its profile matched the mtDNA profile of Anna Anderson Manahan, supporting the hypothesis that the woman's true identity was Franzisca Schanzkowska, not the Duchess Anastasia.

## See Also

**Anthropology:** Determination of Racial Affinity; Role of DNA; **DNA:** Basic Principles; Ethics of Forensic Applications and Databanks; Statistical Analysis; Risk of Contamination; Postmortem Analysis for Heritable Channelopathies and Selected Cardiomyopathies

## Further Reading

Anderson S, Bankier AT, Barrell BG, et al. (1981) Sequence and organisation of the human mitochondrial genome. *Nature* 290: 457–465.

Carracedo A, Bär W, Lincoln P, et al. (2000) DNA Commission of the International Society for Forensic Genetics: Guidelines for mitochondrial DNA typing. *Forensic Science International* 110: 79–85.

Cavalli-Sforza LL, Menozzi P, Piazza A (1996) *The History and Geography of Human Genes.* Princeton, NJ: Princeton University Press.

Chinnery PF, Thorburn DR, Samuels DC, et al. (2000) The inheritance of mitochondrial DNA heteroplasmy: random drift, selection or both? *Trends in Genetics* 16: 500–505.

Forster L, Forster P, Lutz-Bonengel S, Willkomm H, Brikmann B (2002) Natural radioactivity and human mitochondrial DNA mutations. *Proceedings of the National Academy of Sciences USA* 99: 13950–13954.

Gill P, Ivanov PL, Kimpton C, et al. (1994) Identification of the remains of the Romanov family by DNA analysis. *Nature Genetics* 6: 130–135.

Hirata S, Hosel K, Shoda T, Mabuchi T (2002) Spermatozoon and mitochondrial DNA. *Reproductive Medicine and Biology* 1: 41–47.

Howell N, Smejkal CB, Mackey DA, et al. (2003) The pedigree rate of sequence divergence in the human mitochondrial genome: there is a difference between phylogenetic and pedigree rates. *American Journal of Human Genetics* 72: 659–670.

Lincoln PJ, Thomson J (eds.) (1998) *Methods in Molecular Biology 98: Forensic DNA Profiling Protocols.* Clifton, NJ: Humana Press.

Meyer S, Weiss G, von Haeseler A (1999) Pattern of nucleotide substitution and rate heterogeneity in the hypervariable regions I and II of human mtDNA. *Genetics* 152: 1103–1110.

Parsons TJ, Muniec DS, Sullivan K, et al. (1997) A high observed substitution rate in the human mitochondrial DNA control region. *Nature Genetics* 15: 363–368.

Renfrew C, Boyle K (eds.) (2000) *Archaeogenetics: DNA and the Population Prehistory of Europe.* Cambridge, UK: McDonald Institute for Archaeological Research.

Tully G, Bär W, Brinkmann B, et al. (2001) Considerations by the European DNA Profiling (EDNAP) group on the working practices, nomenclature and interpretation of mitochondrial DNA profiles. *Forensic Science International* 124: 83–91.

Vigilant L, Stoneking M, Harpending H, Hawkes K, Wilson AC (1991) African populations and the evolution of human mitochondrial DNA. *Science* 253: 1503–1507.

# Postmortem Analysis for Heritable Channelopathies and Selected Cardiomyopathies

**K A Glatter, N Chiamvimonvat, and J K Park**, University of California – Davis ACC, Sacramento, CA, USA

## Introduction

In the developed world, sudden cardiac death remains the major cause of natural death. Most such cases are due to coronary artery disease and myocardial infarction leading to arrhythmias and sudden death. However, an increasing number of genetic causes of sudden death have been identified, which may strike young, otherwise healthy people.

It is important to be familiar with these genetic causes of sudden cardiac death and the diagnostic difficulties they present so that they can be considered as possible causes of death if the autopsy is otherwise normal. An overview for forensic pathologists on how to collect tissue samples for molecular testing of these entities is provided.

The clinical presentation; genetic, molecular, and cellular abnormalities; and diagnostic evaluation of these causes, including ion channelopathies and cardiomyopathies, are discussed below.

The clinical pathologist should consider these diseases when the autopsy findings do not explain how the person died. There is often a genetic basis for these disorders, and such information could be disseminated to surviving family members, with the hopes that affected persons could be identified and offered treatment while still alive.

Disorders of the ion channel are given as follows:

1. long QT syndromes (LQTS)
2. Brugada syndrome (BS)
3. catecholaminergic polymorphic ventricular tachycardia (ryanodine receptor defect) (CPMVT).

Disorders of the heart muscle are given as follows:

1. hypertrophic cardiomyopathy (HCM)
2. arrhythmogenic right ventricular dysplasia (ARVD).

## Molecular Diagnosis of Sudden Death Diseases

With the explosion of molecular techniques, DNA testing on peripheral blood and tissue has revolutionized the diagnosis of genetic causes of sudden death. The basic methods of tissue preparation and DNA analysis as a useful overview for the clinical pathologist and coroner are described in this article.

### Collection of DNA from Blood Samples

It is easiest to amplify DNA that will be used for genetic testing when it is taken from blood samples. Ideally, the coroner or pathologist would collect 15 ml of blood at the time of autopsy in several tubes which contain ethylenediaminetetraacetic acid (EDTA), to prevent coagulation and degradation of the DNA. The tubes are then stored at 4 °C until the DNA is extracted for analysis, which should be within 1 week, although sometimes it may be 4 months after collection. If the blood samples are collected in tubes which do not contain an anticoagulant, the DNA should be extracted promptly (within days of the initial collection).

### Collection of DNA from Tissue Samples

Extraction of high-quality DNA from tissue that can be used for polymerase chain reaction (PCR) amplification is much more problematic than using blood samples. It is often difficult to amplify long fragments of DNA from formalin-fixed and paraffin-embedded tissue because of the fixation time in the formalin, the often long storage time in the tissue blocks prior to analysis, and the formation of formic acid in the sample. Formic acid hydrolyzes the DNA and creates single-strand nicks in the DNA. In postmortem tissues fixed in nonbuffered formalin (usually in tissue preserved during the early 1980s), DNA fragments longer than 90 bp cannot be amplified.

There are a variety of published methods to extract DNA from preserved tissue. Many involve a phenol–chloroform digestion and washing step. Commercial kits are also available that may simplify the methodology. One paper described a "pre-PCR restoration process" in which the single-stranded DNA nicks are repaired with Taq polymerase prior to PCR amplification, which greatly improved the length of DNA pieces which could be amplified.

An alternative method to obtain usable DNA from tissue is to snap-freeze fresh myocardial tissue collected at autopsy in liquid nitrogen and store at −80 °C until DNA extraction is performed, possibly many months later.

Clearly, the collection and preservation of tissue or blood samples for future DNA analysis are cumbersome, time-intensive, and costly. However, it is very helpful for the pathologist or coroner to preserve such biologic material carefully for future DNA testing in those cases where a genetic cause of sudden death is suspected, as is outlined below.

## Disorders of the Ion Channel

### Long QT Syndromes

LQTS is one of the more common and well-known of the ion channelopathies. It can be inherited as a dominant gene or can be seen in cases of acquired LQTS after taking common drugs, including antipsychotics, antiarrhythmic drugs, or allergy medications.

**Epidemiology** Currently, it is estimated that 1 in 5000 people carry an LQTS genetic mutation. With the inclusion of drug-induced or acquired LQTS cases, many of whom have the same genetic ion channel defects as that seen with congenital LQTS, some

**Table 1**   Genes associated with sudden death

| Disease | Chromosome locus | Gene | Gene product |
|---------|-----------------|------|--------------|
| LQT1 | 11p15.5 | KVLQT1 | $I_{Ks}$, $\alpha$ subunit |
| LQT2 | 7q35-36 | HERG | $I_{Kr}$, $\alpha$ subunit |
| LQT3 | 3p21-24 | SCN5A | Na channel |
| LQT4 | 4q25-27 | ankyrin 2 | Ankyrin-B |
| LQT5 | 21p22.1 | minK (KCNE1) | $I_{Ks}$, $\beta$ subunit |
| LQT6 | 21p22.1 | MiRP1 (KCNE2) | $I_{Kr}$, $\beta$ subunit |

experts believe that the true incidence of LQTS is actually 1 in 1000. Certainly, it is one of the more common genetic causes of sudden death and has been diagnosed with increasing frequency as more coroners are educated regarding LQTS.

**Clinical features**   At least 10% of affected LQTS patients may present with sudden death as their first (and last) symptom. However, most patients with an LQTS mutation will never experience any symptoms. The majority of LQTS families are discovered when a young person tragically dies suddenly with a normal autopsy and other family members are found to have a prolonged QT interval on electrocardiogram (ECG). Each genetic subtype has its own trigger for events (**Table 1**). LQT1 patients usually experience symptoms (syncope, cardiac arrest, or sudden death) during epinephrine (adrenaline)-driven types of activities such as exercise, running, or with strong emotion (e.g., during an argument). An unexplained drowning in a person who is a good swimmer could be due to an LQT1 mutation. LQT2 (HERG) mutations may cause sudden death due to auditory triggers, as with an alarm clock or the telephone ringing. The rare LQT3 (sodium channel) subtype may occur during sleep or during periods of slow heart rates.

Although LQTS is an autosomal disease, females are far more likely to experience symptoms than males. LQTS can be diagnosed in some cases by noting a prolonged QT interval ($>450$ ms) on the ECG. However, up to 30% of gene-positive patients may have a normal or only borderline prolonged QT interval, making diagnosis difficult in some cases.

There is a small association in the literature between sudden infant death syndrome (SIDS) and LQTS, although probably fewer than 5% of all SIDS cases are due to ion channel mutations. SIDS is likely far more commonly associated with risk factors such as placing the infant prone, co-sleeping with adults, or undiagnosed inborn errors of metabolism. Little research has thus far been conducted to determine if other channelopathies besides LQTS are associated with SIDS.

As with many ion channelopathies which cause unexplained sudden death, autopsy findings are unremarkable. Venous blood saved in an EDTA tube (or perhaps snap-frozen myocardial tissue) can be tested at a research laboratory for the presence of LQTS ion channel mutations. It is very difficult to find laboratories willing to test for LQTS mutations given the great expense involved. A USA company based in New Haven, CT, called Genaissance Pharmaceuticals is offering LQTS screening for a fee (their website is http://genaissance.com).

**Pathophysiology**   The fundamental defect in LQTS is prolonged ventricular repolarization and a tendency toward torsades de pointes (polymorphic ventricular tachycardia) and ventricular fibrillation. Beta-blocker medications do not shorten the QT interval; they are believed to act, in part, by blocking early after-depolarizations (EADs), which initiate the ventricular arrhythmias.

**Genetics**   To date, a total of six genes have been identified as causing LQTS. The mutant ion channel which causes clinical LQTS is inherited in an autosomal dominant fashion with incomplete penetrance and was originally known as the Romano–Ward syndrome. With the advent of genetic testing, it has become clear that each LQTS genetic subtype represents a unique disease, with different triggers to arrhythmias. The genes which encode the potassium channels KVLQT1 (on chromosome 11) and minK (on chromosome 21) interact to form the cardiac $I_{Ks}$ (inward slow potassium) current; mutations in each cause LQT1 and LQT5, respectively. The potassium channels HERG (on chromosome 7) and MiRP1 (on chromosome 21) interact to form the $I_{Kr}$ (inward rapid potassium) current, and defects in each cause LQT2 and LQT6, respectively. Mutations in the sodium cardiac channel SCN5A cause LQT3 (on chromosome 3). The gene responsible for LQT4 on chromosome 4 has been identified as ankyrin 2.

The potassium channel mutations cause a "loss of function" in the channel (or a "dominant-negative effect," in the case of the HERG mutation), whereas defects in the sodium channel cause a "gain of function."

In the unlikely event that a mutant copy of the $I_{Ks}$ channel is inherited from each parent (mutations in the KVLQT1 and minK genes), the child will suffer from a clinically severe form of autosomal dominant LQTS and from autosomal recessive congenital deafness. This condition is known as the Jervell and

Lange–Nielsen syndrome (JLNS). It is actually quite rare, with an estimated incidence of 1.6–6 cases per million.

**Treatment**   There is no consensus on how to treat patients with LQTS. Most physicians would advocate an implantable cardiac defibrillator (ICD) for those patients who have survived a cardiac arrest, or possibly even in those with syncopal events. Dual-chamber pacemakers even with beta-blocker therapy have been shown to be ineffective in symptomatic patients. Most physicians would advocate beta-blocker therapy in asymptomatic LQTS patients. The exact dose or type of beta-blocker medication to be used is unclear. In patients unable (or unwilling) to take medications, an ICD may then be recommended. Restriction of heavy physical activity is also suggested in affected patients.

### Brugada syndrome

BS is another inherited ion channelopathy which causes unexplained sudden death, particularly in middle-aged males. It is relatively common in Southeast Asia and should particularly be considered in the autopsy of subjects with this ethnicity.

**Epidemiology**   A BS consensus report published in 2002 estimated the incidence of the disease worldwide at up to 66 cases per 10 000 people. In contrast to LQTS, it affects males more commonly than females, in an 8:1 male-to-female ratio, although it is also an autosomal dominant gene. However, the gene is much more prevalent in Southeast Asia than in the USA. BS is thought to cause the entity known as lai tai ("death during sleep") in Thailand, a relatively common cause of sudden unexplained death among young healthy men.

**Clinical features**   BS was first described in 1992 in patients with right bundle branch block patterns on the ECG who suffered unexplained cardiac arrests. Since then, more has been learned about BS, although much about the disease remains unknown.

It is not known why some Brugada patients become symptomatic and others do not. However, once BS subjects experience a symptom (syncope or aborted cardiac arrest), it becomes a lethal disease with a high clinical penetrance. Several studies have found that the recurrence rate following a resuscitated cardiac arrest was 62% at 5 years of follow-up. Most arrhythmic events occur for the first time when the patient is in the early 40s, but episodes have been described over a wide age range (2–77

years). Symptomatic Brugada patients experience polymorphic ventricular tachycardia degenerating into ventricular fibrillation, leading to syncope or even death. The episodes occur most commonly during sleep but may also happen with exercise or at rest.

The ECG in the Brugada patient is frequently abnormal and represents the best way to diagnose BS (**Figure 1**). A right bundle branch block type of pattern is often noted in the right precordial leads V1–V3 with ST-segment elevation. In many patients with BS, the ECG abnormalities can normalize or be unmasked by pharmacologic challenge with a sodium channel-blocking drug like procainamide, flecainide, or ajmaline. The ECG of a 28-year-old man with BS is provided in **Figure 1**.

Many Brugada patients will have abnormal test results during invasive electrophysiology (EP) study. Inducibility of malignant ventricular arrhythmias is not rare and portends a worse clinical prognosis than for those patients who have normal EP studies. The usual cardiac tests in BS are normal, including echocardiogram, cardiac magnetic resonance imaging (MRI), and biopsy. Autopsy findings of the heart in BS patients are also unremarkable.

**Pathophysiology**   The mutation in the *SCN5A* gene results in either a reduced sodium channel current or failure of the sodium channel to express. The disease is caused by a defect in the $\alpha$-subunit of the cardiac sodium channel gene (*SCN5A*). Numerous *SCN5A* mutations have been described which produce BS, but most lead to a "loss of function" in the cardiac sodium channel. Interestingly, LQT3 (a completely different disease) is also due to mutations in the *SCN5A* gene but leads to a "gain of function" in the sodium channel.

The mutant sodium channel demonstrates more abnormal function at higher temperatures. There are numerous reports in the literature of BS patients experiencing symptoms during febrile illnesses.

**Genetics**   BS is an ion channelopathy inherited in an autosomal dominant fashion. To date, only 20% of Brugada cases have been linked to the *SCN5A* gene; the precise ion channel mutations causing the remaining 80% of cases are unknown. The *SCN5A* gene is one of the largest ion channel genes known, with at least 28 exons identified thus far.

**Treatment**   Medications are largely ineffective at treating BS. Amiodarone, beta-blocker, and calcium channel-blocking agents have all been tried and do not prevent sudden death in high-risk patients. The

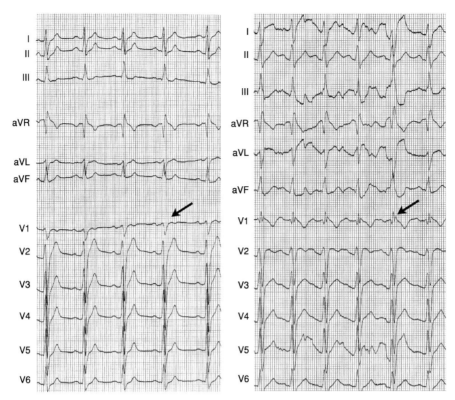

**Figure 1**   Twelve-lead electrocardiogram on a 28-year-old asymptomatic man with Brugada syndrome. Note the QRS prolongation and pseudo-right bundle branch block with ST-segment elevation in leads $V_1$–$V_3$ (arrow). His two older affected brothers suffered cardiac arrests. All three received defibrillators.

recommended treatment for symptomatic patients with BS is ICD implantation, particularly as the recurrence rate for such subjects is high. Patients who have not yet experienced an arrhythmic event but spontaneously exhibit the abnormal ECG findings are at intermediate risk for an episode and may benefit from prophylactic ICD therapy.

## Catecholaminergic Polymorphic Ventricular Tachycardia

CPMVT is a newly described inherited disorder of cardiac calcium channels. It is another arrhythmogenic disorder characterized by sudden unexplained death associated with exercise.

**Epidemiology**   The disease has thus far been characterized in several Finnish and Italian families. The epidemiology of this disorder has not yet been fully described and so far is limited to small case series. Its true incidence is likely much higher than is currently appreciated since most cases are undiagnosed.

**Clinical features**   CPMVT was first described in 1995 in 21 children. This disorder is characterized

by syncopal spells in childhood and adolescence which are often triggered by exercise or stress (catecholamines) as well as cardiac arrest and sudden death. The disease has a mortality of 30–50% by the age of 30 in affected individuals. Due to its autosomal dominant nature, there is often a family history of unexplained sudden death.

The resting ECG of a patient with this disorder is usually unremarkable, as are cardiac imaging studies (echocardiogram, angiogram, cardiac MRI). Patients with CPMVT may experience bidirectional or polymorphic ventricular tachycardia with exercise stress testing, with emotional stress, or during infusion of epinephrine (isoproterenol). Up to 30% of such patients were initially misdiagnosed as having LQTS in one study. Autopsy findings in CPMVT subjects are generally normal.

**Pathophysiology**   Defective calcium channels formed as a result of the mutations in the ryanodine receptor gene *RyR2* lead to abnormal conduction, which predispose the heart to ventricular tachycardia and sudden death. *RyR2*, the gene encoding the cardiac calcium channel, is responsible for mediating the coupling of the cell's electrical excitation and mechanical contraction. Cellular depolarization leads to release of $Ca^{2+}$ from the sarcoplasmic reticulum via *RyR2* and mechanical contraction. Sudden death is hypothesized to occur as the result of torsades de pointes or ventricular fibrillation due to abnormal calcium channel handling.

**Genetics** CPMVT is due to a defect in the cardiac ryanodine receptor (*RyR2*) gene, which is inherited in an autosomal dominant fashion. Ryanodine receptors are intracellular calcium channels that regulate the release of calcium from different cell sites. Three different isoforms of the ryanodine receptor are known, and each is encoded by a different gene. They are the largest ion channels yet described. *RyR2* (encoded by 105 exons) is characteristically found in the heart while *RyR1* is found in skeletal muscle. Because this entity is newly described and the genes encoding the mutant calcium channel are so large, no commercial genetic screening is currently available for CPMVT.

**Treatment** Beta-blockers form the mainstay of therapy in this condition. In patients who have survived cardiac arrest or are felt to be at particularly high risk for sudden death, an ICD is offered.

## Arrhythmogenic Right Ventricular Dysplasia

ARVD is a newly recognized disorder that is a cause of unexplained sudden death in otherwise healthy young adults, particularly in young athletic men. Especially in the early stages, affected patients may have grossly normal heart function.

**Epidemiology** The true incidence of ARVD is unknown. In a prospective, autopsy-based study in the Veneto region of northern Italy, 20% of unexplained sudden deaths in subjects under age 35 were found to have ARVD, including 22% of young athletic men who died suddenly in the region. It is unclear if northern Italy simply has an abnormally high incidence of the disease or if this reflects the true incidence of the disease. However, it is likely a much more common entity than initially appreciated as most cases go undetected.

**Clinical features** Unfortunately, the initial presentation of ARVD clinically is often unexplained sudden death in a healthy, athletic male. Patients experience ventricular arrhythmias from the diseased right ventricle ranging from benign premature ventricular complexes (PVCs) to ventricular tachycardia or even ventricular fibrillation and cardiac arrest. It was first described briefly in 1961 and, in greater detail, in

**Table 2** Arrhythmogenic right ventricular dysplasia diagnostic criteria

| |
|---|
| *Family history* |
| Confirmed at autopsy |
| *Structural findings* |
| Right ventricular global hypokinesis with preserved left ventricular function |
| *Arrhythmias* |
| Right ventricular tachycardia or premature beats |
| *Electrocardiogram findings* |
| Epsilon wave of QRS in leads $V_1–V_3$ |
| Late potentials on signal-averaged electrocardiogram |

1977. The Study Group on ARVD has defined specific criteria to aid in the diagnosis of ARVD (**Table 2**).

ECG findings include a complete or incomplete right bundle branch block during normal sinus rhythm with T-wave inversion in leads $V_1$ to $V_3$. An epsilon wave, a terminal notch in the QRS, may also be present. A signal-averaged ECG is also characteristically abnormal. Echocardiographic findings may be normal or reveal a variety of abnormalities in the right ventricle, including right ventricular wall thinning, dilatation, or dysfunction. Cardiac MRI can sometimes be useful as it may reveal the fibrofatty infiltration of the right ventricular free wall. Biopsy of the right ventricular septum (done in the septum and not in the free wall, due to free wall thinning) is often not helpful, because involvement of the septum in ARVD is sporadic.

ARVD represents one of the few genetically based causes of sudden death which can be identified at autopsy, at least in grossly abnormal cases. The pathologist may find diffuse or segmental loss of myocardium in the right ventricular free wall, with concomitant replacement with fibrofatty tissue. Two-thirds of such patients have patchy, acute myocarditis-type of findings with lymphocytic infiltration and cell death. Up to 50% of ARVD patients have right ventricular aneurysms at autopsy. Patients can have progressive dilatation and failure of the right ventricle over time, which can also occasionally involve the left ventricle, leading to a diffuse cardiomyopathy. One study found that 76% of ARVD subjects had histologic involvement of the left ventricle.

**Pathophysiology** The pathophysiology of ARVD is unclear. It likely represents a complex interplay between genetic predisposition, cellular mechanisms, and unknown environmental factors. Several consistent features of ARVD can be noted: apoptosis (programmed cell death), a component of inflammatory heart disease (e.g., acute myocarditis), and myocardial dystrophy. The disease is progressive over decades in some patients, whereas it is relatively quiescent, for unknown reasons, in others.

**Genetics**  At least seven distinct chromosomal loci have so far been located in association with ARVD. These loci include two on chromosome 10, two on chromosome 14, and one each on chromosomes 1, 2, and 3. One autosomal recessive form of ARVD, called Naxos syndrome, is associated with palmoplantar keratoderma and woolly hair. It is due to a mutation in the gene for plakoglobin. Another syndrome found in Ecuador involves a recessive mutation in the gene for desmoplakin. Both are components of desmosomes, which form the major cell adhesion junctions. Currently there is no commercial genetic testing available to diagnose ARVD. For most cases of ARVD, the genetic linkage is unclear. Up to 30–50% of cases will have an associated family history consistent with ARVD (including sudden death).

**Treatment**  There is no consensus for how to treat ARVD. In those patients who have survived cardiac arrest, implantation of an ICD is generally recommended to avoid sudden death. Pharmacologic therapy with beta-blocker or antiarrhythmic medications has also been suggested. Radiofrequency ablation during electrophysiology study of ventricular arrhythmias has also been attempted.

## Hypertrophic Cardiomyopathy

HCM was first described in 1958. It has been called hypertrophic obstructive cardiomyopathy, and also idiopathic hypertrophic subaortic stenosis, despite the fact that 75% of affected patients do not have a sizeable resting outflow gradient. It is a polygenic, relatively common genetic cause of sudden death, particularly in young athletes.

**Epidemiology**  HCM is actually the most common genetically associated form of sudden cardiac death. It is estimated that 1 in 500 people (0.2% of the general population) carry an HCM genetic mutation. However, the phenotypic presentation or clinical penetrance of the disease is much lower. Most patients with an HCM mutation will not show signs of the disease during life.

**Clinical features**  When present, the hallmark feature of HCM is myocyte disarray. The clinical diagnosis of HCM during life is made most reliably by echocardiography. Severe ventricular wall thickening can be seen. A normal left ventricular wall thickness is generally <12 mm, and thicknesses >30 mm are not unusual in severe cases of HCM. This marked septal hypertrophy is often an age-dependent effect and may not be seen initially in young patients. In most cases, the left ventricle may be affected diffusely or may demonstrate asymmetric septal hypertrophy. In contrast, in the Japanese variant of HCM, the apical left ventricle is primary affected and shows abnormal thickening.

At autopsy, using detailed pathologic examination, one can frequently see hypertrophied myocytes with bizarre shapes, chaotic cellular alignment, and gross cellular disarray in the left ventricle. Patchy areas of myocardial scarring and fibrosis can sometimes be noted, and this is believed to be due to abnormal intramural coronary arteries.

**Pathophysiology**  Syncope in these subjects may occur due to arrhythmias or from obstruction due to ventricular hypertrophy and cavity obliteration. Dehydration can trigger a syncopal event in such patients. Sudden death is expected to occur in HCM due to a primary electrical abnormality by ventricular arrhythmias. In support of this view, one large study of HCM patients in whom defibrillators were implanted demonstrated that nearly 25% of the patients had documented ventricular arrhythmias over a 3-year follow-up period.

The disease may be progressive in some patients. The myocyte hypertrophy continues over years in a clinically silent manner and may lead ultimately to an end-stage, dilated cardiomyopathic picture. Depending upon the time frame during which the patient is evaluated, the HCM-affected heart could appear grossly normal, markedly hypertrophied, or even dilated, making the diagnosis difficult.

## Genetics

The polygenic and multicellular nature of HCM makes it a frustratingly complicated disease to diagnose unless gross histopathologic abnormalities are found on echocardiogram or at autopsy. At least 10 different genes encoding the cardiac sarcomere have been implicated in HCM. Over 150 unique mutations have been reported to date since the first genetic cause for HCM was identified in 1990. Most such mutations are missense mutations found in the proteins of the cardiac sarcomere and are located in the β-myosin heavy chain, cardiac troponin T, or myosin-binding protein C. Although the disease is autosomal dominant, a family history of syncope or sudden death may be lacking, and the disease has widely variable clinical penetrance.

Within the β-myosin heavy-chain gene (*MYH7*), numerous mutations have been described as malignant mutations associated with a poor clinical

**Table 3** High-risk features in hypertrophic cardiomyopathy (HCM)

Family history of sudden death
High-risk genotype (e.g., Arg719Gln)
History of sustained ventricular arrhythmias
Previous cardiac arrest
Exertional syncope
Massive left ventricular hypertrophy ($\geq 30\,mm$)

prognosis. These particular mutations seemed to be associated with a severe clinical phenotype, including progression to end-stage heart failure or sudden death, a relatively high penetrance of the disease, and extreme left ventricular wall thickness (**Table 3**).

**Treatment** There are no formal guidelines for treating asymptomatic patients with HCM. In those patients with symptoms of shortness of breath, medical therapy with medications that reduce the outflow gradient remains the mainstay of therapy. Such medications include beta-blockers or calcium channel blockers. In very symptomatic patients with a large ($>50\,mm$) gradient, the outflow gradient can be reduced by surgical myomectomy or by catheter-based alcohol ablation. The latter is a relatively new technique which causes a controlled myocardial infarction and thus reduces the outflow gradient. In those patients deemed high-risk for an arrhythmic event (**Table 3**), an ICD may be implanted to avert sudden death.

## See Also

**Sudden Natural Death:** Cardiovascular

## Further Reading

Ackerman MJ, Siu BL, Sturner WQ, *et al.* (2001) Postmortem molecular analysis of SCN5A defects in sudden infant death syndrome. *JAMA* 286: 2264–2269.

Al-Khatib SM, LaPointe NM, Kramer JM, *et al.* (2003) What clinicians should know about the QT interval. *JAMA* 289: 2120–2127.

Antzelevitch C, Brugada P, Brugada J, *et al.* (2002) Brugada syndrome: a decade of progress. *Circulation Research* 91: 1114–1118.

Basso C, Calabrese F, Corrado D, *et al.* (2001) Postmortem diagnosis in sudden cardiac death victims: macroscopic, microscopic, and molecular findings. *Cardiovascular Research* 50: 290–300.

Batra AS, Hohn AR (2003) Consultation with the specialist: palpitations, syncope, and sudden cardiac death in children: who's at risk? *Pediatric Review* 24: 269–275.

Elliott PM, Poloniecki J, Dickie S, *et al.* (2000) Sudden death in hypertrophic cardiomyopathy: identification of high risk patients. *Journal of the American College of Cardiology* 36: 2212–2218.

Josephson ME (2002) *Clinical Cardiac Electrophysiology.* Philadelphia, PA: Lippincott/Williams and Wilkins.

Priori SG, Napolitano C, Memmi M, *et al.* (2002) Clinical and molecular characterization of patients with catecholaminergic polymorphic ventricular tachycardia. *Circulation* 106: 69–74.

Seidman JG, Seidman C (2001) The genetic basis for cardiomyopathy: from mutation identification to mechanistic paradigms. *Cell* 104: 557–567.

Thiene G, Basso C (2001) Arrhythmogenic right ventricular cardiomyopathy: an update. *Cardiovascular Pathology* 10: 109–117.

Zipes DP, Jalife J (1995) *Cardiac Electrophysiology. From Cell to Bedside.* Philadelphia, PA: WB Saunders.

# Hair Analysis

**E A Graffy and D R Foran**, Michigan State University, East Lansing, MI, USA

## Introduction

Human hair is one of the most frequently recovered types of biological forensic evidence, and the accurate identification of its origin can be paramount to the success of an investigation. As forensic biological techniques have improved, DNA testing of trace samples like single hairs has become possible and even routine. Depending on which parts of a hair are present, analysis of nuclear DNA, found on the chromosomes, or mitochondrial DNA (mtDNA), a maternally inherited molecule, may be conducted. Both techniques allow for simple exclusion of a potential source, or, if the profiles match, a statistical measure of the accuracy of identification. Hair, having a different structure than other biological samples, requires some changes to standard DNA extraction processes, and all DNA testing must be conducted with special attention to contamination prevention.

## Background

Traditional forensic analysis of hair involves microscopic comparison between an evidence specimen and a collection of exemplar hairs, examining morphological features such as structural measurements, color, cross-section shape, pigmentation, cosmetic treatment, and disease. While these criteria have been used since the early twentieth century to include or exclude a person as a potential source of change to evidentiary hair, no statistical analyses can be generated from microscopic comparisons, making it impossible to state objectively what weight should be afforded to an evidence/exemplar match. Recent postconviction exonerations in cases where morphological comparison of evidence hairs played a key role in conviction have contributed to the movement toward DNA-based analysis of hair. Microscopic examination remains useful for determining species of origin, body area of origin (head, pubic, axillary), and the presence of any tissue or foreign substance adhering to the hair, but the availability of population statistics and its more objective nature make DNA analysis the preferred identification method for forensic hair samples.

DNA testing of hair, with the goal of matching a crime scene sample to a known source, has become routine in many forensic laboratories. In general, testing will examine one of two forms of DNA found in cells: nuclear DNA or mtDNA. Nuclear DNA, the large chromosomes found in the cell's nucleus with which most people are familiar, is inherited in two copies, one from each parent. Mitochondria (singular: mitochondrion), the energy-producing organelles in a cell, also carry their own genetic material. MTDNA is inherited solely from the maternal parent (via the egg), and is present in hundreds to thousands of copies per cell. The information that can be gleaned from an evidence specimen through analysis of either DNA type varies, as does the suitability of each for forensic testing over the course of hair development.

## Hair Anatomy and Physiology

While hair is an outgrowth of soft tissue, its complex structure requires special considerations for forensic testing. A basic knowledge of the biology of hair growth and development is useful to appreciate fully both the capabilities of DNA testing of hair samples and the circumstances in which a certain technique for DNA extraction or analysis may be appropriate.

Hair consists of three primary structures (**Figure 1**). The medulla is a central shaft that in humans is usually filled with air. Surrounding the medulla is the cortex, the layer that contains the various pigments (mostly melanin) that confer color to the hair. The primary component of the cortex is keratin, the protein that gives hair its hardened quality, which is also the major component in finger and toe nails, as well

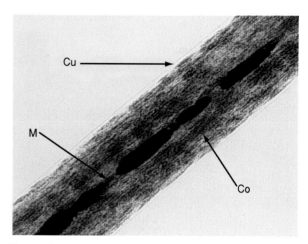

**Figure 1**  Magnified photograph of a human hair shaft. The medulla (M) is fragmented and appears dark. Within the cortex (Co) the long thin layers are bundles of keratin, interspersed with the pigment melanin. The outermost layer, or cuticle (Cu), is mostly transparent, and barely visible along the edge of the hair.

as animal hoof and horns. The outermost layer of the hair shaft is the cuticle, whose function is to protect the inner components and anchor the hair in the skin during growth.

Each hair on the human body grows from an epithelial organ lying just below the skin surface, called a follicle (**Figure 2**). The follicle's structure consists of an underlying layer of tissue, termed the dermal papilla, and an enlarged bulb of cells, called the matrix. Within this root bulb are two types of cells: actively multiplying germinal cells, which in their mature forms comprise the entirety of the hair shaft, and slowly dividing cells called melanocytes. Melanocytes remain in the bulb matrix throughout the life cycle of the hair but contribute cellular products, such as pigment grains, and cellular organs, such as mitochondria, to the developing shaft.

### Hair Development

Stimulated by growth factors secreted by the dermal papilla, germinal cells multiply in the root bulb at the base of the follicle. This germination feeds the growing hair with new cells, contributing to the lengthening of the hair shaft. As germinal cells are released from the matrix, they begin the process of differentiation into medullary, cortical, and cuticle cells. Precortical cells passing through the bulb matrix engulf protruding portions of melanocytes and carry the absorbed material into the hair shaft. This process distributes pigments produced by the melanocytes throughout the cortex.

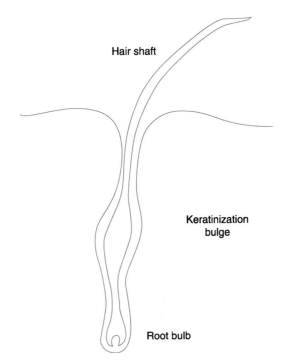

**Figure 2** Hair follicle and emerging hair shaft. Germinal cells multiply in the root bulb, feeding the growing hair with new cells. Medullary, cortical, and cuticle cells undergo keratinization at the keratinization bulge, and continue to migrate toward the skin surface, forming the hair shaft.

As the hair lengthens, cells move away from the bulb. At the keratinization bulge, synthesis of keratin becomes the major cellular activity. Eventually the cells are filled with bundles of keratin fibers to the point that they burst, and many of the cellular components disintegrate. Before a region of hair even emerges from the skin surface, the shaft consists of a mass of keratin fibers interspersed with the debris of dead cells. The cell nuclei have lost their DNA, and mitochondria and other membrane-bound organelles, although possibly intact, are subject to extensive damage.

### Growth Stages

Hair growth and regeneration is a cyclic process encompassing three distinct stages: (1) anagen, (2) catagen, and (3) telogen. The active growth stage (anagen) is described above, consisting of the genesis of a new hair in the follicle, followed by lengthening of the hair up to the point where it stops growing. This stage lasts several years for human head hairs, and shorter periods for other body hairs. Melanocytes cease releasing pigment granules prior to the end of growth, so the basal segment of hairs in the subsequent stages is nonpigmented. Forced removal of a hair during the anagen stage often produces a specimen with follicular tissue adhering to the root end, which may harbor intact nuclear DNA, ideal for forensic analysis.

The catagen stage is characterized by the termination of cell division in the matrix and the regression of the root bulb toward the skin surface. The root bulb shrinks and rounds off to produce a club-like structure of loosely organized cells. The catagen phase is fleeting, and hairs in this stage are not likely to be recovered as forensic specimens.

The telogen stage is considered the resting period before a hair is shed, and usually lasts several months for head hairs, longer for other body hairs. Some tissue does serve to anchor the root club in the skin during this stage, but removal of the hair is relatively simple by mechanical means (e.g., brushing) or due to growth of a new anagen hair beneath it. An estimated 100–150 telogen hairs may be shed from a human head each day. Not surprisingly, these represent the majority of hairs recovered from crime scenes and submitted to the laboratory for forensic DNA testing.

### Nuclear DNA Analysis of Hair

Nuclear DNA typing of hairs is the most precise method for matching a hair to an individual. Although nuclear DNA is lost during keratinization of the hair shaft, the root bulb remains populated with nucleated cells and is strongly anchored in the surrounding tissue throughout the anagen stage. Prior to the development of the polymerase chain reaction (PCR) technique, a method that is now widely used by forensic biologists to amplify DNA from minute specimens, about 15 fresh roots were required to carry out nuclear DNA typing of hair samples. In a forensic situation however, the assumption that 15 hairs collected at a scene are all derived from the same source is not easily made.

Fortunately, the PCR process allows for DNA typing from far less starting material. A forcibly removed anagen hair has been estimated to contain between 30 and 200 ng of DNA, easily enough for PCR-based analysis. Even a telogen hair club, loosely anchored in the surrounding tissue, may be shed with some follicular cells adhering to its end. Pubic hairs are often found in this state, as they exist longer in the telogen stage than any other. The small amount of tissue on a telogen root club can be appropriate for nuclear DNA analysis, but may produce only a partial profile. Hairs should be examined under a

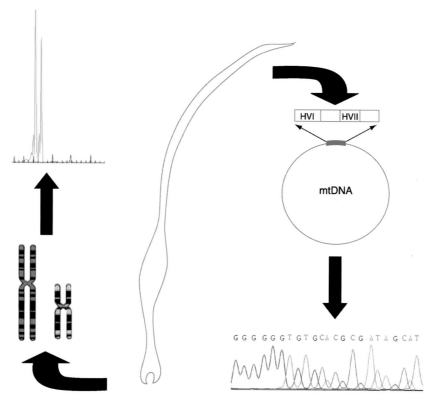

**Figure 3** DNA analysis from hair. If a root is present, nuclear DNA, or that contained on the chromosomes, can be analyzed. Short tandem repeat analysis can generate a random match probability of greater than one trillion to one, functionally individualizing the hair. If no root is present, mitochondrial DNA (mtDNA) analysis of the hair shaft can be conducted. The control region of the circular mtDNA contains two hypervariable regions, HVI and HVII, which harbor most of the variation among unrelated individuals. The nucleotide sequence of these regions determines an individual's mtDNA haplotype, which is useful for excluding a person as the source of the sample, or providing evidence that he/she may be the donor of the hair.

microscope to detect the presence of any adhering follicular tissue before a decision is made on how to proceed with DNA extraction and analysis.

### Sample Preparation, DNA Extraction, and Analysis

If follicular tissue is observed on the hair and nuclear DNA analysis is a possibility, then the portion of the hair with adhering tissue should be isolated away from the rest of the shaft. Care should be taken to avoid transferring keratinized and pigmented portions of the hair, as these can inhibit subsequent PCR reactions. Since most nucleated cells from a follicle or root bulb originate from the skin, procedures for extracting the DNA from hair roots are similar to those for standard buccal (cheek) swabs or similar sources. This may include incubation of the sample in detergents and a protease (an enzyme that breaks down proteins) followed by removal of unwanted materials using a solvent such as phenol. If some

keratinized shaft is present, it may be necessary to add dithiothreitol (DTT) – a chemical that helps to break down highly structured proteins like keratin – to the incubation. Alternatively, many other DNA isolation methods, some utilizing kits available commercially, can be used with equal success.

While methods for analyzing nuclear DNA vary among jurisdictions, the most exacting method of nuclear DNA testing in widespread use today is short tandem repeat (STR) analysis, a PCR-based process that allows typing from very small amounts of sample, including single hair roots (**Figure 3**). At many locations on the chromosomes, short segments of DNA exist as series of head-to-tail repeats, or STRs. A person might, for instance, inherit six repeat units from one parent and seven from the other at a given chromosomal location, and thus would type as a "6/7" for that marker. Multiple STRs are analyzed for each sample, creating a DNA profile. Once this nuclear DNA profile is obtained from a questioned hair, it is compared to the DNA profile generated from the suspected source. If these do not match, the source is excluded as the origin of that hair.

However, if the two profiles are the same, then the probability of the two profiles matching by chance, or the random match probability, must be calculated. The question is asked: how likely is it that the hair originated from someone else in the same population, and not the suspected source? Using the example above, the frequency of "6/7" can be determined for a given population or ethnic group, along with the frequency of the results of other STRs examined. Because they are independent of one another, these frequencies can be multiplied together, generating the probability of a random match between any two unrelated samples. When a full nuclear DNA STR profile is obtained, the random match probability between an evidentiary DNA sample and a suspected source's profile can surpass one in a trillion, far exceeding the number of people on Earth, thus effectively individualizing the source of the questioned sample. Given that its power of discrimination is so high, it is clear that typing of nuclear markers should be attempted if cells with intact nuclei are possibly present in the evidence sample.

## Mitochondrial DNA Analysis of Hair

Most hairs recovered in a forensic context are naturally shed in the telogen stage, and thus have little or no follicular tissue attached. In these situations, nuclear DNA analysis is often unsuccessful; thus, the only option available for genetic testing is mtDNA analysis, as this latter form of DNA can survive the keratinization process. Exactly why mtDNA analysis remains possible in challenging forensic samples when nuclear DNA has apparently degraded is unknown. Although frequently attributed to the large numbers of mtDNA molecules present in a cell, their location within the mitochondrion, the circular structure of the molecule, or other factors could just as easily contribute to this hardiness. Whatever the case, mtDNA seems to survive the process of keratinization well enough to allow successful typing of single hair shafts, even those 1 cm in length or less. A brief description of mtDNA and its analysis follows.

MTDNA is a small, circular molecule that is inherited solely via the egg, and thus persists through maternal lines over generations. The segment of mtDNA used for forensic identification is known as the D-loop or control region, an area that accumulates mutations over long periods of time, and thus

tends to differ among unrelated individuals. Forensic mtDNA analysis is generally performed by PCR-amplifying this region and determining the exact order or sequence of nucleotides (the individual building blocks of DNA) in the area amplified. In particular, two sections of the control region that show the largest amount of variation among individuals – the hypervariable regions, coined HVI and HVII – are usually analyzed. The collection of DNA nucleotide differences between a given sample and the human reference mtDNA (termed the Anderson sequence, or, in its updated form, the Cambridge reference sequence) comprise the mtDNA profile, or haplotype (also termed mitotype), of the sample.

Given the maternal inheritance of mitochondria, a mtDNA profile, unlike nuclear DNA, is not unique to an individual but is shared among siblings and other maternal relatives. This characteristic has major advantages and disadvantages from a forensic point of view. A benefit of sequence identity among maternal relatives is that it allows for a large pool of potential reference samples, meaning a mtDNA type can be compared not only to the original source, but to all maternal siblings, cousins, grandchildren, etc. In this manner, sample identifications or associations may be made over periods of generational time. Cases involving long-lost or long-dead familial relations may be resolved with mtDNA analysis, whereas nuclear DNA analysis is difficult without parents, siblings, or children of the person of interest. For instance, mtDNA analysis is the method of choice at the US Armed Forces DNA Identification Laboratory for the identification of war dead from past overseas conflicts such as Vietnam and Korea. Reference samples may be obtained from any living maternal relative for comparison with mtDNA data obtained from recovered remains. A similar sample collection process may be used for hairs or other biological evidence recovered in a missing person or mass disaster case, where a reference sample from the victim may not be otherwise available. For example, extensive DNA testing (including mtDNA analysis) was carried out on biological material recovered from the World Trade Center, the Pentagon, and the Pennsylvania plane crash sites in the September 11, 2001 attacks. Using a list of possible victims, reference samples were obtained from personal effects (e.g., toothbrushes) or relatives for comparison to recovered remains.

While sequence sharing among maternal relatives is an advantage with respect to sample gathering, the specificity of mtDNA analysis suffers. With potentially large groups of people sharing the same mtDNA sequence, random match probabilities are higher than those obtained using nuclear DNA analysis. Depending on the mtDNA sequence observed and the population or ethnic group with which the sequence is compared, a mtDNA profile may be somewhat common (as high as 5% of unrelated individuals for the most common haplotype) or extremely rare (never before observed). In general, approximately half of unrelated individuals fall into the latter category. However, even in the case of an extremely rare profile, the person in question shares that sequence with any number of maternal relatives; thus, individualization of a sample by mtDNA typing is not possible. This makes mtDNA far more powerful for exclusions than inclusions. If mtDNA from a sample such as a hair differs from an individual thought to have left it at a scene (e.g., a suspect), it readily excludes that individual as the source of the evidence. Alternatively, if the hair and the suspect have the same mtDNA type, the match is potentially strong evidence but certainly not individualizing. This was the case in the *State of Tennessee* v. *Paul Ware* (1999), the first criminal conviction in the USA involving mtDNA, in which a hair consistent with the accused was found in the throat of a sexually assaulted and asphyxiated girl.

### Sample Preparation, DNA Extraction, and Analysis

Hair samples of evidentiary value are often recovered in less than ideal conditions. Forensic hair specimens may have traces of soil, blood, semen, saliva, and any number of other contaminating substances adhering to the shaft, all of which may generate confounding DNA results or inhibit the genetic testing that is to be conducted. In many instances these contaminants can be detected through microscopic examination; if the substance is of forensic interest (e.g., a blood stain), it should be carefully isolated away from the hair, usually by swabbing. Even with guarded handling, traces of the contaminating material are commonly left behind and must be removed before DNA extraction from the hair itself. For this reason most DNA extraction methods from hair shafts are preceded by some form of cleaning or rinsing. These protocols vary by laboratory, but usually involve soaking the hair in sterile water, detergents, alcohol, or the like. Some protocols call for extended wash periods in a sonic bath or shaker, while others are fulfilled with a brief vortex or vigorous shaking. The cleaning method of choice is based on equipment and supplies available, the degree and type of contamination suspected, and the protocols that have been tested and validated in each laboratory.

DNA extraction from a hair shaft, with its abundant keratin and pigments, is somewhat more laborious than that from roots, and the unique challenges of hair as a substrate for DNA extraction and analysis must be considered when developing and adopting a protocol. Both mechanical and chemical means have been employed to break down the hair shaft and release mtDNA into solution. Additional hair components are also released, such as melanin and other pigments, which have been demonstrated to act as PCR inhibitors. The success of mtDNA typing from heavily pigmented hair often depends on neutralizing these effects, either by removing inhibitors during extraction or modifying PCR additives to counteract their activity.

Most methods of DNA extraction from hair shafts are similar to those used for other biological samples, with the additional inclusion of large amounts of proteases and DTT. Hair samples may also be diced or ground to help break down the hair shaft, but this level of handling also increases the risk of DNA contamination from outside sources. An alternate method for dissolving the hair shaft involves soaking it in a strong alkaline (high-pH) solution such as sodium hydroxide. DNA is resistant to high pH, but proteins are functionally dissolved and thus easily removed. Following any of these procedures, the DNA is purified and concentrated and is ready for analysis.

If the mtDNA has been cleanly extracted from the hair shaft (i.e., it does not contain substances that will inhibit chemical reactions such as PCR), subsequent genetic testing is generally routine; the hypervariable regions are PCR-amplified and their DNA sequence determined (**Figure 3**). The segment of mtDNA that can be amplified from a hair shaft is often not as extensive as can be obtained from fresher tissue, presumably because mtDNA slowly degrades over the period it is exposed to damage in the keratinized hair. One remedy for this limitation is to amplify a variety of fragment sizes from each sample, then use the longest amplified fragment as a template for sequencing reactions. Multiple amplifications require more DNA than single reactions, but the limited amount of DNA required for PCR should not consume large portions of the sample, even from small hairs. Some laboratories have found it most useful to amplify shorter, overlapping segments of mtDNA, the products of which must be sequenced individually. Again, multiple PCR reactions consume more starting DNA, but the rationale is to maximize amplification efficiency while still covering the entirety of both hypervariable regions. Other laboratories have turned to nested PCR, in which the first PCR product amplified is used as a template for a second, shorter PCR product. Nested PCR increases the sensitivity of the analysis, making up for difficulties of low DNA yield, but also increases the chances of obtaining results from any contaminating DNA. The sensitivity of these techniques necessitates great care throughout the process, and all forensic laboratories must run strict controls to ensure the results obtained are valid.

Methods for determining DNA sequences vary among laboratories depending on the equipment available and which procedures have been validated at each facility. Whenever possible, sequence data should be obtained from both DNA strands so as to identify each base clearly. The mtDNA region for which a sequence has been obtained and the differences in that region from the human reference sequence are entered into a mtDNA population database (maintained by a forensic entity, such as the Federal Bureau of Investigation) along with the appropriate population/ethnic group (if known). These criteria will produce the frequency of the mtDNA type within the group chosen.

## Special Considerations for mtDNA Analysis

The large number of mtDNA molecules found in a cell makes it possible that some may be different than others, simply due to natural mutations that occur over one's lifetime. Generally, these random mutations are not observed when analyzing mtDNA, as they are masked by the more prevalent original mtDNA type. However, if a mutation occurs very early in development, or exists in the egg, it may become common enough to detect later. The existence of more than one mtDNA type in an individual is termed heteroplasmy. While its occurrence in general is relatively uncommon, some researchers have reported elevated levels of heteroplasmy in hair samples. Others contradict these findings with challenges to their methodology and counter with studies that show that mtDNA sequences are stable over a variety of tissues from an individual. As the debate continues, the possibility of heteroplasmy should still be considered when studying a mtDNA sequence. Due to the phenomenon of heteroplasmy, a single nucleotide difference between samples is usually considered insufficient for exclusion of the suspected source. Any ambiguous base should be confirmed by replicate sequencing, or better, a new DNA preparation and analysis should be carried out on the original sample.

The high copy number of mtDNA in a biological sample is advantageous when faced with trace amounts of evidence, but its ubiquity can be detrimental if proper precautions against sample contamination are not taken. The extremely small quantities of mtDNA in some forensic samples (e.g., hair, fingernails, aged bone, or teeth) can be overwhelmed by a secondary source, including persons who have handled the evidence or work in the laboratory. Another major source of contamination is DNA that was previously PCR-amplified, which can be present in millions or billions more copies than the evidentiary material. To help prevent sample contamination by amplified DNA, laboratories where DNA extraction occurs (pre-PCR) and laboratories where amplification and subsequent analysis take place (PCR and post-PCR) should always be housed separately, as is true for any type of forensic DNA analysis. No equipment, supplies, or samples should be brought into the DNA extraction area after having been in the amplification laboratory without undergoing decontamination. Within the pre-PCR laboratory, a specific space (hood or bench) should be designated as the mtDNA extraction area, as samples undergoing nuclear DNA analysis may contain bountiful mtDNA. Further, reference samples plentiful in DNA, such as blood or buccal swabs, should be extracted separately from evidence samples to avoid cross-contamination. A set of reagents and supplies should also be designated solely for mtDNA typing. The mtDNA extraction area and all reagents and supplies should regularly undergo a decontamination process, which may include ultraviolet-irradiation and washing with bleach to destroy any residual DNA. A reagent blank, in which a mock sample – minus the actual hair or other evidentiary material – is carried in tandem through the entire DNA preparation and analysis procedures, should be included. Any positive result from the blank indicates reagent contamination, and the process should be repeated. Finally, positive and negative PCR controls, containing known or no DNA respectively, let the scientist know that PCR reagents are functioning and are pure.

## Summary

Forensic DNA testing of hairs can be conducted in two ways: analysis of nuclear DNA or analysis of mtDNA. During hair development, germinal cells in the root, rich in both types of DNA, multiply, allowing the hair to grow outward from the follicle. Cells making up the hair shaft undergo keratinization, a hardening process that destroys nuclear DNA, while mitochondria and their small circular DNA are left largely intact. When the root structure is present in a hair sample, nuclear DNA testing – specifically STR analysis – can be conducted. A full STR analysis can produce a DNA profile so unique that it effectively individualizes the source of an evidence hair. If a hair is shed naturally, however, a root or follicular tissue may not be present, and mtDNA analysis is the only available option. Although this form of testing is not as discriminating, a mtDNA profile is valuable for excluding an individual as the source of a hair, and can be strong evidence of association if the mtDNA haplotype from a hair and an individual are the same. Further, the maternally derived nature of mtDNA means any maternal relative can act as a source of mtDNA for comparison. DNA analysis of any trace sample (e.g., a hair shaft), especially mtDNA testing, must be conducted with the goal of minimizing sample contamination in order to ensure the accuracy of the results. Regardless of the testing performed, DNA analysis is a more accurate means of associating a hair with an individual than is microscopic comparison, and has the added advantage of allowing for a statistical measurement of random match probability between evidence material and a suspected source.

## See Also

**DNA:** Basic Principles; Risk of Contamination; Mitochondrial; **Parentage Testing**

## Further Reading

Anderson S, Bankier AT, Barrell BG, *et al.* (1981) Sequence and organization of the human mitochondrial genome. *Nature* 290: 457–465.

Bisbing RE (1982) The forensic identification of human hair. In: Saferstein R (ed.) *Forensic Science Handbook*, vol. I, pp. 184–221. Englewood Cliffs, NJ: Prentice Hall Regents.

Butler J (2001) *Forensic DNA Typing, Biology and Technology Behind STR Markers.* San Diego, CA: Academic Press.

Holland MM, Parsons TJ (1999) Mitochondrial DNA sequence analysis – validation and use for forensic casework. *Forensic Science Review* 11: 22–50.

Linch CA, Whiting DA, Holland MM (2001) Human hair histogenesis for the mitochondrial DNA forensic scientist. *Journal of Forensic Sciences* 46: 844–853.

Parsons TJ, Coble MD (2001) Increasing the forensic discrimination of mitochondrial DNA testing through analysis of the entire mitochondrial DNA genome. *Croatian Medical Journal* 42: 304–309.

Wilson MR, Stoneking M, Holland MM, DiZinno JA, Budowle B (1993) Guidelines for the use of mitochondrial DNA sequencing in forensic science. *Crime Laboratory Digest* 20: 68–77.

Wilson MR, Polanskey D, Butler J, *et al.* (1995) Extraction, amplification and sequencing of mitochondrial DNA from human hair shafts. *BioTechniques* 18: 662–669.

---

**DNA, Anthropological Use**    *See* **Anthropology:** Role of DNA

---

**DNA, Paternity Testing**    *See* **Parentage Testing**

# DOGS, USE IN POLICE INVESTIGATIONS

**B Weakley-Jones**, Office of the Chief Medical Examiner, Louisville, KY, USA
**A J Rebmann**, Connecticut State Police, Kent, WA, USA

## Introduction

Dogs in police investigation represent part of a multidisciplinary investigative team that may include the medical examiner, anthropologist, law enforcement officers, volunteer search groups, and others. Each group has different strengths and weaknesses, but together provide valuable expertise to gather evidence, find an individual, or recover human remains.

## History

The first documented case of dogs being used for search and rescue was the dogs at Mount St. Bernard Hospice and other alpine passes in the 1800s. By 1899, in Europe, military ambulance dogs were used to search for injured soldiers in war, or missing persons during peace times. Later, these dogs carried small packs on their backs containing first-aid material, water, and small flasks of brandy. Based on the work done in Europe, people in the USA developed Red Cross dogs, also known as casualty dogs, for use in World War II. Today, much of the search and rescue dog training done in the USA is based on the methods used to train military dogs.

## Smell and Scenting Ability

The dog has an ability far superior to that of a human to detect odors. Factors enabling odor detection include the following.

- The dog's nostrils are wider and larger than a human's.
- A specialized vomeronasal gland behind the canine tooth is specialized for smell.
- Almost one-eighth of a dog's brain is committed to olfaction, whereas the human olfactory lobes in the brain are much smaller.
- There is a greater variation of olfactory sensory cells within the nose of the dog as compared to the human's nose. It is estimated that 220 million of these cells specialized for smell are present in the dog, while a human may have only 5 million.

There are many different theories on the exact molecular nature of odor. Scent is interpreted as all those combinations of odors or smells that characterize an individual. The human body is a source of human scent. Degeneration of human tissue takes place both internally and externally. Our individual scent is believed to be based upon our particular DNA properties. Inherited genes play a role in the functions of our physical body, our emotional processes, and the distribution of sweat glands in our system. Cultural and dietary variations also have some effect, as do the living conditions and the metabolism and excretion of certain types of foods.

The human body is made up of 60 trillion cells. Each cell has a DNA component and each cell has a particular life span. Dead cells from the skin, respiratory tract, or digestive tract are constantly shed from the body. These cells are called rafts. These rafts, exhaled or shed, fall to the ground, and can be detected by the scenting dog.

In summary, the scent of human beings is derived from cells and vapors, which are individualized as a result of heredity, diet, and physiological response to emotions, metabolism, and environment. Human odor is very complex and very individualistic.

The transmission of the scent of an individual body into the atmosphere can also be somewhat complex. It is believed that the rafts or tiny pieces of exfoliated skin are shed into the environment as we move. There is also a layer of air around the body that is warmer and less dense than the surrounding air. The body's own air current moves the rafts around, such as exhaled air or movement of the body itself. The rafts fall to the ground and continue to degenerate. Bacteria grow on dead human cells, creating an additional specific scent. The combination of rafts, bacteria growing on dead human cells, body secretions, a specific individual's proteins, and DNA creates a mathematical combination that approaches infinity as to each characteristic individual.

Specialty search dogs are trained to detect and indicate a spectrum of scent included within the target odor. For example, the cadaver (human remains) detection dog is trained to detect human decomposition in the spectrum at the time of biological death through the bloat, putrefaction, and liquefaction stages to the skeletal stage. Narcotic detector dogs are normally trained for a minimum of six distinctive odors, and arson dogs for at least 17 different possible accelerants.

## Types of Dog and Training

Depending on the needs of a particular agency or group, individual dogs can be specially trained in a variety of areas. These specialty areas include:

1. Live search
   - patrol or police service dogs – used in criminal searches and police protection
   - wilderness – human scent-specific tracking, trailing (**Figure 1**), or air scent.
2. Specialty search dogs
   - narcotics – identification of drugs
   - explosives – powder residue, explosive scent
   - arson (accelerant) – identification of accelerants associated with fire
   - land cadaver (also referred to as human remains detection dogs) – human decomposition scent on land
   - water cadaver – human decomposition scent in water
   - articles – human scent on articles
   - evidence – articles with decomposing human scent
   - avalanche – human scent (either live or deceased) under snow
   - disaster – human scent, live or dead, in natural disaster or one caused by humans
   - other – organic material, preseizure detection, cancer detection.

There are also multipurpose dogs, which are cross-trained in several of these areas. A single dog may be trained in areas of wilderness, cadaver, and articles. A trained cadaver dog may be used in land cadaver and/or water cadaver and may be trained for evidence (articles with decomposing human scent but not trained in article searches). Many police services dogs are cross-trained for apprehension work and narcotics, explosive, or cadaver detection (**Figure 2**).

Depending on the specialty area of canine training, the breed of dog can vary widely, from a German Shepherd to a Jack Russell terrier. The dog should be receptive to training with a steady disposition and proven olfactory ability. It is generally recognized that some dogs are more suited for a particular task than others, such as the bloodhound used in wilderness searches. Working dogs are a combination of body build, stamina, and drive. They should be calm, bold, confident, and not too aggressive. Generally, the ideal breed falls into the working, herding, or sporting categories; however, no one breed is better than another. Temperature and terrain also affect the choices or types of dogs used in a particular location. Most working dogs must have significant stamina, especially in wilderness, patrol, or cadaver searches.

There are many types of search performed by canine units. Each type requires special training, experience, and expertise. These may include missing or lost person's searches, criminal searches, article searches, line searches, land cadaver searches, water cadaver searches, and evidence or article searches. A lost person will help you find them, whereas a missing person may not want to be found. An Alzheimer's patient may not realize that he/she is missing or lost. Searches for dangerous criminals must be done carefully since safety for the team is a major priority. Different environments may also require different procedures and equipment for the search.

There are some limitations for the search dog team. A dog cannot search many acres in one day. Dogs must be within a certain range from the scent source, depending on the scent source. There is a limit to the length of time the dog can work and this often depends on the dog, temperature, weather, and type of search. It is important to narrow down the search area and provide as much information as possible to the search team.

**Figure 1**  Trailing bloodhound.

**Figure 2**  Water cadaver dog.

**Figure 3**  Lying down with bark alert.

## Training

The initial training process can vary from a few weeks to a year, depending on the desired task(s). The training involves both the handler and the dog since the handler must be able to read the dog and the dog must be able to indicate to the handler its trained indication (alert). This trained alert can be active (digging, barking) or passive (sitting, lying down). Many agencies prefer a passive alert to prevent disturbance of a crime scene (i.e., explosive or article dogs). Other agencies use an active alert (i.e., narcotic or cadaver dogs) (**Figure 3**). The handler may capitalize on a natural reaction that the dog demonstrated when it was working on imprinting problems or the handler can pick a specific action for the dog to perform. Once initial training is completed, the K-9 team (one handler with one dog) should be evaluated and certified.

Certification standards currently available for the K-9 teams are:

- those developed by the user agency
- standards developed by national K-9 associations (e.g., US Police Canine Association, North American Police Work Dog Association, National Association for Search and Rescue, and other groups)
- standards developed by a particular training authority (e.g., local volunteer search groups).

Certification evaluations should be conducted at regular intervals to maintain operational proficiency of the K-9 and handler. There are few states that have statewide search dog certification. A record must be kept of all training and operational evaluations. A subpoena may be issued in court cases for all training and operational records, along with certification evaluations of both the handler and search dog.

A well-trained K-9 team can be an invaluable asset in a police investigation.

## See Also

**Crime-scene Investigation and Examination:** Recovery of Human Remains

## Further Reading

Bulanda S (1994) *Ready, The Training of the Search and Rescue Dog.* Portland, OR: Doral.

Koehler WR (1984) *The Koehler Method of Training Tracking Dogs.* New York: Howell Book House.

Rebmann A, David E, Sorg MH (2000) *Cadaver Dog Handbook, Forensic Training and Tactics for the Recovery of Human Remains.* Boca Raton, FL: CRC Press.

Scheon A, Haack, Rund (2003) K-9 *Suspect Discrimination* Calgary, AB: Detselig Enterprises Ltd.

Syrotuck WG (1972) *Scent and the Scenting Dog.* Canastota, NY: Arner.

Tolhurst B (2000) *The Silent Witness Scent.* Lockport, NY: Library of Congress.

# DOMESTIC VIOLENCE

**C E Jordan**, University of Kentucky, Lexington, KY, USA

## Introduction

Violence against women is widespread in the USA and around the globe. It must be emphasized that a small proportion of males will also be victims of domestic violence from the female partner. This article focuses on the female perspective. Not only do a substantial number of women experience violence at the hands of an intimate, the negative effects on a woman's health and mental health are profound. Intimate-partner violence is associated with higher mortality rates, acute injury, and chronic illness in women. It is also related to somatic complaints, poor pregnancy outcomes, chronic pain, worse overall general health, and higher medical service utilization. Most of the major nonorganic forms of mental disorders have also been associated with at least one form of interpersonal victimization in women. Women who experience intimate-partner violence most often encounter multiple forms of abuse in a chronic, recurring pattern. Thousands of women each year ultimately lose their lives to violence from an intimate; in fact, intimate partners are the most common perpetrators of all forms of violence against a woman. While the most common circumstance of family murder is a husband killing his spouse, there are cases in which women abused by a partner strike back and kill the battering partner. The complexity of these cases and the tendency of the court system to decontextualize an abused woman's actions from the violent environment in which she lives has led to the development of syndromes that have been applied to aid the court in understanding the behavior of battered women who kill. The key to a court's understanding, however, lies in application of the traditional standard of self-defense with testimony to the special circumstances that confront battered women and contribute to their reasonable perception of imminent danger.

This article explores the prevalence and types of violence experienced specifically by women in intimate relationships and the health and mental health effects often seen in abused women. Cases in which battered women kill are also briefly considered.

## Defining the Phenomenon: Prevalence and Categories of Domestic Violence

### Prevalence of Intimate-Partner Violence Against Women

During the 1970s in the USA, the first National Family Violence Survey was conducted to measure the extent of violence occurring in the family setting. That nationally representative survey, in addition to one conducted a decade later, found that 25% of American couples had experienced at least one incident of violence in the course of their relationship. In 1995, the National Violence Against Women (NVAW) survey, using a telephone survey of 8000 females and 8000 males, found a lifetime rate of approximately 52% of women reporting being physically assaulted; almost 18% reporting being victims of rape or attempted rape; and 8% reporting being stalked at some point during their lifetime. Taken together, the last three decades of national incidence and prevalence research suggest that, in any given year, as many as 4 million women in the USA will experience severe or life-threatening physical assault perpetrated by a male partner.

While the USA tends to have higher overall violent crime rates than other countries, prevalence data on violence against women emphasize the multicultural nature of domestic violence: lifetime rates of violence against women have been documented at 60% of Chilean women; 25% of women in Canada; and 25% of Norwegian women aged 20–49. In Switzerland, lifetime rates of partner violence have been reported at 12.6%, and in Ireland, 10.3%. The British Crime Survey reports 22.7% of women in England and Wales have the lifetime experience of physical violence by a male intimate. A total of 37.5% of Korean women report battering by a spouse in the past year.

While prevalence rates offer some indication of the breadth of violence experienced by women across the world, cross-cultural comparisons are hampered by inconsistent measures and definitions of domestic or intimate-partner violence, language barriers, the sociocultural context within which women live, and a myriad of other confounding factors. A more international understanding of the problem is also limited by the lack of prevalence data in many nations, as gendered violence is not safely discussed and a fuller grasp of the problem is restricted to the qualitative voices of women whose private stories have yet to inform the global public debate fully.

### Types of Intimate-Partner Violence

A woman's experience of intimate-partner violence most often occurs as a chronic, repeated exposure to multiple forms of abuse. Different forms of abuse are interspersed with one another in a recurrent pattern, manifesting an overall abusive quality to the relationship. The most common forms of violence experienced by women include physical assault, sexual assault, psychological maltreatment, and stalking. Studies show that every year in the USA, approximately 8% of women experience physical abuse by a partner, and that more than three out of every 100, or 1.8 million women, are severely assaulted in any given year. The lifetime prevalence of sexual violence within intimate relationships is 9–14% in the general population of US women, and 40–46% in the population of battered women. Among women who seek protective shelter from intimate-partner violence, prevalence rates of marital rape incidence are typically higher than other populations of women, reaching almost two-thirds of sheltered women. Sexual violence can include rape involving vaginal, anal, or oral penetration with objects or fingers; forced oral sex; forced sex with others; overt and covert threats to have sex; and the use of other forms of physical violence during sex.

The majority of women who experience physical or sexual assault by a partner are also psychologically maltreated, and in fact physical aggression rarely occurs in the absence of psychological abuse. Psychological maltreatment, often used as a method of instilling fear, can include overt threats of harm or abuse to the woman, her children, or her family. Threats might also include threatening to leave or abandon the family if she does not comply with the wishes of the offender. Control of a victim may also result from actions or words that erode her self-esteem and produce the perception that she has no alternatives to the relationship. Finally, psychological abuse can take the form of physically controlling a woman's environment such that she is isolated from others and unable to access money, resources, or independence. This becomes acutely problematic for women in rural areas across the globe where access to resources and safety is scarce. Because these forms of psychological abuse target a woman's thoughts, feelings, and perceptions, they can profoundly impact how she views herself, her relationship with her partner, and her relationship with the world. This is particularly true when the abusive partner juxtaposes physical violence and psychological abuse with loving behaviors in a way that increases the victim's uncertainty about herself and the accuracy of her perceptions. Battered women often describe psychological maltreatment as the most debilitating form of abuse they experience, leading some to suggest that many of the negative effects typically attributed to physical violence may actually result from the coexisting psychological abuse.

The decade of the 1990s saw stalking created as a crime for the first time in the laws of a number of nations. In 1990, the first antistalking law was passed in the USA, and in less than a decade, every state in the country had some form of law addressing the crime. Stalking was first treated as a criminal offense by the state of California after the murder of a young actress who was shot to death by a man who had repeatedly stalked her before her death. Her murder, and within a month and a half, the murder of four battered women, demonstrated the inadequacy of the law in addressing patterns of stalking and the danger that stalkers can pose to victims. Canada introduced a criminal harassment statute aimed at stalking behavior in 1993; and by 1995 each state and territory in Australia had an antistalking law. In 1997, a Protection from Harassment Act encompassing stalking-type conduct was passed and applied to England, Wales, Scotland, and Northern Ireland. The passage of legal reforms has been followed by limited prevalence studies. Studies of stalking-related phenomena indicate a prevalence rate of up to 24% of US women. The first epidemiological study of stalking in Australia found 15% of women reporting being stalked by a man at some point in their lifetime.

## Violence Inflicted by Male Intimates

Most of the time, when a woman is harmed by violence, it is perpetrated not by a stranger, but by someone she knows. Women are more likely to be physically or sexually assaulted or killed by an intimate male partner than by any other type of offender. A recent National Crime Victimization Survey in the USA reported that nearly 30% of female homicide victims were killed by their husbands, former husbands, or boyfriends; whereas just over 3% of male homicide victims were known to have been killed by their wives, former wives, or girlfriends. In 2001, nearly nine times as many women were murdered by an intimate than were murdered by a male stranger, and the NVAW survey found that the majority of women over the age of 18 who reported an experience with victimization said they were raped (62%), physically assaulted (72%), or stalked (60%) by an intimate partner. By comparison, about 16% of the women surveyed reported that their victimization had been committed by an acquaintance, 15% reported victimization by a stranger, and 6% reported victimization by a relative other than a marital partner. In the UK, almost half of all homicides of women are carried out by a partner or ex-partner of the victim. While most studies find intimate partners as the most common offenders, there are exceptions, as is the case of stalking perpetrated against women in Australia, which has been documented to be perpetrated more often by strangers than intimates.

When intimate partners are violent toward women, the egregious nature of assaults tends to increase. Women are more likely to be injured in physical assaults committed by intimates than assaults committed by strangers, and the closer the relationship between the victim and the offender, the more violent a rape becomes. Similarly, the most likely stalkers to be violent are individuals who have had a previous sexually intimate relationship with the victim. When women are harmed by an intimate, they are also more likely to sustain multiple assaults than when an attack is perpetrated by a stranger. The higher severity and chronicity of violence in intimate contexts may occur because close partners have daily access to their victims, substantial time in which to commit abusive acts, and a veil of privacy behind which their assaults can be hidden.

## Intimate-Partner Violence: Legal Definitions Versus the Victim Experience

The intersection between victims and the legal system is not always smooth. First, some victimization experiences, while significant to the woman, are not considered criminal, a truism for most forms of psychological maltreatment. Remedies for this form of abuse are limited to therapeutic interventions; rarely can they be civilly or criminally prosecuted.

In the criminal arena, interpersonal violence can also be problematic in that, in a different context, the behaviors that make up these offenses are not crimes. For example, sexual intercourse, intimate touching, frequent phone calls, or surprise visits to workplaces or residences are positive experiences when they are consensual or experienced as romantic gestures. When these experiences are forced on a woman and create fear in her, they are no longer positive. In jurisdictions where lack of victim consent and the presence of fear are components of rape and stalking offenses, these same behaviors may now meet the legal definition for criminal behavior. The distinguishing feature between the experiences described here is the emotional experience of the victim (i.e., whether she was afraid), and whether she consented to the behavior, not necessarily the behavior of the offender. The effect of this structure of the law is that, during the prosecution of rape and stalking offenses, the focus of the court is not just on the objective element of the offender's conduct, but also on the subjective element of whether a victim consented to the behavior and whether the experience elicited fear in her. This stands in contrast to other crimes, such as robbery, where the law merely requires that the offender commit a particular act without simultaneously requiring that the victim react in a prescribed way. Victims of interpersonal violence, as a result, experience heightened levels of scrutiny directed at their behavior, motives, and psychological reactions. The requirement in the course of a criminal prosecution that a victim acknowledge a certain level of fear in response to her experience of crime can also be problematic, as not all victims will have such a reaction. Particularly for victims experiencing severe post-trauma reactions or those suffering from long-term abuse, articulating the emotion of fear may not be possible.

## Physical Health Implications of Intimate-Partner Violence

### Acute Injury and Injury Patterns

Victimization at the hands of an intimate poses significant risk of harm to the physical health of a woman. Violence is associated with higher mortality rates, acute injury, and chronic illness. It is also related to somatic complaints, poor pregnancy outcomes, chronic pain, worse overall general health, and higher medical service utilization by a woman. The NVAW survey reported that 41.5% of female victims of physical violence by an intimate and over 36% of women sexually assaulted by an intimate reported injuries as a result of their most recent victimization; and in a single year, 500 000 sought medical treatment for their injuries. Studies in hospital emergency rooms have documented that more than one-third of women seeking emergency medical care for violence-related injuries have been injured by a current or former spouse.

Numerous studies have analyzed the injuries sustained by women as a result of intimate-partner victimization, with most finding that minor injuries are the most common (scratches, bruises, welts, lacerations); knife wounds, broken bones, head injuries, sore muscles, internal injuries, broken teeth, burns, and bullet wounds are also experienced by women. In a study of over 4500 women presenting with injuries to emergency departments, intimate-partner violence victims were more likely to be injured in the face, head, and neck than women injured by other means. In addition to facial injuries, traumatic brain injury is not uncommon in battered women. In a study of 53 victims, 92% reported having been hit in the head or face during a violent episode, and 40% reported at least one instance of having lost consciousness after being hit or shaken by a partner. In a study of intimate-partner violence victims seeking treatment in an emergency department, 30% had experienced a loss of consciousness and 67% reported symptoms consistent with traumatic head injury. While additional research on battering and closed-head injury in victims is needed, current data suggest a risk of this type of injury for intimate-partner violence victims, as well as postconcussional symptoms such as headache, fatigue, dizziness, insomnia, difficulty concentrating, and memory problems. Sexual assault by an intimate can cause superficial bruising and tearing to serious internal injuries and scarring.

While these types of injuries are common among battered women, studies that have attempted to isolate an identifiable pattern of injury in victims of intimate-partner violence have not been successful, leading some to recommend universal screening for intimate-partner violence in healthcare settings.

### Chronic Illness and Health Effects

In addition to the short-term consequences of acute injury, violence in intimate relationships is associated with long-term physical health problems for women, including headaches, back pain, fainting, seizures, or related central nervous system complaints. Chronic pain, miscarriage, irritable bowel syndrome, and psychosomatic and somatic complaints have also been associated with victimization.

Sexual assault appears to cause a number of specific health consequences. Victims of intimate-partner violence are more likely than other women to have gynecological symptoms, including sexually transmitted diseases, vaginal bleeding or infection, fibroids, pelvic pain, and urinary tract infections. Notably, poor pregnancy outcomes have been associated with intimate-partner violence, including low birth weight and miscarriage and spontaneous abortion. Additionally, women who suffer abuse during pregnancy are at increased risk of homicide; in fact, homicide is the leading cause of mortality in women in the time-period immediately before and after delivery of the infant.

The psychological maltreatment that is often a component of intimate-partner violence can also be the source of harm to a woman's health; increasingly, research suggests that this specific form of abuse is strongly related to the range of negative health outcomes. Through the more indirect pathway of psychological abuse and chronic stress, symptoms and illnesses evidenced in women include stomach ulcers, spastic colon, hypertension, functional gastrointestinal disorders and appetite loss, viral infections, and cardiac problems. Finally, in addition to specific physical sequelae associated with physical and sexual assault, women experiencing harm from an intimate also report worse general physical health than do other women. Victims see primary care physicians, specialists, and emergency room physicians more frequently than do nonvictims.

## Mental Health Implications of Intimate-Partner Violence

### Types of Mental Health Effects

The mental health effects of violence against women are widely documented. Most of the major nonorganic forms of mental disorder have been associated with at least one form of interpersonal victimization in women. Assaults by an intimate have been strongly associated with depression in the victim, with studies of women in domestic violence shelters finding rates of depression ranging from 28 to 47%. Women seeking treatment in outpatient and inpatient programs often show elevated rates of depression. Intimate-partner violence is also a significant risk factor for suicidal behavior among women; it has been associated with increased anxiety, feelings of hopelessness and low self-esteem, dissociation, somatization, and substance abuse. Women victimized by rape, stalking, or physical violence also frequently present symptoms of posttraumatic stress disorder. Finally, studies consistently find that a majority of women diagnosed with a serious mental illness report experiencing physical and sexual assault at some point during their lifetime.

### Factors Associated with Mental Health Sequelae

Understanding who will respond to violence with depression, anxiety, or posttrauma reactions is not a random exercise. Generally, four key factors are associated with more severe psychological reactions to trauma: (1) the nature of the victimization experience (e.g., frequency, severity, chronicity, recency, life threat, injury, and substantial use of force); (2) the victim's reaction to the event (e.g., extreme fearfulness, horror, panic, high levels of helplessness, guilt or shame, and dissociation); (3) historical characteristics of the victim (e.g., comorbid mental disorder, previous trauma, family dysfunction or mental disorder); and (4) the absence of social support following the event. Unfortunately, most research limits itself to linking these factors to the severity of a given symptom rather than explaining why one woman might develop posttraumatic stress disorder in response to victimization while another might become depressed or begin to abuse drugs or alcohol.

## The Other Side of Homicide: When Battered Women Kill

### Characteristics of Intimate-Partner Homicide and Cases Involving Female Offenders

The most common form of family murder is a husband killing his spouse, and the most typical murder–suicide involves a male killing his partner and then himself. In 2001, the homicide rate among female victims murdered by males in the USA was 1.35 per 100 000, and African-American women in the USA suffer a homicide rate fully three times that of white women. In Canada, homicide rates of women by intimate partners are comparable, averaging 1.3 women per 100 000 per year. In the USA, the number of white women killed by an intimate increased 15% between 1997 and 1998, making this population the only category for whom intimate-partner homicide has not shown a substantial decline since 1976. In the USA, female intimate partners are more likely to be murdered with a firearm than all other means combined.

While the majority of domestic homicides are committed by male partners, there are cases in which women abused by a partner strike back and kill the offender. Research suggests that the motivations for murders of intimate partners committed by males are qualitatively different from cases where women kill. Women are less likely to kill out of anger and more likely to kill as a response to fear, with studies suggesting that up to two-thirds of men killed by a partner were assaulting or threatening to injure the partner at the time of the homicide. Additionally, studies consistently show that the experience of battering is the most frequent precursor to a woman's commission of homicide. Similarly, homicides committed by women are more likely than homicides by men to have been victim-precipitated, that is, women are far more likely to kill a partner during an incident in which the person killed was the first to commit a violent act.

A number of studies have compared battered women who kill the intimate-partner offender to battered women who do not commit a violent act. Collectively, these studies show that battered women who kill differ from those who do not based on the severity of the violence they experienced at the hands of the man they ultimately killed. Additionally, the relationships of battered women who kill tend to be of longer duration and to be characterized by more frequent and more recent abuse, higher rates of sexual assault, more severe injuries sustained by the woman, and more death threats. In comparison to other women, those who kill an intimate also perceive themselves as having fewer social supports, have higher levels of alcohol and drug abuse, and are more likely to believe that their lives are in danger. A review of the factors that differentiate cases of abused women who kill compared to those who do not find the most significant differences, not among the women themselves, but in the severity of actions by the domestic violence offender.

## When Battered Women Kill: Contextualizing the Court's Understanding

The majority of battered women who kill their offenders do not have a history of committing other criminal offenses; in fact, some have suggested that battered women who kill have the least extensive criminal histories of all types of female offenders. Additionally, when battered women kill the offending partner, there is often ample evidence of a long history of severe abuse against the woman. Women who kill are often reacting to some trigger in the current environment that, based on the totality of their past experience, leads them to believe that harm to them or their children is imminent. As a result, they may take action to protect themselves when the domestic violence offender is, to a naive observer, not posing a threat (e.g., while the man is sleeping or debilitated by alcohol). For the woman, the perceived threat is present, and she takes action at a time when she feels she can best survive the size disparity or retaliation she would otherwise encounter. The justice system, on the other hand, tends to decontextualize the homicide by separating the woman's actions from her abuse experience. As a result, the behavior does not appear

to be a response to imminent threat or provocation and therefore does not meet the traditional legal definition of self-defense. Without an understanding of the dynamics of the abuse experience, a woman's perceptions of imminent threat borne out of years of previous experience with the offender are subordinated to the law's strict definition of self-defense and provocation.

Helping the courts understand the context within which a battered woman kills her abusive husband has been aided by a construct that describes the psychological effects of intimate-partner violence. The battered-woman syndrome (BWS) was conceived by psychologist Lenore Walker after interviews with over 400 battered women, and was intended, in part, to redirect the focus away from a woman's personality features to the external context of violence associated with subsequent psychological responses. This contextualization of a woman's emotional, cognitive, and behavior reactions promoted an understanding that victimization experiences were the cause, not the result, of subsequent mental health problems for a battered woman. Empirical studies have generally supported the sequelae described in the BWS, particularly with respect to posttrauma-related symptoms.

Walker's ground-breaking work with BWS pushed the courts to view abuse experienced by a woman as an appropriate evidentiary matter and helped expand the application of self-defense to incorporate a woman's perceptions of imminent threat. Although expert testimony about BWS was intended simply to contextualize a woman's actions in light of her abuse experience and thereby to allow use of a self-defense or justifiable homicide defense, the application of the syndrome has had unintended consequences. Some authors have argued that the positive courtroom effects achieved on behalf of battered women carried a high price, which is the use of a psychological construct built on the presumption that a woman who strikes back at a battering partner is operating under diminished capacity. Several authors have pointed out that BWS was not intended as a diminished-capacity defense, but it may, in application, have this effect.

Rather than relying on a syndrome that can imply diminished capacity or an inability to employ reason, the key to a court's understanding of battered women who kill lies in realizing the inadequacy of a decontextualized account of a woman's behavior. Understanding battered women who kill may also rely on the application of the traditional standard of self-defense with testimony to the special circumstances that confront battered women and contribute to their reasonable perception of imminent danger.

## Conclusion

Violence against women is a widespread phenomenon with profound implications for the physical and mental health of women. Women experiencing violence at the hands of an intimate see primary care physicians, specialists, and emergency room physicians more frequently than do nonvictims. While most often criminal justice interventions in cases of intimate-partner violence relate to remedies for women in response to a male offender's criminal conduct, in rarer circumstances, female victims of violence strike back and kill the offender. Battered women who kill are not so different from those who do not; the distinguishing features of these cases derive primarily from the behavior of domestic violence offenders and the severity and chronicity of their abuse. Fair treatment of battered women by the courts depends on expanding the construct of self-defense to contextualize abused women's actions within the abusive environments in which they live.

## See Also

**Forensic Psychiatry and Forensic Psychology:** Stalking; **Murder–Suicide**

## Further Reading

Bachman R, Saltzman L (1995) *Violence Against Women: Estimates from the Redesigned Survey*. NCJ-154348. Washington, DC: Bureau of Justice Statistics, US Department of Justice.

Briere J, Jordan CE (2004) Violence against women: Outcome complexity and implications for treatment. *Journal of Interpersonal Violence* 19(12): 1252–1282.

Browne A (1987) *When Battered Women Kill*. New York: Free Press.

Campbell JC (1995) Prediction of homicide of and by battered women. In: Campbell JC (ed.) *Assessing Dangerousness: Violence by Sexual Offenders, Batterers, and Child Abusers*, pp. 96–113. Thousand Oaks, CA: Sage.

Campbell J, Jones AS, Dienemann J, *et al.* (2002) Intimate-partner violence and physical health consequences. *Archives of Internal Medicine* 162: 1157–1163.

Coker AL, Smith PH, Bethea L, King MR, McKeown RE (2000) Physical health consequences of physical and psychological intimate-partner violence. *Archives of Family Medicine* 9: 451–457.

Downs DA (1996) *More than Victims: Battered Women, the Syndrome Society, and the Law*. Chicago, IL: University of Chicago Press.

Dutton MA (1992) *Empowering and Healing the Battered Woman: A Model for Assessment and Intervention*. New York: Springer.

Follingstad DR, Brennan AF, Hause ES, Polek DS, Rutledge LL (1991) Factors moderating physical and psychological symptoms of battered women. *Journal of Family Violence* 6: 81–95.

Jordan CE, Nietzel MT, Walker R, Logan TK (2004) *Intimate Partner Violence: Clinical and Practice Issues for Mental Health Professionals*. New York: Springer.

Kelly L, Römkens R, Stanko B (eds.) (2001) Special issue: European perspectives on violence against women. *Violence Against Women: An International and Interdisciplinary Journal* 7: 727–850.

Plichta SB (1996) Violence and abuse: implications for women's health. In: Falik MM, Collins KS (eds.) *Women's Health: The Commonwealth Survey*, pp. 237–272. Baltimore, MD: Johns Hopkins University Press.

Raitt FE, Zeekyk MS (2000) *The Implicit Relation of Psychology and Law: Women and Syndrome Evidence*. Philadelphia, PA: Taylor & Francis.

Straus MA, Gelles R (1990) *Physical Violence in American Families: Risk Factors and Adaptation to Violence in 8145 Families*. New Brunswick, NJ: Transaction.

Tjaden P, Thoennes N (2000) Prevalence and consequences of male-to-female and female-to-male intimate-partner violence as measured by the National Violence Against Women Survey. *Violence Against Women* 6: 142–161.

Walker LE (1984) *The Battered Woman Syndrome*. New York: Springer.

---

**Drowning** *See* **Autopsy, Findings:** Drowning

---

**Drug-Facilitated Sexual Assault** *See* **Sexual Offenses, Adult:** Drug-Facilitated Sexual Assault

# DRUG-INDUCED INJURY, ACCIDENTAL AND IATROGENIC

**A Aggrawal**, Maulana Azad Medical College, New Delhi, India

## Introduction

Drugs have been causing unintended injuries since time immemorial, but it is only in recent times that this phenomenon has attracted greater attention. An unprecedented proliferation of new and novel drugs and a greater legal awareness among the public have been two most important factors responsible for this change. Drug-induced injuries have been dubbed the cost of modern medical therapy. A few definitions may be discussed at the outset, if only for the purposes of recapitulation.

## Drug

A drug may be defined as a single chemical substance or product that is used to prevent, diagnose, or treat disease or to alter the physiological state of the body. This definition includes substances, such as aspirin, which are ordinarily perceived as drugs, substances such as vaccines (used to prevent disease), radiocontrast agents (used to diagnose disease), and oral contraceptives (used to alter the physiological state of the body). Chemical substances such as heroin, cocaine, phencyclidine (PCP) and lysergic acid diethylamide (LSD) do alter the physiological state of the body, and in that sense, they can be construed as drugs. But for the purposes of this article, it would be more useful to conceive of them as "drugs of abuse," rather than simply drugs. Their injurious effects will be dealt with in more detail elsewhere.

## Medicine

A medicine is a mixture of one or more drugs with other ingredients which allow it to be delivered to the patient in a useful, stable, and palatable form. In addition to one or more drugs, a medicine includes stabilizers, sweeteners, and coloring matters. These excipients or pharmaceutical adjuvants can cause injuries in their own right.

## Injury

Injury – in a legal sense, in most jurisdictions – is defined as any harm whatever done to a person in body, mind, reputation, and property. However, in a medical sense, injury can be defined as any harm done to a person in body and mind. Injury in a medical sense is of more immediate concern for the purposes of this article.

## Drug-Induced Injury

A drug-induced injury can be defined as an injury caused by a drug to a person. In rare cases, this injury can extend to, or even be limited to, some other person. Thus the sedative–hypnotic thalidomide caused no injury to pregnant mothers, but it caused phocomelia in their babies. Drug-induced injury can be intentional, as in parasuicide, but in this article, will only discuss accidental and iatrogenic drug-induced injuries.

## Adverse Drug Reaction (ADR)

An ADR has been defined by the World Health Organization as an effect that is noxious and unintended, and that occurs at doses used in humans for prophylaxis, diagnosis, or therapy.

## Medication Error

A medication error can be defined as an error in ordering, transcribing, dispensing, or administering a drug or medicine. A medication error may or may not cause injury.

## Adverse Drug Event (ADE)

An ADE has been defined as an injury resulting from medical intervention related to a drug. This includes injuries related to a medication error and ADRs. The term "drug-induced injuries" roughly corresponds to "adverse drug events."

## Historical Overview

Drug-induced injuries have had medicolegal implications since the very dawn of recorded human history. As early as 2200 BC, the Code of Hammurabi stated that doctors should lose their hands if they caused the death of their patients. In the ninth century BC, Homer appears to have been aware of injuries caused by drugs. In *Odyssey* he mentions the fatal nature of drugs. Hippocrates, Galen, Rhazes, and Paracelsus were all aware of injurious effects of drugs. One of the earliest examples of a drug being officially banned due to severe adverse reactions was antimony, which was banned in 1566 by the Faculty of Medicine in Paris. William Withering (1741–1799), the discoverer of digitalis, wrote about the injurious effects of digitalis as well. Recognizing the injurious effects of drugs, a preliminary kind of regulation on sales of drugs was passed in France in 1781.

The twentieth century witnessed some of the classical cases of drug-induced injuries, not the least important of which was the sulfanilamide–Massengill disaster of 1937, the Stalinon disaster of 1954, and the well-known thalidomide disaster of 1961. These three drug-induced disasters, occurring within a span of 25 years, took more than 200 lives and made more than 5000 people invalid. Sulfanilamide was a popular sulfa drug marketed in tablet and capsule form since the mid-1930s by the Massengill Company of the USA. During September–October 1937, the company decided to sell the drug in the form of an elixir too. Though an elixir could only be prepared in ethyl alcohol, the company decided to sell sulfanilamide in a solution of diethylene glycol without doing any preliminary testing in animals. Indeed, such testing was not legally required at that time. More than 100 people perished as a result of diethylene glycol poisoning. This disaster led to the passing of the Food, Drug and Cosmetic Act in the USA in 1938, and the Drugs and Cosmetics Act in India in 1940. Through these Acts, controls were exercised on the manufacture, sale, and distribution of drugs.

In 1954, the Stalinon disaster occurred in France. A French pharmacist invented Stalinon for boils. The medication contained 15 mg diiodoethyltin and 100 mg isolinoleic acid esters. Tin is toxic to the human central nervous system. Several people showed signs of raised intracranial pressure, such as headache, confusion, and vomiting. About 102 people died and about 100 more were permanently affected. Some survivors had residual paraplegia. It was discovered that clinical trials had been done, but with capsules containing just 3 mg diiodoethyltin – instead of the supposed 50 mg – due to a dispensing error. The patients thus received five times the drug that had been tested in clinical trials. In 1957, the pharmacist was sentenced to two years imprisonment and heavily fined.

The biggest of all drug-induced disasters was undoubtedly the thalidomide disaster, occurring in the late 1950s and early 1960s. During this period, this drug was marketed in more than 40 countries – mainly in West Germany, the UK, and Japan. In Germany, it was manufactured by Chemie Grünenthal and marketed by it as Contergan from 1956, and enjoyed good sales. In the UK it was licenced by Chemie Grünenthal to the Distillers Company. It was available in the UK from the beginning of 1958 as Distaval. In Sweden, the license was given to a local company, Astra. The drug could not enter the USA,

thanks to the Food, Drug and Cosmetic Act, 1938, which had been passed because of the earlier sulfanilamide–Massengill disaster. It was being used by pregnant women to counteract nausea, which is usually seen in early pregnancy. It also acted as a sedative, and was touted as the safest sedative–hypnotic in the field. Yet it proved to be a strong teratogen, causing limb deformities in newborns known as amelia (absence of limbs) and phocomelia (seal limbs). Women who took it between the fourth and eighth week of pregnancy suffered most, as limb buds start to form during this period. An estimated 5000–10 000 deformed children were born around the world due to this drug. It was finally taken off the shelf in 1961. Nevertheless it was responsible for the amendment of the Drugs and Cosmetics Act, 1940 of India (in 1964), and the passing of the Medicines Act in the UK (in 1968). It is an unfortunate fact that it has taken some of the worst drug-induced disasters of history for the governments around the world to pass acts related to safe use of drugs.

Table 1 gives some recent examples of drugs being withdrawn because of drug-induced injury, or that resulted in heavy compensation claims.

## Therapeutic Index

The dose of a drug required to produce a specified beneficial effect in 50% of the population is called the "median effective dose," and this is abbreviated as $ED_{50}$. The median lethal dose of a drug – as determined in experimental animals – is the dose that would kill 50% of the population. It is abbreviated as $LD_{50}$. Clearly the relationship between $LD_{50}$ and $ED_{50}$ would determine the safety of any given drug. The higher the ratio, the safer the drug. Mathematically speaking: Therapeutic index of a drug $= LD_{50}/ED_{50}$.

Figures 1 and 2 clarify the concept. Figure 1 shows the dose–response curve of a very safe drug. On the $x$-axis is represented the logarithm of the drug dose and on the $y$-axis, the percentage of people showing a given effect – beneficial or lethal. Fifty percent of the population shows a beneficial effect with 100 mg of the drug. $LD_1$ of the drug – the dose at which just 1% of the population will show fatal results – is around 450 mg, which is far greater than 250 mg, at which 99% of the population shows the beneficial effect ($ED_{99}$). This is a very safe drug, having a very high therapeutic index (8.0). There is practically no chance of fatality occurring with this drug.

Figure 2 shows the dose–response curve of an unsafe drug. The two curves – those for the beneficial effect and lethal effect – are very closely spaced. Its $ED_{50}$ is 200 mg, while $LD_{50}$ is 400 mg. The therapeutic index is just 2.0.

**Table 1** Recent cases of drugs being withdrawn because of drug-induced injury, and/or resulting in heavy compensation claims

| Drug | Chemical name | Company | Indicated for | Mode of action | Why withdrawn | Date withdrawn |
|---|---|---|---|---|---|---|
| Alosetron hydrochloride | lotronex | Glaxo Wellcome | Diarrhea-predominant irritable bowel syndrome (IBS) in women only. Not found effective in male patients | Controversial. Could be its highly selective antagonism of $5HT_3$-receptors | Ischemic colitis, severe constipation leading to intestinal obstruction and ruptured bowels. Some of the patients who survived required surgical removal of sections of their intestines | November 28, 2000 (approved on February 9, 2000) |
| Baycol | cerivastatin | Bayer Pharmaceutical Division | Lowering cholesterol | Belongs to a class of drugs known as statins. These drugs are competitive inhibitors of 3-hydroxy-3-methylglutaryl coenzyme A (HMG-CoA) reductase, which catalyzes an early rate-limiting step in cholesterol biosynthesis | Reported to cause myopathy or rhabdomyolysis which can lead to kidney damage and death from acute renal (kidney) failure | August 8, 2001 |
| Celebrex | celecoxib | Pharmacia | Rheumatoid arthritis, osteoarthritis, reducing the number of intestinal polyps in patients with a rare genetic disorder called familial adenomatous polyposis (FAP) | Selective inhibitor of cyclooxygenase-2 (COX-2), thereby inhibiting the synthesis of prostaglandins and thromboxane. Drugs that inhibit both COX-1 and COX-2 (such as aspirin) cause more side-effects such as gastric ulcer (due to inhibition of COX-1) | Increased the risk of heart attack and stroke | A "warning letter" was sent on February 1, 2001, by US FDA to Pharmacia |
| Fen/Phen | fenfluramine + phentermine | American Home Products | Weight reduction | Same as that of redux | Same as that of redux | Not yet recalled |
| Pondimin | fenfluramine | American Home Products | Weight reduction | Same as that of redux | Same as that of redux | September 1997 |
| PPA | phenylpropanolamine | Several | An active ingredient of medications for nasal decongestion and weight reduction | Sympathomimetic amine | Increases the risk of hemorrhagic stroke in women. Men may also be at risk | 2000 |
| Raxar | grepafloxacin | Glaxo Wellcome | An antibiotic used to treat bacterial infections such as bronchitis, community-acquired pneumonia, gonorrhea, urethritis, and cervicitis | Similar to those of quinolones | Prolongation of the QT interval resulting in ventricular arrhythmias in some patients | October 1999 |

| Drug | Generic name | Company | Indication | Mechanism | Reason | Action |
|---|---|---|---|---|---|---|
| Redux | dexfenfluramine (dextro-isomer of fenfluramine) | American Home Products | Weight reduction | Controversial. Sympathomimetic amine. Promotes rapid release of serotonin and inhibits its reuptake, thus causing profound changes in its levels in the brain | Heart valve damage, primary pulmonary hypertension | September 1997 |
| Rezulin | troglitazone (belongs to a class of drugs known as thiazolidinediones) | Warner-Lambert | Diabetes | Selective agonist for nuclear peroxisome proliferator-activated receptor-gamma (PPAR) | Severe hepatic toxicity | March 2000 (had been marketed since March 1997) |
| Serzone | nefazodone HCl | Bristol-Myers Squibb | Antidepressant | Atypical antidepressant | Severe hepatic toxicity. Concomitant use of Serzone and Zocor can cause rhabdomyolysis | January 2003 (from the European market) because of its link to 25 reports of liver failure and 18 deaths. November 2003, from Canada. A "black-box" warning on the labels is necessary in other places. (Had been approved by the FDA in 1994) |
| Vioxx | rofecoxib | Merck | Osteoarthritis, menstrual pain, management of acute pain in adults | Same as that of Celebrex | Same reasons as those for Celebrex | A "warning letter" was sent on September 17, 2001, by US FDA to Merck |
| Xenadrine | ephedra | Cytodyne Technologies | Weight reduction | Controversial | Associated with a number of side-effects: high blood pressure, irregular heartbeat and heart palpitations, insomnia, nervousness, dizziness gastrointestinal distress, hepatitis, psychosis, tremors, headaches, seizures, heart attack, stroke, death | Not yet withdrawn, but a number of compensation claims have been made against the manufacturing company |

FDA, Food and Drug Administration.

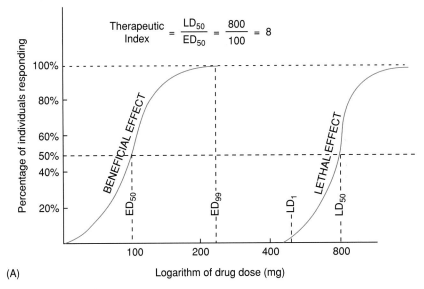

**Figure 1**   Dose–response curve of a safe drug.

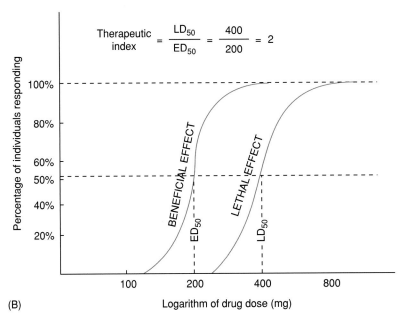

**Figure 2**   Dose–response curve of an unsafe drug.

## Adverse Drug Reactions

ADRs have been grouped into two main categories – type A or augmented reactions and type B or bizarre reactions. Type A ADRs are simply the exaggerated manifestations of the drug's very own pharmacological actions. Typical examples include hypoglycemia occurring with insulin, bradycardia with beta-adrenoceptor antagonists, suppression of bone marrow with anticancer drugs, hemorrhage with anticoagulants, loss of coordination with anticonvulsants, drowsiness with benzodiazepine anxiolytics, and unstable heart rhythms with digoxin. Type A reactions are largely predictable on the basis of the drug's known pharmacology. Their incidence and morbidity in the community are quite high, but their mortality is generally low. Generally, type A reactions are more likely and more serious for drugs that have a low therapeutic index.

Type B ADRs are totally aberrant effects that cannot be predicted; nor do they bear any semblance to the drug's normal pharmacological actions.

Malignant hyperthermia of anesthesia and allergic reactions to penicillin, iodine-containing radiopaque dyes used in radiology, and various vaccines and sera fall into this category. Their incidence and morbidity in the community are usually low, but their mortality may be quite high. Since their incidence in the community is low, they are not usually observed during conventional toxicological screening programs.

Some commentators have added three more categories. These are: (1) type C or chronic treatment reactions; (2) type D or delayed reactions; and (3) type E or end-of-treatment adverse effects. Type C reactions only become apparent after very long treatment. Typical examples are iatrogenic Cushing's syndrome, produced after months of treatment with corticosteroid drugs, and orofacial dyskinesia following long treatment with chlorpromazine.

Type D, or delayed-type ADRs, are seen many months or years after the treatment has ceased. They can even be seen in future generations – those that did not ingest the drug at all. The classical example here of course is teratogenicity induced by thalidomide and other teratogenic agents, and stilboestrol producing clear-cell carcinoma of the vagina in the daughters of mothers treated with it in pregnancy. Another good example is the appearance of fetal calvarial hypoplasia and kidney failure in newborns after their mothers have been exposed to angiotensin-converting enzyme (ACE) inhibitors such as lisinopril, captopril, and enalapril.

Type E or end-of-treatment adverse effects appear at or after the end of treatment, and mostly represent "rebound phenomena." Examples are rebound anxiety and insomnia after cessation of treatment with benzodiazepines, rebound hypertension after cessation of treatment with clonidine, and unstable angina appearing after abrupt withdrawal of beta-blockers.

## Medication Errors

Medication errors are frequent causes of legal actions being brought against pharmacists, nurses, and doctors. Fortunately they are completely avoidable. A quick look into how medication errors occur will help the healthcare provider avoid them.

### Failed Communication

Communication errors between the prescribing physician and the dispensing chemist can occur because of a number of reasons. Poor handwriting, drugs dictated over the telephone, drugs with similar names, a confusion with zeros and decimal points, a confusion of metric and apothecary systems, and ambiguous abbreviations can all cause failed communication,

leading to a medication error. Look-alike names such as Losec (omeprazol, a gastrointestinal drug) and Lasix (furosemide (frusemide), a diuretic) – combined with poor handwriting – can lead to a medication error, as can sound-alike names such as Taxol (paclitaxel, an anticancer agent) and Paxil (paroxetine, an antidepressant) spoken over the phone. In addition, it is quite possible for a patient to hear "two tablespoonsful," when what the physician actually said was "two teaspoonsful." For these reasons, as far as possible, the physician should avoid prescribing over the phone. The only situation where a physician can perhaps be excused for prescribing over the phone is when an emergency situation has arisen, and the physician thinks that he/she can probably save a life by prescribing over the phone.

### Confirmation Bias

Paradoxically, an experienced pharmacist is more likely to fall prey to this than a newcomer. Confirmation bias refers to a person's tendency to extrapolate what he/she has seen, without actually seeing.

Figure 3 presents an example of confirmation bias. Familiarity with the name of a book can make many readers extrapolate what they have seen, and be blind to an inherent mistake. The figure here shows a repetition of "of." A chemist who has been dispensing heparin frequently (and is thus familiar with its name), would tend to read a prescription of Hespan (hetastarch, sodium chloride) as heparin. Cases have occurred where nurses have infused heparin when they should have infused Hespan.

### Dose Miscalculations

Doses usually have to be calculated according to the weight of the patient; this is particularly true of pediatric patients. A simple mistake in division can cause a 10-fold mistake in dosages. Studies have shown that 10-fold mistakes in dosage calculations can occur as frequently as 15% of the time.

### Incorrect Drug Administration

Cases have occurred where a medicine meant for one patient has been given to another patient. This mistake can occur when two patients in the same ward had the same name or similar-sounding names and the dispensing nurse was careless. Drugs may be given through a wrong route. BAL meant for deep intramuscular injection, if given by the intravenous route

ENCYCLOPEDIA OF
OF FORENSIC AND
LEGAL MEDICINE

**Figure 3**   What is wrong here? Example of confirmation bias.

can cause serious fat embolism (it comes dissolved in arachis oil). Drugs meant for the oral route (enteral feeding supplements), or irrigations meant for the bladder, given through the intravenous route can cause disaster. Instances of topical medications being swallowed and ear medications being instilled in the eye (and vice versa) are well known.

### Poor Drug Distribution Practices

Poor drug distribution practices that have resulted in medication errors include keeping a dangerous product next to one which looks just like it (causing drug mix-ups), relying too much on computer-generated labels, and automated dispensing equipment (if wrong information was inadvertently fed into the computer, it can lead to serious errors), and untrained persons gaining access to the pharmacy. Night-duty nurses are known to enter the pharmacy after regular hours (when the regular pharmacist has left), and pick up drugs on their own.

### Nearly Identical Labeling

Two separate items are sometimes labeled with quite similar-looking labels. This can cause a dispensing error. There was a time when the packaging for the antibiotic metronidazole was quite similar to that of mivacurium, a neuromuscular blocking agent. This caused several mix-ups. The labeling has now been revised. Extemporaneously prepared labeling produced by in-house pharmacists can sometimes cause unintentional mix-ups.

### Lack of Patient Education

Studies have shown that if a patient is properly educated about a medication, e.g., what it looks like, its correct route of administration, permissible alternative routes of administration, correct dosage, when it should or should not be taken, there are fewer chances of an incorrect administration of drug. Thus health professionals should spend more time with their patients, explaining about the medication. Patients should be encouraged to ask questions.

## Medicolegal Aspects

In recent years, there has been an unprecedented growth in medical litigation, especially in relation to drug-induced injuries. In these cases, it is usual for the defendant to challenge the causation – the fact that the drug was responsible for the injury alleged. In a case as straightforward as that of thalidomide, all the nine senior members of Chemie Grünenthal (who were tried in a criminal court in Aachen) disputed the causation, and experiments had to be conducted in rabbits to demonstrate a similar teratogenic effect

(despite this, the criminal trial was abandoned after two years, and the civil case was decided out of court for 114 million Deutschmarks).

### Causation

In determining the real link between the drug and the injury (the causation) the court usually has recourse to a few standard pointers:

1. The patient must have been exposed to the drug.
2. The exposure must have occurred before the alleged injury.
3. The time period between the exposure and injury should be sufficient.
4. The extent of exposure must account for the alleged injury (i.e., a sufficient quantity of drug was given for a sufficient time).
5. Where the injury is temporary it must disappear with the cessation of drug and reappear with the start of reexposure (a strong pointer).
6. The alleged injury must be a known complication of the drug, if the drug is already in use.
7. The injury can best be explained in terms of exposure to the drug, and not by any other concomitant factor.
8. In the case of new and novel drugs, experimentation in animal models must produce a similar injury.

The physician must show that he/she had taken "reasonable care" when prescribing the drug. This means that an average physician of his/her rank, specialty, experience, expertise, and seniority would have done the same. A recent case that illustrates this legal principle aptly is *Cranley v. The Medical Board of Western Australia* [1992] Med LR 94. In this case a physician, Cranley, prescribed drugs like diazepam, dextroproproxyphene, and flunitrazepam to drug addicts for self-administration, including by injection. This was not normal "mainstream practice" as defined in the Australian National Methadone Guidelines, which envisaged the substitution of only oral methadone for intravenous heroin. However, the Supreme Court of Western Australia held Cranley not guilty (of a charge of misconduct) and found that there was a reputable minority approving of the policy adopted by Cranley. It also accepted the evidence of Dr. Pols, a leading expert in the treatment of addiction, who gave evidence that in appropriate circumstances, parenteral diazepam for self-administration could be prescribed.

The following cases do not pretend to give a comprehensive coverage of drug-related litigation, but serve as useful pointers to various facts courts take into consideration when pronouncing a health-care provider liable or not liable.

## Decisions Against the Healthcare Providers

In *Murray* v. *Thrifty Drug Store*, Cal. Super. Ct., Sacramento Co., docket no. 209949, 1972, a 70-year-old woman, a sufferer of arteriosclerotic heart disease with chronic atrial fibrillation, congestive heart failure, anginal syndrome, and uncontrolled diabetes mellitus was wrongly given gout medication by the pharmacist. She suffered a heart attack subsequently and claimed that the wrong medication was responsible for it. Although a claim for $75 000 was made, the jury awarded her $3000.

In *Snell* v. *Curtis*, Mich. Cir. Ct., Wayne Co., docket no. 119586, 1971, a physician gave methotrexate to his patient continuously for 43 months as a treatment for psoriasis. Chronic administration of methotrexate is known to cause hepatic fibrosis and cirrhosis, which can be detected in its early stages by regularly conducting liver function tests. The physician however not only failed to conduct these tests, but continued to administer the drug even after spider angiomas developed (a sign of hepatic cirrhosis). The treatment was continued for 11 months after the angiomas first appeared. Finally the patient was admitted to a hospital where a diagnosis of cirrhosis of the liver was made. The patient died after five months. The court awarded $200 000 to the patient's estate.

## Decisions in Favor of Healthcare Providers

In one case (US Dist. Ct. District of Columbia, no. 1356–58, August 1963), a four-year-old girl died of aplastic anemia after she was prescribed chloramphenicol by a doctor. Aplastic anemia is a known complication of chloramphenicol, but it occurs only in one case out of approximately 800 000. The court maintained that negligence cannot be inferred simply from the fact that treatment was unfavorable. It was the family's responsibility to prove that the doctor was unskillful or negligent, and they had failed to prove that. A rare complication of a drug is not sufficient to prove the doctor's negligence. The father of the deceased child also argued that the pharmaceutical firm manufacturing the drug had failed to warn. To this, the judge said that chloramphenicol was a prescription drug and could only be obtained on a doctor's prescription. Thus the manufacturer had no duty to warn the public directly (the learned intermediary principle).

In *Mickles* v. *State of New York*, 252 N.Y.S. 2d 629, the plaintiff, who had been suffering from *Shigella flexneri* dysentery, was prescribed tetracycline (Tetrex), following which she had a reaction with high fever. In its judgment, the court held that there was evidence that this was a routine treatment in such cases and if a qualified doctor stays within approved methods, he/she is not required to anticipate results from a patient's peculiar characteristics.

## Drugs Prescribed via Telephone

If the physician has to prescribe via telephone, he/she must maintain a proper telephone message form detailing the name, age, sex, address, and telephone number of the patient, the date and time of call, the symptoms the patient described, and the drug, dosage, and route the physician advised. This form should be properly filed in the patient's folder if he/she is a current patient. In the case of new patients, a new patient folder must be created, and the form kept there. All telephone prescriptions must be confirmed with the pharmacist as far as possible. If the patient does not contact the physician again, it would be a good idea for the doctor to make an unsolicited call to the patient and confirm the medications the patient has been taking, and if he/she has been experiencing any new symptoms. These simple measures can go far in preventing any uncalled-for litigation.

The following case (citation 25: 147, Sept 1, 1972, published by American Medical Association) aptly illustrates the hazards of prescribing over the telephone. In 1962, a patient saw a physician for a skin rash for which he was prescribed triamcinolone (Aristocort) to be taken orally. It was apparently effective. From that point onwards, whenever the patient had the rash, he was always prescribed the same drug. This went on for four years. In 1966, the patient went to another clinic where he was seen by another physician (physician 2), who also prescribed the same medication. Thereafter the second physician would always prescribe Aristocort over the phone, without bothering to make a physical examination. In 1967, the patient visited the clinic again, where he was examined by a third physician (physician 3), who found that the patient had developed Cushing's syndrome, and stopped the medication. The patient sued physician 2, because he had been prescribing him over the phone without caring to make a physical examination. The jury agreed and awarded him $460 358 in damages.

## Vaccine-Induced Damages

Vaccines have been known to cause injuries, and one of the best examples is that of pertussis vaccine causing irreversible brain damage in children. Several court cases have been fought over this issue. (According to one estimate, in 1985 in the USA an estimated 11 lawsuits were filed for every million doses of vaccine distributed. The vaccine manufacturers spent $16.2 million in settling 52 of them out of court.) In many cases the court found that the doctor was not guilty. One of the most publicized of these was the so-called Susan Loveday case (*Loveday* v. *Renton and the Wellcome Foundation* [1990] 1 Med LR 117). In this case Susan Loveday, a young child, suffered irreversible brain damage after being administered pertussis vaccine by a general practitioner. Boroughs Wellcome – the manufacturers of the vaccine – were never sued in the first place, but they became co-defendants at their own request. Lord Justice Stuart-Smith in his 300-page judgment held that the general practitioner and the manufacturing company were not liable.

In all cases where a vaccine has to be administered, the doctor would do well to obtain written informed consent from the parents, whereby all risks and benefits are explained to them.

### Packaging and Storage of Medicines

The use of outdated medicines can result in adverse reactions. Manufacturers must ensure that the date of expiry is prominently displayed on all medications supplied by them. The medicine must remain safe during this period. An outbreak of Fanconi's syndrome has been linked to the use of old tetracycline, which had become chemically degraded.

### Drug Automatism

Some drug-induced deaths, especially those involving barbiturates, have been explained away as being due to a rather mythical phenomenon called "drug automatism." This means that a patient – in a kind of automatic behavior – repeatedly took the drug, poisoning him/herself to death. This has been stated to be due to confusional states. Another explanation is that the patient forgot that he/she had taken a pill, before taking another, and the cycle went on until the patient poisoned him/herself to death (according to this explanation, the ingested drug itself was responsible for the patient's amnesia). These arguments were undoubtedly raised to beat the "no-benefit-in-case-of-suicide" clause inherent in most life insurance policies. With our current knowledge of therapeutic, toxic, and lethal blood levels of drugs, such an argument is unacceptable today. For instance, even if a patient started taking, say, barbiturates in a confusional, somnolentic, or amnesic state, he/she would fall unconscious well before blood levels reached fatal levels.

### Prevention of Drug-Induced Injuries

Drug-induced injuries may be almost unavoidable in the modern setting. We may wonder what we would do if given the choice of risking a deadly disease versus swallowing a risky pill to counteract it. Nevertheless, if we do not want the risk of a disease, we have to take the risk of the drug! What we must ensure however is that the risk–benefit ratio of any given drug is in the patient's favor. This can be ensured by tight drug monitoring and control systems and a stringent toxicovigilance program.

### See Also

**Complaints Against Doctors, Healthcare Workers and Institutions**; **Drugs, Prescribed:** Product Liability; **Medical Malpractice – Medico-legal Perspectives:** Negligence Quantum; **Pharmacology of Legal and Illicit Drugs**; **Substance Misuse:** Miscellaneous Drugs

### Further Reading

Bates DW, Leape L (2000) Adverse drug reactions. In: Carruthers SG, Hoffman BB, Melmon KL, Nierenberg DW (eds.) *Melmon and Morrelli's Clinical Pharmacology*, 4th edn., pp. 1223–1256. New York: McGraw-Hill Medical.

Cohen MR (ed.) (2000) *Medication Errors – Causes, Prevention and Risk Management*. Sudbury, MA: Jones and Bartlett.

D'Arcy PF, Griffin JP (eds.) (1986) *Iatrogenic Diseases*, 3rd edn. Oxford, UK: Oxford University Press.

Davies DM (ed.) (1985) *Textbook of Adverse Drug Reactions*, 3rd edn. Oxford, UK: Oxford University Press.

Ferner RE (1996) *Forensic Pharmacology – Medicines, Mayhem, and Malpractice*. Oxford, UK: Oxford University Press.

Ficarra BJ (1977) Therapeutic misadventures: drugs prescribed, tried and decried. In: Tedeschi CG, Eckert WG, Tedeschi LG (eds.) *Forensic Medicine: A Study in Trauma and Environmental Hazards*, pp. 1195–1225. Philadelphia, PA: WB Saunders.

Hardman JG, Limbird LE, Gilman AG (2001) *Goodman and Gilman's The Pharmacological Basis of Therapeutics*, 10th edn. New York: McGraw-Hill Medical.

McNulty H, Spurr P (1979) Drug names that look or sound alike. *British Medical Journal* 2: 836.

Pillay VV (2003) *Comprehensive Medical Toxicology*. Hyderabad, India: Paras.

Sneader W (1985) *Drug Discovery: The Evolution of Modern Medicines*. New York: John Wiley.

# DRUGS, PRESCRIBED

Contents
Licencing and Registration
Product Liability
Testamentary Capacity

## Licensing and Registration

**G J Sewell**, University of Bath, Bath, UK

## Introduction

Healthcare professionals and patients have an expectation that modern medicines, whether prescribed or purchased over the counter, have been thoroughly tested and evaluated. This process provides assurance to prescribers and their patients that medicines are relatively safe, offer therapeutic benefit, and are manufactured to exacting quality standards. In attempting to meet these expectations the pharmaceutical industry is, arguably, the most highly regulated of all industrial sectors.

The regulatory framework controlling the production and use of medicines was not constructed overnight. As more potent, and therefore potentially more harmful, medicines were developed in the latter half of the twentieth century, the need for preclinical and clinical testing became increasingly obvious. It was also clear that data produced by such tests should be subjected to rigorous assessment of safety and efficacy by an independent expert body. The tragic consequences of side-effects from medicines brought these requirements into sharp focus. A well-documented example is the case of thalidomide, which was administered to pregnant women to treat morning sickness. The drug proved to be teratogenic and resulted in the birth of babies with severe deformities.

The regulatory process in the health sector will continue to evolve. This is partly due to efforts to harmonize regulatory procedures on a regional and global basis, partly in response to public expectation and political sensitivity in healthcare, and undoubtedly a result of new technological developments. Medicines developed from molecular biology or from the manipulation of genetic material will present particular challenges to regulatory authorities.

A detailed review of worldwide medicine licensing procedures is beyond the scope of this article. Instead, the licensing systems applied to the UK and the European Union (EU) will be described as examples of national and centralized schemes, respectively. National licensing systems such as that described for the UK will also contribute to the decentralized licensing system of the EU. Licensing authorities in other countries, including the Australian Therapeutic Goods Administration, the US Food and Drug Administration, and the Japanese Ministry of Health, Labor, and Welfare, may differ in procedural detail and emphasis. However, all licensing systems in the developed world share the same objectives and key elements.

A variety of different terminologies is in common use to describe the approval of medicinal products by the designated authorities. These include licensing, product licensing, registration, and marketing authorization. The term marketing authorization has been adopted in the UK and EU, although all of these terms can be considered synonymous.

## National Licensing: UK Procedure

In the UK the licensing authority for human medicines is comprised of government ministers. The Secretary of State for Health has overall responsibility for issues relating to the control of medicines but it is the responsibility of the Medicines and Healthcare Regulatory Agency (MHRA) to implement and enforce policy on behalf of the government. The MHRA was created in 2003 from the merger of the Medical Devices Agency (MDA) and the Medicines Control Agency (MCA). The role of the MHRA is to administer the licensing of medicines in the UK, either as a sole agency or as part of the EU mutual recognition and centralized systems.

In the context of UK licensing, the MHRA will receive from the applicant pharmaceutical company a file containing data and information on the composition and formulation of the medicine, preclinical studies, and clinical studies conducted on healthy volunteers and/or patients.

Following an initial assessment by MRHA staff, the application is passed to the Committee on Safety of Medicines (CSM) for detailed review. The CSM is an advisory body set up under the UK Medicines Act and provides advice and guidance to the licensing authority on safety, efficacy, and quality issues in respect of new medicines submitted for licensing. The CSM also has an important role in the postmarket surveillance of medicines already in clinical use, particularly in respect of monitoring adverse drug reactions. In considering the application, the CSM may request further information from the applicant before it can reach a decision. Eventually, the CSM will recommend to the licensing authority either that the application is approved and a license is granted, or that the application is rejected. In some cases, approval of the application is subject to certain conditions or changes required by the CSM. If, following CSM advice, the licensing authority believes the new medicine to be acceptable in terms of safety, efficacy, and quality, a license will be granted. No consideration is given to the relative efficacy of the new medicine with respect to medicines of the same therapeutic class already on the market.

If the application is rejected, the applicant has the right to appeal to the Medicines Commission. The Medicines Commission is another advisory body to the licensing authority and was also established under the Medicines Act. The membership of this committee is appointed by ministers and includes experts from a range of medical, pharmaceutical, and scientific disciplines. In addition to hearing appeals, the Medicines Commission provides advice to the licensing authority on all matters relating to the implementation of the Medicines Act. Following reassessment of the application, the Medicines Commission will advise the licensing authority whether the rejection should be upheld or alternatively that a license should be granted.

If the application for marketing authorization or licensing is approved, the applicant can then enter into discussions with the government to introduce or launch the medicine on to the market. The launch of a medicine may be delayed by protracted price negotiations or because the medicine is subjected to a technical appraisal by the UK National Institute of Clinical Excellence (NICE). Under EU proposals, marketing authorization will be withdrawn from medicines that have not been launched within 3 years of approval.

## Mutual Recognition: EU Procedure

The mutual recognition procedure is an alternative to the centralized procedure as a means of licensing a medicinal product in more than one EU member state. The procedure is coordinated by the Committee for Proprietary Medicinal Products (CPMP), which is a committee of the European Medicines Evaluation Agency (EMEA). The CPMP, on receiving an application, will contract with an EU member state to assess the application. The applicant has the right to select the contracted member state, also known as the reference member state (RMS). The RMS has 210 days to evaluate the application through its own licensing system. In the UK, for example, the evaluation would be conducted by the MHRA.

If the RMS approves the application, other EU member states have up to 90 days to recognize the approval through the mutual recognition scheme. Member states may raise concerns about clinical or safety issues and any objections are arbitrated by the CPMP, which has 30 days to reach a decision. The CPMP will then advise the EU Commission of its decision, which is binding for all member states. If the application is successful, each member state issues its own license or marketing authorization for the new medicinal product.

## The EU Centralized System

The centralized procedure has been compulsory for medicines derived from biotechnology processes since 1995. It is currently optional for other new medicines, although it is likely to become compulsory for medicines used to treat human immunodeficiency virus (HIV), cancer, diabetes, and neurodegenerative diseases in the near future. The centralized system enables EU-wide marketing authorization to be obtained from a single application. For pharmaceutical manufacturers the centralized system also offers the advantage of 10 years' exclusivity, as opposed to 8 years under the mutual recognition scheme.

Applications are submitted directly to the EMEA and the process is administered and managed by the CPMP. The CPMP then appoints representatives of two member states to serve as rapporteur and co-rapporteur. The rapporteurs undertake a professional assessment of the application and produce a detailed report. This forms the basis of discussion as the application is considered by other member states within the CPMP.

A total of 210 days is allowed for the CPMP to deliver an opinion on the application. However, a preliminary review is conducted during the early stages of the process to identify any major issues and to give the applicant the opportunity to withdraw the application and make improvements prior to resubmission. Member states are given 28 days in which to comment on the CPMP opinion and any objections raised are considered by the CPMP.

If the EU Commission receives a recommendation from the CPMP that an EU-wide license should be granted, a European public assessment report is published on the EMEA website. This gives the applicant marketing authorization in all EU countries. This authorization is normally valid for 5 years and applications for extension of the license must be made 3 months before expiry.

The EU-wide license of a medicine does not automatically result in its launch in every EU country. Pharmaceutical companies may decide not to launch in some member states for commercial or logistical reasons.

## Implications of Licensing in Clinical Practice

Although most healthcare professionals accept the licensing of medicines as a positive step, there are occasions when the prescriptive nature of licenses can create practical difficulties. Marketing authorization restricts the use of medicines to the indications specified on the product license. As clinical experience with new medicines develops, new indications often emerge for which the medicine has therapeutic value. However, clinicians prescribing medicines for indications outside those specified on the license are considered to be using the medicine outside the terms of the license (often termed "off-label" use).

A similar situation often arises in prescribing for children. Ethical and commercial considerations often preclude testing of medicines in children for licensing purposes. This results in many medicines being licensed for use only in adults, and a lack of data on dosing, bioavailability, and clinical outcomes to support prescribing in children. It is recognized that patients could be denied effective treatments and new initiatives are under consideration to encourage pharmaceutical companies to license medicines for pediatric use. These include incentives such as extended exclusivity rights.

When prescribing medicines "off-label" or outside the terms of the license, the liability for patient harm resulting from the use of the medicine passes to the prescriber or his/her employer. Such prescribing is relatively common in secondary care, and many institutions have developed policies to manage the perceived risks associated with "off-label" and "unlicensed" prescribing. These include the requirement for a sound evidence base to support and justify the unlicensed use of medicines and obtaining informed consent from the patient (or their parent/carer) before the medicine is prescribed.

## Special Categories of Medicinal Products

### Orphan Drugs

Orphan drug status is granted to medicines that are considered vital in the treatment of life-threatening diseases but are not commercially viable to produce because the disease affects fewer than 5 in 10 000 EU inhabitants. Various EU incentives are available to pharmaceutical companies to undertake research and development on these medicines which otherwise offer no financial benefit to the company.

Applications for licensing of orphan drugs are considered by the EMEA Committee for Orphan Medicinal Products (COMP). If COMP recommends the issue of a license, the period of exclusivity for orphan drugs marketed within the EU is 10 years.

### Medicinal Products Derived from Plasma

National medicine regulatory authorities (e.g., MHRA in the UK) are responsible for the licensing of plasma-derived medicines. However, since these products present additional scientific and technological challenges, the World Health Organization (WHO) has produced international standards to ensure global harmonization in safety and efficacy. National authorities are therefore advised to consider WHO standards on documentation and traceability of donor blood, control of purification, virus removal, virus inactivation processes, and standardization of biological methods used to characterize the activity of the end product. It is also recommended that systems of postmarketing surveillance should be established for plasma products.

### Homeopathic Medicines

Licensing of homeopathic medicines was virtually impossible because of difficulties in proving efficacy in conventional clinical trials. Until 1994 the only homeopathic medicines available in the UK were those introduced before the implementation of the Medicines Act 1971, and such medicines were entitled to a product license of right.

The European Directive 92/73 EEC introduced the homeopathic registration scheme in 1994. Under this scheme, homeopathic medicines are only assessed for safety and quality. To qualify for registration, homeopathic medicines must be for oral administration or external use only, must be sufficiently dilute to guarantee safety, and must not make any therapeutic claims.

Registration, which is administered in the UK by the MHRA, is compulsory for all new homeopathic medicines and allows these products to be marketed without any specific medicinal claim.

### Herbal Medicines

In the UK there are two alternative regulatory routes for herbal medicines:

1. Herbal medicines may be licensed in exactly the same way as any other medicine.

2. Herbal remedies may be exempt from the licensing requirements under Section 12 of the Medicines Act 1968. This exemption allows herbal preparations to be supplied to individual patients following a consultation with the patient. The herbal remedy must also be produced by simple processes (drying, crushing, or comminuting) and must be supplied without any written recommendations as to its use.

Difficulties in proving efficacy of herbal medicines using conventional clinical trials have resulted in new initiatives. In the EU, the Traditional Herbal Medicinal Products Directive has been proposed, with the formal proposals being adopted by the EU Commission in January 2002. Several drafts of these proposals have been produced following consultation with member states. Proposed amendments include the expansion of the directive to cover minerals and vitamins. It seems likely that the EU Council of Ministers will endorse final amendments to the directive early in 2004. Member states will then have 18 months to implement the directive into their national law.

## Manufacturer's License

In addition to the requirements for a product license or marketing authorization, a pharmaceutical company will also require a manufacturer's license (ML) to enable it to manufacture and package the licensed medicines in its portfolio. Similarly, contract manufacturers who manufacture on behalf of a company holding the product license also need to obtain an ML. The ML signifies compliance with the principles of good manufacturing practice (GMP). The requirements for EU member states are set out in the EU *Guide to Good Pharmaceutical Manufacturing Practice*, also known in the UK as the *Orange Guide*. This document sets out the principles of GMP and quality assurance, and also gives details of the quality systems and documentation required to control pharmaceutical manufacturing processes. Qualifications, training, and responsibilities of personnel involved in the manufacturing process are considered alongside premises and equipment, record-keeping, and validation of manufacturing operations. Additional sections of the guide cover some of the more critical pharmaceutical processes such as sterilization and aseptic manipulation. The general principles of GMP also apply to "assembly" operations where bulk supplies of medicines are repackaged and labeled ready for patient use.

The responsibility for inspection of manufacturing sites and enforcement of GMP in pharmaceutical manufacturing rests with national licensing authorities (e.g., MHRA). All production sites of a given company will be subject to audit and inspection.

Defects are classified as critical, major, and other, and these will be detailed in a postinspection report. If the inspector is satisfied that compliance with GMP is achieved and that, if necessary, any defects have been corrected, a recommendation is made to the licensing authority, through its agency, that the site should be granted an ML. Normally, MLs are valid for 5 years, although in most cases pharmaceutical manufacturing sites are reinspected annually.

In the UK, the MHRA also grants a different type of license, known as a "specials" ML. This permits manufacturers to prepare unlicensed medicines (medicines without a product license or marketing authorization). The purpose of a "specials" ML is to enable small-scale manufacturers or hospital pharmacy departments to supply noncommercially available medicines to meet specific patient or clinical needs.

## See Also

**Drugs, Prescribed:** Product Liability; Testamentary Capacity

## Further Reading

Bouayed S (2003) The European Agency for Evaluation of Medicinal Products (EMEA). *European Journal of Hospital Pharmacy* 9: 38.

Commission of the European Communities (1998) The rules governing medicinal products in the EC, vol. 1. *Pharmaceutical Legislation: Medicinal Products for Human Use.* Luxembourg: Office for Official Publications of the EC.

Commission of the European Communities (1998) The rules governing medicinal products in the EC, vol. 3. *Medicinal Products for Human Use: Guidelines.* Luxembourg: Office for Official Publications of the EC.

Commission of the European Communities (1998) The rules governing medicinal products in the EC, vol. IV. *Good Manufacturing Practice for Medicinal Products.* Luxembourg: Office for Official Publications of the EC.

Commission of the European Communities (1998) The rules governing medicinal products in the EC, vol. IX. *Pharmacovigilance.* Luxembourg: Office for Official Publications of the EC.

Department of Health. *The Medicines Act 1968 and its Various Orders and Statutory Instruments.* London: HM Stationery Office.

Medicines Control Agency (2002) *Rules and Guidance for Pharmaceutical Manufacturers and Distributors 2002.* London: Medicines Control Agency.

MHRA (1997) *Towards Safe Medicines. A Guide to the Control of Safety, Quality and Efficacy of Human Medicines in the United Kingdom.* London: MHRA.

World Health Organization *Requirements for the Collection, Processing and Quality Control of Blood, Blood Components and Plasma Derivatives.* WHO technical report series no. 840 (annex 2), Geneva: WHO.

# Product Liability

**A Aggrawal**, Maulana Azad Medical College, New Delhi, India

## Introduction

### Law of Torts

Tort is a wide and amorphous area of common law which includes all instances of harmful behavior, from personal physical attack to interference with personal material possessions and usage and this also includes personal honor, reputation, and privacy. This concept encompasses only those civil wrongs independent of contracts, and recognized by law as grounds for a lawsuit. These wrongs result in an injury or harm which constitute the basis for a claim by the injured party. The primary aim of tort law is to provide relief for the damages incurred and deter others from committing the same. The injured person may sue for an injunction to prevent the continuation of the conduct causing the injury or for monetary damages.

### Product Liability

Product liability is an important concept under tort law, which holds not just the manufacturer of a defective product liable for damages, but also any or all parties along the chain of manufacture of that product. This includes the manufacturer of component parts (at the top of the chain), an assembling manufacturer, the wholesaler, and the retailer (at the bottom of the chain). Pharmaceutical products including prescription drugs are "products" within the meaning of this concept. Hence, any damage caused to the patient by prescription drugs may attract the provisions of this concept.

## Historical Overview of the Product Liability Law

To understand pharmaceutical product liability, it is important to appreciate how the product liability law evolved during the last two centuries. The first important case to attempt to determine product liability occurred in 1842 (*Winterbottom* v. *Wright*). In this case, one Mr. Winterbottom was seriously injured when he was driving a poorly constructed mail coach drawn by horses. The mail coach had been sold to the Postmaster General by its manufacturer, Mr. Wright. The Postmaster had a contract with a company to supply horses to pull the coach. It was that company (contracted by the Postmaster) which hired Mr. Winterbottom to drive the coach.

Mr. Winterbottom sued Mr. Wright for damages, but his case was dismissed – rather contemptuously – because there was no privity of contract between Mr. Winterbottom and Mr. Wright. In effect, this decision established that a product seller cannot be sued, even for proven negligence, by someone with whom he has not contracted, or, in the words of the law, someone with whom he is not in privity (**Figure 1**).

### The Era of Absolute Consumer Liability

It is interesting to conjecture what would have happened at this time if a similar case had occurred then in relation to prescribed drugs. Fortunately parallels can be drawn. A drug manufacturer supplies a spurious or outdated drug to a retailer; the retailer passes it on to the prescribing doctor and the doctor finally prescribes the drug to the ultimate consumer, the patient. If the patient suffers some injury because of this defective drug, despite the fact the manufacturer was negligent, the patient could not sue him because he was not in privity of contract with the manufacturer. This was, in a way, an era of absolute consumer liability (**Figure 2**).

### The Fall of the Privity of Contract

Just ten years after the Winterbottom case, in 1852, the New York Court of Appeals discarded the concept of privity of contract, but only in cases of inherently dangerous medicines (see **Table 1**). For other products absence of contract continued to be an important defense for the manufacturer.

The next important case in product liability law occurred in 1916 (*Macpherson* v. *Buick Motor Co.*). In this case, the defendant, Buick Motor Co., a manufacturer of automobiles, sold an automobile to a retail dealer (X). The retail dealer resold it to MacPherson, the plaintiff. While the plaintiff was in

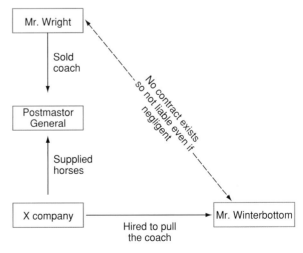

**Figure 1**   Product liability law as under Winterbottom (1842).

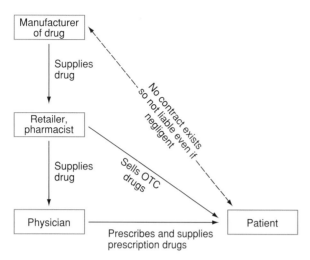

**Figure 2** Equivalent pharmaceutical product liability law as under Winterbottom (1842).

the car it suddenly collapsed. He was thrown out and injured. One of the wheels was made of defective wood, and its spokes crumbled into fragments.

The wheel was not made by the Buick Motor Co., but had been bought in from some other manufacturer (Y). There was, however, evidence that its defects could have been discovered by a reasonable inspection by the Buick Motor Co., but that inspection was not done. The charge brought against the company was of negligence. The question to be determined was whether the defendant owed a duty of care and vigilance to any one but the immediate purchaser.

Had this case been judged by the older *Winterbottom* standard, Buick Motor Co. would not have had to pay any damages to MacPherson, simply because it never entered into a contract with him. It was the retail dealer (X) who had sold the car to MacPherson and thus he (MacPherson) had a contractual relationship only with the retail dealer (X). But in a remarkable conceptual leap, Judge Cardozo of the New York Court of Appeals held that if a company was negligent (as Buick Motor Co. had been in not inspecting the defective wheel), then it was liable, even if it had no privity of contract with the sufferer (**Figure 3**). For the first time, the concept of "privity of contract" was discarded in a case *not* involving dangerous medicines. For many legal commentators of the time, it was "the conquest of tort over contract."

Parallels can be drawn here too. A drug manufacturer gets a chemical component from a supplier (Y). Y supplies a defective chemical (it may be of a low potency, or completely deteriorated). The drug manufacturer – by a reasonable inspection – could have discovered that it was defective but fails to do the inspection and subsequently manufactures the drug, which is sold to the pharmacist (X). The consumer

buys the drug from X and suffers injury. The consumer is fully entitled to get a compensation from the drug manufacturer (**Figure 4**).

### The Rise of Strict Liability

It is important to note that in *MacPherson* although there was no privity of contract between MacPherson and the Buick Motor Co., the damages were awarded to MacPherson, because the company was negligent. It is interesting to conjecture what would have happened if the company had not been negligent, i.e., if it had taken all reasonable precautions (such as careful inspection of the wheels, etc.) to see that a defective part was not incorporated in their automobile and yet somehow it got incorporated in the automobile. If the very same MacPherson had sued the company for damages in this hypothetical case, it is almost sure he would not have won. It is important to appreciate that he had won on the concept of negligence, and in the absence of negligence on the part of Buick Motor Co., no damages could have been awarded to him. The next 50 years were to see a radical change in this concept.

### Implied Warranty of Safety

The early 1960s saw the rise of two very interesting concepts in product liability law: those of implied warranty of safety and strict liability. The former of these came with *Henningsen* v. *Bloomfield Motors, Inc.* In this case Henningsen (H) bought a car from D's dealership. Just ten days after delivery, the steering malfunctioned and H's wife was involved in an accident. H sued the dealer and the car manufacturer. The dealer (D) argued that there was a clause in the warranty signed by H that freed D from any liability for personal injuries. The warranty was only for replacement of defective parts for the period of 90 days or 4000 miles (6400 km). But the court awarded damages to Henningsen. It argued that with the sale of every object there was an implied warranty of safety. Nor could the defendant argue that since it was Henningsen's wife (who had not bought the car from him) who suffered damages, he was not responsible. According to the court, the warranty extended "to every foreseeable user of the product." Even if, for example, Henningsen's friend had used the car and had suffered injury, he could have claimed for damages (**Figure 5**).

**Figure 6** depicts the equivalent pharmaceutical product liability as under *Henningsen*.

### Strict or Absolute Liability

The modern concept of strict liability (also sometimes referred to as absolute liability) arose with *Greenman* v. *Yuba Power Products, Inc.* Strict liability is liability

**Table 1**  Twenty major events in the evolution of the concept of product liability

| Event number | Year | Event |
|---|---|---|
| 1 | 1700–1800 | English doctrine of *caveat emptor* (let the buyer beware) adopted by the American colonies. This principle in the law of commercial transactions meant that the buyer purchases at his own risk in the absence of an express warranty in the contract. The concept of product liability does not exist at all |
| 2 | 1842 | *Winterbottom* v. *Wright* establishes that there *has* to be a contractual relationship between the injured party and the party supplying defective products, before the injured party can sue and be awarded damages. In other words, privity of contract is a must in order to get compensation |
| 3 | 1852 | The New York Court of Appeals takes the first step towards abolishing the privity of contract, but only in respect of extremely dangerous medicines. In *Thomas* v. *Winchester*, Mrs. Thomas sustained injuries from the effects of a quantity of extract of belladonna, administered to her by mistake as extract of dandelion (because of careless labeling). Court awards damages to Mrs. Thomas despite the fact there is no privity of contract between Thomas and Winchester. The court observes: ''The liability of the dealer in such case arises, not out of any contract or direct privity between him and the person injured, but out of the duty which the law imposes upon him to avoid acts in their nature dangerous to the lives of others. He is liable therefore, though the poisonous drug with such label may have passed through many intermediate sales before it reaches the hands of the person injured'' |
| 4 | Early1900s | States begin to pass workmen's compensation statutes |
| 5 | 1916 | Justice Cardozo of the New York Court of Appeals in *MacPherson* v. *Buick Motor Co.* makes a sharp shift from *Winterbottom* and lays foundation to the origin of modern product liability law. Among other things, the case establishes the following concepts:<br>1. It is the manufacturer's duty to conduct necessary tests to ensure safety of product<br>2. The negligent manufacturer could now be held liable to the ultimate purchaser, despite lack of a contractual relationship. Privity of contract defense in negligence (established 75 years earlier by *Winterbottom*) eviscerated<br>3. It is the seller's responsibility for design and manufacturing integrity |
| 6 | 1923 | The American Law Institute (ALI) embarks upon an effort to collect and organize the divergent decisional law which define the common law rules of torts throughout the USA. The efforts were to culminate in the first ever *Restatement of Torts*. University of Pennsylvania Professor Francis H. Bohlen appointed by the ALI as the original Reporter |
| 7 | 1934–1939 | Restatement of Torts adopted by the ALI |
| 8 | 1954 | Berkeley's then Dean William L. Prosser appointed as the Reporter to revise the *Restatement of Torts*. The task of compiling the *Restatement of Torts (Second)* begins |
| 9 | 1960 | The New Jersey Supreme Court in *Henningsen* v. *Bloomfield Motors, Inc.*, disallows the defense of privity of contract in the case where negligence was absent. The implied warranty of safety, extends to all products and to every foreseeable user of the product |
| 10 | 1963 | Chief Justice Roger Traynor of the California Supreme Court in *Greenman* v. *Yuba Power Products, Inc.* introduces strict tort liability as a viable concept. Within a few years, the majority of states would adopt strict tort liability. Under strict tort liability, it is no longer necessary to prove negligence |
| 11 | 1965 | ALI promulgates *Restatement (Second) of Torts* §420A, which ushers in the concept of strict liability. It is no more necessary for the plaintiff to show negligence. Only two things need be shown: (1) that the product was unduly dangerous and (2) that injury occurred as a result of that product. No matter how careful the manufacturer was, he would still be liable under the concept of strict liability |
| 12 | 1979 | Uniform Product Liability Act (UPLA) proposed by US Commerce Department as model law for adoption by states to standardize product liability statutes and insurance premiums |
| 13 | 1981 | Product Liability Risk Retention Act allowed for self-insurance and collective bargaining for lower commercial liability premiums |
| 14 | 1984 | First of many US Congressional bills to limit product liability fails |
| 15 | 1996 | President Clinton vetoes the Product Liability Legal Reform Bill. Among other things it proposed: (1) a US $250 000 cap on punitive damages for small business, (2) a drug and alcohol defense, which would bar a claim if a plaintiff was under the influence when an accident occurred and intoxication was the principal cause of the accident, (3) severe restrictions of the claims of persons who grossly misuse a product and then sue the defendant (with an eye to monetary gain). Studies had earlier shown that when states pass tort reform, productivity and employment increase |
| 16 | 1997 | Senator Ashcroft introduces the Product Liability Reform Bill of 1997. The bill is an exact replica of the failed legislation of 1996. Defeated again |
| 17 | 1998 | The ALI recognizes that the subject of torts had become too broad and too intricate to be encompassed in a single project and undertakes to compile the *Restatement (Third)* in segments. Adopts *Restatement (Third) of Torts: Products Liability*. §6 and §10 of this *Restatement* relate specifically to pharmaceutical product liability. §6 defines the liability of seller or other distributor for harm caused by defective prescription drugs and medical devices. §10 deals with the liability of commercial product seller or distribution for harm caused by post-sale failure to warn |

Continued

**Table 1**  Continued

| Event number | Year | Event |
|---|---|---|
| 18 | 1999 | In *Perez* v. *Wyeth Laboratories, Inc.*, the New Jersey Supreme Court jettisons the well-established and well-entrenched "learned intermediary doctrine." It effectively means that the manufacturers of prescribed drugs owe a kind of strict liability towards consumers |
| 19 | 2001 | In *Yugler* v. *Pharmacia & Upjohn Co.* the court asserts that the manufacturers cannot take the defense of learned intermediary doctrine even if physician recommended the over-the-counter drug. This means that the manufacturer continues to owe a duty to warn to the patient regarding an OTC drug, even if it were prescribed by a physician |
| 20 | 2004 | Manufacturers continue to seek – unsuccessfully – federal tort reform |

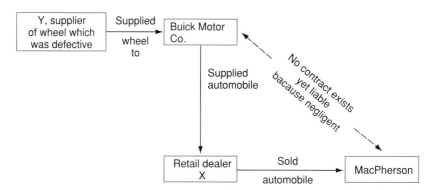

**Figure 3**  Product liability as it emerged under *MacPherson* (1916).

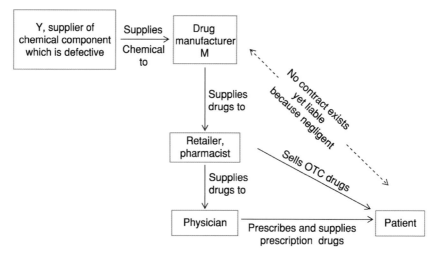

**Figure 4**  Equivalent pharmaceutical product liability law as under *MacPherson* (1916).

without privity of contract and even without negligence. If MacPhersons case had been judged by standards of strict liability, he would have won even in the latter hypothetical case, where the Buick Motor Co. had not been negligent. In *Greenman* v. *Yuba*, Greenman (the plaintiff) had bought a gadget called "Shopsmith," which was a combination power tool that could be used as a saw, drill, and wood lathe. The plaintiff watched a Shopsmith being demonstrated by the retailer and studied a brochure prepared by the manufacturer. He decided to buy a Shopsmith for his home workshop. However, his wife bought and gave him one for Christmas in 1955. In 1957 he bought the necessary attachments to use the Shopsmith as a lathe for turning a large piece of wood he wished to make into a chalice. After he had worked on the piece of wood several times without difficulty, it suddenly flew out of the machine and struck him on the forehead, inflicting serious injuries. He sued both the retailer and the manufacturer. During the trial he

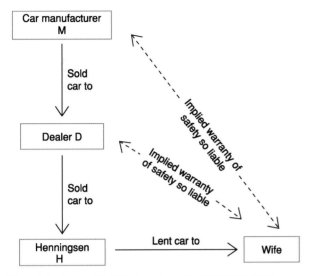

**Figure 5**  Product liability law as under *Henningsen* (1960).

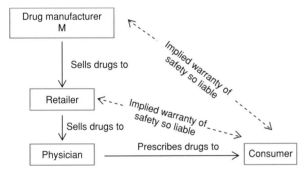

**Figure 6**  Equivalent pharmaceutical product liability law as under *Henningsen* (1960).

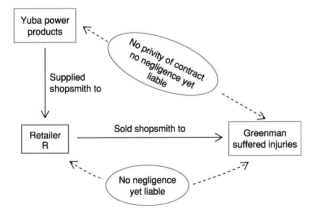

**Figure 7**  Product liability law under *Greenman* (1963).

introduced substantial evidence that his injuries were caused by defective design and construction of the Shopsmith. No evidence was found that the retailer and manufacturer were negligent or had breached any express warranty, yet the court ruled in favor of Greenman. According to the court, the only thing that needed to be shown now was that a product was defective and that it was being used in a way it was intended to be used and yet injury had occurred (**Figure 7**). The plaintiff need not demonstrate any negligence on the part of manufacturer or retailer.

An analogy can perhaps make the concept simpler to understand. Suppose a person (X) decides to keep a dangerous snake as a pet in his house. He takes utmost precautions to contain the snake in a cage and yet the snake escapes somehow and injures a neighbor (Y). It is no defense for X to assert that he had taken utmost precautions to contain the snake and that he was not negligent at all. The only facts that Y needs to prove (to be awarded damages) are (1) X had an exceedingly and inherently dangerous animal as his pet and (2) he suffered an injury due to that pet.

The concept of strict liability is mostly used in connection with objects which are exceedingly and inherently dangerous (sometimes termed as "unavoidably unsafe") such as dangerous animals, radioactive material, explosives, guns (and prescription drugs as some jurisdictions would assert), but various jurisdictions have applied this concept to other objects also. Used in connection with prescription drugs, it implies that if a defective drug causes injury to a patient, he is entitled for recovery of damages. It is not a defense for the manufacturer to show that he was not negligent. Only three things need be demonstrated by the patient to get damages: (1) that the drug was deficient; (2) that he used it as it was intended to be used (i.e., he did not, for example, ingest a syrup meant to be instilled in his eye); and (3) injury occurred as a result (**Figure 8**).

## Restatement (Third) of Torts: Products Liability

As stated at the beginning of this article, the law of torts is a vast and amorphous body of law which lies scattered in various judicial rulings. To crystallize and codify these concepts, the American Law Institute (ALI) started an effort in 1923 and produced the first *Restatement of Torts*. The *Restatement* was exactly what the name implied – a "re-statement" of the common law. As case law kept growing, the restatement needed to be revised. ALI brought out the *Restatement (Second) of Torts* in 1965. § 402A of this dealt with the complex area of products liability. *Comment k* under this section dealt mainly with pharmaceutical product liability.

It gradually became apparent that such a complex subject as product liability law needed a separate codification. In 1998, the ALI brought out *Restatement (Third) of Torts: Products Liability*, a separate body of law dealing just with products liability. It has 21 sections (distributed in four chapters) and as of

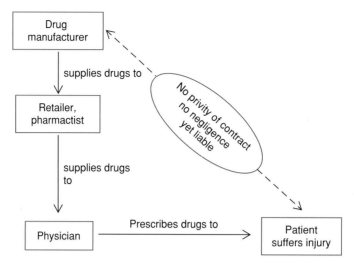

**Figure 8**    Equivalent pharmaceutical product liability law as developed under *Greenman* (1963).

now this body of law is the guiding principle in all cases of products liability. This *Restatement*, which supersedes the earlier *Restatement (Second) of Torts*, represents a thorough reformulation and expansion of § 402A and related sections of the *Restatement (Second)*. Especially notable are the careful separation of product defect into distinct categories and the development of separate rules for special products and their markets. Also covered in detail is liability of product sellers not based upon defects at the time of sale, including liability for post-sale failure to warn, and successor liability.

Many states have enacted their own comprehensive product liability statutes. These state-specific statutory provisions can be very diverse. Because of this, the US Department of Commerce produced the "Model Uniform Products Liability Act" (MUPLA), which serves as a voluntary guide for use by the states. At present there is no federal products liability law. In several other countries such as India and the UK, pharmaceutical product liability is addressed mainly under various Consumer Protection Acts, although various inherent provisions of the law of torts also apply.

## Legal Theories behind Product Liability Claims

Product liability claims can be based on three legal theories – negligence, breach of warranty of fitness, and strict liability.

### Negligence

Negligence is a relatively simple concept. In short, negligence is the failure to exercise ordinary care to avoid injuring someone to whom one owes the duty of care. Ordinary care is the care that a reasonable person would take based on the circumstances known to him at the time. Thus it is the manufacturer's duty to inform the patient that a particular drug is meant only for oral consumption, or that it must only be taken under instructions from the prescribing physician. To establish a charge under negligence, the traditional four Ds must be proved: duty, dereliction, damage, and direct causation. Stated plainly and simply, the sufferer must show that the manufacturer owed a duty to him; he was derelict in his duty; a damage occurred as a result of that dereliction; and finally damage was a direct result of that dereliction.

Ignorance is not a defense to the manufacturer in such cases. There raises the question of what a reasonable person would have been aware of under the circumstances. This is known as "constructive knowledge" in contrast to "actual knowledge." If a person actually knows that he is driving at, say, $120\,km\,h^{-1}$ in a busy street (actual knowledge), he should know that someone may get hurt (constructive knowledge). If a manufacturer is selling drugs without proper instructions and warnings (actual knowledge), the manufacturer must know that someone may suffer injuries because of this lack of instructions (constructive knowledge).

A claim of negligence focuses on the actions of the drug manufacturer in designing and producing a product. In other words, did the company fail to exercise reasonable care in the manufacture of the product, and/or did it ignore its own (or industry standard) production, inspection, and safety guidelines?

It is important to realize that each and every person in the drug distribution chain may be held liable for negligence. It is, however, the manufacturer who is most likely to have been negligent. He may be found negligent because of a number of reasons:

1. Careless design of the product. (Thalidomide has been said to be an example of a design defect. Some even assert that the capacity of aspirin to cause gastric bleeding or of carbimazole to cause agranulocytosis are also examples of design defects).
2. Careless manufacture.
3. Careless performance of (or failure to perform) reasonable inspections and tests of finished products (drugs).
4. Failure to package and ship in a reasonably safe way.
5. Failure to take reasonable care to obtain quality components from a reliable source.
6. Failure to provide sufficient instructions and warnings.

It may be extremely difficult for an injured customer to bring a product liability claim under negligence, simply because he has to prove too many things (the four Ds). It would be much better if he brought the claim under the theory of strict liability. Why then in the first place would anyone sue a manufacturer under negligence? One simple answer is because it is possible. Although the sufferer needs just one theory (negligence, breach of warranty, or strict liability), pleading all three claims usually serves a strategic purpose. By asserting more than one theory, a plaintiff is allowed to obtain more kinds of information about the defendant (drug manufacturer) during the discovery phase of the litigation, information that the defendant may not want the plaintiff to discover about its operation. For example, by alleging negligence, a plaintiff may be able to discover detailed information about how the product was manufactured, information that would not be relevant if the only issue was whether the product was defective (as in a strict liability claim). Similarly, by alleging the breach of an express warranty a plaintiff may be entitled to obtain information about how the product is marketed – information to which the plaintiff might not otherwise be entitled if he had alleged only a strict liability claim. Most courts would, however, restrict a plaintiff to one or two theories at trial to avoid confusing the jury.

## Breach of Warranty

Warranty claims are governed by contract law. In simple terms, a warranty is a promise, claim, or representation made about the quality or performance of a product. After *Henningsen* v. *Bloomfield Motors* (see above), the law assumes that a seller always provides some kind of warranty concerning the product sold and is required to meet the obligation created by the warranty. Under the Uniform Commercial Code (UCC) – adopted in every state of the USA – there are two kinds of warranties: express and implied.

**Express warranty**   An express warranty can be created in several ways. It can be made in the following ways:

- through an affirmation of fact made by the seller to the buyer
- written into a sales contract
- by spoken words during negotiations
- by silence in situations where not saying something has the effect of creating a mistaken impression about the quality of the goods sold
- by samples shown to the buyer
- by design specifications
- by an earlier purchase of the same kind of product (where the buyer reasonably assumed that a second shipment would be of the same quality as the first)
- by advertising or marketing claims.

**Implied warranty**   While an express warranty is created by an affirmative act, an implied warranty is presumed to exist unless the buyer clearly and unambiguously disclaims it in writing as a part of the sales agreement (that is why so many disclaimers are found on drug labels).

There are two kinds of implied warranties in the UCC. The "implied warranty of merchantability" is a kind of minimum requirements warranty. It means that the goods supplied "will pass without objection in the trade" and that "they are fit for the ordinary purposes for which such goods are used." Typically, the implied warranty also includes a warranty of reasonable safety (see *Henningsen* v. *Bloomfield Motors, Inc.* above).

The "implied warranty of fitness for a particular purpose" imposes a similar requirement in cases where the seller knows or has reason to know of a particular purpose for which the goods are required. In such a case, where the buyer relies on the seller to select or furnish goods that are suitable for a particular purpose, and the seller in fact has such expertise, an implied warranty of fitness for a particular purpose is created by law. If a school teacher requests a doctor to supply cough lozenges, for example, to 10–12-year-old children in her school, there is an implied warranty that the lozenges would be fit for that particular purpose, i.e., to soothe cough in 10–12-year-old children. If the lozenges contained a component suitable only for adults (say codeine), and the children suffered damages as a result, the teacher would be entitled to recover damages.

## Strict Liability

Strict liability is the most straightforward head under which damages can be claimed. For a plaintiff to claim damages under this head, he need not show that he entered into any contract with the manufacturer; indeed he does not even have to show the manufacturer was negligent. The only two things he need to prove are (1) that the product (drug) was defective and (2) that injury occurred as a result.

A manufacturer would generally be liable under this heading when his product is deemed to be both defective and unsafe. It is a finer point of law however, because by and large, an unsafe product is presumed to be defective. A product can be rendered defective and unsafe when there was (1) a design defect, (2) a manufacturing defect, or (3) a failure to warn.

Strict product liability applies not only to the product's manufacturer, but also to its retailer, and indeed any other person in the chain of distribution (e.g., a wholesaler) who is in the business of selling such products.

**Strict liability versus negligence**   A difference between strict liability and negligence is enunciated here. While the important guiding factor in claims of strict liability is the quality of product, the guiding factor in claims of negligence is the manufacturer's behavior or conduct in producing the product. The demonstration of utmost carefulness by the drug manufacturer during manufacture is a reasonably good defense in claims of negligence, but of no consequence under claims of strict liability.

## Successor Liability

A drug manufacturer who discovers that spurious medicines manufactured by him have reached the ultimate consumer and have started causing injuries, may try to evade the law by selling his company to an unsuspecting buyer, merging it with some other company, altering its name, or some such other device. Attempts such as this are thwarted by the concept of successor liability enshrined under § 12 of the *Restatement (Third)*. The following is the verbatim statement of § 12

> § 12 – *Liability of Successor for Human Caused by Defective Products Sold Commercially by Predecessor. A successor corporation or the business entity that acquires assets of a predecessor corporation or other business entity is subject to liability for harm to persons or property caused by a defective product sold or otherwise distributed commercially by the predecessor if the acquisition:*
> *(a) is accompanied by an agreement for the successor to assume such liability; or*

> *(b) results from a fraudulent conveyance to escape liability for the debts or liabilities of the processor;*
> *(c) constitutes a consolidation or merger with the predecessor; or*
> *(d) results in the successor becoming a continuation of the predecessor.*

## Joint and Several Liability

The common law rule of joint and several liability makes each and every defendant in a tort lawsuit liable for the entire amount of plaintiff's damages, regardless of that defendant's proportion of fault for the damage done. In other words, it allows a person to recover damages from one or more defendants. Even if a defendant is found to be 1% liable, he may be required to pay the entire amount of the judgment.

## Defenses against Pharmaceutical Product Liability Suits

The manufacturer of drugs has the following valid defense against pharmaceutical product liability suits.

### Statute of Limitations

A sufferer cannot wait to sue the manufacturer according to his whims and fancies. He must file a suit within a stipulated period of time, which varies from country to country. The time limit defined by the "Trade Practices Act of 1992" is three years from the time he or she becomes aware (or ought reasonably to have become aware) of the loss, the defect, and the identity of the manufacturer.

### Statutes of Repose

Statutes of repose are similar to statutes of limitations but, instead of running from a date of injury, the time limitation usually runs from the date on which the product was made or sold. This time varies from place to place, but is generally ten years.

### Contributory Negligence

When the injury occurred as a result of both the manufacturer and the user being negligent, it becomes a case of contributory negligence. There are at least five types of contributory negligence as listed below.

**Comparative fault**   If the jury determines that the user was, for example, 20% responsible for his injuries, then he would get only 80% of the damages that he would have got if he had not been negligent at all. In other words, the damages are apportioned between the manufacturer and the sufferer depending on their quantum of negligence. In several jurisdictions, if the patient was more than 50% negligent, he would not get any claim at all.

**Assumption of risk**   This doctrine is also known by its Latin equivalent *Violenti non fit injuria*. It effectively means that when a patient voluntarily exposes himself to some medication (after proper warning), he assumes the risk contingent upon taking that medicine.

**Misuse**   In this case an injury occurs as a result of misuse of the drug by the patient, as for example instilling a medicine in the eye, which was meant for oral ingestion.

**Alteration**   This arises when the patient alters the medication in some way and then takes it (as when he boils it "to sterilize" it).

**Failure to mitigate**   If a patient discovers that he is, for example, developing some adverse reactions to a drug, he should immediately stop taking that drug and report the matter to the physician. Instead, if he keeps taking the drug and aggravates his injury, the damages he would receive would be reduced by the amount by which he aggravated his own injury.

### Federal Preemption

When there is a federal law on a particular subject, it shall override any state law on the same subject.

### Intervening or Superseding Negligence

This defense, also known by its Latin equivalent "*Novus actus interveniens*," effectively implies that the negligence on which the suit is based springs from the negligence of a third party, and that the negligence was unforeseeable. The success of this kind of defense is highly dependent on individual facts of a particular case. For example, if a doctor writes a (supposedly) illegible prescription, which the pharmacist reads incorrectly and does not confirm from the doctor and then dispenses the wrong medicine to the patient, who suffers an injury. The doctor could perhaps take this defense in this case.

### The Learned Intermediary Doctrine

"Learned intermediary rule" is yet another defense for the drug manufacturer and retailer. According to this rule, the manufacturer of a prescription drug is only required to warn a patient's prescribing physician, and once an adequate warning is given, the drug manufacturer is relieved of any duty to warn the patient directly. The doctor or the healthcare provider is the "learned intermediary" (between the manufacturer and the patient) who must give adequate warning to the patients. At least four rationales have traditionally been forwarded to support this rule. First and foremost, a special and unique relationship exists between the physicians and patients. Physicians "know" their patients better and are in a better position to weigh the benefits and risks of prescription drugs for each patient. Second, they also have a direct communication with their patients (unlike the manufacturer) and are thus in a better position to convey warnings of prescription drugs. Indeed, they have a duty to do so under the doctrine of informed consent. Third, direct-to-consumer warnings (by the manufacturer) simply are not practicable. Not only do pharmaceutical manufacturers lack the means to effectively communicate warnings to consumers, but it is virtually impossible for manufacturers to reach every patient. Finally, the complexity of the warnings and risks inherent in prescription drugs makes it extremely difficult for pharmaceutical manufacturers to warn lay patients in a manner that is not unduly complicated and confusing.

By and large, the learned intermediary doctrine is inapplicable to cases involving over-the-counter (OTC) drugs. With respect to OTC drugs, there is no "learned intermediary" to warn. Therefore, a manufacturer has a duty to warn the consumer directly of the foreseeable risks of harm associated with an OTC drug.

One of the most recent cases illustrating this defense is *Vitanza* v. *The Upjohn Co.* In this case, the plaintiff brought a product liability action against The Upjohn Company, after her husband died as a result of ingesting an anti-inflammatory drug manufactured by Upjohn. Upjohn manufactured the drugs and distributed them to the plaintiff's physician who in turn gave them to the plaintiff as a sample. The plaintiff's husband took the drugs even though they were not prescribed to him, and died from an allergic reaction. Plaintiff's suit was based on the assertion that Upjohn should have provided adequate warnings on the drug package. The defendant Upjohn could successfully invoke this doctrine as a defense.

This doctrine however has fallen in rough weather recently. In 1999, in *Perez* v. *Wyeth Laboratories, Inc.*, the New Jersey Supreme Court abandoned this doctrine. The reasoning given by the court was that there had been a phenomenal rise in direct manufacturer-to-consumer advertising through newspapers, magazines, radio, television, and even the internet, known as "direct-to-consumer" (DTC) advertising. It influenced the patients so much that they requested their doctor for a particular drug (for example, a birth control pill). If the manufacturer had the capacity to influence the patient's decision to take a particular drug manufactured by him, he also owed a responsibility – that of providing adequate warnings. This reasoning, in effect, makes the prescribing physician merely a conduit between the manufacturer and the patient. The patient – who is so influenced by advertisements that he has already decided to take a particular drug – needs a doctor only because a valid prescription to buy this drug is needed. Many legal commentators – quite rightly – consider that the *Perez* decision has perhaps gone too far in applying the concept of strict liability to the manufacturers.

## Summary

A manufacturer of defective medical equipment or a spurious medicine is liable for damages under the concept of product liability. In the beginning of the evolution of this concept, in order to defend himself the manufacturer only needed to show that he was not in privity of contract with the consumer. But this concept was discarded as legal theories concerning product liability evolved. The concept of product liability is now based mainly on the concept of strict liability, where in order to get compensation the patient needs only to show that he used the drug in the way it was intended to be used, and yet it caused injury. The manufacturer can no longer take the defense that he was not in privity of contract with the patient. However, the manufacturer can take certain defenses such as the statute of limitations, contributory negligence by the patient, federal preemption, and intervening or superceding negligence. One of the most convincing of these defenses has been that of the learned intermediary doctrine, whereby it is assumed that it is the doctor – the learned intermediary – who is in a better position to warn the patient about the ill-effects of the drug. The manufacturer is therefore absolved of any liability to warn the patients. In a recent case – *Perez* v. *Wyeth Laboratories* – this defense has however been set aside. Many legal commentators think that this decision has been rather harsh on the manufacturers. As legal theories regarding product liability continue to evolve, we may see further twists and turns in this fascinating area of medical law.

## See Also

**Complaints Against Doctors, Healthcare Workers and Institutions**; **Drug-Induced Injury, Accidental and Iatrogenic**; **Medical Malpractice – Medico-legal Perspectives:** Negligence, Standard of Care

## Further Reading

Ausness RC (2002) Will more aggressive marketing practices lead to greater tort liability for prescription drug manufacturers? *Wake Forest Law Review* 37: 97–139.

Ben-Shahar O (1998) Should product liability be based on hindsight? *Journal of Law, Economics and Organization* 14(2): 325–357.

Davidoff DJ, Walker PE (1977) Products liability. In: Tedeschi CG, Eckert WG, Tedeschi LG (eds.) *Forensic Medicine: A Study in Trauma and Environmental Hazards,* pp. 1656–1660. Philadelphia, PA: W. B. Saunders.

Diamond AL, Laurence DR (1986) Product liability in respect of drugs. In: D'Arcy PF, Griffin JP (eds.) *Iatrogenic Diseases,* 3rd edn., pp. 117–123. Oxford, UK: Oxford University Press.

Macneill MJ (1995) Pharmaceutical products liability. In: Sanbar SS, Gibofsky A, Firestone MH, LeBlang TR (eds.) *Legal Medicine,* pp. 168–179. St Louis, MI: Mosby.

Rabin RL (1997) Restating the law: the dilemmas of products liability. *University of Michigan Journal of Law Reform* 197: 201.

Schwartz VE (1998) *The Restatement (Third) of Torts: Products Liability – A Guide to its Highlights.* Washington, DC: National Legal Center for the Public Interest.

Sharma RK (2003) *Legal Aspects of Patient Care,* 2nd edn. New Delhi, India: Modern Publishers.

Stapleton J (2000) Restatement (Third) of torts: products liability, an Anglo-Australian perspective. *Washburn Law Journal* 39: 363–403.

# Testamentary Capacity

**R E Ferner, N J Langford, and A R Cox**, West Midlands Centre for Adverse Drug Reaction Reporting, Birmingham, UK

## Introduction

In the UK, the number of older people has grown rapidly. In 1961, there were 2.1 million people over the age of 75 years in the UK. By 2001, there were 4.5 million over the age of 75 years, and 336 000 of those were aged 90 or more.

Despite concerns about the elderly having to use capital to fund nursing care in their old age, the over-50s in the UK hold 80% of all wealth and 60% of all savings. In comparison to the working population they are asset-rich and income-poor. Such assets can become the subject of bitter internal family disputes after the death of a relative.

A will stipulates how assets are to be dispersed after the maker's death. Doctors may be asked whether a patient is or was in a fit state to make a will, on the basis of their clinical judgment. Mental capacity is a legal concept, and ultimately, any decision made as to whether a person does or does not have mental capacity is a decision for a court of law. The decision is made on the balance of probabilities. The assessing doctor therefore addresses the question: Is it more probable than not that this person possesses testamentary capacity? The assessing doctor and solicitor need to be aware that with certain conditions and treatments, including drug therapy, a person's capacity may change. Indeed, the mental capacity of a patient may fluctuate widely. However, a will made during a lucid period can be upheld.

The criteria for testamentary capacity were set out in the case of *Banks* v. *Goodfellow* 1870 (L.R. 5 Q.B. 549). The law makes three basic demands of a prospective testator for a will to be valid. Testators have, first, to understand the nature of making a will and what its effects will be once they have died; that is, testators understand that they are giving their property to one or more objects of their regard. Second, testators must understand the extent of the property of which they are disposing. Testators are not required to have an exact knowledge of their estate, but they should have an idea of what form their property takes and in what proportion. They should also be aware of any debts or other financial considerations that they have. It follows that the more complex the estate, the greater the degree of testamentary capacity required. The third requirement for testamentary capacity is that the testators appreciate the claims to which they ought to give effect, that is, they recognize where responsibilities lie in deciding how to apportion their estate. It is not enough to say that the will is unfair, malicious, or capricious. Testators may leave their estate to charity rather than a relative. However, testators would not have the necessary capacity to make a will if they were unaware that the person who visited regularly was in fact their spouse, for whose welfare they might reasonably be responsible.

## Undue Influence

Undue influence is a more complex and vague concept. To be considered "undue," the influence must include coercion, compulsion, or restraint. The testator's mind must have been subjugated to that of another, his/her free agency destroyed, or will overpowered by another. This is especially considered where the accused party played an active role in procuring the will or codicil, the accused was a close relative or advisor of the testator and had control of the testator's functioning and movements, the accused profited unduly from the will, and the testator's mental state was such that he/she could easily have been influenced by another.

When testamentary capacity is assessed retrospectively, the contemporary observations and records of others will become important. The documented statements, behavior, or thought processes of the testator made by hospital or nursing-home staff, friends, business associates, or family members become important. The expected information about the testator's cognitive functioning and grasp of reality, personality traits and attitudes, and statements relating to their assets and relatives are also required. If it is alleged that a drug affected the testamentary capacity of an individual, contemporary drug histories and medical notes may have to be relied upon.

Prescribed medication and any of its adverse effects on an individual may be poorly documented within the medical records. Certainly, only 5% of adverse reactions are reported to regulatory agencies, and only half of general medical patients who believe themselves allergic to penicillin have this fact recorded within hospital notes. Changes in therapy, which could have a bearing on the testamentary capacity of an individual, may not be fully explained within the notes. Even if a relevant adverse drug reaction is recorded in the notes, this does not necessarily mean an individual lacked testamentary capacity at the time of writing the will.

Testamentary capacity requires discernment and memory. Disease states affecting memory, particularly the dementias, are common in the elderly and a common basis on which to question the mental capacity of the testator. While in the past the effects of drugs have mainly been considered in the context of alcohol abuse, professionals now have to reckon with the very large number of drugs that can potentially affect the mind and alter mental capacity. Although many drugs have evanescent effects that will last only as long as the drug is in the body, they will be relevant if the testator was taking them at the relevant time. An obvious, if extreme, example is general anesthesia.

Drugs can also be suspected of making people more susceptible to suggestion and less ready to resist the influence of others. This will be true for drugs of addiction, including alcohol, where a person's free will is corroded by a desire for the drug. Another extreme example is the "date-rape" drug flunitrazepam, which is used to induce both subjugation and amnesia.

The dangers of drug therapy are greater in older persons than younger ones. Older people are more likely to be treated with several different drugs simultaneously, as they are more likely to suffer from more than one condition. There is a greater risk of interactions between drugs as the number of drugs increases. For example, it would be commonplace for an elderly patient with heart problems to be taking seven or eight drugs regularly. If the patient takes four drugs, the number of possible interactions between two drugs is six; with six drugs, it is 15; and with eight drugs, it is 28. This means that there is a high chance of one drug affecting the action of another. Where several drugs have similar adverse effects, such as sedation, for example, then the position may be even worse, since the effects of the drugs together can be additive.

The elimination of drugs by the kidneys is slower in older people, as renal function declines. This increases the risk of adverse effects that are the result of high concentrations of drug in the body, and these include effects on the mind. A decline in drug elimination, with a corresponding rise in drug concentration, can provoke adverse effects even in a patient who has taken a drug for many years without difficulties.

Concerns about the prescribing of psychoactive drugs in the elderly population are well known. In the USA, before the Nursing Home Reform Act was implemented in 1990, psychoactive drugs were prescribed to half of the patients in nursing homes. Although improvements have been made, psychoactive drugs are still prescribed in these areas. Reports from UK nursing homes also suggest that problems exist with the prescribing of psychoactive drugs, and efforts to improve prescribing in the elderly are ongoing.

The risk of adverse psychiatric reactions is increased in the presence of disease that causes preexisting impairment of the brain. Some traits may be inherited, for example, a family history of mania may make such an adverse effect of a drug more likely. However, the lack of a previous history of mental impairment does not provide an individual with a guarantee that drug-induced psychiatric reactions will be avoided.

## The Effects of Drugs on Testamentary Capacity

Drugs that affect the brain may vary from having subtle and subjective effects at one end of the spectrum to rendering a patient unconscious at the other. In between there are various degrees of drug befuddlement, and it is often difficult to know to what extent drugs may have affected testamentary capacity.

## The Drugs

### Opiates

Opiates (such as morphine, diamorphine, pethidine, codeine, and dihydrocodeine) are commonly prescribed, particularly in patients suffering pain or distress at the end of their lives. Their main uses are as analgesics, anxiolytics, and in the treatment of intractable cough. In addition to the relief of pain, morphine can also confer a state of euphoria and mental detachment. In palliative care oral morphine is the treatment of choice.

Patients vary greatly in their sensitivity to the actions and adverse effects of a given opioid. Even within an individual, the effects of a given dose of an opioid can change with time. The most extreme example of this phenomenon is the ability of heroin addicts to tolerate doses of the drug many times higher than what would be a lethal dose in nonusers.

On initiating therapy and during short-term use, opiates can cause nausea and vomiting, constipation, dizziness, and sedation. Stimulation and euphoria may also occur. Hallucinations and dysphoria occur in some patients, with others reporting nightmares. Large doses can result in respiratory depression. Addiction to, or dependence on, opiates represents an infrequent but undesirable consequence of its use, though in the elderly such an effect is rare. Sedation and cognitive effects are early adverse effects to which tolerance occurs with continued use once stable dosing has been achieved. There is little current evidence that the long-term use of scheduled opiate therapy in stable doses causes clinically significant cognitive or psychomotor deficits in patients with chronic pain. Indeed, recent evidence suggests that pain itself can have adverse effects on cognitive performance that is improved with opiate analgesia. Opiate addicts taking methadone for over 30 years showed no increase in markers of cognitive dysfunction, such as motor vehicle accidents or infractions of driving codes. Cognitive deficits in opiate-treated patients are more often due to the concurrent use of sedative medications, such as benzodiazepines. However, in patients taking opiates, the early adverse effects of the drug can reemerge if the dose is altered.

### Benzodiazepines and Hypnotics

Benzodiazepines (such as diazepam, nitrazepam, and temazepam) and related drugs (e.g. zopiclone) are widely prescribed within the UK. All the drugs have anxiolytic, hypnotic, muscle relaxant, and anticonvulsant properties to varying degrees. Their effects differ, and depend on the rate at which they are metabolized and excreted from the body. Benzodiazepines can be used therapeutically to inhibit the formation of memories, particularly in patients who have to undergo unpleasant therapeutic procedures. The amnesia that is produced is classified as being antegrade, that is, an event occurring after the medication has been administered may not be recalled. Episodic memory (the remembering of recent events, the circumstances in which they occurred, and their time sequences) is particularly impaired, and more markedly so in heavy alcohol drinkers. These effects may persist even after the hypnotic effect has worn off. Within the elderly, cognitive impairment is common. Indeed, cognitive deterioration associated with the normal aging process and with dementia can be worsened by benzodiazepine administration.

In some cases, patients taking the medication may appear superficially to function as normal despite being under the influence of the drug. Fugue-like states have been reported, where people taking these drugs can perform complex actions, but have no recall of actual events occurring. Indeed, several cases of shoplifting have been recorded in previously law-abiding individuals who were under the influence of these drugs.

Tolerance to the effects of these drugs usually occurs. However, chronic use of the benzodiazepines and other hypnotic agents can lead to dependence or a need to increase the dose to maintain efficacy.

## Antidepressants

Antidepressants are commonly prescribed to the elderly. Tricyclic antidepressants (such as clomipramine, amitriptyline, imipramine, and dosulepin) can cause toxic delirium, delusions, and visual hallucinations associated with their anticholinergic properties. These adverse effects appear to be dose-dependent and in one study occurred in 13% of patients. The additive effect of further drugs with anticholinergic properties, including neuroleptics, increases the risk of toxicity. Usually the psychiatric effects subside quickly when the drug is withdrawn.

Sedation is an important adverse effect of tricyclic antidepressants and can cause cognitive impairment. Long-term use of amitriptyline and imipramine has been associated with cognitive impairment. In psychiatric patients the incidence of confusional episodes is increased, with memory being affected in both acute and long-term use. Age appears to increase the susceptibility to these reactions.

Manic and hypomanic reactions have been reported with all antidepressant drugs and existing mania may be worsened. Tricyclic antidepressants can precipitate mania, especially in those with bipolar depression. Mania on withdrawal of tricyclic antidepressants has also been reported. Other drugs, including selective serotonin reuptake inhibitors (SSRIs), such as fluoxetine, paroxetine, citalopram, and sertraline, and the atypical antidepressant trazadone can also provoke mania. Tricyclic antidepressants and monoamine oxidase inhibitors (MAOIs) may have occasionally precipitated paranoid pychosis.

## Antipsychotic Drugs

The phenothiazines, such as chlorpromazine, methotrimeprazine, pericyazine, pipothiazine, promazine, promethiazine, and thioridazine, can cause hyperactive delirium preceded by restlessness and agitation. This is suspected to be due to their anticholinergic effects. Antipsychotics with little anticholinergic activity can also induce delirium alone or with anticholinergic agents.

In normal subjects, the effects of neuroleptics on memory and cognitive performance are mild and variable. Higher cognitive functions are largely unaffected, and in some individuals, performance may improve as an existing illness improves. For example, in schizophrenic patients trifluoperazine and haloperidol have been shown to improve short-term memory. Chlorpromazine and thioridazine slightly impair short-term memory but not immediate or long-term visual memory.

In those already suffering from dementia, neuroleptic drugs can accelerate cognitive deterioration. There is evidence to show that Alzheimer patients taking neuroleptic drugs have a greater risk of cognitive decline.

## Anticonvulsant Drugs

Anticonvulsants can impair cognitive function, especially when patients need several different drugs to achieve control of their epilepsy. Effects may be related to drug concentrations, but cognitive impairment can occur even within the therapeutic concentration range of some drugs. Patients often complain of a poor or slow memory. Older drugs such as phenobarbital, primidone, and phenytoin are more likely to cause cognitive impairment than newer drugs such as carbamazepine, sodium valproate, and gabapentin.

Dose-related delirium could also be caused by anticonvulsants. Hallucinations, delusions, and paranoid schizophreniform psychoses can be caused by phenytoin. Exacerbations of acute and chronic schizophrenia have been reported with carbamazepine, as well as with ethosuximide and clonazepam. Psychosis has been listed as an adverse drug reaction to vigabatrin, and abnormal behavior and emotional lability have been reported with topiramate. Most anticonvulsants also have some sedative effects and can disturb the emotions of patients, potentially making patients susceptible to "undue influence" when drawing up their wills.

## Lithium

Around 30% of patients taking lithium complain of memory problems. Formal studies have shown small but significant impairment in a wide range of cognitive tests, including memory tests. Effects seem to be dose-related and early signs of neurotoxicity to lithium can occur at serum concentrations in the range of $1.3$–$2 \, mmol \, l^{-1}$ (therapeutic range $0.4$–$1 \, mmol \, l^{-1}$). However, even within normal serum concentrations, changes such as reversible confusion, cognitive impairments, lassitude, and disorientation may be evident. More severe and partly irreversible effects can occur at higher dosages. Toxicity may be related to interactions with other drugs, most notably with diuretics and nonsteroidal antiinflammatory agents.

## Antiparkinsonian Agents

The psychiatric effects of drug treatment may complicate the management of Parkinson disease. The dopamine precursor levodopa can induce dose-related hypomania or mania in patients with Parkinson disease, with an incidence of 1.5–3.6%. The onset of such symptoms can be delayed for several months after the start of treatment. Bromocriptine, a dopamine receptor agonist, can provoke similar reactions, but these can be more severe and protracted in nature. Other psychiatric complications, such as delirium, depression, agitation, and paranoid psychosis are more common. Other dopamine receptor agonists such as amantidine have also precipitated mania. Other drugs used in the treatment of Parkinson disease such as apomorphine, lysuride, and pergolide, and the type B MAOI selegiline, have been known to cause psychiatric effects such as euphoria, restlessness, confusion, and psychosis.

Anticholinergic agents such as procyclidine, trihexyphenidyl, benztropine, orphenadrine, biperiden, and others can cause delirium and visual hallucinations. When used in combination with other drugs with anticholinergic properties (such as the neuroleptic agent thioridazine), the effects may be additive.

## Metabolic Disturbances

Not all effects on the mental capacity of an individual are due to a direct effect on the brain. Biochemical changes secondary to drug treatment can also lead to reversible intellectual impairment.

Hyponatremia (a reduction in the sodium concentration in the blood) can be caused by a variety of drugs, leading to a variety of symptoms including slowed thought processes, drowsiness, and in severe cases, convulsions. The anticonvulsant drug carbamazepine is a noteworthy cause. Other implicated drugs include tricyclic antidepressants, SSRIs, MAOIs, and antipsychotic drugs. However, hyponatremia is not restricted to those drugs with neurological actions. Other drugs used to treat conditions of a more general nature can also exert an effect on the intellect by biochemical means. Both the antidiabetic drug chlorpropamide and combination diuretics used to treat elderly patients can cause hyponatremia. Other drugs that can cause hyponatremia include the anticancer drugs cyclophosphamide, vincristine, and vinblastine. The widely prescribed nonsteroidal antiinflammatory drugs (NSAIDs) such as naproxen, ibuprofen, and indometacin can also cause hyponatremia by potentiating the action of antidiuretic hormone.

## Drugs of Abuse

### Cannabis

Laboratory investigations demonstrate that social doses of cannabis have minimal effects on the performance of simple motor tasks, but can cause significant impairment in complex thought processes. Cannabis causes specific deficit in short-term memory that can be seen even when small doses have been taken. The principal deficit appears to be in acquisition of memory. This is thought to result from an attentional deficit combined with an inability to filter out irrelevant information. The impact of long-term cannabis use is controversial. In some studies, heavy cannabis users who stopped using the drug showed mild persistence of impairment of attentional function while others suggest that cannabis-associated cognitive deficits are reversible. Impairment of cognitive dysfunction appears more likely related to recent cannabis exposure rather than cumulative lifetime use.

### Opiates

The illicit use of opiates within this group of patients is rare. Addiction to, or dependence on, opiates represents an infrequent but undesirable consequence of its therapeutic use. The effects on mental cognition are similar to those outlined above under opiates.

### Ethanol (Ethyl Alcohol)

The effects of alcohol are well known. Drinking alcohol impairs executive cognitive functioning. This includes cognitive abilities such as planning, abstract reasoning, and the capacity to govern self-directed behavior. The degree of impairment is proportional to the amount of alcohol consumed and relates to the blood alcohol concentration. Following acute alcohol intoxication the memory retrieval processes remain significantly impaired during the alcohol-induced hangover. These effects may be worse for binge drinkers.

The effects of chronic alcohol consumption are variable. Some studies suggest that mild to moderate alcohol consumption improves cognitive function in an aging population. However, chronic heavy alcohol consumption leads to a number of neuropsychological impairments, including memory deficits. Up to 7% of the elderly population chronically abuse alcohol. Problems include impairments of a range of memory tasks such as learning word lists, short- and long-term logical memory, and general working memory and executive function. In certain cases, alcohol abuse can lead to chronic vitamin deficiencies, particularly of vitamin $B_1$ (thiamine) and the acute presentation of Wernicke's encephalopathy that, if left untreated, results in Korsakoff psychosis, when mental capacity is lost.

## Specific Problems

### Drug Withdrawal

Although the main concern about the effect of drugs on testamentary capacity focuses on the drug's direct effect on the cognitive process while the drug is being taken, many drugs can cause disruptions in thought patterns after their withdrawal.

Withdrawal reactions affect homeostatic control in the nervous, endocrine, hematological, and cardiovascular systems, leading to complex effects on the body. Both physical and psychological symptoms can arise.

An obvious example of a withdrawal reaction is delirium tremens. Occurring within 48–72 hours of stopping chronic excessive alcohol use, its symptoms include disorientation, hallucination, convulsions, and changes in psychomotor and autonomic activity.

The withdrawal of benzodiazepines can cause anxiety and insomnia after short-term use. Withdrawal of benzodiazepines after long-term use can potentially lead to more severe adverse effects, such as severe anxiety, perceptual changes, convulsions, and delirium. Following at least three months of treatment, 90% of patients can experience withdrawal reactions when benzodiazepines are stopped abruptly.

Another major group of drugs associated with withdrawal problems is the antidepressants. Abrupt cessation of tricyclic antidepressants can also induce anxiety, nightmares, and headache. More severe effects are seen with withdrawal from MAOIs, with approximately one-third of patients experiencing reactions after abrupt withdrawal. These can include delirium, auditory and visual hallucinations, and schizophreniform psychoses. With both of these groups of drugs, symptoms can appear within a few days to two weeks after stopping treatment.

Ongoing concerns have been expressed about the withdrawal reactions to SSRIs. Abrupt withdrawal leads to behavioral problems, tremor, and dyskinesia. Emotional lability and confusion may also occur. Although all SSRIs have been associated with withdrawal reactions, it is thought that SSRIs with shorter half-lives, such as paroxetine, may be more likely to cause such reactions.

Cases of mania have also been reported after discontinuation of isocarboxazid and isoniazid. Withdrawal of bromocriptine in Parkinson patients has also caused psychosis.

### Drug Tolerance

Repeated administration of a drug may lead to an alteration in its effect on the body, often reducing its impact. This diminution of effect of a drug despite the same dose being used is known as tolerance. For example, with diazepam in a novel user, sedation may be achieved with 5–10 mg. In a habituated user, over 1000 mg may be required to have a similar effect. Similarly, in the novel user cognition may be severely impaired, while in the habituated user at the same dose cognition may be normal. Tolerance to one effect of a drug may occur before tolerance to another effect. For example, with dihydrocodeine there is rapid tolerance to the sedation and cognitive impairment, but little or no tolerance occurs toward constipation. However, tolerance toward a drug may be rapidly lost if the dose is altered, or not taken regularly. Furthermore, simply being on a drug known to have the ability to cause cognitive impairment does not necessarily mean that cognitive impairment will definitely occur.

## Conclusion

Testamentary capacity involves both understanding and an appreciation of specific decisions relating to drawing up a will. Drugs, or their withdrawal, may cause changes in consciousness, reasoning ability, perception of reality, and memory, affecting an individual's testamentary capacity. For those asked to assess a person's capacity either prospectively or retrospectively, the impact of such drugs should be taken into account.

## See Also

**Drugs, Prescribed:** Product Liability; **Pharmacology of Legal and Illicit Drugs**; **Substance Misuse:** Medical Effects; Patterns and Statistics

## Further Reading

Armour D, Cairns C (2002) *Medicines in the Elderly.* London: Pharmaceutical Press.

British Medical Association and Law Society (1995) *Assessment of Medical Capacity: Guidance for Doctors and Lawyers.* London: British Medical Association.

British Medical Association and the Royal Pharmaceutical Society of Great Britain (2002) *British National Formulary,* 46th edn. London: British Medical Association and the Royal Pharmaceutical Society of Great Britain.

Davies DM, Ferner RE, de Glanville H (1998) *Davies's Textbook of Adverse Drug Reactions,* 5th edn. London: Chapman & Hall Medical.

Dollery C (1999) *Therapeutic Drugs,* 2nd edn. Edinburgh, UK: Churchill Livingstone.

Dukes M, Aronson J (2000) *Meyler's Side Effects of Drugs,* 14th edn. Amsterdam: Elsevier Science.

Ferner RE (1996) *Forensic Pharmacology. Medicines, Mayhem and Malpractice.* Oxford, UK: Oxford University Press.

Ferner RE (1997) Drugs and testamentary capacity. *Journal of Clinical Forensic Medicine* 4: 185–187.

McClelland HA (1990) The forensic implications of benzodiazepine usage. In: Hindmarch IA (ed.) *Benzodiazepines: Current Concepts,* pp. 227–250. Chichester, UK: John Wiley.

Sweetman SC (ed.) (2002) *Martindale – The Complete Drug Reference,* 33rd edn. London: Pharmaceutical Press.

Weir E (2001) Drug-facilitated date rape. *Canadian Medical Association Journal* 165: 80.

## Drugs: Back-tracking Calculations   *See* Back-tracking Calculations

## Dyadic Deaths   *See* Murder–Suicide

# ELECTRIC SHOCKS AND ELECTROCUTION, CLINICAL EFFECTS AND PATHOLOGY

**B Marc**, Compiegne Hospital, Compiegne, France

## Introduction

Many workers are exposed to electrical devices and currents during their daily work. Given the widespread use of electrical devices in the home, many other people are also at risk, particularly the very young and very old. Many people know that the principal danger from electricity is electrocution, but few really understand just how small a quantity of electrical energy is required for electrocution. In reality, a normal household current may be lethal and electrocutions may result from contact with an object as seemingly innocuous as a broken light bulb or as lethal as an overhead powerline. Electrocutions have affected workers and users since the beginning of the use of "la fée Electricité" at the end of the nineteenth century. In fact, the first electrical fatality was recorded in France in 1879 when a stage carpenter was killed by an alternating current of 250 V.

Three types of electrical injury and fatality may be encountered by the forensic or emergency physician. First, powerline contacts account for serious injuries and fatalities at job sites and less often at home. In the USA, the National Institute for Occupational Safety and Health estimates that an average of 411 deaths per year occur on job sites as a result of electrical contact. Machines that are mostly involved in powerline contacts are cranes, bucket trucks, drill rigs, fork lifts, manlifts, and other aerial lifts. Second, electric power is used to commit suicide, either by people throwing electric devices into a bath in which they are lying or by individuals connecting electric wires to each hand or arm, inducing an electric current that passes through the heart fibers. Third, electric power may be used with the criminal intent of committing murder, often by a husband, a wife, or a close friend.

Various systems have been used to kill using electric power. Accurate and attentive clinical and pathological examinations may explain the cause of death and help to differentiate suicide from murder in such cases. Electrocution as a death sentence must also be mentioned.

## Some Short Useful Definitions

Electricity is the flow of electrons, containing a negative charge, through a conductor. If the electrons flow from an object through a conductor, the flow is called electric current. Four primary terms are used in discussing electricity: (1) voltage; (2) resistance; (3) current; and (4) ground.

Voltage is the fundamental force or pressure that causes electricity to flow through a conductor and is measured in volts (V). Resistance is anything that impedes the flow of electricity through a conductor and is measured in ohms ($\Omega$). Current is the flow of electrons from a source of voltage through a conductor and is measured in amperes (A). If the current flows back and forth (a cycle) through a conductor, it is called alternating current (AC). AC is most widely used because it is possible to step up or step down (i.e., increase or decrease) the current through a transformer. For example, when current from an overhead powerline is run through a pole-mounted transformer, it can be stepped down to normal household current.

In each cycle the electrons flow first in one direction, then the other. The rate is given in cycles per second, also called hertz (Hz). If current flows in one direction only (as in a car battery), it is called direct current (DC).

Ohm's law mathematically relates current, voltage, and resistance: voltage = current × resistance.

A ground is a conducting connection, whether or not it is intentional, between an electrical circuit or equipment and the earth, or some conducting body that serves in place of the earth. It may be of primary importance in forensic enquiries to establish what the ground is.

## Pathologic Effects of Electrical Energy

Electrical injuries consist of three main types: (1) fatal electrocution; (2) electric shock; and (3) burns, as a result of contact with electrical energy. Electrocution results when an individual is exposed to a lethal amount of electrical energy. It is important for the forensic examiner to determine how contact with an electrical source has occurred and to evaluate the characteristics of the electrical source before the time of the incident. When death has occurred, the human body has been part of an active electrical circuit that has a current capable of overstimulating the nervous system or causing damage to internal organs. The extent of injuries received depends on the current's magnitude (how many amps?), the pathway of the current through the body, and the duration of current flow through the body.

Electrical injuries may occur in various ways: from direct contact with electrical energy, injuries that occur when electricity arcs (the electrons flow through a gas, such as air) to a victim at ground potential (supplying an alternative path to ground), flash burns from the heat generated by an electrical arc, and flame burns from the ignition of clothing or any other combustible material.

Direct contact and arcing injuries produce similar effects on the skin. Burns at the point of contact with electrical energy can be caused by arcing to the skin, heating at the point of contact by a high-resistance contact, or higher-voltage currents (**Figure 1**). Contact with a source of electrical energy can cause external as well as internal burns. Exposure to higher voltages will normally result in burns at the sites where the electric current enters and exits the human body. High-voltage contact burns may result in only small superficial injury; however, there is a

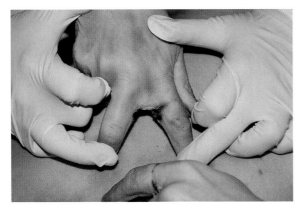

**Figure 1** Black electric burns between fingers.

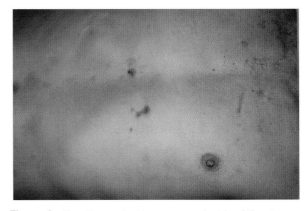

**Figure 2** Two tiny contact burns on each side of the sternum (accidental death).

danger that these small but deep burns will destroy tissue subcutaneously. Internal effects of electrical energy also include blood-vessel clotting, damage to the nerves in the area of the contact point, and major muscle contractions that may cause skeletal fractures. Low-voltage electrocution is associated with poorly visible marks to the body of the victim (**Figure 2**).

Flash burns and flame burns are actually thermal burns since electric current does not flow through the victim and injuries are often confined to the skin. Moreover, contact with electric current could cause a muscular contraction or a startle reaction that may be hazardous if it leads to a fall from a height (from a ladder, aerial bucket, etc.) or contact with dangerous equipment.

## Pathologic Effects Related to Voltage

Standard voltages produce currents passing through a human body in the milliampere (mA) range (1000 mA = 1 A). The estimated effects of 60-Hz AC currents which pass through the chest are as follows :

- 1 mA: barely perceptible
- 16 mA: the maximum current an average individual can grasp and "let go"
- 20 mA: paralysis of respiratory muscles
- 100 mA: ventricular fibrillation threshold
- 2 A: cardiac standstill and internal organ damage
- 15–20 A: usually fatal for a human being: a common fuse or breaker opens the circuit.

When current greater than the 16 mA "let-go" current passes through the forearm, it stimulates involuntary contraction of both flexor and extensor muscles. If current exceeding 20 mA continues to pass through the chest for an extended time, death may occur from respiratory paralysis. Currents of 100 mA or more, up to 2 A, may cause ventricular fibrillation, which is probably the most common cause of death from electric shock.

The presence of moisture from environmental conditions, such as standing water, wet clothing, high humidity, or perspiration, increases the possibility of low-voltage electrocution. The level of current passing through the human body is directly related to the resistance of its path through the body. Under dry conditions, the resistance offered by the human body may be as high as $100\,000\,\Omega$, but wet or broken skin may reduce the body's resistance to $1000\,\Omega$. Applying Ohm's law, it is easy to understand low-voltage electrocution. Under dry conditions, current $= V/\Omega$ is 110 or $220/100\,000 = 1$ or $2\,mA$, which corresponds to a barely perceptible level of current. Under wet conditions, current $= V/\Omega$ is 110 or $220/1000 = 120\,mA$, which is sufficient to cause ventricular fibrillation.

Wet conditions are often found at the death scene of low-voltage electrocutions.

High voltage is usually defined as greater than $600\,V$ AC. Most circuits and equipment operate at voltages lower than $600\,V$, including common household circuits ($110/120\,V$ in the USA and UK and $220/240\,V$ in most European countries), most overhead lighting systems used in industry, buildings, and department stores, and much of the electrical machinery used in industry and manufacturing. High voltages over $600\,V$ can rupture human skin, greatly reducing the resistance of the human body, allowing more current to flow and causing greater damage to internal organs. The most common high voltages are transmission voltages (typically over $13\,800\,V$) and distribution voltages. High voltage is mainly observed in fatal occupational accidents but can also be seen in people who have accidentally come into contact with high-energy electric wires or been struck by lightning.

High-voltage electrical energy rapidly breaks down human skin, reducing the human body's resistance to $500\,\Omega$. Once the skin is punctured, the lowered resistance results in massive current flow, measured in amps. Again, Ohm's law demonstrates the action. For example, at $1000\,V$, current $= V/\Omega$ means $1000/500 = 2\,A$, which can cause cardiac standstill and serious damage to internal organs.

Only one in four cases of high-voltage accidents show current entrance and exit points resembling "typical" electric marks, as they are known from exposure to domestic voltage. Half the bodies exhibit major surface burns as a result of involvement in electric arcs. About one-third of fatal accidents are accompanied by secondary mechanical trauma. Nonspecific signs of asphyxial findings (petechial hemorrhage in the eyelids and conjunctivae, as well as under the pleura and the epicardium) may also be noticed

(10–15%), similar to when death is caused by domestic voltage. After a long exposure to high-tension electricity, fat and gas embolism into the right ventricle due to local tissue heating may be observed.

Latent current marks (LCMs) produced on corpses using electrodes of the metals that are most frequently involved in electrocution (iron, copper, zinc, aluminum, chrome, nickel, and brass) can be investigated by means of macroscopic detection of metallization. Single metals can be identified by spraying specific reagents on the suspected skin marks of accidental electrocution. Instead of appearing on the skin, metallization can sometimes be found on clothes or shoes. A macroscopic search for LCM metallization is a simple method and it is recommended in suspected electrocution, as well as in cases of sudden unexpected death, particularly during work.

High levels of muscular enzymes (creatine phosphokinase, lactate dehydrogenase) in bood samples can be correlated to the cardiac mechanism of electric death. Electrical injury can affect many organ systems and electrical injuries to the heart are far less frequent, and thus, less known. In victims without coronary risk factors, a rise in enzyme levels and electrocardiographic changes suggestive of acute myocardial infarction have been reported after AC electrocution. This rise can also be observed in fatal electrocution victims.

Moreover it is recognised that contact with current, especially high-voltage current, may produce violent electrically induced muscle contractions and therefore an increase in muscle enzymes.

Muscular contraction is observed when an individual contacts an electrified source that has a current of $50\,mA$ or greater. Whether the current is low or high voltage, these contractions can fracture bones. Fractures have been seen as a complication of electroconvulsive therapy.

## Most Frequent Electric Deaths

Occupational fatalities associated with electrocution are a significant problem. Electrocution is one of the leading causes of work-related traumatic deaths. The industries with the highest percentage of electrocutions are construction, transportation, public utilities, manufacturing, and agriculture. Over a 13-year survey period in the USA, 61% of electrocutions occurred in two occupational divisions: 46% among craftworkers and 15% among laborers. These two groups also had the highest rates of death by electrocution: 1.4 per $100\,000$ workers each.

Certain circumstances of death are easily identifiable. Victims may touch a vehicle, ladder, or scaffolding that is in contact with an energized power source. They can also contact short-circuited, damaged, or improperly installed wire or equipment. Almost all the accidents (except lightning) involve AC. A third of deaths are attributed to lower-voltage electrocutions involving a household current of 120–240 V, while two-thirds involve 600 V or more, mainly due to distribution voltages (7200–13 800 V).

## Suicidal Electric Deaths

Fatalities caused by electrocution often lack specific morphologic evidence. Investigation of the death scene together with technical inspection of the electrical apparatus may help to clarify the cause and manner of death (**Figure 3**). Cutaneous current marks may be the only sign of low-voltage-associated fatalities.

Often, a professional such as an electrician may use electric power to commit suicide. This fact is stressed by published case reports.

Electrodes (coins, metal pieces) can be fixed with adhesive tape at the height of the heart to the front and back of the left side of the chest, on each wrist or arm (**Figure 4**), or on one finger of each hand. In at least two published cases, a timer was used.

Autopsy reveals blackish linear marks on the skin, tissue, and muscles under the cutaneous current marks. Current-related and heat-related changes, such as hypercontraction muscle bands and coagulative changes of the peripheral nerves, can be found on histologic examination.

## Homicidal Electric Deaths

Very rare cases of homicide and attempted homicide have been reported. In half of reported cases, the current has been applied to wet towels placed on parts of the sleeping victim. In other cases, flexible conducting wires have been placed around the limbs

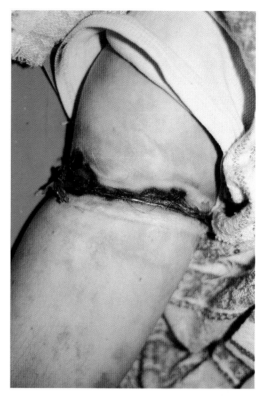

**Figure 4**  Cutaneous electric burns under naked wires (suicide by electrocution).

of the victims and the current switched on. The attempt may be unsuccessful and only result in burns. Diagnosis is assisted by high levels of muscle enzymes in the blood samples of victims who do not have any history of coronary risk factors or renal insufficiency. The significance of pathological findings in forensic investigations of electrocution is principally of interest in fatal cases.

## Other Electrical Accidents and Deaths

Some cases of electrocution in the operating room have been reported. The manner in which a patient sustains an electric-shock injury from improperly wired equipment during the course of an operation often happens in the same way. For example, a patient requiring surgical treatment has the ground plate of an electrocauterization unit placed under the buttocks and the electrodes of an electrocardiogram unit attached to the shoulders and the precordium. During the course of the operation, electrical interference may take place, followed by electrical injury of varying severity.

Electrocution during autoerotic practice has also been reported in recent years. In one case, two wet green terry cloths were placed in the cups of a bra and connected to the house current via two metal

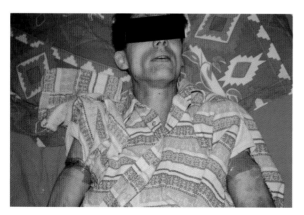

**Figure 3**  An electrocution system linked to a timer in a suicide by electrocution.

washers and a bifid electrical cord. Death was attributed to accidental self-electrocution. In another case of fatal electrocution during autoerotic practice, the accident was related to the attachment of one electrode to the anus and accidental touching of the other electrode with the hand and chest when attempting to attach it to the penis. Autopsy revealed second- and third-degree burns and myocardial lesions.

## Electric Accidents and Deaths in Childhood

Childhood deaths due to electrocution are rare and are more likely to occur when children are playing around electrical wires or equipment, and often result from either faulty apparatus or a lack of understanding of the potential dangers involved. Most deaths occur in the home, while playing with or near faulty electrical equipment while in the bath or in any other room. In contrast to adult electrical deaths, high-voltage electrocutions, suicides, and workplace deaths are uncommon. Strategies for eliminating childhood electrocution should concentrate on ensuring safe domestic environments with properly maintained electrical devices.

## Further Reading

Bailey B, Forget S, Gaudreault P (2001) Prevalence of potential risk factors in victims of electrocution. *Forensic Science International* 123: 58–62.

Byard RW, Hanson KA, Gilbert JD, *et al.* (2003) Death due to electrocution in childhood and early adolescence. *Journal of Paediatrics and Child Health* 39: 46–48.

Casini VJ (1993) Occupational electrocutions: investigation and prevention. *Professional Safety* 38: 34–39.

Di Maio VJ, Di Maio D (2001) Electrocution. In: *Forensic Pathology,* 2nd edn., pp. 409–418. Boca Raton, FL: CRC Press.

Fatovich DM (1992) Electrocution in Western Australia, 1976–1990. *Medical Journal of Australia* 157: 762–764.

Goldman RD, Einarson A, Koren G (2003) Electric shock during pregnancy. *Canadian Family Physician* 49: 297–298.

Harvey-Sutton PL, Driscoll TR, Frommer MS, Harrison JE (1992) Work-related electrical fatalities in Australia, 1982–1984. *Scandinavian Journal of Work and Environmental Health* 18: 293–297.

Jenkins EL, Kisner SM, Fosbroke DE, *et al.* (1993) *Fatal Injuries to Workers in the United States, 1980–1989: A Decade of Surveillance: National Profile,* pp. 93–108. Washington, DC: US Government Printing Office.

Marc B, Baudry F, Douceron H, *et al.* (2000) Suicide by electrocution with low-voltage current. *Journal of Forensic Science* 45: 216–222.

Pfeiffer H, Karger B (1998) Attempted homicide by electrocution. *International Journal of Legal Medicine* 111: 331–333.

Schott JC, Davis GJ, Hunsaker JC, 3rd (2003) Accidental electrocution during autoeroticism: a shocking case. *American Journal of Forensic Medicine and Pathology* 24: 92–95.

Stout N, Jenkins EL, Pizatella T (1996) Occupational injury mortality rates in the United States: changes from 1980 to 1989. *American Journal of Public Health* 86: 73–77.

# ENTOMOLOGY

**M L Goff**, Chaminade University of Honolulu, Honolulu, HI, USA

## Introduction

Entomology is defined as the study of insects, members of the arthropod class Hexapoda. Insects are probably the most successful and numerous organisms on earth, with almost 1 million species currently known and it is believed that this accounts for only a small portion of the actual number of species present. Insects are a highly adaptable group and have successfully exploited almost every conceivable habitat.

While insects are a major component of the earth's fauna, the vast majority of insects have no direct relationship to humans or are beneficial to us. Insects act as pollinators of most agricultural crops, serve as biological control agents for many pest species, and produce products used by humans, such as wax and honey. The flip side of this coin is that insects are also in direct competition with us for food and space. They are significant pests in agriculture, consuming and/or damaging considerable parts of agricultural crops. Termites and ants, among others, consume our homes and other buildings, as well as stored materials. Insects, particularly the "true flies" (order Diptera), are vectors of major human diseases, such as yellow fever, and malaria. Additionally, some species are significant for their nuisance value – it generally requires only one mosquito to disturb a good night's sleep.

Forensic entomology can be broadly defined as the application of entomological evidence to legal proceedings. Within this broad definition there are three generally recognized subspecialties: stored-product entomology; structural/urban entomology; and medicolegal entomology. Stored-product entomology involves insect damage to stored materials such as food or materials that leaves the stored product unsuitable for human or animal consumption, as in the case of beetles or moths feeding on cereals. In structural/urban entomology the situation is similar, but most often involves damage to structures by insects such as termites (order Isoptera) or carpenter ants (order Hymenoptera). Additional situations include problems related to infestation of roaches, biting insects, or other disagreeable insects. In both stored-product and structural/urban entomology the problems generally involve damage, need for an assessment of actions to assign blame, a solution, and, typically, some form of monetary adjustment. The entomologist's role is in assessing what the extent of the problem is, what should be done to correct the problem, and what should have been done, if anything, to prevent the problem. While some of the problems may result from intentional acts, the vast majority is not considered "criminal" in nature.

By contrast, the third area, medicolegal entomology, is directly related to investigations of deliberate criminal acts, most frequently a homicide. This area of investigation is what has most commonly been associated with the term "forensic entomology" by the general public and, in fact, by most of the entomological community. The most common application of entomological evidence in this subspecialty is the estimation of the time since death or postmortem interval. In reality, time since death is not what is actually being estimated but rather the period of insect activity on a dead body, as will be explained later. In addition to this application, under certain circumstances, insects can also provide significant information with respect to postmortem movement of a body, assessment of trauma, and characterization of the crime scene. Insects can serve as alternate specimens for toxicological analyses when the body is too decomposed to allow for normal sampling, and blood-feeding ectoparasites can provide DNA materials from victims and/or potential suspects. More recently, insects have been involved as evidence in cases of abuse and neglect of children and the elderly, particularly those species of Diptera or true flies which feed on living tissues as maggots.

## Basis for Forensic Use of Insects

Decomposing remains will provide a temporary habitat for a wide variety of organisms ranging from bacteria and fungi to vertebrate scavengers. The arthropods are the major component of this fauna and predominate among these insects in terrestrial habitats both in terms of diversity and total numbers. Typically, insects, particularly blow flies (family Calliphoridae) and flesh flies (family Sarcophagidae), are the first "witnesses" to arrive at a dead body. This often occurs within minutes of death. The female fly will deposit eggs or living maggots at natural body openings or wounds. When this occurs, a biological clock is started. This clock is stopped with the discovery of the body and collection of the insects. Use of insects to estimate a minimum postmortem interval requires an understanding of the insect's life cycle, relation of the insect to the body, and also to the habitat in which the body is discovered.

Insects pass through a distinct series of stages of development as they move through their life cycle. This process is termed metamorphosis and can be well illustrated using a blow fly in the family Calliphoridae as an example (**Figure 1**). The female fly arriving at the body will investigate the natural body openings associated with head, anus, and genitals, as well as any wounds that may be present on the body. Eggs will be deposited in these openings (**Figure 2**) and will hatch into larvae, commonly called maggots. There are three larval stages in the development of the blow fly (**Figure 3**), termed instars, with a molt between each stage. Once the maggot has reached maturity, it ceases feeding and moves away from the body to enter the puparial stage (**Figure 4**). During this inactive stage the larval tissues are reorganized to produce the adult fly (**Figure 5**). As different species of insects have been shown to develop at predictable rates under a given set of environmental conditions,

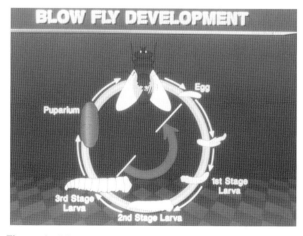

**Figure 1** Life cycle of a blow fly, family Calliphoridae.

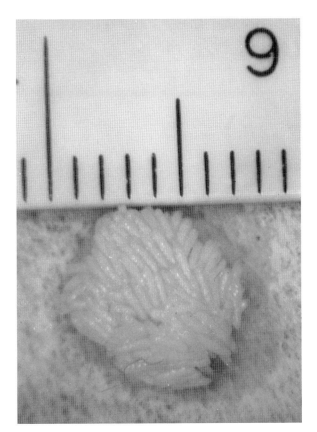

**Figure 2** Eggs of the oriental latrine fly *Chrysomya megacephala* (family Calliphoridae).

**Figure 3** Larval stages of the oriental latrine fly, *Chrysomya megacephala* (family Calliphoridae). Top, first instar; middle, second instar; bottom, third instar.

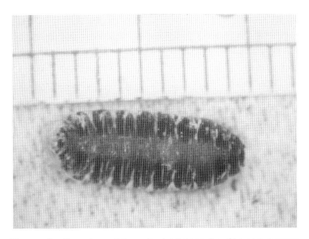

**Figure 4** Puparium of the oriental latrine fly, *Chrysomya megacephala* (family Calliphoridae).

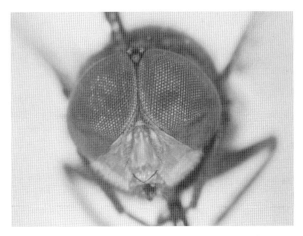

**Figure 5** Head of adult male oriental latrine fly, *Chrysomya megacephala* (family Calliphoridae).

given a species identification it is possible to estimate the period of time required for the most developed specimens to reach the stage collected from the body. This time period is an estimate of the minimum period of time since death. There are two aspects that must be emphasized in this estimate. First, it is only an estimate, not an absolute time. Second, it is an estimate of the period of insect activity on the body, not the actual postmortem interval. There may be factors, such as wrapping of the body, concealment, or repellent substances on the body that will delay the invasion of the body. The actual postmortem interval may be longer than indicated simply by the insect activity.

The above technique works well for the first portion of the decomposition process, which lasts about 2 weeks in most instances. After this time period, most of the initial invading organisms have completed their development and departed the body. After this, we must make use of the concept of succession. A dead body is not unlike a newly emerged volcanic island in the middle of the ocean. The island has no plants or animals. As the island cools, plants brought by wind and ocean currents arrive and begin to grow. These plants change the character of the island and make it attractive and habitable to other groups of organisms. The dead body shows a similar pattern. The first flies that oviposit or larviposit on the body initiate a series of changes to the body as their larvae feed and mature. These changes make the body attractive to other groups of insects. These in turn alter the body, attracting still other insects. Unlike the island, which reaches equilibrium, the dead body is a temporary habitat and is eventually depleted. During this process, the total numbers of insects attracted to the changing body, actually a food resource, is quite large. In Hawaii, for example, over 320 different species of insects have been recorded during decomposition studies. In continental areas, the numbers are even higher. In order to estimate the period of insect activity on the body, all of the insect species, stages of development present, and relative arrival times must be evaluated. In order to accomplish this, the decomposition processes and the relationships of the different species of insects to the body must be understood.

## Decomposition

Over the years, decomposition studies have been conducted in many different parts of the world and using a wide variety of animal models. Most of these studies were conducted in temperate areas and relatively few in tropical to subtropical habitats. One common attribute of these studies has been an attempt to divide the processes of decomposition into a series of discrete stages. It is important to note that decomposition in nature is a continuous process and no discrete combinations of physical parameters and assemblages of insects actually exist. In spite of this, there is a value to these stages as points of reference when faced with the problem of explaining events to a jury. Regardless of locality, there are certain patterns that are common to most decomposition studies. There are regional variations in the faunas involved, although some species of true flies (Diptera) are widely distributed. Generally, the families of insects involved are somewhat stable. Division of decomposition into a series of five stages appears to be a generalized pattern that can be easily applied to most existing studies:

1. Fresh stage: This stage begins at the moment of death and continues until bloating of the abdomen is first observed. The first insects to arrive are the true flies in the families Calliphoridae (blow flies) and Sarcophagidae (flesh flies). These insects investigate the corpse and then the females will deposit either eggs or first-instar larvae in the natural body openings, most often associated with the head, followed by the anus and genitals, and finally wounds that may be present on the body.

2. Bloated stage: Putrefaction, the principal component of decomposition, begins during this stage. Gas produced by the metabolic activities of the anaerobic bacteria in the digestive system first causes a slight inflation of the abdomen and this continues until the corpse is fully inflated and appears balloon-like. During this stage, the internal temperature of the corpse begins to rise as a combination of the activities of the maggots and bacterial decay processes. As internal pressures begin to increase, fluids begin to seep from the natural body openings into the substrate below the body. These fluids are combined with the metabolic byproducts (ammonia, etc.) of maggot activities, turning the soil beneath the body alkaline, and the normal soil fauna departs.

3. Decay stage: The decay stage is the only stage that actually has a definite physical event marking its start point. When the skin is broken, gases escape, and the corpse deflates, and the decay stage is considered to begin. Diptera larvae form large feeding masses and are the predominant taxa present. Some predators and parasites were present during the bloated stage; these along with necrophagous species are present in large numbers during the later portions of the decay stage. By the end of this stage, the Diptera larvae will have removed most of the soft tissues of the body and completed their development and left the corpse to pupariate in the soil.

4. Postdecay stage: As the corpse is reduced to skin cartilage and bone, Diptera species cease to be the predominant species present. Various Coleoptera (beetles) predominate through this stage in xerophytic (dry) and mesophytic (temperate) habitats and the diversity of these taxa increases. Associated with this is an increase in the numbers of parasites and predators of the beetle species. In wet habitats, such as a swamp or rainforest, the beetles do not dominate and these are replaced functionally by other groups, primarily Diptera and their associated predators and parasites.

5. Skeletal stage: This stage is reached when only bones and hair remain. There are generally no obvious carrion-frequenting species present and there is a gradual return of the normal soil fauna to the area beneath the corpse. Activities of carrion-associated species are generally restricted to the soil beneath the corpse and these species may be valuable in estimating the period of activity. There is no actual endpoint to this stage and it may be possible to detect changes in the soil fauna months or even years following death, depending on local environmental and soil conditions.

## Relationships of Insects to the Body

Generally, we recognize four basic types of association between the insect and the decomposing body.

First are the necrophagous species that feed on the corpse. In this classification we find many of the true flies (Calliphoridae and Sarcophagidae) and beetles (Silphidae and Dermestidae). Many species in this category are of major significance during the early stages of decomposition, defined as days 1–14.

As the necrophagous species feed on the corpse, their presence and activities attract a second group, the parasites and predators. These insects are the second most significant category of carrion-associated insects. These taxa are predictable in their arrival at the corpse and are often quite specific in their host/prey selection. Included in this category are many of the beetles (Silphidae, Staphylinidae, and Histeridae), true flies (Calliphoridae and Stratiomyidae), and wasps parasitic on larvae and puparia of fly species. In some instances, a species which begins its life as a necrophage may become a predator as the corpse is consumed.

The omnivores comprise the third category. These species feed on both the decomposing corpse and the associated insects and other arthropods. In some instances, these species may severely retard the consumption of the carcass by other arthropod species by their predatory activities.

The last category is termed the adventives. These are species with no real relationship to the decomposing body, but simply use it as an extension of their normal habitat. Included in this group are spiders, centipedes, Collembola, and mites.

Species in all of these categories can potentially provide valuable information concerning the estimation of the postmortem interval. Typically, as the time since death becomes longer, the parameters of the estimated period of insect activity widen. Thus, during the early stages of decomposition, it is possible to provide an estimate in terms of a period of hours, giving way to days, weeks, months, seasons, and finally estimates based on entomology are not possible.

## The Postmortem Interval Estimate

It must be recognized that each case is unique; however, the process tends to follow the same general sequence. This sequence has been detailed previously and will be only summarized here as follows:

1. The stage or physical stage of decomposition of the body should be determined. Any indications of disturbance or dismemberment of the corpse should be noted following the death. From locally conducted decomposition studies, determine what species and/or groups should be anticipated from the scene, time of year, and conditions of the corpse. Insects and other arthropods collected from the corpse should be examined briefly to determine if there are any gaps (missing stages or groups). If such gaps are noted, additional examination of the corpse and surrounding areas should be made.

2. Samples of insects collected from the corpse must be identified as completely as possible. Often, immature stages must be reared to the adult stage in the laboratory for accurate identification. Representative samples of adults and immatures must be properly fixed and preserved, using techniques appropriate for each group. For many taxa, an expert in the group may be required for species level identification. Some preliminary identification may be desirable to assist in a preliminary estimate of the period of insect activity on the corpse.

3. Climatic data (temperatures, rainfall, cloud cover, etc.) should be obtained from weather stations and on-site observations for outdoor scenes. Factors in addition to climatic factors that may serve to delay invasion of the corpse (shading by trees, slope of ground, wrapping, or burial) must be recorded. For indoor scenes, temperatures possible for the time period in question may be derived from air-conditioning or thermostat settings. The position of the corpse relative to doors and windows may also prove significant.

4. Sites of insect infestations on the corpse must be noted both at the scene and later during autopsy. Determine if there was any antemortem administration of drugs or toxins as these may influence the rate and pattern of development of insects feeding on the corpse.

5. The postmortem interval can then be estimated. During the early stages of decomposition, this process is most often based on development of Diptera larvae. The period of time required for the earliest-arriving species to reach the stage of development collected from the corpse represents the period of insect development on the corpse and this corresponds to the minimum postmortem interval. Further consideration must be given to factors that may alter this time period (climatic factors, wrapping, burial, indoors). When these factors are considered, the final postmortem interval estimate may be longer than the estimated faunal ages. As decomposition progresses, the estimate will be based largely on comparisons with results of decomposition studies conducted in

similar habitats during similar times of the year. These comparisons will reveal time periods during which similar populations will occur on both the corpse and the decomposition studies, both in terms of species composition and developmental stages present. In this comparison, both the presence and absence of taxa must be considered. Generally, as the postmortem interval increases, the parameters for the estimate of insect activity will become wider. During the early stages of decomposition, the estimate may be in terms of hours or days, later months, years, or seasons, and finally "a long, long time."

## Movement of the Corpse

While insects and other arthropods are the most widely distributed animals on the earth, many species have very limited geographic distributions. The fauna associated with a decomposing corpse will consist of elements specific to the decomposition process and other elements specific to the geographic habitat in which the corpse is discovered. Discovery of insects normally associated with a habitat different from that in which the corpse is discovered indicates that the victim was originally killed in one habitat, colonized by insects, and subsequently moved to another habitat where further colonization occurred. Comparisons of developmental stages for both groups of insects can reveal approximations of the periods of time the corpse spent in each habitat. These differences in species composition may involve large geographic distances (state to state transport) or simple differences between urban and rural habitats in relatively close geographic proximity.

## Assessment of Trauma

The normal pattern of insect invasion of a corpse is for the natural body openings of the head, anus, and genitals to be the first sites for oviposition or larviposition by Diptera species. The presence of blood associated with wounds is also attractive to many species and these sites will serve as additional sites for invasion. A wound inflicted prior to death, while the heart is still beating, produces large quantities of blood. By contrast, a wound inflicted following death does not produce similar quantities of blood and is not as attractive to flies. If a corpse during the earlier stages of decomposition has infestations in areas other than the natural body openings, consideration must be given to the possibility that antemortem wounds are present. If wounds are present on

the corpse but invasions are restricted to the natural body openings, these wounds may well have been inflicted following death.

## Crime-Scene Characterization

In this instance, insects or insect bites may be used to tie a suspect or victim to a particular scene. As noted above, insects and other arthropods often have limited geographic distributions. These limitations may be quite specific and the geographic distances short. This was the situation in a case where bites of larval Trombiculidae or chiggers were used to tie a suspect to a particular crime scene in California. The distribution of these mites was restricted to a particular habitat in the larger geographic area. Bites on the suspect could logically only have been acquired if he was in that particular location.

## Entomotoxicology

This field covers two basic areas of concern. There has been an increase in recent years in the number of drug-related deaths in the USA and the rest of the world. Frequently these deaths are not discovered for a period of time and it is not unusual for the corpse to be highly decomposed or skeletal. At this point there is not sufficient tissue for toxicological analysis. However, there are frequently still insects, cast larval skins, or puparial skins present. As has been noted in several publications, it is possible to detect various toxins and controlled substances by analyzing these tissues. Typically, the insects and skins have been homogenized and treated as other tissues or fluids of toxicological interest. Methods used for analyses have included radioimmunoassay (RIA), gas chromatography (GC), thin-layer chromatography (TLC), and high-performance liquid chromatography–mass spectrometry (HPLC-MS).

Due to decompositional processes, estimates of the postmortem interval in these cases are based on entomological analyses. As these estimates are based on the patterns of development and succession of the insects, it is essential that any effects of the toxins, drugs, or metabolites in the tissues be understood and incorporated into formulation of the estimate. Studies by various workers have demonstrated that, particularly during the first 2–4 weeks of decomposition, various drugs influence the rates and patterns of development of Diptera larvae. Substances investigated to date include cocaine, heroin, methamphetamines, phencyclidine, methylenedioxymethamphetamine (MDMA), and amitryptyline. Effects on development varied, dependent on the drug, but all resulted in changes to the development of larvae.

## Sources of Human DNA

DNA technology has provided forensic workers with the ability to isolate, amplify, and analyze minute amounts of DNA. Polymerase chain reaction (PCR) DNA techniques have been used to extract host DNA material from insects, including mosquitoes and crab lice. These extractions have been from both insect gut contents and fecal materials and have been used to identify successfully individual hosts on which the insects had fed. Mitochondrial DNA (mtDNA) analyses have been used to identify human remains on which Diptera larvae had fed as well as identifying the species of the larvae themselves. More recently, mtDNA material has been extracted successfully from nitidulid beetle larvae feeding on bone, thus increasing the timeframe for recovery of mtDNA from insect species associated with later stages of decomposition.

## Abuse and Neglect of Children and the Elderly

In most cases, entomological evidence is restricted to the dead. There is an increasing incidence of abuse and/or neglect of children, the elderly, or others incapable of caring for themselves. In these instances, entomological evidence may be of use in documenting the period of abuse or neglect. The insects most frequently involved are those fly species involved in myiasis. Myiasis is the feeding by fly larvae on living human tissues. Within this there is a range from those that have this as an obligatory condition to those involved in a facultative myiasis. Facultative myiasis most frequently involves feeding by larvae on dead tissues associated with a wound or open sore. This condition, while disturbing, is not in itself generally hazardous to the victim and maggots have been deliberately introduced into wounds as a therapeutic measure. In these cases, the maggots can be analyzed to determine the period of abuse or neglect. An additional problem may occur in cases where myiasis occurred prior to death of a victim. If sites of infestation are not noted, the period of development for these more developed maggots may be added to postmortem development, thus increasing the estimated time since death. Any departure from the normal pattern of invasion of the corpse should be the cause for care in interpretation of entomological evidence.

## Conclusions

There has been a significant increase in the applications of entomological evidence to forensic investigations since the 1980s. The major application remains in the estimation of the period of insect activity on a corpse as an indication of the minimum postmortem interval. While there have been many advances in this aspect, there remains a need for basic research on the life cycles, behavior, and distributions of many species, particularly beetles or Coleoptera. Research has also allowed for the expansion of entomological evidence into other areas, such as toxicology, DNA analyses, and aspects of crime-scene analyses. A current underlying problem lies in the lack of trained forensic entomologists. The majority of individuals working in the field are associated with various academic institutions where only a small part of their research activities is related to the forensic sciences. Insect evidence is not present in all cases, but when it is and is analyzed properly, it has the potential to be a powerful tool in forensic investigations.

## See Also

**Anthropology:** Archeology, Excavation and Retrieval of Remains; Taphonomy

## Further Reading

Byrd JA, Castner JL (eds.) (2001) *Forensic Entomology: The Utility of Arthropods in Legal Investigations.* New York: CRC Press.

Catts EP, Haskell NH (eds.) (1990) *Entomology and Death: A Procedural Guide.* Clemson, SC: Joyce's Print Shop.

Goff ML (1993) Estimation of postmortem interval using arthropod developmental and successional patterns. *Forensic Sciences Review* 5: 81–94.

Goff ML (2001) *A Fly for the Prosecution.* Cambridge, MA: Harvard University Press.

Goff ML, Lord WD (1994) Entomotoxicology: a new area for forensic investigation. *American Journal of Forensic Medicine and Pathology* 15: 151–157.

Greenberg B, Kunich JC (2002) *Entomology and the Law: Flies as Forensic Indicators.* Cambridge, UK: Cambridge University Press.

Haglund WD, Sorg MH (eds.) (1997) *Forensic Taphonomy: The Postmortem Fate of Human Remains.* New York: CRC Press.

Romoser WS, Stoffolano JG (1998) *The Science of Entomology,* 4th edn. Boston, MA: WCB McGraw Hill.

Smith KVG (1986) *A Manual of Forensic Entomology.* Ithaca, NY: Cornell University Press.

# EVIDENCE, RULES OF

**I Freckelton**, Monash University, Melbourne,
VIC, Australia

## Evidence

Most legal disputes principally raise the need to evaluate competing versions of fact, each purporting to
be "true" and reliable. Rules of evidence in both
common-law (accusatorial or adversarial) and civil
(inquisitorial) systems play the important role of
regulating how "facts" are to be assessed and what
proof is required, ultimately determining whether an
accused person is guilty or not guilty and whether
a noncriminal case is proved or not proved to the
requisite standard. They also sit at the intersection
between the rights of the individual (especially the
accused and witnesses, their privacy and corporal
integrity) and the rights of society, as well as regulating the junction between law and forensic medicine and forensic science. Rules of evidence feature
in constitutions (such as the Italian, Portuguese,
Canadian, and the US Bill of Rights), as well as in
international law such as the European Convention
on Human Rights.

Rules of evidence exist in some form in both
common-law systems (accusatorial or adversarial
systems like the United Kingdom, the USA, and
Australia) and civilian inquisitorial jurisdictions
(like the Netherlands, France, Germany, and Italy).
It is important to note that virtually no modern legal
system is purely adversarial or inquisitorial. Although
the dichotomy is idealized, it nevertheless provides a
convenient structure for the purposes of this article.
The two systems, although not mutually exclusive,
range from almost complete freedom of evidence to
restrictive rules of admissibility; although the question of admissibility or freedom of evidence does not
always arise – in common-law systems which accept
the accused's guilty plea without requiring a full trial,
the judge can pronounce a sentence and evidentiary
issues may have limited importance. In general,
courts of the Anglo-American-Australasian tradition
have elaborate judge-made and statutory frameworks
which classify evidence as able to be adduced before a
court (admissible) or not able to be adduced (inadmissible). Fundamental criteria on the basis of which
the rules are formulated are reliability and probative
value – the extent to which an alleged fact materially bears upon questions to be decided by the
decision-maker(s).

This article considers the frameworks for rules
of evidence, focusing upon criminal trials in both
legal systems, exploring the general principles of
evidence law and illustrating and expanding upon
those principles with examples from a variety of countries. Rules of evidence and their application can
differ in criminal and civil trials. For the purposes of
this article and with a focus on forensic medicine, the
principal focus is upon criminal evidence rules. On
the differences between criminal and civil evidence
in the United Kingdom, see for example PIQR P175
published in 1992 by Halford and Brookes where a
civil action for damages was brought for murder,
despite one of the defendants' acquittal in earlier
criminal proceedings.

## Common-Law (Accusatorial or Adversarial) Evidence

### Common-Law Development

Central to the common-law system of justice is adver-
sarialism, a contest between two competing parties
before an impartial and passive umpire-like judge,
with a jury to pronounce one version of facts as
true. Rules of evidence grew in response to this system, principally from common-law judges during the
seventeenth and eighteenth centuries. As lay persons
were involved in the legal system in juries, judges
adopted paternalistic and protective rules of evidence,
excluding matters such as hearsay, evidence of character, information about prior convictions, and the
opinions of nonexperts for fear that juries might misinterpret or overvalue the probative value of such
information, concluding that where there is smoke
there may be fire. The courts were also concerned to
prevent manipulation or deliberate fabrication of evidence from those with a vested interest, and to classify some (such as young children or persons with
serious mental illnesses) to be incompetent witnesses.

According to Harvey, evidence was "founded apparently on the propositions that all jurymen are deaf
to reason, that all witnesses are presumptively liars
and that all documents are presumptively forgeries."
Such extreme criticisms aside, modern rules of evidence play an important role in protecting accused
persons from prejudice and procedural unfairness,
in ensuring the efficiency and expediency of justice
and ultimately in facilitating fact-finding accuracy
and predictability. Many similar considerations also
apply in noncriminal matters. However, as Twining
suggests, the law of evidence resembles gruyère, a

**Table 1** Table of statutes

*Common-law jurisdictions*
Police and Criminal Evidence Act 1984 (UK)
Youth Justice and Criminal Evidence Act 1999 (UK)
Criminal Justice Act 1988 (UK)
Federal Rules of Evidence 1975 (USA)
Evidence Act 1995 (Commonwealth, Australia)
Criminal Code (Canada)
*Civilian inquisitorial jurisdictions*
Codice di procedura penale (Italian Criminal Code)
Code de Procédure Pénale (French Code of Criminal Procedure)
Wetboek van Strafrecht (Dutch Criminal Code)
Strafprozeßordnung (Criminal Procedure Order of 1.2.1877)
 (Germany)

cheese riddled with holes – evidence law is not a complete instrument in any common-law jurisdiction. As there are several common-law jurisdictions (**Table 1**), each with its own common law and statutory regimes regulating the admissibility and use of evidence, this article considers the general framework of evidence law with specific reference to the UK, the USA, and Australia.

In the UK, evidence "is a common law construction overlaid with a statutory veneer," governed by both case law and statute, particularly the Police and Criminal Evidence Act 1984 (UK), which limits police powers and provides the statutory regime for the admissibility of evidence; and the Youth Justice and Criminal Evidence Act 1999 (UK) which, among other things, regulates the competence of children to give sworn and unsworn evidence. In the USA, the Federal Rules of Evidence 1975 (US) are not a complete code and do not bind the states, but generally apply in federal courts and have been adopted or closely followed by more than half of all American states. In Australia, while all individual states and territories also have their own evidence legislation, the Commonwealth Evidence Act 1995 (substantially adopted in New South Wales and Tasmania) applies in federal courts and acts as a guide for other states and territories to follow.

## Common-Law Rules of Evidence

### Relevance

For evidence to be admissible in the common-law tradition, it must first be deemed relevant; although not all relevant evidence will necessarily be admissible. Relevance functions as the most significant gateway for evidence, demarcating the admissible from the inadmissible in courts on the basis of whether it is (sufficiently) pertinent to the matters to be traversed in the proceeding.

In his *Digest of the Law of Evidence*, Stephen defined relevance as:

> any two facts to which it is applied are so related to each other that according to the common course of events one either taken by itself or in connection with other facts proves or renders probable the past, present or future existence or non-existence of the other.

In the USA, Rule 401 Federal Rules of Evidence similarly defines relevance as evidence which makes a fact at issue "more probable or less probable than it would be without the evidence." In practice, whether a fact is relevant is a question of degree, depending on the circumstances and issues in the case at hand, on other evidence, and common sense.

### Competence

Competence is another threshold test. It demarcates who can be a witness and thus who can give sworn (or unsworn) evidence. Traditionally, certain witnesses who were thought apt to mislead rather than aid a court were deemed incompetent, often due to their antecedents of relationship with the parties or matter (see, e.g., R *v*. White 1899).

In the UK, any person is a competent witness in any proceedings, whatever their age, both at common law and under 53(1)s of the Youth Justice and Criminal Evidence Act 1999 (UK). Young children and persons of "unsound mind" or defective intellect are not incompetent *per se*, but must satisfy 53(3)s of the Act: a witness must: (1) understand the questions put to him/her as a witness; and (2) be able to give answers that can be understood. (The age or mental incapacity or illness of a witness may nevertheless affect his/her need to give sworn evidence under oath: see 55(1)–(4)s of the Youth Justice Act.) In Australia and the USA, similar requirements apply: in Australia, a witness cannot give sworn evidence if he/she is incapable of understanding the obligation to give truthful evidence, although the witness may be able to give unsworn evidence if he/she can understand the difference between the truth and a lie, and can give a rational reply which can be understood: see Evidence Act 1995 (Comm Aus), ss 13–14. Likewise, under US federal law, an incompetent witness may be barred from giving evidence due to mental disease (Federal Rules of Evidence 1975 (US), Rule 601).

If a witness is competent, he/she is generally compellable to testify in court. A compellable witness may be entitled to refuse to answer some or all questions on the grounds of public policy or privilege. However, under most common-law systems there are some general exceptions to the compellability rules, the most significant of which is that an accused person is not a compellable witness.

Another category of noncompellable witnesses is often persons closely related to the accused person. In Australia, for instance, a spouse of the accused can object to giving evidence as a prosecution witness against the defendant, depending on such matters as the nature of their relationship, the nature of the offense, the substance, and importance of the evidence (Evidence Act 1995 (Comm Aus, s18)).

## Opinion Evidence

In the Anglo-American-Australasian systems, opinion evidence, save as to shorthand expressions of fact, is generally inadmissible. This means that lay people generally cannot give opinion evidence. Experts are permitted to give such evidence, as well as evidence in the form of facts, but subject to a number of limitations. Expert evidence historically has been significantly mistrusted, because under the common-law systems experts are picked accordingly as their views are known to incline, because perjury proceedings against experts are problematic, because expert evidence can be difficult to cross-examine, and because expert evidence can be misunderstood and misconstrued. The result has been that the exclusionary rules of expert evidence have been fashioned so as to confine its ambit.

In many jurisdictions, "experts" have been narrowly defined. It is not enough, for instance, that they be tertiary-educated; they must have specialized knowledge on the matter upon which they are to give evidence, such knowledge having been acquired by skill, training, or experience. In some countries, such as the USA, the evidence must be "reliable;" this is determined by reference to factors such as the falsifiability of the technique or theory, the use of controls, the extent to which the technique or theory has been the subject of peer-reviewed publications, and the extent to which it has gained general acceptance within the relevant scientific community. Such a test has been used in civil cases, in particular, to exclude evidence that is "novel" in the sense of not yet having been accepted within the scientific or medical communities as sound and orthodox in terms of theory and technique.

The "common knowledge" rule historically has confined experts to giving evidence about matters outside the general ken of lay persons; it has particularly circumscribed the evidence that might otherwise be given by mental health professionals. However, in many jurisdictions, the common-knowledge rule has been attenuated or repealed by legislation (see, e.g., Evidence Act 1995 (Aust Cth), s80).

Historically experts have been precluded from giving evidence upon the ultimate issue to be determined by a court, especially by a jury. The law now is variable, the ultimate issue rule being retained, for instance, for criminal trials in the USA, but having been substantially abolished in Australia.

Where expert evidence is substantially more prejudicial than it is probative, Rule 403 of the US Federal Rules of Evidence and s135 and s137 of the Evidence Act 1995 (Aust Cth) allow it to be excluded. The question is often how confusing, misleading, or time-consuming the expert evidence is, together with the extent to which it assists in establishing a fact in issue between the parties.

Courts in the common-law tradition have depended substantially upon the check and balance of cross-examination to test out the strengths and weaknesses of expert evidence, enabling informed assessment. This has not been so pronounced a feature of the inquisitorial systems of justice. However, a number of calls have been made latterly on the continent for more robust testing of expert evidence adduced against accused persons, lest overmuch deference is shown to experts who may not be sufficiently rigorous in their analyses.

The likelihood of expert witnesses being made accountable for their evidence is a factor of the questions asked of the expert (whether that be by the court or by lawyers for the parties) and also of the potential for counterexpert evidence to be called by the defense in criminal trials to contest the opinions proffered by the experts for the prosecution. There is a tradition of such independent sources of evidence in the Anglo-American-Australasian systems but not so pronounced as one in some civil-law countries. It may be that this will change.

## Hearsay Evidence

In the Anglo-American-Australasian systems, hearsay evidence has traditionally been classified as inadmissible, subject to a complex set of exceptions.

While Wigmore regarded the hearsay exclusionary rule as the "most characteristic rule of the Anglo-American system of evidence" and "the greatest contribution of that eminently practical legal system," Lord Reid and Lord Diplock characterized it as "absurd." The hearsay rule is widely regarded as complex and confusing, although it has been simplified by statute in most common-law jurisdictions. (In the UK, see especially Criminal Justice Act 1988 (UK), ss9, 23–28; Children and Young Persons Act 1933 (UK), s43.)

Hearsay, is "any statement, other than one made by a witness in the course of giving his evidence in the proceedings in question, by any person, whether it was made on oath or unsworn and whether it was made orally, in writing or by signs and gestures, which is offered as evidence of the truth of its contents." More simply, hearsay evidence is information given by a person about what he/she did not personally witness, or evidence he/she obtained from a third party who is absent from the court. It is excluded because the reliability of the evidence cannot easily be tested for mistake, insincerity, or ambiguity: the actual witness cannot swear an oath or be cross-examined or interrogated.

The hearsay rule is not strictly about the apparent reliability of the evidence; rather the issue is the difficulty of deciding what weight to give the evidence. Its admissibility therefore depends on the purpose for which the evidence is being used. If the statement is not tendered to prove the truth of its contents, but only seeks to prove that the statement was made, or to prove the state of mind of the person who made the original statement, then it is not hearsay but "original evidence." (In Australia, see s60 of the Evidence Act 1995 (Cth).) If the original evidence is relevant, it is admissible. Where evidence is relevant for both hearsay and nonhearsay purposes, it is generally admissible, although the judge can exercise his/her discretion to warn the jury about its limitations or even to exclude the evidence.

However, there are numerous exceptions to the hearsay rule, often based on complex case law, and which differ between jurisdictions. A voluntarily made confession by the accused to a police officer outside court is admissible (see Police and Criminal Evidence Act 1984 (UK) on the admissibility of confessions in the UK), as is an informal admission proved against the party who made it. At common law, generally deathbed statements (Rule 804 Federal Rules of Evidence in the USA), declarations against the interests of the declarer and spontaneous statements are also often admissible, even though technically hearsay. Early complaints of sexual assault are also a common exception to the hearsay rule. In the UK and Australia, first-hand hearsay contained in documents (evidence forming part of a record, such as computer files) is generally admissible in both civil and criminal proceedings, provided that the person who made the statement is unable to attend court as a witness (see Section 23 Criminal Justice Act 1988 (UK); Australia: s65 Evidence Act 1995 (Cth)). Hearsay statements contained in documents created or received by a person in the course of trade, business, profession, or occupation, are also generally admissible, with some exceptions (see Section 24 Criminal Justice Act. This applies whether the hearsay is first-hand, second-hand, or multiple. Australia: Evidence Act 1995 (Cth) s 69). In the UK, hearsay statements may also be admissible where they are expert reports, statements, and depositions in criminal proceedings,

committal statements and depositions at trial, written statements under s9 of the Criminal Justice Act, depositions of children and young persons, and transcripts at retrials.

## Character and Similar Fact Evidence

Evidence of the character of a party may be admissible if it is directly relevant or in issue, such as where a previous conviction is an essential element of the current charges, where relevant in sentencing, or where an accused pleads "autrefois convict."

The accused can introduce evidence of his/her good character when it goes to the issue of guilt or innocence, when it supports the credibility of the accused, or even to predispose the jury to favor the accused. Such evidence tends to suggest that he/she is not the kind of person to have committed the crime or, when he/she denies having committed it, that he/she should be believed.

Generally evidence about the accused's character, reputation, history of wrongdoing, or other acts of misconduct cannot be adduced by the prosecution in common-law jurisdictions, as the risk that a tribunal of fact will attach greater than justifiable weight to the evidence outweighs its probative value. (In Australia, Evidence Act 1995 (Cth) s97 and in the USA Federal Rules of Evidence 1975, Rule 401, 608, and 609 are exceptions.) This exclusionary rule is designed to protect the accused from wrongful conviction and preserve the presumption of innocence, as a person should be judged by what he/she has done rather than what acts he/she might have committed in the past.

In criminal proceedings in the UK and Australia, evidence of character is only admissible if it is directly relevant or is in issue. If the accused has put his/her character in issue, the prosecution may be able to rebut evidence of good character with evidence of bad character, either through cross-examination or by leading extrinsic evidence (see also Article 666 of the Canadian Criminal Code). In most common-law jurisdictions, the prosecution can raise "similar fact" evidence "bearing the same signature." (However, the terminology of "similar fact" is less common in the USA and can be misleading.) This means, for example, that while the prosecution cannot raise evidence of another murder committed by the accused at a different time and in different circumstances, the prosecution can adduce evidence of a murder committed in very similar circumstances. In the USA, evidence of a witness' character is only admissible if probative to his/her truthfulness or untruthfulness (Federal Rules of Evidence 1975, Rule 608). Evidence of prior convictions is admissible only if punishable by death or imprisonment in excess of 1 year, where probative of the witness' truthfulness, and where its disclosure outweighs its prejudicial effect to the accused.

### Privilege

In common-law jurisdictions, evidence can be excluded because of extrinsic considerations (such as legal privilege), which outweigh the value that evidence would have at a trial. In the UK, for instance, there are three main kinds of "privilege": (1) privilege against self-incrimination; (2) legal professional privilege; and (3) privilege in "without prejudice" negotiations. In Australia s127 of the Evidence Act 1995 (Cth) also extends privilege to religious confessions but not to interactions between doctors and patients.

In the USA and Australia, suspects have a right to remain silent in pretrial investigations. At trial, the court cannot infer guilt from the silence (Australia: Evidence Act 1975 (Cth), s89). However, in the UK, the court can draw adverse inferences from: (1) the accused's silence in failing to testify or selectively answering questions; (2) the accused's failure or refusal to consent to the taking of samples; and (3) the accused's failure to provide advance disclosure of the defense's case.

Privilege also upholds the confidentiality of a lawyer–client relationship (see Police and Criminal Evidence Act 1984 (UK)), generally protecting communications between clients and their lawyers and lawyers and experts where the dominant purpose of such communications was provision of legal advice or preparation for litigation.

### Public Interest Evidence

Evidence in common-law jurisdictions can be withheld in the public interest or to protect national interests or security. It is generally in the public interest to exclude evidence on the grounds of national security, good diplomatic relations, and international comity. Information relevant to the detection of crime, such as the identity of informers or notifiers (such as those providing information about suspected sexual abuse of children), can also be excluded, as can documents central to government and related to nongovernmental bodies and agencies performing public functions. Thus, it has been held that a trial judge should balance the public interest underlying nondisclosure of evidence against the interests of justice in the particular circumstances, particularly liberty and occasionally even life.

### Unfairly Obtained Evidence

In the UK, under s78 of the Police and Criminal Evidence Act, courts have the discretion to exclude unfairly obtained evidence where it would have a prejudicial effect on the fairness of a criminal trial; under s76, a confession before a police officer will be rejected if the prosecutor cannot prove that it was obtained freely. The situation is similar in the USA, where evidence can be nullified where it was obtained in contravention of constitutional rights; however, there are two significant exceptions: first, evidence can still be admissible where the rights of a third party were disregarded, rather than the rights of the accused. Second, illegally obtained evidence will still be admissible if it would have been discovered even without the illegality.

In the UK and the USA, the doctrine of "the fruits of the poisonous tree" can apply where subsequent evidence linked to illegally obtained evidence can be rejected, such as where a knife found in an illegal search later leads to an accused confessing. In Australia, evidence obtained improperly or illegally is not admitted unless the desirability of admitting the evidence outweighs the undesirability of admitting it (Evidence Act 1995 (Cth), s138).

## Civil-Law (Inquisitorial) Systems

In some respects, rules of evidence are primarily a common-law construction, designed to protect juries from information they could misinterpret. Juries are rarely used in civilian inquisitorial systems, so rules of evidence serve a different purpose.

### Civil Law: Development

In civilian inquisitorial legal systems like the Netherlands, France, Italy, and Germany, the court examines the facts itself and the judge is typically involved in both the preparation and presentation of facts. While cross-examination and orality are central to the common-law system, in the inquisitorial system, cross-examination is less well regarded, on occasions being described as an attempt to corner the witness. A public hearing is not the climax as it is in the accusatorial system; instead the public hearing is a continuation of truth-finding where the court can scrutinize the dossier and interrogate the evidence gathered before the trial.

### Civil Law: Rules of Evidence

Rules of evidence in the inquisitorial system are often less technical and restrictive and do not govern admissibility, but emphasize what value is placed on the evidence. The continental system is characterized by free appreciation of proof so "the court is not fettered by any formal rules of evidence, but can evaluate the evidence produced by the parties or taken *sua sponte*, in its own free and reasonable evidence, including happenings in the courtroom, which are not evidence in the strict sense." In Germany, the principle of "unfettered consideration of evidence" (Grundsatz der freien richterlichen Beweiswürigung) places no legal compulsion on the judge to consider evidence in a particular way (Rules 244 and 261 Strafprozeßordnung (StPo) (Criminal Procedure Order of 1.2.1877). Likewise in France, under Article 81 of the Code of Criminal Procedure, the judge "undertakes all investigating acts which he judges necessary to the revelation of the truth" and under Article 427, "except in cases where the law rules differently, offenses may be established by any means of evidence." However, it is important to note that major differences in rules of evidence and practice exist between civil-law jurisdictions. For instance, while Germany and the Netherlands both have the principle of immediacy (Unmittelbarkeit in Germany, and onmiddellijkheid in the Netherlands), witnesses or experts rarely appear in Dutch courts, as trials are based on the dossier (or case file). While in France, all evidence is admissible and the court can determine the relative weight or value of any evidence (Article 427 Code of Criminal Practice), in the Netherlands, Article 338 of the Dutch criminal code exhaustively regulates the evidence upon which a conviction can be based. (Article 338 Dutch Criminal Code: a conviction must be based on "lawful means of proof" – the personal observations of the judge, the declaration of the accused, a witness or an expert, or official documents. The Code also stipulates that, while some forms of evidence alone are sufficient for conviction, other forms require a combination of proof.)

Evidence must still be relevant in inquisitorial jurisdictions. Italy, for example, takes a strict approach to relevance, allowing the judge to exercise discretion to exclude irrelevant evidence. In Italy, a judge can exclude statements which have no relation to the issue of the case and set aside testimonies that are too detailed (Article 469 Italian Criminal Code). Under Article 494, the judge can prohibit the accused from speaking where he/she goes beyond the subject of the trial and can preclude the parties from asking nonpertinent questions (Article 468). Under the French Code of Criminal Procedure, the president of an assize court can reject any evidence that might impair the dignity of the proceedings or prolong their duration without bringing greater probity (French Code de Procédure Pénal (Code of Criminal Procedure) Article 309).

There are no rules of evidence to exclude hearsay, for example. Instead the court decides how much weight to attach to the evidence. Courts in Germany have the exclusive right to appoint expert witnesses, which the state or defense can challenge (Rule 73–74 StPo). The court is also not bound by expert evidence, and can refuse further expert evidence when it considers it already has sufficient expertise (Rule 244 StPo).

In France, Germany, and Italy, exclusionary evidence rules of some form exist to deter violations of legal process during police interviews and interrogation. While there are restrictions on certain means of obtaining evidence, evidence obtained through prohibited methods is usually admissible in Germany. In France, usually the court alone can decide whether procedural requirements have been breached so seriously as to justify nullification of the relevant evidence. This can occur where there has been prejudice to the accused or breach of a rule of public order (such as competence) (Article 171 Code of Criminal Procedure). Likewise, in Belgium, case law disapproves of evidence obtained illegally or in breach of procedure. Violations such as evidence obtained through narcoanalysis, even with the accused's consent, can result in nullity. Procedural rules are stricter in Italy, where any procedural irregularity can result in inadmissibility of evidence and even a complete rejection of the verdict (Italian Code of Criminal Procedure, 1989, article 191).

## Role of Rules of Evidence

Rules governing the admissibility of evidence exist in some form in both common-law and civil inquisitorial legal systems. They provide articulated yardsticks in relation to evidence classified as worthy to be relied upon in significant decision-making by courts. While the developed sets of rules existing in the common-law systems have been criticized as excessively paternalistic, complex, and restrictive, they have evolved to protect against juries and, to a lesser degree, judges giving inappropriate weight to evidence without the hallmarks of reliability but which can be highly prejudicial to the case of one party to litigation. In those jurisdictions where more confidence is exhibited in the abilities of juries, and where juries are less used, rules of evidence, to the extent that they exist, tend to be looser and more flexible.

## See Also

**Court Systems:** Sharii'ah Law; Law, China; Law, United Kingdom; Law, United States of America

## Further Reading

Bell J, Boyron S, Whittaker S (1998) *Principles of French Law.* Oxford, UK: Oxford University Press.
Fisher HD (1999) *The German Legal System and Legal Language,* 2nd edn. London: Cavendish.

Fishman CS (1992) *Jones on Evidence: Civil and Criminal,* 7th edn. New York: Lawyers Cooperative.

Foster N (1996) *German Legal System and Laws,* 2nd edn. London: Blackstone Press Ltd.

Freckelton I, Selby H (2005) *Expert Evidence: Law, Practice, Procedure and Advocacy,* 3rd edn. Law Book Co.

Keane A (2000) *The Modern Law of Evidence,* 5th edn. London: Butterworths.

Kralik W (1963) *Introduction to the Continental Judicial Organisation and Civil Procedure.* Pretoria: Unisa.

Meintjes-Van Der Walt L (2001) *Expert Evidence in the Criminal Justice Process: A Comparative Perspective.* Amsterdam: Rozenberg.

Nijboer H (2000) The significance of comparative legal studies. In: Nijboer JF and Sprangers WJJM (eds.) *Harmonisation in Forensic Expertise* 402–410.

Nijboer JF, Sprangers WJJM (2000) *Harmonisation in Forensic Expertise.* Thesis. Amsterdam: Thelia. Thesis.

Pakter W (1985) Exclusionary rules in France, Germany, and Italy. *Hastings International and Comparative Law Review* 9(1): 1.

Sopinka J, Lederman S, Bryant A (1992) *The Law of Evidence in Canada.* Toronto: Butterworths.

Tapper C (1999) *Cross and Tapper on Evidence,* 9th edn. London: Butterworths.

Twining W (1989) *Theories of Evidence: Bentham and Wigmore.* Stanford: Stanford University Press.

Twining W (1990) *Rethinking Evidence: Exploratory Essays.* Evanston, IL: Northwestern University Press.

Van Kampen P (1998) *Expert Evidence Compared: Rules and Procedures in the Dutch and American Criminal Justice Systems.* Leiden, The Netherlands: Intersentia.

Waight P, Williams R (2002) *Evidence: Commentary and Materials,* 6th edn. Sydney: Lawbook.

Wigmore IH *Evidence in Trials at the Common Law,* 4th edn. Boston, MA: Little Brown.

# EXCITED DELIRIUM

**C V Wetli**, Suffolk County Department of Health Services, Hauppauge, NY, USA

## Introduction

Delirium is a transient, acute, confusional state characterized by disturbances of cognition, attention, and perception, disorganized and incoherent thinking, memory impairment, and defective orientation. Victims of this organic mental disorder may be apathetic or depressed, or excited with fear or rage, accompanied by sympathetic nervous system arousal (e.g., tachycardia, elevated blood pressure, sweating, pallor, flushing, and mydriasis). Causes include cerebral and systemic diseases, exogenous toxins (including prescriptive and recreational drugs), and substance abuse withdrawal.

In recent years, attention has been drawn to victims of delirium who present in a highly agitated state and die suddenly, often in police custody and while being restrained. Such victims of excited delirium have provoked allegations of police misconduct. The cause and mechanism of these deaths have become controversial, with theories ranging from catecholamine-induced cardiac arrhythmia, to restraint or positional asphyxia, and to the neuroleptic malignant syndrome among others.

This review traces the evolution of the concept of excited delirium from its first description by Dr. Luther Bell in 1849 up to the present. This will hopefully provide a perspective and cohesive focus to guide forensic investigations into the etiology of excited delirium and the mechanisms responsible for sudden death.

## New Form of Disease

Dr. Luther Bell presented his paper in May 1849 at the meeting of the Association of the Medical Superintendents of the American Institution for the Insane. Dr. Bell had spent more than 12 years treating the insane at one asylum. From 1836 through 1848, over 1700 cases were admitted, and among these were 40 cases which manifested a peculiar form of delirium. At least three-quarters of these cases terminated fatally, and "the remainder promptly and entirely recovered – so much so in fact, that one of my distinguishing marks will be found to be deduced from this speedy and sequel-less restoration."

The general presentation and description of symptoms by Dr. Bell bear quoting:

> The type of the aberration is like the low mutterings of typhoid fever, except that the faculties can be stimulated by a direct inquiry to a momentary correct action. Your patient, in his general, dull apprehension of impending danger, makes constant attempts to get out of bed, and if permitted to do so, will stand until exhausted. I find by our record that almost every one of these cases was treated with the bed-strap to secure recumbency – a measure scarcely ever employed with us in any other

case. Oftentimes this sensation of danger will exhibit itself in the patient's attacking any one who approaches him, with a blind fury. If held, he will struggle with the utmost desperation, irrespective of the number or strength of those who may be endeavoring to restrain him. There is no just calculation of numbers supposed to be attacking, no disposition to yield to an overpowering force, noticeable in some degree in the blindest fury of the most intense forms of ordinary mania.

I have had but few opportunities of making autopsic examinations of this class of cases, and the results of these represented a very meager and scarcely appreciable amount of changes. The slight cerebral and meningeal engorgements which constituted the only marks of diseased change were not greater than the incidents of sleeplessness, agitation and death might be expected to leave, independent of any great morbid action behind these.

In addition to the symptoms described above, there were noted occasional instances of muscular rigidity and attempts to remove clothing. In his series of cases, the course of the illness lasted 2–3 weeks, after which there was either death or complete recovery accompanied by exhaustion, malnutrition, diarrhea, and dehydration. In addition, the onset of symptoms was sudden but took about a week to attain the severity that would precipitate admission to the asylum.

The differential diagnosis included delirium tremens, "some inflammatory action of the brain or meninges," advanced typhoid fever, "muttering delirium of typhus," and passive congestion of the brain (or other deficiency in the cerebral circulation). Treatment was "expectant" and it was noted that blood loss (from accidental venesection resulting in loss of a quart (1 l) of blood, drawing 8 oz. (225 g) of blood from the temporal artery, and application of three leeches to withdraw $1\frac{1}{2}$ oz. (40 g) of blood) had no effect.

## Delineation of Bell's Mania

As Derby described: "One does not find in the literature much in reference to exhaustion as a cause of death." Yet he found that "exhaustion" was in fact listed as a cause of death in 48% of the 386 manic-depressive patients who died at Brooklyn State hospital between 1927 and 1932. Dr. Derby, a pathologist, further analyzed the death certificates and compared them with the autopsy findings. In about 20% of cases pathologic changes found at autopsy proved the clinical diagnosis of death erroneous, but the death certificate did not incorporate the autopsy findings. Nonetheless, "exhaustion" (with various modifiers) remained the most common cause of death among manic-depressive patients. It should be noted that the exhaustion was invariably

accompanied by (due to?) excitement. Also it was noted that temperature elevations were common, particularly terminally, when extreme levels could be attained. Dr. Derby concluded:

The picture of exhaustion at autopsy is: (1) absence of positive findings which it is admitted may be missed (foci in the brain or cord, or small foci not observed elsewhere); (2) an expression of a terminal toxic condition represented by a subacute nephritic reaction grossly and microscopically, general dehydration and evidence of insufficient feeding; and (3) a dilated heart with thinned walls which is an expression of the manner of death.

A year later, the literature concerning deaths occurring during acute mental excitement was reviewed by Davidson. The common features of those victims were continuous psychomotor excitement, rapid weight loss, and fluctuating temperature. Autopsies uniformly failed to reveal an adequate explanation for the death. Underlying diagnoses were most often schizophrenia or acute dementia praecox. Of his own series of cases observed at the Manhattan State Hospital between 1929 and 1934, all were females, and diagnoses also included postpartum psychosis and manic-depressive psychosis. Ages ranged from 21 to 34 years. "The majority died" reflects a lack of rigid scientific observation compared to present standards, but the overall description of the clinical course revealed the emergence of a fairly distinct syndrome.

The majority of cases showed sudden onset of illness, there was a history of delusions and hallucinations, they showed extreme psychomotor excitement, restlessness and resistiveness to the point of negatism. They screamed and yelled as if in reaction to terrifying hallucinations. They showed an apprehensive affect changeable with blankness, stuporous rigidity, wetting and soiling, were mute and had to be tube fed in many instances. The manic-depressive cases who showed at onset a manic syndrome were in the final stage undistinguishable from the others. Sensorium could not be evaluated.

Physically, the patients showed rapid bodily decline, severe metabolic disturbances, fluctuating temperature, and leukocytosis. Blood pressure was falling . . . The most interesting feature was the heart-action. The heart in such cases beats vigorously. The contraction is very weak, volume small, suggestive of emptiness, and of arterial oligemia. Finally it comes to cessation of the heart-action. We believe however that paralysis of the heart can be excluded, and that what really happens is a collapse of the cardio-vascular system. All cases expired under the same circumstances.

Davidson recognized that a correct diagnosis could only be achieved by careful consideration of both clinical and pathological features. He concluded that death was due to "capillary toxicosis" from the release of toxins "tentatively identified with the

H-substances of Lewis" which lead to "extreme opening of visceral capillaries" leading to "arterial oligemia and consequent cardiovascular collapse."

Kraines also reviewed the literature and noted that the earliest description of those cases was by Bell, as discussed above. He also noted a subset of cases "that got well and that the fever never rises very high". He proposed the term "Bell's mania" be applied to all these cases based upon the symptoms and regardless of the original diagnosis or ultimate outcome.

Shulack added 12 additional cases to the literature in 1938 and noted that most cases occurred in females. Subsequently, in 1944, he noted that no further reports of "psychotic furors" appeared in the literature between 1938 and 1943. He then reported four additional cases. One was a psychiatric patient:

> For one month, [he] displayed episodes of acute anxiety and tenseness, then on November 19, 1942, he suddenly became excited, restless and assaultive. He was violently disturbed and in constant hyperactive furor for 28 hours, during which he required frequent restraint and barbiturate sedation. He perspired profusely. At 4:10 P.M., November 20, 1942, his pulse collapsed; his respirations were rapid, shallow, and irregular. His temperature was 109 °F. He died suddenly at 4:55 p.m. after 45 minutes of pronounced shock [with a marked terminal hyperpyrexia which was not recorded].
>
> The postmortem findings were: grossly visceral and encephalic vascular congestion; microscopic, sections from cerebral and cerebellar cortex, basal nuclei, and brainstem displayed a well-preserved parenchyma, but marked congestion of the parenchymal vessels. The liver cells were swollen, containing numerous tiny vacuoles. There were no alterations in the pancreas, heart, adrenals, bone-marrow, and skeletal muscles.

The remaining patients were treated with pharmacologic agents (morphine, barbiturates, paraldehyde, and hyoscine hydrobromide), which may have attenuated both the behavior and the temperature elevations. Two of the four patients survived after large doses of sodium chloride and adrenocortical hormone were administered.

In 1946 Madow and Stauffer analyzed 101 deaths of 2547 nonsenile patients admitted to an acute psychopathic department. Cardiovascular diseases followed by alcoholism and general paresis were the commonest causes of death. However, 10% died of "agitation of unknown etiology." The reported cases included male gender and hyperthermia.

Another quite thorough literature review of the acute exhaustive psychosis was published in 1947 by Adland. He noted that hyperpyrexia was a hallmark of the syndrome, but not invariable, and quoted one source as noting a "body temperature elevated and cutaneous temperature lowered." Adland concluded that the syndrome of "acute exhaustive psychosis" was of a psychogenic etiology "originating in a need for self-annihilation as a solution of a problem." Not surprisingly, treatment recommendations focused on medical management to overcome this self-destructive phase and thought that recovery, albeit infrequent, would depend on psychotherapy.

Since Adland's article in 1947, the literature appears virtually silent for discussion or reports of Bell's mania (acute exhaustive mania, psychic furors, etc.). One can only speculate about the dearth of reported cases since the mid-1940s. Likely possibilities would include simple lack of reporting, the development of psychotropic drugs (major and minor tranquilizers, etc.), and, as noted by Wendkos, some of these cases of sudden death may have been attributed to cardiac arrhythmia induced by phenothiazines. Wendkos also cited three essential features for the diagnosis of acute exhaustive mania in hospitalized psychotic patients: (1) persistent, extremely violent, psychotic behavior which is not related to the ingestion of substances; (2) a sudden fatal outcome which dramatically terminates the maniacal behavior; and (3) the absence of any meaningful anatomic changes at the postmortem examination. Interestingly, hyperthermia was not included in the diagnostic criteria. It is also noteworthy that this syndrome had hitherto only been described in hospitalized psychotic patients.

## Excited Delirium

In 1980, Fishbain recognized the syndrome of excited delirium in a cocaine body packer, and within the next few years the syndrome was recognized in recreational cocaine users as well. By this point, the entity of delirium was regarded as either stuporous or excited, and the excited variety was considered to be (often) a medical emergency with a psychiatric presentation. The etiology could be metabolic, pharmacologic, or infectious (e.g., meningitis, encephalitis). In addition, hyperthermia was a hallmark of the syndrome (particularly when due to cocaine toxicity); death occurred frequently outside the hospital setting, and nearly always involved males. Of the many possible causes for excited delirium, the syndrome today appears to be mostly associated with the abuse of cocaine or amphetamine, and with endogenous mental disease such as schizophrenia (especially following cessation of neuroleptic medication).

The neuroleptic malignant syndrome was described in the 1960s as a potentially fatal complication of antipsychotic drugs. The syndrome was characterized by fever, muscular rigidity, autonomic instability, and altered consciousness. In 1988 Koster and Kleber proposed that cocaine-induced excited delirium may well be a variant of the neuroleptic malignant syndrome. Alternatively, one could consider the neuroleptic malignant syndrome to be an attenuated variation of acute exhaustive mania/excited delirium. Recent studies support the thesis that the neuroleptic malignant syndrome and excited delirium from cocaine toxicity are in fact related and due to impaired dopamine transport in the brain.

At present, therefore, it appears that there are three related syndromes: (1) acute exhaustive mania, as originally described by Bell and elaborated upon by others and occurring in hospitalized psychiatric patients; (2) excited delirium, due to many causes, including stimulant drugs and psychiatric illness; and (3) the attenuated variant of acute exhaustive mania – the neuroleptic malignant syndrome.

## Typical Case Presentation

Victims usually display the sudden onset of paranoia manifested initially by attempts to hide and then to flee the area. The behavior is bizarre, such as taping over pinholes in window blinds or jumping through a closed window despite an open door. Often individuals begin to smash objects, particularly windows and glass shower doors, and partial or total disrobing is fairly common regardless of ambient temperature. They frequently scream and shout, alternating unintelligible utterances with expressions of paranoia ("Don't let them get me, they're trying to kill me"). They frequently alternate between calm behavior and behavior that is highly agitated. Attempts to escape the figment pursuers lead to hiding beneath cars and behind bushes, and attempts to run through heavy vehicular traffic, jump from the roof of one building to another, or swim to perceived safety. When confronted by the police who are invariably called to the scene, the victim intensifies the violence and paranoia. An intense struggle ensues when the victim displays incredible "superhuman" strength and is impervious to the usual police techniques of pain control, including applications of pepper spray, electric stun guns, and peroneal baton strikes. The intense struggle often continues for several minutes and involves the efforts of several police officers who are finally able to fasten handcuffs behind the victim's back. Ankle restraints are often needed and, because of continued thrashing and kicking, the handcuffs and ankle restraints may be connected together. This prone position, with the knees flexed and ankle restraints and handcuffs connected by another strap, is often referred to as "hog-tying" or maximal restraint. Usually within seconds of being restrained, the victim loses all vital signs.

As with any medical syndrome, there are a variety of presentations and scenarios that may unfold. In some instances the syndrome is precipitated by the police who merely want to prevent an obviously mentally disturbed person from darting into traffic. Some lose vital signs or die during transport to a medical facility or gaol, and some remain calm during transport but become violent again upon arrival at the hospital or a detention facility.

Core body temperatures (viz. rectal or hepatic in postmortem cases) average about $105\,°F$ ($40.5\,°C$); but, as noted by others, the temperature may not be elevated. Hyperthermia is, therefore, considered strong supportive evidence for the diagnosis of excited delirium but not a *sine qua non*. Anecdotally, hyperthermia is regarded as a harbinger of inevitable death, with survivors of the syndrome often not having the markedly elevated core temperature.

Initially successful resuscitation often leads to a stormy hospital course characterized by an ultimately fatal sequence of rhabdomyolysis, renal failure, and disseminated intravascular coagulation with multiorgan failure.

The syndrome induced by cocaine is perhaps the best studied to date. The victims are chronic users who are frequently engaged in a binge of drug ingestion, often by smoking freebase ("crack") cocaine. They have been known to have a failure to upregulate receptor sites in the brain and this in turn leads to the psychotic symptoms and the hyperthermia. Methamphetamine is also known to induce excited delirium as well as lysergic acid diethylamide (LSD) and phencyclidine (PCP). Schizophrenics who cease taking their medications form the largest category of victims not related to drug abuse. Rarely, the syndrome may occur in a previously mentally healthy, drug-free individual who receives severe psychological trauma (e.g., an acquired immunodeficiency syndrome (AIDS) victim who learns he has less than a few months to live).

It is important to note that the diagnosis of excited delirium is based on the overall scenario and behavior of the victim, not just one or two signs and symptoms. The key features are sudden intense paranoia accompanied by continued bizarre behavior (shouting, hallucinating), violent resistance to restraint, and continued thrashing after being restrained. Unexpected strength and imperviousness to pain compliance techniques are also hallmarks. Although hyperthermia (by core temperature determination) is a frequent finding, its presence is not required for the diagnosis.

## Why Do They Die?: The Mechanism(s) of Death

The violent and bizarre behavior naturally predisposes the victim to severe injury and traumatic death, including drowning, jumps from buildings, and fatal cuts from broken glass.

Most, however, simply collapse shortly after being restrained. Emergency medical responders often find them in pulseless electrical activity. If initial resuscitative efforts are successful, they often die days later with rhabdomyolysis, renal failure, and disseminated intravascular coagulation. At autopsy, the changes imparted by the severe and prolonged rhabdomyolysis may be dramatic.

Death occurring in police custody following a violent confrontation often leads to allegations of improper police procedure or the excessive application of force to subdue the victim. Lawsuits have alleged that the use of pepper spray, stun guns, and law enforcement neck restraints (lateral vascular neck restraint or LVNR) caused the death.

Reay and O'Halloran have postulated that death may result from positional or restraint asphyxia. The contention is that the prone position (particularly if the victim is somewhat obese), coupled with the "hog-tie" restraint, impairs the mobility of the chest and diaphragm, thereby defeating the bellows action of the chest necessary for breathing. The most compelling evidence to support this mechanism of death in excited delirium is the association of the loss of vital signs while being restrained. However, this does not account for those who die without being maximally restrained. More recent scientific studies have shown there is no significant impairment of breathing mechanism or oxygen restriction from being maximally restrained after intense physical activity. Parkes has shown that recovery for pulse rate is slower in the prone position (which had no effect on oxygen saturation) and concluded that the restraint position may only be a factor in combination with other contributory factors (which were not specified).

It has been lamented that there is "much journalism, little evidence" to explain the deaths of victims with excited delirium. One possibility that appears quite likely, if not readily demonstrable, is simply a catecholamine effect on the heart. This theory is bolstered by the observation that the sudden loss of vital signs in these cases is primarily cardiac in nature; the victim is usually found in asystole or with pulseless electrical bradycardia. The intense physical activity immediately preceding the loss of vital signs has also been associated with a severe lactic acidosis with the blood pH often less than 7.0.

The "art" of forensic pathology is to anticipate the questions that will be asked the next day, next month, and several years later during criminal and civil proceedings. Therefore, a death from excited delirium requires the pathologist to learn as much as possible about the incident prior to the commencement of the autopsy. Aside from the usual procedures required for deaths in police custody, swabs should be taken from the nose and mouth for oleoresin capsicum (pepper spray), and the body should be carefully scrutinized for the presence of marks consistent with the application of a stun gun. Petechiae, or their absence, should be carefully and photographically documented in the bulbar conjunctiva (including observations after the globe has been collapsed upon the withdrawal of vitreous fluid), the palpebral conjunctivae, the upper airway, and the lining membrane of the sphenoid sinus. A photographically documented layerwise neck dissection is necessary. Toxicological analysis is also crucial, with determinations of prescribed drugs as well as drugs of abuse and their metabolites in various organs and fluids. For cocaine, it is most helpful to measure the amount of cocaine and its metabolites in peripheral (usually femoral) blood, urine, and brain. Freezing a 2-cm mid coronal portion of the brain for the determination of cocaine receptor sites should also be considered since the patterns differ between cocaine users who die with and without excited delirium.

Continued detailed analysis of individual cases as well as series of cases, and continuing research, should eventually elucidate the cause of these syndromes and the mechanism(s) of death that have eluded the medical profession since Dr. Bell's description of a "new form of disease" in 1849.

## See Also

**Asphyxia**; **Chemical Crowd Control Agents**; **Custody:** Death in, United Kingdom and Continental Europe; Death in, United States of America; **Injuries and Deaths During Police Operations:** Special Weapons and Training Teams

## Further Reading

Akpaffiong MJ, Ruiz P (1991) Neuroleptic malignant syndrome: a complication of neuroleptics and cocaine. *Psychiatric Quarterly* 62: 299–309.

Bell LV (1849) On a form of disease resembling some advanced stages of mania and fever, but so contradistinguished from any ordinarily observed or described combination of symptoms, as to render it probable that it may be an overlooked and hitherto unrecorded malady. *American Journal of Insanity* 6: 97–127.

Chan TC, Vilke GM, Neuman T, Clausen JL (1997) Restraint position and positional asphyxia. *American Journal of Emergency Medicine* 30: 578–586.

Davidson GM (1937) Death in certain psychoses. *American Journal of Psychiatry* 91: 41–49.

Derby JM (1933) Manic-depressive "exhaustive" deaths. *Psychiatric Quarterly* 7: 436–449.

Kosten T, Kleber H (1988) Rapid death during cocaine abuse: a variant of the neuroleptic malignant syndrome? *American Journal of Drug and Alcohol Abuse* 14: 335–346.

Kraines SH (1988) Bell's mania (acute delirium). *American Journal of Psychiatry* 91: 29–40.

O'Halloran RL, Frank JG (1988) Asphyxial death during prone restraint revised – a report of 21 cases. *American Journal of Forensic Medicine and Pathology* 21: 39–52.

Parkes JM (1988) Sudden death during restraint: a study to measure the effect of restraint positions on the rate of recovery from exercise. *Medicine, Science and the Law* 40: 39–43.

Reay DJ, Fligner CL, Stilwell AD, *et al.* (1988) Positional asphyxia during law enforcement transport. *American Journal of Forensic Medicine and Pathology* 13: 90–97.

Ruttenber AJ, Lawler-Heavener J, Yin M, *et al.* (1988) Fatal excited delirium following cocaine use: epidemiologic findings provide new evidence for mechanisms of cocaine toxicity. *Journal of Forensic Science* 42: 25–31.

Shulack NR (1988) Sudden "exhaustive" deaths in excited patients. *Psychiatric Quarterly* 18: 3–11.

Wendkos MH (1988) In: *Acute Exhaustive Mania in Sudden Death and Psychiatric Illness*, pp. 165–175. New York: Spectrum Publications.

Wetli CV, Fishbain DA (1988) Cocaine induced psychosis and sudden death in recreational cocaine users. *Journal of Forensic Science* 30: 873–880.

Wetli CV, Mash DC, Karch SB (1988) Cocaine-associated agitated delirium and the neuroleptic malignant syndrome. *American Journal of Emergency Medicine* 14: 425–428.

# EXHUMATION

**H B Baldwin**, Forensic Enterprises, Inc., Orland Park, IL, USA
**C P May**, Criminal Justice Institute, Little Rock, AR, USA

For the purpose of this article, "exhumation" will be defined as the authorized removal of a dead person from his/her grave. An exhumation takes place when it is necessary to remove the remains for a second autopsy to verify the cause of death or identify the deceased. Exhumations may also become necessary if at the time of death foul play was not suspected but later new facts come to light that require additional information from the body. Exhumations may also be needed to rebury the remains at a different location or at the request of the family to recover an object placed with the remains.

As with all investigative procedures, the scene must be documented prior to the exhumation. This documentation is usually accomplished through photography and notes, but sketching may also be used. Photography will document the scene as it is observed but also the method and procedures of the exhumation. The entire process should be documented from beginning to end or reburial.

Prior to the exhumation the information and location of the remains need to be verified. The reason for the exhumation must be clear and well documented. Is the exhumation for identification, a second autopsy for cause of death, or for retrieval of forensic evidence? All of these and more reasons will guide the authorities in the exhumation technique to be used and dictate the specific course of action to be taken after the remains have been exhumed.

Proper, legal, and documented authority must be obtained prior to an exhumation. Always verify this information before any exhumation activity takes place. If a grave is going to be opened then all attempts should be made to verify that it is the correct one.

Exhumations are relatively simple. The investigator needs to photograph the grave prior to digging, during the exhumation, and after the casket is removed. Of course, a court order or written consent must be obtained before any exhumation. Before the exhumation is started, detailed information about the alleged deceased, name, age, height, weight, sex, and cause of death is necessary. Additional information that may be helpful is a description of the clothes worn by the deceased at the time of burial. A positive identification of the deceased will be required.

The deceased may be buried in a casket or wrapped in a linen cloth or a variety of other methods depending on the country and religious traditions. In the USA the deceased is normally buried in a casket made of wood, plastic, or metal and then placed in a concrete burial vault. The body may or may not be embalmed. Most of the buried remains in modern times in the USA are embalmed. All this information is needed before an exhumation is attempted.

Burial practices in the USA vary depending on the religious background of the deceased. Some religions do not believe in embalming while others embrace it. Embalming is normally conducted to prevent infection to those who handle the remains and also for public safety. The second reason for embalming is to delay the decay of the body to allow adequate viewing time for the family of the deceased.

The embalming procedure is not complex. Chemicals called embalming fluids are added to the body. The embalming fluid of choice has historically been formaldehyde, which replaced arsenic as the fluid of choice since the early 1900s. Modern embalmers use a combination of disinfectant and preservatives to slow decomposition and prevent health hazards.

Identifying the type of embalming fluid used will be necessary to eliminate it from the results of forensic toxicology screening. Besides the variety of fluids used in the embalming process, there are other artifacts that may be associated with the embalming and cosmetic process. The process itself may leave additional marks on the body. In addition, a variety of techniques and products are used cosmetically to make the deceased more presentable for viewing. This information may be needed to explain or identify additional postmortem wounds or other changes to the body.

The burial vault houses the casket and is constructed to withstand several thousand kilograms of dynamic weight loads. This is a standard in the USA. The concrete vault is used to stop the soil from collapsing and creating a depression in the cemetery. The weight of the cemetery equipment or poor casket construction may also cause collapse. Some concrete vaults are sealed and lined to prevent water seepage. Depending on when the body was buried and where in the USA, the top of the concrete vault may be from 45 cm (18 in.) to 1.8 m (6 ft) below ground.

Bodies are buried in a variety of caskets, some just wrapped in linen cloths. The mechanism used to bury the body may be different in different parts of the world. Caskets, for instance, are made with a variety of materials such as wood, steel, bronze, cooper, particleboard, fiberglass, plastic, and ivory. There are other possible construction materials used in the manufacturing of the casket, including all types of woods, from the simple pine box to an elaborate hand-rubbed rare wood. While this information may seem minor, it may be very important in civil cases where the family has paid for a service or product and that service or product was not provided. The thorough documentation of the burial vault, casket, and body is necessary to demonstrate the conditions present at the time of exhumation.

Once the information about the burial site has been verified, then the exhumation process can begin.

When the site has been documented, soil samples from the gravesite should be collected. The soil samples are collected to prove that any toxins found in the body after the exhumation did not leach from the surrounding ground. These soil samples should be taken from all four sides of the grave and from above and beneath the vault. A soil standard is also required and should be taken from an area adjacent to the grave.

Typically the gravesite in a cemetery is covered with sod. Once the sod is removed then the soil can be removed. The soil is either removed by hand, digging with shovels, or by the use of mechanical equipment such as a backhoe. Typically the hole is dug straight down so as not to disturb the adjacent grave sites. It is recommended that a soil sample be collected from the surface of the grave prior to any digging. Then soil samples should be collected just above the vault and again under the vault once it has been removed.

If the vault is not removed then a soil sample can be collected from outside the vault, however this sample must be collected from below the vault.

Soil samples should be collected using proper forensic evidence collection techniques. This means that the container must be either an unlined sterile metal container or a sterile glass jar. The metal container is typically the preferred container. This container should be at least a half-liter or pint size, but 1-l or quart-sized containers are preferred. The soil is collected using a new gardening trowel or other similar type of instrument and then placed in the container. The container is then marked and sealed. Markings on the container should include an incident number, the date, exhibit number, the collector's initials or name, and a brief description of the contents. A tape seal is placed over the lid of the can to ensure the integrity of the contents. Notes and photography should be used to document this procedure.

Before the concrete vault lid is removed, careful examination must be made for possible cracks in the vault lid. If a crack is found, then it must be documented. If the vault was damaged during the exhumation process it should be documented also.

Once the lid has been removed, then additional photographs are taken to demonstrate the condition of the inside of the vault with the casket in place. Using off-camera flash photography can capture the inside sides and bottom of the vault.

After examining and documenting the opened vault, the casket can be removed. Again, these procedures should be photographed or videotaped.

Once the casket is removed, evidence or integrity tape should be used to seal the coffin lid and, in doing so, the integrity of the contents during handling and transportation is ensured. The person in charge of the exhumation or nominee must put his/her initials and date across the tape. The casket is then ready to be transported to a secured location.

In most exhumations, the vault is typically left in place at the gravesite. The lid is placed back on the vault and covered. This makes the reburial process less complicated.

Depending on the situation, time lapsed and local protocol will determine when the body will be positively identified. It is imperative that identification be done as soon as possible. Positive identification includes but is not limited to the primary methods of fingerprint comparison, DNA analysis, and dental and medical record comparison.

Other identification methods such as comparison X-ray radiology, facial reconstruction, photographic superimposition, and general anthropological assessments can be used but are secondary to the primary methods of positive identification.

The casket and body should be transported to a secured facility for examination, second autopsy, or tissue sample recovery. When the sealed casket arrives at the secured facility, it is then rephotographed to show the integrity of the casket intact.

The casket is then opened and photographed. General overall photographs of the casket and contents are needed. Close-up or macrophotography may be required. If the body is removed from the casket, then general overall photographs should be taken of the body. If a second autopsy is done, then the photographs should be taken during the autopsy process.

The reburial process is just the reverse of the exhumation process. The entire sequence of events should be documented just as it was when the body was exhumed.

Documentation in exhumation cases remains the same whether it is for criminal prosecution or for civil procedures.

There are places in the world that use crypts or mausoleums for the internment of the body. A crypt or mausoleum is generally a structure that may be a repository for more than one person. In these circumstances, there will be no soil to recover. Swabbing of the interior of the crypt would be sufficient for comparison purposes. Details of the burial process must be obtained before removing a body from such structures. In some situations there may be a family tomb where several bodies are co-mixed after they are skeletonized. This prior information would greatly influence the procedure to follow to remove the remains properly.

Cases involving cremation are more complicated, but do not necessarily eliminate potential evidence. Older cremation methods which leave very small pieces of bone still intact are amenable to forensic anthropological analyses and evaluations. Newer methods, however, turn the entire body to ash with no bone structure left. Even if the remains are all ash, there is still a potential, through particle-induced X-ray emission analysis, to determine if the ash exhibits a composition consistent with human bone.

Mass gravesites are those sites where a large number of bodies are buried in one communal grave. The manner of burial may differ. The common facts of mass burials are the commingling of bodies, lack of material and documentation that are useful in identification and potential difficulty in determining the cause and manner in which the individuals died. Some mass burials may have occurred because of an epidemic and the remains were buried quickly to prevent further contamination to others. Other mass burials are conducted to hide the evidence of mass executions. Mass burial sites should be considered as excavation sites and not exhumations.

The technique differs in the examination and collection of artifacts, human bones, and teeth from the surface and all underlying soils in a systematic excavation and search. A more thorough discussion of this is beyond the scope of this article.

In summary, the exhumation techniques described in this article are recommended techniques that can be used in most circumstances. Gathering and verifying the information and proceeding by thoroughly documenting the exhumation site and procedures used in the exhumation are emphasized. The type of case, whether criminal or civil, or type of death investigation, i.e., homicide, suicide, accidental, or natural, will not change the techniques and procedures to be used. All exhumations should be handled the same way to gain the maximum amount of information from the burial process and the body.

## See Also

**Anthropology:** Archeology, Excavation and Retrieval of Remains; Bone Pathology and Antemortem Trauma; Cremated Bones

## Further Reading

Geberth VJ (1990) *Practical Homicide Investigation,* 3rd edn. New York: Elsevier Science.
Mayer RG (2000) *Embalming: History, Theory and Practice,* 3rd edn. New York: McGraw-Hill.
Sansone SJ (1998) *Police Photography,* 4th edn. Cincinnati, OH: Anderson.

Siegel JA, Saukko PJ, Knupfer GC (eds.) (2000) *Encyclopedia of Forensic Sciences.* San Diego, CA: Academic Press.

Spitz WV, Fisher RS (1993) *Medicolegal Investigation of Death,* 2nd edn. Springfield, IL: Charles C. Thomas.

Svenson A, Wendel O, Fisher BAJ (1993) *Techniques of Crime Scene Investigation,* 5th edn. New York: Elsevier Science.

US Department of Justice (2000) *Crime Scene Investigation: A Guide for Law Enforcement.* Washington, DC: US Department of Justice.

US Department of Justice (2001) *Medicolegal Death Investigation Guidelines.* Washington, DC: US Department of Justice.

# EXPERT WITNESS

Contents

**Qualifications, Testimony and Malpractice**
**Medical**
**Daubert and Beyond**

## Qualifications, Testimony and Malpractice

**C Henderson**, Stetson University College of Law, Gulfport, FL, USA

This article is adapted from 'Expert Witness: Qualifications and Testimony' in *Encyclopedia of Forensic Sciences*, pp. 724–729, © 2000, Elsevier Ltd.

### Introduction

Expert testimony continues to play an important role in the twenty-first century; however, an expert's scientific findings, no matter how important, have no real meaning in law until they are presented to the judge or jury.

This article will first examine the admissibility of scientific evidence in the USA, including the leading Supreme Court decisions and the Federal Rules of Evidence. Next, the article will address experts' qualifications and how to use those qualifications to project credibility and expertise to a judge or jury. Finally, the article will examine how jurors perceive expert witnesses. Various studies will be discussed in order to examine whether jurors' perceptions of experts have changed over the years. While this article is written from a US perspective, many of the issues discussed here are applicable to expert-witness testimony worldwide.

### Admissibility of Expert Testimony

The admissibility of expert testimony is a question of law to be decided by the judge presiding over the case.

In the USA there are two tests for admissibility: The Frye test and the Daubert test. The older Frye test also known as the general acceptance test, received its name from the 1923 case of *Frye* v. *United States*, 293 F. 1013 (D.C.Cir. 1923). Frye dealt with the admissibility of the precursor of the polygraph. The court stated the test as follows:

> Just when a scientific principle or discovery crosses the line between the experimental and demonstrable stages is difficult to define. Somewhere in this twilight zone the evidential force of the principle must be recognized, and while courts will go a long way in admitting expert testimony deduced from a well-recognized scientific principle or discovery, the thing from which the deduction is made must be sufficiently established to have gained general acceptance in the particular field in which it belongs.

The court held that the systolic blood pressure test had not yet gained recognition in the physiological and psychological communities, therefore, the evidence was not admitted.

The Frye test was the test used by most states and the federal courts in the USA for many years. In 1975, the Federal Rules of Evidence were enacted. Rule 702 provided:

> If scientific, technical, or other specialized knowledge will assist the trier of fact to understand the evidence or to determine a fact in issue, a witness qualified as an expert by knowledge, skill, experience, training, or education may testify thereto in the form of an opinion or otherwise.

Therefore, to be admissible, such evidence needed to be helpful, relevant, and reliable.

After 1975, there arose a question whether Rule 702 superseded the Frye test. In 1993, the US

Supreme Court answered the question in the affirmative in *Daubert* v. *Merrell Dow Pharmaceuticals, Inc.*, 509 U.S. 579 (1993). In Daubert, the plaintiffs alleged that the ingestion of Bendectin, a prescription anti-nausea drug marketed by Merrell Dow Pharmaceuticals, caused birth defects such as limb deformation. The Supreme Court held that proof that establishes the scientific reliability of expert testimony must be produced before it may be admitted. Daubert required that the judges become the gatekeepers of scientific evidence. Daubert also required the trial judges to decide whether the expert testimony will assist the trier of fact and whether it amounts to scientific knowledge, that is, whether the theory or test is derived by the scientific method. The US Supreme Court listed factors that the judges should consider in making their decision; however, the court stated the list was not a definitive checklist, nor was one factor determinative:

1. whether the proposition is testable
2. whether the proposition has been tested
3. whether the proposition has been subjected to peer review and publication
4. whether the methodology or technique has a known or potential error rate
5. whether there are standards for using the technique
6. whether the methodology is generally accepted.

When the Daubert case was remanded to the Ninth Circuit Court of Appeals to apply the factors, the court held that the evidence did not amount to scientific knowledge and was therefore inadmissible (*Daubert* v. *Merrell Dow Pharmaceuticals, Inc.*, 43 F. 3d 1311 (9th Cir. 1995)). The Ninth Circuit also noted that the technique was developed solely for the litigation in the case and the proffered expert testimony was not based on independent research, thus not subjected to peer review and publication.

The Daubert ruling had a great impact on states that had evidence codes modeled after the Federal Rules of Evidence (by mid-1993 35 states had such evidence codes). At present, the majority of states have adopted the Daubert test of admissibility, while a minority has retained the Frye test.

In 1999 the US Supreme Court had to decide whether the gatekeeper function of courts, as outlined in Daubert, reached the testimony of all experts, not just scientific experts. *Kumho Tire Co. Ltd.* v. *Carmichael*, 526 US 137 (1999) involved an accident that occurred after a tire ruptured. The survivors and decedent's representative sued the tire's manufacturer and distributor, alleging that a defect in the tire caused the rupture that led to the accident. The trial court excluded the plaintiffs' expert's testimony for failing to meet the Daubert criteria. The Eleventh Circuit Court of Appeals reversed, reviewing *de novo* the district court's decision to apply Daubert. The Circuit Court ruled that the Daubert test is restricted to those cases involving scientific evidence and not those involving skill or experience-based knowledge.

The Supreme Court reversed and held that the admissibility of expert testimony based upon technical or specialized knowledge should be subjected to the analysis and facts set forth in Daubert. The Supreme Court also reaffirmed that the Daubert factors were not restrictive, but flexible, and should be applied on a case-by-case basis.

The greatest impact of the Kumho decision has been in the areas of "soft science" and pattern recognition: handwriting, fingerprints, psychological testing, psychiatric testimony, bite marks, tool marks, and drug recognition experts. The Kumho decision opened the door to increased litigation in these areas (*United States* v. *Llera-Plaza*, 179 F. Supp. 2d 492 (E.D. Pa. 2002); *United States* v. *Llera-Plaza*, 188 F. Supp. 2d 549 (E.D. Pa. 2002) (Fingerprints); *Ramirez* v. *State*, 810 So.2d 836 (Fla. 2001) (Frye jurisdiction, but rejected tool mark evidence based on Daubert/Kumho factors)).

In December 2000 a revised Rule 702 of the Federal Rules of Evidence went into effect:

> If scientific, technical, or other specialized knowledge will assist the trier of fact to understand the evidence or to determine a fact in issue, a witness qualified as an expert by knowledge, skill, experience, training, or education may testify thereto in the form of an opinion or otherwise, provided that (1) the testimony is sufficiently based upon reliable facts or data, (2) the testimony is the product of reliable principles and methods, and (3) the witness has applied the principles and methods reliably to the facts of the case.

This amended rule was drafted in response to the Daubert decision and to the many cases applying Daubert. The amendment does not distinguish between scientific and other forms of expert testimony. The Committee Notes state that the court's gatekeeper function applies to testimony by any expert and that "[t]he trial judges in all cases of expert testimony must find it is properly grounded, well-reasoned, and not speculative before it can be admitted" (Fed. R. Evid. 702 (Comm. Notes)).

The Committee Notes point out that if a witness is relying primarily on experience to reach an opinion, the witness must explain how that experience leads to the opinion. The Committee Notes also caution that the more controversial and subjective an opinion, the more likely the testimony should be excluded as unreliable. The rule requires that expert testimony must be based upon reliable and sufficient underlying "facts or data." These "data" include reliable opinions of other experts.

Once a judge determines that scientific evidence is admissible, the judge must still address whether the probative value of the evidence is outweighed by prejudice or whether such evidence may confuse the jury. Federal Rule of Evidence 403 provides:

> Although relevant, evidence may be excluded if its probative value is substantially outweighed by the danger of unfair prejudice, confusion of the issues, or misleading the jury, or by considerations of undue delay, waste of time, or needless presentation of cumulative evidence.

A judge's decision regarding the admissibility of expert evidence will only be overturned on appeal if the appellate court determines the judge abused his/her discretion. The US Supreme Court adopted the abuse of discretion standard for reviewing a trial court's admissibility decision under Daubert in *General Electric Co. v. Joiner*, 522 US 136 (1997).

## Qualifications

Once the issue of admissibility of scientific evidence is resolved, the judge must determine whether a witness is qualified to render an opinion as an expert. In the USA, Federal Rule of Evidence 702 states that a witness may qualify as an expert on the basis of knowledge, skill, training, experience, or education.

An expert witness needs only to possess one of these traits for the judge to find the expert qualified to give an opinion. In making this evaluation, the judge may consider the expert's educational background, work experience, publications, awards, teaching or training positions, licenses or certification, speaking or other professional engagements, prior expert-witness testimony, and membership of professional associations. In the majority of jurisdictions, the determination of a witness's qualification to express an expert opinion is within the discretion of the trial judge and will only be overturned for abuse of discretion. In the minority of jurisdictions, the appellate courts will not reverse the judge's decision in the absence of a clear showing of error. Often, the expert may have to educate the attorney proffering the expert regarding the significance of particular experience, achievements, and certifications to ensure that they receive the appropriate emphasis. An expert must be prepared to explain board certification and licensure in detail, including the recertification and relicensing requirements.

## Experience as an Expert Witness

Experience and training are often more significant than academic background and are accorded more weight by jurors, according to a jury study evaluating fingerprint experts. However, experience as an expert witness, standing alone, does not qualify someone as an expert in later cases. For example, in *Bogosian v. Mercedes-Benz of North America Inc.*, 104 F.3d 472, 477 (1st Cir. 1997), the court rejected an opinion of a witness who had testified as an expert 126 times. One court even noted "it would be absurd to conclude that one can become an expert by accumulating experience in testifying" (*Thomas J. Kline, Inc. v. Lonillard, Inc.*, 878 F.2d 791, 800 (4th Cir. 1989)). Conversely, a lack of previous experience as an expert witness does not disqualify one from testifying as an expert. (*United States v. Locascio*, 6 F.3d 924, 937 (2d Cir. 1993: "even the most qualified expert must have his first day in court").

## Education and Training

An expert may be qualified based on his/her academic credentials, i.e., undergraduate, graduate, and/or postgraduate work. While distance learning is the way of the future, the proliferation of the internet has rekindled the old-fashioned diploma mill. One such business, Deplomas 4U, provides bachelors, masters, MBA, or PhD degrees in your field of choice. Their advertisements assure that no one is turned down and there are no bothersome tests, classes, books, or interviews.

An expert should participate only in accredited educational programs. The Technical Working Group on Education and Training in Forensic Science (TWGED), sponsored by the National Institute of Justice and West Virginia University, recently developed a guide, *Education and Training in Forensic Science: A Guide for Forensic Science Laboratories, Educational Institutions and Students. (NCJ 203099, June 2004, Special Report National Institute of Justice)*. The guide is a valuable resource for evaluating forensic science academic programs as well as training and continuing education programs.

An expert also needs to keep researching and publishing, preferably in peer-reviewed publications. In the past, one of the criticisms of the document examination field was a lack of research and studies. That criticism has been rebutted, but the debate is still ongoing.

Teaching experience is another of the qualifications that judges will evaluate: all forms of teaching – regular, specialty, as well as guest lecturing, visiting professorship, continuing education, and short courses – weigh in as credentials. An expert also needs to keep up-to-date with developments in his/her field by reading the literature (journals, treatises, newsletters, and books), as well as through continuing education, joining professional societies, and attending professional meetings.

## Membership of Professional Associations

A study published by the US Department of Justice in 1987 found that jurors perceived those fingerprint experts who belonged to professional associations to be more credible than other experts, and presumed experts would belong to such groups. Joining such associations aids in making contacts, in interaction with peers, and provides speaking and publishing opportunities as well as educational opportunities. At professional meetings experts have opportunities to hear and discuss cutting-edge ideas and theories with their peers.

Annual payment of dues alone, in order to be a member of a professional association, is not as prestigious as having to be invited for membership or needing referees or requiring an examination for membership. It is important for an expert to remain active and participate in professional societies. The expert's credibility is diminished if the expert has not attended a professional meeting recently.

It is wise for an expert to be selective about which professional associations to join. The February 8, 1999 issue of the *Wall Street Journal* noted that the American College of Forensic Examiners (ACFE), a 6-year-old organization, had "mail-order" credentialing, for which the applicants need only pay $350 and pass an ethics exam. There were no examinations for board certifications in various specialties during their waiver of examination periods – all one needed to do was verify possession of 200 "experience points" and send in a fee.

A 2001 *New York Times* article discussed the case of a doctor who was board-certified in forensic medicine by the ACFE's sister organization, the American Board of Forensic Medicine (ABFM), while serving time in prison for the manslaughter of his wife. In his application, he signed a statement saying he had never been convicted of a felony and that he was on sabbatical from his job. The business address he provided was that of the state prison. After learning of the doctor's conviction from the *New York Times* reporter, the ABFM stated they would strip the doctor of his membership.

One expert, Dr. Steve KD Eichel, was so tired of organizations easily granting questionable credentials that he exposed the ease by which they were granted by obtaining board certification by the American Psychotherapy Association for his cat Zoe. Dr. Eichel planted numerous hints about Zoe's true identity in the curriculum vitae he sent to the credentialing bodies. For example, she was given a consulting position with the Tacayllaermai Friends School. Tacayllaermai is "I am really a cat" spelled backwards. The cat's tale was exposed when a reporter requested an interview with Dr. Zoe D Katze regarding an article on hypnosis. "Dr. Katze" was listed on the American Association of Professional Hypnotherapists' website. Zoe's credentials have been revoked since the cat was let out of the bag.

## Increased Scrutiny of Experts

Experts have come under increased scrutiny for either fabricating or inflating their qualifications. For example, in 1998, in Florida, a person who had been testifying as an expert in toxicology for 3 years, for both the prosecution and defense in criminal cases, was prosecuted for perjury for testifying with fraudulent credentials. A prosecutor noticed some discrepancies between two of the expert's resumés and began checking into his claimed credentials. The expert claimed to possess a masters and doctorate degree from Florida Atlantic University. The registrar's office had no record of his attending or of his receiving a degree from the university. In fact, the university did not even offer a PhD in organic chemistry, the program from which the expert claimed to graduate. The expert also handed out a copy of his master's degree dated 1971. It was signed by "Lawton Chiles, Governor." Chiles was a US Senator in 1971. He did not serve as Florida's Governor until 1991. The expert was eventually charged with three counts of second-degree perjury (one count for each first-degree murder case in which the expert testified as a defense witness). The "expert" pled guilty and received a sentence of 3 years in prison, followed by 5 years' probation.

In addition to perjury prosecutions for false qualifications, some jurisdictions will also prosecute for academic fraud. For example, in Florida, a person who misrepresents association with, or academic standing at, a postsecondary educational institution is guilty of a first-degree misdemeanor.

In another matter, a Harvard medical professor was sued for trademark infringement for falsely claiming to be board-certified by the American Board of Psychiatry and Neurology (ABPN) in five trials. The board sought to seize the expert witness fees and treble damages (*ABPN* v. *Johnson-Powell*, 129 F.3d 1 (1st Cir. 1997)). The trial court denied relief because it believed she was unlikely to infringe in the future. The appellate court affirmed, stating that the trial court did not abuse its discretion.

Courts have also overturned convictions where the experts testified outside their field of expertise. For example, in *Gilliam* v. *State* (514 So.2d 1098 (Fla. 1987)), the court held that the medical examiner was not qualified as an expert in shoe pattern analysis; therefore, it was an error for the trial court to allow her to testify that the defendant's sneaker left marks on the decedent's body. See also *Kelvin* v. *State* (610 So.2d 1359 (Fla. App. 1992)), in which an evidence technician was found not qualified to give expert testimony about the trajectory of bullets depicted by dowels stuck into bullet holes in a sofa at a crime scene, as he was not a crime-scene reconstructionist and had no training in ballistics.

Since the Daubert and Kumho decisions, courts have been more willing to exclude expert testimony. A Federal Judicial Center study compared a 1998 survey of 303 federal judges with a 1991 survey. In 1998 41% of the judges excluded expert testimony whereas only 25% of the judges did so in 1991.

Likewise a RAND study by Lloyd Dixon and Brian Gill found that judges were becoming more vigilant gatekeepers; for example, in the Third Circuit (Court of Appeals) the exclusion rate in products liability cases rose from 53% to 70%.

## Weight of the Evidence

Once a judge decides that an expert may testify, the jury must then decide the weight to accord the expert's opinion. Expert witnesses and attorneys should be aware of the studies that have been conducted regarding jurors' perceptions of expert witnesses. These studies have shown that jurors give great weight to expert testimony. Many of these studies discuss jurors' evaluations of the experts' qualifications as well as the experts' appearance, demeanor, and communication skills.

In 1978, Rich Tanton published a study in the *Journal of Forensic Sciences*. Tanton found that jurors held stereotypical views of experts: for example, the male expert was expected to be 44 years old, upper-middle-class, white, neat, intelligent, wearing a dark suit and glasses, professional, calm, and serious; the female expert was expected to be white, 37 years old, dressed conservatively, neat, pleasant, and honest.

In 1984, Saks and Wissler conducted a telephone survey of potential jurors. The respondents were asked the following: whether they would believe testimony from the experts; whether they perceive the testimony to be honest; and whether they perceive the witnesses from different fields to have adequate experience to testify. The study concluded that physicians, chemists, and firearm experts ranked the highest in believability, honesty, and experience. Next-highest ranked were accountants, psychiatrists, psychologists, and eyewitnesses. Lowest-ranked were police officers, handwriting experts, and polygraph examiners.

Dr. Joseph Peterson conducted three studies on forensic evidence and the courts from 1984 to 1987.

His studies concluded that jurors accorded great weight to expert testimony and found that in criminal cases in which expert witnesses testified for the prosecution, jurors were more likely to render guilty verdicts.

In 1992, the *National Law Journal*, a legal publication in the USA, conducted a survey of jurors and their views of the jury system. The study concluded that jurors were influenced by expert witnesses and accorded their opinions great weight. In the civil and criminal cases surveyed, 89% of the jurors thought the experts were believable. Overall, 71% of the jurors said the experts' testimony made a difference in the verdict rendered.

A more recent study of experts' and jurors' preconceived notions of experts was carried out in 1994 by Daniel W Shuman and coworkers. They conducted an extensive survey of American lawyers, judges, jurors, and expert witnesses. A fascinating aspect of the study was the tabulation of the characteristics of experts that jurors considered important in determining the experts' credibility. Their determined willingness to draw firm conclusions and the ability to convey technical information nontechnically were the most important characteristics of a credible expert.

Shuman and coworkers published another study which concluded that an expert witness's believability was linked to the expert's qualifications, familiarity with the facts of the case, good reasoning, and perceived impartiality. Jurors were also influenced by independent research that corresponded with the expert's opinion.

A 1997 study of jurors' perceptions of expert witnesses in death penalty cases by Scott F Sundby found that defenses based solely on expert testimony are likely to fail, but defenses that integrate expert testimony with persuasive lay testimony are more likely to prevail.

A 1998 *National Law Journal*/Decision Quest Study exposed jurors as a more skeptical, cynical group. Among the findings, the study concluded that 50% of those surveyed thought that expert witnesses say only what they are paid to say; 33% do not believe police testimony; and 75% said they would set aside what a judge says the law requires and reach a verdict the jurors feel is right.

Increasing awareness of errant experts and exonerations of the wrongly accused has influenced how jurors perceive scientific evidence. Schklar and Diamond found that background beliefs about the possibility of laboratory errors and intentional tampering affected the weight jurors afforded a DNA report. Jurors with such beliefs gave probability estimates less weight. The *Daily Oklahoman* newspaper and Oklahoma University conducted a poll regarding forensic fraud and its impact on potential jurors and found that 32% think wrongful convictions happen frequently; 23% said that wrongful convictions are rarely an accident.

Today, 40% of the jury pool in the USA consists of Generation Xers, those born between 1966 and 1977. In order to communicate most effectively with this generation of jurors it is important to understand defining experiences that have influenced their lives. This generation grew up with the television as a babysitter, no institutional stability, high divorce rates, gangs, and the specter of acquired immunodeficiency syndrome (AIDS). This is a generation that grew up fending for themselves and is cautious and practical. They do not readily trust institutions and show little deference to authority. Generation X is also the first generation to grow up computer-literate; therefore, they are media- and technology-savvy and expect to be entertained in the courtroom. Effective communication with these jurors requires organized content, and great use of visual presentation techniques. Experts should assume a role, not a profession, for example, a teacher, not a scientist, when testifying to Generation X jurors.

The *National Law Journal*/Decision Quest annual juror outlook survey of 2000 confirms those conclusions regarding Generation X and those even younger. The survey found that 64% of jurors overall believe the police tell the truth when they testify, but only 51% of jurors aged 18–24 years old. Sixty percent overall and 72% of those aged 18–25 viewed presentations using videos, simulations, and computers positively.

## Conclusion

Expert testimony will continue to play an important role in the future. Expert witnesses have been facing increased scrutiny in the USA and worldwide. For more effective expert testimony, lawyers and experts must be aware of the legal tests for admissibility of scientific evidence, the factors courts will evaluate in order to determine whether an expert is qualified to testify, and jurors' perceptions of experts.

## See Also

**Court Systems:** Jewish (Halacha) Law; Sharii'ah Law; Law, China; Law, Japan; Law, United Kingdom; Law, United States of America; **Expert Witness:** Medical; Daubert and Beyond; **Preparation of Witnesses:** Scotland; United States of America; **Professional Bodies, France – Forensic, Medical and Scientific Training**; **Professional Bodies:** United Kingdom; Rest of the World

## Further Reading

Babitsky S, Mangraviti J, Todd C (2000) *The Comprehensive Forensic Services Manual.* Falmouth, MA: Seak.

Feder HA (2000) *Succeeding as an Expert Witness.* Colorado Springs, Co: Tageh Press.

Freckelton I, Selby H (2004) *Expert Evidence: Law, Practice, Procedure and Advocacy,* 3rd edn. Sydney, Australia: Law Book.

Froede RC (1997) *The Scientific Expert in Court.* Washington, DC: AACC Press.

Hamlin S (1998) *What Makes Juries Listen Today.* Little Falls, NJ: Glasser Legal Works.

Lubet S (1998) *Expert Testimony, A Guide for Expert Witnesses and the Lawyers who Examine Them.* Notre Dame: NITA.

McDonald E (1999) The making of an expert witness: it's in the credentials. *Wall Street Journal* February 8: B1.

Meintjes-Van Der Walt L (2001) *Expert Evidence in the Criminal Justice Process: A Comparative Perspective.* Amsterdam: Rozenberg.

Moenssens AA (1997) Handwriting identification in a post-Daubert world. 66 U. M. K.C. L. REV. 251.

Peterson J (1987) *Use of Forensic Evidence by the Police and Courts.* Series no. NCJ 107206. National Institute of Justice Research in Brief.

Peterson J, Milhajlovic S, Gilliland M (1984) *Forensic Evidence and the Police: The Effects of Scientific Evidence on Criminal Investigations.* National Institute of Justice Research Report.

Peterson J, et al. (1986) *Forensic Science and The Courts: The Uses and Effects of Scientific Evidence in Criminal Case Processing.* Chicago, IL: Chicago Center for Research in Law and Justice, University of Illinois at Chicago.

Rabinoff M, Holmes S (1996) *The Forensic Expert's Guide to Litigation.* Palm Beach Gardens, FL: LRP.

Risinger DM, Saks MJ (1996) Science and nonscience in the courts: Daubert meets handwriting identification expertise. 82 *Iowa Law Review* 21.

Risinger DM, Denbeaux MP, Saks MS (1998) Brave new "post-Daubert world," – a reply to Professor Moenssens. 29 *Seton Hall Law Review* 405.

Risinger DM, Denbeaux MP, Saks MJ (1989) Exorcism of ignorance as a proxy for rational knowledge: the lessons of handwriting identification expertise. 137 *University of Pennysylvania Law Review* 731.

Rossi F (1991) *Expert Witnesses.* Chicago, IL: American Bar Association.

Slapper G, Kelly D (2001) *The English Legal System,* 5th edn. London: Cavendish Publishing Ltd.

Saks M, Wissler R (1984) Legal and psychological bases of expert testimony: surveys of the law and jurors. *Behavioral Science and Law* 2: 435.

Smith FC, Bace RG (2003) *A Guide to Forensic Testimony: The Art and Practice of Presenting Testimony as an Expert Technical Witness.* Boston, MA: Addison Wesley.

Tanton R (1978) Jury preconceptions and their effect on expert scientific testimony. *Journal of Forensic Sciences* 24: 681.

http://users.snip.net/~drsteve/Articles/Dr_Zoe.htm and Mark Hansen, *See the Cat? See the Credentials?* ABA e-journal, October 25, 2002.

# Medical

**H F Krous**, Children's Hospital and Health Center, San Diego, CA, USA
**R W Byard**, Forensic Science Centre, Adelaide, SA, Australia

## Introduction

There are approximately 18 million civil lawsuits filed annually in the USA, two-thirds of which are judged to be without merit, and countless more criminal prosecutions. Nevertheless, there are legitimate differences of opinion brought to bear in cases where patients are injured or the outcomes are deemed suboptimal given the variation in treatments and the lack of universally accepted practice pathways for particular diagnoses. Consequently, the need for ethical, qualified, and competent testimony that acknowledges the currently accepted methods of diagnosis and treatment is necessary.

Analyses of injuries and deaths caused by criminal assault may be less complex than those caused by medical malpractice. Many of the former are catastrophic events, the analysis of which is not complicated by prolonged hospitalizations. Nevertheless, the proper adjudication in both areas still depends upon ethical and competent testimony by expert witnesses.

Given the complexity of events leading to many of these legal actions, lay juries must rely on the testimony of expert witnesses who are asked to provide clarification. The unfortunate reality is, however, that some experts are often selected because of their willingness to serve as a highly paid partisan witness rather than as an advocate for the truth and expert to the court; such traits are unbecoming to the ideals and practice of medicine and law. As a result, civil litigation, which has flourished, is often frivolous and without merit. Although physicians question the ethics of attorneys' behavior; they must acknowledge that this situation could not occur without the participation of members of their own profession.

Expert witnesses are drawn from a vast array of professional disciplines ranging from aeronautics and engineering to zoology and medicine. Even within medicine, given its diversity and complexity, it is hardly surprising that medical specialties, e.g., perinatology and geriatrics, may have little, if any, overlap. Legal actions also involve an equally wide range of areas from medical mishaps to criminal activity. In medical matters, one would assume that only physicians with appropriate expertise and experience would testify in civil and criminal cases. Sadly, this is not the case.

Today's courts exercise little discretion in credentialing medical experts, with the result that suboptimal and unethical expert testimony is not infrequent.

Actions against physicians have been divided into medical maloccurrence and medical malpractice. Maloccurrence is a result of unavoidable complications of disease, poor outcome despite appropriate medical care, and individual patient vulnerabilities. Medical malpractice is defined as the "failure to exercise ordinary and reasonable care, diligence, or skill," i.e., in terms of negligence. The Harvard Medical Malpractice Study, published in 1990, concluded that most malpractice lawsuits do not involve genuine negligence.

Physicians often blame attorneys for the increase in litigation and complain they have little influence over the courts. The sad reality is that unqualified physicians have enabled attorneys to generate large amounts of litigation that is so disruptive not only to the practice of medicine, but also to our society. We have complete control over our personal professional integrity when we provide expert testimony. With this in mind, this article is aimed at providing a framework for ethical and competent expert medical testimony for doctors who are primarily working in a hospital setting.

## Ethical Considerations

An expert witness is bound above all to the truth. Anything less is unethical, irresponsible, and serves to undermine the public's confidence in physicians and the justice system.

All interpretations of an expert witness must be objective and impartial. Serving as advocates for their clients, attorneys are highly partisan practitioners. It is imperative, however, that medical experts avoid joining attorneys as partisan witnesses. The testimony is for the court and the jury. An expert witness is charged with providing an informed, complete, and ethical analysis of the data, and not to sit in judgment of the defendant.

Professional opinions should not be developed, and written reports and expert testimony should not be given until all of the pertinent materials and information have been made available from the attorneys and reviewed carefully. Opinions based on incomplete records are likely to be partisan, incorrect, and misleading.

## Qualifications

To qualify as a competent medical expert, the physician must fulfill several criteria. The physician must be properly educated, trained, certified when applicable, and licenced. Hospital privileges may be desirable as well. Obviously, a medical expert witness must possess a degree from an accredited medical school. The development of expertise in cases of homicide begins, for example, with residency and fellowship training in general and forensic pathology. An expert testifying in matters of child abuse and neglect must have previous training in general pediatrics with advanced training specifically in the neglect, and physical and sexual abuse of children. The expert should be able to document for the court evidence of continuing education through attendance and participation at relevant conferences. Board certification from national medical boards, where available, ensures a minimum level of competence. State licensure and hospital privileges are further screens for current levels of competence and ethical standards.

Experience is a critical measure of competence. It is acquired through formal training, clinical practice, and participation in multidisciplinary morbidity and mortality conferences. In general, the greater the experience, the greater the expertise. An expert's experience should be current given the progression of knowledge and clarification of concepts over time.

Relevant academic activities also enhance the credibility of an expert witness and can be achieved through several avenues. Regular and continuing contributions of one's own research to the medical literature, especially peer-reviewed journals, confirm a depth of intellectual curiosity, and acquisition of scientific skills. This translates into an ability to pursue competent and defensible answers to important questions posed in the judicial arena. Experts should be able to cite relevant publications in support of their opinions. Memberships in professional societies suggest regular communication with colleagues with similar interests, practices, and research interests.

How the expert witness occupies his/her professional time is also important. It is critical that physicians spend the majority of their practice achieving and maintaining a level of expertise that allows them to testify as experts. Physicians who spend most of their time testifying become known as "professional witnesses." Expert testimony should comprise only a small amount of a physician's professional activities, thereby allowing sufficient time to attain and maintain a position of expertise in any given area.

## Expert-Witness Fees

Since expert witnesses are typically paid very well, they are often asked about their fees during their testimony. It is difficult to establish levels of reasonable compensation, especially across wide geographic areas with differing economies. Obviously, a witness deserves compensation for time and expertise, and it generally greatly exceeds that of the jurors listening to the testimony. When levels are exceedingly high, the credibility of the witness comes into question. A juror may wonder if the witness testifying is simply a "hired gun." Placing the expert's fee into context with other professionals can be a helpful gauge for comparison by jurors. For example, witnesses can point out that their fees are similar to those received by senior attorneys in the community.

## Unethical Testimony

Unethical testimony must be avoided. As with the practice of medicine, physicians must obey the dictum *primum non nocere* (first do no harm) when they serve as medical experts. Careful scrutiny of written reports, notes, and transcripts may help to rebut unethical witnesses. There are many forms of unethical testimony, several of which are delineated here.

### Absence of Proper Qualifications

The absence of proper qualifications should immediately disqualify a physician from serving as an expert witness. The frequency with which courts disregard the need for an expert to be properly qualified is dismaying. One wonders why a court would allow a clinical pathologist working in an adult hospital to testify in a case of pediatric forensic pathology without proper training, certification, or experience in the latter. One would think that if hospitals prevent physicians from performing operations for which they are unqualified, courts could prevent an unqualified witness from testifying. Yet, to date, neither the legal nor the medical professional associations and societies have provided protective remedies for this unfortunate situation. Until they or the courts do, it remains up to the professional integrity of individual attorneys to insist upon ethical qualified witnesses, a simplistic and ineffective system plagued by recurrent historical failures.

### Unsupported Theories of Causation

The American Academy of Pediatrics and other physicians have stated that the use of novel theories of causation to explain a set of medical findings to a jury is unethical. One should not testify, for example, that congenital anomalies known to be a result of chromosomal abnormalities are due to a woman sustaining abdominal trauma during her pregnancy.

### Atypical Interpretation of Medical Findings

The use of unsubstantiated interpretations of medical findings is another type of unethical testimony. For example, one medical expert hired by the defense testified under oath that the presence of histiocytes in a child's spleen caused a coagulopathy that led to fatal intracranial hemorrhage. The prosecution presented compelling and convincing evidence that the child had actually died from abusive head trauma, and that it had been the cause of the prolonged coagulation tests. A separate medical expert, an internationally preeminent and extensively published pediatric pathologist, retained before the trial, had stated in his written report that there was no evidence of an underlying coagulopathy. Interestingly, this second defense witness was not asked to testify in the original trial.

### Allegation of Nonexistent Medical Findings

Another kind of unethical testimony occurs when an expert alleges nonexistent medical findings or laboratory data to bolster a partisan opinion favorable to one side. For example, a witness alleged that flattening of the occipital skull was a congenital anomaly to support his manufactured view that an infant had a dysmorphic syndrome. Evidence that the infant had been chronically restrained in a car seat thereby causing the skull deformity rebutted this testimony.

### Misquoting of Medical Journals

Misquoting of medical journals or widely used medical texts is a form of unethical testimony. An example would be asserting that a widely accepted text states that particular cardiac enzymes are not elevated in the blood for several days when it is recognized that the established interval is a few hours. Using this statement to alter the proper dating of a myocardial injury based on an incorrect quoting of enzyme analyses could have the effect of removing from consideration an aggressive act toward a vulnerable victim by a defendant. Other examples are asserting incorrectly that specific citations in the neurosurgical literature state that short-distance falls can cause death, or that chronic subdural hematomas in infants can spontaneously rebleed and cause catastrophic clinical deterioration and death. Rebleeding of chronic subdural hematomas is well established in adults and children, but its association with rapid deterioration and death has yet to be documented in infants. Rebuttal witnesses can only refute such testimony if the attorneys demand that these unethical experts cite the specific medical references supporting their position.

### Omission of Facts or Knowledge

Deliberate omission of important facts or knowledge is another kind of unethical testimony. For example,

an expert might opine that the etiology of hypocalcemia implicated in an infant's sudden death was unknown despite knowledge of the baby being chronically starved by its caretakers.

### Deliberate Deceit

Another kind of unethical testimony is willful dishonesty. It is impossible to assess its frequency given the lack of peer review of expert testimony. This kind of unethical testimony can be illustrated using the above scenario of an infant with hypocalcemia. A witness could have asserted that the infant had parathyroid hypoplasia even though undocumented at the postmortem examination, and then claimed that the autopsy was substandard or that the infant suffered a syndrome, such as DiGeorge syndrome, that included hypocalcemia as part of its characteristics. If the jury were convinced of this latter consideration, then they might conclude that the manner of death was natural rather than homicidal. When confronted during cross-examination with apparent lying, an expert witness might claim in retrospect that a particular question placed to him/her was not correctly understood. Rebuttal of such testimony requires close cooperation between the opposing attorney and his/her expert witness.

Unethical testimony is not limited to the types mentioned above. Ethical lawyers and physicians must be diligent in identifying other types and in working toward their prevention.

## Preparation of Reports in Anticipation of Testimony

Attorneys employing medical experts are inconsistent in their request for medical experts to provide a written report prior to their testimony. Depending upon their strategy, they may not want the medical expert to provide a written report that could be obtained during the discovery process by the other side, thereby allowing them to prepare a more comprehensive and effective cross-examination. When a report is requested, however, there are several guidelines that should be followed.

The report, usually in the form of a letter to the attorney requesting an expert opinion, should first include acknowledgment that the opinion is being requested. Then, it should include an itemization of all the materials that were reviewed, followed by a description of the relevant observations used to base one's opinion on the questions being posed. This may include such matters as cause and manner of death or whether there had been evidence of medical malpractice or negligence.

## Court Testimony

Medical experts should appear in proper attire and maintain a professional demeanor befitting the intended dignity of the court. Questions during direct and cross-examination should be answered in a similar fashion to avoid the impression of showing favoritism to the prosecution, plaintiff, or defense rather than the truth. Speaking clearly, slowly, and coherently should be accompanied by the use of appropriate vocabulary in order for maximum understanding by lay juries. Anger, defensiveness, arrogance, dismissiveness, and impatience are to be avoided, despite provocation by an examining attorney.

Observations should be clearly differentiated from opinions. There should be consistency in the observations by competent experts representing both sides; however, their interpretations may differ radically. When this happens, an ethical and competent expert should be able to provide a clear and coherent explanation, supported, when necessary, by additional observations or widely accepted medical literature. Significant literature should always be acknowledged, even if it fails to support a stated opinion. An explanation as to why a particular study is being disagreed with is far preferable to facile downplaying of its importance.

## Visual Aids

Juries are typically composed of individuals from the lay public, and matters contested in court are often complex and highly specialized. For example, the issue being adjudicated may entail anatomical relationships, physiologic functions, and cascades of calculations, none of which are easy to follow without assistance. Patterns of injury, paths of projectiles, types of operations, and calculations are but a few specific examples. It is not surprising, therefore, that visual aids can help to clarify these issues for a jury and a court. Therefore, the attorney of record in consultation with the expert witness should request permission from the court to use these aids when they would assist in the clarification of complex testimony.

## Conclusions and Recommendations

Ethical and competent testimony of expert witnesses is important to the general well-being of society. It contributes to civil discourse and behavior, protects innocents from false charges, and assists in punishing the guilty. It compels production of safe products. In addition, it provides incentives to practice careful and thorough medicine. To these ends, several recommendations to improve expert testimony have been suggested.

The integrity and competence of prior expert testimony could be used as a criterion to determine eligibility for and maintenance of hospital staff privileges and membership for physicians in professional societies and associations. Having medical societies declare that medical testimony carries the same responsibilities as medicine practice might stimulate the authority to create procedures to implement this measure.

The importance and responsibilities of serving as an expert witness need greater emphasis in medical and graduate education, especially in those areas where it is an inevitable part of medical practice, such as in forensic pathology and in the evaluation and treatment of maltreatment of children, spouses, and elders.

Peer review of medical testimony deserves serious consideration. Although expensive and difficult, it offers numerous opportunities to improve the quality and integrity of medical testimony. Publication of irresponsible testimony in medical or society journals with appropriate annotation and discussion by acknowledged experts in a field may discourage these individuals from this practice, especially when their peers become aware of their unacceptable professional behavior. Identifying irresponsible testimony in such a manner provides an additional basis for questioning future testimony.

Professional societies often have an ethics code to which its members are expected to adhere in order to maintain their membership. Unfortunately, the vast majority of these medical societies do not have the financial resources to fund the litigation that might be brought against them when an individual's membership is revoked for violation of the society's code of ethics.

Therefore, the courts should, and seemingly could, be much more rigorous in their credentialing of physicians as expert witnesses. It seems indefensible and inexplicable that the courts will allow patently unqualified individuals to testify as experts. If hospital medical staff can prevent unqualified physicians from performing surgery, then surely the courts could better police the competence of experts appearing before them.

It seems that the competence of testimony could also be enhanced if a court, rather than attorneys who have adversarial roles, selected experts. Courts seek the truth, as opposed to attorneys, who are trying to win a case for clients. Pretrial conferences and communication between experts to determine common ground and areas of disagreement would seem useful ways to achieve accepted consensus and to identify aberrant opinions.

In the final analysis, an expert is expected to be truthful, adequately qualified, experienced, and scholarly. The expert should be capable of providing competent opinions and "telling the story" in an understandable way to a lay jury or judge.

## See Also

**Expert Witness:** Qualifications, Testimony and Malpractice; Daubert and Beyond

## Further Reading

Brent RL (1967) Medicolegal aspects of teratology. *Journal of Pediatrics* 71: 288–298.

Brent RL (1977) Litigation-produced pain, disease and suffering: an experience with congenital malformation lawsuits. *Teratology* 16: 1–13.

Brent RL (1980) Radiation teratogenesis. *Teratology* 21: 281–298.

Brent R (1982) The irresponsible expert witness: a failure of biomedical graduate education and professional accountability. *Pediatrics* 70: 754–762.

Chadwick DL (1990) Preparation for court testimony in child abuse cases. *Pediatric Clinics of North America* 37: 955–970.

Chadwick DL, Krous HF (1997) Irresponsible testimony by medical experts in cases involving the physical abuse and neglect of children. *Child Maltreatment* 2: 313–321.

Committee on Medical Liability (1989) Guidelines for expert witness testimony. *Pediatrics* 83: 312–313.

Committee on Medical Liability and American Academy of Pediatrics (2002) Guidelines for expert witness testimony in medical malpractice litigation. *Pediatrics* 109: 974–979.

Diamond BL (1959) The fallacy of the impartial expert. *Archives of Criminal Psychodynamics* 2: 221–236.

Harvard Medical Malpractice Study (1990) *Parents, Doctors and Lawyers: Medical Injury, Malpractice Litigation and Patient Compensation in New York – the Report of the Harvard Medical Practice Study to the State of New York*. Cambridge, MA: Harvard University Press.

Kassirer JP, Cecil JS (2002) Inconsistency in evidentiary standards for medical testimony: disorder in the courts. *Journal of the American Medical Association* 288: 1382–1387.

Milunsky A (2003) Lies, damned lies, and medical experts: the abrogation of responsibility by specialty organizations and a call for action. *Journal of Child Neurology* 18: 413–419.

Physician Insurers Association of America (1994) *Data Sharing System*. Pennington, NJ: Physician Insurers Association of America.

Weintraub MI (1995) Expert witness testimony: a time for self-regulation. *Neurology* 45: 855–858.

Weintraub MI (1999) Expert witness testimony: an update. *Neurologic Clinics* 17: 363–369.

# Daubert and Beyond

**E J Imwinkelried**, University of California at Davis, Davis, CA, USA

## Introduction

Expert testimony is frequently offered at trial. In one study of the use of expert testimony in California, experts were called as witnesses in 86% of trials; on average, there were 3.3 experts per trial. Some commentators have asserted that, in the USA, trial by jury is becoming trial by expert. In many cases, the quality of the justice dispensed depends heavily on the quality of the expert testimony submitted to the trier of fact.

Moreover, there have been disturbing revelations of flawed expert testimony. In *Galileo's Revenge: Junk Science in The Courtroom* (1991), Peter Huber claimed that spurious expert testimony is increasingly common in civil lawsuits. In the mid-1970s, the Law Enforcement Assistance Administration conducted the Laboratory Proficiency Testing Program. Over 200 laboratories participated. The researchers sent 21 blind samples to the laboratories for analysis. On three samples, fewer than half the laboratories reached correct, complete results. In the 1980s, the Centers for Disease Control conducted a proficiency study of laboratories engaged in immunoassay testing, a screening test for contraband drugs. One laboratory tested had an error rate of 60%. During the same period, the Forensic Science Foundation tested the proficiency of questioned document examiners. On one test, the error rate was 87%. Finally, in the 1990s there were the initial proficiency tests of fingerprint analysts. In one test, 22% of the identifications were erroneous. Nor was the concern about junk expert testimony confined to the USA. For example, in the early 1900s Judith Ward's conviction was set aside in England partially on the basis of suspect expert testimony.

The twin realizations of the extensive use of expert testimony and the incidence of expert error have prompted a reassessment of the standards for admitting expert testimony. In particular, there has been intense focus on the question of which types of theories and techniques experts may base their testimony on. The first part of this article describes the traditional *Frye* test addressing that question. The second part reviews the competing *Daubert* standard, announced by the US Supreme Court in 1993. The third part analyzes the impact that the advent of the *Daubert* standard has already had on, for example, the admissibility of novel scientific theories and "soft" science such as psychological expertise. The final part offers some predictions about the long-term effects that *Daubert* will have on the legal system, other government decision-making, and the expert community.

## The Pre-Daubert Frye Test

Before *Daubert*, the leading case governing the types of theories and techniques on which an expert may rely was *Frye* v. *United States*, 293 F. 1013 (D.C.Cir. 1923). In that case, an accused offered testimony of an expert prepared to describe the results of a systolic blood test administered to the accused. That test was a crude forerunner of the contemporary polygraph test. The expert's theory was that a person's systolic blood pressure changes markedly when the person consciously attempts to engage in deception. The expert would have testified that during the test the accused's blood pressure did not change and that therefore, the accused was being truthful when he denied committing the offense. The trial judge excluded the expert's testimony. On appeal, the court affirmed. In explaining the basis for its holding, the court remarked:

> Just when a scientific principle or discovery crosses the line between the experimental and demonstrable stages is difficult to define. Somewhere in this twilight zone the evidential force of the principle must be recognized, and while courts will go a long way in admitting expert testimony deduced from a well-recognized scientific principle or discovery, the thing from which the deduction is made must be sufficiently established to have gained general acceptance in the particular field in which it belongs.

The court found that the systolic blood pressure test was not generally accepted by either psychologists or physiologists. Given the lack of general acceptance, the testimony was inadmissible.

Although the *Frye* court announced the general acceptance test, the court neither cited precedent supporting the test nor advanced a policy argument justifying the test. However, later courts developed rationales for the test. In essence, the rationale rests on two contentions. One is that lay triers of fact such as jurors tend to attach too much weight to expert testimony. If that is so, it makes sense for courts to take a cautious, restrictive approach to the introduction of such testimony. The second rationale is that even judges are incompetent to directly pass on the merit of scientific reasoning. If even judges lack that competence, the wisest course may be in effect to delegate the decision to the scientific community.

*Frye* does that. If the controlling standard requires a showing of general acceptance of the theory and most experts in the relevant scientific fields reject the theory, testimony about the theory is inadmissible. The state of the sentiment in pertinent scientific circles is dispositive.

Support for the *Frye* test gradually grew. Although the test originated in a jury trial and the rationale for the test rests partially on an assumption about lay jurors' tendency to overvalue expert testimony, the test was extended to bench trials without a jury. Moreover, the test became the overwhelming majority view in the USA. At one point in the early 1970s, the *Frye* decision had been approvingly cited in 46 states and virtually all the federal circuits. Finally, although *Frye* was an American decision, the concern about "junk science" became an international phenomenon; the wisdom of the *Frye* test was debated in jurisdictions such as the UK, Canada, and Australia.

While it was a popular standard, the *Frye* test was a creature of case law. The *Frye* court created the test by decisional process, and the other jurisdictions following the test similarly adopted it as a matter of case law. In 1975, however, the statutory Federal Rules of Evidence took effect. Those statutes are still in effect in federal practice in the USA, and more than 40 states have adopted evidence codes patterned directly after the Federal Rules. The question naturally arose: Did *Frye* remain good law after the enactment of the Federal Rules?

## The Competing Daubert Test

The US Supreme Court answered that question in 1993 in a now celebrated decision. In that case, both the majority opinion authored by Justice Blackmun and the partial dissent by Chief Justice Rehnquist are noteworthy.

In his opinion, Justice Blackmun announced two holdings. First, *Frye* had been superseded by the adoption of the statutory Federal Rules of Evidence. The justice pointed to Federal Rule 402 in pertinent part reading:

> All relevant evidence is admissible, except as otherwise provided by the Constitution of the United States, by Act of Congress, by these rules, or other rules prescribed by the Supreme Court pursuant to statutory authority such as the Federal Rules of Civil and Criminal Procedure.

The justice cited an article by the late Professor Edward Cleary, the Reporter for the committee, which drafted the Federal Rules. The justice quoted Professor Cleary as stating that after the enactment of the Federal Rules, "[i]n principle, no common law of evidence remains." The justice described the Federal

Rules as "liberal" and "permissive;" if evidence is relevant and it satisfies all the express statutory restrictions set out in the Rules, the evidence is admissible. Again, the *Frye* test was a creature of case law. Justice Blackmun stated that he could not find any language in the text of the Federal Rules that could reasonably bear the interpretation that it codified a general acceptance test.

The justice's second holding was that, while trial judges should no longer enforce the *Frye* test, they nevertheless have a "gatekeeping" or "screening" role to perform. Justice Blackmun derived that role from the wording of a second provision in the Federal Rules, namely, Rule 702. At the time of the *Daubert* decision, Rule 702 provided:

> If scientific, technical, or other specialized knowledge will assist the trier of fact to understand the evidence or to determine a fact in issue, a witness qualified as an expert by knowledge, skill, training, or education may testify thereto in the form of an opinion or otherwise.

The statutory text thus indicated that a witness is an expert only by virtue of his/her possession of "scientific, technical, or other specialized knowledge." The statute implied that the substance of the witness's testimony must qualify as "scientific, technical, or other specialized knowledge." In the context of *Daubert*, the key question was the definition of the expression, "scientific . . . knowledge."

The justice did not equate that expression with any particular body of scientific propositions. Rather, he adopted a methodological definition. He asserted that science is essentially a validation methodology. Hence, to establish the admissibility of scientific testimony, its proponent must demonstrate that it is the product of sound scientific methodology. The justice adopted a classical definition of science, that is, formulating hypotheses and conducting systematic experimentation or observation either to verify or falsify the hypothesis. The justice listed a number of factors that trial judges ought to consider in deciding whether the expert's theory or technique rests on appropriate scientific methodology: (1) whether the theory is testable and has been tested; (2) whether there is a known or ascertainable error rate; (3) whether there are standards for applying the theory or technique; (4) whether it has been subjected to peer review; and (5) whether it is generally accepted. Although the justice mentioned "general acceptance," he demoted it from the status of a test to that of a mere factor. It is a relevant factor only insofar as it provides circumstantial evidence that the expert employed a sound scientific methodology. If the theory has been current for a lengthy enough time to have gained general acceptance, presumably many other experts have had an opportunity to review the underlying research. The theory would not enjoy general acceptance unless those experts were convinced that the methodology was sound.

Justice Blackmun added one caveat. He explained that the modern understanding of the scientific process is that "[a]rguably, there are no certainties," even in hard sciences such as physics, chemistry, and biology. It is always possible to conduct another experiment testing a theory or technique; and so long as there is another conceivable experiment, there remains a possibility of falsification. No matter how impressive the results of the research to date, a scientific proposition may never be accepted as a certainty; it can be accepted only tentatively or provisionally. However, the justice expressed his belief that lay jurors can properly evaluate the weight of scientific testimony with the benefit of cross-examination, rebuttal expert testimony, and judicial instructions. As we shall see, that caveat has an important implication for the admissibility of expert testimony about statistical analyses.

For his part, Chief Justice Rehnquist agreed that *Frye* had not survived the enactment of the Federal Rules of Evidence. However, he dissented from Justice Blackmun's description of the new validation standard. The chief justice had serious misgivings about Justice Blackmun's test. The chief justice feared that, in order to apply the test, trial judges would have to become "amateur scientists."

## The Immediate Impact of the New Daubert Test

Shortly after the Supreme Court's rendition of the *Daubert* decision, commentators debated the question of whether the new standard represented a liberalization or tightening of the prior standards for admitting expert testimony. In truth, the results have been mixed. In some cases *Daubert* represents a liberalization of the previous *Frye* standard while in other cases *Daubert* operates more conservatively. Rather than relying on gross generalizations, it is necessary to consider specific types of expert testimony.

### Novel Expert Theories and Techniques

When the witness proposes premising testimony on a novel theory, *Daubert* is a more liberal standard than the earlier *Frye* test. Under *Frye*, testimony about *avant garde* theories is automatically inadmissible. The *Frye* test requires the proponent to establish that the technique has won a certain level of acceptance or support in the relevant scientific circles. If the technique is so novel that the majority of specialists within a field are not familiar with the theory, much less embrace the theory; *Frye* dictates the exclusion of the testimony.

In contrast, under *Daubert* the judge may accept testimony about even a novel theory so long as the proponent can show that the expert witness derived the theory by sound scientific methodology. To be sure, general acceptance is a pertinent factor; and the proponent will have an uphill battle with a truly new theory. However, when the expert's validation methodology is impressive enough, the expert's testimony can be admitted. If the expert derived a high validity rate from a large, representative database and the experimental conditions approximate the conditions in the pending case, the prospects for admission are good.

## Statistical Testimony

Statistical testimony did not fare well under the traditional *Frye* test; the courts were hesitant to admit that type of expert testimony. There were two stated reasons for the hesitancy. One was a variation on one of the rationales for *Frye*. One justification for *Frye* is the supposed danger that lay jurors will ascribe undue weight to expert testimony. On many occasions, courts in *Frye* jurisdictions asserted that statistical testimony posed that danger to an acute degree. In the words of one court following *Frye*, statistical evidence is "a veritable sorcerer in our computerized age." The second reason was that the courts were reluctant explicitly to confront lay triers of fact with the reality that even momentous decisions in death-penalty cases must be based on testimony subject to an unavoidable element of uncertainty. The legitimacy of the judicial dispute resolution system requires widespread public faith in the findings yielded by the system, and the courts were frankly squeamish about expert testimony couched in probabilistic terms.

In *Daubert*, Justice Blackmun voiced his faith in the ability of lay jurors to evaluate critically expert testimony and assign it appropriate weight. He also acknowledged the uncertainty of the scientific process. In light of the tone of his opinion, it was predictable that statistical evidence would be accepted more readily under *Daubert*. *Daubert* does not expressly require the more liberal admissibility of statistical testimony, but most courts interpret its spirit in that fashion. The end result has been greater judicial receptivity to testimony about random-match probabilities, Bayes' theorem, confidence intervals, and regression analyses. In short, as in the case of novel scientific theories, *Daubert* has lowered the standard for introducing statistical evidence.

## Traditional Theories and Techniques

In the two respects above, *Daubert* represents a more liberal standard of admissibility. However, it would be a mistake to conclude that, as a general proposition, *Daubert* makes it easier for proponents to introduce expert testimony. In several respects, the opposite is true. To understand those respects, we must revisit *Frye*. *Frye* dealt with the systolic blood pressure test – a novel, purportedly scientific theory using hardware or instrumentation. In many, if not most, *Frye* jurisdictions, the scope of the test was confined to that type of expertise, novel hard science. If the scope of the test is so limited, several types of expertise are exempt from *Frye* scrutiny. Hence, a traditional theory, "soft" science or nonscientific expertise is not subject to the requirement of showing general acceptance. The judge may still inquire whether the witness qualifies as an expert and whether the subject matter is so arcane that the jury will benefit from expert guidance, but the witness's proponent need not demonstrate that the expert's underlying theory or technique has gained general acceptance. The issue is whether those types of expertise are still exempt under *Daubert*.

Justice Blackmun suggested an answer to that question about traditional techniques in his opinions. There he pointed out that one of the differences between his test and the *Frye* test is that the latter test is limited to novel theories and techniques. That footnote strongly implied that the new test is not so limited. If so, the requirement for a showing of appropriate validation applies to traditional as well as *avant garde* theories. Under *Daubert*, a theory cannot be "grandfathered" into admissibility.

Beginning in 1995, the lower courts began adopting that implication from footnote 11. In that year, a federal district court handed down its decision in *United States* v. *Starzecpyzel*, 880 F.Supp. 1027 (SDNY 1995). *Starzecpyzel* involved a challenge to the admissibility of testimony by a questioned document examiner. Such testimony had been routinely admitted in *Frye* jurisdictions for decades. Yet, in *Starzecpyzel*, the court interpreted footnote 11 to mean that questioned document testimony was not admissible merely because it was a traditional, widely accepted technique. In *Starzecpyzel*, the prosecution proffered evidence of studies conducted by a Dr. Kam, which tended to show that experienced question document examiners can identify handwriting more accurately than laypersons. The opinion suggested that, without Kam's research, the court might have altogether excluded the expert testimony. Even given the research, the court ruled that questioned document testimony qualifies only as nonscientific expertise. The court added that it would give the jury a cautionary instruction that the witness was not a scientist and that the witness's expertise was based on experience rather than fully fledged scientific analysis.

Some subsequent decisions have gone farther and excluded questioned document testimony. Other decisions have entertained attacks to such traditional techniques as microscopic analysis of hair, bite mark analysis, and firearms identification. In one decision, a federal district court went to the length of excluding an identification by a fingerprint examiner. The court reversed itself a few months later; but even in the second opinion, the court followed the lead of *Starzecpyzel* and concluded that in the current state of the research, fingerprint analysis is not a truly scientific technique. In a well-written decision that is likely to be influential, the US Court of Appeals for the Third Circuit came to essentially the same conclusion.

### "Soft" Science

As previously stated, many *Frye* jurisdictions have exempted "soft" science from scrutiny. *People* v. *McDonald*, 690 P.2d 709 (Cal. 1984) is illustrative. There the defense attempted to introduce a psychologist's testimony about the supposed unreliability of eyewitness identification. The prosecutor objected, arguing that the defense had failed to lay a *Frye* foundation demonstrating that it is widely accepted in psychological circles that eyewitness identification is error-prone. The California Supreme Court overruled the objection. The court noted that, in the past, it had applied *Frye* to only instrumental or hardware techniques. The court argued that it is justifiable to limit *Frye*; the court reasoned that *Frye* rests on the fear of juror overvaluation of expert testimony and that "soft" science does not present that risk to the same extent as "hard" science.

In *Daubert*, Justice Blackmun adopted a broad definition of science. The definition is so expansive that it includes "soft" as well as "hard" science. The breadth of his definition has persuaded the lower courts that "soft" science is not exempt from *Daubert* scrutiny. Alternatively, propositions in "soft" science cannot be validated in the same manner or with the same precision as propositions in "hard" science such as physics. However, many propositions asserted by psychologists, psychiatrists, and social scientists are empirically testable; when they can be tested in that manner, a complete lack of testing should lead to the exclusion of testimony based on the proposition. The proposition may be plausible, but scientific methodology precludes equating the plausible with the proven. If the proposition is plausible, it may warrant serious scientific investigation; but until that investigation has been undertaken, the proposition cannot constitute "scientific ... knowledge" within the meaning of that expression in Federal Rule of Evidence 702.

### Nonscientific Expertise

Federal Rule of Evidence 702 refers in the alternative to "scientific, technical, or other specialized knowledge." Thus, the face of the statute reflects that science is not the only type of expertise that may serve as a basis for admissible testimony. However, in the past most *Frye* jurisdictions exempted nonscientific expertise from scrutiny. The courts took an essentially *laissez-faire* attitude toward the theories underlying nonscientific expert testimony.

In *Starzecpyzel*, after finding that questioned document examination does not qualify as "scientific" knowledge, the court turned to the question of whether such testimony could be admitted as nonscientific expertise without any showing of reliability. The court concluded that testimony about any species of expertise can only be admitted after a showing of reliability. Dr. Kam's research was key to the court's decision to admit the testimony. In 1999 in *Kumho Tire Co., Ltd* v. *Carmichael*, 526 US 137 (1999), the US Supreme Court ruled definitively on the issue. The Court held that, although testimony about nonscientific expertise need not be validated by controlled scientific experimentation, there must be some showing of reliability. Rule 702 demands that any type of expert testimony qualify as reliable "knowledge," not merely subjective belief or unsubstantiated speculation. If the nonscientific expert proposes testifying about the existence of a convention, custom, or practice in his/her field, the foundation must demonstrate the extent of the expert's familiarity with that convention, custom, or practice. If the nonscientific expert wants to go farther and employ a technique to draw an inference from observed facts, the expert must be prepared to show that the results of the prior use of the technique establish that the theory enables the witness to draw the inference reliably. Thus, if a dog handler contemplates testifying that his/her dog's conduct constituted an alert indicating the presence of cocaine in a piece of luggage, the dog's previous track record must demonstrate the dog's ability to detect cocaine. A rigorous scientific study is unnecessary, but the expert's *ipse dixit* is insufficient.

What, then, has been the overall impact of *Daubert*? In 1991 and 1998, the Federal Judicial Center asked federal district court judges whether, in their last trial, they had accepted all the expert testimony submitted to them. In 1998, a much smaller percentage responded "yes." Similarly, in both years the center asked judges whether they had ever excluded expert testimony. In 1998, a much higher percentage answered "yes." In sum, largely by ending the exemptions recognized under *Frye*, *Daubert* has toughened the standards for introducing expert testimony.

## The Long-Term Impact of the New Daubert Test

To date, most of the effects of the *Daubert* test have taken the form of changed admissibility standards during the guilt or liability phase of judicial trials. However, in the long term there will be other effects, many of which will occur outside the context of judicial trials.

During the guilt or liability phase, we shall probably see the growing use of specialized jury instructions about expert testimony. In *Daubert*, Justice Blackmun mentioned that careful jury instructions are a tool which judges can employ to prevent the misuse of expert testimony. The *Starzecpyzel* court developed such an instruction for questioned document expertise, and counsel are requesting such instructions in a growing number of cases involving other types of expertise. Further, there has already been a modest increase in the number of cases in which judges have appointed experts under Federal Rule of Evidence 706. In the past, juries sometimes struggled to resolve a "battle of the experts" because the only experts testifying were partisan witnesses called by the litigants. A court-appointed expert can give the jury and judge a tutorial on the basic principles in a scientific discipline to permit them to make a more informed choice between the partisan experts.

While those developments will affect the guilt or liability phase, trials often involve separate sentencing and damages phases. In some instances, the formal rules of evidence are not fully applicable to these later stages. Nevertheless, judges are employing *Daubert*-style analysis in these stages. Judges have begun to realize that a *Daubert* analysis can be a helpful framework for deciding how much weight to accord testimony. For instance, all other things being equal, during the sentencing phase it is sensible for a judge to believe testimony based on a technique with a low error rate and reject opposing testimony resting on a technique with a higher rate.

Nor will *Daubert*'s impact be felt only in the judicial context. The impact will reach administrative proceedings such as investigations conducted by the Environmental Protection Agency (EPA). In conducting its inquiries, the EPA need not limit its consideration to information admissible under the rules of evidence enforceable at judicial trials. Nevertheless, the *Daubert* mode of inquiry into such factors as error rates and peer review can help an administrative agency select the best possible basis for its decision.

Although the above impacts relate to society's dispute resolution mechanisms, *Daubert* will influence other components of society. Law schools will be under greater pressure to integrate the study of scientific methodology into their curricula. Likewise, Daubert will encourage forensic science disciplines such as questioned document examination and fingerprint analysis to conduct proficiency studies and, more importantly, to undertake the sort of basic research needed to validate their underlying assumptions.

## Conclusion

It would be a mistake to think that even in the USA there is unanimity that *Daubert* is the ideal standard for evaluating the admissibility of expert testimony. Sixteen states, including California, Florida, Illinois, New York, Pennsylvania, and Washington, still adhere to some variation of *Frye*. Since those states are among the most populous and litigious, most state trials in the USA are still conducted under the *Frye* standard. However, even in jurisdictions purportedly rejecting *Daubert*, many courts have subtly modified their *Frye* variant to incorporate one or more of the reliability factors listed in *Daubert*.

In the final analysis, the question is the institutional competence of the courts: are judges up to the task of directly passing on the soundness of the methodology underlying an expert's opinion? In his dissent in *Daubert*, Chief Justice Rehnquist expressed his doubts about the wisdom of requiring judges to do so. A recent survey of state court judges seems to bear out those doubts. In that survey, the researchers contacted over 400 judges. A majority of the judges indicated that they had grave self-doubts about their ability to assess scientific reasoning, and a large percentage of the judges had difficulty applying some of the reliability factors mentioned in *Daubert*.

However, there is reason for hope. In the first few post-*Daubert* years, when federal judges endeavored to analyze the reliability of proffered testimony, they tended to focus on Judge Blackmun's list of factors and use the list in a simplistic, checklist manner. In the past few years, though, the judges have begun to exhibit a much more sophisticated understanding of scientific methodology. The improvement might be simply due to greater experience with *Daubert*, but it is probably at least partially attributable to the fact that there has been a large number of judicial education programs devoted to scientific evidence. Judges tend to be bright, educable persons, and they can learn to ask the right questions to gauge the soundness of scientific reasoning. In the long term, if the federal judicial experience with *Daubert* is satisfactory, the *Daubert* mode of analysis is likely to spread to other state courts, influence nonjudicial decision-makers, and have a broader social impact.

## See Also

**Court Systems:** Sharii'ah Law; Law, China; Law, United Kingdom; Law, United States of America; **Courts, Report Writing; Expert Witness:** Qualifications, Testimony and Malpractice; Medical

## Further Reading

Black B, Ayala F, Saffran-Brinks C (1994) Science and law in the wake of Daubert: a new search for scientific knowledge. *Texas Law Review* 72: 715.

Cecil J, Willging T (1994) Accepting Daubert's invitation: defining a role for court-appointed experts in assessing scientific validity. *Emory Law Journal* 43: 995.
Daubert v. Merrell Dow Pharmaceuticals, Inc., 509 US 579(1993).
Faigman D, Kaye D, Saks M, Sanders J (2002) *Modern Scientific Evidence: The Law and Science of Expert Testimony*, 2nd edn. West St. Paul, MN.
Giannelli P (1980) The admissibility of novel scientific evidence: Frye *v.* United states, a half century later. *Columbia Law Review* 80: 1197.
Giannelli P, Imwinkelried E (1999) *Scientific Evidence*, 3rd edn. Charlottesville, VI: Lesix.
Huber P (1991) *Galileo's Revenge: Junk Science in the Courtroom.* New York: Basic Book.
Moenssens A, Starrs J, Henderson C, Inbau F (1995) *Scientific Evidence in Civil and Criminal Cases*, 4th edn.
*People v. Collins*, 439 P.2d 33 (Cal. 1968).
R v. Ward [1993] 2 All.E.R. 577.
Risinger D (2000a) Defining the 'task at hand': non-science forensic science after *Kumho Tire Co.* v. *Carmichael. Washington and Lee Law Review* 57: 767.
Slobogin C (1998) Psychiatric evidence in criminal trials: to junk or not to junk? *William & Mary Law Review* 40: 1.
United States v. Llera Plaza, 188 F.Supp.2d 492 (E.D.Pa. 2002), rev'g, 179 F.Supp.2d 492 (E.D.Pa. 2002).
*United States v. Mitchell*, 365 F.3d 215 (3d Cir. 2004).

# EXTREMES OF TEMPERATURE

**Å Vege**, University of Oslo, Oslo, Norway

## Introduction

Humans are uniquely capable of adjusting to different circumstances. This can be seen in the inclination to settle in the most unfriendly environments, even in areas of extreme cold and extreme heat. Mostly, humans have found ways to cope with extreme temperatures, but the climate may be a real challenge to the human body. Those who are most vulnerable are individuals at the very extremes of life: infants and small children and elderly people.

Hypothermia may result from a low environmental temperature. However, the temperature may be above 0 °C and yet still be harmful, exacerbated by wind and rainfall. Diseases and use of alcohol and drugs may also play a role. Likewise, hyperthermia may be precipitated by high environmental temperature, often acting in combination with disease processes, alcohol, and drugs.

## Hypothermia

### Definition

At body temperatures of 35 to 36 °C an individual may feel discomfort but without harmful effect on the body. Accidental hypothermia is determined by an unintentional decline in core temperature below 35 °C. Hypothermia may be classified as mild (32–35 °C), moderate (28–32 °C), or severe (<28 °C).

### Manifestations

The initial manifestations of hypothermia are simply shivering; and vasoconstriction occurs in an attempt to warm the body. However, even at temperatures consistent with mild hypothermia there is an effect on the central nervous system, resulting in impaired judgment. The initial tachycardia changes to bradycardia and respiration is affected. Initially the cold temperature induces an increase in catecholamines and thyroid hormones. The initial constriction of the skin vasculature eventually fails due to paralysis of the arterial nerves, resulting in flow of relatively warmer blood from the core to the skin, creating a feeling of warmth. Moderately hypothermic individuals show progressive mental deterioration and paradoxical undressing is a not uncommon finding. Electrocardiographic recording of victims of hypothermia reveals a characteristic J-wave, which has been claimed to be pathognomonic for the condition. As the air temperature drops further, hypoventilation worsens and there is an absence of airway reflexes. The pupils are dilated and their reaction to light is poor. When the body temperature falls below 28 °C, there is collapse of the cerebrovascular autoregulation and eventually coma occurs. There is a progressive decrease in blood pressure and heart rate, and ventricular arrhythmias ultimately lead to asystole. Death usually takes place when the temperature drops below 24–26 °C, although there are reported cases of survivors of far lower temperatures, among them a young woman who survived suffering from a rectal temperature of 18 °C.

## Death from Exposure

Heat loss occurs through radiation, convection, conduction, respiration, and evaporation. Most heat is lost through radiation (55–65%). Heat loss due to conduction amounts to 10–15% and this is increased if the body is immersed in cold water. Similarly, heat loss is greater in windy weather. The degree of evaporation depends on the temperature and humidity of the surroundings.

The temperature does not have to be below freezing point to be harmful. Environmental temperatures below 10 °C are probably sufficient to cause harmful hypothermia in vulnerable individuals.

**Outdoor deaths** It is usually healthy individuals who succumb to death from hypothermia caused by a cold environment. Various forms of skiing – downhill, cross-country, and telemark – are popular outdoor activities. Skiers are often caught in bad weather and some set out without sufficient knowledge of the terrain or an awareness of what to do if they are surprised by bad weather (**Figure 1**). Furthermore, many are inappropriately dressed in the event of sudden winter storms. In addition, as a result of the ensuing hypothermia, cerebral function deteriorates and the phenomenon of paradoxical undressing may be seen, which worsens the situation further. Unfortunately, some skiers are also hit by avalanches, although deaths in avalanches are mostly due to asphyxia and blunt trauma, and hypothermia only plays a minor role. Alcohol consumption worsens hypothermia as it causes vascular dilatation and increased heat radiation. Various drugs may also be of significance by, for instance, reducing consciousness and thereby making it less likely that the individual will be able to seek shelter. Furthermore, hypothermia may disturb the effect of necessary medication.

Wind and rainfall exacerbate the drop in body temperature, since wet clothing offers much less insulation against cold.

Furthermore, the body may rapidly lose temperature when immersed in cold water, as water has a cooling effect that is 20–30 times that of dry air. This usually happens after accidents in leisure activities, such as falling from a boat, or in shipwrecks. In

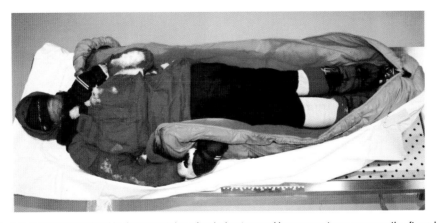

**Figure 1** A young woman was found dead in the mountains after being trapped in a snow storm, apparently after a long skiing trip. The body was frozen stiff and still covered by snow when brought to autopsy.

winter, people walking on unsafe ice may fall into the water when the ice breaks.

**Indoor deaths**    Age is a risk factor *per se*. It is evident that infants and small children are particularly at risk. They have a relatively greater surface area compared to body mass than do adults and hence may rapidly lose heat through radiation if they are not properly taken care of and protected from the cold. Elderly individuals are also at risk; it has been claimed that adults over 75 years of age have a five times greater risk of dying from hypothermia as compared to younger people. Aging is associated with reduced vasoconstriction and shivering response (as compared to younger people) when subjected to cold challenge. A delayed and reduced norepinephrine (noradrenaline) response and a decreased vasomotor responsiveness to endogenous norepinephrine production is thought to explain this reduced vasoconstriction. The reduced shivering and associated heat production in elderly people does not appear to be solely caused by differences in body mass.

Hypothermia in the elderly may easily be overlooked, as it may mimic several conditions such as cerebrovascular disease, cognitive decline, hypothyroidism, or myxedematous coma. Socially isolated elderly people with problems such as reduced mobility, confusion, poor hygiene, malnutrition, and various other diseases are at greatest risk of hypothermia. They also tend to have the heating switched off, even during cold winter times. Paradoxical undressing may also be seen in elderly persons. In these instances it should be borne in mind that the undressing may be due to dementia and that this is the underlying cause of the hypothermia.

Occasionally, victims of hypothermia may be found totally or partly undressed and hiding out of sight, a condition which has been termed "hide-and-die" syndrome. The victims are usually elderly people and are often found indoors, hiding under a pile of clothes, newspapers, or household articles, or hidden in cupboards, wardrobes, or under beds.

## Autopsy Findings

The examination of supposedly hypothermic individuals may pose a challenge to the forensic pathologist, since there may be no findings whatever during the autopsy. The diagnosis may thus primarily rest on information concerning the circumstances. However, fatal hypothermia may be overlooked, due to a lack of findings.

**External findings**    In classical hypothermia deaths the skin will show a pink to red-brown discoloration,

usually on the extensor surfaces of arms and legs, and over large joints such as the hips, knees, and elbows. The demarcation of the patches is blurred and they may have an element of brown coloring, indicating that some hemolysis has occurred. The skin on the face and on the nose and hands can also be reddish and edematous. Furthermore, there is often cyanosis, especially of the fingers and nail beds. The extremities may also look blue, or they may be white (**Figures 2** and **3**). The feet and lower parts of the legs may be edematous; however, many victims who died from hypothermia may have edema due to preexisting cardiac failure. Livor mortis may be bright red, although this discoloration may also develop if the body is exposed to frost after death.

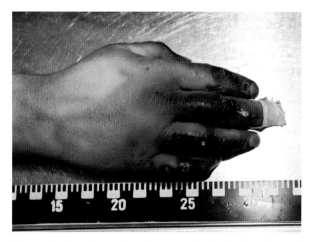

**Figure 2**    A hand showing edema, red-black discoloration, and some blister formation.

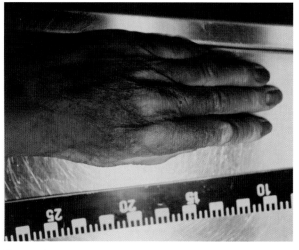

**Figure 3**    A hand showing reddish discoloration and bluish nail beds.

*Frostbite* Localized injuries caused by cold can also be found in individuals dying of hypothermia, but they are rarely fatal in themselves. When the tissue temperature drops below 0 °C, ice crystals form and the cell architecture is destroyed. There is stasis of blood flow and thrombus formation in the microvasculature. Superficial frostbite does not induce any loss of tissue. Deep frostbite is graded like burns. Grade 1 frostbite (first-degree frostbite) is characterized by redness and numbness of the skin; in grade 2 frostbite lesions, vesicles are surrounded by edema and erythema; grade 3 lesions exhibit hemorrhagic vesicles as a sign of serious damage to the microvasculature; a grade 4 lesion affects deeper structures such as the subcutis, muscles, and bones. The classical signs of second- to fourth-degree frostbite are absent in death due to acute hypothermia, and none of the lesions described appear in skin that is frozen after death.

Chilblain is due to repeated exposure to dry cold. The persistent spasticity and inflammation of the vessels can eventually lead to the formation of plaques, nodules, and ulcerations, typically on the hands and feet.

Immersion or trench foot is due to repetitive exposure to damp cold, at a temperature above freezing point. The skin is cyanotic, cold, and edematous and subsequently there is formation of bullae with ulceration and gangrene.

### Internal findings
*Acute gastric erosions* The most frequent finding is acute gastric erosions (Wischnewski ulcers) or hemorrhagic gastritis (**Figure 4**). The mucosa of the stomach may exhibit numerous small, shallow ulcerations

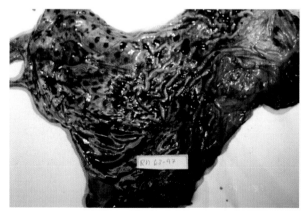

**Figure 4** Gastric mucosa studded with small ulcerations covered by blood. The stomach shown is of a young man who was found dead outside in winter, dressed in only a t-shirt and underpants. The rest of his clothes were found close by. The cause of death was hypothermia.

covered by a black or dark-brown layer of partly digested blood.

*Acute pancreatitis* This finding is consistently quoted in textbooks and papers about hypothermia but it seems to be a less frequent finding than gastric ulcers. Some authors state that they have not observed pancreatitis in deaths due to rapidly developing hypothermia, and that such a finding probably indicates protracted hypothermia. Areas of suspected hemorrhage in the pancreas should be distinguished from the discoloration that occurs as a result of autolysis after death. Histologic examination showing areas of necrosis and infiltration of leukocytes will confirm the suggested macroscopic diagnosis.

*Other findings* Small infarcts in the heart and perivascular hemorrhages in the brain, in the region of the third ventricle, have also been described. These findings are believed to be due to the blood sludging in peripheral vessels, as a result of the formation of cold agglutinins. However, it should be kept in mind that most victims of hypothermia are elderly people suffering from various diseases that could be responsible for the infarctions. The same holds true for the occasional finding of thrombosis in veins in the legs or lungs.

Furthermore, pulmonary edema is a frequent finding, but again this is a very common finding in cardiac failure, from which many hypothermia victims may suffer.

Catecholamines are excreted in the urine in increased amounts during cold stress, and epinephrine (adrenaline) increases proportionally more than norepinephrine. This probably reflects the roles of the catecholamines; epinephrine is more effective at mobilizing glucose, an important fuel for thermogenesis. The catecholamine concentration depends on the duration of hypothermia.

## Hyperthermia

### Definition

Body temperature is normally strictly regulated by the hypothalamus to 37 °C. Normal pyrexia is defined as any temperature up to 41.5 °C, and such temperatures may be seen in various infectious diseases. A fever above 41.5 °C is termed hyperpyrexia. Such high temperatures will cause the uncoupling of oxidative phosphorylation; the function of the enzyme systems will consequently be brought to an end, and cell damage and failure of the control mechanisms ensue. Subsequently, there is widespread organ damage. Hyperpyrexia may develop in patients with severe infectious disease, but is more often due to central nervous system hemorrhage or drug reactions.

Hyperthermia may develop after prolonged exposure to high environmental temperatures and may result in several conditions of varying severity.

### Manifestations

**Heat cramps** Heat cramps result from loss of salt and water through sweating. They are characterized by cramps in voluntary muscles, especially in connection with exercise. Removing the patient from the hot environment and giving fluid is usually enough to resolve the situation.

**Heat exhaustion** Heat exhaustion is a form of heat illness that is characterized by headache, nausea, and vomiting. Heat cramps and profuse sweating are present. There is usually an intact mental function, but there may be poor judgment and irritability. The patient usually recovers rapidly if removed from the hot environment and given fluids. If untreated, the condition may progress to heatstroke.

**Heatstroke** Heatstroke is a severe condition in which temperature regulation collapses. There is a dramatic sudden onset and heatstroke is accompanied by a core temperature that often exceeds 42 °C. There is typically photophobia, delirium, seizures and progressive vasodilatation, tachycardia, and tachypnea. As core temperature rises there is decreasing myocardial contractility with ensuing bradycardia and myocardial irritability. Mortality is approximately 30%.

There are two types of heatstroke: exertional and classic. Exertional heatstroke mostly occurs in athletes, military personnel, or other persons working hard in a hot environment. The heat gain is thus greater and accumulates faster than the body can cope. Persistent sweating as a result of increased catecholamine production can be seen in about 50% of individuals suffering from exertional heatstroke, while sweating is usually absent in the classic form.

Classic heatstroke usually occurs in periods of sustained high temperatures and humidity, such as during heat waves. Elderly persons, especially those with a preexisting disease, are particularly at risk. However, only a small proportion of these deaths fulfill the strict clinical criteria of hyperthermia – documented antemortem temperature above 40.6 °C. From a forensic point of view it is therefore advised that other criteria are used to decide whether death is heat-related. A recent publication recommends that elderly, frail individuals with or without known preexisting illness and younger persons with evidence of acute or chronic illness should be considered the victims of heat-related deaths when there is substantial environmental or circumstantial evidence of heat as a contributing factor. For instance, that the deceased was found in a hot room with the windows closed and without cooling devices. Furthermore, obesity seems to constitute an additional risk factor. Medication such as diuretics and major tranquilizers, anticholinergic, or antiparkinsonian drugs may also add to the risk.

Saunas may likewise precipitate heat illness, exposing individuals to high temperatures and humidity, and thus making it difficult to get rid of heat through sweating and evaporation.

As in hypothermia, babies and small children are also at risk of succumbing to hyperthermia. Heatstroke can be caused by too much clothing or placing the baby or child in a hot environment such as an unventilated car, or too close to a heating device (**Figure 5**). From a forensic point of view it should also be mentioned that hyperthermia is a well-known risk factor for sudden infant death syndrome (SIDS).

**Figure 5** A 2-year-old boy was found unconscious between the bed and the heater in the morning. The room was extremely hot; the furniture was so warm that it was unpleasant to touch. An examination of the heater showed a failure in the thermostat. The boy died 2 days later due to brain edema.

**Malignant hyperthermia** Malignant hyperthermia is an inherited disorder of skeletal muscles that causes a rapid increase in intracellular calcium in response to commonly used inhalational anesthetics and depolarizing muscle relaxants of the succinylcholine type. There is a variable clinical expression: tachycardia and arrhythmia are the earliest and most frequent symptoms. These and other symptoms, such as raised temperature, muscular rigidity, rhabdomyolysis, and acidosis may develop rapidly, and the incidence of fulminant crisis is 6.5% of cases. The literature indicates that this figure may be too high as milder forms are prone to be overlooked.

Family members of a patient who has suffered from malignant hyperthermia should be tested for this condition in order to avoid a similar incident. The only way to do this – as there is no specific mutation occurring in all potential patients – is to take an open biopsy from the thigh muscle (quadriceps femoris). The diagnosis of malignant hyperthermia is established if a pathological muscle contracture occurs after administration of the anesthetic.

Although there is no specific mutation in malignant hyperthermia, more than 20 different point mutations in the calcium release channel of the sarcoplasmic reticulum (ryanodine receptor) on chromosome 19 have been identified. The incidence of such mutations in families with malignant hypertension is 2–10%. In addition mutations have been identified in loci on chromosomes 1, 3, 5, 7, and 17.

**Malignant neuroleptic syndrome** This condition is induced by chronic abuse of psychoactive drugs, particularly phenothiazines, haloperidol, lithium, and monoamine oxidase inhibitors. It seems to be caused by inhibition of dopamine receptors in the hypothalamus, causing increased heat generation and decreased heat loss. Unlike malignant hypertension, malignant neuroleptic syndrome develops slowly, is not triggered by succinylcholine, and is not inherited.

**Ecstasy** The ring-substituted amphetamine derivative 3,4-methylenedioxymethamphetamine (MDMA) or "ecstasy" is increasingly used by young people, especially those involved in rave dance culture. The symptoms of ecstasy intoxication are anxiety, agitation, mental confusion, tremors, muscle rigidity, tachycardia, hypertension, and hyperthermia. Of these, hyperthermia is the most life-threatening. Ecstasy induces release of serotonin in the brain. Animal experiments have shown that it also induces the release of catecholamines and, to a lesser extent, dopamine. There also is inhibition of the reuptake and metabolism of these substances. Serotonin stimulates the thermal control regions in the hypothalamus, possibly by increasing the temperature set point.

## Autopsy Findings

The findings at autopsy after hyperthermia are quite nonspecific and may be minimal. Any finding is also dependent on how long the patient survived in hospital before death. Petechial hemorrhages may be seen on the lungs and other organs and there may be pulmonary congestion and edema, as well as cerebral edema and meningeal congestion. As disseminated intravascular coagulation is often a cause of death, widespread microthrombi may be seen. Furthermore, there may be focal necrosis in the myocardium; tubular necrosis in the kidneys, with intratubular myoglobin as a sign of rhabdomyolysis; and focal vacuolar necrosis and perivenular necrosis in the liver. The brain may also show degenerative changes and there may be pneumonia.

## See Also

**Autopsy, Findings:** Fire

## Further Reading

Ballester JM, Harchelroad FP (1999) Hypothermia: an easy-to-miss, dangerous disorder in winter weather. *Geriatrics* 54: 51–52, 55–57.

Cooper PN (2003) Injuries and death caused by heat and electricity. In: Payne-James J, Busuttil A, Smock W (eds.) *Forensic Medicine. Clinical and Pathological Aspects*, Chapter 14, pp. 181–199. London: Greenwich Medical Media.

Danzl DF (2003) Hypothermia and frostbite. In: Kasper DL, Braunwald E, Fauci AS, *et al.* (eds.) *Harrison's Online. Harrison's Principles of Internal Medicine*, 16th edn., part 2, section 2, chapter 19. http://harrisson's.accessmedicine.com.

Danzl DF, Pozos RS (1994) Accidental hypothermia. *New England Journal of Medicine* 331: 1756–1760.

Dinarello CA, Gelfand JA (2003) Fever and hyperthermia. In: Kasper DL, Braunwald E, Fauci AS, *et al.* (eds.) *Harrison's Online. Harrison's Principles of Internal Medicine*, 16th edn. part 2, section 2, chapter 16. http://harrison's.accessmedicine.com.

Emslie-Smith D (1958) Accidental hypothermia. A common condition with a pathognomonic electrocardiogram. *Lancet* 2: 492–495.

Frank SM, Raja SN, Bulcado C, Goldstein DS (2000) Age-related thermoregulatory differences during core cooling in humans. *American Journal of Physiology - Regulatory, Integrative and Comparative Physiology* 279: R349–354.

Grossman MD, Saffle JR, Thomas F, Tremper B (1989) Avalanche trauma. *Journal of Trauma* 29: 1705–1709.

Hirvonen J (2000) Some aspects on death in the cold and concomitant frostbites. *International Journal of Circumpolar Health* 59: 131–136.

Hirvonen J, Huttunen PM (1982) Increased urinary concentration of catecholamines in hypothermia deaths. *Journal of Forensic Science* 27: 264–271.

Hislop LJ, Wyatt JP, McNaughton GW, *et al.* (1995) Urban hypothermia in the west of Scotland. West of Scotland Accident and Emergency Trainees Research Group. *British Medical Journal* 311: 725.

Kibayashi K, Shojo H (2003) Accidental fatal hypothermia in elderly people with Alzheimer's disease. *Medicine, Science and the Law* 43: 127–131.

Knight B (1996) Neglect, starvation and hypothermia. In: Knight B (ed.) *Forensic Pathology,* 2nd edn, pp. 407–416. London: Arnold.

Laufman H (1951) Hypothermia. *Journal of the American Medical Association* 47: 1201–1212.

Mirchandani HG, McDonald G, Hood ICMB, Fonesca C (1996) Heat-related deaths in Philadelphia – 1993. *American Journal of Forensic Medicine and Pathology* 17: 106–108.

Walubo A, Seger D (1999) Fatal multi-organ failure after suicidal overdose with MDMA, "Ecstasy": case report and review of the literature. *Human Experimental Toxicology* 18: 119–125.

Wappler F (2001) Malignant hyperthermia. *European Journal of Anaesthesiology* 18: 632–652.

Weinmann M (2003) Hot on the inside. *Emergency Medical Services* 32: 34.

Wyatt JP (2003) Environmental factors causing disease and death. In: Payne-James J, Busuttil A, Smock W (eds.) *Forensic Medicine. Clinical and Pathological Aspects*, Chapter 13, pp. 169–180. London: Greenwich Medical Media.

# F

# FALLS FROM HEIGHT, PHYSICAL FINDINGS

Contents
**In Children**
**In Adults**

## In Children

**B S Spivack**, Office of the Chief Medical Examiner,
Louisville, KY, USA

### Childhood Falls from a Height

As with adults there is a paucity of pathologic data concerning childhood falls from a height. Pathologic series of childhood-fall deaths have concentrated on short-fall deaths and have only enumerated the deaths following falls from a height, rather than giving detailed descriptions of the associated pathology. More data can be gleaned from clinical series of children presenting to the emergency departments after falls, including falls from a height. Information concerning these patients is principally derived from radiologic and clinical findings; findings at postmortem examination of fatalities are patchy at best. Metaanalysis of these studies is difficult because of the differing classification of falls; falls from a height are variously described as falls exceeding 3 ft/1 m, 2 m, 10 ft/one story, 12 ft, 15 ft, 2 stories, or unspecified heights. The only consistent finding among the clinical studies is that mortality is unusual, with 36 deaths in 851 falls exceeding 3 m (10 ft) or one story (4.23%). Deaths were increased, but by no means universal, in falls of described height exceeding four stories (7 of 36, 19.4%). Some of the studies report on height fallen in fatal cases, but do not provide a full distribution of heights, so no fatality rate exceeding a given height can be determined from the studies as a group. In an important seminal paper, Barlow and coworkers described no mortality in falls under three stories and 25% mortality at four stories; this study did not find a mortality rate above 50% until the fall exceeded five stories in height. In the largest series published, by Wang and coworkers, fatality rates were much decreased, with only 10% mortality in falls of at least four stories. This decrease in mortality rate may reflect improvement in emergency and critical care services between the eras of Barlow's study (1970–1980) and Wang's study (1992–1998). See **Table 1** for mortality rates in published studies.

Reporting of physical injuries was inconsistent. In studies citing occurrence of multiple injuries, they occurred in a sizable minority of cases, ranging from 14% to 24%.

In all studies reporting physical findings, fractures and head injuries were the most common injuries reported, in some order. See **Table 2** for a summary of findings; the data of Wang and coworkers are not included because the method of reporting data is inconsistent with the classification. Barlow and coworkers found fractures to be the most common major injury in their series of 61 children who fell more than 3 m (10 ft). Seventy fractures were seen, not including skull fractures, with marked predominance of radius/ulna (21) and femur (20). Head injury was the next most frequent finding (56 injuries), with concussion (25), skull fracture (17), and cortical contusion (13) predominating. Abdominal injuries were also common (44 injuries), with predominance of renal injuries (19), liver laceration (11), and splenic rupture (8). Thoracic injuries were far less frequent, with only 6 cases each of hemopneumothorax and rib fracture, and only 3 cases of pulmonary contusions. Studies with follow-up indicated that approximately 30% of children who fell from a building required intensive care, while 10% had long-term neurologic sequelae.

Fracture patterns and frequency varied according to age. Total fracture frequency rose with age.

Adolescents were more likely to have vertebral fractures than younger children. Long-bone fracture rates were similar among infants and adolescents but significantly higher among the children. Fracture rates were surprisingly low in the study of Wang and coworkers, with only 77 fractures reported in 336 pediatric falls of 4.5 m (15 ft) or more (0.23 fractures per patient). This may reflect the very high percentage of infants and toddlers in this series.

Minor injuries are surprisingly frequent, ranging from 16% to 44%. Children under 3 years of age are more likely to avoid serious injury. In falls exceeding three stories, the rate of significant injury was markedly increased, approaching 100%.

In summary, fatality rates for falls from a height are low in childhood, and major injuries are surprisingly uncommon in falls of less than 10 m (30 ft). Significant injuries are most likely to include fractures and head injuries.

## Childhood Short Falls

Short falls are common events of early childhood; young toddlers may fall many times each day as they learn skills related to walking, running, and climbing. Most of these events do not come to medical attention, leading to difficulty in assessing "risk of injury" in childhood short falls. Studies of short falls are also limited by wide variations in heights considered to be "short," with limits ranging from 1 m (3 ft) to 4.5 m (15 ft). Nevertheless, there are several clinical studies, including surveys, retrospective studies, and prospective studies of childhood short falls, some involving publicly witnessed events (**Tables 3** and **4**). In over 1200 short falls documented in these studies, there were no fatalities in children under age 3 and few significant intracranial injuries. Wang and coworkers reported three deaths in children falling from 1.5 m (5 ft) or less; they were aged 3, 8, and 11 years. In contrast, six of nine deaths after falls of 3.5–22.5 m (12–75 ft) were in children under 3 years of age. In the short-fall group of Wang and coworkers (up to 4.5 m (15 ft)), five children required craniotomy for intracranial clot removal; the authors do not specify whether these were for subdural or epidural hemorrhage.

It would be a mistake, however, to state that, since no fatalities and few serious traumatic brain injury occurred in infants or toddlers, these outcomes are not possible results of short falls in this age group. A more realistic conclusion would be that these outcomes are not frequent enough that they did not appear in this series, although it was sizable. Since there are many millions of toddler short falls annually, there is ample opportunity for exceptionally rare events to occur,

**Table 1** Fatality frequency in published series of pediatric falls from a height

| Study | Subgroup | Number | Deaths | Percent |
|---|---|---|---|---|
| Sieben | >3 m (10 ft),15 ≥ 4 stories | 55 | 5 | 9 |
| Smith | 1–3 stories | 37 | 0 | 0 |
| Smith | ≥4 stories | 5 | 2 | 40 |
| Barlow | Fatal all >3 stories | 14 | 14 | |
| Barlow | Nonfatal | 47 | 0 | |
| Barlow | Total | 61 | 14 | 23 |
| Meller | | 48 | 1 | 2.10 |
| Musemeche | 1–17 stories | 70 | 0 | 0 |
| Roshkow | 1–3 stories | 33 | 1 | 3.03 |
| Roshkow | 4–6 stories | 12 | 1 | 8.33 |
| Lehman | 1–3 stories/ 1–13 m (3–45 ft) | 151 | 1 | 0.67 |
| Lallier | >3 m (10 ft) | 64 | 1 | 1.50 |
| Williams | 3–6.5 m (10–22 ft) | 59 | 0 | 0 |
| Williams | 6.5–12 m (22–40 ft) | 3 | 0 | 0 |
| Williams | 21 m (70 ft) | 1 | 1 | 100 |
| Williams | Total | 63 | 1 | 1.59 |
| Chadwick | 3–13.5 m (10–45 ft) | 118 | 1 | 0.90 |
| Wang | 4.5–22.5 m (15–75 ft) | 336 | 8 | 2.38 |
| Total | | 851 | 36 | 4.23 |

**Table 2** Injury frequency in published series of pediatric falls from a height

| Series (n) | Intracranial injury | Skull fracture | Other fracture | Thoracic injury | Abdominal injury | Insignificant Injury |
|---|---|---|---|---|---|---|
| Barlow (61) | 39 | 17 | 70 | 17 | 44 | 6 |
| Smith (66) | 18 | 10 | 39 | 0 | 11 | 11 |
| Musemeche (70) | 22 | 17 | 36 | 1 | 1 | 15 |
| Roshkow (45) | 16 | 17 | 21 patients 33 fractures | 5 | 1 | 11 |
| Meller (48) | 5 | 4 | 35 | 0 | 11 | 22 |
| Lallier (64) | 15 | 10 | 22 | 0 | 8 | 2 |
| Total (354) | 115 (32.4%) | 75 (21.1%) | 234 fractures (0.7 fracture per patient) | 23 (6.4%) | 76 (21.5%) | 67 (18.9%) |

**Table 3**  Studies of short falls

| Study | Subgroup | n | Head impact | SDH | Death |
|---|---|---|---|---|---|
| Lyons | Cribs | 124 | 15 | 0 | 0 |
| Lyons | Beds | 83 | 12 | 0 | 0 |
| Helfer | Home | 219 | NR | 0 | 0 |
| Helfer | Hospital | 85 | NR | 0 | 0 |
| Nimityongskul | Hospital | 76 | 26 | 0 | 0 |
| Kravitz | Clinic | 154 | 120 | 0 | 0 |
| Kravitz | Practice | 101 | 83 | 1 | 0 |
| Williams | Home (ED) | 43 | NR | 0 | 0 |
| Wang | Varied (ED) | 393 | NR | 16[a] | 4[b] |
| Totals | | 1278 | 256 of 538 (47.6%) | 17 (1.3%) | 4 (0.3%) |

SDH, subdural hemorrhage; ED, Emergency Department; NR, not recorded.
[a]Wang does not record how many of these SDH required specific medical intervention. One child in this group died after a recorded fall of 1 m (3 ft); that child had a Glasgow Coma Score of 3 on admission and underwent emergency craniotomy.
[b]Three of 4 deaths were from 1.5 m (5 ft) or less, and no deaths occurred in children younger than 3 years; younger children accounted for approximately 50% of cases.

**Table 4**  Morbidity and mortality of publicly witnessed short falls

| Study | n | Head impact | Skull fractures | SDH | Death |
|---|---|---|---|---|---|
| Lyons | 207 | 27 | 1 | 0 | 0 |
| Helfer | 85 | NR | 1 | 0 | 0 |
| Nimityongskul | 76 | 26 | 1 | 0 | 0 |
| Williams | 43 | NR | 3 | 0 | 0 |
| Total | 411 | 53 of 283 (18.7%) | 6 (1.5%) | 0 (0%) | 0 (0%) |

SDH, subdural hemorrhage.

**Table 5**  Pathology described in fatal short falls

| Study | n | Mass-effect injury: (SDH/EDH) | Lucid interval | Cerebral edema | Skull fracture | RH |
|---|---|---|---|---|---|---|
| Claydon | 1 | 1 (0/1) | 1 | 0 | 0 | 0 |
| Reiber | 2 | 2 (2/0) | Not described | 2 | 0 | 0 |
| Plunkett | 18 | 15 (14/1) | 12 | 11 | 7 | 4 |
| Denton | 1 | 0 (small subdural only) | 1 | 1 | 1 | 0 |
| Total | 22[a] | 18 (16/2) | 14 | 14 | 8 | 4 |

SDH, subdural hemorrhage; EDH, epidural hemorrhage; RH, retinal hemorrhage.
[a]8 < 3 years of age.

which would not be expected in a much smaller sample.

There are several series and case reports describing pathology in fatal childhood short falls (**Table 5**). In the best-documented cases, most fatalities result from mass-effect extraaxial hemorrhage, subdural or epidural, and a minority have skull fractures. Initial loss of consciousness is unusual, and in the reported series, appears to have occurred only in events imparting significant angular momentum, such as falls from swings. However, lucid intervals are typically very short, with a majority less than 1 h in length. The longest interval

between fall and subsequent neurologic deterioration is described by Denton and Mileusnic. This 72-h apparently lucid interval in a 10-month-old is currently an outlier case; unless and until other cases like this emerge, it is impossible to predict the likelihood of this type of event. While four cases with retinal hemorrhages are described in Plunkett's series, none of the children were examined by an ophthalmologist, nor were ocular globes examined postmortem. At the writing of this article, no well-documented cases of retinal hemorrhages arising from an early childhood short fall are found in the medical literature.

## See Also

**Head Trauma:** Pediatric and Adult, Clinical Aspects; **Falls from Height, Physical Findings:** In Adults

## References

Barlow B, Niemirska M, Gandhi RP, Leblanc W (1983) Ten years experience with falls from a height in children. *Journal of Pediatric Surgery* 18: 509–511.

Chadwick DL, Chin S, Salerno C, Landsverk J, Kitchen L (1991) Deaths from falls in children: how far is fatal? *Journal of Trauma* 31: 1353–1355.

Claydon SM (1996) Fatal extradural hemorrhage following a fall from a baby bouncer. *Pediatric Emergency Care* 12: 432–434.

Denton S, Mileusnic D (2003) Delayed sudden death in an infant following an accidental fall: a case report with review of the literature. *American Journal of Forensic Medicine Pathology* 24: 371.

Hall JR, Reyes HM, Horvat M, *et al.* (1989) The mortality of childhood falls. *Journal of Trauma* 29: 1273–1275.

Helfer RE, Slovis TL, Black M (1977) Injuries resulting when small children fall out of bed. *Pediatrics* 60: 533–535.

Kravitz H, Driessen G, Gomberg R, *et al.* (1969) Accidental falls from elevated surfaces in infants from birth to one year of age. *Pediatrics* 44(suppl.): 869–876.

Lallier M, Bouschard S, St-Vil D, Dupont J, Tucci M (1999) Falls from heights among children: a retrospective review. *Journal of Pediatric Surgery* 34: 1060–1063.

Lehman D, Schonfeld N (1993) Falls from heights: a problem not just in the northeast. *Pediatrics* 92: 121–124.

Lyons TJ, Oates RK (1993) Falling out of bed: a relatively benign occurrence. *Pediatrics* 92: 125–127.

Meller JL, Shermeta DW (1987) Falls in urban children: a problem revisited. *American Journal of Diseases of Childhood* 41: 1271–1275.

Musemeche CA, Barthel M, Cosentino C, Reynolds M (1991) Pediatric falls from heights. *Journal of Trauma* 31: 1347–1349.

Nimityongskul P, Anderson LD (1987) The likelihood of injuries when children fall out of bed. *Journal of Pediatric Orthopedics* 7: 184–186.

Plunkett J (2001) Fatal pediatric head injuries caused by short-distance falls. *American Journal of Forensic Medicine Pathology* 22: 1–12.

Reiber GD (1993) Fatal falls in childhood. *American Journal of Forensic Medicine Pathology* 14: 201–207.

Reiber GD (1993) Fatal falls in childhood: how far must children fall to sustain fatal head injury? Report of cases and review of the literature. *American Journal of Forensic Medicine Pathology* 14: 201–207.

Roshkow JE, Haller JO, Hotson GC, *et al.* (1990) Imaging evaluation of children after falls from a height: review of 45 cases. *Radiology* 175: 359–363.

Sawyer JR, Flynn JM, Dormans JP, Catalano J, Drummond DS (2000) Fracture patterns in children and young adults who fall from significant heights. *Journal of Pediatric Orthopedics* 20: 197–200.

Smith MD, Burrington JD, Woolf AD (1975) Injuries in children sustained in free falls: an analysis of 66 cases. *Journal of Trauma* 15: 987–991.

Wang MY, Kim KA, Griffin PM, *et al.* (2001) Injuries from falls in the pediatric population: an analysis of 729 cases. *Journal of Pediatric Surgery* 36: 1528–1534.

Williams RA (1991) Injuries in infants and small children resulting from witnessed and corroborated free falls. *Journal of Trauma* 31: 1350–1352.

# In Adults

**G Lau**, Centre for Forensic Medicine, Health Sciences Authority, Singapore

## Introduction

Deaths due to falls from considerable heights are by no means rare in major cities around the world. Certainly, one would expect to find a significant number of such deaths in any urbanized locality dominated by high-rise apartments or skyscrapers, be they suicidal, accidental, dyadic, or even homicidal in nature. Surprisingly, however, there is a relative paucity of published scientific literature on the pathology of trauma resulting from fatal falls from a height, particularly in relation to patterns of injury, injury severity, and pathogenesis.

The following description of the nature, severity, and patterns of injury from abrupt vertical deceleration represents a synthesis of the collective experience of forensic pathologists from the Centre for Forensic Medicine, Health Sciences Authority in Singapore, who, for several decades, have been conducting coroner's autopsies on 300–400 cases of fatal falls from heights, annually. This department undertakes all coronial casework nationally, serving a population of some 4 million, of whom about 90% reside in high-rise apartments (mostly ≤25–30 floors in height). Accordingly, it mainly applies to individuals (mostly adults) who have fallen from heights of 3–90 m (with some 60–70% having fallen through distances of 20–40 m) and largely landed on unyielding concrete surfaces.

## Overview

There has been a marked preponderance of males (2:1) dying from falling from a height, with just over one-half of victims aged between 20 and 40 years, while nearly one-fifth were ≥60 years; nearly 40–45% were retired or unemployed. The vast majority of victims (approximately 80%) died on site, while the remainder died at emergency departments or after admission. Only one-tenth of them survived for more than an hour, and, one-third of these died within 3 h of the incident.

Police investigations revealed that 80% were either unequivocal or highly probable suicides, while industrial and domestic accidents accounted for 11% and 2% of cases, respectively. Less than 0.5% were dyadic deaths and 3.5% were uncertain in nature. Notably, homicides have been rare; over a 10-year period (1991–2000), only four cases (comprising five victims) of homicides and nine cases (19 individulas) of homicide–suicide, involving falls from heights, were encountered in Singapore. In approximately one-fifth of all cases, a definite history of psychosis or depression was obtained.

As with vehicular and other deceleration injuries, it is the rate of change of the direction and speed of movement that result in tissue injury. Assuming that the victims had been subjected to vertical freefall, the often extensive and severe injuries sustained by them would largely be the consequence of their bodies coming to an abrupt halt upon impact with the ground or some other structure and absorbing the forces of deceleration.

It should be noted that these theoretical considerations may be confounded by collision with intermediate objects or barriers, such as protruding masonry, that are sufficiently sturdy to retard the fall and, thereby, reduce the final velocity at impact. Contact with these structures could also result in serious injuries, such as decapitation or dismemberment of limbs or even the trunk of the body. Moreover, secondary impact with the ground due to the body bouncing up after primary impact may also result in more extensive injuries.

## Injury Severity

It appears that injury severity is primarily correlated with the height of fall and, to a lesser extent, the age of the individual, but not with sex, size (vis-à-vis the body mass index), or site of primary impact, as suggested by a mathematical model. In this context, the application of the injury severity score (ISS), derived from the abbreviated injury scale (AIS), demonstrated a progressive increase in the frequency of serious to clearly fatal injuries (AIS 3–6) to the head, thorax, abdomen, pelvis, and spine, in relation to the height of fall (Table 1).

The same study revealed that only 1.5% of subjects in this series had ISS ≤14, while the remaining 98.5%

**Table 1** Distribution of injuries (mostly abbreviated injury scale ≥3) in overlapping frequencies (%) in relation to known height of fall (n = 416)

| Height bands (m) | 3–<10 | 10–<20 | 20–<30 | 30–<40 | 40–<70 |
|---|---|---|---|---|---|
| Head | 9 | 27 | 34 | 47 | 68 |
| Thoracic aorta | 12.5 | 34 | 56 | 68 | 76 |
| Heart | 9 | 36 | 47 | 64 | 68 |
| Lungs | 22 | 36 | 55 | 67 | 82 |
| Liver | 6 | 24 | 62 | 85 | 92 |
| Kidneys | 3 | 15 | 19 | 35.5 | 54 |
| Spleen | 12.5 | 23 | 38 | 58 | 82 |
| Pelvic fractures | 25 | 34 | 64 | 69 | 72 |
| Spinal injuries | 19 | 31 | 32 | 48 | 56 |

Reproduced with permission from Lau G, Ooi PL, Phoon B (1998) Fatal falls from a height: the use of mathematical models to estimate the height of fall from the injuries sustained. *Forensic Science International* 93: 33–44.

had values of ≥16. Not surprisingly, half had an ISS of 75, while fewer than 3% had an ISS of 66. Among the remainder, approximately one-third had ISS values ranging from 34 to 59. A mathematical equation correlating the height of fall to the severity of injuries was also constructed (Table 2).

## Patterns of Injury

### Distribution of Injuries

In an earlier study of over 600 fatal cases, the following anatomical distribution of injuries (with overlapping frequencies) was observed: thorax (98%); head and face (82%); abdomen (79%); pelvic girdle (55%); and vertebral column (35%). Nearly half (49%) showed a combination of head, thoracic, and abdominal injuries, while a further 16% had injuries of the pelvic girdle and vertebral column as well. Approximately 13% showed a combination of head and thoracic injuries, while about 11% showed thoracic and abdominal injuries, and <1% suffered head and abdominal injuries. The full spectrum of injuries in the various anatomical regions is summarized below.

### External Appearance

A combination of grazes, scratches, imprint abrasions, lacerations, and bruises is usually seen. They tend to be variable in both anatomical distribution and prominence and are ubiquitous in all but a minority (<1%) of subjects who have landed on grass patches. It is conceivable that the thickness and the number of layers of attire worn by the victims

**Table 2** Multivariate analysis using multiple linear regression to adjust for mutual confounding between independent variables with height of fall (height band: HB) as the dependent variable

| Independent variables | | Regression coefficient | | Standard error | | t-test | | P-value |
|---|---|---|---|---|---|---|---|---|
| Intercept | | 1.883 | | 0.233 | | 8.076 | | |
| Age | | −0.013 | | 0.003 | | −5.103 | | <0.0001 |
| ISSB | | 0.098 | | 0.051 | | 1.928 | | 0.055 |
| Brain | 0.354 | | 0.108 | | | 3.283 | | 0.001 |
| Pelvis | 0.284 | | 0.105 | | | 2.706 | | 0.007 |
| Spine | | 0.400 | | 0.103 | | 3.875 | | <0.0001 |
| Heart | 0.304 | | 0.121 | | | 2.510 | | 0.012 |
| Aorta | 0.151 | | 0.067 | | | 2.236 | | 0.026 |
| Liver | | 0.769 | | 0.115 | | 6.711 | | <0.0001 |
| Kidneys | | 0.307 | | 0.120 | | 2.567 | | 0.011 |
| Spleen | 0.301 | | 0.111 | | | 2.719 | | 0.007 |

ISSB, injury severity score band (see below).

Excluded variables: sex, airways, lungs, gastrointestinal tract.

Sample size = 416; $r^2 = 0.466$.

$HB = k - k_aA + k_iI + k_bB + k_cC + k_lL + k_pP + k_rR + k_sS + k_tT + k_vV$

where $A$ = age in years; $I$ = ISSB; $B$ = brain extrusion/lacerations (1 for abbreviated injury scale (AIS) $\geq$ 4, 0 for AIS < 4); $C$ = myocardial/valvular ruptures/lacerations (1 for AIS $\geq$ 3, 0 for AIS < 3); $L$ = liver ruptures/lacerations (1 for AIS $\geq$ 3, 0 for AIS < 3); $P$ = pelvic girdle fractures (1 for AIS $\geq$ 3, 0 for AIS < 3); $R$ = renal ruptures/lacerations (1 for AIS $\geq$ 3, 0 for AIS < 3); $S$ = splenic ruptures/lacerations (1 for AIS $\geq$ 3, 0 for AIS < 3); $T$ = thoracic aortic laceration/rupture/transection (1 for AIS $\geq$ 4, 0 for AIS < 4); $V$ = vertebral/spinal cord injuries (1 for present, 0 for absent); and $k$ = 1.88 (95% confidence interval, 1.42–2.34); $k_a$ = 0.01 (0.008–0.02); $k_i$ = 0.10 (0.00–1.97); $k_b$ = 2.59 (0.50–4.65); $k_c$ = 0.30 (0.07–5.43); $k_l$ = 0.77 (0.54–1.00), $k_p$ = 0.28 (0.08–0.49); $k_r$ = 0.31 (0.07–0.54); $k_s$ = 0.30 (0.08–0.52), $k_t$ = 0.15 (0.02–0.28), $k_v$ = 0.40 (0.20–0.60). In this model, HB values $\leq$1 = height <10 m; 2 = 10–20 m; 3 = 20–30 m; 4 = 30–40 m and $\geq$5 = 40–70 m.

Reproduced with permission from Lau G, Ooi PL, Phoon B (1998) Fatal falls from a height: the use of mathematical models to estimate the height of fall from the injuries sustained. *Forensic Science International* 93: 33–44.

might have a bearing on the appearance of these injuries.

Lacerations of the scalp, when present, may be superficial or deep: deep lacerations are often (but not invariably) accompanied by open skull fractures, or even massive craniofacial disruption and disfigurement. Similarly, lacerations along the upper and lower limbs may be associated with open fractures of the long bones.

Occasionally, extensive and severe internal visceral and skeletal injuries may occur in the absence, or near absence, of any significant external injury. This discrepancy tends to be observed when the body lands upon a relatively "soft" surface, such as a grass patch or a body of water (such as a swimming or landscape pool).

### Head, Face, and Neck

Massive destruction of the brain (in approximately 20% of head injuries) is accompanied by extensive, open, comminuted fractures of the calvaria, the base of the skull, the hard palate, as well as nasal, mandibular, and maxillofacial fractures. There may be partial or complete extrusion of the severely lacerated or disrupted brain matter, which may not be retrievable, especially if it was dispersed over an appreciable area after primary head impact (**Figure 1**). Less severe

direct head impact, or primary feet/lower-limb impact, with resultant ring fractures of the base of the skull, may nevertheless be associated with laceration, transection, or contusion of the brainstem.

In cases with craniofacial fractures (70–80%), the following distribution of intracranial hemorrhage may be observed: epidural (4–5%), subdural (30%), subarachnoid (60–65%), intracerebral (6–7%), and cerebral contusions (approximately 10%).

However, even without skull fractures, cerebral contusions (2–3%), subdural hemorrhage (5–7%), and, more commonly, subarachnoid hemorrhage (about 30%) may be encountered. Not infrequently, there may be patchy, acute subarachnoid hemorrhage (particularly along the parasagittal regions of the cerebral hemispheres and at the base of the brain) in the absence of any evidence of direct impact to the head or face, thereby suggesting that rotational or shearing forces were at work. Occasionally, lacerations of the corpus callosum may be seen, even when the macroscopic and histological features of diffuse axonal injury are absent, probably because death occurred rapidly, or instantaneously.

Internal injuries to the soft tissues of the neck, when present, tend to be limited to mild or moderate subcutaneous, fascial, and muscular hemorrhage, as well as bruising of the thyroid gland. Fractures of the hyoid bone and of the laryngeal cartilages are rare,

**Figure 1**   Disruptive head injury with extrusion of the brain (primary head impact).

although focal bruising of the base of the tongue, laryngeal mucosa, and upper airways is not uncommon. Similarly, major neural and vascular injuries (of the carotid arteries and the internal jugular veins) are also extremely infrequent.

## Thorax

In nearly 50% of victims, rupture or laceration of the heart (in approximately 50% of victims) occurs. The free walls of the right cardiac chambers and the interventricular septum are 2–3 times more prone to rupture than those of the left cardiac chambers and the interatrial septum. Conceivably, this may be due to the fact that the vascular attachments of the right atrium and the right ventricle (the superior and inferior venae cavae, and the pulmonary trunk, respectively) as well as the right ventricular free wall are structurally less robust than the counterparts of the left heart (the thoracic aorta and the relatively thick left ventricular wall). However, not uncommonly, both atria and the interventricular septum may be ruptured (**Figure 2**), while the ventricles remain intact.

Laceration and rupture of the cardiac valves, often in association with injuries to the corresponding or other cardiac chambers, have been described, with a clear predilection for the mitral and tricuspid valves.

Rupture or laceration of one or more principal coronary arteries is sometimes observed. However, the significance of these ruptures is uncertain, as inevitably they are accompanied by full-thickness ventricular ruptures.

Rupture or laceration of the pericardial sac is present in approximately 30% of all cases (both with and without corresponding cardiac injury) and in 60% of subjects with cardiac rupture or lacerations.

Rupture of the thoracic aorta occurs in approximately 50% of subjects. Of these ruptures, approximately 70% present as complete, or circumferential, traumatic transections, while the remaining 30% are full-thickness ruptures (often located anteriorly), with incomplete circumferential involvement (**Figure 3**). Hemorrhage may be limited to the mediastinum or extend into the pleural cavities. In nearly all of these cases, the principal site of rupture is the junction of the aortic arch with the descending thoracic aorta (1–2 cm distal to the origin of the left subclavian artery) and the margins may sometimes be so well delineated even as to mimic transection with a sharp instrument. The predilection of the thoracic arch to rupture at this site may be attributed to the fact that, while the descending thoracic and abdominal segments of the aorta are firmly adherent to the vertebral column, the aortic arch and ascending aorta project into the thoracic cavity. This arrangement renders the initial segment of the aorta relatively mobile, with the result that it and the heart continue their descent for a short time after primary impact, causing the distal part of the aortic arch to tear. This theory seems to be supported by the observation that

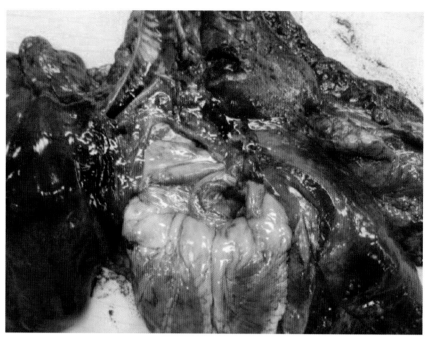

**Figure 2** Ruptures of both atria, the right main bronchus, and the right lung (posterior view).

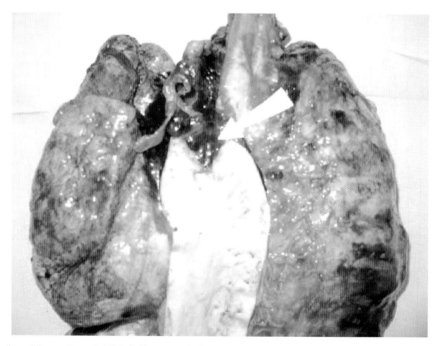

**Figure 3** Transection of the aortic arch (distal). The arrow indicates the distal margin of aortic transection at the junction of the aortic arch with the descending thoracic aorta.

aortic ruptures accompany almost 75% of cardiac ruptures.

Not infrequently, complete or partial ruptures of the ascending aorta are found, either in isolation, or in combination with a similar injury in the distal part of the aortic arch. Isolated injuries to the ascending aortic arch may be due largely to anteroposterior compression of the chest wall, as a consequence of primary or secondary impact to the front of the trunk. In addition, intimal tears are often seen along the thoracic and the abdominal aorta. Rupture or laceration of the pulmonary trunk, arteries, and veins, as well as of the superior and inferior venae cavae, is also sometimes found, although these ruptures appear to be less frequent than might be expected.

Pulmonary contusions of variable extent and severity tend to be ubiquitous, or nearly so. Rupture or laceration of the lungs, whether unilateral or bilateral and involving one lobe or several lobes, may be found in 50–60% of all cases (**Figure 2**). Nearly 90% of subjects with pulmonary ruptures or lacerations had accompanying penetrating rib fractures, suggesting that, in the remainder, marked anteroposterior or lateral compression of the thoracic cage may generate sufficient intrathoracic pressure to cause a disruptive injury to the lungs, in the absence of rib fractures. This could well be the principal mechanism of pulmonary injury in a substantial proportion of children and young adults, who have pliable chest walls.

Ruptures of the trachea and the main extrapulmonary bronchi occur in approximately 15% of subjects; most are accompanied by corresponding ruptures or lacerations of the lungs.

Rib fractures are found in approximately 80% of victims with thoracic injuries (**Figure 4**). These tend to be multiple, bilateral fractures, which would have resulted in flail segments had these individuals survived the initial impact, although solitary fractures are sometimes encountered. Not uncommonly, the thoracic cage may be literally shattered and the sternum and thoracic spine fractured in victims who have fallen from heights of $\geq$40 m.

Overall, approximately 70% of victims in our study presented with hemothorax at autopsy. Of these, almost half had a total of 100–500 ml blood and/or blood clots in their pleural cavities, while nearly a quarter had 500–1000 ml; only 10% presented with >1000 ml. Most subjects with hemopericardia (<15%) had <100 ml of blood or blood clots.

Notably, in a third of all cases, there may be no evidence of any significant hemothorax, despite the extent and severity of the intrathoracic injuries sustained. Thus, up to 30% of victims with fractured ribs may show almost no evidence of hemothorax at autopsy, while <10% present with minimal hemothorax. A similar observation applies to victims with pulmonary rupture or laceration, as well as those with a combination of rib fractures and pulmonary rupture.

Also, 25–30% of cases of partial or complete rupture of the thoracic aorta were not associated with hemothorax, while about 40% showed only minimal hemorrhage into the pleural cavities.

Far greater incongruity was observed with regard to cardiac ruptures. Thus, >70% of subjects with traumatic cardiac perforations or lacerations showed no evidence of hemopericardium, while <10% showed minimal hemorrhage.

The marked discordance between the degree of intrathoracic hemorrhage and the magnitude of the injuries found may be attributed to the fact that, in many of these cases, death would have occurred very rapidly or even instantaneously upon impact. One might well be tempted to postulate that cardiorespiratory arrest could have occurred before impact, possibly as a result of some form of vasovagal response.

Other visceral injuries include unilateral or bilateral ruptures of the diaphragmatic dome, with herniation of the corresponding abdominal organs

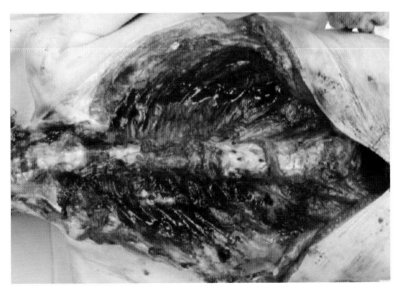

**Figure 4** Bilateral, multiple rib fractures.

into the pleural cavities, as well as the occasional perforation or rupture of the thoracic esophagus. In young children and adolescents, bruising of the thymus may sometimes be observed.

## Abdomen

Variable combinations of organ contusion, laceration, and rupture of equally variable severity may be found (**Figures 5** and **6**). As with the thoracic injuries, there may be a marked discrepancy between the severity and extent of the visceral damage and the amount of bleeding observed at autopsy. Thus, no significant hemoperitoneum is present in approximately 60% of victims, while only 10–15% would show minimal hemorrhage. Approximately 20% would contain 100–150 ml of blood within the abdominal cavity, while 5–6% might have >500 ml of blood.

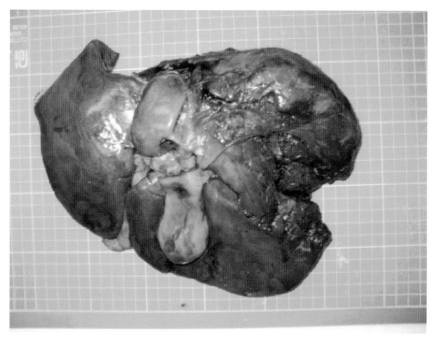

**Figure 5**  Rupture and laceration of the liver.

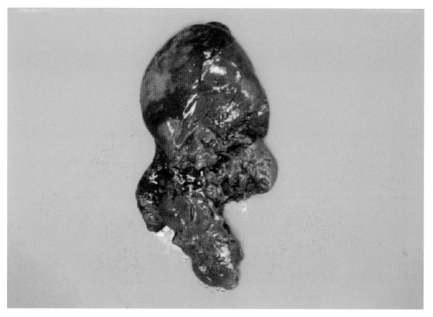

**Figure 6**  A ruptured kidney.

The approximate distribution (in overlapping frequencies) of organ rupture, laceration, or perforation is as follows: liver (60%), spleen (40–45%), kidney(s) (25–30%), and gastrointestinal (2%).

A combination of hepatic, renal, and splenic ruptures is not uncommon (in about 15% of cases). Although complete vascular avulsion of the liver appears to be rare, extensive hepatic parenchymal disruption may be accompanied by lacerations or ruptures of the retrohepatic vena cava or the hepatic veins and arteries, or, occasionally, the portal vein.

Similarly, vascular avulsion and hilar or massive disruption of the spleen are also commonly observed.

By comparison, traumatic renal lesions tend to be less severe and usually present as cortical lacerations, although hilar avulsion of one or, rarely, both kidneys, with or without perinephric hematomas, are found in some cases.

Mesenteric bruising, often focal or patchy, is not uncommon, as is retroperitoneal bruising (in contrast to intraperitoneal hemorrhage), which tends to coexist with pelvic retropubic and retroperitoneal hemorrhage. However, traumatic perforation or disruption of the esophagus, stomach, and intestines is somewhat rare, perhaps owing to their inherent compliance and relative mobility.

Not infrequently, rupture or transection of the abdominal aorta occurs either in isolation or, much more commonly, together with similar injuries of the thoracic aorta.

Less commonly, ruptures of the adrenal glands, pancreas, and urinary bladder (usually in association with severe pelvic fractures) are found.

## Spine and Pelvic Girdle

Approximately one-third of victims sustain vertebral dislocations and fractures (**Figure 7**), which may be accompanied by contusions, lacerations, or even transection of the spinal cord. The relative distribution of these injuries (in overlapping frequencies) is as follows: atlantooccipital (5–6%), cervical (<40%), thoracic (60%), and lumbosacral (25%).

Combined thoracocervical and thoracoabdominal spinal injuries may occur with equal frequency (10–15%).

These spinal injuries are likely the result of the vertical transmission of the forces of deceleration, upwards along the axial skeleton, which would explain their concurrence with fractures of the lower limbs and of the pelvic girdle. Alternatively, primary or secondary impact with the back or the buttocks could also result in vertebral injuries.

Fractures of the pelvic girdle, ranging from solitary fractures of the body of the pubis or the pubic rami, to marked disruption and deformation, with severe retroperitoneal hemorrhage may be seen in 55% of cases (amongst these subjects 40% would also have sustained spinal injuries and pelvic fractures).

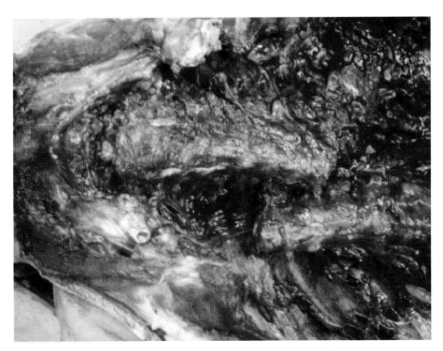

**Figure 7** Dislocation of the thoracic vertebral column (with transection of the spinal cord).

## Primary Impact

The determination of the probable anatomical site of primary impact may be applied to the reconstruction of the fatal fall, particularly in homicides or suspicious deaths. Generally, this is not an easy task, as the victims would usually have fallen from considerable heights, sustained a multiplicity of injuries and, occasionally, collided with intermediate objects.

Thus, in 30–40% of cases, an "educated guess" would be made concerning the probable site of primary impact, based in part on the distribution of the most severe and extensive external and internal injuries. Vertical deceleration with primary feet impact typically (although not invariably) results in open, comminuted fractures of the bones of the feet (and possibly fractures of the ankles, tibiae, and femurs), as well as often severe pelvic fractures and vertebral dislocations, associated with spinal cord laceration or transection, a ring fracture of the base of the skull, and contusion or laceration of the brainstem. Clearly, a careful consideration of the pattern of the injuries in their totality is as important as an assessment of their severity.

In this respect, the author would consider the presence of open, comminuted calcaneal (**Figure 8**) and other tarsal and metatarsal fractures, which often coexist with fractures of the ankles, together with rupture or transection of the distal part of the aortic arch, as being *sine qua non* of primary feet impact. The obvious caveats are that: (1) collision with intermediate objects must be excluded (ideally, by an examination of the scene of death); and (2) not every anatomical region of the body is severely injured, thereby precluding any sensible attempt at determining the probable site of primary impact.

Cases where head injuries are clearly predominant or are overwhelmingly severe or fatal (as when there is partial or complete extrusion of the brain) and where the injuries to the other parts of the body are relatively mild or minimal are likely to be consistent with primary head impact. However, this tends to be complicated by the fact that serious or even fatal head injuries, with open, comminuted or depressed skull fractures, brain lacerations, or partial extrusion of brain matter, may sometimes be seen in cases of probable primary feet/lower-limb impact, with subsequent anterior, lateral, or posterior, secondary head impact. Similar principles apply to fractures of the upper limbs and pectoral girdle.

One study estimated the distribution of the probable sites of primary impact to be as follows: head/face (11%), feet/lower limbs (61%), hands/upper limbs (5–6%), upper and lower limbs (2–3%), front of body (5%), back of body (6%), side of body (4%), and indeterminate (4–6%). Thus, it appears that the feet, or the lower limbs, are the most common probable sites of primary impact.

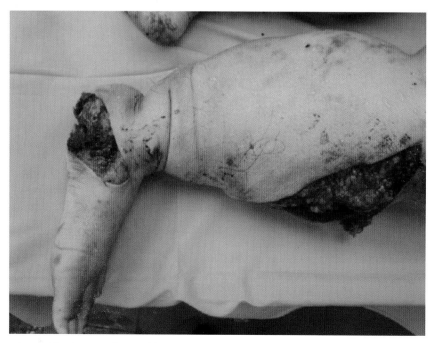

**Figure 8**  An open calcaneal fracture consistent with primary feet impact.

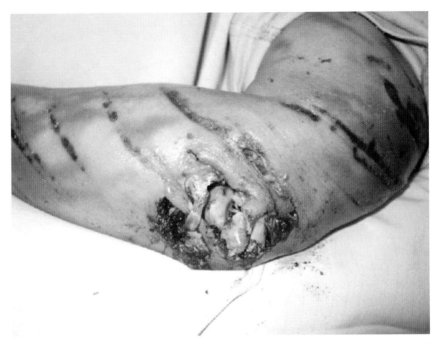

**Figure 9** Patterned, imprint abrasions (with open fracture–dislocation of the right elbow joint), consistent with primary upper limb impact.

Occasionally, distinct imprint abrasions or bruises, such as the pattern of a grille drain cover (**Figure 9**), might indicate the likely anatomical site of primary impact.

## See Also

**Falls from Height, Physical Findings:** In Children; **Injury, Recreational:** Airborne Sports; **Injury, Transportation:** Air Disasters

## Further Reading

Agalar F, Cakmakci M, Sayek I (1999) Factors affecting mortality in urban vertical free falls: evaluation of 180 cases. *International Surgery* 84: 271–274.

Agnew J (1993) Age and fatal work-related falls. *Human Factors* 35: 731–736.

Association for the Advancement of Automotive Medicine (1998) *The Abbreviated Injury Scale*, 1990 revision, update 98. Des Plaines, IL: AAAM.

Chao TC, Lau G, Teo CES (2000) Falls from a height: the pathology trauma from vertical deceleration. In: Mason JK, Purdue BN (eds.) *The Pathology of Trauma*, 3rd edn, pp. 313–326. London: Arnold.

Copeland AR (1989) Suicide by jumping from buildings. *American Journal of Forensic Medicine and Pathology* 10: 295–298.

De Haven H (1942) Mechanical analysis of survival in falls from heights of fifty to one hundred and fifty feet. *War Medicine* 2: 586–596. Reprinted in *Injury Prevention* (2000) 6: 62–68.

Isbister ES, Roberts JA (1992) Autokabalesis: a study of intentional vertical deceleration injuries. *Injury* 2: 119–122.

Lau G (2004) Homicidal and dyadic falls from a height: rarities in Singapore. *Forensic Science International* 44: 93–106.

Lau G, Teo CES, Chao TC (2003) The pathology of trauma and death associated with falls from heights. In: Payne-James J, Busuttil A, Smock W (eds.) *Forensic Medicine – Clinical and Pathological Aspects*, pp. 337–348. London: Greenwich Medical Media.

Li L (1994) The investigations of fatal falls and jumps from height in Maryland (1987–1992). *American Journal of Forensic Medicine and Pathology* 15: 295–299.

Rozycki GS (1991) Injuries sustained by falls. *Archives of Emergency Medicine* 8: 245–252.

Sorock GS (1993) Fatal occupational injuries in the New Jersey construction industry, 1983 to 1989. *Journal of Occupational Medicine* 35: 916–921.

Steedman DJ (1989) Severity of free fall injury. *Injury* 20: 259–261.

Warner KG, Dremling RH (1996) The pathophysiology of free-fall injury. *Annals of Emergency Medicine* 15: 1088–1093.

Wyatt JP, Beale JP, Graham CA, Beard D, Busuttil A (2000) Suicidal high falls. *Journal of Clinical Forensic Medicine* 7: 1–5.

# FEMALE GENITAL ALTERATION

**B Swift and G N Rutty**, Forensic Pathology Unit,
Leicester, UK

## Introduction

The act of modifying the female genitalia is one that remains contentious and controversial within modern western society. Though the definition could theoretically include the internal genitalia, such modifications fall purely in the realm of surgical procedures and are generally performed for the purpose of eradication of symptoms or pathological disease processes. The exception is the cosmetic alteration of the vulvovaginal region, which will be discussed later. The female genitalia, as with other aspects of the feminine form, are revered in social literature and regarded as features of sexual empowerment or reproductive capability. As such any alteration, and hence a possible loss or adjustment of this apparent societal role, even if entirely consensual, is regarded with revulsion by society as a whole.

The modifications fall broadly into three groups:

1. decorative alterations
2. temporary alterations
3. permanent (or surgical) alterations.

Complications of genital trauma also fall within the latter group and may be self-inflicted or induced by a second party, causing injuries such as burns, lacerations, or incised wounds, whether intentional or accidental. Physical complications of the injury, e.g., sepsis, stenosis, grafting, scarring, contractures, or prolapse, may occur as well as psychological and psychosocial sequelae, including fear of pain or loss of excretory or sexual function, loss of libido, or orgasmic dysfunction. Injury can occur at any age from infants to the elderly (the youngest example witnessed by the authors was in an infant of 2 months). The causation, examination, documentation, and evidence gathering from such injuries, however, are not considered here as they are covered in more dedicated texts.

## Decorative Alterations

As with all aspects of body art or modification, the beauty of the body is subjective to the individual. A desire to alter one's appearance may relate to a psychological wish to be individual or, conversely, to conform to a social group or cliché. Thus, the choice remains with the individual, and personal pleasure is gained through such alteration, though not necessarily as a means of becoming desirable to others. Therefore, alterations should ideally be viewed in a nonjudgmental manner.

### Pubic Hair

The most frequently altered aspect of the female external genitalia is the pubic hair. Like head hair, pubic hair may be groomed or altered to produce a fashionable appearance. Current trends include the epilation of the region to create either a limited region of hair, or to remove the hair *in toto*. The methods by which such hair removal may be performed include trimming, shaving, waxing, or electrolysis treatment. These are all associated with their own risks or side-effects, notably localized skin reactions due to chemical applications or hair-tip regrowth. Electrolysis aims to produce a permanent hairless area, whereas the former three are temporary means of epilation. The reasons for removing hair may be to make one feel more sexually attractive, as a means of feeling more hygienic, or to achieve a socially acceptable appearance when wearing certain items of feminine clothing, notably swimwear or narrow underwear. It is for this purpose that the "Brazilian wax" has become more prevalent in the western hemisphere; wax is applied to the pubic region and the hair removed to leave a single narrow vertical line of hair. Alternatively, the hair may be dyed, usually to match altered head-hair coloration.

Historically the bare pubic region was associated with disease; prostitutes exposed to venereal diseases during the eighteenth and nineteenth centuries developed sores and pustules which they needed to conceal to ensure further business. Likewise, syphilitic treatments of the day included the administration of mercury that resulted in hair loss. Again concealment was required to ensure that no clients suspected the presence of diseases. The merkin was thus devised, a pubic wig worn to conceal such infections. Its removal and cleaning also allowed the eradication of pubic louse infestations. With the decline in the prevalence of syphilis and the development of antimicrobial agents, the use of the merkin has declined to the extent of being obsolete.

Pubic hair modifications are mostly reversible or semipermanent. However, decorations may also be produced in more permanent ways, such as tattooing and body piercing.

## Tattoos and Body Piercing

Tattooing refers to the permanent implantation of nonnative pigmentation into the dermis or mucosal-lined surfaces. Though tattoos in general may be seen in relation to religion, culture, and employment (such as coal mining), radiotherapy treatment or the recent close-range discharge of a firearm, the term is generally applied to the insertion of pigments for decorative purposes. This may be performed professionally by a licenced tattoo artist or nonprofessionally such as is seen in penal institutions worldwide.

The female genitalia are an uncommon site for tattoos, although such decorations may occasionally be seen and are historically associated with a tribal initiation. These may provide points of identification in forensic cases, though few tattoos are truly unique. The risks and sequelae (infections or otherwise) of tattooing are well documented elsewhere and will not be discussed here.

Body piercing refers to the production of a semipermanent or permanent opening through the skin or a mucosal-lined surface such that a decorative item of jewelry may be inserted. Though the most common examples, by far, are earlobe piercings, the frequency of female genital piercing is surprising. Studies have shown it to be prevalent in women of all ages and social classes (**Figure 1**).

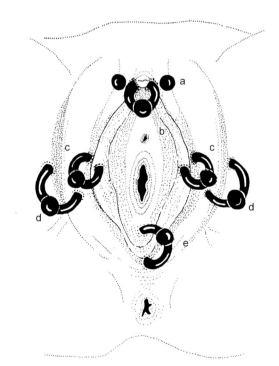

**Figure 1** Common forms of female genital piercing: (a) the prepuce or ''hood'' passing superficially to the clitoris; (b) clitoral; (c) inner labial; (d) outer labial; and (e) fourchette.

Genital piercing, especially for women, continues to be requested today for the purposes of decoration, but increasingly also for sexual arousal. Considering the region as a whole, the clitoris region is the most frequently identified area for piercing the external genitalia. Such piercings do not denote sexual orientation, being seen (as with all piercings) in both heterosexual and homosexual individuals alike. Numerous forms of piercing exist, often given eponymous or fanciful names by those who developed the act. However, despite the frequency of its use, female genital piercing is currently technically illegal, at least within the UK where the parliamentary bill The Prohibition of Female Circumcision Act 1985 denotes it as a felonious act by perpetuating the World Health Organization's categorization of genital modification (type IV: unclassified ... pricking, piercing ... of the clitoris and/or labia). The recent Female Genital Mutilation Bill 2003, designed to repeal and reenact the provision of the earlier act, failed to alter this definition or address this issue. No prosecutions have to date been brought against body-piercing establishments in respect of these acts within the UK. The literature on the risks and complications of body piercing is also well documented in other, more specific texts (**Figure 2**).

## Temporary Alterations

Temporary or semipermanent alterations may equally be performed for decorative or sexual reasons. Through their very nature and innervation, the genitalia are a focus of attention for stimulation and alteration. Either performed by others or, commonly, by the individual as a means of masturbation or sexual play, the genitalia are transformed through physical means. Self-inflicted fictitious injuries, e.g., the gluing together of the labia, may be seen occasionally to make false claims of sexual abuse against another individual.

### Play-Piercing

Play-piercing is a form of sex play, often performed alone as a means of stimulating the genitals, and extragenital sites, inducing a global state of arousal. It differs from the definition of body piercing in that no decorative item is placed into the site of interest; the act is performed purely to insert a sharp item into the region. Typically (for reasons of personal health) disposable hypodermic needles are used, though pins, sewing needles, or even nails may be used. The application of removable clips (often metal) may cause localized swelling or minor trauma. With regard to the female genitalia, hypodermic needles are

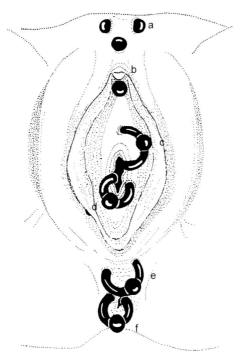

**Figure 2** Uncommon forms of genital piercing: (a) pubic, a superficial skin piercing; (b) "Isabella," with the metal shaft passing deep to the clitoris (this has a high risk of pudendal nerve injury); (c) "Princess Albertina," a rare piercing emulating the Prince Albert in men: the piercing passes from the urethra through to the anterior vaginal vault; (d) hymen; (e) guiche, piercing the perineum; (f) anal. Rare forms not illustrated here also include the "Christina" (a surface vertical piercing from the apex of the prepuce hood to the mons pubis), the "scrunty" (a transverse piercing through the urethral meatus), and the "suitcase" (a very rare piercing from the posterior vaginal vault to the anal canal; this holds a risk of peritonitis due to damage to the pouch of Douglas).

frequently inserted into the labia majora and minora, usually in large numbers and placed decoratively at evenly spaced points bilaterally. The clitoris and prepuce are also focused upon. The pleasure of the act lies in the ritual nature and the pain associated with each insertion. It may form part of an individual's fantasy, thus associated with masturbation, or may be part of an overall sadomasochistic experience. Even though the latter is usually consensual in nature and performed in private between adults, national and international rulings have resulted in custodial sentences for such sexual acts (albeit more in males, often homosexuals), arguing that it represents acts of torture or sexual and physical assaults from which individuals in society require protecting. It is therefore essential to recognize the existence of "play-piercing" as a differential cause of multiple small injuries to the genitalia when considering potential human rights abuses.

## Proportional Alterations

The physical proportions of the female genitalia may be altered, albeit temporarily, through the acts of saline injections or "pumping." Saline solutions may be injected, typically into the labia majora and minora. The effect is to produce swollen, engorged-appearing genitalia with the aim of increasing stimulation. Again the purpose is for sexual stimulation, though risks of vulvitis and sepsis may be raised.

Pumping ("vacuum pumping") describes the application of suction pressure to a region to enhance the natural dimensions. A plastic cylinder is usually applied and suction applied with a hand-pump device. A slow application of pressure results in localized edema and vascular engorgement which, when applied over numerous sessions, result in a semipermanent state of enhancement. The labia and clitoris are often enlarged in such a manner; the reason behind such alterations may be to comply with the individual's desired physical ideal. The risks are minimal and include localized bruising, petechial hemorrhages, and tissue-fluid-filled blisters.

Theoretically, though not described, the risk of local thrombosis or tissue ischemia may also be increased. The number of online groups and pornography-based web pages devoted to both topics reflects the popularity and increased prevalence of such activities.

## Vaginal Stretching

A temporary alteration of the internal genitalia, notably the vagina, may also be induced during sexual activities. Vaginal stretching, either through the insertion of increasingly larger objects (sex toys, vegetables, or household objects) or "fisting," may also be performed by a small percentage of the population. Fisting involves the insertion of the hand(s), or fist, into the vagina following stretching of the orifice. Though occasional deaths have been associated with the practice through trauma or air embolism, again the extent of pornographic material and internet groups shows that the activity is not uncommon and thus fatal outcomes must be very rare.

## Permanent Alterations

Permanent genital alterations generally refer to the surgical modification of the external genitalia which, as will be discussed, may or may not be performed in aseptic clinical settings. The acts may fall into the following three major categories:

1. cosmetic surgery
2. gender reassignment
3. female circumcision/female genital mutilation.

The excision of the external genitalia for the purpose of the diagnosis or eradication of malignancy, or tears and incisions (episiotomy) caused during childbirth, is not discussed in this article, which instead focuses on the alterations that are for psychological or social conformation to the believed feminine ideal.

## Cosmetic Surgery

The desire to achieve physical beauty is one that possesses a long cultural history; one could argue that it dates back to prehistoric times when natural pigments were applied to enhance and attract the opposite sex. The social ideal of physical beauty has altered over millennia and is increasingly being applied to the female genitalia. The desire to possess the most beautiful or sexually attractive genitalia is a frequently held one, though few possess the desire or actual means of achieving it surgically.

Cosmetic surgeons are, more and more, being requested to perform surgical procedures upon the female genitalia in order to achieve desired perfection. The most frequently performed operation is labia minora reduction. The size of the labia is considered hereditary in origin, though parity, sexual activity, and trauma may all alter its size and appearance. Women may consider their appearance sexually compromised and some also experience discomfort during physical activities. As such, enlarged or asymmetrical areas may be resected to produce a desired effect.

It should be noted that some alterations in labial dimension may be performed by nonsurgical operators, including the woman herself. The desire to cut or alter the appearance of a woman's own genitalia may result in a fetish that achieves gratification through the incision and resection of portions or the entire labia. When performed by the individual this is distinct to female genital circumcision/mutilation and as such is not banned by the legislation in place. Should a second individual perform the procedure, even with the consent of the individual, then this is regarded legally as circumcision and thus is illegal in most developed countries. Such second parties are known as "cutters" and are regarded as underground surgical practitioners, though many are not medically qualified, instead being body piercers or sadomasochistic masters. Care should be taken in investigating such cases, as described later.

Interestingly, some cultures find labia more attractive when longer and actively stretch their genitalia through the application of weights or repeated forceful pressure. Though this represents a small proportion of the female population as a whole, their presence on the worldwide web holds testament to the apparent difference between cultural ideals and illustrates the nonuniversal notion of beauty.

The mons pubis may be altered, usually as part of a general abdominal "lipoplasty" procedure. Labia majora may also be regarded as asymmetrical or unsightly. Alteration of the size and shape is performed through liposuction or fat injection, depending upon the desired effect. Alternatively, graft material or injections may produce similar effects. The surgery is usually requested purely as a means of cosmetic remodeling.

Vaginal reconstruction, however, is a purely sexual or functional surgical procedure. Although the procedure has been used for the repair of prolapse, incontinence, or pelvic malignancy, the operation is being requested more for the purpose of increased sexual stimulation. By increasing the tone and narrowing the vaginal space, the experience is considered more arousing for both partners.

The more extreme and purely cosmetic forms available also include hymen-reconstruction surgery. Some cultures still regard the presence of an intact hymen as the only true measure of virginity, despite its natural absence in many or the fact that it is commonly torn during physical activity in late adolescence. By reconstructing the hymen, the more affluent may ensure that the appearance of virginity is achieved for the purpose of securing marriage.

## Gender Reassignment

Gender reassignment represents the most complete means of modifying the genitalia. It is reserved for the treatment of sexual dysphorias, though prior to acceptance for the surgical procedure, extensive counseling and psychiatric documentation are required. Specialist surgical centers are located throughout the world; thus, individuals may elect to be operated upon abroad, depending upon financial aspects and the reputation of the clinics involved.

Complete female-to-male reassignments require the combined use of hormonal treatments, prosthetic implants, and surgery. First exogenous testosterones are administered to aid in the deepening of the voice and to induce a masculine-type distribution of hair growth. One of the oft-desired side-effects is hypertrophy of the clitoris. This may be detached surgically at the base to increase its length.

Metoidoplasties aim to produce a functioning urinary outflow enclosed within a hypertrophied clitoris, akin to the male form utilizing the embryological counterparts. The intention is to create the ability to void whilst standing and not to function as a sexual organ necessarily, as the neophallus is too small for implants. The internal genitalia are removed during a total abdominal hysterectomy and bilateral salpingo-oophorectomy, though some centers offer this procedure laparoscopically, thus shortening the postoperative recovery period. The labia minora are sutured together in the midline and testicular prosthetic implants inserted, possibly at a later outpatient appointment.

Phalloplasties, conversely, are used to create a more functional neophallus. These are fashioned from neurovascular skin flaps from either the abdominal wall or the individual's nondominant forearm. The skin flap is sutured around a urinary catheter inserted into the bladder. Various techniques are used for the siting of the clitoris; some surgeons amputate and reimplant the clitoris as a neoglans, though reinnervation may not occur. Other authorities recommend that the clitoris be left at the base of the neophallus, allowing continued stimulation and the ability to achieve orgasm.

Despite the continued requirement for testosterone therapy, there appears to be no increased risks of atherosclerosis or ischemic heart disease in this population.

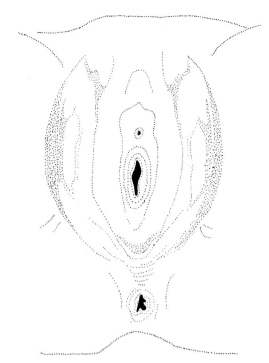

**Figure 3**   Female genital mutilation, type I as classified by the World Health Organization.

## Female Genital Alteration/Mutilation

The perpetuation of the act of female circumcision remains controversial worldwide, to the extent that the west refers to it solely as "female genital mutilation." The ease with which individuals can now cross continents, to emigrate or seek asylum, has led to the recognition of the act in multicultural societies in developed countries. Though locally the name of the procedure may still be known as "circumcision" or being "closed" (as opposed to the "open" state of nonaltered genitalia) the United Nations and World Health Organization have developed the definition of female genital mutilation, which may be divided into four subtypes:

1. Type I: excision of the prepuce with or without excision of part or all of the clitoris (**Figure 3**)
2. Type II: excision of the clitoris with partial or total amputation of the labia minora (**Figure 4**)
3. Type III: excision of any part of the external genitalia with narrowing of the vulval introitus, often through stitching (**Figure 5**)
4. Unclassified – this includes the pricking, piercing, or incision of the clitoris and/or the labia; cauterization of the genitalia; "angurya cuts" (incisions to the vulval introitus); and "gishiri" cuts (incised wounds to the vagina).

The history of the procedure is poorly documented, although examples exist in the writings of Strabone, a

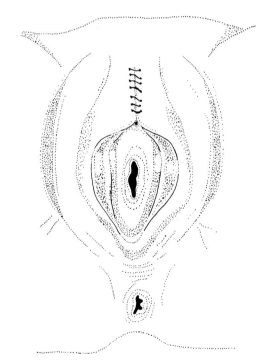

**Figure 4**   Female genital mutilation, type II as classified by the World Health Organization.

Greek historian, in 25 BC and circumcision *per se* is evident in writings dating back to 2200 BC. It continues to be performed, typically, in sub-Saharan Africa and areas of the Arabian peninsula, though the increasing public outcry has resulted in many countries following international organizations in banning it at a local level. Despite this, it is estimated that 2 million girls undergo forced genital alteration each year, with approximately 137 million women worldwide affected in a similar manner. In some countries the proportion of women on whom the practice has been performed approaches 98%. It has been recorded as being inflicted on all age ranges, from newborns to adults, though typically it occurs before 10 years of age.

Medically trained personnel rarely perform female genital mutilation; instead the task is delegated to the elderly members of the societies, and completed in the absence of anesthesia, analgesia, or aseptic conditions. Incisions are made with knives, razors, or shards of glass, often not being cleaned between girls. Remedies made from herbs or ashes may be applied to achieve hemostasis and the legs bound together for up to 1 month or more. Due to the poor conditions in which the procedure is performed, with poor instruments and often by people with failing eyesight, damage is often inflicted upon adjacent anatomical structures. Vesicovaginal or rectovaginal fistulae are not uncommon.

Worldwide, type I and II alterations constitute up to 85% of all female genital mutilations, though in certain countries other forms may be more prevalent. The process is reversed through repeated dilatation during intercourse, though it may require reincising. This also must be performed during childbirth, only to be reinstated after delivery.

The legislation put in place by developed countries differentiates between true female genital mutilation and the alteration of the genitals as a means of eradicating pathological conditions (such as premalignant or malignant disease). It is argued that the alteration of the external genitalia for cosmetic reasons is being performed for psychological purposes and thus is not illegal. (The issues regarding decoration have been discussed previously.) Although developed countries have had legislation in place for nearly 20 years, few actions have been brought (no prosecutions have been brought in the UK since the inception of The Prohibition of Female Circumcision Act 1985). Such laws have recently been altered to include the removal of a child from the country of birth for the expressed purpose of female circumcision.

The reasons for female genital mutilation are numerous (**Table 1**). A religious precedent for female genital mutilation is often cited; it is performed by Christians (Copts, Catholics, and Protestants), Muslims, Jews (Falasha), animists, and atheists alike. Despite being deeply embedded within such societies,

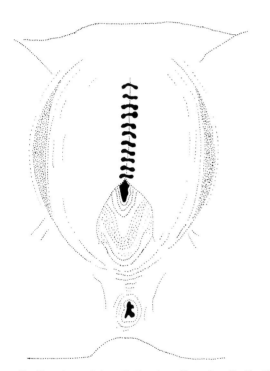

**Figure 5**   Female genital mutilation, type III as classified by the World Health Organization.

**Table 1**   Frequently cited reasons for female genital mutilation

| Reason proffered | Explanation |
| --- | --- |
| Psychosexual reasons | Reduction or elimination of the sexual tissue to attenuate desire, maintain chastity and virginity before and fidelity during marriage, and to increase male pleasure |
| Sociological reasons | Cultural identity, initiation into womanhood, social integration and maintenance of social cohesion |
| Hygiene and esthetic reasons | Considered "dirty" or "unesthetic" in natural state |
| Myths | To enhance fertility and survival of the child once born |
| Religious reasons | Though some Muslim communities practice genital alteration, the act predates Islam. No authentic religious doctrine for any faith demands it |

**Table 2** Health complications associated with female genital mutilation

| Physical complications | Short-term | Death – severe bleeding from incision of the clitoral artery |
|---|---|---|
| | | Shock – hypovolemic, septic, or neurogenic from the pain |
| | | Tetanus – lack of sterilization or immunization |
| | | Injury – perineal, anal, urethral, or vaginal |
| | | Acute urinary retention – periurethral edema or dysuria |
| | | Dislocation or fracture – due to forceful restraint |
| | | Infection – local or systemic |
| | | Poor wound healing – infection, irritation, or malnutrition |
| | Long-term | Recurrent ascending urinary tract infections |
| | | Keloid scars |
| | | Abscesses and dermoid cysts – around the vulva, labia, and clitoris |
| | | Neuroma – typically traumatic in origin, located around the clitoris |
| | | Urethral scarring and stricture formation |
| | | Vaginal calculus formation – inability to shed menses, resulting in debris accumulation and calcification |
| | | Fistulae – vesicovaginal or rectovaginal. Caused either by the procedure or subsequent trauma, including deinfibulation, intercourse, or labor |
| | | Pseudovagina formation – dilatation and scarring following repeated attempts at intercourse |
| | | Sexual dysfunction – mechanical obstruction, infection, or dyspareunia |
| | | Limited obstetric or gynecological examination due to narrowing of the introitus |
| | | Pelvic inflammation or infection |
| | | Infertility – due to traumatic damage or secondary infections |
| Psychological and sexual complications | Psychological | Posttraumatic stress disorder, anxiety, depression, neuroses, behavioral disturbances, psychosis, and suicide |
| | | Altered self-identity when with nonaltered western women in immigrant populations |
| | Sexual | Marital conflicts, inability to achieve sexual fulfillment, loss of interest in sexual intercourse due to dyspareunia, intercourse difficulties due to scarring, and vaginal stenosis |
| Social consequences | | Ostracism of uncircumcised girls |
| | | Acts to inhibit or suppress females culturally and often includes violence, coercion, and deception by next of kin |

no authentic religious doctrine exists that demands its use; many are aware of this, instead regarding it as a means of "controlling" female sexuality.

No statistics exist regarding the psychological or physiological complications associated with female genital mutilation (**Table 2**). Less than one-quarter are reported, probably due to poor access to medical care, a lack of knowledge, or a fear of retribution. However, it should be noted that it continues to be performed by females upon females, reinforcing the cultural nature of the act, and is not always unwanted by the individual.

The supporters of the act compare it to male circumcision, in that no proven medical benefits exist for the removal of the male prepuce and yet it is routinely performed soon after birth when the individual cannot grant consent. Why should male circumcision be deemed acceptable to western culture, being rarely described as mutilation, and yet female genital alteration not be regarded as a different means of cultural identification?

## See Also

**Medical Malpractice:** Plastic and Cosmetic Surgery

## Further Reading

Andrews G (ed.) (2001) *Women's Sexual Health*, 2nd edn. London: Baillière Tindall (Harcourt).

Girardin BW, Faugno DK, Seneski PC, Slaughter L, Whelan M (1997) *Color Atlas of Sexual Assault*. St. Louis, MO: Mosby.

Swift B (2003) Body art and modification. In: Rutty GN (ed.) *Essentials of Autopsy Practice: Recent Advances, Topics and Developments*. London: Springer.

World Health Organization (1995) *Female Genital Mutilation Report of a WHO Technical Working Group*. Geneva: World Health Organization.

# FIRE INVESTIGATION, EVIDENCE RECOVERY

**P J Thatcher**, Forensic Science Centre, Darwin, NT, Australia

## Introduction

Many agencies have a legislative, corporate, financial, or scientific requirement to ensure that the cause of a fire is reliably determined. In many instances, resources and information are shared and the investigation into the cause of the fire and the circumstances surrounding the fire are undertaken by a team representing multiple agencies (e.g., police, fire, and coronial services). However, it is not uncommon for members of the team to report independently to their own agencies in such a way that the specific requirements and responsibilities of the agency are met.

Whether agencies conduct independent investigations or contribute to a team approach, it is expected that their investigators will recover any evidence that contributes to the determination of the cause of fire and other circumstances surrounding the starting, progression, and suppression of the fire.

This article provides some basic information concerning investigation of the scene of fire, particularly with respect to the determination of the fire starting point and the cause of the fire. It is intended to provide an overview of the subject and there is an emphasis on the information that can be obtained by a careful examination of any human remains found at the scene.

## Scene and Evidence Recording

While fire scenes can often require specialist skills, particularly with regard to the determination of the fire starting point and cause, some requirements are common to the scientific investigation of any incident or scene of crime. Scene and evidence recording is one such example.

The methods used to record a fire scene are determined by the severity of the fire and the expertise and technical preferences of the investigator. Notwithstanding the range of recording media available to investigators, all investigators should be competent in the application of video techniques. This medium provides a rapid and simple means of recording the entire situation and provides an opportunity to obtain a second opinion on contentious matters at a time when the scene no longer exists in its original condition. Through the use of video, there is also an opportunity to record information that, while deemed apparently insignificant at the time of the inspection, can become important at a later date.

As with video recording, there is always the need to take photographs, either by traditional photographic techniques or by the use of digital photography. In addition to general photographs of the scene, photographs of the seat of the fire and any item that appears related to the starting of the fire should be photographed. These photographs can often be difficult to take because of the poor lighting available and the large amount of light-absorbing materials present. For this reason, photographic skills that exceed those needed to operate a camera in "automatic" mode are appropriate and, for specific photographs taken at the fire seat, a second photograph should be taken using the next "f stop" aperture setting.

When photography is used to record a scene, it is desirable that it is complemented with comprehensive notes and sketches. In this way, the relationship between items of interest can be determined and important measurements recorded for later reference.

## The Determination of Fire Starting Points

Before any evidence of the cause of the fire can be recovered, it is necessary to determine as precisely as possible the point where the fire started.

It is beyond the scope of this article to provide details concerning how this is done, but there are various fire travel indicators that assist in determining the fire starting point. Before listing the major fire travel indicators, it must be understood that these are only indicators. Although generally reliable, they can be invalidated and they can be contradictory, depending on circumstances.

### Fundamental Indicators

**Areas of most severe damage** The most severe damage usually occurs where the fire has burnt for the longest time, and this logically indicates where the fire must have started. This is fundamentally true, but localized areas of high fire load can produce a similar effect. Furthermore, while the indicator might be correctly read, the burn time might be the result of fire suppression operations being focused on other areas for strategic purposes (i.e., the fire did burn in that position for the longest time but only because the fire services allowed it to do so – not because it actually originated there).

**Lowest point of burning**   The basis for using this indicator is that fire travel is predominantly upward, due to convection effects, while spreading outward due to radiation effects. Therefore, it is reasonable to assume that the fire must have started at the lowest point of burning. However, while this is often the case, burning curtains and general debris can invalidate this indicator.

**Holes in flooring**   This has a similar basis as the previous indicators, but severely burnt areas where large amounts of flammable materials are stored at floor level can also result in a misinterpretation of this indicator.

**Other fire indicators**   Other fire indicators that suggest that a flammable liquid has been involved in the ignition and spread of the fire include characteristic "tongue-and-groove" burning in floorboards, which can also result in holes in the flooring, the appearance of "spill-pattern" burns in floor coverings, heavy sooting, and so on.

It should be mentioned here that several discredited fire travel indicators are still referred to in numerous fire investigation references. These include spalling in concrete, "alligatoring" patterns on burnt wood, depth of charring (as concerns the duration of burning), and some heat damage to electrical wiring.

## The Recovery of Evidence

Through the use of scientifically validated indicators, fire investigators "read" the fire travel and work back to the point of origin. Note that different investigators place different emphasis on these indicators, but, in general, competent fire investigators should independently arrive at the same designated starting point. Once the starting point of the fire has been identified, this area must be meticulously searched for any item or remains of an item that could have provided the ignition source for the fire. Items collected from the diagnosed seat of a fire are sampled for the following:

1. To confirm the presence of an item or substance that could have the potential to act as an ignition source or assist fire spread. An example of this situation is where there is an odor of flammable liquids and/or the burning and explosion characteristics suggest a very rapid fire spread typical of when a flammable liquid has been employed. A search of the identified fire seat, while not restricted to the recovery of flammable liquid residues, would certainly be targeting their

recovery for laboratory confirmation. However, in this situation, if any subsequent laboratory results fail to confirm the diagnosis of the cause of fire, the laboratory results might not necessarily be regarded as significant if there is a scientifically valid explanation for this apparent contradiction. For example, the burn characteristics on the floor coverings might suggest that it is likely that all the flammable liquids would have been completely burnt and therefore the absence is not only explicable but expected.

2. To provide any evidence that will support or refute a plausible fire cause in the absence of a likely or obvious cause. In these cases, the presence of this item will have limited investigative value unless more information becomes available through a subsequent scientific examination of the item or more circumstantial evidence concerning the spread and progress of the fire. For example, an examination of the electrical wiring or an electrical appliance recovered at or near the diagnosed fire origin might reveal evidence of an electrical malfunction. However, this damage can indicate either the cause of fire or an effect of the fire, so unless a reliable scientific examination can solve this dilemma, the fire investigator may have to rely heavily on eyewitness accounts before providing an opinion on the cause of ignition. In this instance, the scientific examination becomes more subjective and less independent.

When recovering items that have potential evidentiary value, the main considerations are:

1. Recording and labeling. The precise location of any item must be recorded in the case file notes as well as its condition at the time of sampling. Sufficient labeling should be added to the item packaging to ensure that the item can be fully identified at any time in the future. This information will include a description of the item and details of the collection (i.e., times, dates, and signatures).

2. Packaging. The packaging for the item must be sufficiently resilient to ensure that the contents are not damaged in the period before inspection. Furthermore, in the case of flammable liquids, the packaging must protect the item from any losses due to evaporation prior to the laboratory extraction and identification procedures. Steel cans and bottles meet both these requirements, but because of the bulk, mass, and expense of these containers, commercial oven and freezer bags are now commonly used for this purpose. Note that paper bags and plastic (polythene) bags are not suitable.

3. Sample numbers and size. Although the presence of microliters of flammable liquids can be recovered and identified using modern extraction and identification techniques, occasionally additional laboratory tests are necessary for these samples. As a consequence, it is preferable that large samples, such as a square meter of carpet or 2–3 kg of soil and debris, are submitted to the laboratory for analysis. It is also good practice in the case of structure fires to submit numerous samples taken from different rooms, although it will not always be necessary to analyze all of these samples.

4. Reference samples. If floor coverings are submitted for flammable liquid testing, a similar-sized sample that is not suspected to contain flammable liquid residues should be taken for laboratory reference purposes. For identical reasons, consideration should also be given to taking reference samples when items are collected that are suspected to have been involved in the ignition of the fire, for example, if an electrical motor in an exhaust fan is diagnosed as the probable ignition source, it is important that the condition of a similar motor also recovered from the fire scene be examined.

5. Continuity. As is the case with any item taken from an incident scene and that has the potential to assume forensic significance, there must be a guarantee for the integrity of that item at all times. Effectively, this means that the item must be secured at all times and that access will be denied to all persons other than the individual responsible for the item at any particular time. Furthermore, the chain of possession must be maintained and documented.

## Evidence Obtained from Bodies Present at Fire Scenes

In the case of fire scenes where deaths have occurred, police and coroners will routinely require information concerning the cause of death and the identity of the deceased. However, the position and condition of bodies recovered at crime scenes can also provide other valuable evidence concerning patterns of fire spread and the fire starting point (origin).

Therefore, although it is desirable that a forensic pathologist attends the scene and conducts a preliminary examination of the body *in situ*, it is essential that the body is not unnecessarily or excessively disturbed before the investigation of the cause of fire commences. Of particular interest to the fire investigator will be the position, condition, and attitude of the body, as well as the presence of any clothing on the body.

### Position of the Body

Where the body is sited can sometimes assist in determining what events took place during the fire. Most people will attempt to escape through doors or windows during a fire, and it is not uncommon to recover bodies from these locations. If a body is located some distance from an exit opportunity, it is important to determine answers to the following questions:

- What is the position of the body with respect to the diagnosed fire origin and could the position of the fire have prevented the deceased from reaching an egress point?
- If the deceased was near an egress point, what could have prevented an exit from the building?
- Was the deceased familiar with the premises?
- Had the deceased been immobilized prior to the commencement of the fire or was the deceased immobilized during the progress of the fire?

The answers to these questions could give rise to the scenario that the deceased died before or very soon after the fire started. Obviously, the forensic pathologist will be able to answer these questions (depending on the condition of the remains) after a postmortem examination is conducted. However, this usually takes considerable time, especially if toxicology results are required, and the fire investigator is in no position to defer any examination of the scene until all the test results are available.

If the situation suggests that the deceased has been injured or killed before the fire was started, the investigator will examine the scene for evidence of the fire starting point and cause, as well as search for any circumstantial evidence (e.g., the presence of a weapon) concerning the assault/murder.

### Condition and Attitude of the Body

The condition and attitude of the body will depend on the following: fire intensity, size of the body, period that the fire burnt, and position of the body in the fire.

The body can suffer different degrees of damage. The damage can range from literally no damage to a situation where only a few bones remain, although theoretically it is also possible that the situation is reached where there are no recognizable remains at all. However, the remains recovered after formal cremations indicate how difficult it is to destroy a body totally and since the "ideal" conditions of a cremation are rarely reached in any fire, significant amounts of remains are usually recovered.

Most commonly, bodies are recovered that have severe tissue loss with the resultant exposure and extrusion of internal organs. In these cases, the tissue at the extremities is usually severely charred and there are missing toes and fingers.

A feature of this severity of damage is that the body adopts the "pugilistic pose" (i.e., arms and legs are bent in simulation of a boxer's stance). This condition was originally regarded as evidence that the victim was defending himself/herself prior to death. It is now known that the reason for this body attitude is a consequence of muscle contraction. On exposure to severe heat, the flexor muscles contract more than the extensors due to their natural dominance.

Another significant feature that must be closely examined is the presence of any damage, such as holes or fractures, to the skull.

Any bursting of the cranium during severe exposure to heat is usually, but not always, along the sutures. The damage is caused by very rapid heating that causes steam pressure in the skull. This pressure can burst the skull before the palate, eyes, and ears are damaged to such an extent that this pressure can be released.

Any skull damage of this nature requires close examination because: (1) the skull damage might be due to a gunshot wound or other traumatic event; and (2) if the skull damage is due to a rapid heat rise, this could be a strong indication that flammable liquids were involved in the starting and spread of the fire. In either case, there will be additional and serious complications for the scene examiner, who might require the assistance of experts from other scientific disciplines, particularly forensic pathology.

## The Presence of Clothing on the Body

Contrary to popular opinion, it is extremely difficult to destroy a body by burning, particularly when it is subjected to less-than-ideal conditions. It is also reasonable to expect that the presence of clothing will significantly protect the body by insulating it against flames and heat. While this can be true in particular cases where woollen materials are concerned, it is generally not the case. In fact, the presence of clothing often assists the burning of a body by acting as a "wick" in an identical fashion to that of a wick in an oil lamp. The heat from the fire first liquefies the body fats, which then soak through the clothing and burn, which can leave the clothing relatively unaffected. As a consequence, the process continues and can become self-sustaining. This is a very efficient mechanism to burn a body and is the scientific explanation for the so-called "spontaneous human combustion" phenomenon that has for the past 200 years been credited for the complete destruction of bodies. Interestingly, the phenomenon has usually been reported

in situations where the fire damage to the structure is not particularly severe and often has been confined to a single room. These incidents are neither a result of a phenomenon nor are they spontaneous. The ignition of a body without an external ignition source is scientifically impossible.

As a further consequence of this explanation for the destruction of bodies in fires, it is predictable that it should be more difficult to burn an unclad body. This is confirmed by observations by experienced fire investigators. However, the situation is complicated when there is some involvement of flammable liquids in the starting and spread of the fire. The presence of these substances is often explained by a deliberate attempt to destroy a body or, alternatively, that the deceased has become a victim in a fire of his/her own making. In either case, the situation can arise that the fire was of such intensity that the only materials remaining to confirm the presence of any flammable liquid residues are those remnants of clothing that the deceased is lying on and/or the floor coverings directly under the body. It is therefore imperative that these items be collected and analyzed routinely for the presence of flammable liquid residues.

The foregoing discussion serves to stress the importance of understanding the basic principles involved in the destruction of bodies in fires. An incorrect interpretation can misdirect the investigation and several days can be lost before more precise pathology and laboratory results might become available that could correct the situation.

## Recording and Recovering the Remains

It is critical that the recording of any body parts is meticulous and that all accepted crime scene investigation standards are met. The recording should be by means of a combination of sketches and notes, orthodox photography, and video taping. However, any use of digital technology, while providing a convenient means of recording, might require compliance with local jurisdictional and government standards and policies.

In most instances, the actual recovery and transport of the body require few special considerations and will be done according to jurisdictional policies and procedures. However, in the case of bodies that have been reduced to bones and bone fragments, there are additional recording and recovery requirements.

In order to determine the number of deceased, any prior disturbance to the remains and the relationship of the remains to other items in the vicinity, it is necessary to construct a grid over the area. Each sector should measure approximately $1 \times 1$ m (although a smaller grid pattern might be more appropriate) and the sectors should be appropriately identified, for example, A1, A2 ... A5 and A1, B1 ... E1, resulting in 25 sectors.

The debris in each sector should then be screened, and all bone fragments and other items of interest from that sector should be placed in a plastic bag with the sector number identified. The screening is conducted using a series of screens ranging from 10 mm (#3) to 5 mm (#6).

In a recent case in Darwin, Australia, the combined results of the crime scene investigators, the forensic pathologist, and a fire expert showed that a body burnt in a camp fire had been severely disrupted before the remaining bones were collected. This proved that the accused had deliberately attempted to dispose of the body by raking the fire over, whereas it was claimed that the victim merely stumbled into the fire and was burnt to death. This was a critical factor in determining the circumstances of the incident and what the appropriate charges should be.

### Identification of the Deceased

While this discussion has concentrated on the evidence available for the incident investigation, it must always be remembered that one of the most vital pieces of evidence that can be gained from the deceased is his/her identity.

Although dental records are often available, a more speedy identification is often available through tattoos and other identifying features, jewelry and other artifacts, and identification papers in a wallet. This is a common method of identification because deceased persons are often found lying face-upward and any wallet is usually present in the back pocket. Thus, the personal papers are protected from the fire.

Notwithstanding the application of these convenient and obvious aids for establishing identity, fingerprints and DNA are now widely used to confirm identity. However, despite the recent scientific advances in these identification sciences, both methods have limitations.

If a deceased's fingerprints are on record, then there is no doubt that this technique represents the most efficient means of determining identity. Limitations for the use of the technique arise when the extremities of the body are destroyed through prolonged exposure to a significant fire. This effectively removes fingerprints and palm prints as a means of identification.

In the case of DNA, severe heating can also threaten the use of this technique by denaturing the nuclear DNA to such an extent that it can no longer be profiled. However, it will require a significantly longer exposure at high temperatures to denature nuclear DNA

deep in the body cavity than is required to destroy the skin on digits and palms. Therefore, to maximize the chance of success using nuclear DNA technology for identification purposes, multiple samples should be taken, particularly from internal organs and, if possible, a sample of blood should be taken from the heart.

In some instances, the problems caused by denaturing might be avoided by resorting to an analysis of mitochondrial DNA present in bone. However, this is a more difficult and expensive procedure and there is still no guarantee of success. Of course, regardless of any scientific difficulties encountered in these identification processes, there still remains the need to obtain the deceased's fingerprints or DNA profile for comparison purposes. This information might be available through the fingerprint and DNA databases held by the police forces and forensic science laboratories. However, if this is not the case, but there is some suspicion as to the identity of the deceased, confirmation samples might be available from personal items, such as hairbrushes, toothbrushes, electric shavers, and so on. If this is also not possible, then it will be necessary to collect samples from close relatives, particularly parents, children, and the mother of the children. The results from these persons will allow a deductive process to be undertaken that will result in a statistical probability for the identity of the deceased.

### Summary

The examination of human remains recovered from crime scenes can provide vital evidence to fire (cause) investigators and to police investigators. The position and attitude of the body and the severity of burning suffered by the deceased can assist in the determination of the fire starting point, the cause of the fire, and its progress. Furthermore, the identity of the deceased and the cause of death can provide information concerning circumstances leading to the incident. The potential of burnt bodies to provide this evidence demands that there always be a detailed examination of human remains at fire scenes and that the recording, recovery, and labeling of the remains comply with the strictly controlled procedures implemented for other types of evidence.

### See Also

**Anthropology:** Cremated Bones; **Autopsy, Findings:** Fire; **Carbon Monoxide Poisoning:** Incidence and Findings at Postmortem; **Crime-scene Investigation and Examination:** Recovery of Human Remains; **Injury, Fatal and Nonfatal:** Burns and Scalds

## Further Reading

DeHaan J (1997) Fire related deaths and injuries. In: Simon, Schuster (ed.) *Kirk's Fire Investigation*, 4th edn., pp. 362–391. New Jersey: Brady Prentice Hall.

Horswell J (1998) Crime scene examination. In: Selby H, Freckleton I (eds.) *Expert Evidence*, vol. 4, pp. 8-7303–8-7612. London: Law Book Company.

Ide RH (2000) Fire-scene. In: Seigel JA, Saukko PJ, Knupfer GC (eds.) *Encyclopedia of Forensic Sciences*, pp. 911–916. London: Academic Press.

Leitch DA (1993) *Guide to Fatal Fire Investigations*. Leicester, UK: Institution of Fire Engineers.

Pounder DJ (2000) Burns and scalds. In: Seigel JA, Saukko PJ, Knupfer GC (eds.) *Encyclopedia of Forensic Sciences*, pp. 326–331. London: Academic Press.

Simpson K, Knight B (1985) The ultimate effects of injury. In: *Forensic Medicine*, 9th edn., pp. 131–135. Maryland: Edward Arnold.

Stimson PG, Mertz CA (1997) *Forensic Dentistry*. New York: CRC Press.

Thatcher PJ (2000) Fire investigation. In: Selby H, Freckleton I (eds.) *Expert Evidence*, vol. 3, pp. 8-1401–8-1715. London: The Law Book Company.

Thatcher PJ, Kelleher JD (2000) Evidence recovery at the fire scene. In: Seigel JA, Saukko PJ, Knupfer GC (eds.) *Encyclopedia of Forensic Sciences*, pp. 905–911. London: Academic Press.

---

**Fire, Deaths**  *See* **Autopsy, Findings:** Fire

---

**Fire, Injuries**  *See* **Injury, Fatal and Nonfatal:** Burns and Scalds

---

# FORENSIC BOTANY

**J H Bock and D O Norris**, University of Colorado at Boulder, CO, USA

## Introduction

This article introduces aspects of botany that are useful in courtroom evidence concerned with crime-scene investigations, relationships among victims, associations between victims and suspects, victims/suspects and crime scenes, and the time of death of a victim. Botanical science is also useful in finding clandestine graves. Forensic botany applies the knowledge and techniques of plant science to legal matters, especially those related to crime. This article is based upon experience with the applications of three aspects of botany in criminal, especially homicide, investigations. These uses come from: (1) plant anatomy; (2) plant taxonomy; and (3) plant ecology. Two other aspects of botany used in forensics, plant DNA and palynology, are discussed in passing. Examples from cases can be found in the journal articles cited below. The cases we have dealt with have originated from investigators and attorneys involved in criminal justice.

## Plant Anatomy

Plant anatomy is the study of plant cells. This botanical subdivision has received little attention by forensic scientists. It is here that certain aspects of forensic botany have developed lately, although the techniques used are as old as the field itself. Every kind of plant, including plants used for food, has specific patterns of cell types with distinctive sizes, shapes, and inclusions. These characteristics allow individual food plants to be identified readily in samples from the human digestive tract. Plant cells pass through the human digestive tract without losing their identifying characteristics. They also maintain these characteristics in fecal material. This is because cellular size, shape, and structure are defined by the plant's cell wall. Cell walls of plants have cellulose as their principal structural component. Cellulose is nonliving and it surrounds the internal contents of cells by means of interwoven strands. Cellulose is a polysaccharide. It is indigestible by humans and passes through the human digestive tract intact. Therefore, as long as some or all of a victim's digestive tract is present we can often identify specific plant foods from their cells in stomach, intestinal, and fecal samples from meals near the time of death.

The forensic use of plant cells from the human digestive tract requires a limited amount of special training, but the laboratory techniques are simple. For example, food contents of a victim's last meal may indicate the place where the meal took place, with whom the meal was or was not taken, false testimony and, within broad scientific guidelines, general information about the time of death. This evidence has been widely accepted in criminal courts.

The technique used for identification of food plant cells is as follows. Samples of digestive tract contents are received. Slides are prepared from those samples for light microscope examination. Staining is not essential, but a drop of safranin or similar stain may be used. These slides are examined, and indications of food plant possibilities are likely to be suggested to the experienced plant anatomist. Slides are then prepared from known food plants. The plants to be used for comparison usually are obtained from a grocery store. Whether the store's material is fresh, canned, or frozen is irrelevant. The guidance for identification may come from either our out-of-print guide which was widely distributed at publication to investigators and to forensic laboratories in the USA and Canada, or, quite often, from the plant anatomist's previous experiences. In order to double-check our identifications, known samples are prepared and compared. It is highly desirable that at least two people, working independently, affirm the identification.

Plant cells in a victim's stomach contents sometimes provide clues about the time of death. At death the pyloric valve at the base of the stomach closes and remains closed until decay is advanced, holding most, if not all, the contents of the last meal in place (**Table 1**). This is not true of food found elsewhere in the digestive tract where valves do not necessarily seal at the time of death. Only stomach contents have been used in discussions and testimony concerning time of death.

## Plant Taxonomy

A second kind of useful botanical evidence in crime-scene investigation uses information from plant taxonomy. This field includes plant species identification. Plant materials may be found in and on vehicles. Such materials have been used to link suspects to a crime

**Table 1** Human digestion times for a meal: times are compiled from scientific literature concerned with human digestion[a]

| Location | Range of time |
|---|---|
| Mouth | 1 s–2 min |
| Stomach | 2–6 h |
| Small intestine | 2–8 h |
| Large intestine | 6–9 h |
| Total time | 10–23 h |

[a]These figures are only rough guides and may be influenced by drugs, diseases and many other factors.

scene, a suspect to a victim, and victims who have relocated have been linked to the original crime scene. Materials have also been identified from the clothing of suspects and victims, and from the bodies of victims. Very small pieces of leaves, twigs, and flowers can often be identified from species using relatively simple and readily available guides. This work has led us to encourage crime-scene investigators to look for plant fragments before using a vacuum sweeper. People with the appropriate backgrounds to carry out such identifications in an expert way are readily available throughout most of the world.

## Plant Ecology

Plant ecology is the discipline that investigates plants and their environmental relationships. In the search for clandestine graves, ecological knowledge of patterns of plant succession is useful. Disturbance patterns of the soil and vegetation over graves vary in known ways and are dependent upon time since burial, decomposition of the corpse, and regional climate, among other factors. In addition, ecological knowledge of patterns of plant distribution has been useful in pinpointing crime scenes. Regional experts are available in most parts of the world. Ecological knowledge often complements the findings of plant taxonomy because plants are often highly specific in their environmental requirements and their natural distributions. For example, in Colorado, we have been able to associate plants from a crime scene with certain mountain elevations that were distinctive from the plants found elsewhere in the state.

## Palynology

Palynology is a subdivision of plant science and geology that deals with pollen and spores. Pollen grains carry the sperm involved in sexual reproduction of vascular plants. Spores are cells that are involved with nonsexual reproduction in fungi and plants. Geologists have long made use of fossil pollen and spore patterns in their searches for fossil fuel deposits. Such cells can also be used to reconstruct climates of past times as well. For example, near Boulder, CO, in the USA, there are many pollen fossils of palms and red-wood trees, bearing witness to a milder, wetter climate than exists there at present. Forensic scientists make use of pollen and spores as well. If pollen and spores are identified on the clothing of a victim or a suspect, they can act as witness to where these people have been. In addition, seasonality may figure in an investigation because pollen and spore dispersal are seasonal as well as place-specific.

## DNA Analysis for Botanical Materials

DNA work on plants is available from a myriad of sources that carry out DNA analyses. The most common practice is to use chloroplast DNA for such purposes; but mitochondrial and nuclear DNA from plants can also be used. Such evidence has been useful in a few well-publicized cases, but it is less useful in general for plant evidence than for that involving humans because humans belong to only one species and our entire complement of DNA has been analyzed. The DNA of most of the 270 000 species of flowering plants has not been investigated.

## Education

Presently, there are no formal training programs or board certifications in forensic botany. The persons who qualify as expert witnesses in plant anatomy work have rather specific educational and experiential requirements. Advanced training in botany is essential (masters or doctoral degree) and some training in crime-scene investigation, courtroom testimony and evidence presentation, as well as appropriate professional affiliations, is important. Certainly, self-education is possible to a considerable extent if the investigator can obtain a plant anatomy textbook for serious study and, using a light microscope, prepare and examine food plant materials.

## The Use of Botanical Evidence in Forensic Testimony

Far too few forensic laboratories make use of the inexpensive, strong evidence that can come from forensic botany. Many aspects of botanical knowledge are useful in detection and in courtroom testimony in criminal

cases. Sometimes expert witnesses require highly specialized training to be received as experts in court, but there are many botanists throughout the world with credentials and knowledge that will fit them for giving testimony and depositions. Botanical evidence as described here calls for relatively inexpensive techniques to produce credible evidence.

## See Also

**Autopsy, Findings:** Organic Toxins

## Further Reading

Barbour MG, Burk JH, Pitts WD, Gilliam FS, Schwartz MW (1999) *Terrestrial Plant Ecology,* 2nd edn. London: Addison Wesley Longman.

Bock JH, Norris DO (1997) Forensic botany: an under-utilized resource. *Journal of Forensic Sciences* 42: 364–367.

Bock JH, Lane MA, Norris DO (1988) *Identifying Plant Food Cells in Gastric Contents for Use in Forensic Investigations: A Laboratory Manual.* Washington, DC: US Department of Justice, NIJ.

Crawley MJ (ed.) (1997) *Plant Ecology,* 3rd edn. Oxford, UK: Blackwell Science.

Dickenson WC (2000) *Integrative Plant Anatomy.* London: Academic Press.

Esau K (1977) *Anatomy of Seed Plants,* 2nd edn. New York: Wiley.

Jackson S (2002) *No Stone Unturned.* Boston, MA: Kensington.

Judd WS, Campbell CS, Kellogg EA, Stevens PF, Donahue MJ (2002) *Plant Systematics: A Phylogenetic Approach.* Sunderland, MA: Sinauer Associates.

Lane MA, Anderson LC, Barkley TM, *et al.* (1990) Forensic botany: plants, perpetrators, pests, poisons, and pot. *BioScience* 40: 34–40.

Mertens J (2003) Forensics follows foliage. *Law Enforcement Technology* 30: 62–67.

Norris DO, Bock JH (2000) Use of fecal material to associate a suspect with a crime scene: report of two cases. *Journal of Forensic Sciences* 45: 184–187.

Norris DO, Bock JH (2001) Method for examination of fecal material from a crime scene using plant fragments. *Journal of Forensic Investigation* 52: 367–377.

Sachs JS (2001) *Corpse: Nature, Forensics, and the Struggle to Pinpoint Time of Death.* Cambridge, MA: Perseus Publishing.

Sachs JS (2003) Crime seen: tiny clues from a "gentle drowning." *Popular Science* 28–31.

# FORENSIC JOURNALS, BIBLIOMETRICS AND JOURNAL IMPACT FACTORS

**A W Jones**, University Hospital, Linköping, Sweden

## Introduction

In its broadest sense forensic science is concerned with the application of scientific methods and procedures to investigate crimes, including the gathering and interpretation of evidence and presenting the findings in an unbiased and objective way in courts of law. In this connection, forensic science is a perfect example of a multidisciplinary topic and its practitioners require knowledge and training in many areas of the pure, applied, and biomedical sciences. Most forensic scientists work at government-controlled laboratories or at private enterprise organizations that offer forensic science services. Indeed, there is an increasing commercialization of the forensic sciences in some countries and this is especially evident in the UK.

The typical forensic scientist differs from an academic or university-based scientist in several ways. Among others, there is less pressure to publish the results of research and development work and to place this information in the public domain. Accordingly, forensic scientists are less inclined to write up the results of their research work or case files in the form of a scientific paper and participate in the often time-consuming process of submitting the work for peer review and publication. People who do not publish scientific articles regularly do not cite the published work of authors, a fact that has obvious consequences when journal impact factors are concerned, because these are derived from counting citations. Accordingly, the prestige rating of forensic science journals, as reflected in citation counts and impact factors, is low compared with many other disciplines.

The multidisciplinary nature of forensic science and the size of the field can be roughly gauged by considering the American Academy of Forensic Sciences (AAFS) and the scientific sessions at the annual AAFS meeting, which was held in New Orleans, Louisiana, USA in 2005. These covered themes such as criminalistics, engineering sciences, general subjects, jurisprudence, odontology, pathology/biology, physical anthropology, psychiatry, engineering science, behavioral sciences, questioned documents, and toxicology. The current membership of AAFS (founded in 1948) is 5520 and this can be compared with the Forensic Science Society (FSS) in UK (founded in 1959), which has a current membership of over 2500.

The traditional information sources for acquiring knowledge and expertise in forensic and legal medicine are books and monographs written by some authority or established expert on a topic such as a prominent forensic pathologist. However, the past 50 years have seen the emergence of forensic science journals as an alternative way of spreading information and keeping abreast of developments in the subject. The official journal of the AAFS, the *Journal of Forensic Sciences* (JFS), first appeared in 1956 as a quarterly periodical and became bimonthly in 1987 and considers for publication original research articles, reviews of the literature, technical notes, brief communications, letters to the editor, and book reviews on all aspects of the forensic sciences.

Some forensic journals deal with subspecialties such as legal medicine and pathology, which is one of the major themes of the present encyclopedia. However, even the smaller forensic science disciplines have acquired their own journals and forums for disseminating information and publication of research. Indeed, publishing papers in scientific journals has become part and parcel of the scientific process and is the primary means of spreading information to colleagues and also gaining priority for the particular research and development work. One truism in science is that research does not exist until it is published.

This article deals with citation trends and practices among international journals specializing in forensic science and legal medicine with major focus on English-language periodicals. In particular, the ranking of these journals according to the Institute for Scientific Information (ISI) in terms of their impact factors and other bibliometric indicators is reviewed and discussed.

## Forensic Science Journals

Table 1 contains information about the leading forensic and legal medicine journals, including the year they first appeared, with the original journal title if this has changed over the years, the country of origin and publisher, the name of the current editor, and the size of the journal as reflected in the number of printed pages in the 2002 editions. All the journals listed are English-language journals, although *Science*

**Table 1**  The major forensic science and legal medicine journals, the year they first appeared, the country of origin and publisher, the current editor-in-chief and the number of pages in the 2002 editions

| Current name of journal (earlier title) | First appeared | Country and publisher | Current editor (2003) | Printed pages (2002) |
|---|---|---|---|---|
| International Journal of Legal Medicine (Zeitschrift für Rechtsmedizin) | 1990 | Germany, Springer | B Brinkmann | 374 |
| Forensic Science International (Forensic Science) | 1978 | Ireland, Elsevier | P Saukko | 1415 |
| Journal of Forensic Sciences | 1956 | USA, American Society for Testing of Materials | M Peat | 1413 |
| American Journal of Forensic Medicine and Pathology | 1980 | USA, Lippincott, Williams & Wilkins | VJ DiMaio | 403 |
| Medicine, Science and Law | 1960 | UK, Barsbury | AW Goode | 361 |
| Science and Justice (Journal of the Forensic Science Society) | 1995 | UK, Forensic Science Society | ARW Forrest | 245 |
| Journal of Clinical Forensic Medicine[a] (Police Surgeon) | 1994 | UK, Elsevier | JJ Payne-James | 209 |
| Legal Medicine[a] | 1999 | Ireland, Elsevier | H Takizawa | 256 |

[a]Not yet included among the journals covered by the Institute for Scientific Information (ISI).

*and Justice* (the official journal of the UK FSS) includes abstracts of the articles in German, French, and Spanish. The *International Journal of Legal Medicine*, which was originally called *Zeitschrift für Rechtsmedizin*, now publishes only in the English language. The current German-language journal that specializes in forensic and legal medicine is entitled *Rechtsmedizin* (Springer Verlag) and is the official organ for *der Deutschen Gesellschaft für Rechtsmedizin*. A primarily French-language journal is entitled *Journal de Médicine Légal Droit Médical* and deals with all aspects of medicine, science, and the law. Another primarily French-language journal is devoted to analytical and forensic toxicology, namely *Annales de Toxicologie Analytique*.

Besides the major forensic science and legal medicine journals listed in **Table 1**, there are also more specialist periodicals that cover various domains of forensic science and legal medicine, including:

- *International Journal of Forensic Dentistry*
- *Journal of Forensic Odontostomatology*
- *Journal of Forensic Identification*
- *Journal of Forensic Psychiatry*
- *Forensic Linguistics*
- *Environmental Forensics.*

The most significant journals in terms of their size and circulation are *JFS* (1413 pages in 2002) and *Forensic Science International* (1415 pages in 2002), both of which cover all aspects of research and development in forensic science, including pathology. The UK journal *Science and Justice* is seemingly becoming slimmer and slimmer in size, which might reflect the increasing commercialization of the forensic science services in the UK, allowing less time and motivation to prepare scientific papers for publication. Examples of smaller-circulation forensic society journals include *The Canadian Society Forensic Science Journal* and *The Australian Journal of Forensic Sciences*, although these are not covered by the ISI and therefore have not acquired an impact factor. Another non-ISI journal is entitled *Blutalkohol* (blood alcohol), which is primarily a German-language journal (Steintor Verlag, Lübeck) that specializes in publishing articles dealing with forensic science aspects of alcohol (alcohology), particularly alcohol, drugs, and traffic safety.

## Review Journals

Review articles constitute an important source of information in all branches of science, not least in the forensic sciences. Many forensic journals solicit for publication critical reviews of the literature on a given topic. Much can be learnt from reading and writing a comprehensive review article. The publishing house Springer Verlag embarked on publishing a series of monographs entitled *Forensic Science Progress*, but the project was terminated after the first five volumes were produced. The editors-in-chief of this series were Drs A Maehly and R L Williams and most of the articles were penned by invited authors and specialists in a particular area of the forensic sciences. The most current ongoing review journal is *Forensic Science Review* (chief editor Dr. Ray H Liu), which appears twice annually and the first volume dates from 1989. Some of the issues of *Forensic Science Review* are devoted to a particular topic or theme of current interest, for example the state of knowledge about drugs and driving was recently covered.

Those journals specializing in publishing review articles often become highly cited and accordingly enjoy a high impact factor, as illustrated by the annual review volumes listed in **Table 2**. The bibliography of a comprehensive up-to-date review article might include several hundred references to scientific articles, which is one reason why they tend to become highly cited.

The impact factors of forensic science journals such as *JFS* and *Journal of Analytical Toxicology* have seemingly fluctuated year by year over the past 6 years (**Table 3**). The reason for this uneven citation rate can be attributed to a single biannual review of the forensic science literature, which appears in a special edition of *Analytical Chemistry* called *Application Reviews*. These reviews contain extensive bibliographies with 843, 811, 782, 243, and 461 reference items for the years 1995, 1997, 1999, 2001, and 2003, respectively. Because most of the citations are to recent published articles in *JFS* and *Journal of Analytical Toxicology*, within the 2-year window, this is beneficial when impact factors are computed. The drop in number of references in 2001 was a direct request from the publisher of *Analytical Chemistry* – the American Chemical Society. Other comprehensive reviews of forensic science and analytical

toxicology that might contain hundreds of references to recently published articles (over the previous 2 years) will help to boost journal impact factors.

## Institute for Scientific Information

The ISI, with its head offices in Philadelphia, was founded by Eugene Garfield (**Figure 1**) in the early 1960s and has developed into a worldwide organization now owned by the Thomson Corporation, Toronto. Although probably best recognized for producing the weekly booklet *Current Contents*, which contained a collection of the contents pages from several hundred scientific journals, ISI's most sophisticated tool for citation analysis research is the *Science Citation Index*. This product has now been renamed *Web of Science* and this enormous citation database is now searchable online. The citation records for millions of published articles can be investigated and this allows the developments in a topic to be traced forward in time. With the help of web-of-science, it has become a fairly simple matter to scrutinize a person's output of papers (quantity) and the associated citation record (quality).

*Journal Citation Reports* (*JCR*) is the ISI product that contains journal impact factors and other bibliometric information for ranking, evaluating, categorizing, and comparing different journals according to the number of times the articles they publish become cited. Indeed, impact factors are

**Table 2** Examples of periodicals (book series) having high impact factors and fairly low numbers of citable items, as shown by data for 2002

| Review journal | Impact factor 2002 | Citable items |
|---|---|---|
| Annual Review of Immunology | 54.4 | 26 |
| Annual Review of Biochemistry | 36.2 | 28 |
| Annual Review of Neuroscience | 24.1 | 19 |
| Annual Review of Pharmacology and Toxicology | 19.6 | 23 |
| Annual Review of Physiology | 15.9 | 32 |
| Annual Review of Medicine | 7.9 | 34 |

**Table 3** Citations from *Analytical Chemistry* (AC) to articles published in *Journal of Forensic Sciences* and *Journal of Analytical Toxicology* and fluctuations in their impact factors between 1997 and 2002

| Year | Journal of Forensic Sciences | | Journal of Analytical Toxicology | |
|---|---|---|---|---|
| | Impact factor | Cites from AC[a] | Impact factor | Cites from AC[a] |
| 2002 | 0.787 | 7 | 1.256 | 12 |
| 2001 | 0.883 | 53 | 1.417 | 6 |
| 2000 | 0.939 | 8 | 1.592 | 6 |
| 1999 | 1.394 | 156 | 2.221 | 124 |
| 1998 | 0.769 | 10 | 1.395 | 8 |
| 1997 | 1.404 | 192 | 2.168 | 144 |

[a]*Analytical Chemistry*.

**Figure 1** Eugene Garfield PhD (born 1925), founder of the Institute for Scientific Information, Philadelphia, the company that produces *Journal Citation Reports* and other bibliographic tools, including *Science Citation Index*, which is now called *Web of Science*. Courtesy of Eugene Garfield, PhD. Reproduced with permission.

now much discussed and debated because many people consider them a marker of journal quality and prestige. The *JCR* has been available online since 1997 and usually appears in July each year and contain impact factors and other information for close to 6000 scientific journals published worldwide.

## What are Impact Factors?

Impact is a nice-sounding word that conjures up the idea of quality and prestige in something. The idea to create a journal impact factor was apparently conceived by Eugene Garfield in 1955, ostensibly to help librarians manage their journal collections and select what they should or should not include. Garfield has been a prolific writer on all aspects of information science and is the undisputed guru of bibliometrics and citation analysis. There is a treasure trove of information available in Garfield's personal website (www.garfield.library.upenn.edu). Besides biographical details and notes about historical development of the *Science Citation Index* and impact factors, the site contains most of Garfield's published works, including hundreds of essays of an information scientist, all of which are available in portable document format (pdf), making them easy to copy and print.

The ISI product *JCR* lists both citing and cited journals and these can be rank-ordered according to various bibliometric parameters, including impact factor, immediacy index, and number of times cited. The best way to use *JCR* is to select a journal category that includes the discipline of main interest and, in this connection, forensic science and legal medicine journals are located under the rubric "Medicine, legal." In 2002 this category comprised just nine journals, which are listed below in rank order of decreasing impact factor:

1. *International Journal of Legal Medicine* 1.918
2. *Regulatory Toxicology and Pharmacology* 1.528
3. *Expert Opinion on Therapeutic Patents* 1.369

4. *Journal of Law and Medical Ethics* 1.288
5. *Forensic Science International* 1.023
6. *Journal of Forensic Sciences* 0.787
7. *American Journal of Forensic Medicine and Pathology* 0.521
8. *Medicine, Science and Law* 0.371
9. *Science and Justice* 0.229.

The reason for including journals 2, 3, and 4 in this subject category is not clear and they will not be considered further. However, *Journal of Clinical Forensic Medicine* (Elsevier), now in its ninth year of publication, is a perfect candidate for inclusion in this category (**Table 1**) , along with *Legal Medicine* (Elsevier), although neither are as yet included by ISI and they have not been assigned an impact factor.

**Table 4** gives additional information about the journal category "Medicine, legal" based on the 2002 edition of *JCR*. The total cites column indicates the total number of times that articles from these journals were cited by all journals included in the ISI database within the current product year. This is followed by the impact factor for the current year and next the immediacy index. The immediacy index is a bibliometric parameter used to measure how fast the "average article" in a journal gets cited and is the ratio between current-year citations to the number of articles published in the current year. The immediacy index is a kind of 1-year journal impact factor. Journals that appear late in the year or experience a delay in publication have a disadvantage when the immediacy index is calculated, because current-year articles appear too late to be cited in articles published the same year. Many journals now make available online details of the articles pending publication and preprints can often be downloaded. This service should eventually lead to a higher immediacy index for these periodicals.

**Table 4** also shows the number of articles published in the current year (articles + reviews) and the number of citable items – these are important in the

**Table 4** Forensic and legal medicine journals ranked according to impact factor and listing of other bibliometric details according to the Institute for Scientific Information's journal citation reports for 2002, which covered 5876 journal titles with a median impact factor of 0.85. See text for a fuller description of terms used

| Journal | ISSN | Total cites 2002 | Impact factor | Immediacy index | Articles 2002 | Cited half-life |
|---|---|---|---|---|---|---|
| International Journal of Legal Medicine | 0937 9827 | 1199 | 1.918 | 0.250 | 76 | 4.6 |
| Forensic Science International | 0379 0738 | 2073 | 1.023 | 0.150 | 240 | 5.3 |
| Journal of Forensic Science | 0022 1198 | 2467 | 0.787 | 0.094 | 254 | 7.5 |
| American Journal of Forensic Medicine and Pathology | 0195 7910 | 704 | 0.521 | 0.062 | 81 | 7.5 |
| Medicine, Science and Law | 0025 8024 | 432 | 0.371 | 0.044 | 45 | >10 |
| Science and Justice | 1355 0306 | 92 | 0.329 | 0.000 | 22 | a |

[a]Not available because total cites were fewer than 100.

**Table 5** Definitions and explanation of selected terms relevant for studies on bibliometrics and citation analysis (modified from information provided by the Institute for Scientific Information (ISI), Philadelphia)

| Term or word | Definition/explanation |
| --- | --- |
| Abstract | Brief summary or description of the essential content of an article, book chapter, or book |
| Author | The writer of an article, book chapter, or complete book. Many articles have multiple authors, although the first author is generally considered the primary author or major contributor to the work produced |
| Bibliographic reference | The citation that refers the end-user to an original source of information and usually includes the names of the authors, title of the article, and the source of the publication, such as name of the journal and the volume number, year of publication, and pagination |
| Bibliography | A list of references to source material on a given topic, usually appearing at the end of an article or book chapter. References can be listed in numeric order as used in the text or alphabetically by name of first author |
| Citation | A citation is a reference usually published at the end of a journal article and comprises one item in the bibliography |
| Citation density | The ratio of total number of citations in all the articles published in a journal in a particular year divided by the total number of articles published during that year |
| Citation index | A bibliographic tool formerly in printed format but now electronic that lists all referenced or cited source items published in a given time span |
| Cited half-life | The number of years going back from the current year, which accounts for 50% of the total citations received by the cited journal in the current year |
| Cited journal | The journal that receives a citation either cited in one of its own articles (self-citation) or in some other journal |
| Cited reference search | A search for papers that have cited a particular target reference or author or journal |
| Citing half-life | The number of journal publication years, going back from the current year, that accounts for 50% of the total citations given by the citing journal in the current year |
| Citing journal | The journal that gives a citation or bibliographic reference to an article published in the same (self-citation) or another journal |
| Immediacy index | The average number of times an article published in a specific year in a target journal is cited over the course of that same year |
| Impact factor | The number of current-year citations to articles published in a specific journal 2 years previously divided by the total number of articles published in the same journal in the corresponding 2 years |
| ISBN | International standard book number, a unique 10-digit number for a specific edition of a book |
| ISSN | International standard serial number, a unique 8-digit number that identifies a specific periodical title |
| Journal | A periodical (quarterly, bimonthly, monthly, or weekly) usually devoted to a specific field or subject such as forensic science, forensic medicine, or legal medicine. Also the Annual Reviews series are treated as journals by ISI |
| Peer review | The process by which an article is evaluated by experts, the author's peers in the subject area covered in the article submitted for publication |
| Self-citation | When a journal article cites an article previously published in the same journal or when an author cites another article that he or she has written previously |

impact factor calculation and form part of the denominator. Finally, **Table 4** shows the cited half-life of the journals listed, which is defined as the number of publication years from the current year, and which accounts for 50% of the current citations received. This factor helps to evaluate the age of the majority of cited articles published in a journal. Only those journals receiving more than 100 citations are given a cited half-life.

## Bibliometrics

The subject of bibliometrics is concerned with evaluating groups of publications and the quantitative relationships between the cited and citing information, including the source journals and the articles they publish. These citation records are used to evaluate the importance of the journals in their discipline, the productivity of the authors, and the frequency of citation to published work. There is an increasing acceptance among science administrators and scientists themselves that the number of citations received is more meritorious than the number of published articles produced. Many of the terms and expressions used in articles dealing with bibliometrics, citation analysis, and impact factors are explained in the miniglossary shown in **Table 5**, which is a modified version of information provided by ISI.

## Calculating Journal Impact Factor

The impact factor of a scientific journal is a measure of the frequency with which the "average published article" is cited in a particular time period, usually 2 years after the year of publication. The calculation starts with a breakdown of the reference lists included in all the articles published in all the journals covered by ISI. The first task is to count the number of times a particular target journal's articles are cited as a function of the year the articles were published. However, only recent articles count in the journal impact factor calculation and those older than 2 years won't help, as illustrated by the following example.

Article title: Time adjusted urine/blood ratios of ethanol in drinking drivers.

Source journal: *Journal of Analytical Toxicology* 27: 167–168 (2003).

This article contained the following five cited works in the list of references.

1. A W Jones. Reference limits for urine/blood ratios of ethanol in two successive voids from drinking drivers. *Journal of Analytical Toxicology* 26: 333–339 (2002).
2. A W Jones. Disappearance rate of ethanol from blood in human subjects; Implications in forensic toxicology. *Journal of Forensic Sciences* 38: 104–118 (1993).
3. A W Jones and L Andersson. Influence of age, gender, and blood-alcohol concentration on the disappearance rate of alcohol from blood in drinking drivers. *Journal of Forensic Sciences* 41: 922–926 (1996).
4. A W Jones and B Sternebring. Kinetics of ethanol and methanol in alcoholics during detoxification. *Alcohol & Alcoholism* 27: 641–647 (1992).
5. R Iffland and A W Jones. Evaluating alleged drinking after driving – the hip flask defense. Part 1. Double blood samples and urine-to-blood alcohol relationship. *Medicine, Science and Law* 42: 207–224 (2002).

References 1 and 5 contribute to the impact factor of *Journal of Analytical Toxicology* and *Medicine, Science and Law* for the year 2003 because the articles appeared in print within the 2-year window (2002 and 2001). By contrast, citations to the articles from *Journal of Forensic Sciences* (2) and *Alcohol & Alcoholism* (3) will not help the impact factor for 2003 because the articles cited were published more than 2 years earlier, that is, before 2001.

The impact factor is therefore simply a ratio consisting of a numerator, the number of citations in the current year to items published in the target journal in the previous 2 years, and a denominator, the number of citable items (articles and reviews) published in the journal during the same 2 years. The impact factor can therefore be considered to represent the annual citation rate for the average journal article published in the previous 2 years. The impact factor for a particular journal in 2003 is calculated as follows:

$$\text{Impact factor} = \frac{\text{Cites in 2003 to articles published in 2002 and 2001}}{\text{Number of citable items published in 2002 and 2001}}$$

Restricting citations and citable items to just 2 years after the current year is a device to compensate for journals that differ widely in number of articles and issues published each year. Indeed, some journals appear quarterly, others bimonthly or monthly, and a few even weekly. Use of a 2-year window also prevents a seminal work that gets highly cited year after year from skewing the data by including these citations in the impact factor calculation. Such articles are known as "citation classics" and can generate many thousands of citations. Some consider that stipulating a 2-year window after the year of publication is too narrow, especially for slow-moving fields like forensic science, giving an unfair advantage to hot research topics like molecular biology and immunology. However, studies have shown that the 2-year and 5-year impact factors for a selection of forensic and toxicology journals were very similar.

## Analyzing Self-Citations

When citations to a journal's articles are counted, these numbers also include self-citations, that is, when journal articles cite articles from the same journal. The self-citing rate of *International Journal of Legal Medicine* was especially high (41%), compared with the other journals listed in **Table 6**. The impact factor is easy to recalculate after self-citations are removed and after this was done, the score for *International Journal of Legal Medicine* dropped appreciably, from 1.918 to 0.745. Note that a high self-citation rate does not necessarily reflect on the quality of a journal and may simply mean that the bulk of the research on a particular topic is reported in that journal.

Journal impact factors range from zero for the least cited journal to over 40 for some of the highest-impact journals. The median impact factor for all journals included in the ISI database for 2002 ($n = 5876$ titles) was 0.85, which means that the average article was cited less than once each year during the first 2 years after publication. Only two forensic journals had an impact factor above this median for all journals (**Table 6**). In a relatively small discipline like forensic and legal medicine, the journal impact factors are generally lower compared with broader disciplines like the biological and

**Table 6** Comparison of self-cited rate and impact factor (2002) before and after adjusting for self-cites for selected forensic science and legal medicine journals

| Cited journal | Impact factor | Total cites[a] | Self-cites[b] | Percent self-cites | Impact factor without self-cites | Citation density[c] |
|---|---|---|---|---|---|---|
| International Journal of Legal Medicine | 1.918 | 1199 | 498 | 41% | 0.754 | 21.2 |
| Forensic Science International | 1.023 | 2073 | 440 | 21% | 0.745 | 17.8 |
| Journal of Forensic Science | 0.787 | 2467 | 509 | 21% | 0.576 | 15.9 |
| American Journal of Forensic and Legal Medicine | 0.521 | 704 | 110 | 16% | 0.371 | 19.4 |
| Medicine, Science and Law | 0.371 | 432 | 39 | 9% | 0.276 | 19.8 |
| Science and Justice | 0.329 | 92 | 15 | 16% | 0.253 | 15.3 |

[a]Total cites in 2002 from all journals and to all publication years.
[b]Self-cites in 2002 to all publication years.
[c]Ratio of number of references to number of articles.

**Table 7** Changes in impact factors of selected forensic science and toxicology journals between 1997 and 2002. Data from the online version of *Journal Citation Reports* (JCR), a product of the Institute for Scientific Information (ISI)

| Journal | 1997 | 1998 | 1999 | 2000 | 2001 | 2002 |
|---|---|---|---|---|---|---|
| Journal of Analytical Toxicology | 2.16 | 1.83 | 2.22 | 1.59 | 1.41 | 1.26 |
| Therapeutic Drug Monitoring | 1.83 | 1.54 | 1.38 | 1.73 | 2.04 | 2.14 |
| Journal of Toxicology-Clinical Toxicology | 0.93 | 1.17 | 1.73 | 1.30 | 1.36 | 1.17 |
| Human Experimental Toxicology | 0.71 | 0.95 | 1.06 | 0.82 | 1.30 | 0.95 |
| International Journal of Legal Medicine | 1.95 | 1.81 | 1.63 | 1.50 | 1.13 | 1.92 |
| Journal of Forensic Science | 1.40 | 0.77 | 0.99 | 0.94 | 0.88 | 0.79 |
| Forensic Science International | 1.32 | 0.82 | 1.39 | 0.83 | 1.05 | 1.02 |
| Science and Justice | 1.10 | 0.71 | 1.07 | 0.91 | 0.56 | 0.33 |
| American Journal of Forensic Medicine and Pathology | 0.39 | 0.60 | 0.37 | 0.60 | 0.41 | 0.52 |
| Medicine, Science and Law | 0.39 | 0.29 | 0.41 | 0.47 | 0.40 | 0.37 |

life sciences or clinical medicine and much lower than fields like genetics and molecular biology. The existence of field-dependent citation rates means that impact factors and citation analysis should not be used to compare journals or scientists from different disciplines.

Table 7 shows some trends in journal impact factors for major forensic, legal medicine, and toxicology journals between 1997 and 2002. Very few of these acquired an impact factor exceeding 2.0 and many were less than 0.5 over the 6-year period.

According to information provided by ISI, only original articles and reviews are counted as citable items and therefore included in the denominator of the impact factor calculation. However, citations to all kinds of items, e.g., editorial, debate, opinion, letters to the editor, are counted and included in the numerator of the calculation. This gives a definite advantage to journals like *Nature* and *Science* that include many news items and commentaries in each issue, which also tend to attract citations.

## Cited versus Citing Journals

Table 8 shows the relationship between cited journals and the journals that cite them, making it clear that a

small core of closely related journals account for most of the citations entering into the impact factor calculation. As well as showing total cites (all journals all years), the total cites awarded by the top four citing journals are also listed, along with a breakdown of these citations only to articles appearing in print 2 years earlier. The latter numbers are used in the impact factor equation.

## Importance of Peer Review

Publishing articles in scientific journals and learning to deal with the peer-review process is an essential part of training necessary to develop into an independent scientist. Indeed, accumulating a long list of publications in well-known international journals helps to establish an individual's reputation and standing in the sciences.

Peer review is the term used to describe the process by which a manuscript submitted for publication to a scientific journal is evaluated by outside experts for correctness, novelty, and validity of the data presented. The peer review is a kind of quality control of the information in the published article. Only a scientist's peers or equals in a particular area of research are considered qualified to serve as critics and

**Table 8** Relationship between cited and citing journals showing total number of cites in the current year (2002), the number of cites from the top four citing journals and the cites to 2001 and 2000 article only

| Cited journal | Top four citing journal | Total cites | Cites to 2001 and 2000 articles |
|---|---|---|---|
| International Journal of Legal Medicine | All journals | 1199[a] | 328[b] |
| | International Journal of Legal Medicine | 498 | 199 |
| | Forensic Science International | 150 | 34 |
| | Journal of Forensic Science | 132 | 6 |
| | American Journal of Forensic Medicine and Pathology | 82 | 4 |
| Forensic Science International | All journals | 2073[a] | 567[b] |
| | Forensic Science International | 440 | 154 |
| | International Journal of Legal Medicine | 179 | 52 |
| | Journal of Forensic Science | 173 | 44 |
| | Journal of Analytical Toxicology | 79 | 21 |
| Journal of Forensic Science | All journals | 2467[a] | 366[b] |
| | Journal of Forensic Science | 509 | 98 |
| | Forensic Science International | 239 | 43 |
| | International Journal of Legal Medicine | 144 | 20 |
| | American Journal of Forensic Medicine and Pathology | 111 | 11 |
| American Journal of Forensic and Legal Medicine | All journals | 704[a] | 87[b] |
| | American Journal of Forensic Medicine and Pathology | 110 | 25 |
| | Journal of Forensic Science | 66 | 4 |
| | International Journal of Legal Medicine | 54 | 5 |
| | Forensic Science International | 43 | 5 |
| Medicine, Science and Law | All journals | 432[a] | 39[b] |
| | Medicine, Science and Law | 39 | 10 |
| | Forensic Science International | 31 | 0 |
| | Journal of Forensic Psychiatry | 21 | 7 |
| | American Journal of Forensic Medicine and Pathology | 14 | 0 |
| Science and Justice | All journals | 92[a] | 26[b] |
| | Journal of Forensic Science | 16 | 5 |
| | Science and Justice | 15 | 6 |
| | Forensic Science International | 14 | 2 |
| | International Journal of Legal Medicine | 10 | 3 |

[a]Total cites in 2002 from all journals to articles published in all years.
[b]Citations from all journals to articles published in 2001 and 2000; these form the numerator in the impact factor calculation.

to assess the worthiness of the article being proffered for publication. The peer reviewers or referees of the manuscript serve as advisors to the editor-in-chief of the journal who makes the final decision to accept or reject the article for publication. Besides members of the editorial board, most journals have a large pool of peer reviewers to choose from, depending on the subject matter of the manuscript in question. Some of the most prestigious journals like *Nature, Science, Lancet*, and *New England Journal of Medicine* have very high rejection rates for unsolicited manuscripts – often exceeding 90%.

Peer review of articles submitted for publication is generally done single-blind, that is, the reviewer knows the identity of the authors of the manuscript and their affiliation, but not vice versa. Some journals operate a double-blind review system, e.g., *Science and Justice*, whereas others prefer a completely open

system, e.g., *British Medical Journal*, and the peer reviewers are expected to sign their report that often contains a critical appraisal of the manuscript. The pros and cons of blind versus open peer review are much discussed and debated, owing to allegations of bias and conflicts of interest on the part of referees. However, there is still no better system available for judging the scientific merits of an article and worthiness for publication than having it read by specialists in the field.

Some journals might ask three independent peer reviewers to look at the article and also solicit comments from a specialist editor, although two referees is the norm. The peer-review reports are expected back in the editor's office within 2–4 weeks after receipt of the manuscript, although longer delays are usually inevitable. The manuscript should be considered a confidential document for the reviewer's eyes only, although asking a colleague's opinion is permitted, provided that the journal editor is informed about this. As well as making detailed comments and recommendations to the authors, the peer reviewers are also encouraged to provide confidential information for use by the editor. Opinions are rendered about the novelty of the work submitted and a recommendation is made to accept, reject, or ask for a revision, which means that the authors are invited to resubmit their article after making minor or extensive changes. Some journals operate a scoring system giving points for originality, timeliness, contribution to the field, correctness of the language, and suitability of illustrations such as graphs and tables. Some of the larger journals might ask the opinion of an expert in statistics, whenever statistical analysis of data was a major part of the study, such as with many epidemiological surveys or reports of meta-analysis or clinical trials, which often have complex study designs.

## Peer Review and Expert Testimony

The importance of peer review and publication for the admissibility of scientific evidence attracted considerable attention after the US Supreme Court made its ruling in the case of *Daubert* v. *Merrill Dow Pharmaceuticals*. This concerned civil litigation about the alleged teratogenic properties of the antinausea drug Bendectin. Use of this drug during early pregnancy was alleged to have caused serious birth defects, including various malformations such as shorter limbs. Both parties in the case mustered considerable expert opinion for and against the dangers of this medication. Those experts appearing for the plaintive were criticized in part for relying on arguments gleaned from unpublished sources and also animal testing instead of looking at epidemiology surveys and relative risk calculations involving case-control and cohort studies. The Supreme Court made various recommendations for admissibility of expert evidence, including:

- The scientific theory should not only be testable but it should also have been tested.
- Such evidence should be peer-reviewed and published.
- The trial court should consider the accuracy limitations or error rate of the scientific technique.
- The extent to which the theory or scientific technique has been accepted in the scientific community should be a consideration.

Being able to testify that the opinion rendered to the court is based on information obtained from an article published in a peer-reviewed journal, e.g., *JFS*, should receive more weight and credibility compared with information gleaned from textbooks or government reports or studies in progress. Indeed, the material in a textbook represents the opinions of the author and these have not necessarily undergone peer review in the usual sense.

## Concluding Remarks

Much has been written about journal impact factors, not only for comparing and ranking scientific journals but also for judging the significance of the work of individual scientists. The journal impact factor concept has found many applications besides helping libraries manage their journals. These include:

1. Market research by publishers and editors who want to compare their journal with that of a rival periodical
2. Grant funding agencies to compare and contrast the quality of the articles produced by individual scientists or research groups and to use this information to decide on whether a new project should be funded
3. Academic departments often evaluate and compare candidates for promotion or tenure and focus heavily on published work (quantity and quality)
4. To document the publication track records of individual scientists competing for funding or the award of prizes or medals.

Impact factors are calculated as the ratio of current-year citations to articles published in a particular journal in the previous 2 years and adjusted for the number of citable items (articles and reviews) published in the same 2-year period. An impact factor of 1.0 means that the average article published in the journal during the 2-year window was cited once in the year of the *JCR* edition. Citations are derived from a breakdown of the reference lists from all journal articles covered by ISI, including the target journal itself. Indeed, self-citations account for a significant fraction (25%) of all citations to a journal's articles (**Table 6**). Impact factors have become widely regarded as indicators of quality and prestige and journal marketing departments eagerly await publication of the latest *JCR*.

Impact factors differ widely between different scientific disciplines and it is erroneous to compare the journals in different disciplines. It is equally wrong to sum the impact factors of the journals where people publish and use this as a marker of success and standing in a particular discipline. The legal medicine subcategory contains typically low-impact journals compared with biochemistry, cell biology, or immunology, to mention just a few. The reason for this, at least in part, is that fewer people practice forensic science and there are fewer links to academia compared with basic research subjects and biomedical fields. Many forensic scientists are reluctant to spend their time writing articles for publication because a long list of publications is seemingly not necessary for their promotion prospects or salary increments. Keeping abreast of developments in the forensic sciences requires reading widely, and hopefully also contributing to the literature by submitting articles for publication. For those forensic practitioners who intend to testify as expert witnesses a solid publication track record is of considerable merit. Information sources in science have changed appreciably in recent years, with an upsurge of online databases, websites, and home pages, all of which can be used to retrieve information. It should be remembered that the material downloaded from the internet has not been subjected to peer review and therefore needs to be carefully scrutinized.

Writing up the results of research and development work and getting this published is time-consuming but represents an essential part of the scientific process. Although counting the number of publications gives an idea of the quantity of work produced over a certain time period, judging the quality of the work is a much more difficult task. This can only be done by reading carefully the articles concerned and not by summing the impact factors of the journals where the work is published. A basic assumption of citation analysis is that if you cite an article the information it contained has in some way influenced your own work. However, negative citations are also likely, that is, refuting the results in an earlier published article. Although impact factors should not be used to judge the merits or importance of an individual article, there is nothing wrong with noting the number of times a particular article is cited over a given time period after publication, but this requires more work.

Many factors need to be considered when journal impact factors are compared and contrasted, including the size of the discipline, the number of citing journals, long-term versus short-term impact factors, frequency of self-citation, citation density (ratio of citations to number of articles), and the inclusion of many review articles in the journal. Additionally, the accuracy of the information in the list of references is obviously important when citations are counted. Errors in the spelling of a person's name or the use of a wrong or dropped initial can play havoc

with citation counting. Using an incorrect journal title in the list of references might also influence impact factor calculations and foreign-language journals are at a disadvantage because most are not covered by ISI.

Biannual international conferences are organized that focus on peer review in biomedical publication and the program at these meetings also includes many aspects of bibliometrics. High on the agenda are reflections on authorship practices, such as name ordering, criteria for being included as an author, advantages and limitations of blind versus open peer review, ethics and conflicts of interest among reviewers, prevalence of duplicate or salami publications, and issues related to fraud and scientific misconduct. Methods of improving peer review of manuscripts and grant proposals and the entire future of the printed journal as opposed to the rise in web-based publishing are among the topics. The proceedings from these meetings appear in a special number of the *Journal of the American Medical Association* and are well worth reading by those interested in scientific publishing.

A journal's impact factor is taken very seriously by editors and publishers and increasingly also by authors of the submitted articles. Impact factors also play a role in university politics because the journals where a person publishes can influence decisions on promotion and tenure and the amount of money allocated for research projects. Scientists are starting to send their best work to the journals with the highest impact factor. Controversy exists among many journal editors about the use of impact factors to judge the prestige of a journal, as reflected by the titles and subtitles of leading articles and editorials published over the years:

"Impact factors – what do the numbers really mean?"
"Impact factors – like them or not"
"The journal impact factor – a misnamed, misleading, misused measure"
"Journal impact factors – is the tail wagging the dog?"
"Sense and nonsense about the impact factor."

Scientific journals and the articles they publish are the primary means of communication in science for spreading information about new developments in research, whereas books and monographs still play a key role in education and teaching. The recently published *Encyclopedia of Forensic Sciences* (Academic Press), as well as the present encyclopedia, represent a gold mine of information and knowledge about all aspects of the forensic sciences and related fields of scholarship. It should also be mentioned that the articles contained in these encyclopedias have undergone peer review by experts prior to acceptance for publication.

Although forensic scientists should be aware of the existence and meaning of journal impact factors, they need not be too concerned about the relatively low numbers for the legal medicine subject category. Unlike university-based scientists, those working in forensic science and legal medicine are less inclined to write papers for publication and do not need to compete for external funding to survive. Nevertheless, forensic scientists should be encouraged to write up their work for publication or contribute a chapter to a book or encyclopedia. A forensic scientist with a respectable publication track record has a definite advantage when decisions are made about awarding scholarships or prizes and when called to serve as an expert witness in high-profile trials.

Besides impact factors, other attributes of a journal to ponder over are the rigor of the peer-review process, timelines in obtaining the referee reports, a short time from acceptance to publication, whether titles of articles and abstracts are indexed in the major databases (e.g., National Library of Medicine's Pubmed), and the availability of online versions of the journal.

## See Also

**Clinical Trials:** Good Clinical Practice and Ethical Aspects; Legal Aspects and Consent; **Expert Witness:** Qualifications, Testimony and Malpractice

## Further Reading

Adam D (2002) The counting house. *Nature* 415: 726–729.

Chubin DE, Hackett EJ (1990) *Peerless Science; Peer Review and US Science Policy*, pp. 1–267. Albany, NY: State University of New York Press.

Cronin B, Atkins HB (eds.) (2000) *The Web of Knowledge – A Festschrift in Honor of Eugene Garfield*, pp. 1–565. ASIS monograph series. Medford: Information Today Incorporated.

Field KS (ed.) (1998) *History of the American Academy of Forensic Sciences: 50 Years of Progress, 1948–1998*, pp. 1–358. Pennsylvania, PA: American Society for Testing of Materials (ASTM).

Foster KR, Huber PW (1999) *Judging Science: Scientific Knowledge and the Federal Courts*, pp. 1–333. Cambridge, MA: MIT Press.

Garfield E (1996) How can impact factor be improved? *British Medical Journal* 313: 411–413.

Goodlee F, Jefferson T (eds.) (1999) *Peer Review in Health Sciences*, pp. 1–271. London: British Medical Journal Publishing.

Grinnell F (1992) *The Scientific Attitude*, 2nd edn., pp. 1–180. New York: Guilford Press.

Jones AH, McLellen F (eds.) (2000) *Ethical Issues in Biomedical Publication*, pp. 1–374. Baltimore, MD: Johns Hopkins University Press.

Jones AW (1993) The impact of forensic science journals. *Forensic Science International* 62: 173–178.

Jones AW (2003) Impact factors of forensic science and toxicology journals – what do the numbers really mean? *Forensic Science International* 133: 1–8.

Lock S (ed.) (1991) *The Future of Medical Journals*, pp. 1–217. London: British Medical Journal (BMJ) Publishing.

Lock S (1991) *A Difficult Balance; Editorial Peer Review in Medicine*, pp. 1–172. London: British Medical Journal (BMJ) Publishing.

Macrina FL (1995) *Scientific Integrity – An Introductory Text with Cases*, pp. 1–283. Washington, DC: ASM Press.

Resnik DB (1998) *The Ethics of Science: An Introduction*, pp. 1–221. London: Routledge.

# FORENSIC PSYCHIATRY AND FORENSIC PSYCHOLOGY

Contents

**Forensic Psychology, Education, Training and Certification**
**Forensic Psychiatry, Education, Training and Certification**
**Assessment**
**Ethics**
**Psychological Autopsy**
**Forensic Interviewing**
**Suicide Predictors and Statistics**
**Mental Handicap and Learning Disability**
**Drug and Alcohol Addiction**
**Malingering**
**Personality Disorder**
**Multiple Personality Disorder**
**Stalking**
**Sex Offenders**
**Criminal Responsibility**
**Fitness (Competence) To Stand Trial**

## Forensic Psychology, Education, Training and Certification

**S L Golding**, University of Utah, Salt Lake City, UT, USA

### Introduction

Psychologists were involved in the judicial system as early as the late nineteenth century. This article is written from an American perspective on forensic psychology. While roughly comparable developments have occurred in Canada, the UK, Australia, New Zealand, Europe, and a few other countries, the status of training and credentialing is different, and thus local laws and scholarly literatures should be consulted. However, psychologists (as opposed to psychiatrists) did not become significantly involved in forensic applications until the broader field of clinical psychology began to receive funding from the Veterans Administration and the National Institutes of Mental Health (NIMH) to support training and research after the end of World War II. An educational and training model for clinical psychologists, the so-called "Boulder Model" was developed in 1949 and the American Board of Examiners in Professional

Psychology began to grant diplomate status to certify advanced competencies for clinical psychologists at approximately the same time. As psychologists became increasingly involved in the judicial system, an economically based competition with psychiatrists became inevitable, and the American Psychiatric Association, in 1954, attempted to assert that only medically trained psychiatrists should be allowed to offer testimony in judicial forums about mental "illnesses." Forensic psychologists involved in both clinical and research contexts continued to struggle to establish their specialty in a rather uncoordinated fashion until three seminal events occurred.

### The *Jenkins* Case: Status of Expert Witnesses

First, in 1962, Judge David Bazelon, a leading mental health law jurist, wrote the majority opinion in *Jenkins* v. *United States*. The *Jenkins* case was an appeal of a trial judge's instruction to the jury that they could disregard the forensic evidence offered by Jenkins' forensic psychologists because, as psychologists, they were not qualified to offer expert testimony on the issue of mental illness. In a scholarly *tour de force*, Judge Bazelon argued that it was the expert's training, knowledge, and expertise that formed the basis for acceptance or rejection as an expert witness, not the nature of their title or degree. This powerful opinion by a respected jurist helped to remove the previously unchallenged assumption of the superiority of psychiatry and placed the focus directly upon the quality, nature, and extent of an expert's knowledge and the scientific status of that knowledge. Since forensic psychologists differ from forensic psychiatrists primarily by a relatively stronger focus on the empirical foundations of forensic knowledge, this decision had the additional impact of encouraging the formation of empirically based forensic training programs more consistent with traditional psychological than with psychiatric training models.

### Establishment of the Center for Studies of Crime and Delinquency

Second, in 1968, Saleem Shah became the director of the NIMHs Center for Studies of Crime and Delinquency. Between 1968 and his untimely and tragic death in 1992, he spearheaded the funding of a variety of seminal forensic psychology research grants that helped to lay the empirical and conceptual foundations of the discipline. In addition, he helped to introduce many first-generation forensic psychologists to each other thus extending further the development of the discipline by making individuals aware of the work of others.

### The American Psychology-Law Society

The third development, also in 1968, was the organization of the American Psychology-Law Society (APLS) which began formal operations the following year. The formation of this group has proven to be a critical step in the development of forensic psychology as a discipline because it allowed for the routine exchange of scientific and professional knowledge, provided a network for trainers and students, and was pivotal in the development of ethical and professional standards. Eventually, APLS merged with Division 41 (Psychology and Law) of the American Psychological Association (APA), and in 2001, forensic psychology was officially recognized as a specialty by the Commission for the Recognition of Specialties in Professional Psychology (CRSPP), an organizational unit of the APA.

## Definition of the Field of Forensic Psychology

Forensic psychologists organized and defined their discipline, adopted a broad and inclusive definition of their field in recognition of the many areas of psychological scholarship, research, and practical competencies that produced expertise of relevance to the judicial system as a whole. Thus, *Specialty Guidelines for Forensic Psychologists*, a set of ethical and professional guidelines adopted by APLS/Division 41, defined "forensic psychology" as:

> all forms of professional psychological conduct when acting, with definable foreknowledge, as a psychological expert on explicitly psycholegal issues, in direct assistance to courts, parties to legal proceedings, correctional and forensic mental health facilities, and administrative, judicial, and legislative agencies acting in an adjudicative capacity.

When forensic psychology was recognized as a specialty by CRSPP, very similar language was used. Thus, while the majority of forensic psychologists are trained in programs that emphasize applied aspects of psychology such as clinical psychology or neuropsychology, a sizeable group work in areas such as social, developmental, experimental, and physiological psychology. What they share in common is applying psychological knowledge to issues of legal relevance. The result is an extreme broad array of conceptual, empirical, and practical "psycholegal issues," as is apparent from inspection of the table of contents of widely cited "psychology and law" handbooks and from scholarly articles attempting to define forensic psychology. This conceptual, empirical, and practical breadth has some interesting implications for models of education and training. In 1995, a conference organized by the leaders of broadly defined forensic psychology explicitly acknowledged that diversity of appropriate training models was required because of the breadth of the discipline.

## Training Models

There are a wide variety of doctoral training models in forensic psychology. Nine graduate programs offer forensic psychology training in either clinical or nonclinical areas; four of these also offer dual psychology and law degrees (the extent to which individuals with dual degrees remain professionally active in both fields is not clear). Eight graduate programs offer forensic psychology training exclusively oriented towards clinical issues and 11 programs (two of which are dual degree programs) offer exclusively nonclinical forensic training programs. In addition, an unknown number of forensic psychologists are trained in graduate psychology departments without specialized programs but with one or more faculty members who specialize in forensic psychology. A variety of postdoctoral programs, as well as other training in forensic facilities are also available.

Given this wide array of training models, it is difficult to describe "forensic psychology training," but most programs tend to share a common training assumption that derives from the "forensic" aspect of the discipline. That is, the adjective "forensic" implies that the professional and scholarly aspects appear in public and legal settings and subjected to legal scrutiny, debate and cross-examination. While psychological theories and data are subjected to scientific scrutiny in research and scholarly settings, a different set of rules and issues arise when those theories and data are admitted as evidence in a legal setting. While the evidentiary "hurdles" that psychological evidence must pass are increasingly seen in terms familiar to psychological scientists as reflecting a Popperian view of science, legal disputation is fundamentally different from scientific disputation. As a consequence, forensic training programs, whether they emphasize clinical, developmental, experimental, neuropsychological, or social aspects of the discipline must prepare students for the legal scrutiny of their scholarly and professional products. In "normal" clinical work, for example, an assessment report may be reviewed by another professional, but will not be subjected to rigorous scrutiny or cross-examination (perhaps the quality of psychological products, whether published in scientific journals or used in professional settings, would be improved if they were more routinely subjected to such scrutiny). Thus, this fundamental "forensic" assumption gives rise to a series of distinctive characteristics. The nature of some of these is readily seen in forensic clinical psychology. Role relationships between forensic clinicians and those that they evaluate or treat are fundamentally and systematically different to traditional clinician–client role relationships. In fact, the "client" in such relationships is generally an attorney or a court, not the person evaluated or treated. There are corresponding major differences with respect to issues of privilege and confidentiality, record keeping, and reporting requirements. Forensic clinical assessments often involve specialized assessment techniques and instruments that focus on distinct psycholegal constructs and employ special methods that often target deceptiveness and collateral sources of information. Basically, forensic clinical psychologists are trained in the details of the legal issues and adjudicative processes in which they participate, though most often they do not complete law degrees in spite of participation.

## Qualifications in Forensic Psychology

While APA and CRSPP officially recognize forensic psychology as a specialty, these organizations do not award advanced certification of specialization or diplomate status to particular individuals. Within the USA, diplomate status has been traditionally granted by the American Board of Forensic Psychology (ABFP), which is part of a larger organization, the American Board of Professional Psychology (ABPP). ABFP and ABPP have many administrative and professional links with APA, but are separate. Other organizations also grant diplomate status in forensic psychology, but problems associated with their procedures will be discussed subsequently.

Diplomate status from ABFP "attests to the fact that an established organization of peers has examined and accepted the Diplomate as functioning at the highest level of excellence in his or her field of forensic competence." It is important to note that when ABFP was formed in 1978, the original members of the organization did not "arbitrarily declare" themselves as diplomates. Rather, each one was examined by others in the founding group, to ensure that they possessed the higher level of training, skill, and knowledge expected of a "diplomate." The current examination process is extremely rigorous and essentially involves the following steps. An applicant must first be accepted as a candidate. To become a candidate the individual should: 1. Be a doctorate from an accredited institution in the USA or Canada. 2. Be either a licensed psychologist or work as such in a statutorily recognized way. 3. Have at least 1000 h of forensic psychology experience, most of which must be accumulated postdoctorally. 4. Be free from a history of adjudicated ethical or professional complaints. 5. Have at least 100 hours of specialized training in forensic psychology.

The second stage of the ABFP process is an evaluation of professional work. Each applicant is required to submit samples of work in two professional work areas that reflect their advanced expertise in those areas of forensic psychology. These work samples are reviewed by two examiners according to published criteria. Finally, an applicant undertakes both a written examination concerning advanced knowledge of forensic psychology and associated legal issues, and an oral concerning ethical and professional issues and aspects of the candidate's own chosen aspects of particular expertise. Data from a two-year period, for example, 1995–1997 demonstrate the rigors of the examination process. During that period, 39% of the applicants whose credentials were substantiated failed because of the nature of their professional work samples. Of those who qualified for the final stage, 48% failed.

## Vanity Diplomas

Whether due to the rigors of the examination process, economic incentives to obtain "advanced certification or diplomate status" in forensic psychology, or other unknown considerations, a cottage industry of "vanity" diplomate boards has grown up in the USA in the 1990s. Originally, such vanity boards, as described in articles in the *Wall Street Journal*, the *American Bar Association Journal*, and elsewhere were clearly in the business of "sheepskins for sale." They routinely granted diplomate status on the basis of weak criteria, had few or no mechanisms for checking on the validity of claimed experience, never appeared to turn anyone down who had applied, required no peer review of professional work, and had no other mechanisms for verifying the applicant's advanced levels of knowledge, skill, and experience. Sufficient alarm about the impact of the flood of such "vanity" certified experts, in a host of different professional fields, led to strong cautionary statements being published in professional mental health journals and in materials being circulated to sitting judges and practicing attorneys. Although those witnesses not possessing accreditation are not automatically presumed to be unsuitable for providing expert testimony, there is a focus on the necessity to scrutinize carefully the nature of an expert's claimed expertise and certification as a "specialist," "diplomate," or "board certified" expert.

Any internet search using the terms "diplomate" and "forensic" will now uncover a dizzying array of hits and organizations. The real task facing a consumer (whether an attorney, judge, or juror) in understanding what a given expert's "diplomate" status means and does not mean has become enormously more difficult since the first publications analyzing vanity boards, "check-book" diplomates, and the like. Many of the organizations originally criticized for their lax procedures, no meaningful examinations, "grandfathering," or having little or no review of work have now begun to change their publically announced requirements and procedures. Whether or not such announcements reflect any meaningful change awaits further demonstration and documentation. Thus, while many now announce an "examination" as part of the process, it is unclear whether they meaningfully assess the types of advanced competencies and knowledge reflected by the meaning commonly associated with "diplomate" or "board certified." For example, one of the original "examinations" from such organizations contained the following question: "In giving testimony at a deposition, it is appropriate to engage in shouting matches or arguments with abusive attorneys. True or false?". The adoption of meaningful examinations will in part be indexed by the number of applicants who fail.

## Administrative Procedures for Certification and Regulation

Other than the general cautions and caveats published by professional psychological and legal organizations, some states in the USA have begun to adopt more aggressive administrative procedures or institute statutory regulation. For example, California has given the term "board certified" administrative meaning by requiring that physicians may not describe themselves as "board certified" unless the "board" uses meaningful and psychometrically valid testing procedures to examine whether or not the physician has the required education, training, and experience expected of a "board certified" specialist. The regulations which implement this statute specify a set of boards that qualify and also provide a set of criteria by which to evaluate "applicant boards" not specifically listed. This mechanism for regulating use of "board certification" was upheld in a recent decision by the Ninth Circuit Court of Appeals. The logic of this decision comports with other professional analyses of the problem of separating the wanted from the unwanted by focusing upon the meaningfulness and rigor of the review and evaluation process. Logically, it must also be noted that having had one's training, knowledge, and skill examined and "certified" at one time does not guarantee a similar status in future. Similarly, not being a "diplomate" or "board certified" does not carry the logical or empirical implication that a particular expert is less qualified than someone who has undergone a rigorous examination of knowledge and skills. However, having chosen to obtain a "certification" from a vanity board as opposed to rigorous peer scrutiny, does have other logical implications that may be effectively pursued during rigorous cross-examination. If the cross-examiner can effectively link an expert's choice to obtain a "vanity diploma" with questions about the adequacy or rigor of his or her methods and reasoning, a particularly forceful synergy is accomplished. Obviously, having a "traditional" diplomate in forensic psychology does not guarantee current competence, professionalism, or the correctness of opinion. However, it does guarantee that the individual has chosen to have his or her professional work peer-reviewed, has had the nature, quality, and adequacy of their professional forensic training scrutinized, and has stood for a wide-ranging and meaningful examination of specialized and general knowledge of forensic psychology, and of ethical and professional standards of practice. The alternative choices end up speaking for themselves to triers of fact if they are explored in functional detail, either during *voir dire* or cross-examination. An additional and apparently unappreciated legal consequence of presenting himself/herself as a "diplomate" or "board certified" is that this sets the standard of care to which they will be held in any tort action.

## Further Reading

American Board of Forensic Psychology (2004) Brochure. Accessed 1/15/2004 at www.abfp.com/brochure.asp.

Baldwin M, Watts B (1996) A survey of graduate education and training experiences in psychology and law. *American Psychology-Law Society Newsletter* 16: 10–11.

Cattell JM (1895) Measurements of the accuracy of recollection. *Science* 2: 761–766.

Farkas G, DeLeon P, Newman R (1997) Sanity examiner certification: an evolving national agenda. *Professional Psychology: Research and Practice* 28: 73–76.

Foxhall K (2000) What's behind that credential? When it comes to credentialing, *caveat emptor*. *Monitor on Psychology* September.

Goldstein AM (ed.) (2003) *Handbook of Psychology. Forensic Psychology.* vol. 11. New York: John Wiley.

Greenberg S, Shuman D (1997) Irreconcilable conflict between therapeutic and forensic roles. *Professional Psychology: Research and Practice* 28: 50–57.

Grisso T (2003) *Evaluating Competencies: Forensic Assessments and Instruments,* 2nd edn. New York: Kluwer Academic.

Grisso T, Steadman HJ (eds.) (1995) Special section of commemorative articles in memory of Saleem A. Shah. *Law and Human Behavior* 19(1): 1–48.

Hansen M (2000) Expertise to go. *American Bar Association Journal* 86: 44–52.

Heilbrun KS (2001) *Principles of Forensic Mental Health Assessment.* New York: Kluwer Academic.

Hess AK (1999) Defining forensic psychology. In: Hess AK, Weiner IB (eds.) *The Handbook of Forensic Psychology,* 2nd edn., pp. 24–47. New York: John Wiley.

Hess AK, Weiner IB (eds.) (1999) *Handbook of Forensic Psychology.* New York: John Wiley.

Kagehiro DK, Laufer WS (eds.) (1992) *Handbook of Psychology and Law.* New York: Springer-Verlag.

Kaslow FW (1989) Early history of the American Board of Forensic Psychology: a retrospective account. *Forensic Reports* 2: 305–311.

MacDonald E (1999) The making of an expert witness: it's in the credentials. *Wall Street Journal* February. 8, pp. B1.

Munsterberg H (1908) *On the Witness Stand: Essays on Psychology and Crime.* New York: McClure.

Parry J, Drogin EY (2000) *Criminal Law Handbook on Psychiatric and Psychological Evidence and Testimony.* Washington, DC: American Bar Association.

Parry J, Drogin EY (2001) *Civil Law Handbook on Psychiatric and Psychological Evidence and Testimony.* Washington, DC: American Bar Association.

# Forensic Psychiatry, Education, Training and Certification

**R Reeves**, University of Medicine and Dentistry of New Jersey, Newark, NJ, USA
**R Rosner**, New York University School of Medicine, and the Forensic Psychiatry Clinic of Bellevue Hospital Center, New York, NY, USA

## Introduction

Over the past three decades, around the world, education, training, and certification in forensic psychiatry have grown more uniform and systematic. This is particularly true of the USA, which is the primary focus of this article. Education and certification in the UK and Canada are also summarized. Readers who wish to learn about education and certification in any other country are directed to contact that country's national psychiatric association or, if applicable, that country's national association for psychiatry and the law. Finally, an outline for systematic, independent training for those wishing to forgo a formal education in forensic psychiatry is presented.

## USA

### Education

In 1982, the American Academy of Psychiatry and the Law (AAPL) and the American Academy of Forensic Sciences (AAFS) cosponsored a report, *Standards for Fellowship Programs in Forensic Psychiatry.* The report promulgated common didactic and clinical curricula in training programs in the USA and Canada. In 1988, the creation of the Accreditation Council on Fellowships in Forensic Psychiatry (ACFFP), a component of the AAPL, established a process to recognize training programs that met the *Standards for Fellowship Programs in Forensic Psychiatry.* The ACFFP accredited fellowships from 1989 to 1997. Partway through 1997, the ACFFP was supplanted by the Accreditation Council for Graduate Medical Education (ACGME). The ACGME is the recognized accrediting body for all graduate medical education programs in the USA. As of the 2003–2004 academic year, the ACGME had approved 40 residency programs (with a total of 100 trainee positions) as meeting its criteria for accreditation in forensic psychiatry.

The ACGME requires that the training period in forensic psychiatry be 12 months for its approved programs, and that training occurs after completion of a psychiatry residency program accredited by the

ACGME. However, training in forensic psychiatry that occurs during the general residency training is not credited toward this 1-year requirement.

The clinical assignments must include experiences in the following three areas: (1) forensic evaluation of subjects of both genders – including adolescent, adult, and geriatric groups – who represent a broad range of mental disorders and circumstances, in both civil and criminal contexts; (2) consultation to general psychiatric services on issues related to the legal regulation of psychiatric practice such as civil commitment, confidentiality, refusal of treatment, decision-making competence; and (3) treatment of persons involved in the criminal justice system. Residents must have experience in review of written records, and in testifying in court or in mock trials.

The didactic curriculum must include the following components: (1) a psychiatric curriculum; (2) a law curriculum related to forensic psychiatry (e.g., fundamentals of law); (3) a civil law curriculum; (4) a criminal law curriculum; and (5) conferences in forensic psychiatry. The program should also offer a meaningful, individually supervised, scholarly experience for each resident.

The program must be administratively attached to and sponsored by a residency program in psychiatry that is accredited by the ACGME. The program should take place in facilities accredited by the appropriate state and/or federal licencing agencies, the courts, and, where appropriate, the Joint Commission on Accreditation of Healthcare Organizations. Assignments to participating institutions must be based on a clear educational rationale and include written affiliation agreements with clearly stated learning objectives and activities, and identification of faculty and their responsibilities.

The program must include experiences in: (1) facilities in which forensic psychiatric evaluations are performed on subjects with a broad variety of psychiatric disorders (e.g., an inpatient forensic unit); (2) facilities that provide general psychiatric services to patients with a broad variety of psychiatric disorders (e.g., a general outpatient unit); and (3) facilities that treat persons in the correctional system (e.g., a prison). Residents must have access to a major medical library with an adequate number of texts and journals in psychiatry and the law, and online access to medical and legal databases.

The program director must be certified by the American Board of Psychiatry and Neurology (ABPN) in the specialty of forensic psychiatry, or have equivalent qualifications in forensic psychiatry that are acceptable to the ACGME's Psychiatric Residency Review Committee (RRC). The program director organizes and manages the activities of the educational program in all institutions that participate in the program. The program director also prepares a statistical and narrative description of the program as requested by the RRC, and monitors the progress of each resident.

As with the program director, the physician faculty must be certified by the ABPN in the specialty of forensic psychiatry, or have equivalent qualifications in forensic psychiatry satisfactory to the RRC. There must be at least one ABPN-certified child and adolescent psychiatrist on the faculty. The faculty must be qualified by experience in forensic psychiatry to provide the expertise needed to fulfill the didactic, clinical, and research goals of the program, and must devote sufficient time to the educational program. In addition to the psychiatrists, the faculty must include a lawyer and a forensic psychologist.

These represent a partial list of ACGME's requirements. For the complete list, visit the ACGME website and look for "program requirements for residency education in forensic psychiatry."

The Association of Directors of Forensic Psychiatry Fellowships (ADFPF) also plays a role in the effort to ensure quality education in forensic psychiatry. The ADFPF, a council of AAPL, provides a venue for forensic residency directors to exchange ideas and remain up-to-date with developments relevant to training in forensic psychiatry. The ADFPF meets twice a year, at the annual AAPL meeting, and immediately prior to the annual American Psychiatric Association (APA) meeting.

## Certification

The American Board of Forensic Psychiatry (ABFP), established in 1976, was an organization that required candidates for certification to take both a written and an oral examination to demonstrate competence. Successful completion of the ABFP examination conferred a lifetime certification in forensic psychiatry.

In 1990 the AAPL succeeded in obtaining, from the APA, formal recognition of forensic psychiatry as a psychiatric specialty. In the early 1990s, the APA petitioned the ABPN to establish an examination procedure for persons to be certified in the subspecialty of forensic psychiatry. (The ABPN at that time already offered a certifying examination in general, and in child and adolescent psychiatry.) The ABPN then successfully petitioned the American Board of Medical Specialties (ABMS) for authorization to offer a new forensic psychiatry examination. Thus, as of October 1994, the ABFP was supplanted by the examination for Added Qualifications in Forensic Psychiatry of the ABPN, under the supervision of the ABMS.

The ABPN's multiple-choice examination assesses candidates on their knowledge in: legal regulation of psychiatry; civil law and criminal law; corrections and correctional healthcare; legal systems and basic law; children and families; special diagnostic and treatment issues; special procedures in forensic psychiatry; special consultations and investigations; risk management (including violence, dangerousness, criminology, suicide, and psychiatric autopsy); and forensic psychiatry practice issues.

In order to sit for the ABPN forensic exam, an applicant must first be certified by the ABPN in psychiatry. The examination of April 1999 was the last ABPN exam a psychiatrist could take without having graduated from a 1-year fellowship in forensic psychiatry. The examination of April 2001 was the last ABPN exam a psychiatrist could take without having graduated from an "ACGME-approved" residency. Thereafter, all applicants were required to submit documentation of successful completion of 1 year of ACGME-approved residency training in forensic psychiatry.

Unlike the lifelong certification of the ABFP, ABPN certificates for forensic psychiatrists are valid for only 10 years; periodic recertification examinations are required to sustain ABPN forensic certification. The ABPN does not offer a "grandfathering" mechanism; everyone certified by the ABPN must pass its exam. As of January 1, 2003, the ABPN had issued 1384 certificates in forensic psychiatry. Graduation from an ACGME-accredited forensic psychiatry residency and certification by the ABPN is now the preferred route to forensic psychiatry in the USA.

## UK

### Education

In the UK, the Royal College of Psychiatrists (RCPsych) accredits hospitals for training purposes, and offers a certification examination for psychiatrists who have completed specialist training (the equivalent of general psychiatry residency training in the USA). In specialist training, the RCPsych recognizes a placement (rotation, in the USA) in forensic psychiatry as an optional component of training. A placement in forensic psychiatry is subject to the requirements of all placements in basic specialist training, including a job description and timetable. Most placements are of 6 months duration. The RCPsych recommends that a placement in forensic psychiatry include consultations at prisons, hospitals, secure units, remand centers, and other establishments. Trainees are encouraged to prepare shadow reports for discussion with their consultants, and to receive instruction in the principles of forensic psychiatry and medical–legal work.

After completing basic specialist training, and passing the examination for membership of the Royal College of Psychiatrists (MRCPsych), a psychiatrist who wishes to specialize in forensic psychiatry may enter further specialist training. There are six areas of higher specialist training: (1) general (adult) psychiatry; (2) old-age psychiatry; (3) psychiatry of learning disability; (4) psychotherapy; (5) forensic psychiatry and (6) child and adolescent psychiatry. Over the past decade, major changes in the structure of specialist training in the UK have brought the training into accord with European Union medical directives. In July 1992, the UK established a committee under the chairmanship of the Chief Medical Officer, which included presidents of Royal Medical Colleges (including the RCPsych). This committee issued the Calman Report that led to the enactment of the European Specialist Medical Qualifications Order 1995 (ESMQO). This order created both the Specialist Training Authority (STA) and the award of Certificates of Completion of Specialist Training (CCSTs) as the single means of indicating completion of higher specialist training. Since January 1, 1997, all appointees to National Health Service (NHS) consultant posts must possess a CCST.

As a result of the above changes, the RCPsych and the Association of University Teachers of Psychiatry agreed at the end of 1997 that the erstwhile Joint Committee on Higher Psychiatric Training should become a College committee, to be known as the Higher Specialist Training Committee (HSTC), reporting to the Court of Electors. The HSTC has the dual role of setting the standards for training schemes (programs) in psychiatric specialties, and setting the standards (under the aegis of the STA) for the award of CCSTs. The HSTC accomplishes these goals by establishing a series of specialist advisory committees (SACs) reporting to it. Currently, there are five SACs, including a Forensic Psychiatry Specialist Advisory Committee (FPSAC), and these committees produce advisory papers on higher specialist training for the HSTC. The mandate of a SAC, including the FPSAC, is to: (1) assess higher specialist training schemes and report upon their organization and quality to the HSTC; (2) consider applications for approval of new training placements and trainers; (3) consider applications for specific approval of aspects of individual trainees' experience in relation to the requirements for training' in a specialty; and (4) advise the HSTC on policy and give guidance to training program directors and trainees.

The FPSAC meets four times a year at the Royal College. Throughout the year, the FPSAC conducts approval visits to specialist training schemes in forensic psychiatry throughout England, Wales, and Scotland. The FPSAC visiting teams make recommendations based on the overall results of their visits, as well as on the particular needs of individual schemes.

The RCPsych's *Higher Specialist Training Handbook* gives an account of the aims of higher specialist training, basic training requirements, and the range of clinical experience required within forensic psychiatry. In order to be eligible for a CCST in forensic psychiatry, a psychiatrist must complete 3 years of higher training in forensic psychiatry. The duties of a British training-program director are multifarious and similar to those of a program director in the USA. Amendments to the *Higher Specialist Training Handbook* are published in the RCPsych's *Psychiatric Bulletin*.

## Certification

A psychiatrist must pass parts I and II of the MRCPsych to enter higher specialist training. Part II of the MRCPsych contains questions on forensic psychiatry. Passing the MRCPsych of the RCPsych, certifies expertise in general psychiatry. Passing the MRCPsych may be likened to passing the ABPN certification examination in general psychiatry in the USA. In the spring of 2003, 42% and 49% of candidates passed parts I and II of the MRCPsych, respectively.

The UK does not offer a certification examination in forensic psychiatry. Rather, every trainee in forensic psychiatry is annually evaluated by the program director and the HSTC to determine whether the trainee is allowed to progress to the next year and, ultimately, to be awarded a CCST. The end of the first year of higher specialist training is particularly important as it is at this stage that reservations about the performance of a trainee are expected to be made clear.

## Canada

### Education

According to the Canadian Psychiatric Association (CPA), nine of Canada's 16 medical universities offer fellowships in forensic psychiatry. These fellowships take 1 or 2 years, depending on the program. The curriculum also varies from program to program. Entry into a fellowship requires, at a minimum, completion of 4 years of residency in general psychiatry (identical to the requirement for entry into a forensic residency in the USA). A few programs additionally require that the psychiatrist has passed the Royal College of Physicians and Surgeons of Canada (RCPSC) examination in psychiatry. This certifying examination serves a purpose similar to the ABPN examination in general psychiatry in the USA.

From 1989 to 1997, Canadian forensic psychiatry fellowships were accredited by the ACFFP, a component of AAPL. In 1997, the ACGME supplanted the ACFFP in the USA. The ACGME is not authorized to accredit Canadian postgraduate medical programs. The RCPSC is the body that today would otherwise accredit Canadian forensic psychiatry fellowships. However, the RCPSC does not recognize forensic psychiatry as a subspecialty, and therefore does not accredit forensic psychiatry fellowships.

With the goal of receiving subspecialty recognition of forensic psychiatry, the Canadian Academy of Psychiatry and the Law (CAPL), within the auspices of the Canadian Psychiatric Association, created an education committee. In 1996, this committee developed a model training curriculum with the aim of standardizing training across the country. In 1999, CAPL petitioned the RCPSC to recognize forensic psychiatry as a subspecialty. To date, the RCPSC has not granted such recognition (as it also has not recognized the subspecialty status of child psychiatry and geriatric psychiatry).

## Certification

The RCPSC is the body that certifies the expertise of Canadian physicians in their various specialties and subspecialties. However, as the RCPSC does not recognize forensic psychiatry as a subspecialty, it offers no certification examination in that field.

## Independent Training

The USA, the UK, and Canada have made gradual moves toward standardization and quality in education and certification in forensic psychiatry. Nonetheless, the demand for practitioners in forensic psychiatry in these countries makes it possible for individuals to work in forensic psychiatry without having completed a residency, and without having been certified by an accrediting body. Indeed, at the present time, most practicing forensic psychiatrists in these countries (and around the world, for that matter) are not graduates of accredited forensic psychiatry residency programs, and are not certified as to their expertise. They are mostly psychiatrists trained in general psychiatry who are employed in forensic settings. To the extent these general psychiatrists have trained themselves as forensic psychiatrists, they have availed themselves of a variety of forensic employments, have attended continuing medical education programs, and have completed readings in forensic psychiatry. If one wishes to train outside a forensic psychiatry residency or fellowship, and one is willing to abandon specialty certification in forensic psychiatry, then a program of independent training may allow one to develop the requisite skills and knowledge of a competent forensic psychiatrist.

Independent training refers to a self-directed program of education and employment. It rises above mere on-the-job training in that it is systematic and comprehensive. Training will typically take place on a part-time basis, and will continue over many years. A psychiatrist interested in pursuing independent training in the USA can turn to the ACGME's *Program Requirements for Residency Education in Forensic Psychiatry*. Perusal of these standards will allow one to learn not only the likely structure and content of an independent training program, but also the knowledge and skills a practitioner in the subspecialty is expected to possess. In the UK, psychiatrists may turn to the RCP's *Higher Specialist Training Handbook* for similar information. Independent study will have: (1) a series of employments exposing one to the diversity of forensic psychiatric work; (2) a sequence of readings and continuing medical education courses in forensic psychiatry; and (3) a regular schedule of supervision from an experienced and certified forensic psychiatrist.

The series of employments will include work in criminal law, corrections, civil law, and domestic-relations law. The emphasis is on the series. No single employment will provide the necessary range of experiences. The readings and continuing medical education courses will address a similarly broad range of topics. In addition, the training psychiatrist needs to know basic law and the legal system's procedures, and the landmark legal cases in the field. Continuing medical education in forensic psychiatry is available through the programs presented at annual forensic conventions, such as those of AAPL, CAPL, and AAFS. Psychiatric organizations with broader missions, such as the RCP, the CPA, and the APA, also typically offer a small selection of forensic courses and panels at their annual conventions. Finally, the regional chapters of AAPL provide local educational opportunities.

Private instructions and supervision in forensic psychiatry are usually available on a fee-for-service basis. Instruction should include how to conduct a forensic psychiatric assessment, how to write a forensic psychiatric report, and how to testify effectively in court. Supervisors should be formally trained and certified in forensic psychiatry, and, preferably, be on the faculty of an accredited forensic residency or higher specialist training program. AAPL's membership directory offers a list of psychiatrists certified by the ABFP. The ABPN and ABMS offer a list of psychiatrists with ABPN certification.

## Conclusion

A forensic psychiatry residency (and its equivalent in the UK and Canada) provides a more intense and systematic experience than independent training. Residency training ensures exposure to the field's diversity, with close supervision from experienced and certified practitioners. Nonetheless, for the next several decades at least, a mix of self-trained and residency-trained, certified and uncertified, forensic psychiatrists will practice the subspecialty in the USA, the UK, and Canada. Until the practice of forensic psychiatry is made legally contingent on graduation from an accredited forensic residency or certification by an accrediting body, some practitioners will continue to come into the field by independent, on-the-job training.

## See Also

**Accreditation:** Forensic Specialties Accreditation Board; **History of Forensic Medicine**

## Further Reading

American Academy of Forensic Sciences–American Academy of Psychiatry and the Law Joint Committee on Accreditation of Fellowship Programs in Forensic Psychiatry (1982) Standards for fellowship programs in forensic psychiatry. *American Academy of Psychiatry and the Law Bulletin* 10(4).

American Academy of Psychiatry and the Law, www.aapl.org.

American Board of Medical Specialties, www.abms.org.

American Board of Psychiatry and Neurology, www.abpn.com.

American Council for Graduate Medical Education, www.acgme.org.

American Psychiatric Association, www.psych.org.

Canadian Academy of Psychiatry and Law, www.caplnet.org.

Canadian Psychiatric Association, www.cpa-apc.org.

Reeves R, Rosner R (2003) Education and training in forensic psychiatry. In: Rosner R (ed.) *Principles and Practice of Forensic Psychiatry*, 2nd edn., pp. 52–55. London: Arnold.

Royal College of Physicians and Surgeons of Canada, rcpsc.medical.org/index.php3?pass = 1.

Royal College of Psychiatrists, www.rcpsych.ac.uk.

# Assessment

**R Reeves**, University of Medicine and Dentistry of New Jersey, Newark, NJ, USA
**R Rosner**, New York University School of Medicine, and the Forensic Psychiatry Clinic of Bellevue Hospital Center, New York, NY, USA

## Introduction

In the approach to a problem in any field of knowledge, a conceptual framework or method allows one to organize and analyze data rationally. A useful framework for assessment in forensic psychiatry and forensic psychology is a four-step method, articulated by Richard Rosner. These steps are:

1. Issue: What is the specific psychiatric– or psychological–legal issue?
2. Legal criteria: What are the legal criteria that will be used to resolve the issue?
3. Data: What are the data relevant to the legal criteria that will be used to resolve the issue?
4. Reasoning: How may the data be applied to the legal criteria in order to establish a rational psychiatric or psychological opinion?

## Issue

Psychiatric and psychological issues in forensic medicine arise in three broad areas of law: (1) civil law, (2) criminal law, and (3) legal regulation of mental healthcare. Civil law involves issues such as disability, personal injury, fitness for work, child custody, child abuse and neglect, parental competence and termination of parental rights, guardianship, and testamentary capacity. Criminal law involves voluntariness of confessions; juvenile delinquency; waiver to adult court; competence to stand trial, enter a plea, and testify; insanity; diminished capacity; and risk assessment. Legal regulation of mental healthcare includes issues such as voluntary hospitalization, involuntary hospitalization, right to treatment, right to refuse treatment, informed consent, malpractice, and ethics.

In a given case, there may be several potential psychiatric– or psychological–legal issues. The forensic psychiatrist or psychologist must identify the specific legal issue or issues that the referring judge, attorney, or agency wishes the evaluator to address. Such identification is not always easy. A busy judge or attorney may ask for a "psychiatric evaluation" of a defendant and provide no additional information. The evaluator bears the responsibility of contacting the referring person and ascertaining just what psychiatric–legal issue or issues the referrer wishes the evaluator to address.

The completed forensic report may otherwise fail to meet the needs of the legal system.

A referrer may have only a fuzzy idea about which issue should be addressed by the psychiatrist or psychologist. Such confusion is not uncommon. The evaluator should clarify the issue. For example, an attorney involved in a child custody dispute might ask the psychologist to evaluate the opposing attorney's client for evidence of neglect of the child. The perspicacious psychologist might suggest that the attorney broaden the issue to an evaluation of which custody arrangement serves the interest of the child better.

A single case commonly involves more than one issue. For example, an attorney might wish to know whether his or her client's statement to police was voluntary. The attorney might also wish to know whether the client is competent to stand trial and whether the client was insane at the time of the offense. Each issue requires its own evaluation according to the legal criteria applicable in the given jurisdiction.

## Criteria

For any given psychiatric– or psychological–legal issue, there are many legal arenas in which the issue may come into play. Most legal systems, including those of the USA and UK, are arranged hierarchically. The USA has its federal, military, and 50 state jurisdictions plus the District of Columbia. For each of these jurisdictions, there is a separate set of statutes (laws created by a legislature), case law (rulings made by judges), and administrative code (policies created by bureaucracies). (For the arrangement of jurisdictions within a given country, consult a basic law-school text for that country.) In addition, there are the small, private arenas such as the proprietary definition of disability in a disability insurance policy issued by an insurance company. For the purposes of a forensic evaluation, statutes, case law, administrative code, and private policy all function as "law" in that they serve as the legal criteria that define an issue.

These numerous jurisdictions and their subdivisions mean that the legal criteria defining an issue are numerous and diverse. The forensic evaluator must be certain of the legal criteria applicable to an issue within a given jurisdiction. Such knowledge requires, first, familiarity with the arrangement of the legal system within one's country. Second, an evaluator needs to develop a means to access the appropriate criteria. The easiest and most common means of access is for the evaluator simply to ask the referring attorney for a written statement of the appropriate legal criteria. The criteria should be written because an attorney's oral report is unreliable.

The criteria may be vague and are always open to interpretation, but they nonetheless roughly establish the boundaries of the issue. For example, in most jurisdictions in the USA, a legal criterion for competence to stand trial is some version of the capacity to consult with one's lawyer with a reasonable degree of rational understanding. What is "reasonable"? Reasonable people – including judges, attorneys, and forensic evaluators – can and do differ in their interpretation of this criterion. On the other hand, the criterion's requirement that a defendant demonstrate some ability to work with his or her lawyer establishes a higher threshold for competence than if the criterion were nonexistent.

If the attorney works infrequently with mental health issues, the attorney may be uncertain of the criteria. The evaluator should insist that the criteria be made available. Otherwise, one's opinion is logically unsupported. Because the legal criteria are numerous and recondite, the experienced evaluator not uncommonly educates the attorney. Subscriptions to legal publications (e.g., in the USA, *Westlaw* and *LexisNexis*) are an independent means for an evaluator to access the legal criteria. Do not rely on the internet for free access to these criteria. Internet searches in this area are slow, often fruitless, and always tedious.

## Data

After identifying the psychiatric– or psychological–legal issue and the criteria defining the issue, the psychiatrist or psychologist gathers the data relevant to the criteria defining the issue. Unlike routine clinical practice, the data may concern more than the present mental state of the examinee. For example, the examinee's past mental state is relevant to the question of whether the examinee was insane at the time he or she committed a crime. An examinee's future mental state is relevant to the question of which parent is likely to be the better custodian of an infant.

Results of forensic assessments are not confidential in the way that medical and therapeutic records are (generally) confidential. A psychiatric or psychological forensic assessment, being requested by an attorney, judge, or agency, is read by these same entities. These entities then use the assessment to render a legal decision that might benefit or hurt the examinee. Therefore, before proceeding with a forensic assessment, a forensic examiner warns an examinee about the lack of confidentiality and the purpose of the assessment. The warning seeks to dispel any confusion the examinee might have that the assessment is for therapeutic purposes and will stay between the examiner and examinee. Such a warning is typically required by professional ethical guidelines.

Stakes are high in these evaluations because they typically involve matters of liberty, custody, or large amounts of money. The examinee often has good reason to exaggerate, distort, evade, or lie outright. Therefore, the forensic evaluator exercises a healthy skepticism of any claim made by an examinee. Looking deeply into the eyes of the examinee is rarely the means by which the examiner establishes truth. People lie often and well. Rather, scrutiny of the examinee's statements for contradictions, distortions, and evasions may provide evidence of dissembling. Simple but clever questioning techniques may also reveal evidence for malingering of mental illness. The examiner compares the mental state of the examinee to what the examiner knows about genuine psychopathology. Occasionally, the interview is all that is needed to dispose of a case. For example, an interview of a jail inmate may reveal that he is confused and disorganized, and unable to respond to questions, making it perfectly obvious that he does not meet the legal criteria for competence to stand trial. Thus, it is beneficial for the evaluator to be a good diagnostician and to maintain at least a parttime clinical practice.

In addition to the interview of the examinee, and unlike many therapeutic assessments, the forensic psychiatrist or psychologist seeks collateral information to confirm or refute the examinee's statements. Obviously, an examinee's story gains credibility if others consistently corroborate the story. The converse is also true. Typical sources of historical information include medical records, school records, vocational history, criminal history, police reports, and statements from relatives, employers, and caregivers. It is this fastidious, persistent, and unglamorous accumulation and evaluation of historical data that comprises the core of the psychiatric or psychological forensic assessment.

Normative tests, nonnormative structured assessments, and brain imaging are additional diagnostic tools. These types of tools are increasing in number, diversity, and precision, and they are gradually supplanting unsupported and untested individual opinion. Such change is welcome in a field that purports to offer science as the basis of opinion. Buttressed with normative testing, structured assessments, and brain imaging, one's opinion may be disputed in court but is unlikely to be dismissed altogether as being unreliable, invalid, and obscure in its reasoning.

The skill of the forensic psychiatrist or psychologist is revealed by the practitioner's knowledge of what test to use in what forensic situation. A normative test is a test in which the distribution of results is known within a population. Such a test offers an established reliability and validity. For example, the second edition of the Hare Psychopathy Checklist – Revised (PCL-R) is an indispensable 20-item rating scale for assessing psychopathy, a personality construct characterized by remorselessness, irresponsibility, and crime. The PCL-R is normed on various forensic populations, including international forensic populations, and has established reliability and validity data. The Portland Digit Recognition Test is a normative test of feigned memory loss, in which the distribution of results within the population of head-trauma victims is known. A nonnormative structured assessment specifies the factors that are empirically associated with a suspected phenomenon, but leaves the weighting of the factors to the judgment of the evaluator. For example, the Structured Assessment of Violence Risk in Youth (SAVRY) lists the factors that are empirically predictive of future violence in adolescents. In the SAVRY, an examiner assesses an adolescent on each factor but then uses his or her own judgment to combine the factors and render a final opinion as to the adolescent's likelihood of committing future violence. A nonnormative structured assessment lacks the reliability and validity of a normative test. However, a nonnormative structured assessment remains useful because it is based on research, and it makes one's diagnostic method more explicit than in unexplained clinical opinion. Thus, one's opinion rises above the individualism and even idiosyncrasy that is tolerated in clinical practice. Brain imaging is advancing rapidly and may soon play a routine role in a forensic assessment. Today, however, the sensitivity and specificity of the various means of brain imaging in the diagnosis of psychopathology are largely unknown. Thus, the usefulness of brain imaging in forensic assessment is limited.

## Reasoning

Armed with data relevant to the legal criteria, the psychiatrist or psychologist applies the data to the criteria in order to establish a rational psychiatric or psychological opinion. The reasoning process is often the most difficult part of the assessment because it requires logical thinking, and logical thinking is not a skill or talent that is distributed equally among persons. The structure of a psychiatric– or psychological–legal opinion should follow the three generic steps of a syllogism. The first step is the assertion of a premise. The second step is the assertion of a minor premise or fact. The third step is a deductive inference or conclusion that follows from the premise and fact. The following is an example: all dogs are animals (the premise); Fluffy is a dog (the fact); therefore, Fluffy is an animal (the conclusion).

In a psychiatric– or psychological–legal opinion, the premise is the legal criteria. The fact is the data relevant to the criteria. The conclusion is the final opinion. Consider the insanity defense. In the state of New Jersey, a person is not criminally responsible for conduct "if at the time of such conduct he was laboring under such a defect of reason, from disease of the mind as not to know the nature and quality of the act he was doing, or if he did know it, that he did not know what he was doing was wrong" (the premise). Mr. Jones, at the time he committed murder, suffered from schizophrenia ("disease of the mind"), which so impaired his reason that he thought that killing his victim would save humanity. Therefore, he did not know the "nature and quality" of his act (the fact). Thus, Mr. Jones is not criminally responsible for his killing (the conclusion).

Each step in a psychiatric– or psychological–legal opinion may be incorrect and, thus, is subject to challenge. That is, the legal criteria may be incorrect, the data may not relate to the criteria, or the final opinion may have little or no relation to the criteria and data. An example of this last mistake is an opinion that a person suffers from schizophrenia and substance abuse and is subject to disorganized and violent behavior when he/she is not taking his/her medication and is abusing substances. Such an opinion may be entirely true, but it does not answer the question of whether the person was legally insane at the time he/she committed a criminal act.

Skillful reasoning in a forensic assessment requires more than attention to the logic of a syllogism. The forensic practitioner should approach an assessment as if an intelligent and skeptical nonclinician were reading the report (which is usually the case with a judge or an attorney). One should explain that which, by virtue of one's experience, has become clinically obvious. Jargon is better avoided (unless it is subsequently explained) because it impresses few and enlightens none. What are givens in therapeutic practice should be questioned and substantiated in a forensic assessment. For example, clinicians as well as laypersons commonly think that mentally ill patients pose an increased risk of violence relative to persons who are not mentally ill. However, the MacArthur violence risk assessment study, the largest study of violence in civil psychiatric patients in the USA, questions this assumption. The MacArthur study found that there was no difference between the prevalence of violence by patients without symptoms of substance abuse and the prevalence of violence by others living in the same neighborhoods who were also without symptoms of substance abuse. Substance abuse increased the rate of violence in both the patient and the comparison groups, and a higher portion of patients than of others in their neighborhoods reported substance abuse. Furthermore, among those who reported substance abuse, the prevalence of violence among patients was significantly higher than that among others in their neighborhoods. Thus, the MacArthur study suggests that the increased prevalence of violence among psychiatric patients is mediated by substance abuse rather than by mental illness alone. The forensic practitioner is obligated to recognize this distinction and convey this in the practitioner's report because it may have a bearing on a person's parole or release from a hospital.

A judicial outcome commonly differs from the recommendation offered in a forensic assessment. The psychiatrist or psychologist should anticipate that outcome and offer recommendations contingent on different rulings. Uncertainty should be acknowledged. Forensic psychiatry and psychology are, at best, primitive sciences. At their worst, they are about who can spin the best yarn. Acknowledgment of uncertainty is not a condemnation of one's skill or profession but, rather, a recognition that normative data are often unavailable to contribute to an assessment, and that prediction of behavior is fraught with error. Acknowledgment of uncertainty adds to one's credibility because it reflects honesty. It places one's opinion in perspective and allows a judge, jury, or other reviewer to weight the opinion accordingly.

Finally, an assessment invariably takes the form of a written report. Courtroom testimony, despite what television dramas suggest, is but a small part of forensic work. A well-written report may even obviate testimony. Thus, the ability to write logically and well is an indispensable skill for the forensic psychiatrist and psychologist. Following the convention of judicial opinion, the psychiatric– or psychological–legal opinion should be near the beginning of the report. Such placement also allows a busy judge or attorney to learn the upshot of the report without having to wade through the data. The following format is useful for most forensic reports:

- Identifying data – the name and birth date of the examinee, the date of the evaluation, the date of the report, and the name of the evaluator.
- Reason for referral – including the person or agency requesting the referral, the legal issue, and the legal criteria defining the issue.
- Opinion – stated in language meeting the legal standard for the issue at hand.
- Sources of information – including persons interviewed and documents reviewed, and dates of each.

- Warning of lack of confidentiality – a statement (typically required by professional ethical guidelines) warning the examinee of the purpose of the evaluation and who will see the report, and estimating the examinee's comprehension of the report.
- Relevant history – including the offense or incident that led to the referral (as described by the examinee and others), criminal history, psychiatric history, medical history, family history, and social and developmental history.
- Mental status examination – including appearance, attitude, movements, orientation, attention, memory, fund of knowledge, intelligence, speech, mood, range of emotional expression, perception, thought process, thought content, and insight into one's mental illness and/or circumstances precipitating the evaluation.
- Test results – the results of normative testing, structured assessments, brain imaging, etc.
- Diagnostic formulation – an organization of the previously mentioned data supporting a psychiatric or psychological diagnosis, if any, including an acknowledgment of the diagnostic system and criteria that are used.
- Forensic formulation – an organization of the previously mentioned data that applies the data to the legal criteria and issue and identifies the reasoning used to reach one's conclusion.

Rational organization and analysis in a forensic psychiatric or psychological report allows one to manage large amounts of complex data. Because forensic mental health issues rarely reach the level of scientific certainty that other areas of scientific inquiry do (e.g., as in DNA analysis), a common conceptual framework allows areas of uncertainty or disagreement to be highlighted and explained. A common framework also allows efficient communication among colleagues. Finally, rational organization and analysis are likely to make one's presentation more effective.

## See Also

**Forensic Psychiatry and Forensic Psychology:** Ethics; Forensic Interviewing; Malingering

## Further Reading

Melton GB, Petrila J, Poythress NG, Slobogin C (eds.) (1997) The nature and method of forensic assessment. In: *Psychological Evaluations for the Courts – A Handbook for Mental Health Professionals and Lawyers*, 2nd edn, pp. 41–63. New York: Guilford.

Melton GB, Petrila J, Poythress NG, Slobogin C (eds.) (1997) Consultation, report writing, and expert testimony. In: *Psychological Evaluations for the Courts – A Handbook for Mental Health Professionals and Lawyers,* 2nd edn, pp. 519–546. New York: Guilford.

Rosner R (ed.) (2003) A conceptual framework for forensic psychiatry. In: *Principles and Practice of Forensic Psychiatry,* 2nd edn, pp. 3–6. London: Arnold.

Silva JA, Weinstock R, Leong GB (2003) Forensic psychiatric report writing. In: Rosner R (ed.) *Principles and Practice of Forensic Psychiatry,* 2nd edn, pp. 31–36. London: Arnold.

# Ethics

**D Mossman**, Wright State University School of Medicine, Dayton, OH, USA

## Introduction

Psychiatrists and psychologists tread on foreign professional territory when they step into the legal arena, and the customary standards of conduct that clinicians use when making therapeutic decisions often seem inappropriate or inadequate for situations where a legal determination, rather than healing, is the goal. In treatment settings, mental health professionals need to maintain clinical objectivity, but doing so rarely conflicts with their primary role of improving patients' health and functioning. In adversarial legal proceedings, however, no doctor–patient relationship usually exists between the forensic clinician and the litigant, and the mental health expert's official role – providing reliable, impartial information to assist the court – often seems at odds with attorneys' partisan duty to advocate diligently for their side. Whereas treating clinicians usually have straightforward, concrete aims (e.g., helping individual patients) to guide their treatment decisions, the forensic expert's moral allegiance is to abstract principles, such as truthfulness, candor, scientific accuracy, and professional competence. Thus the moral questions that psychiatric and psychological experts face are distinct from, and more complex than, those that mental health clinicians come across in ordinary patient care.

This article describes several ethical issues that mental health experts encounter, with special emphasis on topics covered in guidelines promulgated by the American subspecialty organizations of forensic psychiatrists and psychologists. The article also summarizes the efforts of several authors to articulate the ethical framework within which forensic mental health professionals conduct evaluations and provide other services to the legal system.

## Who is a Forensic Psychiatrist? A Forensic Psychologist?

Having noted that forensic mental health experts face unique ethical issues raises two threshold questions: (1) What activities constitute forensic psychiatry and psychology? (2) Insofar as published ethical guidelines exist, to whom do those guidelines apply?

The ethical guidelines of the American Academy of Psychiatry and the Law (AAPL) describe forensic psychiatry as a medical subspecialty that applies scientific and clinical psychiatric expertise to civil, criminal, and correctional issues, as well as legislative matters. Practitioners of forensic psychiatry should adhere to ethical principles that govern the entire profession of psychiatry, and the AAPL guidelines thus supplement guidelines promulgated by the American Psychiatric Association (APA) and the American Medical Association. AAPL does not handle ethical complaints about psychiatrists' behavior, but directs these toward the APA, its district branches, and/or state medical licencing boards.

*Specialty Guidelines for Forensic Psychologists* were developed by Division 41 of the American Psychological Association, but are not an "official statement" of this organization. The guidelines offer a model of practices to which psychological experts should aspire, and are intended to amplify standards expressed in the American Psychological Association's *Ethical Principles of Psychologists*. The *Specialty Guidelines* define as forensic psychologists those licenced psychologists who regularly function as experts in legal proceedings, who work in correctional and/or forensic mental health facilities, or who serve in agencies that adjudicate judicial or legal matters.

## Specific Issues, Problems, and Areas of Practical Concern

Because the activities of forensic psychiatrists and psychologists are in many respects similar, the ethical guidelines for their subspecialties share much in common. Experts in both subspecialties are advised about the need for special cautions concerning the examination procedures, consent, confidentiality, maintaining objectivity, relationships with evaluees and retaining counsel, and fees. However, forensic psychologists express more concern and assume more responsibility concerning the potential misuse of their expertise than do their psychiatric colleagues.

## Boundary Issues and Role Conflicts

Mental health professionals use the phrase "boundary issues" to designate potentially problematic behavior that can arise when clinicians act outside their proper role. Although the traditional, fiduciary relationship between doctor and patient usually does not apply in forensic practice, forensic clinicians are ideally expected to have no relationship with evaluees or retaining parties beyond that of being an examiner and potential witness. Having a business or romantic relationship with an evaluee, an evaluee's family member, or a retaining attorney is hardly conducive to impartial assessment and would certainly create the appearance of bias.

Mental health professionals also agree that, as a general rule, they should avoid serving as legal experts who would offer expert opinions concerning patients whom they are also treating. This position differs from that taken by many medical specialists, and attorneys sometimes have difficulty appreciating why psychiatrists and psychologists feel as they do. The clinical reasons reflect concern that serving as an expert might so alter a patient's relationship with the therapist as to compromise future treatment irrevocably. Also, treating therapists do not – and should not – approach the evaluation of their patients with the kind of skepticism required of forensic clinicians. Further, respect for patients' privacy usually demands that a treating therapist be very cautious about any contact with other persons who know the patient, whereas such "collateral contacts" are frequent and often necessary parts of forensic assessments.

It is acceptable for a treating clinician to serve as a fact witness concerning a patient, though this is not without potential therapeutic pitfalls. If a patient becomes involved in litigation and a need for expert testimony arises, a treating clinician should recommend that the patient be evaluated for that express purpose by an independent, nontreating clinician. A possible exception to this general rule involves psychiatrists and psychologists who testify about their own patients at civil commitment hearings or who provide court reports concerning the status of defendants found incompetent to stand trial. In these circumstances, reports or expert testimony by a treating clinician may be required by statute or may be the only practical way of letting a patient get needed services. Nonetheless, before accepting a forensic role, a treating clinician should consider whether providing courtroom expertise would compromise his/her patient's care and whether the previous treatment relationship would preclude the clinician's functioning with the impartiality required of an expert witness.

## Establishing and Clarifying the Expert's Role

The forensic expert's need to be honest and objective often conflicts with the desires of litigants and their attorneys to "win" cases. Because of this, forensic clinicians must clearly establish their role as evaluators and impartial experts when they accept referrals, and often must restate this role throughout the course of a consultation.

**Relationships with referring attorneys**   Forensic consultations often begin with a telephone call from an attorney who seeks mental health expertise. When gathering information about the potential referral, the potential expert must explore several ethical matters before agreeing to be retained. These include ruling out conflicts of interest (created, for example, by having treated or had other previous contacts with the litigant). The expert must also decide whether his/her professional background and time constraints will permit him/her to do a proper job in conducting evaluations, reaching conclusions, and preparing for trial. The expert must clarify whether his/her expected role will be that of an impartial evaluator and potential courtroom expert, or a consultant who will help the attorney prepare the case but not testify. Experts should also apprise the referral source about articles they have written and any "skeletons in the closet" that might be relevant to the issues presented in the case.

If none of the just-mentioned considerations preclude accepting the referral, the expert should then discuss fees and payment arrangements. Though remuneration for services may seem like a practical rather than ethical matter, forensic referrals are fraught with potential situations in which concern about payment may influence (or at least appear to influence) the expert's opinion. For example, plaintiffs' attorneys regularly accept contingency fees, but mental health experts should not agree to such payment arrangements, which could detract from the expert's impartiality and objectivity. Retainer fees and other arrangements for advance payment reduce the temptation to alter one's opinion for financial reasons, and are therefore both ethically acceptable and often recommended.

Pressures to identify and "side with" referring attorneys can be explicit or implicit, blunt or subtle, external or internal. Some attorneys start initial discussions with a potential expert by saying, "I need a doctor to testify that..." Other attorneys insinuate that future referrals hinge on the expert's opinion about the current case. Attorneys may encourage experts to rephrase or revise their conclusions to fit their clients' legal positions better. In responding to such overtures, experts must guard against losing objectivity or altering findings out of a desire to please or to be helpful. A more difficult (but crucial) duty is for the expert to recognize when unconscious identification with the retaining side may have unintentionally influenced the expert's views.

**Relationships with evaluees**   A clinician should not undertake a forensic evaluation without receiving appropriate legal authorization, usually from the evaluee's attorney or through a court order. In a situation where consent is not legally required (e.g., a court-ordered evaluation concerning competence or civil commitment), the evaluator should still seek the evaluee's assent and should explain that refusal to participate will be noted in the evaluator's report and/or testimony. When consent is legally necessary and an evaluee cannot give valid consent, the evaluator should not proceed until substituted consent for the evaluation (in accordance with laws of the jurisdiction) has been obtained.

Even when evaluees are competent and have received clear explanations from their attorneys about a pending forensic examination, they may still regard evaluators as their "doctors" and think that the usual features of clinician–patient relationships apply. For this reason, a forensic interview should begin with a clear, simply worded statement of why the evaluation is occurring and what it will involve. Here, for example, is an explanation (using colloquial US English at a 12-year-old reading level) that might precede a court-ordered examination concerning criminal responsibility (i.e., insanity):

> I'm Dr. Smith, and I'm a psychiatrist. The court has asked me to evaluate your mental condition at the time of the crime you are charged with. I need to learn whether you had a mental disorder that was so serious that the court should not hold you criminally responsible.
>
> Although I am a doctor, I am not your doctor. Usually, when you see a doctor, the doctor treats you and doesn't tell anyone what you said. But here, my job is to evaluate you, learn the truth, and report my findings. I won't be treating you, and what I find out may or may not help your case. Also, what we talk about is not confidential. I'll send a report about our interview to the judge, your lawyer, and the prosecutor in your case. Later on, I may testify in court about what you've told me.
>
> It's important that you be honest with me. I'm going to ask about many things, but you don't have to answer all my questions. If you choose not to answer some questions, however, I may need to say that you didn't in my report. The county will pay me for my time, so I won't be billing you. If you need to take short breaks while we're talking, that's fine – just ask me.
>
> Do you have any questions about what I just said? Do I have your permission to continue?

To make sure that evaluees have understood, some examiners will have the evaluees restate what they have been told about the interview's nature, purpose, and nonconfidentiality. Doing this tells the evaluator how well an evaluee has understood matters, which is relevant to ensuring the evaluee's competence to undergo evaluation. The exchange also establishes the nontherapeutic posture of the evaluation, puts the evaluee on notice about the examiner's impartial role, affirms the evaluee's autonomy, and warns the evaluee about potential consequences.

Despite issuing such cautions, forensic evaluators must remain alert to the possibility that, in an evaluee's mind, an examination may become a therapeutic encounter. When evaluators sense this occurring, they should remind evaluees of the evaluator's neutral, nontreatment role.

**Confidentiality**   As the above section explains, forensic evaluations do not take place in a climate of confidentiality, and evaluees must be told how information will be released. Beyond this, however, forensic clinicians should protect evaluees' privacy to the extent that the legal context permits. Before the trial, an expert should not discuss a case with an opposing expert or counsel without first getting the retaining attorney's permission. Although the media sometimes obtain copies of forensic evaluators' reports, it is improper for mental health experts themselves to furnish reports to news organizations.

**Personal examination**   Published ethical guidelines recommend that mental health experts only offer opinions about individuals who have been personally examined. In cases where an expert cannot conduct a personal examination of an individual, it is acceptable to formulate and offer an opinion about that individual based on other available information. Experts should make it clear when they are doing this, however, and should explain how this limitation may affect the accuracy and reliability of their opinion.

**Test security, "raw" data, and legal requirements** The usefulness of many psychological tests (including intelligence scales and personality inventories) depends in part on the public's lacking access to the tests' precise contents. For example, if questions from the Wechsler intelligence scales were easily obtained and evaluees could study them, the test results would no longer be valid indicators of evaluees' native intelligence. For this reason, the American Psychological Association's *Ethical Guidelines* admonish psychologists to maintain test security, i.e., to prevent persons who would not be authorized to administer tests from obtaining questions, manuals, and other test materials. Similarly, psychologists may (and often should) refrain from releasing "raw" test data (e.g., an evaluee's responses) when doing so poses a risk that such data might be misrepresented or misused. Although psychiatrists' ethical guidelines do not explicitly mention these matters, psychiatrists who use tests should observe similar precautions.

During litigation, a mental health expert may be subpoenaed or statutorily required to submit to opposing counsel "all" documents related to a case, which could include raw data and test information printed on scoring forms. Often, however, the expert can satisfy such requirements by asking opposing counsel to designate a licenced psychologist or psychiatrist who can receive the materials directly. This practice preserves test integrity and avoids the risk of misinterpretation by nonmental health professionals, while respecting opposing counsel's need independently to review potential sources of evidence in a case. An expert can respond to a subpoena by filing a motion for a protective order or for quashing the subpoena; the expert might also contact the test publisher, who may intervene with a similar motion to protect "proprietary" materials. If, despite such efforts, a court insists that an expert submit test materials to a nonclinician, the expert may have to obey the court's order.

**Misuse of expertise** Forensic psychiatrists and psychologists recognize that attorneys and legal decision-makers may distort or misuse their findings and opinions. Though psychiatrists find this dismaying, they ascribe such occurrences to the nature of the adversarial process, and feel their ethical obligations are satisfied so long as they remain honest and objective. The forensic psychology guidelines, however, see experts as being further obligated to ensure that their reports and testimony are used responsibly and to communicate findings understandably; to do this, experts should take into account the characteristics of the potential audience for their opinions and communications. American Psychological Association guidelines urge all psychologists to rely on established scientific principles and professional knowledge, to keep up-to-date on knowledge of scientific and professional developments, and to use that knowledge when collecting data and selecting evaluation procedures.

## Theoretical Concerns

The duties and expectations of mental health experts seem at odds with the moral obligations that usually govern interactions between clinicians and those whom they evaluate. As physicians, psychiatrists regard their professional behavior as bound by Hippocratic obligations to heal the sick, alleviate suffering, and *primum non nocere* ("above all, do no harm"). The *Ethical Principles for Psychologists* lists benefiting and not harming clients and evaluees as the first of several general principles toward which psychologists should aspire, adding that considerations of fairness and justice entitle everyone to the benefits of psychology as a scientific and professional discipline.

Yet legal decisions rarely benefit all parties involved: in criminal cases, a conviction may imply fines, incarceration, or (in the USA) death; in civil cases, losing parties experience financial (and not infrequently, emotional) consequences. Recognizing that litigants whom forensic psychiatrists and psychologists examine often end up being adversely affected by the experts' reports or testimony, several commentators have asked whether and how professional ethics can be reconciled with the legal outcomes that mental health expertise often helps produce.

### Avoiding the Courtroom

Some prominent US psychiatrists, including Karl Menninger and Alan Stone, believe that medical ethics and the demands of the legal system are incompatible, and have urged psychiatrists to stay out of courtrooms. Psychiatry, Stone writes, is an error-prone profession, but one that physicians nonetheless practice ethically when their intention is to ease patients' suffering. Without this goal to guide them, psychiatrists lack a moral compass. In court, their knowledge and status may be misused, and they are prone to letting the adversarial legal system sway their views and undermine their integrity. Zealous legal advocacy, Stone writes, combined with the expert's financial interests and emotional responses, encourages experts to adopt polarized, extreme opinions. Some well-meaning clinicians assume antiprosecutorial biases in misguided efforts to help defendants; inexperienced experts often appear to be biased by personal issues that litigation symbolizes for them. Forensic examinations are often ambiguous encounters, Stone believes, during which skillful, empathic interviewers unavoidably create quasitherapeutic relationships that seduce evaluees into revealing information adverse to their cases. Though psychiatrists may think that giving honest testimony only furthers justice, doing so nonetheless violates the doctor's traditional obligation to help individual patients.

### The Defense Psychiatrist

A second solution is explicitly to aim only to help evaluees, by, for example, testifying only in ways that might help the evaluee escape punishment.

Bernard Diamond believed that impartiality and objectivity were impossible aims, and felt a physician should not use his/her skills to enable prosecution and punishment. He therefore held that psychiatrists should testify only for the defense in criminal cases, and believed this position was consonant with a physician's therapeutic role. In this vein, some mental health professionals avoid certain kinds of evaluations (e.g., capital sentencing evaluations) because doing so might risk uncovering information that would adversely affect the defendant.

## Appelbaum's Theory

As Paul Appelbaum has pointed out, if mental health professionals were obligated only to help those whom they examine, the legal system would have little use for their findings and opinions. It is only because accurate evaluations may be adverse to evaluees' interests that the legal system gives forensic testimony any credence. For this reason, Appelbaum believes that forensic subspecialists need ethical principles that are distinct from those of treating clinicians. Because forensic evaluators do not have treatment relationships with their evaluees and do not seek to promote their health, the ethical principles that apply in forensic contexts must differ from those that apply in treatment contexts, and should reflect the goals that society seeks to achieve by having mental health professionals participate in legal proceedings.

Society values courtroom psychiatric input because of its potential to advance the cause of justice, and such input is only valuable if it is truthful. Thus, truth-telling must be the first ethical principle in forensic psychiatry, according to Appelbaum. The legal system's search for truth is always tempered by respect for persons, even those who are suspected of committing crimes. Respect for persons thus is a second principle of forensic ethics, manifested in examiners' clarifying their role with evaluees, explaining the limits of confidentiality, and stating clearly that they are not providing treatment. Beneficence and nonmaleficence are aspects of forensic ethics only insofar as these principles obligate experts always to consider whether their actions are consonant with the aim of seeking justice.

## Critiques of Appelbaum's Approach

Although Appelbaum's formulation is widely respected among forensic clinicians, his theory is not without critics. Ezra Griffith faults Appelbaum for not recognizing how historical experience and political disparities – for example, disparities between whites and blacks in the USA – affect what members of dominant and nondominant groups perceive as the

"truth" about a situation. Full accounts of forensically relevant events, says Griffith, should include cultural formulations. Such formulations, which describe the evaluee's individual perspective and cultural factors that affect his/her illness and social functioning, would promote understanding of the evaluee, his/her personal experience, and his/her psychosocial environment. Expanding upon Griffith's insights, Candilis and colleagues argue that in many forensic consultations, a clinician's professional integrity entails moral responsibilities that go beyond a strictly evaluative role. Such responsibilities may require therapeutic efforts to make sure the problems that generate referrals are resolved in ways that address the legitimate needs of the persons involved.

Mossman asserts that mental health professionals do not and cannot abandon their obligations of beneficence and nonmaleficence when they serve as forensic experts, because these obligations apply to all citizens at all times. Relying on Kant's political theory, Mossman believes that all individuals have given their hypothetical rational consent to the requirements of a reasonably fair criminal justice system, including the requirement that individuals experience consequences (e.g., criminal penalties or civil sanctions) for undesirable acts. No interest is more important to a person than respect for his/her humanity, and truthful psychiatric input into legal determinations helps ensure that the rationality and humanity of the litigant are respected. Mental health professionals therefore fulfill their duties to help and avoid harming evaluees by conducting honest and objective forensic evaluations and by testifying honestly, even when the information so obtained or imparted supports criminal convictions or civil sanctions.

## Integrity versus Advocacy

Shuman and Greenberg note an apparent tension created by psychologists' ethical obligation to be impartial sources of information for courts, and the partisanship of retaining attorneys who advocate zealously for their clients. Even when courts permit testimony that is biased or unfounded, experts may be subject to civil suits or sanctions by licencing boards if they become partisan advocates for litigants. However, Shuman and Greenberg believe that opposing integrity and advocacy represents a false dichotomy for psychological experts. Instead, they regard remaining impartial as the best form of advocacy: an expert must be credible to be an effective advocate for his/her viewpoint; to be credible, the expert must remain impartial and objective.

Mental health experts must simultaneously accommodate the evidentiary requirements of courts, the ethical requirements of their professions and licencing boards, and implicit or explicit economic pressures to please retaining attorneys. Shuman and Greenberg believe experts can respond through adherence to five principles:

1. Experts should know the limits of current scientific knowledge and should not testify beyond those areas where psychological expertise permits adequate certainty.
2. Experts should disclose all information relevant to their opinions, though they have no obligation to disclose other information that would not bear on issues about which they have not been asked.
3. In formulating opinions, experts must evaluate issues from the perspective of all competing parties in litigation, request legal documents that describe competing views of a case, and identify evidence that would support or refute those views.
4. Experts should consider all perspectives and weigh rival hypotheses even-handedly.
5. Experts should present their findings candidly, even if attorneys feel that doing so conflicts with the allegiance the expert owes to retaining counsel.

## Conclusion

This article only introduces some of the ethical issues that confront forensic psychiatrists and psychologists, and is intended to convey the complexity and variety of the ever-changing moral problems these subspecialists encounter. As of this writing, American forensic psychiatrists and psychologists are revising their published ethical guidelines. Mental health professionals are becoming increasingly aware of how their functioning as experts creates possible role conflicts and problems of double agency. They are also recognizing that their expertise concerning sex offenders and predicting violence may be inadvertently misapplied in legal proceedings. Finally, forensic psychiatrists and psychologists know that future social developments and court decisions – such as recent US rulings about restoring competence to stand trial and the execution of prisoners with mental retardation – will create new moral quandaries and require further revisions of ethical standards.

## See Also

**Expert Witness:** Qualifications, Testimony and Malpractice; Medical; Daubert and Beyond

## Further Reading

American Academy of Psychiatry and the Law (1995) *Ethical Guidelines for the Practice of Forensic Psychiatry.* Available at http://www.emory.edu/AAPL/ethics.htm (accessed December 5, 2003).

American Psychological Association (2002) *Ethical Principles of Psychologists and Code of Conduct.* Washington, DC: American Psychological Association. Available at http://www.apa.org/ethics/code2002.html (accessed December 5, 2003).
Appelbaum PS (1997) A theory of ethics for forensic psychiatry. *Journal of the American Academy of Psychiatry and the Law* 25: 233–247.
Candilis PJ, Martinez R, Dording C (2001) Principles and narrative in forensic psychiatry: toward a robust view of professional role. *Journal of the American Academy of Psychiatry and the Law* 29: 167–173.
Committee on Ethical Guidelines for Forensic Psychologists (1991) Specialty guidelines for forensic psychologists. *Law and Human Behavior* 15: 655–665.
Diamond BL (1992) The forensic psychiatrist: consultant v. activist in legal doctrine. *Bulletin of the American Academy of Psychiatry and the Law* 20: 119–132.
Griffith EEH (1998) Ethics in forensic psychiatry: a cultural response to Stone and Appelbaum. *Journal of the American Academy of Psychiatry and the Law* 26: 171–184.
Mossman D (1994) Is forensic testimony fundamentally immoral? *International Journal of Law and Psychiatry* 17: 347–368.
Rosner R, Weinstock R (eds.) (1990) *Ethical Practice in Psychiatry and the Law.* New York: Plenum.
Shuman DW, Greenberg SA (2003) The expert witness, the adversary system, and the voice of reason: reconciling impartiality with advocacy. *Professional Psychology: Research and Practice* 34: 219–224.
Stone AA (1984) *Law, Psychiatry, and Morality.* Washington, DC: American Psychiatric Press.
Stone AA (1994) Revisiting the parable: truth without consequences. *International Journal of Law and Psychiatry* 17: 79–97.
Strasburger LH, Gutheil TG, Brodsky A (1997) On wearing two hats: role conflict in serving as both psychotherapist and expert witness. *American Journal of Psychiatry* 154: 448–456.
Weinstock R, Leong GB, Silva JA (2003) Ethical guidelines. In: Rosner R (ed.) *Principles and Practice of Forensic Psychiatry,* 2nd edn, pp. 56–72. London: Edward Arnold.
Wettstein RM (2002) Ethics and forensic psychiatry. *Psychiatric Clinics of North America* 25: 623–633.

# Psychological Autopsy

**A L Berman**, American Association of Suicidology, Washington, DC, USA

Edwin Shneidman, Norman Farberow, and Robert Litman, then the directors of the Los Angeles Suicide Prevention Center (LASPC), coined the term "psychological autopsy" in 1958. Working in collaboration with the Los Angeles County Medical Examiner's

Office (under the direction of Theodore Curphey), these clinician-researchers devised procedures to assist the medical examiner in medicolegal investigations of equivocal deaths. Equivocal deaths are those that are not immediately descriptive of the manner of death because, for example, they were not witnessed or involved conflicting data. Through these procedures, the medical examiner hoped to make informed judgments and determine the manner of death more accurately.

The first recorded case in which these procedures were used involved a 46-year-old male who drowned off the pier at Santa Monica, CA. The case was equivocal because it involved contradictory eyewitness testimonies as to whether the man had stood in front of the guard rail and then jumped. Dr. Litman visited the site and interviewed both the witnesses and the decedent's relatives. He concluded that the decedent had been in good spirits and showed no signs of depression. On the day of his death, the decedent and another man were drinking heavily outside a bar on the pier. The decedent appeared to witnesses to have fallen asleep and was seen to slip off the bench on which he had been sitting and through the guard rail into the ocean, where he drowned. The death was ruled accidental. Over the next two decades, behavioral scientists from the LASPC investigated and consulted on more than 1000 cases referred by the county medical examiner's office.

The psychological autopsy involves the systematic collection of psychological data through structured interviews of the decedent's family members, friends, coworkers, and fellow students. Data are sought that are relevant to the decedent's characteristic behavior, personality, coping style, cognitive processes, psychiatric history, and general emotional life so that a rich psychological biography emerges. When combined with first-person accounts of the decedent's last days of life – evidence from the site of death; police investigation reports; and archival documents, e.g., medical and mental health records, school and occupational records, criminal records, and financial records – conclusions can be drawn as to the intention of the decedent, therefore the decedent's role in effecting his/her own death. Thus, the simplest definition of a psychological autopsy is:

> a set of postmortem investigative procedures that help ascertain and evaluate the role that physical and psychological factors play in the death of an individual, thus to determine the manner of death to as high a degree of certainty as possible.

Over the years psychological autopsies have been conducted for a variety of purposes. In the research

on suicide they have served to develop detailed understandings of suicidal risk factors, e.g., from case-control studies of suicides versus matched nonsuicidal controls, and suicidal pathways. They are used in clinical work to help survivors of suicide better answer the nagging question "why?" when grieving the loss of a loved one to suicide, thus to help survivors in their grieving process. They have been used in governmental inquiries into major public suicides in the UK (cf., the Hutton Inquiry into the death of biological weapons inspector David Kelly in July 2003) and in the USA (cf., the Office of Independent Counsel's 1996 inquiry into the death of Vincent Foster, Jr., deputy counsel to President Bill Clinton).

Given its birth in the world of forensic pathology, it is no surprise that the psychological autopsy has found its way into the courtroom. The determination and certification of manner of death by the coroner or medical examiner is an opinion. As psychological autopsies are time-consuming, and therefore costly, very few coroner's offices have and can afford the budget to employ consultant-suicidologists to provide this expertise and investigative work necessary to conduct a psychological autopsy routinely on difficult, equivocal cases. If a litigant has reason to challenge the opinion of a coroner or medical examiner, it would ultimately be in the courtroom (or during discovery), where alternative opinions are presented and argued, that such a challenge would take place. Final decisions regarding such contested determinations, assigning responsibility for a death and, if applicable, penalties for that liability, are the province of the court.

The psychological autopsy is most commonly introduced in two broad types of forensic cases, those involving *parens patriae*, or custodial caretaking, and those of contested life insurance claims. In some instances, these issues are joined in the same case. In addition, psychological autopsies have been introduced in criminal cases.

## Parens Patriae

Societies typically assign blame for every death, either to God (natural and accidental) or to humans (homicide and suicide). Where death can be attributed to human negligence, punishments are called for.

The office of the coroner was established, by ordinance, in England in 1194. The coroner was named guardian of the pleas of the crown with a primary responsibility to ensure the Royal Treasury of its revenues. Convicted felons, for example, forfeited their property to the crown, in addition to other punishments, not the least of which was hanging! It was up to the coroner to determine both what

**Table 1** Types of forensic case in which the psychological autopsy is used

- Malpractice
- Institutional care
- Product manufacturers
- Worker's compensation
- Life insurance claims
- Criminal defense

constituted the felon's goods and chattels and how much they were worth. One who completed suicide was considered a *felo de se*, a felon against self, and, like the perpetrator of homicide, suffered forfeiture of property. (This penalty remained in effect until its abolition in 1870.) Moreover, those whose deaths were judged to be suicides were further punished through degradation of the corpse and burial outside consecrated ground.

Modern legal thinking has shifted from blaming the suicide to more enlightened attitudes of vulnerability (case-control psychological autopsy studies affirm that more than 90% of those who complete suicide have one or more mental disorders) and more compassionate concern for survivors. Responsibility, instead, is conferred on those in custodial and caretaking roles of protecting the potential suicide from conditions of predisposing self-harm or from actual self-harm behavior. Where these caretakers can be shown to have deviated from a duty of care, negligence may be found.

There are any number of potentially negligent caretakers and, consequently, targets of tort actions that fall under this rubric. **Table 1** lists the major types of these cases and the following case examples illustrate each.

## Malpractice

Negligence law allows plaintiffs to recover damages where it can be shown that a caregiver, e.g., mental health clinician, breached the standard of care to a patient and that breach (an act of omission or commission) can be shown to be a proximate cause of the suicide of a patient in the care of that clinician.

### Case Illustration

A 37-year-old male was hospitalized briefly for a suicide attempt. One month later his behavior became erratic and threatening. After his wife moved out and threatened divorce, he drank heavily, wrote a suicide note, and ingested a large quantity of over-the-counter sleeping pills. Observed by neighbors rolling around in the gravel in front of his house, he was transported by rescue personnel to a local hospital where his stomach was pumped; he was then admitted against his will to a psychiatric unit. At intake he was evaluated as both homicidal and suicidal. A psychological evaluation assessed him as impulsive but unlikely to be suicidal in the future. After 6 weeks of hospitalization he was discharged with a week's supply of lithium carbonate and an outpatient referral "as needed." Hospital records indicated that at discharge his lithium was below therapeutic levels in his blood. He neither made an outpatient appointment nor refilled his prescribed medication. Two weeks after discharge he assaulted his wife with a hammer, hitting her several times on the head, and tried to strangle her. He then killed himself with a shotgun blast to the chest with a gun he had bought the previous day.

The inpatient facility was sued for improper assessment of suicide risk, improper discharge, inadequate attention to his continuity of care, and a host of other alleged breaches of the standard of care.

## Institutional Care

Jails and prisons have custodial responsibilities for those sentenced to and housed by them. With regard to suicide risk, these institutions have responsibility to assess that risk and take preventive precautions against suicide. When a notably agitated and depressed inmate is either not noticed and evaluated and placed in position to be monitored, or transferred for mental health care, and a suicide results, the institution may be sued by the inmate's estate.

## Product Manufacturer's Liability

Those who produce products for human use have a responsibility to ensure the safety of that product and its user. Since the publication of anecdotal reports of suicides related to selective serotonin reuptake inhibitors (SSRIs) and the subsequent governmental investigations into the safety of these medications, particularly with children and adolescents in both the UK and the USA, suits alleging that these medications have caused suicides among those who have taken them have proliferated. Because those who were prescribed these medications were depressed and possibly suicidal before and, indeed, that this was the reason for them taking these medications, there is a need for intensive investigation to help the court determine causation. Similarly, those who provide services attendant to a product have equal responsibility to ensure that those services are performed in a safe manner.

## Workers' Compensation

Similarly, employers have a responsibility to provide safe working conditions. Workers' compensation laws in the USA provide for the care and support of employees injured on the job. Unsafe job conditions that lead to injuries which, in turn, produce mental distress and subsequent suicide can be shown to be proximate causes of that suicide. Psychological autopsies have been used, and allowed into court, to help determine pathways to suicide, thus proximate causation.

### Case Illustration

A lifelong employee of the railroad injured his back when attempting to pick up a greasy steel coupling. Months of unremitting pain ensued. Unable to resume the work he loved, the engineer became despondent and soon resumed an earlier habit of alcohol abuse. With no hope of ever being able to return to work, he shot himself in the head during a night of binge drinking. His wife sued the railroad for not ensuring safe working conditions, specifying federal regulations requiring no greasy couplings at a job site.

## Life Insurance Cases

Life insurance companies make actuarial bets. As suicide is viewed as an intentional act, an applicant for insurance who may see more value to his/her family in death than in life might take out a life insurance policy with intent to defraud, then complete suicide. To hedge that bet, life insurance contracts typically include a clause that denies payment of benefits if a suicide occurs within 2 years of the date a policy goes into effect. If denied benefits, the insured's beneficiaries may take the insurance company to court to recover denied benefits. As an affirmative defense, the burden of proof rests with the insurance company to prove that the death was a suicide. In the USA, the majority of states have some sort of presumption of law against suicide when the manner of death is equivocal. As the medical examiner or coroner's certification of death is based on opinion, it is not considered legal proof of how a person died. Thus, an opinion regarding the state of mind of the decedent derived from a psychological autopsy and reliant on operational criteria for classifying suicide has equal weight in court.

### Case Illustration

The decedent was found in the closed trunk of a burning car; the body was bound at the ankles and thighs and had jumper cables tightly wrapped twice around his neck. The medical examiner initially determined the cause of death to be strangulation by ligature and the manner of death as homicide. However, as no evidence of trauma to the hyoid bone was found, as would have been expected if sufficient force to cause strangulation were used, the cause of death was amended on the death certificate to strangulation with diffuse thermal burns as a contributing cause; the manner of death was changed to undetermined.

Because life insurance in the amount of US$700 000 was placed less than 2 months before his death and because the decedent had allegedly misrepresented his income on his application, the insurance company denied his widow the insurance policy's benefits.

An independent forensic pathologist opined that the decedent was alive at the time the fire started, that his arms and hands were not bound, and that matches found under his body in the trunk of the car were used to start the fire and disguise his death as a homicide.

Early on the day of his death the decedent told his wife he had a business meeting with some Syrian businessmen with whom he was working on a "million-dollar deal – a deal of a lifetime." He further said to her that he had been suspicious of the source of their money and planned to confront them at this meeting.

A psychological autopsy requested by the insurance company found:

- The decedent had been under severe financial duress, and owed more than $100 000 to his credit card company.
- His marriage was in difficulty. The couple had vacationed separately, slept in separate beds, and did not socialize together.
- He was reported to have been drinking heavily.
- Although generally secretive by nature, in the days before his death he had specifically and uncharacteristically mentioned the name of the alleged Syrian company as his new client. No record of this named company could be found.
- There was no evidence of defensive wounds to the hands, as would have been expected had he been attacked; his vehicle was parked so as to invite discovery.

The psychological autopsy concluded that his death was a suicide and that the primary motive was shame over his inability to support his family financially.

## Criminal Cases

In criminal cases psychological autopsies have been admitted in US courts to help juries decide whether a parent should be held responsible for the suicide of a child (*Jackson v. State*, 553 So.2d 719 (Fla.App. 4 Dist. 1989)) and whether a decedent died by her own hand or at the hand of her husband (*State v. Guthrie*, 627 N.W.2d 401, 2001 SD 61 (S.D. 2001)).

### Case Illustration

In the Guthrie case, the wife of a Presbyterian minister was found naked and unconscious in her bathtub. Efforts to resuscitate her failed and she died, never recovering any brain function. At autopsy, gastric and blood serum toxicology confirmed the presence of subtherapeutic levels of two antianxiety agents and a toxic and debilitating level of temazepam, but not a fatal overdose. The forensic pathologist ruled that she could not have taken that amount of medication by accident; however, the autopsy alone could not resolve whether her death was a suicide or homicide.

A psychological autopsy ascertained that she had no history of mental illness, depression, significant physical illness, chemical dependency, or suicidal ideation or behavior. Nor was there any history of suicidal behavior in her family. On the other hand, Ms. Guthrie had known for more than a year that her husband was having an affair and that he had plans to divorce her. Although heightening possible motivation for suicide, this knowledge was not learned proximate to her death. Contraindicating her risk for suicide were the following findings:

- She was excited about her daughter's upcoming wedding.
- She was self-conscious about her weight and would not have wanted to be found naked.
- The prevalence of suicidal drowning in a bathtub in the USA is less than 2%; she was found face-down, while those who commit suicide are generally found face-up, lying back in the water as if to sleep.

On the basis of this testimony and other evidence, the court found Guthrie guilty of homicide, a conviction that was upheld upon appeal to the state's supreme court.

## The Daubert Standard

In spite of advantages offered to the coroner or medical examiner and the courts, the psychological autopsy has some weaknesses. First, clearly the decedent is not available for observation or questioning, making this type of evaluation different and more complicated than most evaluations conducted by mental health professionals. In addition, in its forensic use,

the contractor for the psychological autopsy has a stake in the outcome of its findings, thus the information gathered from these sources can be biased. Moreover, to date there is no standardized protocol and method of conducting the psychological autopsy, thus raising questions about the procedure's validity and reliability.

This last difficulty poses significant problems in the American courts where it may be deemed inadmissible by court standards using the Federal Rules of Evidence. Admissibility of psychological autopsies has been questioned under the Daubert standard of evidence. The Daubert standard of evidence is derived from the Supreme Court decision, *Daubert v. Merrell Dow Pharmaceuticals, Inc.* (1993). This case essentially stated that the Federal Rules of Evidence, Rule 702 (2001), superseded the Frye test, which relied upon the evidence being based on a well-recognized scientific principle and subject to a standard of "general acceptance" by the relevant scientific community. Not all US states have accepted Daubert as a replacement standard (*Grady and Grady v. Frito-Lay, Inc.*, no. 43 WAP 2002, Pa. Sup.; 2003 Pa LEXIS 25); however, Daubert both incorporates the Frye test's criterion of general acceptance and extends it by establishing criteria that evidence must be "founded on scientific knowledge." The courts found in Daubert that "founded on scientific knowledge" meant that the testimony must be grounded in the methods and procedures of science and possess scientific validity to establish evidentiary reliability. The court listed four additional factors to be used as guidelines for admissibility, leaving the judge to be the final "gate-keeper" in deciding the admissibility of expert testimony. These factors are:

1. whether the theories and techniques employed by the witness have been tested
2. whether they have been subjected to peer review and publication
3. whether the techniques employed have a known error rate
4. whether they are subject to standards governing their application.

While the Daubert standard is based on a US Supreme Court decision and, therefore, has its most immediate impact limited to US federal courts, it provides the most rigorous and sensible guidelines for admissibility to date.

## Intention

The primary criteria for suicide involve evidence that the death resulted from a self-inflicted act and intention. "Intention" means to "have in mind" that death, as we know it to be the cessation of consciousness, will result. Thus, intention refers to the aim, purpose, or goal of the behavior, e.g., to seek an end to/solution for unbearable/perceived unsolvable pain/problems of living.

In equivocal cases, factors descriptive of high intentionality (Table 2) are conscious awareness of consequences; goal of cessation; expectation of fatal outcome; implementation of a method of high lethality; minimal rescuability or precautions; premeditation; and communications. Where evidence exists for one or more of these factors, the probability of suicide increases.

As noted above, a large body of archived data (death scene descriptions, police reports, laboratory data, medical and mental health records, and criminal records) must be reviewed in conjunction with interviews with relevant observers and witnesses to derive sufficient information from which an opinion regarding the decedent's intent to suicide can be formed. The behavioral investigator must weigh such data relative to what is known about suicide (versus, for example, accidental death). Where it can be shown that the decedent had sufficient risk factors and state-of-mind evidence to describe an intent to die, then suicide would be determined as the manner of death. Where data and observations are sufficiently more persuasive to determine that intent to suicide was not present or could not be formed, e.g., because of alcohol or drug intoxication, then the manner of death would be determined to be accident. Needless to say, the behavioral investigator needs to be expert at and current in his/her knowledge of suicide risk factors to arrive at a reasonable opinion as to manner of death.

**Table 2** Factors descriptive of high intentionality

- Conscious awareness of consequences: decedent was aware that an end to earthly existence would result from a self-inflicted, self-destructive act
- Goal: to seek death (as in cessation) as an alternative to a life of perceived, unremitting pain
- Expectancy: of a fatal outcome from self-inflicted action
- Implementation: lethality of method is known to be high; knowledge of method
- Rescuability: timing and location are chosen so as to prevent, thwart, or minimize the possibility of rescue or intervention. No attempt at self-rescue or help-seeking is evident after initiation of attempt
- Planning: premeditation is evident through evidence of active preparation, e.g., hoarding pills, purchase of weapon
- Communications: direct, overt communications of intent are made prior to action

## The Autopsy Protocol

To date, a standardized protocol for conducting the psychological autopsy has not been published. Different researchers, clinicians, and forensic suicidologists have used similar protocols, but with different foci and length. This author has recently proposed such a standard protocol and argued for its common usage and adoption by those in forensic cases to aid in establishing better psychometric properties, notably the reliability and validity of this procedure. The proposed protocol is offered in **Table 3**.

Typically, the information sought through such a protocol is achieved through face-to-face interviews. These may be supplemented, where appropriate, by suicide assessment measures and scales. The overwhelming majority of these instruments were validated as self-report or interviewer-administered scales, all with living persons. Some have been adapted for use with family members of suicide decedents, especially those regarding children and adolescents.

It should be noted that some survivor informants, e.g., minors and the sick elderly, pose special challenges as interviewees. Clearly, minors need parental consent to be an informant. At times, surviving parents withhold such consent, alleging that their child would be adversely affected, i.e., emotionally distressed, by such an interview. A sick elderly interviewee may require family assistance in order to participate and may require special arrangements to facilitate an interview (e.g., multiple short interview sessions). Each potential interviewee should provide informed consent after reasonable discussion of the potential risks and benefits to their participation.

## Conclusion

The psychological autopsy is a powerful tool for the skilled suicidologist. It cannot definitively define cause-and-effect relationships, thus it cannot validly inform an expert that a suicide definitely occurred; rather, it can better inform opinions as to whether a decedent likely completed suicide and provide a better understanding of pathways to the determined manner of death. As such, it informs coroners and medical examiners and the courts which are ultimately the decision-makers.

Information derived from psychological autopsies will necessarily be incomplete and the totality of data sources may serve to create a mosaic that is more impressionistic than factual. The light it shines on its subject is often filtered by the prismatic lenses of many observers. Nevertheless, it illuminates. As an intensive single-case research procedure, the

**Table 3** A psychological autopsy protocol

### Recommended documentation/archival records
- Medical records
- Police records
- Legal records
- Criminal records
- School records
- Financial records
- Suicide note or other documented communication (re: suicidal ideation or death wish)
- Military records
- Autopsy report
  - toxicology report, if available

### Site of death
- Decedent's relationship to site
- Evidence of rescuability vs. precautions against rescuability
- Evidence of planning and/or rehearsal

### Demographics
- Immigrant status
  - acculturation issues
- Residence relative to recent mobility
- Socioeconomic status
- Employment and financial status
- Age/gender/race
- Marital status
- Educational status
- Religion and religiosity
- Adopted vs. biological family status

### Recent symptoms/behaviors
- Appeared depressed, sad, tearful, or moody
- Displayed symptoms of depression
- Expressed suicidal ideation or thoughts of death or dying
- Appeared to have made a change for the better
- Appeared anxious, or complained recently of anxiety or panic attacks
- Appeared agitated
- Behaved in an impulsive manner
- Displayed uncontrolled rage or aggressive behavior
- Demonstrated constricted thinking or "tunnel vision"
- Disclosed feelings of guilt or shame
- Appeared confused, disoriented, or psychotic?
- Expressed feelings of hopelessness, helplessness, or worthlessness?
- Mental status: evidence of:
  - impaired memory?
  - poor comprehension
  - poor judgment
  - hallucinations or delusions?
- Showed an inflated sense of self or signs of magical thinking?
- Engaged in excessive risk-taking behaviors?

### Precipitants to the death
- Had the decedent recently experienced or was the decedent anticipating:
  - Significant loss or losses (relationships, job, finances, prestige, self-concept, family member, moving, anything of importance to the person)?
  - Significant (or perceived significant) disruption of a primary relationship?
  - Legal troubles or difficulties with police?
  - An event which was or was perceived as traumatic
  - Significant life changes? (negative as well as positive, e.g., marriage, birth of child, promotion, etc.)
  - The completed suicide or suicidal behavior of a family member or loved one?

**Table 3** Continued

- The anniversary of an important death, an important other loss, or another significant anniversary?
- Exposure to the suicide of another through the media or personal acquaintance?
- His/her death as evidenced by recently making preparations for death? (e.g., updating will, insurance policies, etc.)
- An expressed wish to reunite with a deceased loved one or to be reborn?

### Psychiatric history
- Of prior suicidal behaviors
- Of any prescribed psychotropic medications for anxiety, depression, or psychosis
- Of ever being hospitalized in a psychiatric setting? Where? When? Diagnosis?
- Of having seen a therapist or psychiatrist/pharmacologist (or other, e.g., PCP) in recent past
  - of being in therapy at the time of death. (If so, duration, quality of therapeutic alliance and compliance with treatment, diagnosis, etc.)
- Of ever expressing concerns about "going crazy" or of losing cognitive functioning

### Physical health
- Recent visit to physician (note for what)
- Experiencing chronic pain
- Recent or past diagnosis or concerns re: chronic, fatal, or disabling disease
- Recent reduction in physical/functional capabilities
- Current medications; if so, compliance, recent changes in dosage or prescription

### Substance abuse
- History of alcohol or drug abuse
- Recent attempts to discontinue alcohol or drug abuse; recent increase in pattern of abuse
- Degree of alcohol or drug use at time of death; evidence of binge drinking?
- Patterns of poly-substance abuse
- History of "accidental overdose"; if so, when?, what drug?

### Family history
- Sibling or parent who died a nonnatural death
- Level of support or observed closeness in nuclear and extended families
- Of significant physical, sexual, or emotional abuse
- Of substance abuse
- Of suicide
- Of violent behavior
- Of affective disorder or other mental health disorders in the family

### Firearm history
- Of firearm ownership
- Recently purchase or otherwise obtaining a weapon?; if so, for what stated purpose?
- Care for weapons; What was the characteristic pattern of cleaning guns?
- Storage patterns for weapon(s)
- Of accidental discharge of firearm

### Attachments/social supports
- Ability to create and maintain close personal relationships? Have a close confidante
- Ability to express feeling as needed (especially grief and anger) in relationships
- Recent talk about feeling unsupported, uncared for, not important in relationships

**Table 3** Continued

- Relative success in:
  - personal relationships
  - work
- Attachment to hobbies, interests, religion, etc.
- Recent change in any relationship to the above attachments

**Emotional reactivity**
- History of violence toward others
- Impulsive behaviors
- Excessive rage or other uncontrolled, aggressive behavior

**Lifestyle/character**
- Typical coping patterns
- Perfectionism
- Self-destructive behaviors (such as self-mutilation, drinking/ driving, etc.)
- Frequent crises, often those appearing self-created
- Victimization behaviors, e.g., bullied

**Access to care**
- History of help-seeking behavior
- Known barriers to healthcare (e.g., lack of insurance, no accessible caregiver)

**Other areas of inquiry**
- Occupational history
- Hobbies/interests
- Gambling history
- Degree of religiosity

psychological autopsy significantly improves manner of death determinations and offers clues to understand better the state of mind of those who complete suicide.

## See Also

**Crime-scene Investigation and Examination:** Death-scene Investigation, United States of America; Suspicious Deaths; **Deliberate Self-Harm, Patterns**; **Expert Witness:** Daubert and Beyond; **Forensic Psychiatry and Forensic Psychology:** Assessment; Suicide Predictors and Statistics; **Medical Malpractice:** Psychiatry

## Further Reading

Berman AL (1993) Forensic suicidology and the psychological autopsy. In: Leenaars AA, Berman AL, Cantor P, Litman RE, Maris RW (eds.) *Suicidology: Essays in Honor of Edwin Shneidman*, pp. 248–266. Northvale, NJ: Jason Aronson.

Brown GK (2003) A review of suicide assessment measures for intervention research with adults and older adults. Available at: Browng@landru.cpr.upenn.edu.

Cavanagh JTO, Carson AJ, Sharpe M, Lawrie SM (2003) Psychological autopsy studies of suicide: a systematic review. *Psychological Medicine* 33: 395–405.

Daubert *v.* Merrell Dow Pharmaceuticals, Inc., 509 US 579 (1993).

Federal Rules of Evidence, as amended, 28 U.S.C., Rule 702 (2001).

Gelles MG (1995) The psychological autopsy: an investigative aid. In: Kurke MI, Scrivner EM (eds.) *Police Psychology into the 21st century*, pp. 337–355. Hillsdale, NJ: Erlbaum.

Gelles MG, Ritchie EC (2002) Psychological autopsies: the current department of defense effort to standardize training and quality assistance. *Journal of Forensic Sciences* 47: 1370–1373.

Goldston DB (2003) *Measuring Suicidal Behavior and Risk in Children and Adolescents*. Washington, DC: American Psychological Association.

Jobes DA, Berman AL, Josselson AR (1986) The impact of psychological autopsies on medical examiners' determination of manner of death. *Journal of Forensic Sciences* 31: 177–189.

Litman RE (1980) Psychological aspects of suicide. In: Curran W, McGarry A, Petty C (eds.) *Modern Legal Medicine*, pp. 841–853. Philadelphia, PA: FA Davis.

Litman RE, Curphey T, Shneidman ES, Fraberow NL, Tabachnick N (1963) Investigations of equivocal suicides. *Journal of the American Medical Association* 184: 924–929.

Rosenberg ML, Davidson LE, Smith JC, *et al.* (1989) Operational criteria for the classification of suicide. *Journal of Forensic Sciences* 33: 1445–1456.

Shneidman ES (1981) The psychological autopsy. *Suicide and Life-Threatening Behavior* 11: 325–340.

Shneidman ES, Farberow NL (1961) Sample investigation of equivocal suicide deaths. In: Farberow N, Shneidman E (eds.) *The Cry for Help*, pp. 118–128. New York: McGraw Hill.

Snider JE, Hane S, Berman AL (submitted for publication) Research note: standardizing the psychological autopsy: addressing the Daubert standard.

Weisman AD, Kastenbaum R (1968) *The Psychological Autopsy: A Study of the Terminal Phase of Life*. Monograph series 4. New York: Community Mental Health Journal.

# Forensic Interviewing

**R P Fisher**, Florida International University, North Miami, FL, USA
**N Schreiber**, University of Miami, Miami, FL, USA

## Introduction

The principal determinant of whether a criminal case is solved is the completeness and accuracy of an eye-witness's account. Whether or not witnesses can provide complete and accurate reports is partially determined by factors not under the legal system's control, such as the viewing conditions at the scene of the crime or the witness's memory and verbal skills. The focus here is on that part of the investigative process that the legal system can control, namely, how they interview witnesses.

## Scientific Research on Interviewing

Prior to 1980 little scientific, experimental research had been conducted on the psychological processes underlying witness recollection. There were many demonstrations that witnesses misidentified innocent suspects or that witnesses incorrectly described the central elements of a crime (perpetrators, weapons, actions). However, little experimental research had been done to examine the causes of these errors, and more important, what can be done to improve witness recollection.

The two primary goals of a forensic interview with a cooperative witness are: (1) to elicit accurate recollections; and (2) to elicit extensive, detailed recollections. What are the psychological principles underlying accuracy and quantity of memory, and how can these principles be translated into effective interviewing techniques?

### Accuracy of Witness Recollection

Although people may occasionally misperceive events, generally our perceptions of the external world are accurate. Therefore, if witnesses are encouraged to describe their perceptions naturally, and to volunteer only those recollections they are certain of, their testimony is likely to be accurate. Unfortunately, various factors inherent in forensic interviews conspire against such pure recollections. First, in response to open-ended questions (e.g., What did the robber look like?), witnesses, and especially young children, often provide short and incomplete answers. Second, witness narratives frequently wander off track into forensically irrelevant topics. In an effort to elicit more informative answers, interviewers ask many specific, closed-ended questions (e.g., How tall was the robber?). The drawback of asking closed-ended questions is that they elicit less accurate responses, as they entice witnesses to volunteer answers that they are not certain of. Forensic interviewers should therefore try to elicit information mainly through the use of open-ended questions. They should explicitly instruct witnesses not to guess, but rather to indicate, "I don't know." This is particularly important when interviewing young children, who might otherwise be motivated to provide answers, whether certain or not, simply to comply with their expected social role of answering questions. In reality,

police interviewers rarely caution witnesses against guessing. If anything, just the opposite occurs when interviewers subtly reinforce or praise witnesses for volunteering answers (e.g., "You seem to remember a lot about the crime") or when interviewers utter the innocent comment, "good," after witnesses provide information. In their zeal to elicit complete, detailed responses, forensic interviewers may create a more serious problem of encouraging witnesses to fabricate incorrect memories.

Another potential threat to accuracy is that memories are sometimes constructed from knowledge sources other than the crime itself. That is, witnesses take in or encode information about a crime from a variety of sources, including conversations with other witnesses, the media, or even the interviewer him/herself. Witnesses may then incorporate these other sources of information into their memories of the crime, and then later forget where they acquired this information or incorrectly remember the source of information (known as "source-monitoring" errors). Interviewers should therefore be careful not to make suggestive comments or to convey their personal beliefs about how the crime was committed.

Well-trained interviewers are unlikely flagrantly to express their personal beliefs to witnesses consciously; however, they may subtly convey their beliefs unconsciously. For instance, in attempting to verify their hunch about the crime, police interviewers may subtly suggest the anticipated answer in the form of a suggestive question: Was it a red shirt? Respondents are sensitive to such implicit suggestions – after all, the police officer is an authority figure and may have knowledge of what transpired during the crime. This inferred belief may then be incorporated into the witness's later memory of the crime.

Of greater practical concern than police interviewers distorting witness recollections is the potential influence of nonpolice interviewers, who may have vested interests in witness recollections being slanted one way or another. For instance, defense attorneys are more successful when prosecution witnesses express doubt or remember the crime in a way that makes the defendant appear not culpable. Just the opposite, prosecutors benefit when witnesses express their memories confidently and remember the crime in a way that makes the defendant more palpably culpable. Clinical psychologists may have a completely different bias. Their main concern is the therapeutic value of the interview, and so they may be more interested in their client's "remembering" an event in a way that leads to a favorable therapeutic outcome, irrespective of its historical accuracy. Certainly, one is not charging any profession with intentionally distorting memories through poor interviewing practices. Nevertheless the potential exists, and in fact, guided distortions of the truth are not rarities among forensic interviews.

### Amount of Witness Recollection

Ideally, witness recollection will not only be accurate, but will also contain extensive information. Fortunately, recent theoretical advances in social and cognitive psychology have given rise to innovative interviewing techniques to increase the amount of information that witnesses recall. The interview process can be divided into three psychological processes: (1) social dynamics; (2) cognition; and (3) communication. For the interview to proceed effectively:

1. Both the witness and the interviewer must establish the proper social dynamics, with each person knowing and playing his or her role in the exchange of ideas.
2. The thought processes of both the witness and the interviewer must be efficient so that the witness can remember the details of the event and the interviewer can ask questions properly and keep track of the witness's description.
3. Both the witness and the interviewer must communicate their thoughts to each other. Witnesses must communicate their memories of the crime to the interviewer, and interviewers must communicate their investigative needs to the witness.

A thumbnail sketch of some of the basic concepts is presented here.

**Social dynamics**    Police interview witnesses because they possess some information about the crime event that police do not know. In conversations between a curious person (police) and an expert (witness), the expert normally does most of the talking, while the curious person takes a more passive role, absorbing the expert's knowledge. In many police interviews, however, this norm is violated, with the police officer playing the dominant role and relegating the witness to a passive role. As a result of having been forced into this passive role, witnesses often generate relatively little information and respond with only brief answers – even though they possess extensive, relevant information. To inculcate the proper social dynamics, the police interviewer should: (1) state explicitly to the witness what are the expected social roles; (2) ask primarily open-ended questions; and (3) not interrupt witnesses before they have completed their answers. Unfortunately, recent studies examining police interviews with victims and witnesses show that interviewers violate all three of these recommendations. They rarely explain the proper social roles; they ask very few open-ended questions (almost all of their questions are closed-ended); and they frequently interrupt witnesses in the middle of their answers.

Because of the emotional and personal nature of many forensic investigations, interviewers should take time to develop a personal rapport with the witness, and especially when interviewing a victim. Police interviewers sometimes fail to develop this basic personal contact effectively, and as a consequence, victims do not feel comfortable divulging all of the details of emotionally charged and personal experiences.

Establishing a personal connection with the respondent is also important when interviewing suspects. Recent studies have shown that suspects are more likely to volunteer relevant information when they are treated respectfully, in a humane fashion, than when they are subjugated by a dominant interviewer who creates an adversarial relationship. This type of confrontational style, however, seems to be the most common approach to interviewing suspects.

**Cognition**    The mental tasks of both the witness and the interviewer are extremely challenging in a criminal interview. Witnesses are asked to remember complex events in great detail. Interviewers must keep track of and notate witnesses' descriptions, which are often disorganized, and formulate insightful questions instantaneously. Fortunately, considerable knowledge about witnesses' and interviewers' mental processes has been amassed by cognitive psychologists and can be applied to the task. Some of the major principles are as follows:

1. Context reinstatement. People's memories for earlier events can be enhanced by putting them back into the same physical, emotional, or mental context as when they experienced the original event. Instructing witnesses at the time of the interview to think about their thoughts or the external environment at the time of the crime should therefore facilitate memory for the crime. The tactic of returning to the scene of the crime works because of context reinstatement.
2. Limited mental resources. People have only a limited amount of mental resources to process information. Any distracting signals (e.g., noises in the environment, or even interviewers asking questions) may therefore deflect a witness's mental resources away from remembering the crime. Interviewers should attempt to maintain a quiet environment, and to ask as few questions

as possible. (Despite the beliefs of many investigators, the most successful interviewers are those who ask the fewest questions.) Interviewers also have limited mental resources, so that having to formulate many questions (rather than asking fewer, but open-ended questions) will impair their ability to understand a witness's narrative. Tape-recording the interview, which frees interviewers from having to take copious notes, should also allow interviewers to listen and create follow-up questions more effectively.

3. Witness-compatible questioning. Each witness's mental representation of the crime is unique. Similarly, witnesses' world knowledge (e.g., about cars) and interests (e.g., hairstyles) differ from one another. To capitalize on these individual differences, interviewers should tailor their questions to each specific witness, exploiting his or her unique strengths. This rule is often violated when interviewers use a standardized crime report sheet to guide the interview, asking all witnesses the same questions and in the same order.

**Communication**  Witnesses may have very good memories of the crime, but they may fail to communicate their knowledge effectively to the investigator. Some witnesses have difficulty because they are not verbally skillful – perhaps they are foreigners, or young children. Some events are difficult to describe because they are inherently nonverbal (e.g., the perpetrator's face). Interviewers can overcome these obstacles by encouraging witnesses to use nonverbal means to convey their knowledge, e.g., drawing a sketch of the crime scene or acting out an action sequence. Another communication problem is that witnesses sometimes withhold information because they do not realize it is forensically relevant. Similarly, witnesses describe events or objects only superficially even though they have detailed memories of the events, because they do not realize that investigators requires detailed descriptions. To overcome these communication problems, police interviewers need to convey their investigative needs clearly.

**Sequence of the interview**  In addition to the individual component techniques, the sequence of the interview is critical to its success. The same questions and instructions will be less valuable if conveyed in the wrong order. The recommended order of conducting the interview is to: (1) develop a good personal rapport with the witness, preview the interview procedure, and establish the proper social role for the witness (actively generate information); (2) elicit an open-ended, uninterrupted narrative of the entire crime event; (3) follow up with more focused questioning (open-ended questions followed by direct probes) of the most informative sections of the narrative; (4) tie up any "loose ends," e.g., additional isolated facts, and account for inconsistencies; (5) review the information gathered; and (6) close the interview in a way that promotes open communication for future contact between the witness and police. Flexibility in the sequence is desirable, as cases vary from one another, although such flexibility increases the difficulty of online decision-making by the investigator.

Several alternatives to the traditional police interview have developed over the past two decades employing some or many of the principles described above. Some of the best-known interviewing protocols are the stepwise method, conversation management, the memorandum of good practice, and the cognitive interview. Excellent reviews of most of these procedures can be found in several sources, listed in Further Reading.

## Scientific Testing: How Do We Know the Techniques Work?

Before adopting any interviewing techniques, there should be some objective evidence that they accomplish their goals. In order to determine objectively whether the aforementioned techniques work, scientists in the USA, Canada, the UK, Germany, and Spain have tested various interviewing procedures under tightly controlled laboratory conditions. In addition, field tests have been done with victims and witnesses of real crime. We summarize here the research to test the cognitive interview procedure, mainly because: (1) it includes most of the techniques described here; and (2) the research is extensive (over 70 published experiments) and has been conducted by a wide variety of researchers.

In typical laboratory studies, volunteer witnesses see a videotape of a simulated crime and then are interviewed about the crime details by someone who has been trained either to use the principles earlier described (cognitive interview) or to conduct a conventional police interview. The witnesses' recollections are tape-recorded and scored for amount recalled and accuracy. The results are stable and show that the cognitive interview elicits 40% more correct information than does the control-comparison interview. The accuracy rates are approximately the same, with only a small advantage for the cognitive interview. Two field studies, with real victims and witnesses of crime, were conducted in the USA and the UK and found similar results. That is, police officers trained to use the cognitive interview elicited considerably more information from victims and witnesses than equally experienced police conducting conventional police interviews. We cannot know in real crimes whether witness recollections are accurate, because we do not know for certain what transpired in the crime. (That is one of the major advantages of conducting laboratory research.) The best estimate of recollection accuracy (based on corroborating testimony from other witnesses) suggests that the cognitive interview yields about the same or slightly more accurate responses than do conventional police interviews. We, therefore, have good reason to believe that the recommended techniques work to elicit considerably more extensive, and slightly more accurate, witness testimony.

There are no apparent costs of using the recommended techniques in terms of the quality and amount of information elicited. There may, however, be a practical cost. Specifically, more time is required to implement these procedures than to conduct a traditional police interview (using many specific, closed-ended questions). British police have commented that they often do not have adequate time to implement all of the component techniques. This is particularly true for the first police officer to respond after the crime. To remedy this situation, current research is being conducted: (1) to determine which of the techniques is most efficient; and (2) to develop a shorter version of the procedure.

## Training Interviewers

How effectively police investigators learn to use proper interviewing techniques depends on the quality of the training they receive. Within the laboratory, some researchers have had remarkably greater success than others in training interviewers. The keys to training are to: (1) use a building-blocks approach, where the core techniques (e.g., asking open-ended questions) are taught first, and more refined techniques added later; (2) schedule the training over an extended period of time, so that learners are not overwhelmed with having to learn many techniques all at once; (3) provide extensive practice opportunities in controlled environments (e.g., role-playing exercises); and (4) provide constructive feedback on the interviewers' performance.

Although scientifically based advances in interviewing have been available for the past 20 or 30 years, they have only recently been incorporated systematically into police training and only in a few countries around the world. The most progressive training programs are to be found in Europe (UK, Sweden, Norway, Germany, the Netherlands) and Australia. Progress has been much slower in North America, although a recent publication by the US Department of Justice Technical Working Group for Eyewitness Evidence may speed up the learning process.

## Interviewing Children

With an increased awareness of child abuse, many legal investigators and research psychologists have become more interested in the skill of interviewing children. Much of the research was motivated by the highly publicized cases of the 1980s in which preschoolers falsely accused their day-care teachers of having sexually abused children. Many of the claims were originally taken at face value. Later investigations, however, found that some of these allegations were false. Of greater concern is that these false allegations may have been promoted by poor interviewing techniques. Some of the questionable interviewing techniques included promising children rewards for making specific statements, informing children about other witnesses' statements, and asking children to speculate about events in question. Other problematic interviewing techniques used in these and other investigations include investigators conveying their preinterview biases to the children, and asking the same questions repeatedly, even after the child has answered the question. Finally, there is a common error of asking children very specific closed-ended suggestive questions. Many of these questioning procedures are problematic when interviewing adults. They are even more problematic when interviewing children, and especially young children, whose testimony is even more malleable. In light of this, more agencies throughout the world have been recording and monitoring child interviews and providing more specialized training for investigators who conduct child interviews.

When interviewed properly, children of all ages can provide useful and accurate information. Based on the extensive research done with child witnesses, many researchers and child protection agencies recommend the following interviewing tactics: (1) developing extensive rapport at the beginning of the interview; (2) asking open-ended questions; (3) adapting the language and questioning style for different age groups; (4) avoiding suggestive questions; and (5) avoiding complex questions. A particularly sensitive area of child interviewing for which guidelines have been developed is how to introduce the topic of the investigation (e.g., alleged incident of abuse) but without using suggestive questions.

Young children who were allegedly sexually abused pose a unique dilemma for interviewers, because of children's limited vocabulary and knowledge about sexual activities and body parts. Some authorities have suggested using anatomically correct dolls to help overcome these limitations. If the dolls are used suggestively, however, that may encourage young children to fabricate sexual events. There is not a strong consensus on the use of these dolls, although most researchers agree that, if an interviewer does use these dolls, the interviewer must first receive a narrative statement on the event in question, i.e., anatomically correct dolls should be used only to clarify parts of a witness' statement made previously. Second, the interviewer must exercise extreme caution to avoid any hint of suggestion.

## Exotic Interviewing Techniques: Hypnosis

Given the difficulty of eliciting extensive, detailed recollections from witnesses when using traditional interviewing methods, some have turned to exotic techniques, such as hypnosis, to assist witness memory. Although, periodically, one hears about breakthroughs in police investigations following a hypnotic witness interview, the research is not nearly so sanguine about the value of hypnosis. First, many people cannot be hypnotized, and even among people who can be hypnotized, many cannot be hypnotized to a deep level. Second, the research on hypnosis shows that it does not work reliably. As many laboratory studies show that it does not enhance memory as studies show that it does enhance memory. Third, and of greater concern, there are important costs associated with hypnotically refreshed memory. Specifically, under laboratory testing, hypnotized witnesses: (1) produce more fabricated recollections than those who are not hypnotized; (2) are more influenced by interviewers' misleading comments and questions than are nonhypnotized witnesses; and (3) are more confident in the accuracy of their recollections than are nonhypnotized witnesses – even when their recollections are false. As a result of these potential costs, hypnosis is often proscribed as an interviewing procedure in many jurisdictions, although note that several countries do permit hypnotically refreshed witness recollections.

## Detecting Deception

When people report about criminal events, there is sometimes the concern that they may be deceptive.

Interviewers therefore attempt to distinguish between truthful and false witnesses. Among many different qualitative approaches, the only approach to assess witness credibility that has been tested empirically is the so-called Criteria Based Content Analyses (CBCA), which is the core component of an elaborate credibility assessment system, Statement Validity Assessment (SVA). This approach is based on Undeutsch's hypothesis that true and false statements differ in quality and quantity and can therefore be distinguished. The SVA consists of three parts: (1) a structured witness interview; (2) an evaluation of the witness's statement according to CBCA criteria; and (3) a validity checklist incorporating information from the interview and the CBCA results. CBCA consists of 18 criteria, which are assumed to be present more often in accounts of true than false events. Examples of these criteria are whether the witness's statement was rich in details, whether it contained verbatim speech, and whether the witness questioned his or her own memory. Empirical research has found mixed results on the usefulness of the criteria, and moderating variables have yet to be fully explored. Although SVA has been recommended as the most useful tool in credibility assessment in some European legal settings, some researchers have expressed doubts concerning the validity of CBCA.

There is broad agreement that the usefulness of the CBCA criteria depends heavily on the way the witness's statement is elicited, and so SVA provides guidelines for conducting the interview. The CBCA criteria distinguish more effectively between true and false witness accounts when interviewers ask open-ended questions (to elicit more narrative responses) and refrain from using techniques to alter the witness's statement (e.g., suggestive questions).

## Interviewing Suspects

Following several recent cases in which high-profile defendants were released from custody because they provided false or coerced confessions, the UK reviewed its policies of interrogating suspects. Current practice has much more in common with interviewing cooperative witnesses, i.e., developing rapport and treating suspects in a humane fashion in an attempt to elicit voluntary information. Police practices in the USA are more traditional, with more psychological ploys to elicit confessions and fewer legal restraints against deceiving suspects. Although there is no universally accepted technique of interrogating suspects, many American police who receive interrogation training are encouraged to minimize the suspect's perceived consequences of confessing.

The interrogator may offer justifications or face-saving excuses for having committed the offense (e.g., she tempted you by being dressed so provocatively) or may suggest that the suspect did not realize the seriousness of the offense, or that the interrogator him/herself might have done the same thing in the situation. There has been little formal research to examine whether this minimization strategy accomplishes its goal, namely, to encourage guilty suspects to confess without promoting false confessions from innocent suspects. Unfortunately, the news from recent laboratory studies is discouraging, as the minimization strategy appears to promote false confessions along with true confessions. In one such study, volunteer participants were more likely to "confess" to cheating in an experiment (providing answers to another, confederate participant) when the interviewer used the minimization strategy than when the interviewer did not use the strategy. Admittedly, generalizing laboratory results to real-world interrogations is tenuous, because laboratory "crimes" and the consequences of laboratory crimes cannot be as severe as those occurring in the real world. That is, we cannot charge research volunteers with having committed serious legal infractions and threaten to detain them if they do not cooperate. Nevertheless, there are grounds for concern. Furthermore, we have good reason to believe that at least some real-world confessions were probably coerced by improper police interrogation practices. Certainly this deserves more research.

## Interviewing Techniques for Other Investigative Tasks

Although the focus here has been on police interviews of cooperative witnesses, there are many other forensic investigations that require eliciting information from people, e.g., internal affairs investigations, debriefing police (or military) after a critical event, war crimes investigations. On the surface, these tasks appear to be very different from interviews with cooperative witnesses. However, many of the described techniques should be equally effective with these tasks, and especially when there is a heavy component of memory and communication, as with debriefing police officers following a criminal investigation.

## See Also

Identification: Facial; **Injuries and Deaths During Police Operations:** Shootings During Police Stops and Arrests; Special Weapons and Training Teams; **Recovered Memory**; **War Crimes:** Pathological Investigation

## Further Reading

Ceci SJ, Bruck M (1995) *Jeopardy in the Courtroom: A Scientific Analysis of Children's Testimony.* Washington, DC: American Psychological Association.
Eisen JL, Quas JA, Goodman GS (2002) *Memory and Suggestibility in the Forensic Interview.* London: Lawrence Erlbaum.
Fisher RP, Geiselman RE (1992) *Memory-Enhancing Techniques in Investigative Interviewing: The Cognitive Interview.* Springfield, IL: CC Thomas.
Fisher RP, Geiselman RE, Raymond DS (1987) Critical analysis of police interviewing techniques. *Journal of Police Science and Administration* 15: 177–185.
Fisher RP, McCauley ML (1995) Information retrieval: interviewing witnesses. In: Brewer N, Wilson C (eds.) *Psychology and Policing*, pp. 81–99. Hillsdale, NJ: Erlbaum.
Flanagan EJ (1981) Interviewing and interrogation techniques. In: Grau J (ed.) *Criminal and Civil Investigation Handbook.* New York: McGraw-Hill.
George RC (1991) *A Field and Experimental Evaluation of the Three Methods Interviewing Witnesses/Victims of Crime.* Unpublished thesis, Polytechnic of East London.
Gudjonsson GH (2003) *The Psychology of Interrogations and Confessions.* New York: Wiley.
Inbau FE, Reid JE, Buckley JP, Jayne BC (2001) *Criminal Interrogation and Confessions*, 4th edn. Gaithersberg, ND: Aspen.
Memon A, Bull RA (1999) *Handbook of the Psychology of Interviewing.* Chichester, UK: Wiley.
*Memorandum of Good Practice on Video Recorded Interviews With Child Witnesses for Criminal Proceedings* (1992) London: Her Majesty's Stationery Office.
Milne R, Bull RA (1999) *Investigative Interviewing: Psychology and Practice.* Chichester, UK: Wiley.
Poole DA, Lamb ME (1998) *Investigative Interviews of Children: A Guide for Helping Professionals.* Washington, DC: American Psychological Association.
Technical Working Group for Eyewitness Evidence (1999) *Eyewitness Evidence: A Guide for Law Enforcement.* Washington, DC: United States Department of Justice, Office of Justice Programs.

# Suicide Predictors and Statistics

**A L Berman and C E Bergeron**, American
Association of Suicidology, Washington, DC, USA

## Introduction

The empirical study of suicide and suicidal behaviors provides the necessary data sets for the understanding of these multifaceted and complex phenomena. The limitations of these statistics and methods of data collection are reviewed first and then both an international and American snapshot of suicide, with particular reference to perpetuating and predisposing risk factors, are given. Finally the perspective toward understanding methods of suicide and how understanding both methods and risk leads to current best practice in suicide prevention are described.

## Limitations

Accurate data are essential for the understanding of suicidal phenomena, efforts to assess and treat those at risk for suicide and suicidal behaviors, and to develop public health prevention programs.

There are several limitations and problems inherent in collecting data on suicide. Suicide is a low base-rate event. In the USA it accounts for 30 000 deaths annually, a rate of 10–11/100 000. Thus, large-scale prospective studies of those at risk are rare given the need to follow inordinately large samples over time. Moreover, retrospective studies must rely on archival documents and third-party data sources, as the object of study is unavailable for interview.

The primary archival document, of course, is the death certificate, but this provides little more than basic demographic information about the decedent. Moreover, coroners, particularly in rural communities and when the death involves a child or a member of a prominent family, may conceal the true manner of death in an effort to spare the family from the stigma associated with suicide or to protect the reputation or memory of the deceased. There is no reliable estimate of how much underreporting of suicides occurs, but best estimates suggest it is in the range of 15–20%. Moreover, underreporting – if it is indeed more common in certain types of suicides, for example, in minority groups – may distort the demographic picture of suicide.

In addition, data sets in the USA have not been linked. Thus, it may be learnt from a study of death certificates that a large proportion of decedents died by a firearm, but specifics such as the type of firearm, its storage, purchase, and whether it was used as a murder weapon immediately before the suicide are not described on the death certificate. Co-occurring events such as homicide–suicides can only be determined by linking police investigation reports to each individual death certificate. This is only now being initiated on a large scale, but on a pilot basis, in the USA through the National Violent Death Reporting System.

One consequence of the difficulties in collecting data on completed suicides is that the overwhelming majority of understanding of suicide originates from studies of nonfatal attempters. After all, these individuals survive their attempt to die by suicide and remain available for interview. However, here also, significant problems are encountered in that only a fraction of nonfatal suicide attempters are comparable in their character to suicide completers. An individual may be a nonfatal suicide attempter because of: (1) miscalculation of the number of pills needed to accomplish death; (2) external intervention or thwarted attempt; or (3) feigning suicide to have interpersonal influence over another person, e.g., to induce guilt. Rarely do studies differentiate or report samples of attempters by level of lethality (medical–biological dangerousness) inherent in the method used and/or circumstances of a nonfatal attempt.

### Nomenclature Issues

Suicide and suicide behaviors reflect a range and variety of behaviors that are distinct from one another, yet overlap. Moreover, there are a number of self-harm behaviors that are not suicidal in intent, yet are self-destructive. For example, self-mutilators cut and/or burn themselves, but are not suicidal. Their intent is to feel pain or see blood. Their actions relieve tension or a dissociative state, or replace feelings of emptiness; the actor figuratively proclaims: "I bleed, therefore I am!" Rather than wanting to be dead, they feel more alive through these behaviors. At the same time, self-mutilators are at heightened risk for suicide. Suicidology's lack of a standardized nomenclature is referred to as a "tower of Babel."

### Data Sources

As noted above, death certificates serve as the primary data source for the study of suicide. In the USA, these are sent to a state's vital statistics office and, ultimately, to the National Center for Health Statistics, which publishes mortality data for the country. The epidemiology of a country's suicide mortality is thus derived from the quality and limitations of death certificates.

From these data certain retrospective surveys are also possible. A "follow-back study" is a variant on the more complex and thorough "psychological autopsy." In a follow-back study, one or two primary informants, typically a spouse or family member, is interviewed, often by phone, about the decedent, using a standardized interview protocol. Archival documents are not included in this form of survey. Case-control formats allow derived data to be compared with other manners of death (e.g., natural or accidental).

Given that more than 90% of completed suicides have retrospectively diagnosable mental disorders, hospital admission and treatment records serve as a significant source of valuable data about patients who commit suicide (or who are admitted for a nonfatal suicidal behavior). Again, case-control formats allow significant comparisons with other at-risk clinical populations who do not have suicidal behavior.

Since 1991, the US Centers for Disease Control and Prevention have conducted biannually large self-report surveys of adolescent risk behaviors including questions regarding suicide ideation and attempt. However, the Youth Risk Behavior Surveillance (YRBS) is only administered to enrolled high-school students, thus does not extract information on more at-risk nonstudents in this age group, e.g., dropouts. Nevertheless it provides a rich database of both the prevalence of and trends in the occurrence of these behaviors. It has also been shown that surveys taken with guaranteed anonymity produce higher rates of positive responses to sensitive questions than survey methods which are not anonymous. In addition, the terminology used in questions varies and determines different observed rates of positive response.

Case studies reflect the idiosyncrasies inherent in suicide. Such qualitative data allow for the development of new hypotheses and exploration of more indepth understandings of suicidal individuals than are possible from quantitative research. For example, the 1961 suicide of author Ernest Hemingway offers a rich portrait of the role that a family history of suicide and mental disorder plays (Hemingway's father, a brother, a sister, and, to date, one granddaughter have also committed suicide). Another example is the classic Egeland and Sussex's 1985 study of affective disorders and suicides, among an Amish community in Pennsylvania, which found that over a 100-year period (1880–1980), 24 of 26 suicides were diagnosed with a major affective disorder. Moreover, almost three-fourths of the suicides clustered in just four families, each of which was also heavily loaded with affective disorders.

Metaanalyses are difficult because samples and methodology vary widely among studies. For example,

Luoma and colleagues examined 40 international studies regarding contact with mental health and primary care providers before suicide. It was found that only one-third of suicides had contact with mental health professionals in the period before death. Similarly, primary care physicians saw more than twice as many suicidal individuals as did mental health care givers in the 30 days prior to death (45% versus 19%). Results such as these point to primary care providers as entry-point targets for prevention models designed to identify and assess suicidal individuals better.

Suicide is a multidimensional behavior, involving aspects such as psychiatric and psychological, biological (genetic and biochemical), sociological, philosophical, and theological. Each domain has its own discipline-specific methods of inquiry and experimental or qualitative methodology. All have contributed to the understanding of this complex phenomenon.

## The Epidemiology of Suicide

### International Statistics

The difficulties in studying suicide are nowhere more apparent than when attempting to study suicide on a worldwide level. It is tempting, for example, to compare countries with very low rates of suicide to those with the highest rates. However, each country has a different method of reporting mortality. Moreover, some have religious and cultural taboos against suicide (e.g., Egypt), making for high rates of reporting errors. In addition, changes made by the World Health Organization's (WHO) International Classification of Disease (ICD) system over the years make temporal comparisons more difficult. The WHO's published rates of suicide for males and females ostensibly allow global comparisons for the most recent available data (**Table 1**). Yet, these data only span from 1984 to 2001. Considering the range of sociocultural events and conditions that span these years, comparisons between and among countries become highly suspicious.

As depicted in **Figure 1**, very few data are available for Africa and some Middle-Eastern countries. Countries with high rates (top 10) are: Lithuania, Russian Federation, Belarus, Latvia, Ukraine, Sri Lanka, Slovenia, Hungary, Estonia, and Kazakhstan. Low-incidence countries include a number of South and Central American countries, Egypt, and Iran. The high rates among the former Soviet Republics have been attributed to their political – thus sociocultural and socioeconomic – instability and significant alcohol use.

As reported by the WHO (2001), the average suicide rate for 1996 of 53 countries was 15.1 per

**Table 1**  Suicide rates per 100 000 by country, year, and gender

| Country | Year | Males | Females |
|---|---|---|---|
| Albania | 2000 | 2.4 | 1.2 |
| Antigua and Barbuda | 1995 | 0.0 | 0.0 |
| Argentina | 1996 | 9.9 | 3.0 |
| Armenia | 2000 | 2.5 | 0.7 |
| Australia | 1999 | 21.2 | 5.1 |
| Austria | 2001 | 27.3 | 9.8 |
| Azerbaijan | 2000 | 1.2 | 0.4 |
| Bahamas | 1995 | 2.2 | 0.0 |
| Bahrain | 1988 | 4.9 | 0.5 |
| Barbados | 1995 | 9.6 | 3.7 |
| Belarus | 2000 | 63.6 | 9.5 |
| Belgium | 1996 | 29.4 | 10.7 |
| Belize | 1995 | 12.1 | 0.9 |
| Bosnia and Herzegovina | 1991 | 20.3 | 3.3 |
| Brazil | 1995 | 6.6 | 1.8 |
| Bulgaria | 2000 | 25.2 | 9.1 |
| Canada | 1998 | 19.5 | 5.1 |
| Chile | 1994 | 10.2 | 1.4 |
| China (selected rural and urban areas) | 1999 | 13.0 | 14.8 |
| China (Hong Kong SAR) | 1999 | 16.7 | 9.8 |
| Colombia | 1994 | 5.5 | 1.5 |
| Costa Rica | 1995 | 9.7 | 2.1 |
| Croatia | 2000 | 32.9 | 10.3 |
| Cuba | 1996 | 24.5 | 12.0 |
| Czech Republic | 2000 | 26.0 | 6.7 |
| Denmark | 1998 | 20.9 | 8.1 |
| Dominican Republic | 1994 | 0.0 | 0.0 |
| Ecuador | 1995 | 6.4 | 3.2 |
| Egypt | 1987 | 0.1 | 0.0 |
| El Salvador | 1993 | 10.4 | 5.5 |
| Estonia | 2000 | 45.8 | 11.9 |
| Finland | 2000 | 34.6 | 10.9 |
| France | 1999 | 26.1 | 9.4 |
| Georgia | 2000 | 4.8 | 1.2 |
| Germany | 1999 | 20.2 | 7.3 |
| Greece | 1999 | 5.7 | 1.6 |
| Guatemala | 1984 | 0.9 | 0.1 |
| Guyana | 1994 | 14.6 | 6.5 |
| Honduras | 1978 | 0.0 | 0.0 |
| Hungary | 2001 | 47.1 | 13.0 |
| Iceland | 1997 | 19.1 | 5.2 |
| India | 1998 | 12.2 | 9.1 |
| Iran | 1991 | 0.3 | 0.1 |
| Ireland | 1999 | 18.4 | 4.3 |
| Israel | 1997 | 10.5 | 2.6 |
| Italy | 1999 | 11.1 | 3.4 |
| Jamaica | 1985 | 0.5 | 0.2 |
| Japan | 1999 | 36.5 | 14.1 |
| Jordan | 1979 | 0.0 | 0.0 |
| Kazakhstan | 1999 | 46.4 | 8.6 |
| Kuwait | 2000 | 1.6 | 1.6 |
| Kyrgyzstan | 1999 | 19.3 | 4.0 |
| Latvia | 2000 | 56.6 | 11.9 |
| Lithuania | 2000 | 75.6 | 16.1 |
| Luxembourg | 2001 | 23.9 | 10.7 |
| Malta | 1999 | 11.7 | 2.6 |
| Mauritius | 1999 | 21.1 | 9.5 |
| Mexico | 1995 | 5.4 | 1.0 |
| Netherlands | 1999 | 13.0 | 6.3 |
| New Zealand | 1998 | 23.7 | 6.9 |

**Table 1**  Continued

| Country | Year | Males | Females |
|---|---|---|---|
| Nicaragua | 1994 | 4.7 | 2.2 |
| Norway | 1999 | 19.5 | 6.8 |
| Panama | 1987 | 5.6 | 1.9 |
| Paraguay | 1994 | 3.4 | 1.2 |
| Peru | 1989 | 0.6 | 0.4 |
| Philippines | 1993 | 2.5 | 1.7 |
| Poland | 2000 | 25.9 | 4.9 |
| Portugal | 2000 | 8.5 | 2.0 |
| Puerto Rico | 1992 | 16.0 | 1.9 |
| Republic of Korea | 2000 | 18.8 | 8.3 |
| Republic of Moldova | 2000 | 26.7 | 4.1 |
| Romania | 2001 | 20.8 | 3.9 |
| Russian Federation | 2000 | 70.6 | 11.9 |
| Saint Kitts and Nevis | 1995 | 0.0 | 0.0 |
| Saint Lucia | 1988 | 9.3 | 5.8 |
| Saint Vincent and the Grenadines | 1986 | 0.0 | 0.0 |
| Sao Tome and Principe | 1987 | 0.0 | 1.8 |
| Seychelles | 1987 | 9.1 | 0.0 |
| Singapore | 2000 | 12.5 | 6.4 |
| Slovakia | 2000 | 22.6 | 4.9 |
| Slovenia | 1999 | 47.3 | 13.4 |
| Spain | 1999 | 12.4 | 4.0 |
| Sir Lanka | 1991 | 44.6 | 16.8 |
| Suriname | 1992 | 16.6 | 7.2 |
| Sweden | 1999 | 19.7 | 8.0 |
| Switzerland | 1999 | 26.5 | 10.0 |
| Syrian Arab Republic | 1985 | 0.2 | 0.0 |
| Tajikistan | 1999 | 4.2 | 1.6 |
| Thailand | 1994 | 5.6 | 2.4 |
| Tfyr Macedonia | 2000 | 10.3 | 4.5 |
| Trinidad and Tobago | 1994 | 17.4 | 5.0 |
| Turkmenistan | 1998 | 13.8 | 3.5 |
| Ukraine | 2000 | 52.1 | 10.0 |
| United Kingdom | 1999 | 11.8 | 3.3 |
| United States of America | 1999 | 17.6 | 4.0 |
| Uruguay | 1990 | 16.6 | 4.2 |
| Uzbekistan | 1998 | 10.5 | 3.8 |
| Venezuela | 1994 | 8.3 | 1.9 |
| Yugoslavia | 1990 | 21.6 | NA[a] |
| Zimbabwe | 1990 | 10.6 | 5.2 |

Source: http://www.who.int/mental_health/prevention/suicide.
[a]NA, not available.

100 000. The rate of suicide is almost universally higher among men compared to women by an aggregate ratio of 3.5 to 1, with an average of 24.0 for males and 6.8 for females (**Table 1**); with the single exception being in rural China, where female suicides are more frequent than male suicides. For both genders, suicide increases with age; for both genders, the peak is in the 75+ age group (**Figure 2**). Between 1950 and 1995, the incidence of suicide among males has steadily risen by about 40%; although females have followed the same trend, the rate of increase is only about half that of males.

Since 1950, the age distribution of individuals who complete suicide has changed. Suicides among those

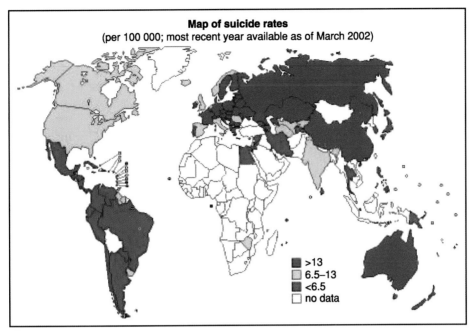

**Figure 1**   Map of suicide rates, international. Reproduced with permission from the Suicide prevention pages, in the Mental Health section of the World Health Organisation's web resource www.who.int

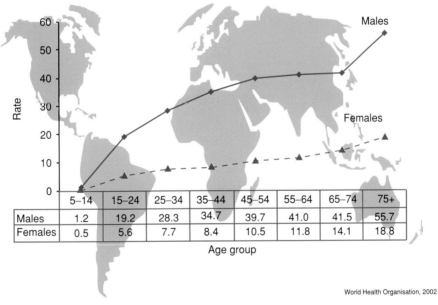

| Age group | 5–14 | 15–24 | 25–34 | 35–44 | 45–54 | 55–64 | 65–74 | 75+ |
|---|---|---|---|---|---|---|---|---|
| Males | 1.2 | 19.2 | 28.3 | 34.7 | 39.7 | 41.0 | 41.5 | 55.7 |
| Females | 0.5 | 5.6 | 7.7 | 8.4 | 10.5 | 11.8 | 14.1 | 18.8 |

World Health Organisation, 2002

**Figure 2**   Change in age/gender distribution, international. Reproduced with permission from the Suicide prevention pages, in the Mental Health section of the World Health Organisation's web resource www.who.int

aged between 5 and 44 increased from 40% to 55% of all completed suicides by 1996 (**Figure 3**). Youth suicides appear to be a problem worldwide. Suicide ranks as one of the top three causes of death among 15–34-year-olds; suicide rates among males between the ages of 15 and 24 have dramatically increased in the last few decades, particularly in Australia, New Zealand, Portugal, Spain, and Greece. Suicide among

the young is now the leading or second leading cause of death after accidental deaths in these countries.

The WHO has estimated that worldwide there are between 815 000 and 1 000 000 suicides annually.

**United States of America**

Suicide is the 11th leading cause of death in the USA; 30 622 suicides were recorded in 2001, accounting

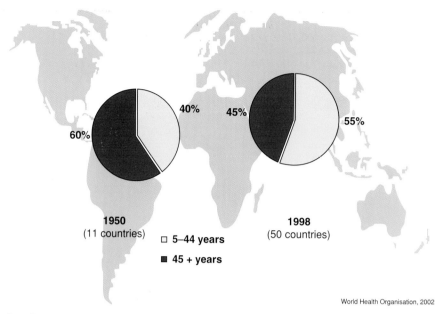

World Health Organisation, 2002

**Figure 3** Distribution of gender per age, international. Reproduced with permission from the Suicide prevention pages, in the Mental Health section of the World Health Organisation's web resource www.who.int

**Table 2** Total suicide rates, USA, 1990–2001

| Year | Suicide rate |
|------|--------------|
| 1990 | 12.4 |
| 1991 | 12.2 |
| 1992 | 12.0 |
| 1993 | 12.1 |
| 1994 | 12.0 |
| 1995 | 11.9 |
| 1996 | 11.6 |
| 1997 | 11.4 |
| 1998 | 11.3 |
| 1999 | 10.7 |
| 2000 | 10.7 |
| 2001 | 10.7 |

Source: http://webapp.cdc.gov/sasweb/ncipc/mortrate.html.

**Table 3** Suicide injury deaths and rates per 100 000, all races, both sexes, all ages in the USA in 2001

| Age group | Number of deaths | Rate |
|-----------|------------------|------|
| 00–04 | 0 | 0.00 |
| 05–09 | 7 | 0.03 |
| 10–14 | 272 | 1.30 |
| 15–19 | 1611 | 7.95 |
| 20–24 | 2360 | 11.97 |
| 25–29 | 2389 | 12.56 |
| 30–34 | 2681 | 12.89 |
| 35–39 | 3176 | 14.23 |
| 40–44 | 3459 | 15.16 |
| 45–49 | 3260 | 15.67 |
| 50–54 | 2682 | 14.55 |
| 55–59 | 1985 | 13.98 |
| 60–64 | 1332 | 11.98 |
| 65–69 | 1212 | 12.71 |
| 70–74 | 1220 | 13.89 |
| 75–79 | 1219 | 16.41 |
| 80–84 | 973 | 18.88 |
| 85+ | 769 | 17.29 |
| Unknown | 15 | |
| Total | 30 622 | 10.73 |

Source: http://webapp.cdc.gov/sasweb/ncipc/mortrate.html.

for a rate of 10.7 per 100 000, a small but steady decrease since 1990 (**Table 2**). Male suicides (17.6 100 000) occur four times as frequently as female suicides (4.1/100 000). The highest rate of suicide across all age groups is for individuals aged 80–84 years (18.9/100 000). The elderly comprise 12.4% of the population, yet represent 17.6% of suicides. **Table 3** shows rates by age group for the USA.

In the USA, Caucasians have the highest rate (11.9/ 100 000), followed by American Indian and Alaska Natives (10.6/100 000), African-Americans (5.36), and Asians and Pacific Islanders (5.1) (**Table 4**). Temporal increases, however, have occurred differentially among gender and racial groups. For example, although the rates for 15–19-year-old Caucasians and

African-Americans of both genders have increased since 1960, there has been a dramatic increase for males. Similarly, the suicide rate for black males increased by a much faster rate than did the rate for white males (234% versus 136%; **Table 5**). These increases have primarily been attributed to parallel increases in the use of firearms in suicide by these groups.

Suicide rates in the USA generally declined among those aged 45 years and higher between 1950 and 2000. For those aged between 15 and 24 years, however, suicide rates increased between 1950 and 1995, but decreased in the last several years (**Figure 4**). Notably, a decrease in the use of firearms and an increase in the prescribing of antidepressant medications have been postulated to explain this more recent decrease in rates.

**Nonfatal suicide attempts** For every completed suicide it has been estimated that there are 25 nonfatal attempts. The great majority of nonfatal attempts

occur among younger individuals, with estimated ratios of attempts to completions in the range of 100:1, compared to 4:1 among the elderly. However, the only large-scale data that exist come from the YRBS. As depicted in **Figure 5**, 18% of US high-school students reported thinking about suicide in the last 12 months, 15% made a plan, more than 8% claimed to have made an attempt, of which about one in three required medical attention. This latter estimate (about 2.5% of all respondents) has remained reasonably steady since 1993 (**Figure 6**). It is also significant to note that, in contrast to data on completed suicides, the gender ratio is reversed for nonfatal attempts: females attempt suicide three times more often than do males.

## Prediction and Risk

The prediction of suicide is impossible. Given its low base-rate of occurrence, any predicted outcome of suicide will have an inordinately high rate of false positives. Even in conditions of high risk, the overwhelming majority of individuals will not die by suicide. For example, it has been estimated that depressed psychiatric inpatients admitted with suicide ideation or attempt behavior have a 6% lifetime risk of suicide; yet this means that for every predicted suicide there will be 15 nonsuicidal deaths. Moreover, although ample knowledge about suicide risk factors exist, comparably little is known about near-term risk, i.e., observations that have both sensitivity and specificity for being associated with suicidal behavior in the next several hours or even days. The 6% prevalence estimate noted above for depressed and suicidal inpatients is for lifetime risk, not near-term risk. The best that can be done is to note individuals who

**Table 4** Suicides (*N*), suicide rates, all ages, both genders, per race, in the USA in 2001

| Ethnic origin | N | Rate |
|---|---|---|
| Caucasian | 27 710 | 11.91 |
| African-American | 1957 | 5.26 |
| American Indian/Alaska Native | 321 | 10.57 |
| Asian/Pacific Islander | 634 | 5.14 |
| Total | 30 622 | 10.73 |

Source: http://webapp.cdc.gov/sasweb/ncipc/mortrate.html.

**Table 5** Suicide rates, 15–19-year-olds, by gender and race, in the USA from 1960 to 2000

| Year | Caucasian | | African-American | |
|---|---|---|---|---|
| | Males | Females | Males | Females |
| 1960 | 5.9 | 1.6 | 2.9 | 1.1 |
| 2000 | 13.9 | 2.9 | 9.7 | 1.5 |
| % increase | 136 | 81 | 234 | 36 |

Source: Centers for Disease Control, National Center for Health Statistics, various years.

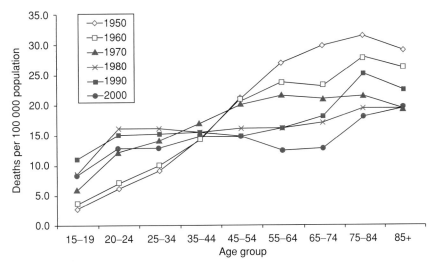

**Figure 4** Suicide rates by age, 1950–2000.

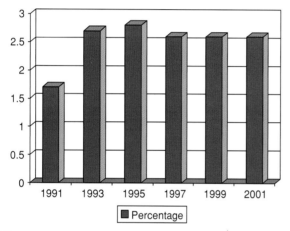

**Figure 5** Youth risk behavior surveillance data in the USA, 2001.

**Figure 6** Youth risk behavior surveillance in the USA from 1991 to 2001, injurious attempt in last 12 months.

**Table 6** Frequency of mental disorder diagnosis in completed suicide

| |
| --- |
| Affective disorders |
| Range: 39–89%; Median: 61% |
| Substance abuse |
| Range: 19–63%; Median: 41% |
| Anxiety disorders |
| Range: 3–27%; Median: 10% |
| Schizophrenias |
| Range: 0–16%; Median: 6% |
| Axis II |
| Range: 31–57%; Median: 42% |

Data from 16 Psychological Autopsy Studies.

carry a greater risk for suicide than others who do not share characteristics known to be associated with those who commit suicide.

## Perpetuating Risk Factors

Perpetuating risk factors for suicide include variables such as family history of suicide, violence, substance abuse, and mental disorder requiring hospitalization. Offspring of parents with these histories have 5–11 times the risk of completing suicide as those without these parental histories. A history of a previous suicide attempt is a significant perpetuating risk factor. One in three of those with a suicide attempt history will make further attempts, with 10–15% ultimately completing. Sexual abuse and a history of multiple personal losses are also classified as perpetuating risk factors. Perpetuating risk factors increase vulnerability to suicide, but are not modifiable or open to change by interventions.

## Predisposing Risk Factors

Predisposing risk factors increase vulnerability to suicidal behavior but are considered modifiable. Examples of significant predisposing risk factors are described below.

**Mental disorder** Acute psychiatric disorders impair coping and resilience, amplify stress, decrease protections, and have associated emotional reactivities and cognitive distortions that heighten risk for suicide. The most commonly observed mental disorders in adult suicides are:

- affective disorders
- schizophrenia
- alcoholism
- axis II (personality), cluster B disorders.

The most commonly observed mental disorders in adolescent suicides are:

- affective disorders
- substance abuse disorders
- conduct disorders.

**Table 6** depicts the range and median frequencies of diagnostic conditions in completed suicides. The co-occurrence of mental disorders, for example depression plus alcoholism, is significantly associated with increased risk. **Table 7** depicts the most common metal diagnoses by gender for teen suicides as derived from case-controlled psychological autopsy studies.

**Suicide ideation** Thoughts of suicide precede suicidal behavior, especially planned behaviors. However it has been estimated that in almost one-third of nearly fatal attempts the thought of suicide preceded the attempt by 5 min or less.

**Hopelessness** Thoughts of self, others, and future which are absolute and negative (e.g., "I'm a terrible person," "Nobody cares about me," "Nothing will ever change") have been found to be more associated with suicidal behavior than depression.

**Social isolation** Individuals who lack social supports, who do not seek or accept help when in need, or who are acutely alone and lonely, who are alienated or in conflict with systems of attachment, e.g., adolescents who drop out of school, tend to be more at risk for suicidal behavior. Suicides are more frequent among divorced and separated adults than among those who are married.

**Medical conditions (axis III disorders)** A number of significant physical diseases and conditions are associated with increased risk for suicide. Table 8 shows the odds ratios for several illnesses which have been found to pase increased risk.

**Decreased protective factors** Suicides are less frequent among those who have:

- positive self-esteem
- confidence in personal abilities to control and cope
- cognitive, such as problem-solving, skills
- accessible and available supports
- internal (e.g., religiosity) and external (e.g., family, children) constraints.

**Table 7** Most common mental disorders from case-control psychological autopsy studies of teen suicides, USA

| Disorder | Male | Female |
|---|---|---|
| | (n = 213) | (n = 46) |
| Mood disorder | 50% | 69% |
| Antisocial disorder | 43% | 24% |
| Substance abuse | 38% | 17% |
| Anxiety disorder | 19% | 48% |

Source: Shaffer D, Gould MS, Fisher P, *et al.* (1996) Psychiatric diagnosis in child and adolescent suicide. *Archives of General Psychiatry* 53(4): 339–348, Brent DA, Baugher M, Bridge J, *et al.* (1999). Age- and sex-related risk factors for adolescant suicide. *Journal of the American Adolescent of Childhood and Adolescent Psychiatry* 38(12): 1497–1505.

**Table 8** AXIS III: medical conditions increasing risk

| Illness | OR |
|---|---|
| HIV/AIDS | 6.6 |
| Malignant neoplasms of head/neck | 11.4 |
| Chronic renal failure – dialysis | 14.5 |
| Spinal cord injuries | 3.8 |
| MS | 2.4 |
| Systemic lupus – erythematosus | 4.3 |
| Peptic ulcer | 2.1 |

Adapted from Kelly MJ, Mufson MJ, Rogers MP (1999) Medical settings and suicide. In: Jacobs DJ (ed.) *The Harvard Medical School Guide to Suicide Assessment and Intervention.* San Francisco, CA: Jossey-Bass.

**Contributing Risk Factors**

Contributing risk factors are conditions that facilitate suicidal behavior and increase risk among those so exposed. Examples of contributing risk factors are described below.

**Exposure to suicidal models** Being exposed to the suicidal behavior of others, even if only through the media, has been found to be associated with imitative (copy-cat) behaviors among vulnerable others. For example, when Marilyn Monroe died by suicide in 1962, there was an immediate, statistically significant, and unexpected increase in suicides among young white females. The assumption is that her death communicated a nonspecific loss of hope among those who might have looked to her as an icon of womanhood, success, and beauty. Clusters of suicides (three or more suicides among individuals in a defined community over a short time span) are commonly observed and account for about 5% of all youth suicides.

**Personality disorders (*Diagnostic and Statistical Manual* axis II)** An axis II diagnosis increases suicide risk, particularly for personality disorders with cluster B traits: antisocial, borderline, histrionic, or narcissistic. Borderline personality disorder has been the subject of considerable study, with the lifetime risk of completed suicide being about 7%. Comorbidity with an axis I depression considerably heightens lifetime risk.

**Access and availability of firearms** Especially in the USA, where firearms account for almost three of five suicides, there is a clear relationship between the ready availability of firearms in the home and suicides by those living there. The risk of suicide of a household member is increased nearly five times in homes with (versus without) guns.

**Acute intoxication** Alcohol decreases controls and increases impulsivity. Often vulnerable individuals use alcohol as an antidepressant. As many as 50% of suicides and attempted suicides have been noted to have elevated blood alcohol at the time of these events.

**Insomnia** Lack of sleep impairs coping ability and cognitive performance and heightens confusion and emotional reactivity.

**Precipitating Risk Factors**

Precipitating risk factors are proximate, triggering life events that serve as the "last straw" to potentiate suicidal behavior among predisposed individuals.

Sometimes these are anticipated versus actual; still, they give rise to acute stress, heightened panic, and feelings of shame and fear that mediate suicidal behavior. Examples of precipitating risk factors are:

- losses of relationship, e.g., a breakup of adolescent romantic involvement, divorce, death of close attachment
- threat of legal action or incarceration
- unemployment
- threat of financial loss or bankruptcy.

## Subpopulation Risk Profiles

Certain subpopulations have been studied with regard to idiosyncratic risk factors. Notable among these are:

1. Persons in jail or prison. Suicides by those behind bars have, necessarily, been studied retrospectively and descriptively. Common characteristics of jail suicides include: younger (under age 32 years), male, unmarried, incarcerated for nonviolent offenses, particularly involving drug or alcohol offenses (and being intoxicated or under the influence at the time of arrest). Suicides typically occur by hanging when staff supervision is less available, when in isolation or seclusion, and soon after incarceration. A majority, although rarely screened, had a diagnosable mental disorder and expressed hopelessness or suicide ideation. Suicides in prisons tended to be among older males, serving long-term sentences for major offenses, and by those with histories of psychiatric illness and suicidal behavior.
2. Psychiatric inpatients. As acute psychiatric disorders are significant predisposing risk factors for suicide, those more at risk are those with disorders necessitating inpatient care. Those hospitalized for affective disorder, schizophrenia, substance abuse disorders, and anxiety disorders have greatest risk, and also of concern are those with comorbidity. Fawcett and colleagues in 1990 particularly noted the role of severe psychic anxiety, anxious ruminations, global insomnia, psychotic delusions, and recent alcohol abuse in the near-term (1-year) risk of suicide among those with major affective disorder. The risk of suicide among hospitalized depressed patients is highest in the first few weeks following discharge from inpatient care and, most probably, among those with incomplete remissions or inadequate attention to continuity of care in a context of increased or renewed stress.
3. Alcoholics. Comorbidity with major depressive episodes particularly characterizes suicides among

alcoholics. In addition, poor social support, unemployment, serious medical illness, social isolation and/or loss, or disruption of a close interpersonal relationship describes those at heightened risk.

## Methods of Suicide

As noted above, the modal method of suicide in the USA is firearms. This is true for both males and females with a higher proportion for males; and among the old and the young, with a higher proportion among the elderly. Hanging is the most commonly used method worldwide and second most frequent method of suicide in the USA. Ingestion is the most frequent method used by nonfatal attempters.

The potential decedent's intention, in part, defines the choice of method. Individuals intent on dying by means of their self-inflicted act typically choose more lethal methods to carry out their intention. This is especially true in planned versus impulsive suicides. However, a number of other factors, working independently and in combination, define the choice of suicide method. These include:

- Accessibility and availability. In jail settings, for example, where other means are limited, hanging is the method of choice. Pesticides are the method of choice in rural China.
- Knowledge, experience, and familiarity. In cultures where firearms are readily available, those comfortable with guns will commit suicide more by firearms than will others not experienced or comfortable with guns.
- Meaning, symbolism, and cultural significance. Drug ingestion may be preferred by females as a method that is not destructive to appearance; drugs are also associated with a peaceful sleep, thus a nonpainful death. In addition, there are a number of popular jumping sites in various countries that serve as suicide magnets because of their association with a new life and beauty.
- State of mind. The more bizarre and/or disfiguring the method, on average, the more likely the decedent was psychotic.

## Linking Statistics to Prevention

Comprehensive data about suicide, its prevalence and risk, shed light on trends, points of entry for intervention, and opportunities for prevention. When based on sound data, a range of targeted prevention approaches have been shown to decrease suicide rates.

For example, a study in Utah found that almost two-thirds of youths who died by suicide had contact with the juvenile justice system, and that there was a direct correlation between the number of contacts and increased suicide risk. Many of these youths were not in contact with the school system. Few had received mental health care. Most had multiple minor offenses over many years. These findings identified the juvenile justice system as the best available point of entry to identify youths at risk for suicide and to deliver mental health care to them.

A number of prevention approaches are based on the concept of risk reduction. These range from case-finding approaches, models of early detection and referral, to treatment of those at risk, such as screening programs and gatekeeper education programs, to means-restriction programs, wherein available access to lethal means is made more difficult. Means-restriction programs offer excellent statistical data on prevention.

- In Washington, DC, the number-one site for suicidal jumpers was the Duke Ellington bridge. Spanning a city park, the bridge offered a 37.5-m (125-ft) fall to the roadbed surface below and averaged about four suicides per year. Of interest, an immediately adjacent and equally high bridge (the Taft bridge) averaged fewer than two suicides per year. In the mid-1980s suicide barriers were constructed on the Ellington bridge. In the succeeding 5 years the frequency of suicidal jumps from this site declined to zero. Correspondingly, jumps from the Taft bridge increased only slightly.
- In the UK, suicide attempts with acetaminophen (paracetamol) were found to have steadily increased from the 1970s and by 1996 nearly half of all overdose admissions to general hospitals in England and Wales involved painkillers, especially acetaminophen, either alone or in combination with other drugs. Moreover, nearly 75% of all attempters reported that they ingested the drug on impulse. Recognizing its potential lethality and the ease of its availability, advocates promoted national legislation that limited the number of tablets sold per sale and instated packet warnings about the dangers of acetaminophen overdose. Consequently, over the subsequent 2 years, the number of deaths due to acetaminophen overdose fell to 18%, a 10% reduction in nonfatal attempts using acetaminophen to overdose, and a 30% reduction in admissions to liver units because of acetaminophen-induced liver damage.
- As noted earlier, the USA has initiated a National Violent Death Reporting System. This system, now being pilot-tested in 13 states, links data sets from multiple sources. Consequently, co-occurring homicides and suicides can now be analyzed, sources and storage patterns of firearms used for suicide can be traced, the role of substance abuse in completed suicides can be better established, and geocoding of neighborhoods of higher risk and the consequent identification of environmental characteristics associated with higher risk conditions can be identified.

## Conclusion

Surveillance of suicide and suicidal behaviors and correlated risk factors is essential to both a better understanding of suicide and to the implementation of promising prevention programs. Accurate data and linked data sets provide a perspective for both clinical and public health approaches to reduce suicide mortality and morbidity.

## See Also

**Forensic Psychiatry and Forensic Psychology:** Psychological Autopsy; **Suicide:** Etiology, Methods and Statistics; Parasuicide; Youth Suicide

## Further Reading

Bonner RL (1992) Isolation, seclusion, and psychosocial vulnerability as risk factors for suicide behind bars. In: Maris RW, Berman AL, Matltsberger JT, Yufit RI (eds.) *Assessment and Prediction of Suicide*, pp. 398–419. New York: Guilford Press.

Brent DA, Baugher M, Bridge J, *et al.* (1999) Age- and sex-related risk factors for adolescent suicide. *Journal of the American Academy of Childhood and Adolescent Psychiatry* 38(12): 1497–1505.

Busch KA, Fawcett J, Jacobs DG (2003) Clinical correlates of inpatient suicide. *Journal of Clinical Psychiatry* 64: 14–19.

Fawcett J, Scheftner WA, Fogg L, *et al.* (1990) Time-related predictors of suicide in major affective disorder. *American Journal of Psychiatry* 147: 1189–1194.

Goldsmith SK, Pellmar TC, Kleinman AM, Bunney W (eds.) (2002) *Reducing Suicide: A National Imperative.* Washington, DC: National Academies Press.

Hawton K (2002) United Kingdom legislation on pack sizes of analgesics: background, rationale, and effects on suicide and deliberate self-harm. *Suicide and Life-Threatening Behavior* 32: 223–229.

Hawton K, van Heeringen K (eds.) *The International Handbook of Suicide and Attempted Suicide.* Chichester, UK: Wiley.

Hayes LM (1998) Suicide prevention in correctional facilities: An overview. In: Puisis M (ed.) *Clinical Practice in Correctional Medicine*, pp. 245–256. St. Louis, MO: Mosby.

Jacobs DG, Brewer M, Klein-Benheim M (1999) Suicide assessment. In: Jacobs DG (ed.) *The Harvard Medical School Guide to Suicide Assessment and Intervention*, pp. 3–39. San Francisco, CA: Jossey-Bass.

Joiner TE, Pettit JW, Rudd MD (2004) Is there a window of heightened risk if patients gain energy in the context of continued depressive symptoms? *Professional Psychology: Research and Practice* 35: 84–89.

Kelly MJ, Mufson MJ, Rogers MP (1999) Medical settings and suicide. In: Jacobs DJ (ed.) *The Harvard Medical School Guide to Suicide Assessment and Intervention.* San Francisco, CA: Jossey-Bass.

Lönnqvist JK (2000) Psychiatric aspects of suicidal behavior: depression. In: Hawton K, van Heeringen K (eds.) *The International Handbook of Suicide and Attempted Suicide,* pp. 107–120. Chichester, UK: John Wiley.

Luoma JB, Martin CE, Pearson JL (2002) Contact with mental health and primary care providers before suicide: a review of the evidence. *American Journal of Psychiatry* 159(6): 909–916.

Maris RW, Berman AL, Silverman MM (2000) *The Comprehensive Textbook of Suicidology.* New York: Guilford Press.

O'Carroll PW, Berman AL, Maris R, *et al.* (1996) Beyond the tower of Babel: a nomenclature for suicidology. *Suicide and Life-Threatening Behavior* 26: 237–252.

Shaffer D, Gould MS, Fisher P, *et al.* (1996) Psychiatric diagnosis in child and adolescent suicide. *Archives of General Psychiatry* 53(4): 339–348.

Tanney BL (1992) Mental disorders, psychiatric patients and suicide. In: Maris RW, Berman AL, Matltsberger JT, Yufit RI (eds.) *Assessment and Prediction of Suicide,* pp. 277–320. New York: Guilford Press.

Tanney BL (2000) Psychiatric diagnoses and suicidal acts. In: Maris RW, Berman AL, Silverman MM (eds.) *Comprehensive Textbook of Suicidology,* pp. 311–341. New York: Guilford Press.

World Health Organization (1999) *Figures and Facts about Suicide.* Geneva: WHO.

# Mental Handicap and Learning Disability

**M Welner**, NYU School of Medicine, New York, NY, USA

## Introduction

Forensic science and mental retardation are unfamiliar acquaintances, with little research completed in forensic contexts on this special population. Traditionally, the mentally handicapped have drawn the interest of the education community, as well as pediatrician and child psychology specialists, given the setting in which mental handicaps first present problems to the individual, or are noticed by loved ones.

Mental handicaps and learning disorders do not translate well into criminal law matters. Perhaps this reflects the frame of reference of designating people as "mentally retarded" or "learning-disordered." Unlike psychiatric diagnostic standards, which identify conditions for treatment and specific treatment protocols, mental handicap and learning disorders are classified and designated in order to denote eligibility for social services, or special education, for example.

Treatment of the mentally retarded only became pertinent in developed nations when abuses of the retarded provoked discomfort over the prospect that these individuals were merely warehoused, sometimes with great neglect. Increasing sensitivity to the rights of the mentally handicapped has prompted examination of victimization patterns, and forensic research has promoted safeguards to the vulnerable among the mentally retarded.

Concerns about sexual exploitation have been offset by trends toward reintegrating the mentally handicapped and enabling them to exercise autonomy over their rights, including their own personal sexuality. The mentally handicapped also pose unique treatment challenges for future risk prevention.

In recent years, mental handicap has received greatest consideration within the criminal law due to concerns about the rights of the mentally handicapped defendant. Particular attention has focused on interrogation and criminal responsibility and accountability. However, workplace antidiscrimination laws, disability assessments, and protection statutes also concern themselves with learning disorders and their significance.

## Definitions and Characteristics

### Mental Retardation

Mental retardation is diagnosed under the *Diagnostic and Statistical Manual,* 4th edition (DSM-IV-TR) as:

1. significantly subaverage intellectual functioning: an IQ of 70 or below on an individually administered IQ test
2. concurrent deficits in present adaptive function (i.e., the person's effectiveness in meeting the standards expected for his/her age by his/her cultural group) in at least two of the following areas: communication, self-care, home living, social/interpersonal skills, use of community resources, self-direction, functional academic skills, work, leisure, health, and safety
3. such limitations present at least prior to the age of 18.

The first criterion reflects that the individual has failed to develop an even remotely comparable intelligence level that would be appropriate for his/her age group. Diagnosis of mental retardation is possible in individuals with an IQ below approximately 70, or two or more standard deviations below the norms established for the given intelligence test administered.

The second criterion, adaptive functioning, encompasses how effectively individuals manage essential life demands and how capable that individual is of independently functioning relative to others of his/her age group, sociocultural background, and community.

Adaptive skills are assessed in the individual's typical environment, across all aspects of life. Difficulties with navigating through the daily course of life are more inclined to respond positively to remedial efforts than is the cognitive IQ, which tends to remain a more invariable trait.

Significant differences exist in the definition adopted by the DSM-IV-TR and the American Association on Mental Retardation (AAMR). DSM-IV-TR is geared toward the clinical and research community, and has avoided the legal arena, while the AAMR advocates for the retarded defendant to be handled extrajudicially, and has revised the criteria for retardation twice in recent years to enhance its advocacy mission.

Most recent AAMR criteria only require general deficits in adaptive function, without greater specificity.

The AAMR generalization of criteria, in keeping with its policy agenda, considerably expands the range of potential convicted killers who would be declared ineligible for capital punishment in the USA (which recently declared execution of the convicted retarded murderer unconstitutional). However, the revised AAMR definition is not rooted in any scientific research, but rather a social policy initiative. Given the problems in the forensic interface of existing diagnosis of mental retardation noted below, the AAMR definition is nothing more than an advocacy statement of little scientific substance.

## Subtypes

Mental retardation is subdivided into levels of severity based on intellectual and functional impairment. The degree of impairment from mental retardation has a wide range, from profoundly impaired to mild or borderline retardation. The level of mental retardation is the main determinant in the degree of outside assistance the person with mental retardation needs to live an independent life.

DSM-IV-TR identifies four degrees of severity that reflect the degree of functional impairment: (1) mild; (2) moderate; (3) severe; and (4) profound.

**Mild mental retardation**   Failure to adapt normally and grow intellectually may become apparent early in life or, in the case of mild retardation, not become recognizable until school age or later. Taken as a whole, those with mild mental retardation account for the greatest segment of the population with the disorder, and are considered to be only a little slower than average in learning new information and skills. IQ scores, by DSM-IV-TR criteria, range from approximately 50 to 70.

As children, signs of mild mental retardation may not be readily apparent. These children may not be identified until they enter school. Social and communication skills progressively develop during the preschool years (0–5 years), as does the acquisition of learned information (through the late teens). As adults, many will be able to lead independent lives in the community, achieving social and vocational success adequate for minimum self-support. Typically, however, many will also require support in the form of supervision, guidance, and assistance, especially when under unusual social or economic stress.

**Moderate mental retardation**   Individuals with moderate mental retardation comprise approximately 10% of the entire population of the mentally retarded. Similar to those with mild mental retardation, those with moderate mental retardation also acquire communication skills during early childhood years. IQ scores range from the 35–40 to 50–55 range.

Those with moderate mental retardation may also benefit from vocational or occupational training and, with guidance and supervision, can often maintain adequate personal care. However, unlike those who are mildly retarded, those with moderate mental retardation are unlikely to progress beyond the second-grade level in academic subjects. By their teen years, such individuals may begin experiencing issues that interfere with the development and growth of peer relationships.

As adults, individuals with moderate mental retardation may be able to perform unskilled or semi-skilled work under supervision, and adapt well to life in a supervised community, provided that they have ample training and support.

**Severe mental retardation**   Of those who are mentally retarded, 3–4% of the population consists of those with severe mental retardation – with IQ scores ranging from the 20–25 to 35–40 range. Individuals with a severe or profound level of mental retardation frequently have additional disabilities beyond mental retardation.

In contrast to the groups with mild and moderate mental retardation, these children, in the early childhood years, attain little or no communication skills. Additionally, children with this level of mental retardation are unlikely to be able to learn to read or write, but may be able to be toilet-trained and learn to dress with assistance. While some learn to talk during the school-age period, they are severely limited in their ability to understand or retain scholastic information.

As adults, this group requires more assistance than persons with mild or moderate mental retardation, as even though they may be able to perform simple tasks in closely supervised settings, they still require considerable basic physical care or supervision to live.

**Profound mental retardation**   Individuals who have a profound level of mental retardation frequently have disabilities such as an identified neurological condition that accounts for their mental retardation. IQ scores fall below the 20–25 range. Early in childhood, such individuals exhibit significant impairments in sensorimotor functioning.

This does not necessarily imply that the deficits are inoperable, as motor development, self-care, and communication skills may all improve if appropriate training is provided. Ideally, development in profoundly retarded individuals transpires in a highly structured environment with consisted, individualized aid and supervision.

**Mental retardation, severity unspecified**   A diagnosis of mental retardation, severity unspecified, is recommended when there is a compelling case to be made for mental retardation but standardized testing instruments cannot successfully evaluate the person – whether it be the result of infancy, extensive impairment, or other characteristic of the examinee. Generally, the younger the individual, the harder it is to assess for the presence or absence of mental retardation.

**Cautions and limitations**   The diagnostic criteria fail application in two major respects: inadequate attention to specific importance of impulsivity, and of judgment. These are the two areas that, arguably, have greatest relevance to forensic questions, be they criminal, employment, civil (intentional infliction of emotional distress, or malpractice actions arising from the conduct of an individual), or parental rights.

### Learning Disorders

According to DSM-IV-TR, learning disorders are diagnosed when the examinee's achievement on individually administered, standardized tests in reading, mathematics, or written expression is substantially below that expected for age, schooling, and level of intelligence. These learning problems first present in childhood and early scholastic settings, and may persist into adulthood. They significantly interfere with academic achievement or activities of daily living that require reading, writing, or mathematical skills.

Those with learning disorders do not demonstrate the otherwise broad intellectual and functional impairments of mental retardation. Ordinarily, testing reveals achievement that is two standard deviations below what would be otherwise expected, given an individual's IQ. Occasionally, if a mental disorder or cultural influence impacts performance on testing, that discrepancy may be one to two standard deviations below the level correlated with IQ testing.

Learning disorders, in assessment, need to be distinguished from poor achievement reflective of a different cultural background, poor teaching, lack of opportunity, and problems adjusting to the school setting.

## Associated Qualities

Criteria to meet a diagnosis of mental retardation or learning disorders must be present before age 18. Examinees who are natives to the USA will have drawn attention to themselves long before that age, however. Unless the child grew up in conditions of considerable neglect, the family would have sought medical and psychiatric consultation for problems relating to behavior, or to "slowness."

In the forensic examination, collateral sources of information must be queried to ascertain a number of associated features.

Peers, family, and significant others can be quite instructive. Retarded individuals are not age-appropriate; peers experience them as younger, and they occupy roles within their families that equate with a noticeably lower level of developmental achievement or maturity. If the defendant is retarded, his/her family may describe a history of emotional and material dependence; they would be involved in a caretaking role, not the other way around. The quality of their relatedness, even within the family, is immature and shallow.

These sources provide additional information to resolve questions of the defendant's ability to live and manage alone, manage finances, care for his/her self, and safety. Documentation of individuals' autonomy and handling of responsibilities, such as that available from banks and landlords, is also helpful and minimizes bias.

Assessing friends and friendships elicits information about the defendant's social function, how he/she fits in with peers, the basis for their friendship, and shared qualities. The retarded defendant may have few friends; those he/she does have may be expected to describe shallow, limited relationships; they may use a mentally retarded male for strength or other material benefit, perhaps as a lookout for a gang. More sinister acquaintances may welcome a retarded defendant because of his explosive temper and willingness to be a soldier for them.

Retarded individuals who attract no friends may rely on their family for companionship. Likewise, parents with retardation may rely on their own parents to assume decision-making responsibilities and more for the child.

Former significant others can demonstrate and reveal much about the age-appropriateness of the defendant's behavior. These witnesses should be questioned about the quality of the relationship, sexuality, and the defendant's relatedness to others. The age and qualities of that significant other should likewise be appraised; a peer-appropriate relationship would be expected when one retarded individual becomes involved with another.

Academic problems, noted from within the school system, would create a baseline of intelligence-testing results that should be available for forensic psychiatric examination.

School records are also pivotal to the assessment of retardation. Grades and scores demonstrate the academic difficulties that are fundamental to a diagnosis of retardation. Academic records in particular further distinguish whether the history is more reflective of learning disorders or of behavioral problems independent of intellectual deficiencies and developmental disorder.

Records of referral to special education also illuminate the nature of a defendant's earlier strengths and limitations as a student. The absence of such referral needs to be followed up with school officials to appraise the likelihood that retardation would be missed, and how.

Academic records may further bear upon the individual's capability of incorporating new information – as well as the mechanisms to train the individual best. In custody, guardianship, and parental rights determinations, this information is particularly vital to courts.

Previous psychiatric records not only enable a diagnosis of retardation to be established, but also contribute to recognizing co-occurring, or comorbid, conditions, and their treatment history. Life events, such as head trauma that causes dementia, or diseases such as encephalitis, can be identified through review of these records as well. Important members of the support system, who can provide additional input on the defendant's behavior and way of relatedness, can also be identified this way.

Counseling records and specific periods of failing may illustrate problem periods for the individual in younger years – but not retardation, especially if these academic difficulties are episodic, or periodic, but not persistent.

Employment records are also helpful. While any work history at all may erroneously suggest that retardation is not present, it is still important to follow up with an employer about the nature of the work the defendant had been performing. Information about how the individual came to be hired, job description, the independence with which the individual worked, and his/her job performance all distinguish whether the defendant had age-appropriate work skills that would surpass what would be expected of someone with retardation.

At the same time, a person who clearly needed close supervision, who was taken in by a caretaker environment that provided a sheltering schedule, may support the diagnostic impression that the defendant has significantly subaverage work performance.

This possibility is further borne out by special arrangements afforded to that employee, including special accommodations. Information from co-workers, especially those who have not been coached, about the competencies and limitations of the defendant, and an accurate understanding of why he/she would have been terminated, is helpful.

The learning-disordered may or may not have deficits that reflect themselves at the workplace. A long-range work history, affording the opportunity to examine closely duties, performance, and reason for termination, will reveal whether a learning disorder manifested during scholastic years persisted into adulthood, and whether it does impair a person's functions at the workplace.

## Diagnostic Testing

To assess an individual properly for the presence of the disorder, it is imperative that the examining professional be diligent in selecting testing instruments and when conducting the subsequent result interpretation. Factors such as physical disabilities, socioeconomic status, and native language, if not accounted for, can limit and possibly skew the diagnostic procedure.

Significantly subaverage functioning and adaptation, on at least two domains, is required for the diagnosis of mental retardation. This information is best ascertained through history. Such history may be gathered in a systematic way using instruments listed in **Table 1**. Nevertheless, as the ratings of

**Table 1** Intelligence tests

| Intelligence test | Used for | What is measured and how | Can it detect malingering? |
| --- | --- | --- | --- |
| Wechsler Adult Intelligence Scale – third edition (WAIS-III) | Ages 16–89 | Measures verbal comprehension (vocabulary, similarities, information), perceptual organization (picture completion, block design, matrix reasoning), working memory (arithmetic, digit span), and processing abilities (sequences). Contains separate verbal and performance scales | Atypical responses may be an indication; however, this should be supplemented by another test. Utilization of multiple psychological tests is the best way to detect faked mental retardation |
| Wechsler Intelligence Scale for Children – third edition (WISC-III) | Ages 6–16 | Verbal Scale measures ability to express and comprehend speech, including vocabulary, short-term auditory memory, and ability to categorize and compute; Performance Scale consists of tasks that measure ability to perceive and act on spatial relationships. Specific pattern of strengths and weaknesses can indicate specific learning disabilities | No |
| Stanford Binet Intelligence Scale, fourth edition | Ages 2–23 | Measures verbal and nonverbal areas of development; also provides assessment of mathematical reasoning and short-term memory capacity. Caution: Large margin of error (5 points) | No |
| Kaufman Assessment Battery for Children (K-ABC) | Ages 2.5–12.5 | Sequential Processing Scale contains hand movement, number recall, and word order subtests; Simultaneous Processing Scale consists of spatial tasks that measure acquired knowledge: Achievement Scale contains subtests that measure expressive vocabulary, arithmetic, reading, etc. Relies on visual stimuli (therefore, not suitable for individuals with visual impairments); applicable to diverse populations because less culturally dependent and focuses on problem-solving process, not content of test items | No |
| Raven's Standard Progressive Matrices (SPM) | Ages 6 and older | Multiple-choice test measures nonverbal intelligence; specifically, the ability to form perceptual relations and reason by analogy, independent of language and formal schooling | Limited – tasks progressively increase in difficulty so performance should steadily decline; malingerers tend to have scattered result pattern |
| Slosson Intelligence Test – Revised (SIT-R) | Ages 0–27 | Measures crystallized verbal intelligence from the following cognitive domains: information, comprehension, arithmetic, similarities and differences, vocabulary, and auditory memory; one of the few measures capable of assessing severely and profoundly mentally handicapped populations because its IQ scales range from 36 to 164. Consists of 187 questions administered orally | No |
| Kaufman Brief Intelligence Test (K-BIT) | Ages 4–90 | Includes both verbal (vocabulary subtest involving word knowledge and concepts) and nonverbal (matrices subtest involving pictures and abstract designs) assessment of problem-solving abilities; can rule out language problems as cause of impairment | No |
| Test of Nonverbal Intelligence 3 (TONI-3) | Ages 6–89 | Subjects examine figures, identify the relationships among them, and select correct response by pointing; instructions are pantomimed. This nonverbal assessment of intelligence, aptitude, abstract reasoning, and problem-solving is well suited for verbally or neurologically impaired, learning-disabled, and mentally retarded individuals | No |
| California Verbal Learning Test (CVLT-II) | Ages 16–89 | Subjects presented with list of words and asked to recall them across series of trials. In addition to assessing verbal learning and memory, there are measures encoding strategies, learning rates, and error types | Yes – low rate of correct responses to forced-choice items may be an indication. Caution: susceptible to coaching |

| Test | Age range | Description | Measures malingering[a] |
|---|---|---|---|
| Columbia Mental Maturity Scale (CMMS) | Ages 3–9 | General reasoning ability is assessed by classification of pictorial figures arranged in series of overlapping levels; each level is equivalent to a specific chronological age | No |
| Stoelting Brief Intelligence Test S-BIT) | Ages 6 and older | Nonverbal measurements of reading, organizational skills, abstract comprehension, and logical reasoning; ideal for measuring intelligence of children and adolescents thought to have communication or neurological impairment | No |
| Wechsler Memory Scale – Revised | Ages 16–74 | Written test; measures both visual and auditory capacities of immediate, general delayed, and working memories. Used with aphasic and organically brain-injured individuals and the elderly | Yes – poor performance on Attention/Concentration index may indicate malingering; severely impaired individuals typically perform well |
| Halstead-Reitan Neuropsychological Battery | Age 5 and older | Consists of 10 tests designed to measure elements of memory, abstract thought, language, sensory-motor integration, imperception, and motor dexterity. Type/location of brain damage can be identified | Yes – formula is applied to scores that take into account history, other test data, and behavioral observations |
| Bender Gestalt test | Ages 4–85 | Subject reproduces figures on cards; visual-motor functioning, visual-perception skills, neurological impairment, and emotional disturbances are assessed based on rotation, distortion, symmetry, and perseveration of these reproductions | Yes – inhibited figure size, changed position, distorted relationships, complex additions, and gross simplification may indicate malingering[a] |
| Luria-Nebraska Neuropsychological Battery | Ages 15 and older | Designed to assess neurologically impaired patients. Generates 14 scores: motor, rhythm, tactile, visual, receptive speech, expressive speech, writing, reading, arithmetic, memory, intellectual processes, pathognomonic, left hemisphere, and right hemisphere functioning | No |
| Wisconsin Card-Sorting Test (WCST) | Ages 6.5–89 | Respondents are required to sort the cards according to different principles (color, form, or number) and to alter their approach when instructed. Primarily used to assess perseveration and abstract thinking; capable of measuring strategic planning, organized searching, goal-directed behavior, and impulsive responding. Sensitive to frontal lobe dysfunction | No |
| Rey Complex Figure Test (RCFT) | Ages 6–69 | Assesses neuropsychological functioning via measurements of visuospatial recognition memory, response bias, processing speed, and visuospatial constructional ability. Discriminates brain-damaged patients with documented memory impairment who are able to live independently from those who are not | Limited – measures response bias |
| Comprehensive Test of Nonverbal Intelligence (CTONI) | Ages 6–90 | Six subtests require subjects to view pictures and engage in problem-solving tasks involving analogies, categorizations, and sequences. Subjects respond by pointing – no reading, writing, or verbalization is required. Useful for testing individuals with language, neurological, or fine motor skill impairment, and non-English speakers | No |
| General Ability Measure for Adults (GAMA) | Ages 18 and older | Assessment of general intelligence; consists of matching, sequence, analogy, and construction tasks. Nonverbal format overcomes cultural, linguistic, and educational barriers | No |
| Slosson Full-Range Intelligence Test (S-FRIT) | Ages 5–21 | Assessment of verbal, performance, and cognitive ability | No |

[a]Schretlen D and Arkowitz H (1990) *Behavioral Sciences and the Law* 8: 75–84.

these scales do not control for forensic examiner bias, they should not be used in forensic evaluations to the exclusion of accounting for all history that these scales inventory.

## Intelligence Testing

The diagnosis of mental retardation is aided through up-to-date standardized intelligence testing. Specifically, testing with standardized psychometric instruments, with scores that fall at least two or more standard deviations below the age-group mean for the standardized psychometric instrument used, support a diagnosis of retardation. In the case of a specific learning disorder, the test results reflect deficits in a particular area, such as reading or arithmetic.

In order to contribute to a valid understanding of the defendant's intelligence, a test must be properly standardized for those of the examinee's age, cultural and racial background, language of fluency, and educational level of achievement.

Commonly employed tests are the Wechsler Memory Scale – Revised, Wechsler Adult Intelligence Scale (WAIS), now in its third version, the Halstead-Reitan Neuropsychological Battery, the Luria-Nebraska Neuropsychological Battery, the Wisconsin Card-Sorting Test, the California Verbal Learning Test, and the Rey Complex Figure test. Brief versions of the IQ tests are demonstrated to be inadequate relative to the full versions of the WAIS and Slosson (**Table 1**).

Tests must be administered with standard protocol by examiners fluent in the language of the examinee, and such practices must be verifiable, analogous to the gathering of physical evidence. Therefore, examiners who administer intelligence testing must offer complete documentation of raw data of the examination when submitting their findings. In addition, when testing is done in the context of an adversarial proceeding, the intelligence testing should be unobtrusively videotaped in order to verify the integrity of the protocols used.

Testing must be administered at the time of the forensic assessment. A defendant diagnosed as retarded or learning-disordered earlier in life may have improved from earlier testing, given the educational or psychosocial interventions previously available, such that intelligence testing no longer reflects that the defendant is retarded or learning-disordered.

Because earlier and later versions of a specific test may be administered, examiners must be prepared to educate the court about the discrepancies one might expect across versions of a test. The WAIS – Revised (WAIS-R), for example, is likely to result in scores that are somewhat lower than those recorded on the WAIS for nonretarded examinees. Retarded examinees tend to show less difference, although the WAIS-R scores higher than the WAIS in the mildly and moderately retarded, especially on the verbal and full-scale domains. For this reason, the moderately retarded may appear, on later testing, to be mildly retarded – though only full assessment of adaptive skills can resolve that question, including performance on standardized measures of adaptive behavior (**Table 2**).

For learning disorders, similar considerations apply. Wechsler Intelligence Scale for Children – third edition (WISC-III) scores are one-half to one-third of a standard deviation lower than comparable scores on the WISC-R. Having been given both tests, learning-disordered students may appear to have worsened as a result of this artifact.

Memory impairment, as measured through the Wechsler Memory Scales, may not correlate as reliable with lower IQ measurements on the WAIS-R. Adjustments in interpretation may be necessary, therefore, in interpreting findings in tested mentally retarded defendants.

## Other Diagnostic Testing

Old records of the retarded will include information crucial to the assessment of the defendant. Specifically, developmental delays would have been noticed by parents or other caregivers, and will have arranged for diagnostic workup of these problems. When a child first appears to be slow, there is enough concern within most families that a search for a cause, particularly a reversible cause, is recommended by the family pediatrician. Previous head trauma, if associated with long-term consequences, would also leave records of assessment.

Medical workup of retardation is likely to yield specific information relevant to legal proceedings only when genetic testing and neurological scanning are done. Positive findings on genetic testing may support the longstanding nature of the neurodevelopmental problems, and the fallout from unsuccessful and inexorably failed attempts to adapt over the life cycle.

Radiological scans, such as magnetic resonance imaging (MRI) and positron emission tomography (PET), may also demonstrate positive findings. However, subtle abnormalities in brain imaging can also be found in normal variants. Furthermore, such structural brain abnormalities may have developed later in life and cannot therefore be used to account for a predisposing condition to mental retardation unless the examinee's history reflects a life of poor adaptation and low function.

Because some medical conditions may have been poorly investigated in the examinee's early years, it is helpful to get a full diagnostic medical workup. Visual, facial, cardiac, neuromuscular, auditory, and other

**Table 2** Measures of adaptive behavior

| Test of adaptive behavior | Used for | Description |
|---|---|---|
| Vineland Adaptive Behavior Scales (VABS) – Expanded Form | 0–18 years; low-functioning adults | Assesses communication, daily living, socialization, and motor skills |
| Adaptive Behavior Assessment System (ABAS) | Ages 5–89 | Assesses individual's ability to perform and frequency of tasks in the following domains: communication, community usage, functional academics, home living, health and safety, leisure, self-care, self-direction, and work. Determines how well the individual responds to daily demands and is capable of living independently |
| Adaptive Behavior Inventory (ABI) | Ages 5–18 | Consists of five scales: Self-Care Skills, Social Skills, Communication Skills, Academic Skills, and Occupational Skills. Third party rates child's task performance on 4-point scale. Useful to screen for mental retardation or emotional disturbance |
| Adaptive Living Skills Curriculum and Checklist (ALSC) | Ages 2+ | Inventory of 80 behaviors in four domains: Personal Living Skills, Home Living Skills, and Community Living Skills, and Employment Skills |
| Inventory for Client and Agency (ICAP) | Children and adults | 16-page booklet completed by third party used to plan and evaluate services for people with disabilities. Includes 77 adaptive behavior items in the following domains: social/communication skills (interactions, language), personal living skills (independence), community living skills (work skills, money management, and motor skills). Includes an overall Service Score, that indicates overall level of care, supervision, or training required |
| Inventory for Client and Agency (ICAP) Problem Behavior Scales[a] | Children and adults | Precisely measures adaptive behavior and problem behaviors in three maladaptive clusters: (1) internalized (self-directed); (2) externalized (directed at others); and (3) asocial (within a social context) |
| Brief Index of Adaptive Behavior | Ages 5–17 | Inventory consisting of 39 items for assessment of three domains: Independent Function, Socialization, and Communication. Useful as a screen for possible behavior disorders and neuropsychological impairment |
| Scales of Independent Behavior, Revised (SIB-R) | Ages 0–80 | Measures functional independence and adaptive functioning in school, home, employment, and community settings; identifies internalized, externalized, and asocial maladaptive behaviors. Also generates Support Score to predict level of support individual will require based on impact of maladaptive behaviors on adaptive functioning |
| Social Skills Rating Scale (SSRS) | Ages 6–18 | Provides detailed analysis of positive and negative behaviors according to three scales: social skills (cooperation, assertion, responsibility, empathy, self-control), problem behaviors (external, internal, hyperactivity), and academic competence |
| Balthazar Scales of Adaptive Behavior | Ages 5–57 | Designed to measure self-care abilities: identifies weaknesses in eating, dressing, and toileting skills. Useful for giving appropriate training or treatment for profoundly and severely mentally retarded individuals |
| Adaptive Behavior Scale-Residential and Community: 2nd edition (ABS-RC:2) | Ages 18–79 | Rates adaptive behavior as measurement of personal routines, interpersonal behavior, and social responsibility. Part I measures personal independence and important coping skills for daily living; Part II measures social behavior and assesses presence of personality and behavioral disorders |

[a]McGrew KS, Bruininks RH, Thurlow ML (1992) Relationship between measures of adaptive functioning and community adjustment for adults with mental retardation. *Exceptional Children* 58: 517–529.

troubles may herald a familiar profile of a causal condition that influenced the examinee from early on.

## Malingering

The incidence of malingering in correctional settings is as high as 50%, and in the setting of more serious charges this figure may be much higher. The adversarial proceeding lends itself to different forms of malingering. This reality forces the forensic examiner to account for this possibility in assessing history, conducting examinations, and in reviewing the work of others.

Faked intellectual deficiency may be difficult to test for. While certain tests – such as the Test of Memory Malingering, Wechsler Memory Scale, Fifteen-item test, Victoria Symptom Validity Test, and forced-choice tests – may reveal a poor effort by the examinee, or even malingering, efforts to downplay intelligence may go unnoticed even on standardized psychological testing, particularly in an examinee who has been coached.

A number of factors can cause someone to perform more poorly on intelligence testing. Fatigue, failure to understand instructions, peripheral neurological difficulties, anxiety, depression, pain, psychosis, antagonism toward the examiner, age, and ethnic and cultural background, and malingering, have all been noted as contributing.

Intellectual test results do not worsen over the course of development from youth to adulthood, and if test results do not improve, they should be expected to remain the same, given the range allowed for margin of error. Test results that worsen from administration in youth should be regarded with suspicion of malingering, either by the defendant or by the examiner administering the tests.

History remains the most important factor in demonstrating the presence or absence of malingered mental retardation. Clear evidence of communication fluency that does not correspond with verbal intelligence testing performance, for example, reflects faking or inadequate testing conditions.

## Causes

Mental retardation originates from a variety of causes. Each of these conditions, be they congenital, perinatal, psychosocial, or illness, have a global impact on the growing central nervous system. As the brain develops mental and neurological networks even after birth, such broad-based deficits affect, depending on the condition, a variety of mental and physical abilities. Some conditions, such as fetal alcohol syndrome, more obviously impact mental abilities, and are also associated with learning disorders. Others, such as cerebral palsy, may cause profound neurological limitations but may relatively spare intellectual abilities.

In 30–40% of those diagnosed with mental retardation in clinical settings, no cause is identified, even after diagnostic workup. Likewise, learning disorders may not be associated with a particular cause (**Table 3**).

Ultimately, changes in the way nerve cells or neurons network together result in multiple and pervasive deficits in the individual's functioning.

## Course

### Onset

Mental retardation refers to below-average general intellectual functioning with typical onset in infancy or birth, that must occur prior to 18 years of age. A preponderance of those with mental retardation have comorbid mental disorders that are estimated to be three to four times greater than in the general population. There is nothing to suggest that the etiology of a given mental disorder is different in individuals who have mental retardation, however.

### Progression

The cause and the severity of mental retardation are contingent upon the age and mode of onset of the disorder in the individual, although, as mentioned previously, symptoms must be present before the age of 18. Factors that may influence the course of mental retardation include, but are not limited to, the presence of underlying medical conditions and environmental considerations such as parental stimulation and access to educational opportunities.

Depending on the severity of the retardation and the extent of the faculties that the disorder impacts (as well as the availability of external resources), a diagnosis of mental retardation is not indicative of a lifelong condition. For example, an individual with mild retardation, diagnosed early in childhood, may not excel in an academia-related environment. However, with sufficient training and support, it is possible for the acquisition of adaptive living skills such that the individual no longer meets the degree of impairment necessary for a diagnosis of mental retardation.

## Differential Diagnosis

Numerous circumstances, such as education, motivation, personality characteristics, social and vocational opportunities, other mental disorders, and general medical conditions that may coexist with mental retardation, influence adaptive functioning.

It is often difficult to diagnose accurately the presence of comorbid mental disorders, as the symptomatology may be impacted or marred by the severity of mental retardation and associated limitations. For example, deficits in verbal exchanges may result in an inaccurate history of the individual, given his/her inability to communicate a comprehensive history.

Individuals with learning and communication disorders may have otherwise normal intellect, impulse control, judgment, and function. Therefore, these persons would not be diagnosed with mental retardation.

Individuals with autism, communication disorder, and Asperger's syndrome are not necessarily retarded. The developmental problems of these conditions contribute to a person's social awkwardness, even ineptitude. However, intelligence testing may demonstrate them to be quite capable.

Learning disorders may affect academic performance from early in scholastic life. However, these learning disorders do not necessarily mean that a person has retardation. The overlap of diagnostic criteria for learning disorders, as well as autism, Asperger's, and other developmental disorders, mandates strict attention to criteria in assessing and diagnosing mental retardation.

A history of scholastic problems may be accompanied by behavioral problems of attention deficit hyperactivity disorder or oppositional defiant disorder. Careful history-taking delineates whether retardation coexisted with these conditions, or whether the diagnoses caused scholastic problems to a severe degree. As these diagnoses may dissipate by late adolescence, evidence for behavior evolution must be carefully tracked as the defendant's history moves into adulthood.

Furthermore, attention deficit hyperactivity disorder and oppositional defiant disorder often graduate into antisocial personality disorder and narcissistic personality disorder, respectively. Diagnostic examination, when these conditions are present in youth, must probe whether such an evolution has transpired in adulthood, or more dramatically, if the defendant evolved into a psychopath.

Depression and anxiety often present with behavioral problems and poor academic performance in school. In such cases, functional impairment may not be persistent, though chronic depression may obscure the nature of the diagnosis, as depression often presents differently in children and adolescents.

Courts may confront individuals who suffered brain injuries from trauma early in life, causing significant intellectual deterioration, including memory problems, but who are otherwise functionally intact. Head trauma, if it is sufficiently severe, will cause a remarkable loss of intellect, and possibly affect other functional domains. The history of changes is more abrupt. These individuals would be diagnosed with dementia. If all the criteria for mental retardation are present, mental retardation would be diagnosed.

A diagnosis of mental retardation should be made whenever the diagnostic criteria are met, even in the presence of another disorder, unless testing for intelligence is substantially affected by the psychosis or intoxication of an examinee.

Deficits in judgment and impulse control may be especially magnified in those who experience other acute conditions, such as intoxication and psychosis. Mental retardation can be diagnosed with other such related diagnoses, such as schizophrenia and alcohol dependence, if testing is performed under conditions that would not be directly influenced by the conditions themselves.

For example, if a person with schizophrenia who was not otherwise psychotic performed exceptionally poorly on intelligence testing, and on impulse control assessment, both diagnoses would be present. Likewise, a person with alcoholism who displays no impulse control problems and less impaired intellect when sober does not meet the criteria for mental retardation.

Even a diagnosis of retardation does not preclude the possibility that criminal behavior may be driven by drug abuse. A history needs to be gathered as to the defendant's use of drugs, their effect on his/her behavior, patterns of abuse, and whether this is done in groups, alone, or otherwise. If toxicology testing – which should be done at the time of arrest for any defendant who is suspected of a mental abnormality – reveals some illicit or prescription substance that affects behavior, the history will assist in the contextual understanding of the crime.

## Ethnic, Gender, and Cultural Variations

Mental retardation cuts across the lines of racial, ethnic, educational, social, and economic backgrounds. It can occur in any family. Measures should be taken to ensure that intelligence-testing procedures, as well as adaptive functioning testing procedures, adequately recognize the individual's ethnic, cultural, or linguistic background.

The prevalence of mental retardation due to known biological factors is similar among children of upper and lower socioeconomic classes. Certain etiological factors are linked to lower socioeconomic status. When the etiology is unknown, and no specific biological causation can be identified, the mental retardation is usually milder and individuals from lower socioeconomic classes are overrepresented. The causal relationship between adequacy of parenting, environment, and mental retardation draws support from this trend.

## Case Considerations

### Interviewing

Unique challenges confront the forensic interviewer of the mentally retarded. Sensitivity must be heightened

**Table 3** Conditions that cause mental retardation

| Condition | Associated symptoms | Medical diagnostic tests | Prognosis |
|---|---|---|---|
| Normal genetic variation | None: normal health, physical ability, appearance | | Mild intellectual impairment unlikely to affect capacity to function |
| Fragile X syndrome | Learning disorders; hyperactivity; anxiety; unstable mood; autistic-like behaviors; long face; flat feet; seizures | DNA-based blood test reveals X-chromosome abnormality | No cure; medication available to treat symptoms |
| Fukutin related-protein (FKRP) gene mutation | Congenital muscular dystrophy; cerebellar cysts | DNA-based test indicates chromosomal mutation on chromosome 19q13.3 | Severe cases will have severe impairment; mild mutations have favorable long-term outcome |
| Lesch–Nyhan syndrome (typically males only) | Compulsive self-mutilating behavior; head-banging; joint swelling; dysphagia; impaired kidney function; athetosis; chorea | Prenatal chorionic biopsy reveals deficiency of the enzyme hypoxanthine guanine phosphoribosyl transferase (HPRT) | Poor: no treatment for neurological defects; build-up of uric acid in body may be fatal; some require restraints and intensive supervision |
| Tuberous sclerosis complex (TSC) | Skin and central nervous system lesions; tumor growth; seizures | Brain MRI, CT scan, renal ultrasound, ECG, eye exam, and Wood's lamp evaluation of the skin | No cure; however, most patients will live normal life span |
| Down syndrome | Low muscle tone; distinguishing physical features; enlarged tongue; heart defects; hypothyroidism; visual and gastrointestinal problems | Triple screen and alpha-fetoprotein blood tests in combination with ultrasound; chorionic villus sampling (CVS); amniocentesis; percutaneous umbilical blood sampling (PUBS); karyotype | No cure; however, mental retardation is typically within mild to moderate range |
| Klinefelter syndrome (males) | Stunted genital development; abnormal body proportions; personality impairment | Rectal exam shows enlarged prostate; karyotype shows 47 chromosomes in each cell instead of normal 46; semen exam shows low sperm count and decreased serum testosterone level | No cure; symptoms can be treated |
| William's syndrome | Abnormal facial features; frequent heart problems | Elevated serum calcium; X-ray of the chest or ECG shows heart abnormalities | Varies: some will be able to master self-help skills; others require lifelong intensive supervision |
| Prader–Willi syndrome | Low muscle tone; incomplete sexual development; problem behaviors; chronic feeling of hunger resulting in life-threatening obesity | Specialized genetic testing on a blood sample | Require lifelong diet supervision and obesity prevention to insure normal life span |
| Tay–Sachs disease | Loss of muscle tone and motor skills; exaggerated response to sudden noises; vision and hearing problems | Prenatal: amniocentesis or CVS indicates abnormal gene<br>After birth: blood test | Classic infantile Tay–Sachs is fatal; long-term prognosis for adults is unknown |
| Cretinism | Dwarfism; body disfigurement; skin defects; motor and speech impairment | Blood test shows lack of thyroid hormone | Treated with thyroid extract and iodine intake; growth and mental facility will improve |
| Turner syndrome (females) | Webbed physical features; lack of ovarian development; cardiovascular, kidney, and thyroid problems | Karyotype indicates complete or partial absence of one of the two X chromosomes | No cure; growth hormone and estrogen replacement therapy improve symptoms |

| Condition | Symptoms | Diagnosis | Prognosis/Treatment |
|---|---|---|---|
| Cerebral palsy | Epilepsy, learning disorders, and various neurological problems | MRI and CT scan may indicate hydrocephalus; diagnosis primarily based on developmental delays as well as muscle tone, movement, and reflex abnormalities | Despite significant neurological limitations, intellectual capacity remains relatively intact |
| Cardiofaciocutaneous (CFC) syndrome | Physical abnormalities; skin discoloration; cardiac defects | No current laboratory test; diagnosis relies on clinician's observations | No cure; treatment varies |
| Phenylketonuria (PKU) | Skin and gastrointestinal problems; unusual behavior; delayed growth; frequent seizures | Blood test revealing high levels of phenylalanine; almost all states require newborn testing within a few days of birth | Requires careful diet monitoring from onset; patients lead normal life |
| Congenital muscular dystrophy (CMD) | Muscle weakness; joint deformity; hypotonia; delayed motor development | Blood test for high levels of muscle enzyme creatine kinase (CK); muscle biopsy reveals muscle fiber size variation; electromyography (EMG) shows unusual activity | No cure; treatment aimed at preventing complications |
| Congenital hypothyroidism | Jaundice; body-shape abnormalities; respiratory distress: slowed mental development | Blood test revealing lack of effective thyroid hormone | Some forms only temporary; treated with thyroid hormone |
| Prenatal toxins: maternal consumption (drugs/alcohol; smoking) and infection (toxoplasmosis, cytomegalovirus, rubella, syphilis, human immunodeficiency virus (HIV)) | | | |
| Fetal acohol syndrome (FAS) | Facial abnormalities; growth deficiency; central nervous system dysfunction; neurological deficits and learning disorders | Abnormal levels as indicated on blood test | Poor; 82% of patients will not be able to live independently |
| Fetal malnutrition | Prematurity; low birth weight; "failure to thrive" conditions at birth | | Poor; those who survive will have lasting impairments |
| Cerebral hypoxia (oxygen deprivation) | Inattentiveness; poor judgment; memory loss; impaired motor coordination | PET scan indicates lack of oxygen in cerebral blood flow | Worse the longer brain has been deprived of oxygen: During recovery, psychological and neurological abnormalities such as amnesia, personality regression, hallucinations, memory loss, and muscle spasms and twitches may appear, persist, and then resolve |
| Head trauma | Headaches, visual and neurological problems | Damage is indicated on CT scan, MRI, or other imaging techniques | Varies; depends on severity of injury |
| Lead/mercury poisoning | Muscular, gastrointestinal, and visual problems; convulsions; agitation; hallucinations; other nervous system abnormalities and learning disorders | Blood chemistry test indicates toxic levels | Treatment is effective; however, chronic exposure may be fatal |
| Childhood diseases: whooping cough, chickenpox, encephalitis, measles, hepatitis B | | | |
| Environmental stressors: poverty, inadequate healthcare and education | | | |

MRI, magnetic resonance imaging; CT, computed tomography; ECG, electrocardiogram; PET, positron emission tomography.

to nonverbal cues in poor communicators. Jocularity and condescension should be avoided. At the same time, questions should be carefully phrased so that the examinee understands the question enough to answer it.

The interviewee's responses may be difficult to understand; alternatively, the examinee may respond so as to please the interviewer, particularly if there is a more pronounced status difference between interviewer and examinee. Interviewers must be careful to avoid overdirecting the interview; furthermore, the examinee may reflect answers to a response set, rather than open-ended information that is more objective to the forensic interview.

Response bias, particularly in the acquiescent, can be reduced by substituting either/or questions for yes/no questions, especially if accompanied by picture representations of each choice.

## Death Investigation

Suicide in the mentally retarded is more frequent in the mildly retarded compared to the severely retarded. However, research on those affected with Down syndrome demonstrated suicidality to be less frequent among the handicapped, compared to an unaffected group. Only nonverbal learning disability has shown any association with suicidality.

The mental health history of the decedent must therefore be considered in any death investigation. While depression may be chronicled in a retarded individual, other psychiatric diagnoses often go undiagnosed. Therefore, special consideration should be taken to gather a history for symptoms such as hopelessness, self-endangerment, or self-mutilation, or other suggestion of progenitors to successful suicide.

Given the functional problems of the retarded, their higher risk for accidents leaves them vulnerable to unexpected and unanticipated death. Evidence from the scene of the investigation will yield additional details as to the likelihood of error or uncoordination in contributing to the decedent's demise.

The retarded are often victimized. Homicide by strangers may involve bullies or other antisocial predators who recognize the retarded individual as a patsy who is easily overcome, as an outlet to discharge anger. As the retarded are unlikely to be very profitable robbery victims, robbery–homicide is more likely to relate to drug-seeking behavior that targets the most readily available victim, or adolescent perpetrators who risk the legal consequences of homicide for even small amounts of money.

Likewise, the retarded may be victimized by overwhelmed or abusive family members, or by live-in significant others who displace antagonistic feelings.

The retarded may be sexually victimized as well. Death under such circumstances does not preclude other motives or likely perpetrators. Such perpetrators may themselves be retarded.

Evidence, from crime investigation, of a sophisticated *modus operandi* reflects on the intellect of the actor. However, a perpetrator may perform poorly on intelligence testing and still show an elaborate and devious methodology and plan to homicide. The more clearly intellectually limited a perpetrator is, the more likely it is that his/her role in a carefully planned or elaborately orchestrated crime was more confined, or as an accessory who followed the instigation of a less intellectually limited prime mover.

## Victimization and Aggression

Rates of violence perpetrated on people with mental retardation are higher than those against the rest of the population. Few are reported to the authorities, and retarded complainants may not inspire a sense of credibility among the police, who may then choose not to investigate or prosecute their complaints.

More aggressive and confrontational tendencies are associated with victimization, as well as more acquiescent personalities. Indeed, many perpetrators have also been victimized. Interpersonal training may decrease vulnerability to victimization, independent of environmental factors.

Medications targeting aggression, and the underlying psychological illness responsible for it, are effective in the mentally retarded. Anger-management programs have demonstrable efficacy in reducing long-term violence potential in the mentally handicapped.

## Sexuality and Expression

Given emerging sensitivity to the exploitation of the retarded, it may be difficult to balance protection of the retarded with an appreciation for their sexuality.

Denying the sexuality of the retarded is passé. Sterilization is out of favor. However, what is maturation, for purposes to give informed consent, in someone whose "mental age" is widely considered to be as a child?

Sex education facilitates an appreciation of the significance of sexual relations, informed consent, sexual hygiene, and conscientious contraception. Even the retarded sex offender is best rehabilitated by sex education, especially in adolescents.

## Miranda and Interrogation Issues

A suspect's Miranda rights in US courts require police to advise suspects, prior to interrogation, that they have a right to remain silent, to an attorney, and that whatever they disclose in an interrogation can and will be used against them in court. Poor intellect alone does not *per se* reflect incompetence to waive Miranda rights. However, since waiving Miranda requires a "knowing" and "intelligent" waiver, mental retardation warrants careful consideration of the defendant's unique awareness.

Competency in the Miranda setting, as well as questions that probe false confessions, requires contextual relevance, and a specific accounting of a defendant's strengths and weaknesses. A diagnosis of retardation, even a noticeably reduced IQ score, does not necessarily deprive the defendant of competence to waive Miranda such that a diligent history need not be performed.

Clearly, a retarded suspect with communication problems may be unable to waive Miranda rights. An illiterate defendant would have to be engaged orally by detectives, who would need to carefully explain these rights and the ramifications of waiving them.

Even then, the impaired anticipation of consequences in a retarded suspect may have to be uniquely accounted for. Unless familiar with the system, suspects may not recognize the possibility that they will have to answer for charges made against them in a court of law. For this reason, the examination of statements and the circumstances of their being provided requires review of how well Miranda rights are explained.

The British have instituted changes in how the retarded are questioned. This reflects research that has demonstrated how the retarded are generally more suggestible, or moved into accepting scenarios of self-incrimination, by questioning interrogators. US courts have also acknowledged and accounted for the importance of suggestibility and compliance of the retarded suspect.

The latter vulnerability, particularly notable to the retarded, may lead to false acceptance of responsibility, or false confessions. So, too, may the retarded suspect's compliance with interrogators who demand an admission of guilt during questioning.

History on the circumstances of the questioning, which should be accompanied by a complete videotaped record of the proceedings, should be obtained to appraise the confessions of the retarded. These sources of information are best appreciated with a full understanding of the defendant's unique way of relating to authority, and how that style compared to the dynamics present in the interrogation setting.

## Competency to Stand Trial

The skills required for such competency include controlling behavior in the courtroom setting, aspects relating to the ability to communicate with counsel, assisting with the planning of a defense, and understanding the roles of the different functionaries and trial procedure. Under most circumstances, defendants are not expected to direct their case.

However, as many cases result in plea negotiations, the defendant's understanding of the ramifications of the plea he/she is accepting may be difficult to determine. The threshold for a finding of competency is typically afforded a higher threshold by examining clinicians when the case is particularly complex, or charges are severe.

The Competency Assessment for Standing Trial for Defendants with Mental Retardation (CAST-MR) is a 50-item inventory, arranged in three sections of multiple-choice and open-ended questions. It enables a standardized competency examination to be carried out with the simple communication needed for special populations.

For a defendant found not competent to proceed, education may assist in complete and essential awareness of the court functionaries and their behavior. The most difficult obstacle to overcome may be the defendant's lack of competency to assist in the planning of his/her case; the ambiguous possibilities of such claims, however, warrant a demonstration of how that limitation is interfering with the attorney–client relationship.

Behavior can also be remedied to become more contained in the courtroom setting, and within a relatively short period of time. Medications for impulse control do not necessarily require many weeks to exert sufficient effect to restore competency. Antipsychotics, similarly, can restore competency within weeks, unless the defendant is exceptionally resistant to them.

## Competency to Proceed *Pro Se*

While the same set of skills for competency to plea are required as for competency to stand trial, one would be hard-pressed to find a situation where a truly retarded defendant could intelligently represent him/herself.

## Competency to Plea

An otherwise retarded defendant may still be competent to accept a plea. Accepting a plea offer may reflect acquiescence or compliance by the defendant, and a full appreciation of what will happen once the plea is accepted may be absent. Therefore, when there is evidence for retardation, care should be made to ensure competency to accept a plea.

## Mens Rea

Individuals with functional and adaptive problems and poor performance on standardized testing may nevertheless form quite criminal intent. The retarded, particularly the mildly mentally retarded, make a variety of choices about their lives without great difficulty, and therefore can make such choices relative to criminal actions.

*Mens rea* is a particularly complex issue in the retarded that does not necessarily correspond to the level of functional impairment, or performance on intelligence testing. The history of a defendant's typical behavior is a more likely guide to resolve these questions.

Crimes that reflect a pattern of the defendant's stealth and concealment, as well as premeditation, demonstrate clear *mens rea*. This issue is less certain when crimes follow impulsive decisions, particularly so when the crimes parallel fairly common behavior by the defendant.

Stalking is a crime that may naturally originate from a retarded person's poor social sensitivity. While some unwanted and persistent annoyances are threatening and menacing, others are simply repeated efforts to maintain contact in the face of rejection or emotional dependence.

Shoplifting may result from kleptomania or other poor impulse control and hoarding that sometimes complicates the behavioral presentation of the retarded.

Likewise, unprovoked minor assaults or destruction of property are commonly described in the more severely mentally retarded. An offended or aggrieved victim may pursue criminal charges; under these circumstances, the defendant's capacity for *mens rea* would require closer study.

History is helpful in this regard. Parents, peers, school officials, and treatment records give additional insight into whether in the past the defendant was one to exhibit proactive or predatory violence – or reactive violence in response to provocation.

Such history should also ascertain the customary settings for such violent behavior, as well as any secondary gain that the defendant may have realized from previous violence. This information better distinguishes whether the defendant is given to engaging in violence in group or solitary settings.

Many of the moderately retarded, and particularly the severely retarded, have a poorly developed sense of boundaries, and sexual interest and curiosity may violate the integrity of another. Sex offenses, particularly those committed in full view of others, warrant closer examination as to the defendant's intent (**Table 4**).

**Table 4** Complicating factors impacting *mens rea* in the mentally retarded

Pattern of stealth and concealment
Premeditation
Realization of secondary gain
Crimes as result of poor social sensitivity and emotional dependence (example: stalking)
Crimes as result of poor impulse control (example: shoplifting)
Crimes as result of poorly developed sense of boundaries
History of violent behavior and unprovoked aggression
Capacity to distinguish right from wrong

In certain instances, the retarded defendant may reflect a clear lack of understanding of the criminality of his/her conduct. However, in other cases, that understanding is as clear as for a person who performs much better on intelligence testing. The question can only be resolved by careful history-gathering that reflects on the choices made – and those opted against – by the defendant, before the crime.

The mere history that a person is institutionalized, or lacks an obvious motive, does not preclude the possibility that the defendant could form *mens rea*. Apart from a careful accounting of the crime, the *mens rea* question is best resolved with history from progress notes on what problem behaviors the defendant had been counseled on in the past, and what degree of understanding he/she had demonstrated. In spite of a defendant having been counseled on such problem behaviors, even repeatedly, the instant offense may reflect his/her acting out when angry or otherwise unsettled.

## Moral Decision-Making and Appreciation of Wrong

While brain and neurological development is impaired in the retarded, decision-making and moral judgment demonstrate significant impairment primarily in those who are moderately to severely retarded. Even then, many with intelligence testing consistent with moderate retardation have adequate moral development to recognize right from wrong. Hence, they live their lives with little need for supervision or institutional placement.

Moral maturity and cognitive reasoning relate more directly to each other rather than to mental age. Ultimately, focusing an assessment on these areas provides greatest insight into the moral capabilities of a defendant.

At the same time, psychotic disorders are underdiagnosed in the retarded. A careful history must also address the possibility that the defendant has a major psychiatric disorder on top of retardation. An additional, or dual diagnosis, may account for why a person with retardation, who would have a well-established ability to appreciate wrong, could be affected by an acute psychotic condition, such as schizophrenia, bipolar disorder, or psychotic depression. Such a major mental illness would affect the defendant's moral decision-making in the same way it does anyone else with those conditions.

## Remorse

Remorse is a potentially misleading concept in the retarded. While they may experience unimpaired regret and remorse, disturbances in communication or social skills may impede a clear expression of remorse. A defendant's capabilities are best distinguished by gathering an adequate history of moral development, including expression of remorse, from caregivers, parents, or other close acquaintances. This includes a history of the behaviors for which he/she expresses remorse, and how this is expressed.

## Ability to Conform Conduct

Impulse control problems are common in the retarded. Not surprisingly, a number of crimes may occur because of the defendant's inability to conform conduct. However, even those with impulse control problems may retain a substantial capacity to conform their conduct to the requirements of the law.

As with other aspects of forensic examination, it is best to answer these questions on a case-by-case basis. An assessment of a particular crime should also examine the history of the defendant's behavior, his/her history of impulse control problems, the circumstances under which he/she demonstrated such impulse control problems, how they manifested themselves, whether he/she was receiving treatment for them, and whether that treatment was successful.

## Appreciation of Consequences of Actions

Poor judgment is a manifestation of limited intelligence, and may contribute to a viable diagnosis of retardation. The defendant's capabilities, however, need to be distinguished from a momentary bad decision or bad judgment *per se* because the actions were criminal. The retarded defendant's poor adaptive skills include impairment in the capacity to foresee the full extent of the consequences of his/her actions. This may be the case even when the defendant is fully aware of the nature of what he/she was doing.

Appreciation of the nature and consequences of actions, such as it is applied in the insanity defense, does not require that the defendant foresee all of the potential consequences. The extent of the defendant's understanding is best examined through observations of other witnesses before, during, and immediately after the crime, including witnesses to the defendant's comments and statements. Therefore, impaired intelligence and functional adaptation, consistent with a diagnosis of retardation, is not a *per se* basis to presume that the defendant lacks the capacity to appreciate the consequences of his/her actions.

Nevertheless, those with severe deficits in adaptive functions and particularly low intelligence testing scores are more likely to lack such capacity. Testing scores and other adaptive problems, however, do not eliminate the need to review the defendant's history pertinent to the time around the crime.

## Prognosis and Future Risk

A person whose retardation was responsible for a crime, either because of impulse control or poor socialization, may or may not continue to demonstrate the same deficits later in life. While retardation is a developmental disorder that does not reverse, individuals with retardation may progress through education. Training and other strategies may be successful in reducing the degree, or number, of functional and adaptive problems.

Nevertheless, the retarded are capable of having antisocial personality features. Under these circumstances, retardation will particularly complicate the expression of antisocial personality disorder, whose symptoms will be particularly difficult to treat. By reviewing the history of the crime and ascertaining the thoughts and motivations behind it, an examiner may be able to delineate the relevance of retardation versus antisocial personality as the prime mover of the crime or the decision to choose criminality.

When crimes are a direct product of retardation, the prognosis is directly affected by the residential arrangements for the defendant's disposition, their suitability for a person of his/her behavior, or medicines that a defendant may be prescribed.

Unlike defendants who recover from illnesses, the retarded defendant will represent a risk when conditions present at the time of the instant offense repeat themselves. Therefore, the supervising institution should account for future risk in its treatment planning – both in the training programs devised for the defendant as well as the level of supervision the defendant receives.

## Mitigation at Sentencing

Mental retardation has been acknowledged as a mitigating factor in capital-eligible cases. The US Supreme Court has ruled in Atkins that the mentally retarded cannot be executed, while assigning responsibility to states to define "retardation" for purposes of capital eligibility.

Given the range of crimes that have not been included in the Atkins ruling, retardation may have a significant impact on the defendant's participation in crime and be appropriately mitigating.

A crime may reflect the retardation of the defendant. Impulsivity may be demonstrated in shoplifting, vandalism, ringing fire alarms, assault – even sexual offenses, and murder.

Poor judgment may also be reflected in the perpetrator's actions. Bad judgment is best reflected in unnecessary crimes, crimes that would obviously result in capture, crimes with bumbling *modus operandi*, for example.

Other aspects of retardation, such as adaptive or intellectual difficulties, may have very little relevance to crimes, and when present, should not be considered as contributing to the mitigating influence *per se* of retardation.

Like other conditions, mental retardation may have a mitigating impact on a crime, as it is indeed a significant illness, but like significant diseases such as pancreatic cancer, it may have little relevance to criminogenic decision-making. Resolving the relevance of a diagnosis of mental retardation to mitigation requires a careful review of the defendant's actions before, during, and after the crime.

### Employment Considerations

**Accommodation and the Americans with Disabilities Act** The Americans with Disabilities Act affords promising protections to those with mental retardation and, in particular, the learning-disabled. With many fairly simple positions very much within the range of capabilities of the retarded, the Americans with Disabilities Act allows that if a person can perform the essential functions of his/her position, an employer must make reasonable accommodations for the disability.

While learning disorders often disappear by adulthood, the potentials that accompany the limitations of the learning-disordered expand the possibilities for their employability.

Adaptation to learning disorders earlier in life may be complicated, however, and the learning-disordered are often hampered by personality problems, even disorders, that originated from coping strategies they developed during earlier scholastic underachievement.

Since the Americans with Disabilities Act does not protect the entitled malcontent, forensic disputes may well arise in employees with personality problems independent of any learning disorder, who

claim disability on the basis of school performance in their youth. The nuances of such cases are reflected in an employer's desire to rid him/herself of a foul employee – not one who is making spelling, mathematics, or reading errors.

The retarded endure conditions, long before they reach the workplace, that engender in them a sense that they are less entitled. Typically, the retarded are not at all litigious, and their low sophistication limits their awareness of legal rights. Complaints on their behalf, therefore, more likely originate from aggrieved family members, if at all. Retarded employees who are unaware of their legal protections are less likely to externalize responsibility to the employer when conveying reasons for an unlawful dismissal.

**Discrimination and harassment** The same natural forces that engender silence among the retarded indeed manifest themselves in hostile work environments. A naturally diminished self-esteem, and a lack of confidence relative to other employees, interferes with the mentally retarded employee's acknowledgment that even if he/she has been victimized and bullied at other times, such treatment at the workplace is unacceptable.

One legacy of harassment and discrimination complaints is that they are brought by individuals who are combative, determined, and sophisticated enough to recognize, and then respond legally, to discrimination. Given the qualities of the mentally retarded, the most likely vehicle for protecting their rights may indeed be their parents or guardians.

The learning-disordered are not affected intellectually, and may be painfully sensitive – in the opposite direction – to the treatment they get from others at the workplace. An economy that affords fewer jobs, downsizing, and decisions of whom to lay off that seem arbitrary may give rise or inspire scrutiny as to whether an employment action was motivated by discrimination.

### Parental Rights

No anticipated reproductive problems necessarily accompany retardation. However, the ability of a retarded mother to parent her child adequately may be in question. Maternal mental retardation is associated with an increased risk of child abuse and neglect. Neglect complaints are particularly overrepresented. Because of their retardation, parents are unable to utilize community resources properly, even as agencies make them available. Retarded parents are often characterized as dependent on others, who may even victimize them. As they may not be able to drive or to make change, and may have unrealistic expectations of their child's development, in a crisis setting, they may destabilize further.

Love, and the capacity to love, is unrelated to retardation *per se*. Given the range of abilities and limitations that a retarded person may possess, the capacity to learn may prove to be the rate-limiting factor in demonstrating whether education can overcome his/her other shortcomings. Better outcomes may be enabled by the presence of a normal functioning adult who is able to provide extended daily support to the retarded adults and their children. Worse outcomes may arise if a child who is already at risk from a genetic standpoint for retardation faces a higher risk from environmental neglect as well.

The moderately retarded, and those more severely impaired, may be encumbered with insurmountable limitations that keep them from mastering their own routines, let alone those of their children. Foster care has been shown to improve the emotional condition of depressed and functionally deteriorating children of the retarded. Older children of the retarded may project a pseudomaturity, endeavoring to care for both parents and younger siblings.

## See Also

**Forensic Psychiatry and Forensic Psychology:** Personality Disorder; Multiple Personality Disorder; Stalking; Criminal Responsibility

## Further Reading

Abramson PR, Parker T, Weisberg SR (1988) Sexual expression of mentally retarded people: educational and legal implications. *American Journal on Mental Retardation* 93: 328–334.

American Psychological Association (2000) *Diagnostic, Statistical Manual of Mental Disorders DSM-IV-TR.* Washington, DC: American Psychological Association.

*Atkins* v. *Virginia* (2002) 260 Va. 375, 534 S. E. 2d 312.

Day K (1988) A hospital-based treatment programme for male mentally handicapped offenders. *British Journal of Psychiatry* 153: 635–644.

Day K (1993) Crime and mental retardation: a review. In: Howells K, Hollin CR (eds.) *Clinical Approaches to the Mentally Disordered Offender,* pp. 111–144. London: Wiley.

Duckworth MS, Radhakrishnan G, Nolan ME, Frasier WI (1993) Initial encounters between people with a mild mental handicap and psychiatrists: an investigation of a method of evaluating interview skills. *Journal of Intellectual Disability Research* 37: 263–276.

Fletcher RJ, Dosen A (1993) *Mental Health Aspects of Mental Retardation: Progress in Assessment and Treatment.* New York: Lexington Books.

In re: Lora Faye Wirsing, Developmental Disabled Person (1998) 456 Mich. 467; 573 N.W.2d 51.

Jacobsen JW (1990) Do some mental disorders occur less frequently among persons with mental retardation? *American Journal on Mental Retardation* 94: 596–602.

Kennedy CH, Niederbuhl J (2000) Establishing criteria for sexual consent capacity. *American Journal on Mental Retardation* 106: 503–510.

Lindsay WR, Allan R, MacLeod F, Smart N, Smith AHW (2003) Long-term treatment and management of violent tendencies of men with intellectual disabilities convicted of assault. *Mental Retardation* 41: 47–56.

Petersilia JR (2001) Crime victims with developmental disabilities: a review essay. *Criminal Justice and Behavior* 28: 655–694.

Santamour M, West B (1977) *Mentally Retarded Offender and Corrections.* Washington, DC: US Department of Justice, National Institute of Law Enforcement and Criminal Justice Law.

Stephens B (1974) Symposium: developmental gains in the reasoning, moral judgment, and moral conduct of retarded and nonretarded persons. *American Journal of Mental Deficiency* 79: 113–115.

# Drug and Alcohol Addiction

**W Flannery**, National Alcohol Unit, London, UK
**M Farrell**, National Addiction Centre, London, UK

## Introduction

Addiction originates from a Latin word, which describes debtors, who are in effect slaves to their creditors. In a similar derivative manner, dependence implies a condition of being beholden or subordinate. This article examines how substance use and its problems relate to a forensic setting. In conceptualizing addiction, three models are used. The first is the disease model, in which by using symptoms and signs, a diagnosis is made and treatment commenced. Alcoholics Anonymous (AA) uses this as the wellspring of its approach and philosophy. Second, the socioeconomic model places substance misuse in the context of the social environment to which individuals belong. Factors from this environment direct the individual to substance misuse. This model has greatly influenced the temperance movement. Finally, substance misuse can be viewed in terms of behavioral theory. Classical conditioning describes how the stimulus and the desire to use a substance lead to a response – the consumption of a substance for its positive effects. The setting where the substance is consumed can then become associated with the substance. This leads to the setting itself becoming the stimulus to use independently of the desire to use. The setting acts as a cue to use. A cue can be a physical location, drug paraphernalia, company of friends, or experiencing the symptoms of stress. Operant conditioning explains how the effects of a substance encourage further use. The positive effects reward the user and so act as a positive reinforcer in that further use is encouraged. Withdrawal symptoms are unpleasant and are relieved by substance use. So, withdrawal symptoms act as a negative reinforcer as they encourage further substance use to alleviate their presence. Social learning theory suggests that when individuals observe the actions of others and their effects, they then copy what they have observed in order to obtain the same effect. The cognitive factors involved in this process, such as anticipation, planning, expectation, and self-efficacy, form the basis of cognitive behavioral therapy and relapse prevention.

Moving from these models explaining how it happens on to what is happening, the Epidemiological Catchment Area study gave lifetime prevalence for substance-related disorders for the general population of 16.7%, which shows the penetration of substance-related problems into society. This is even truer for the forensic and criminal justice settings, as substance misuse is the most common health problem encountered in these settings. Prevalence rates vary, but up to 50% of prisoners meet the criteria for alcohol or drug dependency. Over one-third of fatal road traffic accidents involve drugs or alcohol. Alcohol is a factor in over half of homicides and drugs in over one-third. There is no doubt as to the ubiquity of the malign influence of substances in people's lives.

## Common Drugs of Abuse

The more common drugs of abuse can be grouped in various ways. Drugs of a group have similar effects, use the same biological mechanisms, have cross-tolerance, and display a similar pattern of withdrawal.

### Opiates

Opiates can be opium-derived, such as morphine and codeine, semisynthetic, such as heroin, or synthetic, such as methadone. They all have a dependence potential and, although not fatal, have very unpleasant withdrawal symptoms.

### General Depressants

This group contains alcohol, benzodiazepines, chloral, and paraldehyde. Withdrawal symptoms can be unpleasant and, in the case of alcohol, potentially fatal.

### Stimulants

Stimulants can be plant-derived, e.g., cocaine and coffee, or manufactured, e.g., amphetamines and appetite suppressants. Withdrawal symptoms are less severe than in the case of opiates and general depressants.

### Hallucinogens

These include lysergic acid diethylamide (LSD) and mescaline. There are no withdrawal symptoms, but withdrawal may cause prolonged "flashback" experiences.

### Volatile Organic Substances

This group ranges from anesthetic gases and fluorinated hydrocarbons to petrol, toluene, butane, and amyl nitrite. Acute intoxication can cause death. There is usually no marked dependence or withdrawal.

### Substances with Mixed Properties

These are substances whose effects cross group boundaries. Cannabis has depressant properties and idiosyncratic hallucinogenic properties at higher doses. Nicotine is both a stimulant and a depressive. Methylenedioxymethamphetamine (MDMA, ecstasy) is an amphetamine derivative with both stimulant and hallucinogenic properties.

## Definitions

Various terms are used in the field of substance misuse, and it is useful to understand what each term implies. The following terms, with corresponding descriptions, apply to all substances, i.e., both drugs and alcohol.

- Substance use or abuse: this is the use of mind-altering chemicals, whether they are licit or illicit.
- Substance misuse: this is substance use that causes harm in some form.
- Substance-related problems: these are the full range of problems that can occur due to substance abuse:
  - problems affecting the user, but commonly others as well, e.g., the victim of a drunk driver
  - physical, psychological or social
  - disease processes due to substance abuse. These can be acute or chronic.
- Dependence: this is an interrelated cluster of cognitive, behavioral, and psychological symptoms. Psychological symptoms are listed below and were

originally described in the context of alcohol by Edwards and Gross, but apply to any substance:

- Increased tolerance: greater quantity of the drug is required for the same effect. This is caused by increased metabolic clearance.
- Repeated withdrawal symptoms: this implies that symptoms occur when the drug is withheld. The pattern of symptoms depends on the individual drug being used.
- Subjective awareness of compulsion to use: this compulsion or craving is a constant preoccupation with thoughts and feelings centered on the desire to take drugs.
- Salience of drug-seeking behavior over all other activities: the person gives highest priority to drug use, to the extent that negative social consequences do not deter use.
- Narrowing of the drug-taking repertoire: the person uses the drug in a rigid or stereotyped manner.
- Relief avoidance of withdrawal symptoms: the first use of the substance becomes earlier and earlier in the day, triggered by increasing severity of dependence and withdrawal symptoms.
- Reinstatement after abstinence: if the person abstains for a period and then resumes, the previous dependence is quickly reestablished.

- ICD-10: the features used in the International Classification of Diseases, tenth edition (ICD-10) are based on the above definitions and those used to make a diagnosis are listed in **Table 1**. The same harmful use or dependency criteria are used for each individual substance. Substance misusers often use more than one drug, so if the patient is dependent on more than one substance, the most important substance is classified first.

- Motivation: in terms of substance misuse, this is the willingness of the person to implement change. The degree of willingness is evident by the individual's behavior, which can be seen as a series of stages. A person who is contemplative realizes that there is the need for change and weighs up both sides. If he/she is active he/she will be modifying the problematic behavior. If a person is able to sustain change and modify as necessary, then he/she has the ability to maintain behavior change.

## Statistics

### Alcohol

In the UK, 96% of men and 86% of women drink. The average consumption per week is 16 units for men and 6.3 units for women. The recommended weekly intake is less than 21 units for men and less

**Table 1** International Classification of Diseases, 10th edition (ICD-10): diagnostic features

Harmful use
- Substance caused physical or mental use

Dependency syndrome
Three or more over the past year of the following:
- Compulsion to take the substance
- Escalation of amount used
- Withdrawal syndrome following reduction in use
- Tolerance
- Neglect of other activities in favor of substance use
- Persistent use despite evidence of harm

**Table 2** Statistics of alcohol problems

| | |
|---|---|
| Estimated prevalence rate for alcohol dependence syndrome: | |
| Men | 75/100 000 |
| Women | 21/100 000 |
| Estimated total mortality per year | 5000–40 000 |
| Road traffic accidents, casualties, 2002 | 20 140, 6% of total |
| UK National Health Service Admissions, 2002 | |
| Alcohol as the primary diagnosis | 28 100 |
| Alcohol-related disorders | 90 900 |

than 14 units for women. Twenty-seven percent of men and 14% of women exceed these recommended limits. For men this figure has remained static, but it has been increasing steadily for women. As older people tend to drink less, adjusting the figures gives 35% of men and 18% of women aged 16–24 who are exceeding safe drinking limits. In a previous week 37% of men and 21% of women binge-drank, that is, consumed over 4 units for men and over 3 units for women. Despite the 3.3% contribution of alcohol taxes to the UK government's tax revenues, this level of alcohol consumption is not without problems, as listed in **Table 2**.

### Drugs

In the UK on average, 4 million people use drugs every year. Cannabis is the commonest illicit drug used; however, up to 1 million will have used a class A drug. There are between 100 000 and 250 000 problem drug users in the UK. These drug users are part of a market that is estimated to be £6.6 billion a year. The economic deficit to the country by drug use is estimated to be £4 billion a year. However, there is a huge discrepancy between the estimates of problem users and the number that present for treatment – 40 430 in 2000. This is an increase of 45% since 1995. Accurate statistics are essential in the understanding and treatment of substance problems. However, the statistics available are from a variety

**Table 3** Drug use amongst general population, 2000 (British Crime Survey)

| | |
|---|---|
| Ever used any drug | 34% |
| Used a drug last year | 11% |
| Used a drug last month | 6% |
| Cannabis, ever used lifetime | 27% |
| Cannabis, used last year | 9% |

**Table 4** Drug use amongst 16–29-year-olds, 2000 (British Crime Survey)

| | |
|---|---|
| Used a drug last year | 24% |
| Cannabis, ever used lifetime | 44% |
| Cannabis, used last year | 22% |
| Class A, used last year | 9% |

**Table 5** Drug use amongst those presenting for treatment 2001 (Annual Report on the UK Drug Situation)

| | |
|---|---|
| Heroin as primary drug | 64% |
| Ever injected | 66% |
| Injected last week | 45% |
| Mortality rate | 1.2% |
| Human immunodeficiency virus (HIV) | 0.8% |
| Hepatitis B virus | 5.4% |
| Hepatitis C virus | 29% |

of sources and of variable quality and so give only a snapshot of the possible extent of the problem (Tables 3–5).

## Screening

Screening is the recognition of hazardous alcohol or drug consumption. It can be asking simple, direct questions, using questions in a structured way, or the use of validated and reliable instruments. Essentially, a formal or informal checklist is used to enhance accurate history-taking. In general, the most reliable information will be about the last 24 h; more distant accounts are less reliable, but are required to establish the individual's longitudinal history of pattern of use. The usefulness of screening is that patients may not volunteer any information themselves, as they see their drug or alcohol use as recreational and not problematic, and so the evaluation process in itself can create insight and self-awareness.

### Questionnaires

These request the patient to state the frequency of use of an individual drink or substance over a given period, e.g., a week or month, such as quantity frequency questionnaires. A diary format asks patients simply to write down what they used each day over a period, say, of a week. They are relatively time-consuming, but are reliable and give accurate information.

The Alcohol Use Disorder Identification Test (AUDIT) was developed by the World Health Organization. It asks a series of simple questions which are designed to pick up early signs of alcohol-related problems. It can be extended for a more thorough screening procedure. A five-item AUDIT is displayed in Table 6.

CAGE is a very simple and quick four-item questionnaire (Table 7), where two or more positive replies identify the problem drinker.

The Maudsley Addiction Profile (MAP) covers four areas: (1) substance use; (2) health risk behavior; (3) physical and psychological health; and (4) social functioning. It can be used at assessment and after a period of treatment. A modified version of the MAP is given in Table 8.

## Assessment

In managing alcohol and drug problems, a detailed history is required to assess comprehensively the impact of use on physical, psychological, and social well-being. This assessment is the same irrespective of the presenting complaint, as otherwise valuable clinical information could be lost and also an opportunity to intervene in a substance-related problem. The use of screening tools and routine drug and alcohol testing is a valuable aid to this process. Guidelines relating to the substance use component of a psychiatric history are illustrated in Table 9.

## Drug Testing

Chemical testing of biological fluids is the most objective means of diagnosis of drug use. The European Court of Human Rights stated that testing for substances in all forms is legal. However, the response to that test can be illegal, e.g., a longer period in prison. Testing is of no use if the sample is not what it is meant to be, so ideally the taking of any sample is supervised to prevent substitution or contamination. In general, substance levels are lower in hair or saliva compared to urine or blood. The standard method of detection is immunoassay followed by gas chromatography confirmation with mass spectrometry.

### Urine Assessment

Urine is the biological tool of choice for detection of substance use and as such the most frequently used. Increasingly available are rapid detection devices (near-patient drug-testing devices) for initial

**Table 6** Five-item Alcohol Use Disorder Identification Test (AUDIT)

| Have you consumed *any* alcohol in the last 12 months? (please tick) | | Yes | | No | |

If *no*: do not continue
If *yes*: please answer the following questions

Please circle the appropriate answer and then record the points score for that item in the right-hand column. At the end of the section, add up the scores in the right-hand column and complete the total score box to determine the outcome

| | Points per item | | | | | |
| | 4 | 3 | 2 | 1 | 0 | Score |
|---|---|---|---|---|---|---|
| How often do you have a drink that contains alcohol? | 4+ times weekly | 2–3 times weekly | 2–4 times monthly | Monthly or less | Never | |
| How many drinks containing alcohol do you have on a typical day you are drinking? | 10+ units | 7–9 units | 5 or 6 units | 3 or 4 units | Never | |
| How often during the last year have you found that you were not able to stop drinking once you had started? | Daily or almost daily | Weekly | Monthly | Less than monthly | Never | |
| How often during the last year have you failed to do what is expected of you because of your drinking? | Daily or almost daily | Weekly | Monthly | Less than monthly | Never | |
| Has a relative/friend/doctor or health worker been concerned about your drinking or suggested you cut down? | | | Yes, during the last year | Yes, but not in the last year | No | |
| | | | | | Total score | |

A score of more than 5 suggests problematic use that requires further investigation
Outcome (please circle): | | | | | Negative | Positive |

screening. However, as these devices are not as reliable as laboratory testing, any result should be confirmed. **Table 10** shows the time periods of detection for drugs in urine – individual laboratories may differ on this.

## Saliva Assessment

This sample can be obtained either by spitting or using a swab. To generate sufficient volume, sometimes citric acid crystals or chewing on an inert material is used before sampling. Saliva has great advantages over urine in that it is easy to collect and noninvasive. At the time of writing, this form of assessment is only being developed and so there is a lack of a pool of data to establish standards. The current techniques cannot then be said to give robust results. However, it is likely in the near future that this will change and saliva testing will be available for roadside testing and screening.

## Hair Assessment

Again, like saliva testing, this form of testing is at the developmental stage. The interpretation of results is not fully understood as yet, as the age, anatomical site, ethnicity, and cosmetic treatment can all

**Table 7** CAGE questionnaire

1. Have you ever felt you should **c**ut down your drinking?
2. Have people **a**nnoyed you by criticizing your drinking?
3. Have you ever felt **g**uilty about your drinking?
4. Have you ever had a drink first thing in the morning as an "**e**ye-opener"?

influence results. The drug metabolites are incorporated into the matrix of hair, so hair samples give a measure of long-term use. So, although it is much more expensive than urine testing, it does have an advantage in that this longer detection window gives an idea of the chronicity of the problem.

## Blood Assessment

Blood testing remains the most accurate quantitative measurement. However, the means of obtaining a sample, the risks associated with blood, and the expenses involved limit greatly the use of this method. This is particularly apparent in the need for regular, rapid, on-site screening involving large numbers of samples. It is best suited for therapeutic drug monitoring, as in the case of methadone treatment.

**Table 8** Low-threshold drug screen

| Please read to the patient: In the last 12 months, how often have you used the following illicit substances or prescribed medications? | | |
|---|---|---|
| *Substance* | *Use in the last 12 months* | |
| Cannabis | | |
| Hallucinogens (LSD, ecstasy, mushrooms) | | |
| Ketamine | | |
| Amphetamines (speed) | | |
| Cocaine powder | | |
| Crack cocaine | | |
| Heroin | | |
| | *Prescribed* | *Nonprescribed* |
| Opioids (DF118, Temgesic, morphine, diamorphine, methadone) | | |
| Codeine | | |
| Procyclidine | | |
| Other medications (e.g. asthma, steroids). Please specify name and dose: | | |
| Benzodiazepines (Valium, temazepam, nitrazepam, mogadon) | | |
| Score positive if the client reports having used at any time over the last year: 1. an illicit drug or 2. a prescribed substitute (methadone/DF118) or 3. a prescribed drug that is not prescribed to him/her | | |
| Outcome (please circle) | *Negative* | *Positive* |

## Interventions

The treatment of drug dependence is a combination of pharmacotherapeutic and psychosocial interventions. The role of medication is fourfold. It can be used: (1) to alleviate withdrawal; (2) to detoxify; (3) as maintenance; and (4) to support abstinence. Psychosocial interventions are used as patients request this form of treatment; they improve the outcome of pharmacological treatments and are more effective than nonintervention. Most services combine these approaches, but there is more emphasis on psychosocial and briefer interventions in the alcohol field, where the pharmacotherapeutic options are more specific. Trials report the benefits of addiction treatment, but typically only 20% report abstinence over the past year and often there is a 50% dropout rate. However, this is consistent with a model of a chronic behavioral disorder. The evidence available on the efficacy of these interventions is very variable. This becomes important as when suggesting a treatment plan there must be confidence in its effectiveness, which can only be based on robust research.

## Harm Reduction

The goal of substance misuse treatment is reduction of individual and public harm. The emergence of human immunodeficiency virus (HIV) necessitated this approach, as the spread of HIV is a greater danger than drug misuse. The aims are to reduce injecting, sharing, and drug use, to encourage safe sexual practices, and to reduce crime. Central to this approach are needle exchanges, education, particularly about safe injecting, viral screening with hepatitis B vaccination, and methadone maintenance. More recently, the need for patients to have education about resuscitation has also been appreciated, as opiate misusers have ten times the mortality of an age-matched general population. The success of this approach is shown by the National Treatment Outcome Research Study (NTORS), for example, for every £1 spent on treatment, £3 is saved on crime.

## Treatment Retention

Retention of treatment is an important aspect, as the evidence shows that the longer the patient spends in treatment, the greater the gains and the greater the lifestyle changes. This gives more weight to maintenance treatment, as short interventions do not work for the more severely dependent.

## Pharmacotherapy, Alcohol

### Drugs used for withdrawal

**Benzodiazepines** Accompanied by vitamin supplements, benzodiazepines are used to manage alcohol withdrawal. Long-acting benzodiazepines, such as

**Table 9**   Substance use history

*Reason for presentation*

*Current substance use*
Use past 24 h
Use past month
Average use last 6 months
*Longitudinal substance use*
First ever use
Age of first use for each substance/age for regular use each substance
Age of dependent use each substance
Routes of drug use
Age regular weekend drinking/age regular evening drinking
Age regular lunchtime drinking/age early-morning drinking
Features of dependence
Withdrawal symptoms/delirium tremens
Periods of abstinence
*Substance-related problems*
Physical
Psychological
Social
*Motivation*
Coping capacity
Past stress, which caused relapse
Stages of behavioral change
*Injecting history*
First episode in detail/age first time injected
Duration of injecting/daily frequency of injecting
Injection sites and problems
Sharing/use of sterile injecting equipment
Knowledge about viral transmission
*Risk of HIV/hepatitis viruses*
Frequency of sharing/people shared with
Knowledge of cleaning equipment
Sexual risk-taking
*Previous treatment history*
General practitioner/specialist
Medication/maintenance/detoxification
*Forensic history*
Drinking and driving/drunk and disorderly
Prison sentences
Court cases/pending court cases
*Present lifestyle*
Marital/occupational/leisure
Social support/nonsubstance-using network

HIV, human immunodeficiency virus.

**Table 10**   Period of detection in urine

| | |
|---|---|
| Amphetamines | 48 h |
| Methamphetamines | 48 h |
| Benzodiazepines | |
|    Therapeutic dose | 3 days |
|    Long-acting | 7 days |
| Cocaine | 2–3 days |
| Methadone | 7–9 days |
| Heroin | 48 h |
| Cannabis | |
|    Single use | 3 days |
|    Daily use | 10 days |
| Chronic heavy use | 21–27 days |

chlordiazepoxide, are used and for a limited period only. Chlormethiazole is also used, but only in an inpatient setting, as its use with alcohol can cause respiratory depression.

### Drugs Used to Prevent Relapse

**Alcohol-Sensitizing (Deterrent) Medications**   Disulfiram and citrated calcium carbimide act by inhibiting the action of aldehyde dehydrogenase. If alcohol is consumed then this causes the build-up of acetaldehyde, which causes an unpleasant systemic reaction. Ideally, the drug is given under supervision after the nature of the drug–alcohol interaction is fully explained. It is the possibility of this reaction that makes these drugs contraindicated in certain vulnerable groups, particularly disulfiram and cardiovascular disease. The usefulness of these drugs is controversial, as those who do better on their use are compliant, attend the accompanying psychosocial interventions, and have good motivation, which are themselves good prognostic factors.

**Gamma-Aminobutyric Acid (GABA) Analog: Acamprosate**   This drug acts by restoring normal activity to the glutamate and GABA system disrupted by chronic alcohol use. There is good evidence that acamprosate enhances abstinence and reduces drinking days, but has little effect on craving or rates of severe relapse.

**Opiate Antagonist: Naltrexone**   Naltrexone acts by inhibiting the pleasurable effect of alcohol. It has been shown to reduce relapse and the number of drinking days. The evidence also suggests that it reduces craving and enhances abstinence.

## Pharmacotherapy, Drugs

### Drugs Used for Detoxification

Detoxification is one of the most widely used treatments but one of the least effective. Research has shown that the majority of opiate addicts cannot sustain abstinence on a long-term basis.

**Opioid Agonist: Methadone**   Methadone is a full opioid agonist with a half-life of 24 h. This allows once-a-day dosing, but a steady state is not achieved until 4–5 days. However, it does have an opioid withdrawal syndrome and, once the patient is stabilized, detoxification is done gradually to ensure that the symptoms are tolerable.

**Alpha$_2$-adrenoreceptor Agonists** These include clonidine and lofexidine; the latter induces less hypotension and sedation than clonidine. These reduce the somatic symptoms of withdrawal. There is no difference in outcome between these agents and methadone in detoxification.

**Ultrarapid Opiate Detoxification** This technique induces acute withdrawal using naloxone and naltrexone while the patient is under general anesthesia. There is no evidence for effectiveness and serious concerns about safety.

### Drugs Used for Maintenance

**Opioid Agonist: Methadone** The safety and efficacy of methadone maintenance have been unequivocally established. It has been shown to reduce crime, drug use, HIV transmission, and mortality as well as to improve general health and social status. Over the past decade, there has been a major growth in the use of methadone across Europe. To ensure a good outcome requires induction, stabilization, and maintenance, which usually requires a dose above 60 mg a day, and must be accompanied by appropriate psychosocial intervention.

**Partial Opioid Agonist: Buprenorphine** Buprenorphine is comparable in effectiveness to methadone. Its advantages are that there is less risk of overdose, less dependence, and a smoother withdrawal, but it is more expensive and has a higher risk of being injected.

### Drugs Used to Prevent Relapse

**Opioid Antagonist: Naltrexone** Naltrexone prevents the euphoria or other effects of heroin. As for alcohol, most patients describe reduced cravings. However, there is mixed evidence for benefits.

## Stimulants

Many agents have been tried with stimulant users. For withdrawal relief, antidepressants (such as tricylics) or dopamine agonists (such as bromocriptine) have been tried. Dopamine antagonists and anticonvulsants potentially counter the pleasurable effects of stimulants. However, thus far, the evidence for their effectiveness is not convincing. This is unlike the evidence for psychosocial interventions, which is the treatment of choice for stimulant-related problems.

## Psychosocial Interventions

### Brief Interventions for Alcohol

Brief interventions are aimed at patients who are drinking at harmful levels. The structured intervention usually takes the form of advice, education, self-management training, group therapy, or motivational interviewing. It has been shown to be effective in reducing alcohol consumption.

### Alcoholics Anonymous/Narcotics Anonymous

These organizations use the disease model, stress abstinence, and adopt a 12-step approach. Although there are no rigorous trials, the evidence suggests that these are as effective as other psychotherapies.

### Relapse Prevention and Cognitive Behavior Therapy

This therapy is based on the work of Marlatt and Gordon. The assumption is made that substance misuse is a means of coping and the patient is taught how to manage high-risk situations. Typically, patients attend only 50% of the time, but all the same there is a modest overall effect.

### Motivational Interviewing

This has been described by Miller and Rollnick. As a technique it is based on cognitive dissonance and encourages patients to find their own reasons to attempt change. It has a good research base that shows effectiveness.

### Contingency Management

This uses positive control techniques in the form of rewards in response to abstinence. It has generally been used for opiates and cocaine and has been shown to be effective.

### Community Reinforcement, Couple and Family Therapies

Here the patient is rewarded for abstinence by agreed strategies. These therapies do have some effectiveness.

### Residential Rehabilitation

This is a planned and usually highly structured program of counseling and other support services aiming for global lifestyle changes. There are three broad types: (1) therapeutic communities, which have the biggest research base; (2) 12-step programs, based on the Minnesota Model; and (3) general or Christian houses. Completion rates are often below 20%. Residential programs are as effective as community programs, but at a much greater cost.

## The Law

### Responsibilities of the Doctor

The use of drugs and the consequences of drug use (e.g., prison, viral transmission) may be associated with prejudice and stigma. However, the UK General Medical Council has firmly stated that it is unethical to withhold treatment from any patient based on that patient's lifestyle or location of that patient. The principle behind this treatment is the harm reduction model. A doctor should offer a treatment once that treatment can be shown to reduce the degree of overall harm either to the individual or society. All individuals are entitled to the same standard and range of treatments.

In a custodial setting, there can be demands to prescribe excess quantities or an institutional ethos to resist demands for medication. This has to be avoided. Usually, the most pressing need is with the competent management of withdrawal. If a doctor is placed in a situation where this competency is not possible then it is advisable to refer the patient to a location where this is possible. Ideally, the institution has a set policy for prescribing and the circumstances of substance withdrawal.

With all consultations, confidentiality is important, but particularly so with drug problems. This is because part of a thorough assessment inquires about prohibited activities used to fund drug use. If patients do not feel secure, it will hinder their ability to access treatment. Confidentiality can only be broken in extreme circumstances, e.g., threat to the life of another. However, it is appropriate to raise concerns over criminal activity or prostitution. It is advisable to warn the patient about the risks of driving motor vehicles or the use of machinery. With shared care or in a multidisciplinary team setting it is helpful to have guidelines on shared and individual professional responsibility.

There are three circumstances where confidentially is impinged upon. The first is compilation of statistics. There are regional drug misuse databases, to which reporting is voluntary and done at a local level. They give a broad overview since all drug use and a wide range of providers are included. The second circumstance relates to HIV, hepatitis B or hepatitis C, usually acquired by injecting drug use. There is a statutory requirement to notify in the case of these infections, and the data are used for epidemiological

purposes. Finally, the UK Home Office scrutinizes the dispensing of controlled drugs.

### Guidelines on Prescribing

In the UK a prescription for a controlled drug must be written in the doctor's handwriting and state the form, strength, dose, and total quantity. A doctor whose practice entails a large amount of prescribing of controlled drugs can apply for a handwriting exception. In a hospital setting, there is a special prescription form for opiates and cocaine in the treatment of addiction. A general practitioner has a special prescription form to issue daily dispensing. A patient can travel abroad freely with under 500 mg of prescribed methadone, although it is useful to have a "To whom it may concern" letter indicating the exact circumstances. Any amount above 500 mg requires the patient to apply for a license to the Home Office. Of course, this license only covers exit and entry to the UK and the visited country may have separate and different protocols.

In general, drugs that have an abuse potential should be used very cautiously in dependency. These are drugs that have a high black-market value, especially pharmaceutical or synthetic opiates, or drugs that can be injected despite being in oral form, such as buprenorphine or capsules of temazepam. Heroin, cocaine, and synthetic opiate dipipanone are prohibited in drug dependence. These can be used for other conditions, but even if these are present in a drug addict, such drugs are still not to be used.

### Capacity

Drug dependency is not seen as a reason in itself to cause impaired capacity. In law, a person is deemed to be responsible for his/her actions irrespective of the presence of a state of intoxication. In other words, being intoxicated is no defense. This is so as the person willingly placed him/herself in an intoxicated state and so is conscious of the possible consequences. However, a defense could be made if the person was unaware that he/she was consuming a drug, with which he/she was not familiar, for example, in the case of a "spiked drink."

On the same theme, as capacity is not impaired there are no powers of detention for dependency alone under the current UK mental health legislation. Of course, a person could still be detained if there was another comorbid mental illness or when detaining is for assessment if there was doubt as to the diagnosis. At the time of writing, the UK government is considering introducing new mental health legislation where this would no longer be the case.

The fact that capacity is not impaired is also reflected in the fact that drug addiction by itself does not form the grounds for separating parents and children. Parents might not present for treatment if they feared that this was indeed the case. The guiding principle is the Children Act 1989, which states that "the welfare of the child is paramount." A care order is only given provided it meets two criteria. The first is that the child is suffering or likely to suffer significant harm and, second, that this is attributable to care not being what it would be reasonable to expect from a parent. Of course, parents with substance problems have heightened risk of child care issues.

### Driving

It is an offense to be in charge of a vehicle if "unfit to drive through drink or drugs." A driver who is suspected of being under the influence of either drugs or alcohol can be asked by the police to go forward for urine or blood testing. In the case of suspicion of drug use, the driver will first perform "coordination tests" and then go on for testing if the test is failed. Statistically, there are good reasons for this. As already mentioned, 5% of road traffic accidents involve illegal alcohol levels. In the mid-1980s, for fatal traffic accidents alcohol was implicated in 35% of cases and drugs in 3%. By the year 2000 the percentage for drugs had risen to 24.1%, the majority testing positive for multiple drugs.

The use of substances will affect a person's application for a driving license or place conditions on the license if already held. In general, if the urine screen shows cannabis, the license will be withdrawn for a year; if any other drug has been used, the withdrawal will be for a year, and longer if there is persistent misuse. Under the Road Traffic Act 1988, it is the duty of the holder of the licence or an applicant to disclose any relevant medical disability to the Driving and Vehicle Licensing Agency (DVLA). The use of prescribed medication to treat drug dependency is considered a relevant disability. A driver using a prescribed drug, like methadone, would not automatically be considered unfit to drive. A patient with a group 1 license will have to undergo an independent medical examination and a urine drug screen. If the screen is only positive for methadone, then the license will be issued for 1 year at a time. If the person stops methadone treatment, then this annual supervision is continued for 3 years and if after that time there is no concern, all restrictions are lifted. The methadone must of course be part of a treatment program and should be accompanied by a favorable report from the supervising consultant. If the person is on injectable methadone, he/she is unlikely to receive a license or likely to have it withdrawn. In exceptional cases, with a medical report stating that the person experiences low levels of sedation, a license may be given. A person on methadone treatment will not receive a group 2 (heavy goods vehicle/public service vehicle) license or will have it withdrawn for at least 3 years.

As mentioned, it is the responsibility of driving license holders to inform the DVLA about any treatment they are receiving for substance problems. For a doctor to inform the DVLA is a breach of confidence. However, if a doctor is concerned about a patient's ability to drive, then the General Medical Council advises to discuss it first with the patient and offer a second opinion. If the patient continues to drive, efforts should be made to encourage him/her not to do so, including informing the next of kin. Despite this, if the patient continues to drive, then that doctor should inform the patient that he/she is informing the DVLA. The final step is for the doctor to contact the medical advisor at the DVLA and inform the patient that he/she has done so.

### Legal Framework

The Misuse of Drugs Act 1971 is the main law regulating drug control in the UK. This act fulfills the obligations of the United Nations Single Convention of Narcotic Drugs and the 1971 Convention on Psychotropic Substances. Drugs are classified under Schedule 2 of the Act. A class A drug is harmful and examples are heroin and cocaine. A class B drug is intermediate and examples are amphetamines and barbiturates. However, an injectable preparation of a class B drug is designated as class A. Finally a class C drug is the least harmful and includes anabolic steroids, benzodiazepines, and growth hormone. As for cannabis, after a request by the UK Home Secretary in 2002 to the Advisory Council on the Misuse of Drugs, cannabis has been reclassified from a class B drug to a class C drug as from 2004.

Police contact can be a stimulus to referral for drug treatment. One option is arrest referral schemes, where the police refer persons to their local agency. In other words, the point of arrest is used to encourage the person to avail of treatment. Drug treatment and testing orders were initiated in 2000 for the more persistent offender. These are used for cases with more extended crime, use of class A drugs, or comorbid mental health problems. This involves joint working between the probation and drug treatment services using the harm reduction model. There is a structured support, twice-weekly drug testing, and monthly court reviews. Besides these options, the UK Criminal Justice Act 1991 allows for treatment of drug or alcohol problems as part of a probation order.

## Drug Offenses

In general, drug consumption is not an offense, but possession is. Broadly, there are three different types of drug offenses. The most common drug offense is possession of a named illicit drug such as heroin. If a larger quantity is seized or there is strong circumstantial evidence, the likelihood is that the person is a dealer in drugs and the offense is supply or intention to supply or possession with intention to supply drugs. Finally, the third offense is that of importation if very large quantities of drugs are involved and being brought across national boundaries. It has been shown that substance misuse treatment reduces this type of crime. In NTORS, being on a methadone maintenance program reduces drug selling to 13% of preprogram levels in 1 year. This gradually rises subsequently, but even after 5 years it reaches only 17% of the preprogram level.

## Crime

Substance misuse is a clear generator of crime. In the UK, 120 000 people were sentenced for drug-related offenses in 1999. In 2001, the UK prison population was 65 000; 37 000 of these had contact with the prison substance treatment services. There are well-established epidemiological links between the two. The 2000 New England and Welsh Arrestee Drug Abuse Monitoring report showed a statistical correlation between arrests, being positive for drug use and all criminal behavior. The association was particularly strong for heroin and cocaine. Increasing drug use was shown to correlate with increasing crime. The majority of drug-related offences are due to acquisitive crime, not crimes to the person, homicides, driving and drug offences. The exact causal relationship between substance misuse and acquisitive crime is complex; both are associated with areas of poverty and social deprivation. The offense is usually assumed to be used to support a habit, but in fact the act of offending often precedes drug dependence. However, what has been shown to have a causal relationship is effective treatment and a reduction in crime. One study on methadone maintenance showed that the number of crime days per month fell from 11 to 7. However, effective treatment will not eliminate crime completely. NTORS showed that acquisitive crime fell for methadone maintenance programs to 23% of the intake level at 5-year follow-up. This is a significant drop, confirming the effectiveness of treatment to reduce, but not eliminate, crime. The association between substance misuse and crime as well as the large numbers involved show why one of the central tenets of the harm reduction approach is to decrease crime.

## Violence

There is a strong positive link between substance misuse and violence. The MacArthur Violence Risk Assessment Study showed the 1-year rate of violence for substance misuse, personality, and adjustment disorder to be 43%, the highest for any category. The relationship between substances and violence is complex, as not only do the acute physiological disturbances caused by intoxication, withdrawal, and dependence account for the violence, but so does the context of substance use, the environment, the culture, and individual personal factors. Table 11 lists the substances associated with violence, but in general alcohol has a greater risk than drugs, which are more associated with acquisitive crime. Evidence given to the British All Party Group on Alcohol Misuse stated that in 44% of all violent incidents the assailant was drunk at the time. Alcohol is associated with 70% of stabbings, 70% of beatings, and 50% of domestic assaults. In 1999, Appleby compiled a report of 500 court homicide cases, in which 31% were identified as having a history of alcohol misuse, with 51% having alcohol as a contributing factor. The same report noted that 35% had a history of drug misuse, with 18% having drugs as a contributing factor. Besides homicides, patients with substance problems are at much higher risk of suicide. In people who commit suicide and are in contact with mental health services in the year before their death, 25% have a primary diagnosis of substance dependence or personality disorder and 50% a secondary diagnosis for these groups. Substance misuse greatly contributes to violence of any form, either to self or to others.

## Government

The Home Office and the Home Secretary, since 2001, have overall responsibility for drugs in the

**Table 11**   Associations with violence

| Positive | None |
| --- | --- |
| Alcohol | Sole use of opiates |
| Cocaine | Nicotine |
| Amphetamines | |
| Benzodiazepines | |
| Cannabis | |

UK. The Ministerial Steering Group on Drugs focuses on developing strategy. The UK Anti-Drugs Coordinator and deputy are members of this committee and report to it. This committee produces an annual report summarizing overall events, policies, and interventions in the drug arena. At a local level, 150 drug action teams (DATs) deliver services. At a regional level, the Drug Prevention Advisory Services, of which there are nine, support the DATs. Prisons provide counseling, treatment, referral, advice, and throughcare services. The two most recent major policy documents affecting drugs are *The Effectiveness Review* (1996), and *Tackling Drugs to Build a Better Britain* (1998). The first highlighted the requirement for all substance misusers to have a general practitioner, the role of shared and specialized services, and the centrality of harm minimization. The second puts forward a 10-year strategy to tackle four main areas: (1) young persons; (2) communities; (3) treatment; and (4) drug availability. The most recent policy document affecting alcohol, the *Alcohol Harm Reduction Strategy for England*, places emphasis on prevention by education and voluntary codes for the alcohol-related industry, but less emphasis on brief interventions, changing current alcohol testing procedures for drivers or using price and taxes to control alcohol consumption.

## Summary

Substance misuse is an area of high mortality and morbidity with associated social problems, including criminality. Over the last decade, there have been significant developments in the field of addiction. There are effective pharmacotherapeutic and psychosocial interventions. With greater understanding of each substance-related problem, the constituents of these interventions are being honed further to give more tailored treatments. The results from large-scale outcome evaluations such as NTORS show significant positive benefits for the individual and society. The challenge ahead is for greater detection of substance misuse with increased availability of effective interventions. Due to the high prevalence of substance misuse, this is even truer for the forensic setting.

## See Also

**Road Traffic, Determination of Fitness To Drive:** Sobriety Tests and Drug Recognition; **Substance Misuse:** Medical Effects; Cocaine and Other Stimulants; Heroin; Substitution Drugs; Miscellaneous Drugs; Patterns and Statistics; Crime; **Toxicology:** Methods of Analysis, Antemortem

## Further Reading

Cabinet Office (2004) *Alcohol Harm Reduction Strategy for England*. London: Prime Minister's Strategy Unit.

Cami J, Farre M (2003) Mechanisms of disease: drug addiction. *New England Journal of Medicine* 49: 975–986.

Chick J, Cantwell R (1994) *Seminars in Alcohol and Drug Misuse*. London: Royal College of Psychiatrists.

Department of Health (1996) *Task Force to Review Services for Drug Misusers: Report of an Independent Review of Drug Treatment Services in England*. London: Department of Health.

Department of Health (1998a) *Drug Misuse and Dependence – Guidelines on Clinical Management*. London: Department of Health.

Department of Health (1998b) *Tackling Drugs to Build a Better Britain*. London: Department of Health.

Department of Health (2001) *Annual Report on the UK Drug Situation 2001*. London: Department of Health.

Driver and Vehicle Licensing Agency (1998) *At a Glance Guide to Medical Aspects of Fitness to Drive*. London: Driving and Vehicle Licensing Agency.

Gossop M, Marsden J, Stewart D, Kidd T (2003) The National Treatment Outcome Research Study (NTORS): 4–5 year follow-up results. *Addiction* 98: 291–303.

Kintz P, Samyn N (2002) Use of alternative specimens: drugs of abuse in saliva and doping agents in hair. *Therapeutic Drug Monitoring* 24: 239–246.

Luty J (2003) What works in drug addiction? *Advances in Psychiatric Treatment* 9: 203–288.

Marshall EJ, Farrell M (2003) Substance use and psychiatry. *Psychiatry* 2: 1–35.

Marshall EJ, Farrell M (2004) Substance use and psychiatry. *Psychiatry* 3: 36–39.

Prochaska J, DiClemente C (1992) Stages of change in the modification of problem behaviours. *Progress in Behaviour Modification* 28: 183–218.

Snowden P (2001) Substance misuse and violence: the scope and limitations of forensic psychiatry's role. *Advances in Psychiatric Treatment* 7: 189–196.

Swanson J, Holzer C, Ganju V (1990) Violence and psychiatric disorder in the community: evidence from the Epidemiological Catchment Area Survey. *Hospital and Community Psychiatry* 41: 761–770.

Taylor PJ, Gunn J (1999) Homicides by people with mental illness: myth and reality. *British Journal of Psychiatry* 174: 9–14.

Weatherall D, Ledingham J, Warrell D (1996) *Oxford Textbook of Medicine*, 3rd edn. Oxford: Oxford University Press.

Wolff K, Farrell LM, Marsden J, *et al.* (1999) A review of biological indicators of illicit drug use, practical considerations and clinical usefulness. *Addiction* 94: 1279–1298.

World Health Organization (1992) *The ICD-10 Classification of Mental and Behavioural Disorders*. Geneva: World Health Organization.

# Malingering

**R L Jackson**, Pacific Graduate School of Psychology, Palo Alto, CA, USA
**R Rogers**, University of North Texas, Denton, TX, USA

## Introduction

An implicit assumption in medical and psychological practice is that patients will be open and honest in their self-reports. With the advent of managed care, however, the basis of the assumption has steadily eroded. Moreover, in forensic practice patients may be motivated to be less than forthright with their evaluators. This article provides an overview of malingering and related response styles, focusing primarily on the malingering of mental and cognitive disorders.

Knowledge of malingering and related response styles is imperative for those working in forensic settings. Far from being a rare and trivial event, altered response styles are often encountered in forensic practice. Knowledge and a heightened awareness of its presentation allow for proper identification and treatment of those suspected of malingering. The article begins with an overview of malingering and defines terms commonly encountered in the malingering literature. To provide context for the assessment of malingering in forensic settings, explanatory models of malingering and common myths associated with malingering and its presentation are discussed. Finally, the article concludes with an examination of detection strategies for malingering and evaluates the available measures for malingering.

Malingering is defined by the American Psychiatric Association (APA) as "the intentional production of false or grossly exaggerated physical or psychological symptoms, motivated by external incentives." The two key features of malingering are: (1) intentionality; and (2) motivation. The intentional nature of malingering differentiates it from somatoform disorders, in which the production of symptoms is unintentional. Likewise, malingering is differentiated from "factitious disorder" by its motivation. Factitious disorders are motivated by internal incentives, such as adopting or maintaining a "sick role." External incentives are necessarily absent. In contrast, malingering requires "obvious, external incentives."

As a critically important issue, false symptoms are not necessarily malingering. Similarly, not all altered response styles are malingering. Patients may adopt a range of response styles, including malingering, defensiveness, and honest responding (**Table 1**). In contrast to malingering, defensiveness is the denial or minimization of symptoms and can be reasonably applied to either internal or external motives. The terms "feigning" and "dissimulation" are often used as generic descriptors of altered response styles in that they make no assumptions about motivation (internal or external).

The *Diagnostic and Statistical Manual* (DSM-IV-TR) provides guidelines for when malingering should be suspected. Specifically, the DSM-IV suggests that malingering be "strongly suspected" if two or more of the following indicators are present:

1. The evaluation occurs within a medicolegal context.
2. The person's claimed stress or disability is not consistent with objective findings.
3. The individual is uncooperative with the evaluation and the prescribed treatment regimen.
4. The individual meets criteria for "antisocial personality disorder."

Clearly the DSM-IV-TR advocates for a strong index of suspicion for any clinician working in correctional and forensic contexts, highlighting the fact that malingering may be more common in these settings than previously believed. Although the utility of the DSM criteria have been questioned by some, they do serve to heighten awareness of its existence, particularly in correctional and forensic settings.

The suspicion of malingering must be further tempered by an appreciation of the potentially damaging effects of a malingering classification. Misclassification of patients as either genuine or malingering has grave consequences. In the criminal forensic realm, a genuine patient mistakenly classified as malingering is denied much-needed mental healthcare and returned to face a criminal proceeding with which he/she is ill equipped to handle. Moreover, the mere allegation of malingering serves to discredit the accused. In the civil arena, genuinely impaired individuals (e.g., plaintiffs in personal-injury suits) may seek relief through the courts. Errors in the assessment of malingering deny the person needed healthcare and stymie legal efforts. The importance of such errors has led to the recommendation that all forensic referrals be systematically assessed for malingering and related response styles. Assessment and classification must be approached with utmost care.

Malingering is often perceived as an uncommon phenomenon, particularly in nonforensic settings. For this reason, many practitioners have not received formal training in its assessment and classification. However, malingering may occur in 15% of forensic

**Table 1**   Terms and definitions associated with malingering and other altered response styles

| Term | Definition |
| --- | --- |
| Honest responding | Characterized by the patient's sincere attempt to be forthright in his or her self-reporting |
| Malingering | Conscious fabrication of symptoms chiefly motivated by an external goal |
| Factitious presentation | Fabrication of symptoms chiefly motivated by an internal goal, namely to adopt the patient role |
| Defensiveness | Conscious denial or minimization of symptoms |
| Dissimulation | Primarily used to encompass all nonhonest response styles. However, a few authors have utilized this term as a synonym for defensiveness |
| Feigning | A generic term for "fake-bad" that avoids assigning either internal or external motivation |
| Overreporting | A generic term used to avoid assumptions of intentionality. Overreporting can range from being conscious and intentional to unconscious and out of the patient's awareness |
| Suboptimal effort | Most often used in the cognitive literature. Outright malingering of cognitive deficits must be distinguished from suboptimal effort that may result from a host of legitimate difficulties |

and 7% of nonforensic cases, highlighting its potential importance to all practitioners. Unfortunately, without training, clinicians are left to approach its identification with preconceived notions regarding its etiology and rely on commonly held misbeliefs regarding its presentation. To provide a context for the comprehensive assessment of malingering, the discussion now turns to an overview of explanatory models of malingering and presents some commonly held myths regarding its presentation and identification.

## Explanatory Models

Rogers has outlined three explanatory models of malingering: (1) the pathogenic model; (2) the criminological model; and (3) the adaptational model. Each model attempts to explain the motivation that prompts individuals to malinger. Each of these models is described below.

### Pathogenic Model

The pathogenic model dominated early conceptualizations of malingering and finds its roots in psychoanalytic theory. It postulates that the production of false symptoms serves as a defense against genuine symptoms that are currently being repressed. The patient attempts to contain and control the emergence of disturbing symptoms by consciously producing the symptoms, thereby exerting control of their manifestation.

Because the underlying cause of the malingering is presumed to be a genuine mental disorder, the pathogenic model predicts that malingerers will eventually become genuinely mentally ill. This model has fallen out of favor with the medical and psychological communities, largely because its predictions have often not been borne out. In personal-injury cases, several investigators have observed a dramatic

decrease of symptoms once the motivation to malinger is removed. This observation has led to the coining of pejorative terms such as "accident neurosis," "compensation neurosis," "compensationitis," and "greenback neurosis." Furthermore, a recent prototypical analysis found very little support for the pathogenic model of malingering.

### Criminological Model

Rogers has described a second explanatory model based on the premise that malingerers are "bad" people involved in "bad" circumstances. This model, termed the criminological model, figures prominently in the DSM conceptualizations of malingering. The criminological model has been criticized on several grounds, including its overemphasis on criminality and uncooperativeness. Strict adherence to the criminological model results in a drastic overestimation of malingering in forensic evaluations. For example, nearly all adolescent offenders meet at least two criteria (#1, "medicolegal context" and #3, "uncooperative"), as do many chronic adult offenders (#1, "medicolegal context" and #4, "antisocial personality disorder"). Such individuals are automatically suspected of malingering, with potentially devastating consequences.

### Adaptational Model

Rogers advanced a third explanatory model, namely the adaptational model of malingering, which offers an alternative to classifying malingerers as either mad (pathogenic model) or bad (criminological model). Instead, malingering is seen as an understandable attempt to cope with adversarial circumstances. Facing harsh consequences for their criminal behavior, some defendants may choose to malinger with a mental disorder in an attempt to avoid punishment. In civil cases, individuals may exaggerate or fabricate their symptoms in order to maximize potential benefits (e.g., monetary damages or disability payments). The central premise of the adaptational model is that an individual malingers because he/she perceives it to be a potentially effective strategy for meeting current needs. Healthcare professionals applying the adaptational model to their practices can understand the motivation to malinger and thereby reduce their countertransference at being fooled by their patients. The most recent revision of the *International Classification of Diseases* appears to recognize the adaptational nature of malingering in defining it as "understandable in light of ... the individual's circumstances."

Patients and criminal defendants are not unique in viewing deception as a viable choice in difficult circumstances. In a survey of physicians, Novack and colleagues found that the majority of physicians indicated a willingness to use deception to secure insurance payment. Such deception combines altruism (greater access to services) with self-interest (financial gain). Nearly one-third indicated they would provide misleading information to a patient's family if a medical mistake had led to the patient's death. In all, 89% of the physicians reported that deception is acceptable in certain circumstances.

## Myths of Malingering

Healthcare professionals are often misled by common myths about malingering. Six myths are summarized that may lead to grave errors in the classification of malingering.

### A Patient Who is not Completely Honest is Probably Malingering

Patients may adopt a range of "response styles" in their clinical presentations. These response styles can range from outright denial of symptoms (i.e., defensiveness) to complete fabrication of bogus symptoms (i.e., malingering). **Table 1** provides descriptions of many response styles and defines common terms often encountered in the malingering literature. Most persons, including healthcare professionals, are not completely forthright when faced with adversarial circumstances. To equate a lack of total honesty with malingering is a very serious error.

### Inconsistent Responders are Malingering

Patients are inconsistent in their self-reports and behaviors for many possible reasons, only one of which is malingering. When confronted with an inconsistent presentation, the most prudent course of action is actively to seek out alternative explanations for the inconsistency. Many genuine patients provide inconsistent accounts of their histories and symptoms and manifest erratic (i.e., inconsistent) behaviors as a result of their mental disorders. For instance, severely impaired patients have poor insight and are incapable of providing a consistent, factually accurate account of their symptoms. Patients with long histories of mental disorder may not remember many details of their histories at every interview. Differences in interviewing methods may elicit new or different information, inconsistent with prior findings. Importantly, such inconsistencies are sometimes the product of the assessment rather than the patient.

Grave errors occur when inconsistent responding is equated with malingering. In some cases, inconsistent responding on psychological testing is inaccurately interpreted as evidence of malingering. An example, the Minnesota Multiphasic Personality Inventory-2 (MMPI-2), with over 500 questions, is difficult for some psychiatric patients with a diminished ability to concentrate because of disabling symptoms or possibly from side-effects of their medication. Its eighth-grade reading level is also a significant obstacle in criminal forensic settings where educational achievement is often marginal. Inconsistencies, by themselves, may not necessarily demonstrate malingering.

### Malingerers are so Fantastic in their Presentations, they are Easy to Identify

Many professionals in forensic settings readily recall a remarkable case involving a presentation so outlandish that malingering was the obvious conclusion. Although a small number of malingerers invent incredible symptoms, most malingerers are not remarkable in their presentations. They may be knowledgeable about mental disorder and convincing in their presentations. Taken from the adaptational model, these individuals view feigning as the best possible strategy to meet their current goals. They are, therefore, highly motivated to avoid detection. Systematic and comprehensive assessment is often the best method for identifying the skilled or practiced malingerer. Some of the more common detection strategies are outlined in a subsequent section.

### Malingering Occurs so Infrequently, it is not Really an Issue

Rogers noted in the course of conducting workshops and other educational programs that he is frequently surprised by professionals who claim never to have seen a case of malingering. The implicit assumption is that malingering is quite rare. In contrast, adherence to the criminological model, as outlined earlier, suggests that most criminals involved in forensic evaluations are likely to be malingering. The truth is likely to fall somewhere between these two extremes.

Available data suggest that malingering is likely to occur in a substantial minority of forensic evaluations. For example, Rogers and colleagues found estimates of malingering of 15.7% in forensic settings. Other estimates place the base rate of malingering anywhere from 8% to 17.4%. These estimates assail the notion that malingering is rare and underscore the need for its systematic and routine assessment.

### Projective Methods, e.g., The Rorschach Inkblot Test, Are Immune to Malingering

Early research from the 1930s and 1940s suggested that the Rorschach, as a projection of unconscious dynamics, might be immune to malingering. More recent research, however, has demonstrated its vulnerability to faking. Schretlen's review of malingering on the Rorschach noted most studies were plagued by methodological limitations. However, rigorous studies demonstrated that malingerers can produce Rorschach results that are indistinguishable from genuine psychiatric patients. In summary, no clear signs or scales reliably identify malingering on the Rorschach. In their recent text on insanity evaluations, Rogers and Shuman argue that the Rorschach and other projective measures should not be used for determinations of malingering, nor should the protocols be interpreted in cases where feigning is suspected.

### Malingering and Mental Disorder are Mutually Exclusive

A common pitfall in forensic evaluations is the assumption that individuals who malinger are free from genuine mental disorders. In reality, malingering is much more likely to exist on a continuum ranging from the marked exaggeration of *bona fide* distress to the outright fabrication of preposterous symptoms. This continuum increases the complexity of the assessment task. When faced with an exaggerating patient, it becomes challenging to distinguish malingered from genuine psychopathology. The added complexity requires that evidence of mental disorder (or lack thereof) be established through patient records and collateral interviews. The patient invested in exaggerating his/her level of distress cannot be relied upon to provide accurate self-reports. Third-party interviews with friends and family combined with educational and psychiatric records can often provide the needed information.

## Detection of Malingering

Healthcare professionals, particularly in the forensic domain, are faced with the challenging task of distinguishing malingerers from their genuinely disordered counterparts. Several general approaches to the assessment of malingering have been identified that yield varying levels of success. Of these, three approaches will be examined: (1) unstructured interviews; (2) empirically supported detection strategies; and (3) psychological testing.

### Unstructured Interviews

Unstructured interviews often form the basis of history-taking, psychiatric case formulation, and diagnosis. The primary advantages of the unstructured interview are its flexibility and adaptability across patient populations. On scientific grounds, the unstructured nature of the interview is also its greatest liability. The previous section highlighted some of the pitfalls resulting from total reliance on clinical judgment in classifying malingering. In his classic study, Rosenhan provides compelling evidence regarding the limitations of unstructured methods in accurately identifying feigned presentations. More recent research has demonstrated the inaccuracies of clinical judgment in decision-making, including the detection of malingering.

### Detection Strategies for Feigned Psychopathology

A second approach is the use of well-established detection strategies for malingering and associated response styles (**Table 2**). Four of the strategies are well validated across different research designs and empirical studies: (1) rare symptoms; (2) symptom selectivity; (3) absurd symptoms; and (4) obvious versus subtle. Furthermore, these strategies can be easily incorporated into traditional clinical interviews.

**Rare symptoms**   The rare-symptoms strategy relies on the overendorsement of symptoms that are often infrequent among genuine patients. An example of a rare symptom may be: "Can thoughts be extracted from your mind without you knowing it?" Genuine patients seldom endorse these items. In contrast, malingerers are typically unaware of their rarity and may endorse a substantial proportion of rare symptoms.

**Table 2**  Empirically supported detection strategies for feigned psychopathology

| Strategy | Description |
|---|---|
| Rare symptoms | Overendorsement of symptoms that are very infrequent among genuine patients |
| Symptom selectivity | Indiscriminately endorsing a great number of symptoms without consideration for possible diagnosis |
| Absurd symptoms | Endorsing or creating fantastic or unbelievable symptoms. Although this is rare among malingerers, its presence is highly suggestive of malingering |
| Obvious versus subtle | Endorsing a greater number of symptoms that are obviously related to mental disorder |

**Symptom selectivity**  Past research has suggested that some malingerers indiscriminately endorse a great number of symptoms without any consideration for possible diagnoses. As a benchmark, when presented with a wide array of symptoms, malingering should be suspected when patients endorse two-thirds or more of these symptoms and associated features.

**Absurd symptoms**  The majority of malingerers do not create or endorse preposterous symptoms. Nonetheless, a minority of unsophisticated malingerers are apparently unaware that their symptom presentation lacks believability.

Often, fantastic symptoms are revealed through the use of follow-up questions about symptoms or probes used in a structured interview. For mood disorders, an example of an absurd symptom might be "Do you believe that weeping-willow trees have contributed to your depression?"

**Obvious versus subtle**  Malingerers are likely to endorse a greater number of obvious symptoms than their genuinely mentally ill counterparts. Obvious symptoms refer to those symptoms that are easily recognizable as psychopathology (e.g., suicidal thoughts as a symptom of depression). In contrast, subtle symptoms do not necessarily appear related to mental disorders (e.g., early-morning awakening as a symptom of depression). Malingerers are more likely to endorse a very high proportion of obvious symptoms, because they are easy to recognize and manipulate. This detection strategy is best assessed via standardized methods, such as structured interviews.

One advantage of adopting the use of systematic detection strategies is the ease with which they can be introduced into the traditional clinical interview. During the course of history-taking and review of current symptoms, questions related to detection strategies can be unobtrusively inserted. Endorsement of these items provides initial evidence that a more comprehensive assessment for malingering may be required.

## Validated Measures of Malingering

A third approach is the use of validated measures of malingering and related response styles. Measures of malingering can be classified as either screens or tests. Screens are often useful as brief guides that identify unusual presentations suggestive of possible feigning. Because of their brevity, screens commonly have high rates of false positives. Screens are not intended nor should they be used for the determination of malingering.

Screens are often effective at identifying individuals who require a more comprehensive assessment. Popular screens include the M Test, the Structured Inventory of Malingered Symptomatology, and the Miller Forensic Assessment of Symptoms Test (MFAST). The MFAST appears to be very promising as a screen for feigned mental disorders.

In contrast to screens, tests of malingering are more comprehensive in their assessments and are intended for the determination of feigned mental disorders. The Structured Interview of Reported Symptoms (SIRS) is currently the best-validated test developed specifically for the detection of malingering and related response styles. Based on well-established detection strategies, such as those described above, the SIRS is a structured interview consisting of 172 items. Its eight primary scales assess well-validated detection strategies. Scores on each scale are categorized as one of the following: (1) definite malingering; (2) probable malingering; (3) indeterminate; and (4) honest. Persons malingering mental disorders may be identified by their pattern of scores involving probable and definite feigning categories. Importantly, these patterns result in very few false positives, thereby increasing healthcare professionals' confidence in the SIRS classification.

## Multiscale Inventories in the Assessment of Malingering

Many healthcare professionals and forensic experts are surprised to discover that many commonly used psychological tests have limitations in determinations of malingering. Due to the popularity of the MMPI-2,

Personality Assessment Inventory (PAI), and Millon Clinical Multiaxial Inventory, 3rd edition (MCMI-III) in many psychological and psychiatric assessments, this brief section reviews these tests in the context of malingering.

**MMPI-2** Perhaps the most popular and widely used multiscale inventory is the MMPI-2, which assesses patterns of psychopathology and personality-related features. Importantly, its authors recognized the importance of response styles (e.g., overreporting and even malingering) and integrated "validity" tests into the development of the MMPI-2. Extensive research has been conducted on the MMPI-2 both for assessing patterns of psychopathology and response styles. Because of its length (567 true–false items) and reading level (eighth-grade), patients should be screened regarding their appropriateness in terms of concentration and literacy.

The MMPI-2 is a highly complex psychological test consisting of clinical scales, content scales, validity scales, and specialized scales. The MMPI-2 is potentially a very valuable measure for the assessment of malingering and feigned mental disorders. The key caveat is that healthcare professionals must rely on psychologists who have sophisticated training in the MMPI-2 and malingering. Grave errors can occur in healthcare professionals' attempts to use "canned" (e.g., computerized or cookbook) interpretations or to rely on psychologists that do not have specialized training. It is the responsibility of healthcare professionals to research the backgrounds of clinical psychologists before using them as MMPI-2 consultants.

A recent metaanalysis of the MMPI-2 and malingering integrated the results of 65 feigning studies for 11 feigning scales and indices. Several important findings emerged:

1. The rare-symptoms strategy was the most effective, although certain diagnostic groups (i.e., schizophrenia and posttraumatic stress disorder) evidenced marked elevations on scales F and Fb. Fortunately, a new scale called Fp proved highly effective with a relatively stable cut score.
2. Scales based on "obvious versus subtle" (i.e., O–S) and "symptom selectivity" (i.e., LW) produced positive yet highly variable results that make it difficult to recommend specific cut scores.
3. The MMPI-2 has a unique detection strategy for malingering based on erroneous stereotypes. The use of this Ds scale proved to be very successful as a specialized scale for evaluating feigned mental disorders.

The determinations of malingering on the MMPI-2 require a multistep process. First, psychologists must use specialized scales to rule-out inconsistent responding that could result in false positives for malingering. Second, psychologists must evaluate scales, such as Fp and Ds, to ensure that any observed elevations are very unlikely to occur in patients with genuine disorders. Third, psychologists must seek confirmatory information from other standardized methods.

**PAI** The PAI is a recent multiscale inventory with promising research on malingering. Its strengths include nonoverlapping scales, easy reading comprehension (fourth-grade), and shorter administration time (344 items). Unlike research with the MMPI-2, feigning studies have typically utilized the standard cut scores, with promising results.

The PAI has three primary fake-bad indictors, namely negative impression management (NIM), the malingering index (MAL), and the Rogers' discriminant function (RDF). NIM and MAL have received empirical support in both simulation and known-groups designs; however, Rogers cautions against the use of his RDF in forensic cases. Preliminary guidelines for the screening and detection of malingering have been offered:

1. Rule-out feigning: a NIM score <77T indicates a low probability that the patient is feigning.
2. Screen for feigning: marked elevations on NIM (77–109T) indicate the need to evaluate more thoroughly the issue of feigning, perhaps through the use of a specialized measure such as the SIRS.
3. Likely feigning: extreme elevations on NIM ($\geq$110T) or the MAL ($\geq$5) indicate a strong likelihood of feigning.

**MCMI-III** The MCMI-III includes the debasement index as a measure of feigned psychopathology. Relatively few clinical studies have been conducted, with mixed results. One simulation study demonstrated a moderate effect (Cohen's $d = 0.59$) between simulators and inpatients on the debasement index. A primary concern when utilizing the MCMI-III in cases of suspected malingering is that the debasement index is highly correlated with nine of the clinical scales ($r \geq 0.75$) in the normative sample. For example, major depression is correlated at 0.85 with the debasement index. In other words, genuinely elevated clinical scales are likely to be accompanied by elevated debasement scores, making the determination of feigned versus genuine psychopathology exceedingly difficult.

**Table 3** Empirically supported strategies for the detection of feigned cognitive deficits

| Strategy | Description |
| --- | --- |
| Floor effect | Failing on very simple questions that even very impaired persons can answer correctly |
| Performance curve | A comparison of easy items failed and difficult items passed |
| Violation of learning principles | An individual's performance runs counter to established principles. For example, significantly better performance for delayed versus immediate recall trials |
| Symptom validity testing | Malingering is suspected when performance on a forced-choice test falls below chance levels |

## Feigning Cognitive Deficits

An entirely separate body of literature concerns feigning cognitive deficits. A comprehensive review of this literature is beyond the scope of this article; however, that is the very point that warrants attention here. An all-too-common error is to equate the malingering of cognitive and psychopathological impairments and utilize the same strategies or assessment instruments in their classification (e.g., utilizing the MMPI-2 to assess cognitive malingering). **Table 3** outlines the empirically supported strategies for detection of malingered cognitive deficits.

## Clinical Applications of Strategies and Tests

The far-reaching consequences of malingering determinations require that healthcare professionals go beyond clinical acumen and apply validated detection strategies and standardized malingering measures. Three general reasons for utilizing detection strategies/tests are advanced.

First, the sole reliance on clinical judgment is fallible. Numerous authors have demonstrated the unreliability of unaided clinical intuition. Clinical judgment must be informed by empirically validated strategies and tests. Similar to other diagnostic endeavors, the use of tests facilitates accurate empirically based classification. As an analogy, physicians diagnose heart disease using a range of validated diagnostic tests in addition to their clinical acumen. Likewise, malingering requires both clinical judgment and validated tests in its determination.

Second, the consequences of misdiagnosis of malingering are too grave to be left to chance, particularly in the forensic domain. As outlined earlier, genuine patients misdiagnosed as malingering will almost inevitably be denied treatment and be "tainted" in subsequent legal proceedings. The mere suggestion of malingering is often enough to discredit the patient. In contrast, clinical errors in missing cases of malingering utilize mental health resources and may frustrate the legitimate goals of the legal system. "Successful" malingerers may realize unwarranted gains in civil proceedings or avoid the legal consequences of their criminal behavior. In line with

Heilbrun and Rogers, we recommend the systematic assessment of malingering and related response styles of all forensic referrals.

Third, evidence of malingering gained through empirically tested methods is simply more defensible. In forensic cases, particularly for cross-examination, professionals must support their conclusions with data. Expert witnesses are in a much stronger position if they can defend conclusory opinions with empirically supported research. The use of both detection strategies and malingering measures provide experts with crucial scientific support for their findings.

## Concluding Remarks

Malingering is a challenging diagnostic concern for clinicians, particularly in the forensic arena. The main focus of this article was to acquaint healthcare professionals with some of the issues involved in malingering and its proper assessment. The importance of systematic assessment was emphasized in light of the devastating consequences of misclassification for both individuals (plaintiffs and defendants) and the legal system. The article also provided a framework for approaching the systematic assessment of malingering, including the adaptational model of malingering and the importance of dispelling common myths. Only reliance on well-established detection strategies and malingering measures can yield the accurate and defensible classification of malingering.

## See Also

**Forensic Psychiatry and Forensic Psychology:** Assessment; Personality Disorder; Criminal Responsibility

## Further Reading

American Psychiatric Association (2000) *Diagnostic and Statistical Manual of Mental Disorders*, 4th edn., revised. Washington, DC: American Psychiatric Association.
Garb H (1998) *Studying the Clinician: Judgment Research and Psychological Assessment*. Washington, DC: American Psychological Association.

Heilbrun K (2001) *Principles of Forensic Mental Health Assessment.* New York: Kluwer Academic/Plenum.

Novack DH, Detering BJ, Arnold R, *et al.* (1989) Physicians' attitudes toward using deception to resolve difficult ethical problems. *Journal of the American Medical Association* 261: 2980–2985.

Resnick PJ (1984) The detection of malingered mental illness. *Behavioral Sciences and the Law* 2: 21–38.

Reynolds CR (1998) *Detection of Malingering during Head Injury Litigation.* New York: Plenum.

Rogers R (1990) Models of feigned mental illness. *Professional Psychology: Research and Practice* 21: 182–188.

Rogers R (1990) Development of a new classificatory model of malingering. *Bulletin of the American Academy of Psychiatry and Law* 18: 323–333.

Rogers R (1997) *Clinical Assessment of Malingering and Deception,* 2nd edn. New York: Guilford Press.

Rogers R, Bender SD (2003) Evaluation of malingering and deception. In: Goldstein AM (ed.) *Comprehensive Handbook of Psychology: Forensic Psychology,* vol. 11, pp. 109–129. New York: Wiley.

Rogers R, Shuman DW (2000) *Conducting Insanity Evaluations,* 2nd edn. New York: Guilford Press.

Rogers R, Bagby RM, Dickens SE (1992) *Structured Interview of Reported Symptoms (SIRS) and Professional Manual.* Odessa, FL: Psychological Assessment Resources.

Rogers R, Sewell KW, Martin MA, Vitacco MJ (2003) Detection of feigned mental disorders: a meta-analysis of the MMPI-2 and malingering. *Assessment* 10: 160–177.

Rosenhan D (1973) On being sane in insane places. *Science* 172: 250–258.

# Personality Disorder

**J Frazer**, Cleckheaton, UK
**K J B Rix**, Leeds Mental Health Teaching Trust, Leeds, UK

## Introduction

The concept of personality disorder is one that raises controversy amongst many clinicians in psychology and psychiatry. Its usefulness lies in the potential response to treatment of individuals with this label and also the risks associated with abnormal behaviors, particularly violence and other adverse consequences. There is still a great deal about personality disorders that remains speculative.

Although other mental disorders in psychiatry have been narrowed down in terms of symptom constellations and treatment, personality disorders have not yet achieved this precision. People still regard personality disorder as a pejorative term and, when the label is given to patients, this can lead to therapeutic nihilism, a belief that little can be done and we might as well wash our hands of them. It is important to recognize, however, that personality disorders and mental illnesses often coexist and the fact that someone may have an abnormality of personality development and function does not mean that he/she is untreatable, nor that any intercurrent illnesses cannot be treated. There are however difficulties in distinguishing where mental illness begins and personality disorder ends, as many of the symptom constellations can appear as morbid characteristics in specific mental disorders. As yet there are no specific physical or psychological tests which can be used to diagnose personality disorder formally.

Although instruments have been developed that can accurately measure personality characteristics, little is yet known as to how these personality disorders actually develop, nor their genetic basis. That is for the future. Nevertheless it is important, as clinicians working in forensic psychology or psychiatry, to be able to identify obvious personality disorders, as they can be highly predictive of risk, and also the response of comorbid disorders to treatment.

## Diagnosis of Personality Traits and Disorders

Personality is the characteristic pattern of an individual's attitudes, behaviors, beliefs, feelings, thoughts, and values, the sum of a person's emotional, cognitive, and interpersonal attributes. Personality traits are prominent and characteristic features of an individual's personality and do not imply psychopathology. Aspects of personality are present from early life and personality traits are relatively stable from adolescence onwards, consistent of contributory environments and recognizable by friends and acquaintances. However, the term "personality disorder" should be reserved for those consistent patterns of thoughts, feelings, and behavior, that are inflexible and maladaptive.

Five dimensions of temperament have been described which appear to be somewhat independent and to have strong genetic contributions:

1. neuroticism
2. extroversion, contrasting with introversion
3. openness, contrasting with discomfort with novel experiences
4. agreeableness, contrasting with contrariness
5. conscientiousness, contrasting with fickleness.

These temperamental attributes may have implications for the course of psychotherapies that cut across diagnostic categories. Another dimension of personality not adequately dealt with in the *Diagnostic and Statistical Manual* (DSM-IV) or *International Classification of Diseases* (ICD-10) concerns moral behaviors such as honesty and integrity. The extent to which individuals behave honestly and with integrity differs considerably across individuals and in different situations. Deception and lying are common behaviors that occur in benign forms, e.g., white lies. In its pathological forms, they are psychiatrically important in antisocial personality disorder and sociopathic disorder, pathological liars, and malingerers. Deception and lying may be difficult to assess clinically, in the absence of additional informants. Studies of nonhuman primates suggest that, at least among chimpanzees, deception (equivalent to lying and dishonesty) is relatively common and in some situations adaptive, thus not in itself indicative of personality disorder.

Another proposed personality typology characterizes personality along three dimensions relating to temperamental characteristics presumed to be strongly influenced genetically. These are: (1) harm avoidance; (2) novelty-seeking; and (3) reward dependence. Different personality types may be described according to patterns of scores on these three dimensions, for example, antisocial personalities are characterized by high novelty-seeking, low harm avoidance, and low reward dependence, whereas dependent characters have low novelty-seeking, high harm avoidance, and high reward dependence.

DSM-IV employs a categorical approach to personality. There is a large overlap among the DSM personality disorders and the clustering of these personality disorders under the three broad groups implies a lack of clear boundaries that currently define categories. The three DSM-IV clusters describe: (1) odd or eccentric types (cluster a); (2) dramatic, emotional, and erratic type (cluster b); and (3) anxious and fearful types (cluster c).

The odd or eccentric group includes paranoid, schizoid, and schizotypal personality disorders. Patients with these personality disorders have the core traits of being interpersonally distant and emotionally constricted. People with paranoid personality disorder are quick to feel slighted and jealous, carry grudges, and expect to be exploited and harmed by others. People with schizoid personality disorder lack friendships or close relationships with others and are indifferent to praise or criticism by others. People with schizotypal personality disorder display odd beliefs, engaging odd and eccentric gestures and practices, and exhibit odd speech.

The dramatic, emotional, and erratic group includes borderline, histrionic, narcissistic, and antisocial personality disorders. Patients with these personality disorders characteristically have chaotic lives, emotions, and relationships. People with borderline personality disorder are impulsive, unpredictable, angry, temperamental, unstable in relationships, compulsively interpersonal, and self-damaging with regard to sex, money, and substance misuse. People with histrionic personality disorder are attention-seeking, exhibitionistic, seductive, and self-indulgent. They exhibit exaggerated expressions of emotion and are overconcerned with physical appearance. People with narcissistic personality disorder tend to be hypersensitive to criticism, exploitative of others, egocentric, with an inflated sense of self-importance, feel entitled to special treatment, and demand constant attention. People with antisocial personality disorder are described almost exclusively in behavioral, rather than affective or relational terms. They commit truancy, lie, steal, start fires, break rules, are unable to sustain work or school, and shirk day-to-day responsibilities.

The anxious and fearful group includes patients with avoidant, dependent, and obsessive-compulsive personality disorders. Patients with these disorders are characterized by constricting behaviors that serve to limit risks. People with anxious avoidant personality disorders avoid relationships. People with dependent personality disorder avoid being responsible for decisions, and people with obsessive-compulsive personality disorder use rigid rules that preclude lewd behaviors. People with avoidant personality disorders are hypersensitive to rejection and are reluctant to enter close relationships in spite of strong desires for affection. Those with dependent personality disorders show excessive reliance on others to make major life decisions, stay trapped in abusive relationships for fear of being alone, have difficulty initiating projects on their own, and constantly seek reassurance and praise. Individuals with obsessive-compulsive personality disorders exhibit restricted expressions of warmth, tenderness, and generosity and also exhibit stubbornness, with a need to be right and to control decisions. They are indecisive at times; they often apply rules and morals so rigidly to the point of being inflexible.

There is another example of a personality disorder that is related to brain damage and is referred to as organic personality disorder in the ICD-10 and as personality change due to a general medical condition in DSM-IV. These features include irritability and inappropriate jocularity with euphoria, inappropriate socially disinhibited behavior, and impulsiveness. In contrast, other patients with damage to different areas of the frontal lobe exhibit apathy and indifference.

## ICD-10 or DSM-IV

In ICD-10, personality disorders are described as deeply ingrained, maladaptive patterns of behavior, generally recognized by the time of adolescence or earlier, and continuing throughout most of adult life, though often becoming less obvious in middle or old age. The personality is abnormal, either in the balance of its components, the quality and expression, or in its total aspect; because of this deviation or psychopathy, the patient suffers or others have to suffer and there is an adverse effect upon the individual or society.

Although the ICD-10 definition recognizes that personality disorders are distinct from other mental disorders, in their ingrained nature, it continues to retain them within the main axis of mental disorders, which distinguishes it from the American classification in the DSM-IV. Here it is argued that personality disorders should be placed on a separate axis to ensure that consideration is given to the possible presence of personality disorder that might otherwise be overlooked, when attention is directed to usually more florid axis I disorders.

There are distinctions between the two classification systems, in that schizotypal personality disorder is regarded in ICD-10 as on the spectrum of psychotic disorders, whereas in DSM-IV it is regarded as a personality disorder. Also cyclothymic disorder is regarded by some as a version of manic-depressive psychosis and therefore belongs with mental illness. It has subsequently been dropped from the definition of personality disorders.

In ICD-10 personality accentuation was also included to describe people with exaggerated personality traits, in that individuals who show a relatively mild degree of abnormality may be more liable to develop mental illness when affected by circumstances. These are therefore abnormalities of personality, intermediate between normal personality and personality disorder. The main characteristic is the persistence of personality disorder when other mental abnormalities have been treated and therefore we might consider them to be a continuum.

## The History of Personality Disorders

Aristotle's Pupil, Theophrastus, described a group of characters (**Table 1**), based on his observations of humankind. We can see from the descriptions that many people have these characteristics. However, it is important to note that, although people may have these characteristics at one point in their lives, they may not be persistently prone to these characteristics. The nature of the personality disorder is that we now recognize these are persistent traits in individuals diagnosed as suffering from personality disorders.

**Table 1** Theophrastus' characters

| | | |
|---|---|---|
| *Dissimulator* Affection in acts and words | *Gross man* Obtrusive and objectionable jesting | *Vain man* Paltry desire for distinction |
| *Flatterer* Degrading, self-profiting intercourse | *Unseasonable man* Inopportune attitude | *Boaster* Pretending to have advantages not personally possessed |
| *Chatterer* Mania of talking hugely without thinking | *Officious man* Presumptious benevolence in word and deed | *Arrogant man* Contempt for everyone except himself |
| *Rustic* Grossness which is ignorant of good manners | *Stupid man* Sluggishness of mind | *Coward* Shrinking of the soul caused by fear |
| *Complaisant* Agreeable intercourse without good motives | *Surly man* Lack of amenity in speech | *Oligarch* Domination in power and wealth |
| *Reckless cynic* Effrontery of doing or saying shameful things | *Superstitious man* Cowardice towards divine power | *Late learner* Pursues knowledge at too advanced an age |
| *Loquacious man* Incontinence of speech | *Grumbler* Complaining too much of one's lot | *Slanderer* Malevolent disposition of the soul |
| *Newsmonger* Inventing false events | *Distrustful man* Suspects all men of dishonesty | *Friend of the rabble* Has a taste for vice |
| *Unscrupulous man* Disregard of reputation for sake of base gain | *Offensive man* Repulsive neglect of the person | *Avaricious man* Pursues sordid gain |
| *Penurious man* Economy beyond all measure | *Unpleasant man* Annoyance without being really harmful | *Mean man* Lack of generosity |

Basant Puri, Annie D Hall, *Revision Notes in Psychiatry*. Hodder and Stoughton 1998. Reproduced by permission of Hodder and Stoughton Ltd.

This view of temperament persisted for many years in western traditions, but it was not until Pritchard's work in the 1840s that clinicians started to distinguish between abnormal mental state and abnormal personalities. Pritchard described and coined the term moral insanity.

Toward the end of the century, Koch described psychopathic inferiority and since then personality disorders have carried with them a trait of degeneration which makes them much less respectable than a mental illness and indeed, often clinicians use them as a term of abuse when they dislike patients.

The German psychopathologist Kraepelin further developed Koch's ideas, particularly of psychopathy.

He described personality disorders as "morbid mental states," in which the peculiar disposition of a personality must be considered the real foundation of the malady. He described paranoid types, antisocial types, and hypochondriacal types. We now regard personality disorders as developing early in adult life and lasting with greater or less fluctuation throughout the whole of life.

It was Schneider who produced the definition that is still used today, i.e., psychopathic personalities are such abnormal personalities who suffer through their abnormalities, or through whose abnormalities society suffers. Schneider described 10 types: (1) hypothymic; (2) depressive; (3) insecure; (4) fanatic; (5) self-seeking; (6) emotionally unstable; (7) explosive; (8) affectless; (9) weak-willed; and (10) aesthenic psychopathic personality.

In the USA in 1941, Cleckley discussed the clinical status of psychopathic personality disorder and his approach has been developed further by Robert Hare, who developed the Psychopathy Checklist (PCL), based on historical records. That is the characteristic which distinguishes it from self-report measures of personality disorder. It provides a robust diagnosis of psychopathic disorder. Hare also developed a screen version of the PCL, which is referred to as the PCL SV. This is because many professionals have requested a brief instrument that has a higher validity and reliability similar to the complete revised Hare PCL (PCL-R). The PCL SV was not designed to replace the PCL-R, but rather to offer a tool to screen for the possible presence of psychopathy. It is a tool based on a subset of PCL-R items that could be completed in civic and forensic settings in under 90 min. It can be used in psychiatric evaluations, personal connection, and community studies. Currently, it has been used in a MacArthur risk assessment study to assess risk amongst people hospitalized in acute-care psychiatric facilities. The conclusions of the group in May 2004 suggest that it is highly accurate when compared to other approaches to assessing risk amongst that group of patients. It is also more computationally complex than other approaches. Testing is continuing.

There remains a separation in psychiatric diagnosis between axis I (mental-state problems) and axis II (personality disorders).

## Personality Development

There are two specific theories relating to this concept. The first is based on studies of populations with characteristics which fall beyond normal. These are then regarded as abnormal. These theories are described as nomothetic. Then there are idiographic theories that relate to the specific individuals' uniqueness. This is therefore based on the study of the individual. Kelly, in his personal construct theory, suggests that the individual interprets the world on the basis of his/her past experience. The individual then creates specific constructs and makes predictions about how the world works based on those constructs. Clearly each individual is unique in the way that he/she construes the world and personality will therefore change depending on ongoing experiences.

There are some constructs that are central to the individual's sense of identity and, when other individuals ignore these, this can cause a great deal of distress to the individual. Other constructs are less important. Hostility is an important consequence of the imposition of constructs upon one another.

In the 1980s there was a view that personality traits result from differences in learning experience and that the behavior changes according to the situation in which individuals find themselves. However there is a poor correlation between behavior or attitudes in one situation compared with another and the most likely reality is the interaction of the situation with the personality.

## Genetics and other Influences on the Development of Personality

The risk of developing psychopathology can be considered under the following headings:

1. demographic factors
2. psychosocial factors
3. biological factors
4. genetic factors
5. family environment
6. external environment.

To distinguish clearly between temperament and personality disorder, temperament refers to those characteristics which are found normally distributed in normal individuals, which also have genetic heritability, such as people who are sociable, those who are shy, those who are irritable, and those who are placid. It is only when these traits are maladaptive and cause problems to individuals in their social, occupational, and relational functioning that they are regarded as maladaptive and part of personality.

With respect to the pathogenesis of borderline personality disorder, Torgerson and coworkers have conducted a series of twin studies to estimate the way genes and environment influence personality structure. Twin data allow the estimation of the genetic correlation between two traits and the way that these two traits may share the same genetic predisposition. Factor analysis can then be used to determine traits such as anxiousness, submissiveness, effective ability, cognitive dysregulation, social avoidance, suspiciousness, or narcissism. These studies show that the environment has a substantial effect on personality, accounting for 50% of the variance seen.

It is clear that a single factor can rarely account for the variance between the emergence or any inhibition of a psychiatric disorder. Genetic factors seem to be of particular significance. These are then influenced by numerous other factors. For example, the following factors are regarded as significant in an individual who has been removed from his/her birth family in childhood.

1. genetic influences
2. early separation from parents
3. early childhood environment prior to that separation
4. multiple placements in residential care, rather than in any one establishment
5. physical abuse in residential establishments and other settings
6. emotional abuse in residential establishments and other settings
7. sexual abuse in residential establishments and other settings
8. poor family support on leaving care
9. traumatic experiences in adult life.

Genetic and environmental factors interact in complex ways to influence the risk of personality disorder. Available genetic observations about twins, adoptees, and families are explained by the hypotheses that quantitative inheritance of underlying personality dimensions influences the risk of personality disorder, rather than positing separate inheritance of personality disorder subtypes. More than one-half of the variance in the four major personality traits is inherited.

Temperament traits determine one's susceptibility to specific neurochemical processes, leading to individual differences in basic emotions in biased learning. These antecedent temperament factors, along with the systematic cultural bias and random life events, critically influence character development, which is represented as the interaction between internalized concepts about the self and the external world. Various temperamental types differentially affect one's risk of immature character and personality development. Some configurations (most with high reward dependence) protect against personality disorders, whereas some increase this risk (e.g., the explosive or borderline profile with low reward dependence, high novelty-seeking, and low harm avoidance).

Average scores on the temperament dimensions do not protect against maladaptation and immaturity.

People with average temperament traits have an average, not a decreased, risk of personality disorder. Similarly, extreme temperament variants do not necessarily indicate personality pathology. They are expected to be associated with long-term personal, social, or occupational impairments that warrant the personality diagnosis, only when accompanied by low character traits, in other words, poorly developed character is what makes some behavior traits maladaptive and increases the risk of personality disorders. An individual high in novelty-seeking and low in harm avoidance may have an impulsive personality disorder if he/she is low in self-directedness and cooperativeness, or maybe an energetic business executive or an inquisitive scientist without personality disorder, if he/she is self-directed and cooperative. Mature character traits, i.e., mature concepts about oneself in the external world, optimize adaptation of temperament, i.e., basic emotionality to the environment, by reducing discrepancies between one's emotional needs and norm-favoring social pressures. In personality disorder, immature character traits and extreme temperament configurations mutually perpetuate each other.

Behavioral geneticists have demonstrated that the effect of sociocultural factors on personality is less specific than that of genetic factors and the definitive influence is success in adaptation, rather than formal personality style. This is consistent with recent findings about the importance of family and local culture and character development. The family environment does not influence temperament, but explains 35% of variability of character traits. Hence psychosocial disorganization in the rearing environment of a child substantially influences the risk of personality disorders. This is essential for preventive strategies, as even temperament configurations with a high risk of personality disorder may be overcome in homes and communities that provide security and limit behavior in a warm, compassionate manner, encouraging self-directed choice and respect for other people.

The potential role of a child psychiatrist, therefore, in identifying children with the antecedence of antisocial personality disorder is very important. A critical task is to separate this heterogeneous group, so that those who are most at risk of developing antisocial personality characteristics become the focus of intervention. Since Robins' classic follow-up of children referred to a clinic for conduct problems, numerous studies have shown that the persistence and pervasive, aggressive, and destructive behaviors seen before the age of 11 are strongly associated with the persistence of antisocial behaviors through adolescence and into adult life. Robins described that the risk extends far beyond antisocial behaviors to unstable relationships, unreliable parenting, and underachievement in education and at work. This broad consolation of difficulties is reflected in DSM-IV antisocial personality disorder. Children who do not have conduct problems are very unlikely subsequently to develop antisocial personality disorder, which is rare without a history of conduct problems.

Conduct disorder is a specific diagnosis within DSM-IV which requires antisocial acts generally seen in older children and adolescents. The available research unfortunately does not yet tell us whether differences in parenting or associated features of childhood conduct problems are predictive of distinctive adult outcomes.

It is important to clarify that psychopathy refers to the constellation of traits of deceitfulness, lack of remorse, and failure to learn from previous experiences, as well as callous disregard for others, and when these traits run together, we are discussing a severe form of personality disorder, known as psychopathy. Other individuals with fewer traits may meet the criteria for a personality disorder, but not at the same level of severity, thus psychopathy specifically refers to severe personality disorder, with a far greater number of traits pertaining to that personality disorder type.

Although 50–80% of convicted offenders have DSM-IV antisocial personality, a much smaller group of 15–30% are judged to have characteristics such as grandiosity, callousness, deceitfulness, shallow affect, and lack of remorse. These individuals are much more likely than other offenders to have a history of severe and violent offenses and they may also have a distinctive deficit in interpersonal sensitivity. They are thought to have a severe disturbance of personality structure, also known as psychopathic personality disorder. In addition, compared with other offenders, adults with psychopathic disorder have reduced autonomic responses to distress cues, suggesting a biological determinance to psychopathy. Unfortunately, no studies have yet tested the continuity between child and adult psychopathic traits by following these children into adult life.

It is usual that the universal traits are present in all people in different degrees. It is important to clarify that these personality traits can be measured in normal individuals, and do not represent a personality disorder. It is only when they are present in sufficient numbers and with a sufficient degree of severity that the diagnosis is made continuous.

In general, three aspects of personality change substantially with age. Novelty-seeking decreases by 18%, thus older individuals are less impulsive, perhaps more reflective, less rule-breaking, more orderly and less quick-tempered, and more stoical. Cooperativeness increases markedly in most children during school age and then increases by 12% on average after age 18, and self-directedness increases markedly in most people during adolescence and young adulthood, increasing on average by 9% after the age of 18. The decreasing prevalence of personality disorder with age is attributable to increased development of both self-directedness and cooperativeness, as the individual gets older. The additional tendency for novelty-seeking to decrease with age explains why people with impulsive personality disorders show more improvement than those with anxious or eccentric personality disorders.

The best-documented finding about changing deviant behaviors is the remission of criminal behaviors of an individual with antisocial personality disorder. These individuals nearly always remain impulsive, are novelty-seeking, risk-taking, low harm-avoidant, and aloof, but become mature enough to maintain work and family life in a stable manner, after the age of 30.

Gradually links are being established between core personality disorder traits and some genetic developmental mechanisms. This will hopefully shed light on the task of identification and differentiation of abnormal personalities. Research is increasingly understanding of different factors, including innate dispositions, neurodevelopmental organization, neurocognitive architecture, critical social transitions, and repeated stress episodes on an individual's vulnerability to developing personality disorder. Hopefully, the advances in psychometric detection of the most salient clinical profiles, within each of the personality subtypes, together with the refinement of the neurocognitive and neurohormonal data, will produce better solutions.

## The Genetics of Criminality

Criminality, like other aspects of psychological characteristics of individuals, appears to be significantly inherited. The average heritability of psychological traits seems to be 50%, based on simple measurements, and possibly 70%, when based on estimates of the stable components of the traits, i.e., those that remain stable after repeated measurement. A highly consistent and stable trait like intelligence quotient (IQ) has a heritability on the order of 75% for single measurements, rising to 85% when corrected for instability. IQ may be relevant to criminality because we know that the mean IQ of prison inmates and adjudicated delinquents is somewhat lower than the average population. However, it is possible that some of the brighter offenders are not included in these averages, because they have avoided being caught. For traits of personality, temperament, and interest that seem specifically relevant to criminality, we can estimate that perhaps 50–70% of the stable variance is genetically determined within the general population. Somewhat less than this, 30–40% among the population are now at high risk for delinquency and crime.

## Measurement of Personality Disorder

Personality disorders are felt to differ from the normal variation only in terms of degree. Thus the personality traits of some individuals are sufficiently maladaptive and abnormal to constitute a personality disorder. Catell identified 20 000 words describing personality. Using factor analysis he derived 16 first-order personality factors, his 16 PF questionnaire. Second-order factor analysis resulted in the trait dimensions similar to those of Hans Eysenck. These are sociability, extroversion and introversion, anxiety, and intelligence. Eysenck looked at fractionalities of rating scale data. This yielded orthogonal dimensions, assumed to be normally distributed, of neuroticism, stability, extroversion, introversion, psychoticism or stability, and intelligence. Personality inventories were used to measure these traits, namely the Maudsley Personality Inventory (MPI), which was superseded by the Eysenck's Personality Inventory (EPI), finally superseded by the Eysenck's Personality Questionnaire (EPQ), which measured psychoticism.

The Minnesota Multiphasic Personality Inventory (MMPI) was derived through a process of empirical construction. It was devised as a clinical tool to differentiate between abnormal personalities, but has subsequently been used with normal populations. It consists of a total of 550 statements to which the interviewee responds with a reply of true or false, or cannot say. The MMPI measures traits and is widely used. It appears to be of considerable value in the study of clinically abnormal personalities, but interpretation by an experienced psychologist is required. The scales, which include paranoia, schizophrenia, and hypomania, should be regarded as indicative of the presence of specific personality attributes, rather than of an axis I diagnosis. It is also used in candidate selection and prediction procedures, but is more of value in a clinical setting.

The Personality Assessment Schedule (PAS) was developed in 1976 and has been used to classify personality disorders. This is a hierarchical system in which the personality category that has the highest score for social impairment becomes the named personality disorder. Other major categories

which achieve clinically significant scores can be mentioned in the diagnostic description. Patients who do not reach the scores necessary for diagnosis of personality disorder may still attain the level required for personality difficulty and be coded as such. Severity can also be assessed using the system of Tyrer and Johnson.

Cluster analysis has shown that the four major types of personality disorders can be identified from the PAS. **Table 2** sets out the choice of instruments used to measure the aspects of personality disorder. In forensic populations, the one that is most predictive of measuring risk of recidivism is the Hare PCL-R.

## Personality in Old Age

As people age, they tend to become more introverted. To the extreme level, this can result in the Diogenes syndrome, in which the elderly recluse lives a limited life in advanced squalor with extreme hording of rubbish. It may be that chronic alcohol misuse and chronic frontal lobe dysfunction may play a part in this condition. Characteristically, the syndrome is

**Table 2** Reasons for selecting the Personality Assessment Schedule or other instruments in research studies

| Purposes which may justify selection of PAS | Purposes which suggest the use of other instruments (preferred choice in brackets) |
| --- | --- |
| Need to assess premorbid personality | Need to assess current personality functioning (SCID-11) |
| A population that is unlikely to tolerate an assessment lasting longer than 30 minutes | Compliant population that is predominantly within normal or mildly abnormal range (SNAP or DAPP-BQ) |
| Significant Axis I comorbidity | Quick assessment for ICD-10 diagnosis (SAP) |
| Wish to record personality across severity range | Full assessment for ICD-10 and DSM-IV diagnosis (IPDE) |
| Longitudinal study requiring multiple assessments over a long time period | Forensic use with special attention to reoffending (PCL-R) |
| Studies in which either informant or patient may be required to complete assessment | Rapid screening instrument for DSM personality disorders (Iowa Personality Disorder Screen) |

SCID-11, Structured Clinical Interview for DSM-IV Axis II personality disorders; SNAP, Schedule for Nonadaptive and Adaptive Personality (Clark *et al.*, 1996); DAPP-BQ, (Dimensional Assessment of Personality Pathology-Basic Questionnaire (DAPP-BQ) (Schroeder *et al.*, 1992); SAP, Standardized Assessment of Personality (Mann *et al.*, 1981; Hare Psychopathy Check List – Revised (Hare, 1991); Iowa Personality Disorder Screen (Langbehn *et al.*, 1999).

unaccompanied by any psychiatric disorder to account for the state in which the patient lives. In the UK, the Mental Health Act cannot be used in the absence of a mental disorder. Instead the Public Health Act may be used to deal with these situations if required. Unfortunately, as with other disorders, in old age the prognosis is usually very poor, with almost inevitable relapse. Although in the initial phases, day care may help, institutional care is often the outcome, with the individual being transferred from home into such an institution as the only means of managing the public health problems.

## Treatment and Management of Personality Disorders

### Psychosocial Treatments

Dynamic psychotherapy  In the past, psychoanalysts, such as Jung and Freud, were treating neurotic disorder with associated personality pathology, mainly from the cluster c group. Since the days of these giants, however, no scientific evidence has emerged to show that dynamic psychotherapy is superior to other forms of psychotherapy. A formal evaluation of two forms of dynamic psychotherapy, namely short-term dynamic psychotherapy and brief adaptational psychotherapy, was carried out by Winstone and colleagues in 1991, but excluded patients with borderline, narcissistic personalities. No difference was shown between treatments, but both treatments were better than a waiting-list control group, suggesting that this treatment may have some value.

Research in the past has focused primarily on the management of patients with borderline symptomatology, as these are the patients commonly presenting in clinical practice. Assessment is always difficult, as personality traits tend to be egosyntonic (i.e., the patient does not regard his/her coping style as maladaptive). Patients may not be aware of symptomatology and therefore not complain. It is essential that multiple sources of information are used, including an informant who has known the patient for a considerable time. In order for the diagnosis to be made, personality traits should be enduring and not transient, be pervasive across social situations, and be early in onset and cause distress to the patient or impairment of social functioning.

In a controlled randomized trial, Bateman and Fonagy compared the effectiveness of 18 months of a psychoanalytical-oriented day hospitalization program with routine general psychiatric care for patients with borderline personality disorder. Patients randomly assigned to the day hospital program showed a statistically significant improvement in depressive symptoms and better social and interpersonal functioning, as well as a significant decrease in suicidal and self-mutilatory acts on the number of inpatient days. Although Bateman and Fonagy showed impressive maintenance of treatment effects in an 18-month follow up, this study lacked a treatment manual and therapists' adherence ratings.

Nevertheless, psychotherapy or intensive psychoanalytical psychotherapy has been considered by many psychotherapists to be the treatment of choice for individuals with borderline personality disorder. The duration of therapy varies between 2 and 7 years and treatment consists of the interpretation of the transference and primitive defense mechanisms, the neutrality of the therapist, and consistent limit-setting. Attention is focused on the present, rather than interpreting childhood experience. An alternative is supportive psychotherapy, which aims to strengthen a patient's adaptive functioning through education, suggestion, and facilitating into personal relationship. Interpretation and transference defense mechanisms and regression independence are avoided, since they are considered likely to lead to suicide or other forms of acting out.

Group psychotherapy  Group psychotherapy has been traditionally avoided, particularly in the borderline group, as these patients are considered to be too demanding and disruptive to other group members. Gentle confrontation delivered by the group, however, is considered to be effective, rendering egosyntonic traits more egodystonic. This works by letting individuals know their effects upon other individuals. There is no evidence specifically to recommend group therapy over individual therapy. However, therapeutic communities have operated in the healthcare system since their introduction in the 1950s. Patients who are referred are accepted primarily on the basis of their behavior and then acceptance by the democratic therapeutic community. Studies at the Henderson Hospital, Sutton, UK, which primarily treats individuals with severe personality disorders, used instruments to record personality disorders according to the standard diagnostic systems, i.e., DSM-IV and the personality disorder questionnaire. Individuals tend to have at least four separate personality disorder diagnoses, suggesting that their personality disorders are severe. The treatment given is group psychotherapy and stays variable, but lasts for around 7 months. There have been no randomized controlled trials to study the outcome of therapeutic community intervention, however, as there are major difficulties, including ethics, a lack of objective outcome measures, resistance from the field, or reluctance to compare treatments.

In the course of working among a therapeutic community in an open forensic unit in Bradford, UK, over a period of 8 years, one of the authors (JF) observed several patients with severe personality disorder mature and improve in all aspects of the function in that environment. Clearly, however, these observations are anecdotal and this appears to be the level of the evidence.

**Cognitive analytical therapy** This was first described by Ryle in 1997. It is concerned with describing different self-states and helping patients to identify "reciprocal role procedures." These are patterns of relationships which are learned in early childhood and are relatively resistant to change. The patient is taught to observe and try to change damaging patterns of thinking and behavior, which relate to these self-states, and to become more self-aware. The therapist gathers information about the patient's experience of relationships and the different states the patient experiences. Any accounts of transference reactions experienced by the therapists are considered as useful data as they may represent identification with the patient or some reciprocating response to the patients' overt or covert behavior. Having identified and labeled these, countertransference (i.e., negative feelings toward the patient engendered in the therapist) is reduced to maintain a working alliance with the patient. The therapist's task is to help patients reliably recognize these self-states and to encourage them to become aware of them without dissociating, i.e., psychologically switching their memory off. Although there are no published studies to compare with other psychotherapies, initial work has shown some promising outcome.

**Dialectical behavior therapy** This is a manualized treatment program, particularly for patients with borderline personality disorders. The patients have weekly individual psychotherapy and group psychoeducation about behavioral skills. They receive telephone consultation with their therapist, who remains in 24-h contact with the patient. The treatment consists of teaching a variety of problem-solving skills, helping patients to regulate emotion, tolerate distress, and validate their own perceptions. They also develop behavioral and psychological versions of meditation skills. Patients are encouraged to observe, describe, and participate in events without separating themselves from what is happening. This encourages them to take a nonjudgmental approach to events and interactions and to do what works, rather than what they feel might be the right thing

to do. Again, the evidence base for this intervention does not involve controlled studies.

**Cognitive-behavioral therapy** Linehan and co-workers randomly allocated cognitive-behavioral therapy and "treatment as usual" over a period of 1 year to chronically parasuicidal borderline patients. During that year the cognitive-behavioral therapy group had fewer and less severe incidents of parasuicide and fewer inpatient days, suggesting benefit in this disorder. However, it must be stressed that cognitive therapy for personality disorder remains experimental in approach. It does however aid the therapist in understanding this group of diverse patients to provide a framework in which to formulate problems and interventions.

Particularly in relation to the treatment of dangerous severe personality disorders, a Home Office review is trying to distinguish between treatments that have proven to be effective for men and women. This relies heavily on a "what works" evidence base, which has not been fully established. The evidence base includes 25 studies of cognitive behavioral psychotherapy, eight studies of dialectical behavior therapy, and five studies of cognitive analytical therapy. There were also 32 studies of pharmacological treatment, 35 studies of psychodynamic psychotherapy, ten studies of tricyclics and two of physical approaches to treatment. There were no recommendations for a specific treatment approach deriving directly from the research evidence.

**Inpatient treatment in general psychiatric hospitals**
Currently, long-term admissions for patients suffering borderline personality disorder are not encouraged. The risk of hospitalization to the patient includes stigma, disruption of social and occupational function, loss of freedom and hospital-induced behavioral regression. Many therapists draw up contracts between the patient and care team to improve outcome. The treatment contract should incorporate agreement by all involved parties, specific focused achievable goals and strategies to achieve these and the specific responsibilities of patient and staff, and provision of the minimum degree of instruction necessary. Patients should forgo their usual means of managing intolerable feelings, such as self-harm, and alternative strategies would be provided. Positive reinforcement of desirable behavior is preferable to sanctions, which should not be drawn up to resolve punitive wishes by staff toward the patient. This should be strictly enforced but would have room for negotiating modification. An alternative approach is a brief admission at the time of crisis, but once admitted, it may be difficult to avoid the hazards listed above.

## Pharmacotherapy

Placebo-controlled drug trials amongst those with personality disorder show small specific drug effects, as well as large placebo effects. There is no evidence for large treatment effects to date.

**Neuroleptic drugs**  Low-dose neuroleptic treatment has been shown to be beneficial, particularly in the management of borderline personality disorder in a majority of trials. Low-dose flupenthixol reduced the number of suicide attempts by 6 months, compared to placebo mianserin in a mixed group of parasuicidal personality disorder subjects. Low-dose neuroleptics can improve a broad spectrum of neurotic symptoms, as well as reducing behavioral dyscontrol and the numbers of suicide attempts compared to placebo.

**Tricyclic antidepressants**  Patients with borderline or schizotypal personality disorder improve with tricyclics on rating of depressed mood, impulsive and manipulative behavior. There is a significant potential however for paradoxical effects and rage reactions. They are not recommended in the management of personality disorders, unless there is a comorbidity of major depression. Depression complicated by personality disorder is only half as likely to respond to tricyclic drug treatments compared to poor major depression.

**Monoamine oxidase inhibitors**  If there is a history of childhood hyperactivity, there is some evidence that patients with borderline personality disorder may respond to these drugs.

**Selective serotonin reuptake inhibitors (SSRIs)**  Disruption of the serotonergic system is implicated in depression, impulsivity, and obsessive compulsion. There is some evidence that fluoxetine at doses of 20–80 mg per day can result in improvement in depressed mood and impulsivity, as well as reducing self-harm, while sertraline, used in impulsive and aggressive patients, has resulted in some improvement in overt aggression and irritability from the fourth week of treatment. However, long-term studies have not been carried out.

**Lithium**  This may be helpful in a small number of patients with various personality disorders, particularly with affective features, or a family history of affective disorder with alcoholism. In male convicts with a pattern of recurring, easily triggered violence, a marked reduction in fractions resulted from the treatment with lithium, again over a short period of time.

**Carbamazepine**  Reducing passivity, particularly in behavioral dyscontrol, results in aggression. This is in the absence of epileptic organic features.

**Benzodiazepines**  These are contraindicated because they disinhibit, induce rage reactions, and promote dependence and misuse.

**Psychostimulants**  It has been suggested that individuals with an early history of attention-deficit hyperactivity disorder, which has been responsive to methylphenidate (Ritalin), may respond in adult life to the prescription of psychostimulants, such as dexamphetamine and pemonine. However, because of the psychotogenic effects and addictive properties, extreme caution should be used.

## Conclusions in Respect of Therapies

Despite the fact that there are several controlled trials involving psychotropic drugs and placebos, in the treatment of personality disorder, none showed full efficacy in the sense that the treatment is independent of comorbidity. The treatments are not superior in efficacy to placebo and need to show lasting efficacy for a period of at least 6 months because of the enduring nature of personality disorder.

Ideally, in randomized trials, the outcome of personality disorder should be measured directly by assessing personality status before and after treatment and also after long-term follow up. This is clearly a long-term and difficult process.

With reference to "what works" evidence, the therapeutic community model had the most promising evidence base in this poor field. There was some evidence that psychodynamic day hospital-based programs with highly structured therapeutic programs had promising evidence of effectiveness to treat poorly functioning self-harming, borderline patients. Short-term gains were found with the DBT process to reduce self-harm in higher-functioning female outpatients with borderline personality disorder. The evidence for pharmacological interventions was very poor; also SSRI antidepressants might ameliorate symptomatology and anger, and brofaramine (monoamine oxidase inhibitor) may ameliorate avoidant personality disorders and symptoms of social anxiety.

## Outcome of Personality Disorder

Unfortunately, individuals with personality disorder show a high morbidity and mortality. The standardized mortality ratio for the 39-year age group is six times that of normal individuals, similar to the rise in people suffering from major functional psychoses, such as schizophrenia. Sufferers have high rates of comorbidity, with both axis I and axis II conditions. Response to treatment of the axis I disorder is worse in the presence of personality disorder and patients are at high risk of suicide.

In borderline patients treated with psychotherapy, the aim and support of psychotherapy may be to reduce suicidal behavior and impulsive acts while they are awaiting remission, since the long-term prognosis of this disorder is good. Fifteen years after diagnosis, of 100 borderline patients, 75 were no longer diagnosed as borderline, with reduction of symptomatic behavior on all scales and clear functional improvement. However, there remains a high risk of suicide in this group, with 8.5% completing suicide in the 15-year follow-up period. Those patients with chronic depression, good motivation, psychological mindedness, low impulsiveness, and stable environment are the most responsive to treatment.

With regard to those patients suffering from antisocial personality disorders, there is a significant association between the ability to form a relationship with the therapist and treatment outcome. In settings such as the prison, or military settings, confrontation with peers may change social behaviors and prevalence decreases with increasing age. Schizotypal personality disorder remains relatively stable over time. A small proportion (5–10%) go on to develop schizophrenia. Some other types of antisocial and borderline personality disorders tend to become less evident with age, although this is less true with the obsessive-compulsive personality and schizotypal personality disorder.

## See Also

**Forensic Psychiatry and Forensic Psychology:** Assessment; Suicide Predictors and Statistics; Multiple Personality Disorder

## Further Reading

Adlington R (1925) *A Book of Characters*. London: George Rutledge.
American Psychiatric Association (1994) *Diagnostic and Statistical Manual of Mental Disorders (DSM-IV)*, 4th edn. Washington, DC: American Psychiatric Association.
Basant KP, Anne DH (1998) Revision notes in psychiatry. In: *Personality Disorders*, pp. 336–351. London, Sydney and Auckland: Arnold Publications.
Campbell SB (1995) Behaviour problems in preschool children: a review of recent research. *Journal of Child Psychology and Psychiatry* 36: 113–149.
Chiesa M, Bateman A, Friis S, Wilberg T (2002) Patient characteristics, outcome and cost benefit of hospital based treatment for patients with personality disorder: a comparison of three different programmes. *Psychology and Psychotherapy* 75: 381–393.
David TL (1995) *Anti-social Personalities*. Hillsdale, NJ: Lawrence Erlbaum.
Dunn J, Deater-Deckard K, Pickering K, O'Connor TG, Golding JG (1998) Children's adjustment and pro-social behaviour in step-, single-parent and non-stepfamily settings: finding from a community study. *Journal of Child Psychology and Psychiatry* 39: 1083–1095.
Fergusson DM, Horwood LJ (1998) Conduct problems and later life opportunities. *Journal of Child Psychology and Psychiatry* 39: 1097–1108.
Gelder MG, Lopez-Ibor JJ, Andreasen N (eds.) (2000) *Genetics and Personality: Summary, New Oxford Textbook of Psychiatry*, vol. 1. Oxford University Press.
Hare RD (1991) *The Hare Psychopathy Checklist*, revised. Toronto, Canada: MultiHealth Systems.
Kaplan BS, Sadock VA (2000) *Personality Traits and Disorders, Comprehensive Textbook of Psychiatry*, vol. 1, 7th edn., pp. 821–822. Lippincott/Williams & Wilkins.
Kaplan BS, Sadock VA (2000) *Psychobiological Summary of Personality Disorder, Comprehensive Textbook of Psychiatry*, vol. 2, 7th edn., pp. 1755–1757. Washington, DC: Lippincott/Williams & Wilkins.
Monahan J, Steadman H, Silver E, *et al.* (2001) *Rethinking Risk Assessment: The MacArthur Study of Mental Disorder and Violence*. New York: Oxford University Press.
Plomin R (1994) Genetics and children's experiences in the family. *Journal of Child Psychology and Psychiatry* 36: 33–68.
Roy P, Rutter M, Pickles A (2000) Institutional care: risk from family background or pattern of rearing? *Journal of Child Psychology and Psychiatry* 41: 139–149.
Tyrer P (2000) *Personality Disorders, Diagnosis, Management, Course*, 2nd edn. Heinemann.
Tyrer P, Duggan C, Coid J (2003) *Ramifications of Personality Disorder in Clinical Practice*. London: Royal College of Psychiatrists.
Warren F, *et al.* (2003) *Review of Treatment for Severe Personality Disorder*. Home Office.
World Health Organization (1992) *Tenth Revision of the International Statistical Classification of Diseases in Related Health Problems (ICD-10)*. WHO, Geneva.

# Multiple Personality Disorder

**S J Hucker**, McMaster University, Hamilton, ON, Canada

## Multiple-Personality Disorder in ICD-10

The *International Classification of Diseases*, 10th edn (ICD-10), introduces the section on dissociative (conversion) disorders with the statement that "the common theme shared by dissociative (or conversion) disorders is a partial or complete loss of the normal integration between memories of the past, awareness of identity and immediate sensations, and control of bodily movements." Multiple-personality disorder, so designated in ICD-10, while recognized, is noted to be rare but "the essential feature is the apparent existence of two or more distinct personalities within an individual, with only one of them being evident at a time. Each personality is complete, with its own memories, behavior, and preferences; these may be in marked contrast to the single premorbid personality." This manual notes that, though generally rare, the common form involves two personalities, one of which is dominant; neither have access to the memories of the other and are almost always unaware of each other's existence. Switching from one state to another is usually abrupt in the first instance and associated with trauma, though subsequently often limited to stressful events or occurring during therapeutic sessions. The extent to which iatrogenic or culture-specific factors may influence the development of the disorder is therefore well recognized.

## Dissociative Identity Disorder in DSM-IV

In the *Diagnostic and Statistical Manual*, 4th edn (DSM-IV-TR), dissociative disorders are given their own separate category and multiple-personality disorder is referred to as "dissociative identity disorder." In this classification, the diagnostic criteria are more specific and include the presence of two or more distinct identities or personality states that recurrently take control of the behavior of the individual. Inability to recall important personal information that is more extensive than that which can be explained by ordinary forgetfulness is also necessary. An additional requirement is the exclusion of substance abuse or a general medical condition that might account for the disorder/behavior. Here also the disorder is seen as reflecting "failure to integrate various aspects of identity, memory, and consciousness."

## A Brief History of the Concept of Dissociation and Multiple Personality

The disorder has to be seen in the context of the evolution of the concept of dissociative disorders in general. The origins of the idea evolved largely during the nineteenth century, when the first dynamic psychiatrists became interested in a wide range of phenomena, including hypnosis and psychic phenomena such as automatic writing, crystal gazing, somnambulism, and so on. The notion that psychological trauma predisposed to these conditions became

common. Janet suggested that "psychological automatisms," each representing a complex act and preceded by an idea and accompanying a motion, form the elementary structures of mental life. Normally integrated into a single stream of consciousness, such automatisms could be separated from the rest and function outside awareness and normal voluntary control.

Freud and his disciples quickly replaced the earlier dynamic theories, emphasizing sexuality and hostility, and the notion of repression and the significance of dreams became more influential.

The concept of dissociation however became important again in the second half of the twentieth century and it did become increasingly recognized that some degree of dissociation is a normal phenomenon based on the observation that many mental functions occur unconsciously and automatically.

Early versions of the *Diagnostic and Statistical Manual* were heavily influenced by Freudian psychodynamic theory and its subsequent history. Successive editions have been complex and reflect the considerable debate about the notion of dissociation and related phenomena in general. In the 4th edition, the requirement for amnesia as a diagnostic criterion was reintroduced.

Early reported cases of multiple personality were rare, but reports became much more common in the second half of the twentieth century. Books and movies depicting cases brought the phenomenon to widespread attention, examples include "The Three Faces of Eve" and "Sybil."

By 1990, over 20 000 cases had been reported in the USA. Further media attention, including television appearances, may have contributed to this proliferation.

## Medical–Legal Repercussions of Multiple-Personality Disorder

It was during this epidemic that the potentially serious implications for the criminal justice system became apparent. Individuals accused of serious crimes were able to claim that some personality other than their normal self had been responsible for their behavior.

The possibility of malingering or conscious dissimulation makes the forensic evaluation of a dissociative disorder difficult to assess and to defend. Although various structured interviews and diagnostic instruments have been developed, it remains impossible to be sure whether an accused person's claim of amnesia is genuine or dissimulated. Furthermore, evidentiary questions such as the admissibility of hypnotic or amylobarbital interviews and the independence of testimony by different "alter" personalities have understandably also proved problematic.

At the height of the apparent epidemic, a number of high-profile criminal cases brought the problems into sharp focus. The "Hillside Strangler" (Kenneth Bianchi), along with his cousin, was accused of ten rape-homicides in California in the late 1970s. His defense attorney argued that the crimes were committed by his alter ego and attempted to support this with evidence of his highly hypnotizable nature. His claim was contradicted by other evidence suggesting that he had simulated hypnosis and the identification of inconsistencies in the presentation of his supposed alters. Moreover, there was no independent corroboration of these alters prior to the offenses. Bianchi's history of using bogus credentials to practice as a psychotherapist and acquire psychological knowledge undoubtedly contributed to his ultimate conviction. Bianchi also read a great deal about multiple-personality disorder, though some have noted that "genuine" patients, with no legal involvements, often do so as well.

The use of multiple-personality disorder in support of an insanity defense to serious crimes including murder revolves around two basic issues: the reliability of the diagnosis and the relevance of the diagnosis to the insanity defense.

However, in the USA, a number of disparate judicial decisions reflect the controversies and confusion surrounding the diagnosis and elaborate on the ways in which the basic issues have been approached. Behnke identified three types of legal analysis in these cases. In the first kind, the analysis depends on the assumption that the accused's alter or secondary personality was "in control" of the individual's behavior at the time of the offense. A second type rests on the idea that each personality alter may or may not be criminally responsible for the crime and each must be assessed using the appropriate insanity test. Each alter must be assessed independently of all the others. The third approach focuses on whether or not the dominant personality fulfills the test of criminal responsibility or the "host" personality. Most of the cases he analyzes represent variations on these basic types.

Central to these legal arguments is the psychological and philosophical understanding of what constitutes "a person." The approaches which regard each individual "alter" and the host personality are in some views inappropriate. Behnke, for example, points out that elevating "alter" personalities to the status of persons ignores the fact that only persons can be conscious or unconscious. Moreover, only persons can be criminally responsible and so a court should assess the mental state of the person accused and the nature of the act. On this analysis, alters are mental states and should be evaluated as such. The fact that an individual may have amnesia for a criminal act committed in such an abnormal state would not automatically exonerate the person. The mere presence of a dissociative disorder even in the extreme of a dissociative identity disorder would not in itself be grounds for a defense of insanity. Spiegel has pointed out that, although amnesia is an essential requirement for the diagnosis of dissociative identity disorder, the memories may be easily accessible through hypnosis and other techniques. Failure to be aware of, or think through, the consequences of a criminal act is not a defense; failure to access dissociated aspects of the personality is not in itself a defense either. Thus, the usual insanity standard works fairly satisfactorily with individuals with dissociative identity disorder because the focus of the question asked is narrowed to one that can be answered even if only a personality fragment is dominant.

A completely contrary view is offered by Saks, whose analysis regards alter personalities as independent persons and each should be treated independently under the criminal law. The purported "split" in the personality would, according to Saks, represent absence of *mens rea*.

Generally, most courts have not found dissociation sufficient grounds to absolve an accused of criminal responsibility and have held that the whole human being is responsible for the behavior of any part.

## Conclusion

Although found in official classifications, the diagnosis of multiple-personality or dissociative identity disorder remains controversial. A considerable level of skepticism exists within the mental health professions, whereas others make the diagnosis frequently and argue that critics are blind to the frequent occurrence of the disorder. Given the degree of contentiousness of the very diagnosis, it is not surprising that the law has often had difficulties in coming to terms with the alleged phenomenon.

## See Also

**Forensic Psychiatry and Forensic Psychology:** Personality Disorder

## Further Reading

James D (1998) Multiple personality disorder in the courts: a review of North American experience. *The Journal of Forensic Psychiatry* 9(2): 339–361.

Piper A, Merskey H (2004) The persistence of folly: a critical examination of dissociative identity disorder. Part I. The excesses of an improbable concept. *Canadian Journal of Psychiatry* 49: 592–600.

Piper A, Merskey H (2004) The persistence of folly: a critical examination of dissociative identity disorder. Part II. The defence and decline of multiple personality or dissociative identity disorder. *Canadian Journal of Psychiatry* 49: 678–683.

# Stalking

**J A Reavis**, Relationship Training Institute, San Diego, CA, USA

## Introduction

Although no universal definition has been adopted for the term, it can now safely be stated that the obsessional harassment of one person by another – what is commonly called stalking – occurs with some frequency across the world. This review article will focus on four major studies of stalking behavior, which comprise three large-scale national surveys from different continents, and a metaanalysis of 103 studies comprising nearly 70 000 participants. Definitions of stalking will be reviewed, and prevalence rates examined. Characteristics of stalkers, including the gender of the perpetrator, relationship between perpetrator and victim, duration of pursuit, and putative psychopathology of stalkers, will be discussed. Attachment theory will be introduced and used as an explanatory factor for stalking acts committed by previous sexual intimates of the victim. A model for the assessment and treatment of previously sexually intimate stalkers will be put forth.

## Different Definitions, Different Prevalence Rates

Three national surveys have now been completed on the nature and extent of stalking victimization. In Australia, 6300 adult female respondents were surveyed in a nationally representative random sampling where stalking was defined as unwanted communication, loitering, following, or watching the same person. Two incidents had to occur against the same victim and the perpetrator had to utilize more than one kind of stalking behavior. The survey did not include a fear condition in the definition. Results indicated that 15.1% of the sample had been stalked

at some point in their lives, with 2.4% having been stalked within the last year.

In the UK, a nationally representative sample of nearly 10 000 males and females aged 16–59 years was surveyed on their experience of stalking victimization. Stalking was defined in this study as "persistent and unwanted attention." The definition did not include criteria on behavioral frequency or level of victim fear. Lifetime victimization rate, across gender, was 11.8%. Lifetime rate of female victimization was 16.1%; the male rate was 6.8%. Some 2.9% of the sample reported being victimized within the prior 12 months, again with more females (4.0%) than males (1.7%) reporting being stalked.

The National Violence Against Women survey conducted telephone surveys on 16 000 adult respondents, divided evenly by gender, in 1995 in the USA. In this study, stalking was defined, in part, by a fear condition, where the victim either had to have felt very frightened or feared bodily harm from the perpetrator. This definition, predictably, led to lower rates of observed stalking; lifetime rates of victimization for men and women were 2.2% and 8.1%, respectively. Annual incidence for male and female victimization was 0.4% and 1.0%, respectively. When the fear condition was lessened, victimization rates rose to be roughly equivalent with the two national surveys cited above, with lifetime rates of 4% for men and 12% for women, and annual rates of 1.5% for men and 6% for women.

Spitzberg's recent metaanalysis on stalking and "stalking-related phenomena" represented 103 studies, 108 samples, and 68 615 participants. Across studies, an overall prevalence rate of roughly 21% was found, with a female victimization rate of 23.5%, a male victimization rate of 10.5%, and a female-to-male victimization ratio of 2.5.

It is clear that differences in the way stalking is defined, mainly with regard to behavioral frequency and level of victim fear, lead to discrepant prevalence estimates. However, across three national surveys, when stalking is defined liberally (low levels of fear, or no fear condition, and less stringent behavioral frequency), similar rates are found: lifetime rates of male victimization of 5%, and lifetime rates of female victimization of 15%.

## Gender of Victim

Significantly more women than men are victimized by stalking. Although the Australian survey research did not include data on male victims, other results from that country, comprising a random sample of 3700 male and female respondents from the Australian state of Victoria, found that fully 75% of those reporting stalking were female. Results from the UK were similar, and indicated that approximately three of four (73%) stalking victims were female. The US national survey found that nearly four of five (78%) of the victims were female, and Spitzberg's metaanalysis indicated that three of four victims of stalking are women.

## Gender of Perpetrator

An interesting aspect of stalking crimes is that, although most of these acts are committed by male perpetrators, a significant proportion are also committed by females.

Spitzberg found that males comprised four in five of the total perpetrator sample, and the British survey research found similar numbers. However, this work also indicated that, while 90% of the stalking acts against women were committed by male perpetrators, that number dropped to 57% when considering male victims. Similarly, in the USA, nearly 90% of stalking acts were committed by male perpetrators. Again, while 94% of the perpetrators against females were male, 40% of the stalking acts committed against males were female. In Australia, 84% of the perpetrator sample was male. As we will see, stalking is most likely to occur between current or previous sexual intimates; the relatively high rates of female perpetration is evidence of this.

## Victim–Offender Relationship

In Australia, women reported that they were most often stalked by strangers: 48% of the Australian sample reported being victimized by someone unknown to them, compared to 41% by a previous partner, and 29% by an acquaintance. In the UK, the perpetrator was either a current or former intimate partner of the victim in 29% of cases, an acquaintance 29% of the time, and a stranger to the victim in 34% of cases. By gender, women in the UK were significantly more likely to be stalked by a stranger than were men. In the USA, men were more likely to be stalked by strangers, though, in contrast, female victims were overwhelmingly more likely to be victimized by current or former partners. Drawing on research from 40 studies, Spitzberg indicated that the clear majority of stalking victimizations occurred from previously sexually intimate relationships, followed by acquaintances, and then strangers (**Table 1**).

## Duration of Pursuit

The length of time that stalkers pursue their victims suggests, first, that such behavior is often qualitatively

**Table 1**  Victim–offender relationship

| Country | Sexual intimate/ previous sexual intimate (%) | | Acquaintance (%) | | Stranger (%) | |
|---|---|---|---|---|---|---|
| | Male | Female | Male | Female | Male | Female |
| Australia | NA | 41 | NA | 29 | NA | 48 |
| UK | 27 | 30 | 36 | 30 | 28 | 35* |
| USA | 30 | 59** | 34 | 18** | 36 | 23** |

NA, not available.
*P significant at 0.10 level; **P significant at 0.05 level.

different from what might be considered "normative pursuit" of another, at the termination of a relationship, for example. Second, particularly for the previously sexually intimate stalker, the tenacity suggests the depth of the psychological wound and the perpetrator's putative attachment pathology, as well as the lengths the individual will go in his/her attempts to repair these.

The National Violence Against Women survey results indicated that, although roughly two-thirds of victims reported that their stalker ceased the harassment within 12 months, the average duration of pursuit, across victims, was 1.8 years. Those women who had been stalked by a former intimate partner reported a longer duration of 2.2 years. In the UK, roughly one-third of the victim sample was stalked for less than a month, one-quarter for between 1 and 3 months, and one in five victims were stalked for more than 1 year. Although the Australian survey research did not include data on length of pursuit, other research from that country using a stringent definition for the behavior (a minimum of 10 contacts over a minimum of 4 weeks) found a mean duration of pursuit of 12 months, among a sample of 145 mostly male stalkers referred to a forensic psychiatric clinic for treatment. In the large metaanalytic study, mean duration of pursuit, across 108 samples, was more than 22 months.

Research on length of pursuit as a function of victim–offender relationship has not shown consistent findings. As above, the Violence Against Women survey found that intimate partners stalked for a significantly longer period than perpetrators who were not intimately connected to the victim. The British survey research found similar results: 27% of the female victims who had had a previous intimate relationship with the perpetrator were stalked for at least 1 year, compared to 15% of women who were stalked by a nonintimate. Likewise, Mullen and colleagues found that their group of Australian "rejected stalkers," 79% of whom were former partners of the victim, engaged in the longest absolute duration of pursuit of 41.3 months, though this was not significant at post-hoc analysis. Finally, Purcell and colleagues again in Australia found that previous sexually intimate stalkers engaged in the longest duration of pursuit (mean 16.6 months), compared to nonintimate perpetrators. In contrast, other research has found that "stranger" stalkers pursue the victim longer than previous sexual intimates, while Kropp and colleagues found that duration of pursuit was shortest for strangers, followed by previous sexual intimates, and longest for acquaintances. Further research into this area may help to clarify the relationship between duration of pursuit and victim–perpetrator relationship.

## Stalking and Violence

There is a clear relationship between stalking and physical violence, particularly among those perpetrators currently or previously sexually involved with the victim.

In the USA, four in five female victims stalked by a current or former partner were physically assaulted by that perpetrator; 31% were sexually assaulted. Using these numbers, the authors estimated that in comparison to husbands and partners in the general population who do not stalk, current or former partners who stalk their intimate or other are four times more likely to physically assault, and six times more likely to sexually assault the victim.

The random sample survey research in Australia indicated that nearly one in five stalking victims also reported being physically assaulted, and that 2% reported being sexually assaulted. Those victims who had formerly had an intimate relationship with their perpetrator were more likely than all other groups to be assaulted. In the UK, 19% of women reported being physically assaulted by their stalker, compared to 24% of men; one in 10 women reported being sexually assaulted, compared to 3% of male victims. Similar to the research above, female victims who had had a sexual relationship with the perpetrator were more likely to have been physically and sexually abused than females who did not. Male victims, however, were most likely to be physically abused by stranger stalkers. Finally, across 42 studies, Spitzberg found the rate of physical assault among stalkers to be 33%; the rate of sexual violence, across 17 studies, was 11%.

## Psychopathology

Although there has been much conjecture regarding the psychopathology of individuals who stalk, no systematic research has administered standardized psychological tests to a sample of stalking offenders (that research is underway in the author's lab). The following represents some of the work that has been done.

Although divergent research exists, there appears to be a significant amount of psychiatric illness among stalking offenders, particularly of personality dysfunction. In a sample of 147 males and females referred for evaluation for stalking-related criminal offenses, Rosenfeld found a 17% rate of schizophrenia, 15% rate of delusional disorder, and just over a 10% rate of mood disorder. Just over a third of the sample met criteria for personality pathology; half of these individuals met criteria for full diagnosis or traits associated with the cluster b disorders of borderline, antisocial, or narcissistic personality. Mullen and coworkers reported that half their stalking sample met criteria for an axis I mental disorder and 50% were personality-disordered. In a sample of 50 pretrial British stalkers, Farnham and colleagues reported that over 50% suffered from a psychotic illness.

Although, the delusionally disordered stalker comprises a portion of the perpetrator sample, this percentage is not as high as was once believed. In a sample of 74 stalkers, Zona and colleagues reported that just seven (9.5%) were diagnosed with erotomania, the subtype most often associated with unwanted pursuit. Mullen and Pathe reported that five of 14 stalkers referred for psychiatric evaluation were erotomanic, and Harmon and coworkers found a roughly similar rate (29%). Finally, among Rosenfeld's relatively large sample of 147 male and female stalkers, 15% met criteria for delusional disorder.

With regard to use of substances, fully 50% of Rosenfeld's (2003) sample of male and female stalkers had histories of substance abuse. Meloy and Gothard found a rate of 70% among their sample, although Mullen and colleagues found that just 25% met criteria for a substance-related disorder.

As above, the absence of standardized psychological testing on a sample of stalking offenders makes it difficult to draw firm conclusions regarding the level and extent of psychopathology. In San Diego, California, this author has evaluated or treated 150 males and females for stalking or stalking-related criminal activity. Data collection, including psychological testing, is being carried out. Although the data have not been formally analyzed, preliminary analyses indicate significant amounts of personality pathology (as measured by Millon Clinical Multiaxial Inventory, 3rd edition (MCMI-III)), particularly narcissistic pathology, and substance abuse, particularly alcohol and methamphetamine, among this population. The defensive qualities of the narcissism suggest underlying feelings of inadequacy in the stalker, and, by inference, difficulties with attachment.

## Attachment

In London in the 1950s, John Bowlby and his colleagues, working from psychoanalytic and ethological principles, created a theory of the way an infant "attaches" to its caregiver. Three early, central postulates of their theory were:

1. Attachment between mother and child is genetically determined.
2. Felt anxiety is the emotional response to separation or threat.
3. Grief occurs at the loss of a loved one.

Mary Ainsworth and her colleagues built on Bowlby's work by demonstrating the role of fear in the attachment behavior of infants. When a child feels strongly attached to his mother, he will explore his environment, acquire new information, and assimilate what he learns into the developmental progression. This feeling of "emotional safety" allows the child to learn, mature, and grow. During times of subjective fear or anxiety, however, exploration behavior ceases, information intake stops, and (most importantly for theories on the motivations of stalkers), the child seeks physical proximity to mother. In this scenario, the felt experience of fear stops exploration and leads to attachment. Thus attachment is a genetically determined behavioral system which ensures physical closeness between infant and caretaker.

Modern attachment research conducted by Bartholomew has identified three pathological types of adult attachment. The individual with a dismissing attachment style has experienced rejecting or unresponsive parenting as a child, and thinks highly of self and negatively of others. The fearfully attached person has had similar experiences with his/her parents as a child, but has negative thoughts about both him/herself and others. These individuals are both desirous of intimacy and fearful of being rejected. The preoccupied style of attachment is characterized by inconsistent parenting in childhood, positive perceptions of others, low self-esteem, and a dependence on others to assuage these feelings. While the dismissing attachment style is conceptually similar to elements of the psychopathic personality, the final two styles – the fearful and preoccupied – have special relevance to theory and research on stalking.

Attachment theory has been applied to research on domestic violence, with interesting results. Kesner and McKenry reported that the attachment styles of both male and female batterers were unique predictors of marital violence. The authors further hypothesized that the anger of the male batterer was an attempt to communicate fear of separation. Babcock and colleagues studied a sample of male batterers and reported that violence in the relationship was most likely to occur when the male partner was insecurely attached. Male subjects with a dismissing attachment style were most likely to use instrumental violence, had the most antisocial personality traits, and were most likely to be violent when their partner became defensive during an argument. In contrast, those male batterers who were categorized as preoccupied in their attachment style were most likely to use expressive (reactive) forms of aggression, and their violence was most likely to occur when the female attempted to withdraw from an argument. Wife withdrawal was only a predictor of marital violence among the preoccupied batterers. The authors hypothesized that the function of the violence among these men served to maintain the wife's proximity.

## Assessment

This author is aware of only one other published work on the risk assessment of stalking perpetrators. The following will detail the process of stalking risk assessment used in a forensic outpatient private practice in San Diego, California.

Assessment occurs subsequent to a charge or conviction on a stalking or stalking-related criminal offense. The evaluation attempts to provide answers to three main questions: (1) the extent and nature of the offender's psychopathology; (2) the offender's level of risk for spousal assault, violent, and stalking offense; (3) recommendations to manage the risk level in the community. Following is a list of the battery of psychological tests and self-report instruments utilized in the assessment of persons charged or convicted for stalking or stalking-related criminal activities:

1. history: psychosocial history form (self-report; 37 pages)
2. personality: MCMI-III
3. psychopathy: Psychopathy Checklist Screening Version (PCL SV)
4. instant offense, criminal history: official records
5. substance abuse: Subtle Substance Abuse Screening Inventory (SASSI)

6. attachment: Experiences in Close Relationships Measure – Revised (ECR-R), Relationship Scales Questionnaire (RSQ), Inventory of Personality Organization, risk appraisal: Historical, Clinical, Risk Management-20 (HCR-20), Spousal Assault Risk Assessment (SARA), PCL SV: consideration of stalking recidivism predictors.

New research has been published by Rosenfeld, which comprises the first empirical work on the frequency of recidivism among a stalking population. The author found that among a mixed-gender sample of 148 stalking and harassment offenders, several variables predictive of general and violent reoffense among violent offenders were also predictive among stalkers. These were age, personality disorder diagnosis, and interaction between personality disorder and substance abuse. In contrast, Rosenfeld reported that two strong predictors among other criminal populations – history of violent behavior and previous general criminal history – were unrelated to likelihood of reoffense among stalkers. Finally, the relationship between the stalker and the victim was predictive of reoffense: previously sexually intimate stalkers were the most likely to commit a new crime.

Thus, when a stalking defendant is sent for psychological evaluation, risk levels for general violence, spousal assault, and stalking-specific reoffense are appraised. The PCL SV and HCR-20, a "structured clinical" risk appraisal instrument, are utilized to appraise risk of general and violent offense. The literature on the predictive power of psychopathy is vast; the construct as measured by the original or revised Psychopathy Checklist has been found moderately to predict violence and reoffense among general offenders, sex offenders, and mentally disordered offenders. Although it has been theorized that stalkers as a group will not have high levels of psychopathy (due in part to the theory that these offenders are both fearfully and anxiously attached to their mates), it is likely that those offenders scoring high in psychopathy will be more likely to commit new criminal acts. On the HCR-20, individual subject scores have been found to be associated with inpatient aggression, criminal recidivism, and a history of violence. Further, the instrument's H (for historical) and C (for clinical) subscales have been found to have larger correlations with a number of previous violent charges than those observed for the Psychopathy Checklist or Violence Risk Appraisal Guide. Finally, Douglas and coworkers found that scores on the HCR added incremental validity to subject scores on the PCL SV in predicting violence among 193 civilly committed patients.

To evaluate the likelihood of intimate-partner violence, the SARA, a similar "structured clinical" assessment instrument that has been found to discriminate between recidivistic and nonrecidivistic spousal assaulters, is utilized. Finally, to evaluate the likelihood of stalking-specific recidivism, findings from Rosenfeld's research, mentioned above, are considered.

For each outcome behavior under consideration (general violence, spousal assault, stalking), the offender is given a summary rating of risk, communicated on a three-point ordinal scale (low, moderate, or high). The evaluation process as a whole allows for clear communication between relevant parties (e.g., court, probation) and also aids in the identification of interventions that can be utilized in treatment to lower the offender's level of risk.

## Treatment

To treat this population effectively, the motivations behind stalking acts must be understood. The following rests largely on the author's clinical experience working with a previously sexually intimate stalking population. Future research will put these hypotheses to the test.

Clinical evidence suggests that stalkers have often experienced "shaming" episodes, usually at the hands of a parent, in childhood; Dutton has empirically shown this to be the case in a subset of domestically violent men. These experiences led to a conviction in the stalker of personal deficiency, which lasts to adulthood, and is often managed by narcissistic defenses. In his adult relationships, the stalker often chooses partners who play out these early paradigms of being shamed, confirming the individual's early experience. The initial period in the relationship is idyllic and highly romanticized, as the stalker-to-be desperately hopes that this relationship will satisfy his emotional needs. Soon, however, the individual perceives lack of interest in his partner, a fear that can be reality-based, as the partner begins to feel suffocated by the individual's "neediness," or transference-based, as the individual's early experiences color his adult perceptions. Often, it is a mixture of the two. In time, the partner actually begins to detach herself from the relationship, which signals the confirmation of the individual's worst fear: that he is unworthy, inadequate, and deficient. The narcissistic defenses are "pierced" and the partner has "seen" the individual in all his inadequacy; he has been "publicly shamed." These feelings bring the individual back to the original shaming experiences in childhood, and are defended against by rage. The pursuit of the victim, then, is an attempt by the stalker both to punish the victim for "making" him feel emotions he has long avoided, as well as an indication of his desire for reunification. If he could just rekindle this lost love, perhaps the pain would go away.

Treatment of previously sexually intimate stalkers is done primarily in a single-gender group format; groups meet weekly; individual sessions with each patient are scheduled on a monthly basis. Other types of stalker, such as acquaintance and stranger stalkers, are seen individually, as these are patients who are obstructive to the group process. Psychopathic stalkers, though rarely seen, are initially included in the group, as new research indicates that psychopathy is not associated with the effects of treatment on violence.

Group therapy functions according to a cognitive-behavioral, relapse-prevention model. The focus is on helping the offender gain insight into the emotional, cognitive, and situational precursors to the offense, and on providing him with the skills to manage these "stressors" when they arise in the future. Finally, progress in the group is self-paced, as each offender must complete assignments from the curriculum outside the group, and then present these assignments to the group and receive feedback and suggestions for revision.

The therapist's task in the individual treatment sessions is to provide an environment for the patient to explore early attachment experiences, and losses, with his caregivers, and then to process how these have influenced his functioning in adult relationships. The elicitation of very painful affect is an integral part of this process, as the patient relives early shaming experiences. The hope here is that, in the midst of such painful memories, the patient experiences the therapist as an empathic, caring object, unlike the parental figure who caused the original pain. The patient's shame, then, is tolerated and accepted by the therapist, and is thus rendered somewhat less toxic to the patient. In addition, the therapist's ability to remain with the patient and "not withdraw" during these feelings offers the opportunity for a new "secure" attachment experience. Together, the therapist and patient can examine the old wounds, take their measure, and begin to create new ways of relating to others.

### Pharmacological Interventions

Many stalking perpetrators have rightly been considered as obsessional; certainly the tenacity and duration of pursuit is evidence of this. One author has suggested that discrete diagnoses of obsessive-compulsive disorder, though rarely mentioned in the research literature, may be common in this population. At the end of the relationship, and in the months after, levels of anger, hurt, and rejection are at their apex; it is likely that the frequency and intensity of these feelings are related to the likelihood of the stalker's unwanted contact. These feelings often remain during the treatment process and, although they may attenuate over time, are worthy of clinical attention. When an individual in treatment reports perseverative thoughts of the victim, or when there is clinical or behavioral evidence (e.g., breaking of a restraining order) of obsessionality, a referral is made for evaluation of the benefit to the offender of serotonergic medication, as these have been demonstrated to have antiobsessional elements.

## Extinguishing Stalking

Although the above paragraphs on treatment interventions may, in time, be shown to be effective in decreasing stalking recidivism, this remains an empirical question. Thus, firm conclusions regarding what extinguishes the behavior are difficult to draw. However, the author's clinical impression, which appears to be corroborated by research, is that after the intense emotions have had the opportunity to "cool off," primarily through the passage of time, though perhaps in the future with the assistance of treatment intervention, stalkers may be less likely to pursue their victim. Indeed, Rosenfeld's research, which indicated that previously sexually intimate stalkers, who can be theorized to hold the most intensely felt emotions toward their victims, were the most likely of the different "types" to commit a new crime, lends some credence to this theory. Additional evidence is found in the fact that the vast majority (80%) of stalkers from Rosenfield's sample who recidivated did so within 12 months. This finding, if it can be replicated across studies of stalking offenders, has implications for sentencing dispositions, wherein a year-long sentence to custody might be used to decrease recidivism among previously sexually intimate stalkers.

## Future Directions

This article, and others on the same subject, establishes that stalking is a troubling social phenomenon. Research to this point is only beginning to identify patterns of behavior, and to suggest directions for future work. One clear area in need of explication is the level and extent of psychopathology among this population, achieved through the use of standardized psychological tests. Similarly, the attachment pathology of these offenders should be researched more closely, to identify its relation to stalking and violence. Additionally, if research is able to demarcate specific types of pathological attachment in individuals who stalk, treatment interventions could be created to attempt to remediate these deficits. Treatment interventions utilized in a case of a preoccupied or fearfully attached stalker, for instance, would likely differ markedly from those utilized in a case of a stalker with a dismissive attachment style. Along this line, research which develops a typology of stalkers, similar to work on domestic violence offenders, would prove helpful. It is possible that stalkers differ not only in their relationship to the victim (stranger, acquaintance, previous sexual intimate) and their style of attachment (fearful, preoccupied, dismissive), but also in their overall level of psychopathology, the extent and frequency of physical violence toward the victim, and the intensity and generality of their antisocial behavior in the community (criminal history). A typology of previously sexually intimate stalkers, perhaps the most prevalent, tenacious, and likely to be violent of all types, is an area in particular need of typology work. Similarly to the research on domestic violence, such research may identify different needs among this subpopulation, which will then aid in identification of the type, intensity, and urgency of treatment interventions. Finally, although Kropp and coworkers are doubtful that an actuarially based risk appraisal instrument, similar to ones developed for sex offending populations, can be created for a stalking population, efforts should be expended to in this area, so that more accurate judgments of recidivism risk, including stalking-specific recidivism, can be made.

## See Also

**Forensic Psychiatry and Forensic Psychology:** Assessment; Personality Disorder; Multiple Personality Disorder; Criminal Responsibility

## Further Reading

Australian Bureau of Statistics (1996) *Women's Safety Australia 1996.* Canberra, Australia: Australian Bureau of Statistics.

Bartholomew K (1997) Adult attachment processes: individual and couple perspectives. *British Journal of Medical Psychology* 70: 249–263.

Bowlby J (1958) The nature of the child's tie to his mother. *International Journal of Psychoanalysis* 39: 350–373.

Budd T, Mattinson J (2000) *The Extent and Nature of Stalking: Findings From the 1988 British Crime Survey.* (Home Office research study no. 210.) London: Home Office.

Douglas KS, Webster CD (1999) The HCR-20 violence risk assessment scheme: concurrent validity in a sample of incarcerated offenders. *Criminal Justice and Behavior* 26: 3–19.

Dutton D (1998) *The Abusive Personality.* New York: Guilford Press.

Hare RD (1991) *Manual for the Psychopathy Checklist-Revised.* Toronto, Ontario, Canada: Multi-Health Systems.

Hart S, Cox D, Hare R (1995) *Manual for the Psychopathy Checklist: Screening Version (PCL:SV).* Toronto, Ontario, Canada: Multi-Health Systems.

Hart S, Kropp P, Hare R (1998) Performance of psychopaths following conditional release from prison. *Journal of Consulting and Clinical Psychology* 56: 227–232.

Kesner J, McKenry P (1998) The role of childhood attachment factors in predicting male violence toward female intimates. *Journal of Family Violence* 13: 417–432.

Kropp PR, Hart SD, Lyon DR, LePard D (2002) Managing stalkers: coordinating treatment and supervision. In: Sheridan L, Boon J (eds.) *Stalking and Psychosexual Obsession: Psychological Perspectives for Prevention, Policing and Treatment,* pp. 138–160. Chichester, UK: Wiley.

Meloy JR (2002) Pathologies of attachment, violence, and criminality. In: Goldstein A (ed.) *Handbook of Psychology,* vol. 11. New York: Wiley.

Mullen PE, Pathe M (1994) Stalking and the pathologies of love. *Australian and New Zealand Journal of Psychiatry* 28: 469–477.

Mullen PE, Pathe M, Purcell R, Stuart GW (1999) Study of stalkers. *American Journal of Psychiatry* 156: 1244–1249.

Purcell R, Pathe M, Mullen PE (2001) The prevalence and nature of stalking in the Australian community. *Australian and New Zealand Journal of Psychiatry* 36: 114–120.

Rosenfeld B (2000) Assessment and treatment of obsessional harassment. *Aggression and Violent Behavior* 5: 529–545.

Rosenfeld B (2003) Recidivism in stalking and obsessional harassment. *Law and Human Behavior* 27: 251–265.

Spitzberg BH (2002) The tactical topography of stalking victimization and management. *Trauma, Violence, and Abuse* 3: 261–288.

Tjaden P, Thoennes N (1998) *Stalking in America: Findings from the National Violence Against Women Survey.* Washington, DC: US Department of Justice.

# Sex Offenders

**W C Myers**, University of Florida, Gainesville, FL, USA
**L Marrero**, Shands at Vista, a University of Florida
Affiliate, Gainesville, FL, USA
**M J Herkov**, University of North Florida, Jacksonville,
FL, USA

## Introduction

This article will review the classification, assessment, management, and treatment of persons who sexually offend. For the purposes of this article, the term "sex offenders" will refer to those individuals who commit sexual acts against other, nonconsenting persons. Usually, but not always, the offenders' behavior will be illegal. Sex offenders commonly have paraphilias, that is, recurrent, sexually deviant fantasies, urges, or behaviors. Paraphilias can range from being harmless eccentricities (e.g., fetishes) to public nuisances to psychologically or physically damaging, even deadly acts. Few human behaviors stir up the degree of public reaction as those of sex offenders, particularly child molesters, rapists, and sexual killers. However, as will be addressed in this article, sexual offenders are a more heterogeneous group than those offenders who make the headlines. Moreover, it is not uncommon for an individual offender to have more than one paraphilic diagnosis.

### Etiology and Associated Features

The great majority of sex offenders are male (90–95%). Testosterone, the sex hormone with the greatest effect on male sexual behavior, clearly plays a significant role in the etiology of most sexual offenses. Histories of child sexual and physical abuse and family dysfunction are common. Social skills deficits are a frequent finding, as are low self-esteem, poor capacity for empathy, impaired impulse control, and obsessive deviant sexual fantasy. Sex offenders typically become aware of their deviant predilections around the time of puberty, and in some cases earlier. Fantasies of abnormal sexual behavior often predate their acting upon them by several years. It is important to consider the historical and cultural setting in which sexual offenses occur. What is abnormal can vary from culture to culture. For instance, in some cultures masturbation and homosexuality are still considered deviant.

## Types of Sex Offender

Typology of sex offenders can be divided into three categories: (1) child molesters; (2) rapists; and (3) noncontact offenders (**Table 1**). Female sex offenders do not generally fall under these categories and will be discussed separately.

When sexual offenses are considered collectively, assaulters are often found to know their victims. These offenders may be neighbors, friends, acquaintances, or family members. Overall, approximately 75% of victims are known to some degree by offenders. The younger the victim, the more likely he/she is to know the perpetrator.

### Child Molesters

Child molesters can be divided into fixated and regressed/situational types. This categorization in part refers to how ingrained the paraphilic attraction is to children. According to the American Psychiatric Association's *Diagnostic and Statistical Manual of Mental Disorders* (DSM-IV-TR), pedophilia is further subdivided into exclusive and nonexclusive types. The exclusive type is sexually attracted only to children, whereas the nonexclusive type is also attracted to adults. Moreover, for the DSM-IV-TR diagnosis of pedophilia, the person must be 16 years of age or older, and at least 5 years older than the child. Additionally, the person must have recurrent, intense, sexually arousing fantasies, sexual urges, or behaviors involving sexual activity with a child. In addition, these fantasies, sexual urges, or behaviors must cause clinically significant distress or interpersonal difficulty.

Fixated pedophiles view their attraction to children as permanent and note that this attraction usually begins in adolescence. The chronicity of the disorder is higher for those attracted to males and the recidivism rate is twice that of those attracted to females. Those attracted to females most commonly select children between 8 and 10 years of age, whereas those attracted to males usually prefer children aged 11–15 years old.

Sexual offenses by fixated pedophiles tend to be planned and well-thought-out as opposed to an impulsive action. Manipulation and grooming behavior are used in an attempt to lure children into sexual acts and gain the trust of their parents/guardians. They are outwardly giving and kind to the child, while meeting their own emotional needs through these children. The molester often justifies the offense by projecting his own thoughts and feelings on to the child, desiring the child to enjoy the experience. It is not unusual for this type of offender to profess "love" for the child. In this manner, the fixated pedophile is often convinced that the abusive behavior is not harmful. Further, the pedophile may use rationalization, stating that the abuse added educational value or sexual pleasure to the child's life.

**Table 1**  Types of sexual offender

| Type | Subtypes | Characteristics |
|---|---|---|
| Child molesters | Fixated | Over 16 years of age, at least 5 years older than victim, grooming behavior, usually only attracted to children, rationalizes, professes "love for the child," chronic in nature |
|  | Regressed/situational | Attracted to adult women, offends as a result of stress and feelings of inadequacy |
| Rapists | Anger-motivated | General anger toward women, physical force meant to humiliate women, short interval between rapes, random victims |
|  | Power-motivated | The reassurance type is motivated by doubt and insecurity and watches victims to plan attacks; the assertive type is motivated by dominance over women. Neither type seeks to use excessive force |
|  | Sadism-motivated | Gains pleasure by inflicting pain and suffering on victim: most dangerous type of rapist |
| Noncontact offenders | Voyeur | Aroused by watching unsuspecting strangers naked or disrobing |
|  | Exhibitionist | Aroused by exhibiting genitals to unsuspecting strangers |

The regressed/situational child abuser is primarily attracted to adult females. When asked about their ideal sexual partner they will most frequently describe an adult female and often are involved in relations with an adult partner during the time of the sexual offense. This type of offender is more likely to offend as a result of stress or failures in life. The regressed/situational offender will report feelings of inadequacy and low self-esteem.

Unlike the fixated pedophile, the regressed child abuser is less likely to engage in grooming behavior toward the child and guardians. Rather, the offense is often unplanned and occurs in relation to a stressful life situation. Nevertheless, the abuse may begin before puberty and continue with the child past puberty. The victims of the regressed child abuser may be older than that of the fixated type.

### Rapists

Rapists may be divided into those motivated by anger, power, and sadistic urges. The anger-motivated rapist is driven by a pathological retaliatory fantasy against the victim, and often uses excessive force as a mechanism to express general anger toward a particular gender (in most cases women, but in some cases men). The physical force utilized in the rape is meant to humiliate and degrade the victims. Victims are often random and follow no pattern or obvious characteristics of selection. The rape itself is often of a short interval and ends when the rapist has ventilated his anger.

The power-motivated typology can be subdivided into the power reassurance and power assertive types. The power reassurance type is motivated by doubt and insecurities of his own masculinity and sexual sufficiency. He will often strike by the cloak of night and attempt to use as little force as necessary to subdue the victim. Often this type will even offer

apologies to the victim and endeavor to feign a desire to befriend the victim. In addition, potential victims are often watched in advance and attacks planned with selected victims.

The power assertive rapist utilizes the act of rape to assert his dominance over women. He typically does not doubt his masculinity and, in fact, may make a point to show his "masculine dominance" by repeatedly raping the victim during one attack episode. This offender, like the power reassurance type, does not seek to use more excessive force than is necessary to subdue the victim.

The sadistic subcategory of rapist is characterized by the offender's desire to gain pleasure by inflicting pain and suffering on his victim. The victim's response of fear and pain is sexually stimulating to the offender. Though the sadistic rapist is less prevalent than the other subtypes, he is the most dangerous of the offenders.

Gang rape is not considered a typology in itself. There are often different offender typologies within the individuals involved in the act. Therefore, the above categories should be individually applied to those individuals within the gang.

### Noncontact Offenders

The noncontact offender category includes voyeurs and exhibitionists. A voyeur is defined by DSM-IV-TR as one who, over a period of six months or more, experiences recurrent, intense sexually arousing fantasies, sexual urges, or behaviors involving the act of observing an unsuspecting person who is naked, in the process of disrobing, or engaged in sexual activity. In addition, these fantasies, sexual urges, or behaviors must cause significant distress and/or impairment in functioning. Most often the victim is a stranger and no direct contact is sought. Masturbation at the scene or later to the memories of watching the unsuspecting stranger is normally the source of sexual pleasure. The onset of voyeurism usually occurs before the age of 15 and may be chronic in nature.

An exhibitionist is defined by DSM-IV-TR as one who, over a period of six months or more, experiences recurrent, intense sexually arousing fantasies, sexual urges, or behaviors involving the exposure of one's genitals to an unsuspecting stranger. The fantasies, sexual urges, and behavior must cause significant distress and/or impairment in functioning. The victim of this offender is usually a stranger. Often the exhibitionist masturbates or fantasizes about masturbating in the presence of a stranger. The exhibitionist usually desires no intimate contact with the victim, but is aroused by the startle or shock effect the exposure of his genitals elicits. The condition usually begins before adulthood. As few arrests occur after the age of 40, it is hypothesized that the condition becomes less severe or abates.

### Female Sex Offenders

The predominant typology of female sex offenders has been categorized into teacher/lover, predisposed type, and historical victim (**Table 2**). The teacher/lover is characterized by the offender who believes he or she has "fallen in love" and bears "no malice" toward the victim. In these cases the offender may attempt to justify the offense and involve the victim in the justification.

The predisposed type category of female sex offenders is characterized by difficulty with male relationships, intimacy-seeking, and a loner profile. Those offenders in this typology often see the younger child as fulfilling the emotional need for intimacy. They tend to be regressed in their social skills as well as emotional needs.

The third category of female sex offenders, the historical victim, is characterized by a history of sexual abuse as a child, feelings of powerless in relationships, and involvement in failed abusive male relationships. Offenders who fit this typology tend to displace blame for their own abuse on to the victim. In addition, their victims tend to be adolescent males rather than younger children.

**Table 2** Types of female sexual offender

| Type | Characteristics |
| --- | --- |
| Teacher/lover | Believes she has fallen in love with victim, feels no malice toward him or her, justifies offense |
| Predisposed | Difficulty with male relationships and seeking intimacy, a loner |
| Male-coerced | Often sexually abused as a child, has feelings of powerlessness, has had failed abusive relationships with males |

Female sex offenders tend to differ from male sex offenders by perceiving sexual abuse as more deviant and also believing that sexually deviant behavior cannot be changed. Further, female sex offenders may be more resistant to investigation of their sexual offenses and often use more denial about their deviant activities than male sex offenders.

## Assessment

The assessment of sexual offenders is unique in the field of mental health. Exploration of sexual functioning represents one of the most intimate areas of human experience, making questioning about this topic difficult in any situation. This inherent difficulty is exacerbated by the demand characteristics of the sex-offender interview. The external referral source (i.e., almost exclusively forensic and rarely self), lack of pathology-associated distress (i.e., ego syntonic symptoms and strong pleasure associated with deviancy), societal disdain for offenders and negative consequences associated with positive diagnosis (i.e., incarceration) all offer the evaluee strong incentives to deny any deviant sexual desires or behaviors. As such, traditional assessment techniques like the clinical interview are of less utility in evaluating sex offenders than other diagnostic groups (e.g., "Do you have difficulty sleeping?" as opposed to "Are you sexually attracted to children?"). Therefore, evaluators of sexual offenders have had to augment interview assessment with other measures in an attempt to provide an understanding of the nature and range of psychopathology of these individuals and to provide helpful treatment and disposition recommendations.

Further complicating the issue of assessment of sexual offenders is the pressure by the legal system, and unfortunately the willingness of some evaluators, to use the psychosexual assessment as a method of determining whether the evaluee perpetrated some aberrant sexual behavior. Research over the last several decades has generally shown that current psychosexual assessment measures lack the sensitivity and specificity to provide definitive information as to whether an individual is in fact a sexual offender.

The above-noted limitations in the assessment of sexual offenders does not mean, however, that the mental health field has little to offer in terms of providing valuable information in the diagnosis, treatment, and disposition planning of sex offenders. In fact, the assessment process can provide valuable insights into the nature and scope of the disorder, treatment-planning, and efficacy of interventions. In the paragraphs below are summarized the available literature on the assessment of sexual offenders and a model for comprehensive psychosexual evaluation.

The need to assess the sexual offender may take place at many different points, including preconviction (i.e., accusation, guilt phase of proceedings), postconviction (i.e., sentencing, treatment-planning, intervention), and end-of-sentence disposition planning for convicted sex offenders (e.g., release and parole). The structure of the interview assessment will vary considerably, depending on its point in the above timeline. For example, a preconviction assessment might involve a single forensic interview lasting several hours. A postconviction treatment assessment might involve a series of interviews over weeks or months. Research has shown that these two situations may result in very different assessment information. It is not uncommon for interviewees to provide more information in the latter situation as increased rapport is established with the interviewer. Such rapport is invaluable in the establishment of a therapeutic alliance necessary for the efficacy of the cognitive behavioral treatments.

Assessments may also be used for providing a clinical description of the offender or in determining risk of dangerousness and recidivism. This latter function has gained considerable attention following the US Supreme Court decision in *Kansas* v. *Hendricks*, establishing procedures for civilly committing sexual predators following completion of their prison terms. The literature on this subject is extensive and the validity of procedures is facing both scientific and legal challenges. A comprehensive review is beyond the scope of this article and the reader is referred to other sources for a more in-depth coverage of this area. However, a brief description of this process and common assessment techniques will be reviewed.

## Assessment Process

**Interview**   The first step of the evaluation of the sexual offender should be the clinical interview. Here, in addition to addressing traditional areas of history and psychological functioning, the examiner should conduct a thorough psychosexual history, including such areas as early sexual experiences, sexual victimization, types and numbers of sexual partners, range of sexual behaviors, masturbatory practices, use of pornography, negative consequences of sexual behavior, and sexual dysfunction. This self-report, when compared to other data obtained below, will provide the examiner with useful information regarding the evaluee's level of denial, insight, and amenability to treatment.

**Collateral data**   Because of the factors identified above, sexual offenders show a strong propensity to deny, minimize, and rationalize their sexual deviancy. Therefore, other sources of information must be obtained to augment their self-report. In conducting a psychosexual assessment it is important that the examiner have access to victim and witness statements, interviews of significant others, past arrest records, previous mental health records, and any other information that might shed light on the present referral question.

**Psychological inventories**   Psychometric testing is often useful in the evaluation of the sex offender. Traditional assessment instruments utilize paper-and-pencil self-report inventories to provide information on the offenders' psychosexual and psychological functioning. In general, these tests fall into two categories: general psychological inventories adapted to the sex-offender population (e.g., Minnesota Multiphasic Personality Inventory or MMPI) and specific psychosexual inventories (e.g., Multiphasic Sex Inventory). **Table 3** provides a listing of this category of assessment measures.

Traditional measures of psychopathology such as the MMPI have been used extensively with sex-offender populations. These tests have identified several common profiles among sexual offenders. Although these classification systems often lack specificity, they can provide valuable information on general psychological functioning, including the areas of

**Table 3**   Sex offender assessment instruments

| Test type | |
| --- | --- |
| Self-report: nonsex-offense-specific | Minnesota Multiphasic Personality Inventory |
| | Millon Clinical Multiaxial Inventory |
| | Psychological Inventory of Criminal Thinking Styles |
| Self-report: sex offender-specific | Multiphasic Sex Inventory |
| | Colorado Sex Offender Risk Scale |
| | Clark Sex History Questionnaire |
| | Multidimensional Assessment of Sex and Aggression |
| | Abel Screen for Sexual Interest |
| Actuarial assessment instruments | Rapid Risk Assessment of Sexual Offense Recidivism |
| | Static-99 |
| | Violence Risk Appraisal Guide |
| | Sex Offender Risk Appraisal Guide |
| | Structured Anchored Clinical Judgment |
| | Sexual Violence Risk-20 |
| | California Actuarial Risk Assessment Tables |
| | Minnesota Sex Offender Screening Tool – Revised |

impulsivity, judgment, level of denial, and associated psychopathology.

There are also a number of sex-offense-specific self-report inventories (**Table 3**). These tests offer the advantage of an in-depth assessment of sexual interests and deviancy. Many are psychometrically sound, have internal validity measures, and produce scales that reflect sexual deviant classifications (e.g., pedophilia). However, many of these tests are also rationally derived and thus comprise items that are face-valid. As such, these items are subject to deliberate distortion by individuals seeking to deny or minimize their problems.

**Physiological assessment**   In an attempt to correct for the possible distortions associated with self-report inventories, many evaluators have also utilized physiological measures in assessing sex offenders. These methods seek to provide a more objective assessment of sexual deviant interest and behaviors. The two primary physiologic methods used in the assessment of sex offenders are phallometry and polygraphy.

In phallometric assessment, the individual's penis is connected to an instrument that measures erectile changes to various stimuli (e.g., the person is shown a picture of prepubescent children). This method of assessment can detect patterns of deviant sexual arousal that an individual might verbally deny. Research on phallometric testing indicates good sensitivity and utility, especially in the area of pedophilic interest. However, phallometric testing is less effective in evaluating other types of sexual offender, and can lead to a high rate of false positives (e.g., nonsexual-offending men being aroused by forced-sex scenarios). There is also a risk of false-negative findings in individuals who are able consciously to suppress arousal to deviant stimuli that are in fact stimulating.

Another physiologic measure used in the assessment of sexual offenders is that of polygraphy. In this method, the individual is asked a series of questions regarding his sexual interests and behaviors while undergoing polygraph monitoring. The premise is that deceptive answers will result in physiological changes that are detected by the machine and interpreted by the polygraph examiner.

In summary, physiologic measures, because of issues of measurement error and conscious suppression, have not proven to be the gold standard in the assessment of sexual offenders as had once been touted. However, while certainly not infallible, these methods can be valuable additions to the clinical interview and traditional psychometric testing involved in the assessment of sexual offenders. When used as part of a multimodal assessment and treatment approach, physiologic measures are useful tools in confronting denial, assessing treatment gains, and monitoring recidivism.

**Actuarial assessment**   More recently, a number of structured and semistructured interviews have been developed that assess sexual offense recidivism risks using actuarial data. These instruments have been used extensively in end-of-sentence evaluations of convicted sex offenders as a measure of risk for reoffense and basis for civil commitment. These instruments compare the demographic, offense, and personality characteristics of the offender with established base rate predictors associated with reoffense. Although not widely used in initial assessments, these measures have shown some utility in predicting reoffense. **Table 3** provides a listing of the most frequently used risk assessment measures.

**Summary**   The assessment of sexual offenders is a difficult process where inaccurate classification (both false positives and false negatives) has serious consequences. It is important that the evaluator keep abreast of the research literature, obtain as much information as possible for each case, use a multimodal assessment strategy, and know the limitations of any assessment techniques used. Issues of denial and questionable motivation to change can complicate this process, but if the above caveats are employed, the professional can provide the referral source with competent, informative, and valid psychological assessments of the sexual offender.

## Management of Sexual Offenders

As noted earlier, sexual offenders are a heterogeneous group with varying etiologies, behaviors, clinical courses, and prognoses. Consequently, no single management or treatment approach is suitable for all sexual offenders, nor is there a "cure" *per se*. While treatment can help decrease the chances of reoffending behaviors, it cannot make the desire disappear. Therefore, management and treatment are generally a long-term undertaking – even lifelong in some cases.

Sex offenders benefit most from a carefully designed, multimodal treatment plan resulting from a thorough assessment. Only a small minority of sex offenders will voluntarily seek treatment. Rather, they generally enter treatment after their acts have brought them into contact with law enforcement. It is believed that the earlier management and treatment can be initiated – ideally before adulthood – the better the prognosis for the offender not to enter an ingrained, self-reinforcing pattern of sexual offending.

Persons with more serious paraphilias have a greater likelihood of receiving management and treatment (and incarceration) for their acts than others, particularly those who offend against other members of society. For example, individuals with zoophilia (bestiality, or attraction to animals) or frotteurism (sexual gratification involving touching or rubbing against a nonconsenting person) are going to be in a position to receive sexual offender treatment far less often than the rapist or child molester. And while some sex offenders may not commit technically illegal acts (this can vary from one jurisdiction to the next), their behaviors may still negatively impact their interpersonal and societal adjustment and therefore indicate the need for treatment.

Additionally, there are sexual offenders – such as serial rapists with psychopathic personalities or lust murderers – who are not appropriate candidates for conventional sex-offender treatment. Instead, the management of such an offender is going to be prolonged incarceration to protect society. Perhaps some day treatments will be available for the most egregious of sexual offenders.

## Management and Treatment Approaches for Sexual Offenders

The more common methods for the management and treatment of sexual offenders are listed in **Table 4**. Group therapy is a mainstay of sex-offender treatment in many programs. A cognitive behavioral approach with relapse prevention has been shown to be the most useful of psychotherapeutic approaches.

**Cognitive behavioral treatment** In this therapeutic approach, developing cognitive mediation strategies in the three key modalities of thinking, feeling, and behavior are utilized as techniques in offense reduction as well as in motivation to engage in treatment. Further, personally relevant relapse prevention plans must be put in place in order to prevent relapse when returning to the community. Though cognitive behavioral therapy may differ in its emphasis, the primary focus is usually on changing the structure of the thought process moderating deviant sexual behavior and interests, improving social skills, and developing new strategies for alleviating attitudes and cognitive distortions regarding the offensive behavior.

Cognitive behavioral approaches seek either to reduce deviant sexual arousal or increase appropriate sexual arousal. One such technique to address these areas is covert sensitization, a process in which the offender identifies the events or behaviors that led to the sexual offending. These events or behaviors are

**Table 4** Management and treatment methods for sexual offenders

- Psychotherapy
  - Cognitive behavioral
  - Insight-oriented (limited application)
  - Supportive
  - Other
- Group therapy
- Psychoeducational curricula
- Family therapy
- Marital therapy
- Social skills training
- Relapse-prevention techniques
- Sexual arousal conditioning
- Victim empathy training
- Promotion of community/social support networks
- Support of participation in work/school
- Treatment of accompanying psychiatric disorders
- Substance abuse treatment
- Residential treatment
- Psychopharmacological medications (e.g., selective serotonin reuptake inhibitors)
- Antiandrogen medications
  - Medroxyprogesterone acetate
  - Leuprolide acetate
  - Cyproterone acetate
- Surgical castration
- Community supervision
- Probation
- Imprisonment
- Civil commitment (e.g., sexually violent predator laws)

then paired with highly negative images such as being arrested and going to prison.

The modification of cognitive distortions or cognitive restructuring is an important component of social skills training. Cognitive distortions include such beliefs or attitudes as women who dress in a certain manner deserve sexual abuse or that fondling does not cause psychological damage to a child.

Though cognitive behavioral therapy is generally considered to be a primary treatment factor in reducing recidivism, some studies indicate that offender characteristics rather than treatment type influence recidivism outcome or what is commonly known as effect size.

**Biological treatments** The advent of pharmacotherapies like the selective serotonin receptor inhibitors (SSRIs) and antiandrogens has increased the role of biological treatments for sex offenders. Evidence exists to indicate that SSRIs can help control the obsessive thinking patterns and compulsive behaviors of sexual offenders. Relatedly, antiandrogens can be a helpful treatment component by decreasing the sexual drive (through suppression of male sex hormones) and therefore paraphilic fantasies, urges, and behaviors.

**Implementation of management plans**  It is beyond the scope of this article to provide an in-depth review of the various treatment methods for sexual offenders. Some general comments will be made on the implementation of management plans. At the onset of treatment, the offender's level of denial should be determined. Some degree of denial is to be expected. Acceptance of at least some responsibility for their sexual offenses is an important ingredient in treatment. Significant denial will dramatically interfere with the work of treatment, as in the need for the offender to examine and develop an understanding of the thoughts, feelings, behaviors, and antecedent events involved in the sequence leading to his deviant acts.

Similarly, motivation must be present. Typically, offenders with internal motivation have better prognoses than those who lack it. For a significant number of offenders, external motivation will be necessary, e.g., the threat of revocation of probation and incarceration for not complying with treatment. For those offenders with low motivation, some success has been reported in overcoming this obstacle through the use of motivational interviewing within the context of a cognitive behavioral therapy.

Taken together, factors like level of denial, motivation, remorse, intelligence, personality structure, and family/community support can be considered in determining whether an offender should be in outpatient treatment versus more structured settings versus not being accepted into treatment at all. Those who steadfastly maintain their innocence and show no remorse will not benefit from treatment.

Relatedly, it is important for those administering treatment to sexual offenders to stay in communication with other persons who may be involved in the case, such as parole officers, social service workers, affected family members, and other treating professionals. Feedback from other sources is important in monitoring the offender's commitment to the program, treatment effectiveness, and risk of recidivism.

Typically an approach using a combination of interventions will have the best chance of success (e.g., combined psychotherapeutic, community, and biological treatments). However, treatment interventions must be chosen carefully, and therapeutic options cannot be arbitrarily applied to all sex offenders. For example, social skills training could backfire with certain offenders who might later use these skills to be more effective in procuring victims. Similarly, victim empathy training may actually be sexually stimulating – and thus contraindicated – for the sadist who enjoys learning more about victims'

pain and suffering. In assembling participants for group therapy, an excess of markedly antisocial members may impede the attainment of therapeutic goals. Furthermore, while chemical castration through the use of antiandrogen medications may help lessen deviant sexual desires, it is no guarantee against reoffending.

**Treatment and Recidivism**

Recidivism refers to the proportion of offenders who commit one or more additional offenses. Many persons who commit a first sexual offense will progress to a pattern of repetitive sexual offending. Certain subgroups, such as sadistic rapists and child molesters, particularly those who target boys (homosexual pedophiles), are believed to be at particularly high risk for reoffending. Violent rapists are more likely to reoffend than nonviolent rapists. For child molesters, intrafamilial abusers have a better prognosis than those who victimize nonbiological children. Some pedophiles have admitted to abusing hundreds of victims in their lifetime. Additionally, sex offenders' reoffending may escalate in terms of offense seriousness over time. Thus, recidivism rates are crucial information for the evaluation of sex-offender treatments.

Unfortunately, it is difficult to determine recidivism rates with confidence. The risk of recidivism increases with time. Rearrest rates are unreliable and should not be considered an accurate measurement of recidivism. Most offenders don't get caught for a given sex crime, thus rearrest rates are an underestimate. The accuracy of self-report measures must also be viewed with caution. Sex offenders are usually acutely aware of the legal consequences of their acts, and admitting to having committed a sexual crime in writing, even after being assured anonymity, is often not enough to quell fears of arrest/rearrest fears. Adding to this concern is the special risk certain types of sex offenders have of being assaulted by other inmates when in prison. Lastly, sex offenders not uncommonly have at least some degree of antisocial personality traits that have contributed to their committing sexual offenses in the first place. Dishonesty and lying are core features of persons with antisocial personality disorders, and these qualities decrease the chances of getting a valid report of sexual offenses by questionnaire.

In summary, recidivism rates are dependent on length of follow-up and vary widely in studies, ranging from 10% to 75%. A rough estimate of recidivism at 5 years following treatment would be in the range of 15–25% for sex offenders as a whole.

## See Also

**Children:** Sexual Abuse, Overview; Sexual Abuse, Epidemiology; **Sexual Offenses, Adult:** Human Normal Sexual Response; Injuries and Findings after Sexual Contact; Management Postassault; Male Sexual Assault; Drug-Facilitated Sexual Assault; Global Crime Figures and Statistics

## Further Reading

Allen CM (1991) Women as perpetrators of child sexual abuse: Recognition barriers. In: Horton AL, Johnson BL, Roundy LM, Williams D (eds.) *The Incest Perpetrator: A Family Member No One Wants to Treat*, pp. 108–125. Newburg Park, CA: Sage.

American Psychiatric Association (1999) *Dangerous Sex Offenders. A Task Force Report of The American Psychiatric Association*. Washington, DC: APA.

American Psychiatric Association (2000) *Diagnostic and Statistical Manual of Mental Disorders*, 4th edn., text revision *(DSM-IV-TR)*. Washington, DC: American Psychiatric Press.

Blanchard R, Klassen P, Dickey R, Kuban M, Blak T (2001) Sensitivity and specificity of the phallometric test for pedophilia in non-admitting sex offenders. *Psychological Assessment* 13: 118–126.

Conroy M (2002) Assessment of sexual offenders. In: Vandorster B (ed.) *Forensic Psychology: From Classroom to Courtroom*, pp. 219–246. New York: Kluwer Academic/Plenum.

Craig LA, Browne KD, Stringer I (2003) Risk scales and factors predictive of sexual offense recidivism. *Trauma, Violence and Abuse* 4: 45–69.

Groth AG (1979) *Men Who Rape: The Psychology of the Offender*. New York: Plenum.

Hanson RK, Bussiere MT (1998) Predicting relapse: a meta-analysis of sexual offender recidivism studies. *Journal of Consulting and Clinical Psychology* 66: 348–362.

Hanson RK, Gordon A, Harris AJR, *et al.* (2002) First report of the collaborative outcome data project on the effectiveness of psychological treatment for sex offenders. *Sexual Abuse: A Journal or Research and Treatment* 14: 167–192.

Hazelwood RR, Burgess AW (2001) *Practical Aspects of Rape Investigation: A Multidisciplinary Approach*, 3rd edn. Boca Raton, FL: CRC Press.

Konecek P, Jones C (1996) *Five-Year Recidivism Follow-up of Sex Offender Releases*. Ohio Department of Rehabilitation and Correction Grant, Ohio: Office of Management Information Systems.

Krafft-Ebing R (1882) *Psychopathia Sexualis* (Klaf FS; 1965 translation). New York: Stein and Day.

Marshall WL, McGuire J (2003) Effect sizes in the treatment of sexual offenders. *International Journal of Offender Therapy and Comparative Criminology* 47: 653–663.

Marshall WL, Anderson D, Fernandez Y (1999) *Cognitive Behavioural Treatment of Sexual Offenders*. Hoboken, NJ: John Wiley.

Prentky RA, Burgess AW (2000) *Forensic Management of Sexual Offenders*. New York: Kluwer Academic/Plenum.

Salter AC *A New Look at the Female Offender*. Available online at: www.annasalter.com/hardouts/d1110_Female SexOffenders.pdf.

Schlank M (1995) The utility of the MMPI and the MSI for identifying a sex offender typology. *Sexual Abuse: Journal of Research and Treatment* 7: 185–194.

Schlesinger LB (ed.) (2000) *Serial Offenders: Current Thought, Recent Findings*. Boca Raton, FL: CRC Press.

Shaw JA (ed.) (1999) *Sexual Aggression*. Washington, DC: American Psychiatric Press.

Vick J, McRoy R, Matthews BM (2002) Young female sex offenders: assessment and treatment issues. *Journal of Child Sexual Abuse* 11: 1–23.

Wilcox DT (2000) Application of the clinical polygraph examination to the assessment, treatment and monitoring of sex offenders. *Journal of Sexual Aggression* 5: 134–152.

Witt PH, Bosley JT, Hiscox SP (2002) Evaluation of juvenile sex offenders. *Journal of Psychiatry and Law* 30: 569–592.

# Criminal Responsibility

**S J Hucker and K DeFreitas**, McMaster University, Hamilton, ON, Canada

## Introduction

In western jurisprudence, a crime is held to consist of two components: the *actus reus*, a forbidden act, and the *mens rea*, a guilty state of mind. In order to find a person guilty of a crime, it is not sufficient to prove that he/she committed the alleged act; it must also be proven that he/she had the intent to commit the act. If either of these elements is missing, then criminal responsibility is diminished or absent.

In certain cases, such as those involving young children or those suffering from major mental illness, the accused person may have committed the act but lacked the ability to form the intent to commit the act. In other words, he/she may have lacked the ability to make a rational, conscious decision to do wrong. In these circumstances the accused person may be found not criminally responsible for the act. This defense, when applied to those suffering from mental illness, is called the insanity defense.

However, there are other circumstances in which criminal responsibility may be diminished or absent. In some cases, the accused person may have committed the act in question but had no specific intent to commit the act. In these cases he/she may be found to have diminished criminal responsibility for the act. In others cases, the accused person may have committed the act without being consciously aware that he/she was committing the act. In these cases the act is involuntary, and there is no intent to commit the act. In these cases the accused person may qualify for a finding of automatism, which can lead to either a finding of absent criminal responsibility or an outright acquittal.

The concept of absent or diminished criminal responsibility remains a part of the criminal law in most western jurisdictions. Its purpose is to make allowances for abnormal mental states and to avoid punishing those who did not choose to do wrong. In modern times there has been an emphasis on treatment rather than punishment for those found not criminally responsible for their actions. There has also been an emphasis on protecting the public from dangerous mentally disordered persons, which requires an assessment of the level of risk that insanity acquittees pose to the community.

## The History of the Insanity Defense

The concept of the insanity defense goes back several thousand years. Aristotle wrote: "A person is morally responsible if, with knowledge of the circumstances, and in the absence of external compulsion, he deliberately chooses to commit a specific act." Ancient Hebrew law made a distinction between offenses where blame could be attributed to the offender, and offenses where blame could not be attributed to the offender. Included in this latter category were criminal acts committed by children or by the mentally ill. In the thirteenth century CE (common era) the idea of moral wrongfulness was codified into English law. Thereafter, a crime was held to consist of the two elements of *actus reus* and *mens rea*.

While the concept itself is ancient, there has been much debate throughout recent history about how to determine which persons should qualify for the insanity defense. Several standards were proposed at various times. The 1724 trial of Edward Arnold for the wounding of Lord Onslow produced what is known as the "wild beast test." Justice Tracy held that for a man to be acquitted by reason of insanity he must be "totally deprived of his understanding and memory and doth not know what he is doing, no more than an infant, than a brute, or a wild beast." This test was cognitive in nature. In order for an accused man to qualify for the insanity defense, his cognitive abilities had to be significantly impaired, rendering him little better off than an animal.

In 1800 the criteria for the insanity defense were expanded. In the trial of James Hadfield for attempted regicide, his attorney argued that insanity should include states in which "the mind is under the influence of delusions, where the reasoning proceeds upon something which has no truth ... but vainly built upon some morbid image formed in a distempered imagination." Mr. Hadfield had attempted to assassinate the King as a result of a delusional belief, and was eventually acquitted on the grounds of insanity. This expanded the number of persons who could qualify for the insanity defense. No longer was it necessary to be significantly cognitively impaired. Instead, a person could qualify for the defense if his/her criminal act was the direct product of mental illness, even if he/she was otherwise cognitively intact.

Yet another test for the insanity defense was suggested in the 1840 trial of Edward Oxford, who attempted to assassinate Queen Victoria. The judge in that case stated that: "If some controlling disease was, in truth, the acting power within him, which he could not resist, then he will not be responsible." This test was volitional in nature. It did not examine the accused person's cognitive abilities as the previously discussed tests did, but instead focused on the person's ability to control his/her behavior. An individual qualified for the insanity defense if, because of a mental illness, he/she was unable to resist the impulse to commit the criminal act.

The modern cognitive test for the insanity defense came into being after the 1843 trial of Daniel M'Naghten. Mr. M'Naghten fatally shot Edward Drummond, secretary to the English Prime Minister, and was acquitted on the grounds of insanity. This led to a public outcry, and Queen Victoria summoned the law lords in the House of Lords and asked them to answer various questions about the insanity defense. The so-called M'Naghten rules were derived from their answers. They stated in part that "Every man is to be presumed to be sane ... to establish a defense on the ground of insanity, it must be clearly proved that at the time of the committing of the act, the party accused was labouring under such defect of reason, from disease of the mind, as not to know the nature and quality of the act he was doing, or if he did know it, that he did not know he was doing what was wrong."

## The Insanity Defense Today

The criteria for the insanity defense are jurisdiction-specific. However, most western jurisdictions have adopted some version of a cognitive test based on the M'Naghten rules. Some jurisdictions have added a volitional component to the cognitive test. An example of this is the American Law Institute (ALI) test, modified versions of which were adopted by several states in the USA. The ALI test reads: "A person is not responsible for criminal conduct if at the time of such conduct as a result of mental disease or mental defect he lacks substantial capacity either to appreciate the criminality of his conduct or to conform his conduct to the requirements of the law."

All tests of the insanity defense require that the accused person suffer from a mental disorder. Mental disorder, as used in the insanity defense, is a legal term with a legal definition that varies with jurisdiction. The types of mental disorders that are accepted as meeting the criteria for the insanity defense vary with jurisdiction. Psychotic illnesses, which involve a loss of contact with reality, are accepted by almost all jurisdictions. Other mental disorders may also be accepted, but in most cases the defense is limited to those disorders that are officially recognized by the medical community. Some jurisdictions have specifically excluded certain disorders from qualifying for this defense. Disorders that are sometimes specifically excluded include personality disorders, paraphilias, or sexual perversions, impulse-control disorders such as pyromania and kleptomania, and voluntary intoxication.

The other terms used in the insanity defense, and their interpretations, also vary with jurisdiction. However, in general, the cognitive test for the insanity defense requires that the accused person be unable to understand the nature of his/her criminal act and its potential ramifications and consequences. An example of this is a man who kills another because he believes that the victim is a demon. In such a case, the perpetrator does not understand that he is killing another human being. Even if the perpetrator does understand the nature of his act and its consequences, he may also qualify for the defense if he did not know that his act was wrong. "Wrong" in this context may refer to legal or moral wrongfulness, and this will vary across jurisdictions. An example of lack of knowledge of moral wrongfulness is a man who kills another because he believes that the victim was trying to kill him. In this case, the perpetrator understands that he is killing another human being, but believes that his actions are justified to save his own life.

The volitional component of the insanity defense is not as frequently used as the cognitive test. This test is also known as the "irresistible-impulse test." To satisfy this test, the accused person must have felt compelled to perform a criminal act, and have been unable to resist the urge to commit the act. In practice, this test is problematic because of the difficulty in distinguishing the irresistible impulse from the impulse that was not resisted.

Despite sometimes widespread publicity surrounding the insanity defense, only a very small percentage of felony prosecutions result in a successful insanity defense. In the USA, this number is close to 1%. In the majority of cases both sides agree with respect to psychiatric diagnosis and legal opinion, and there is little contention. The much-discussed "battle of the experts" is in fact an uncommon occurrence, but its frequency is often overestimated because of the media attention that such cases attract.

## Disposition of Those Found Not Guilty by Reason of Insanity

Prior to 1800, in England and Wales, those found not guilty by reason of insanity were released into the community. The detention of insanity acquittees resulted from the 1800 Hadfield trial. When Mr. Hadfield was acquitted of attempted regicide, there was concern that he could be dangerous if released into the community. The judge in that case stated: "The prisoner, for his own sake, and for the sake of society at large, must not be discharged. It is absolutely necessary for the safety of society that he should be properly disposed of." As a result, the Criminal Lunatics Act of 1800 was passed, which led to immediate postacquittal detention of those found not guilty by reason of insanity.

Today, the disposition of persons found not guilty by reason of insanity varies with jurisdiction. In most western jurisdictions they are assessed to determine their level of dangerousness. If they do not pose a danger to the public, they may be released into the community. If they are deemed to be a danger to the public, they can be detained. The circumstances of detention, including whether it is in a prison facility or mental hospital, depends on the jurisdiction. The focus is on providing treatment for the insanity acquittee, and on protecting the public. Several jurisdictions have laws that allow for the indeterminate detention of those found not guilty by reason of insanity for as long as they are deemed a danger to the public. In several jurisdictions, multidisciplinary review boards make these decisions about disposition. These boards often include representatives of the legal and psychiatric communities, as well as members of the public.

It is often assumed by members of the public that insanity acquittees are quickly released back into the community. However, studies in the USA and in Canada show that the majority of insanity acquittees are detained for longer periods than offenders convicted of similar crimes.

## Diminished Responsibility

An accused person who does not qualify for the insanity defense may still claim diminished responsibility for his/her criminal act. Diminished responsibility occurs when a disturbance in mental state negates the intent necessary for a particular offense. In such a case, the accused person may be convicted of a lesser offense.

This defense is based on the fact that the law in many western jurisdictions divides criminal offenses into two groups: (1) general-intent crimes; and (2) specific-intent crimes. General-intent crimes require a lower degree of intent than specific-intent crimes. For example, murder, a specific-intent crime, is generally held to require more intent than manslaughter, a general-intent crime. An accused man charged with murder may claim that a disturbance in his mental state, such as intoxication, prevented him from forming the intent to kill his victim. If he is successful, he may be convicted of manslaughter instead of murder, and face lesser sanctions as a result.

## Automatism

Automatism negates criminal responsibility. The term is used to describe behavior that occurs when a person is unconscious and unaware that the act is taking place. In these cases, the act is not voluntary and there is no intent to commit the act. An example of this is a man who murders his spouse while sleepwalking.

Automatism is often classified into two groups: (1) insane; and (2) noninsane. Insane automatism occurs when the condition giving rise to the automatism is intrinsic to the mind of the accused person. An example of this is automatism due to epilepsy. If this defense is successfully used, the accused person is found not guilty by reason of insanity, and is subject to the same potential detention as anyone found not guilty by reason of insanity. In noninsane automatism, the automatism is due to some factor external to the mind of the accused person. In other words, the accused person has a normal mind that was temporarily affected by some external factor. An example of this is automatism due to severe hypoglycemia. If this defense is successfully used, the accused person receives an absolute acquittal and is no longer under the control of the criminal justice or mental health systems.

## Psychiatric Evaluation for Criminal Responsibility

Decisions concerning criminal responsibility are legal decisions to be made by the court. The role of mental health experts, such as psychiatrists and psychologists, is to provide information to the court about the accused person's psychiatric diagnosis and mental state at the time of the offense. This assists the court in rendering its decision.

When conducting a psychiatric evaluation concerning criminal responsibility, the goal is to obtain information to assist the court in determining whether the person satisfies its jurisdiction's requirements for the insanity defense, diminished responsibility, or automatism. It will be necessary to diagnose any psychiatric condition that is present at the time of the assessment or at the time of the offense. It will also be necessary to explore the person's mental state at the time of the offense, and to determine what effect, if any, his/her mental state had on the commission of the offense.

In order to conduct a comprehensive evaluation, it is necessary to interview the accused person, as well as to obtain information from a variety of collateral sources such as hospital and police reports. It may also be necessary to interview others who can provide information about the accused person. Psychological testing may also play a valuable role.

Because these evaluations are done for legal purposes, certain ethical considerations apply. It is necessary to inform the accused person of the purpose of the assessment, including whether the assessment is being done at the request of his/her attorney, the state's attorney, or the court itself. It must also be made clear that the evaluator is acting as an impartial assessor and not as the accused person's personal physician or advocate. Both the accused person and any collateral information sources must be informed that what is said during the interview is not confidential, and may be incorporated into a report that may be sent to the court. Proper procedure must be followed in obtaining records, especially confidential health records.

There are several potential difficulties in evaluating accused persons for criminal responsibility. Because they have been charged with a criminal offense, and face potential legal sanctions, there is an incentive to attempt to fake mental illness where it does not exist. Even when the mental illness is genuine, there is the temptation to exaggerate the role that the illness played in the commission of the criminal act. There is also the possibility that some mentally ill accused persons will go to the opposite extreme and attempt to deny their mental illness, or minimize its seriousness, often out of a sense of shame. It is therefore incumbent upon the evaluator to assess the credibility of any information provided by the accused person. Because much of the information involved is inherently subjective, this is a difficult task. The evaluator may be helped in this task by collateral information from health records, and interviews with persons who are familiar with the accused.

The evaluation of criminal responsibility requires a retrospective exploration of the accused person's mental state at the time of the offense. The offense may have occurred anywhere from a few hours to several years in the past. This introduces difficulties since the memory of both the accused person and of collateral information sources may have faded in the intervening time. The evaluator may be assisted in this task by health or police records which document the accused person's mental state near the time of the offense.

The evaluator is expected to address his/her clinical opinion to the legal issues involved in the case. However, it may be difficult to adapt the clinical facts of the case to the legal definitions in use. For example, it may be difficult for an evaluator to offer an opinion as to whether or not an accused person knew that his/her act was wrong. The legal definition is a yes–no proposition – either the accused person knew the act was wrong, or he/she did not know that it was wrong. However, the clinical situation may be more ambiguous. The accused person may have felt that his/her act was justified without being completely sure that it was. He/she may have had some doubts about its wrongfulness. He/she may even not have thought about the issue of wrongfulness at all at the time.

## Conclusion

The concept of reduced criminal responsibility is an ancient one. It is still present in western jurisdictions because it serves a valuable purpose. It prevents the punishment of those who could not choose to do wrong, and diminishes the punishment of those who were mentally disturbed at the time of the offense. At the same time, it provides for the detention and possible treatment of those who pose a danger to the public as a result of mental disorder, and as such plays a role in safeguarding public safety. While decisions about criminal responsibility are legal ones, mental health experts such as psychiatrists and psychologists play a valuable role in assisting the courts in formulating their decisions.

## See Also

**Forensic Psychiatry and Forensic Psychology:**
Mental Handicap and Learning Disability; Malingering;
Personality Disorder

# Fitness (Competence) To Stand Trial

**S J Hucker and A Lewis**, McMaster University,
Hamilton, ON, Canada

## Introduction

This article refers to an accused person's mental capacity to participate meaningfully in criminal proceedings against him or her. Few European countries have any specific provisions for this notion but regard mentally disordered offenders as lacking criminal responsibility and therefore not deserving of punishment. Alternatively, all countries with an Anglo-American legal tradition (the UK, Australia, Canada, and the USA), to varying degrees, require an individual to be mentally capable of participating in the proceedings before a trial can proceed.

The terminology varies from one jurisdiction to another. In the UK the term "fitness to plead" is used, as it is in Australia. In Canada the term "fitness to stand trial" is used and in the USA "competence" is usually applied.

## The Law on Fitness in the UK

As a basic principle, fitness to plead was recognized in English law from the Middle Ages, but it has evolved over the centuries. By the eighteenth century a mentally disordered defendant was returned to custody and tried subsequently only after recovery. English law continued to apply this principle and it was incorporated into American practice at the end of the nineteenth century.

The criteria used to determine fitness to plead evolved through nineteenth-century English case law which involved many cases of deaf mutes, who were unable to communicate. The criteria were primarily concerned with intellectual capacity and were summarized in the case of *R.v. Pritchard* (1836), which remains the basis on which fitness to plead is determined in the UK. Pritchard stated that a person must meet the following criteria if he/she is to be considered fit to plead and able "to make a proper defence":

1. be able to understand the charge
2. be able to enter a plea
3. be able to challenge a juror
4. be able to follow court proceedings and understand the evidence
5. be able to instruct counsel.

In the UK the issue of fitness to plead can be raised by the defense, prosecution, or the trial judge.

Although it is possible for courts to postpone consideration of the defendant's fitness to plead until any time after the prosecution has presented its case, in order to ensure that there is a case to be answered, the issue is usually raised and determined at the pretrial stage. A jury is assembled to hear the evidence and determine the accused's fitness to plead. Such a hearing would normally include the oral evidence of a psychiatrist. If the issue of fitness is raised by the defense, the burden of proof rests with them and they must prove their case on a balance of probabilities (*R. v. Podola* 1959). If the question is raised by the prosecution and disputed by the defense, the Crown must prove its case beyond reasonable doubt (*R. v. Robertson* 1968). Similarly, if the issue is raised by the judge and disputed by the defense, it must be proven by the prosecution.

The Criminal Procedure (Insanity) Act 1964 reviewed the concept of fitness to plead but did not comment on the criteria for determining fitness, which remain those outlined in Pritchard, and concentrated primarily on disposal of defendants found unfit. In cases where the defendant was found to be "under disability in bar of trial," the court was required to make an order that the accused be detained in hospital (rather than in custody). This could be a maximum- or medium-security hospital or a local hospital, depending on the gravity of the alleged offense and the apparent risk to the public. The accused was treated as though subject to a restriction order without limit of time for the first 2 years of detention: this had the effect that the person could not be granted leave or discharged without the permission of the Home Secretary. Each person's case was reviewed at 6-month intervals for the first 2 years of his/her detention in hospital to consider his/her fitness. If, at the end of 2 years, the Home Secretary was advised that the person remained unfit then the Home Secretary would review the continuing need for a restriction order and terminate it if satisfied that it was unnecessary for the protection of the public. The person would remain compulsorily detained in hospital until the treatment team concluded that he/she was sufficiently improved for discharge. In practice this meant that most of those found unfit to plead spent lengthy periods detained in hospital, with approximately one-quarter remaining in hospital indefinitely. As a result of these significant consequences, the issue of fitness to plead tended to be raised only in cases involving serious charges.

Before 1982 it was the policy of the Home Office only in exceptional circumstances to remit for trial those patients who regained their capacity to plead. The most common reasons given for failing to remit a person who had become fit were the length of time that had passed since the original offense and the minor nature of the offense. However, if the person insisted on his/her right to trial, Home Office policy was to remit if possible. Policies changed after 1982 and failure to remit had to be justified and there was a marked concomitant rise in the number of people returned to trial.

A study of all 295 defendants who were found unfit to plead between 1976 and 1988 found that a third were detained in maximum-security hospitals and the remainder were detained in medium-security units or local hospitals. Of this population, 135 (46%) eventually regained their capacity to plead, of whom 76 (26%) returned for trial.

The Report of the Committee on Mentally Abnormal Offenders ("The Butler Report," 1975) criticized the way that the 1964 Act dealt with defendants who were found to be "under disability in relation to trial" (its preferred term). The Committee recommended that all such defendants should have an additional trial of the facts, intending to protect those who were not guilty, and also recommended that the courts should have wider powers of disposal.

However, it was not until the Criminal Procedure (Insanity and Unfitness to Plead) Act 1991 that these amendments were made. The 1991 Act requires that, once a jury has found a defendant to be unfit to plead, this jury should be dismissed and a new jury be sworn in to hear a trial of the facts. This second trial determines whether, based on the evidence, it is likely that the person committed the alleged offense. In the case of insubstantial evidence, the charges should be withdrawn and the defendant discharged. If the person is found to have committed the alleged offense then the 1991 Act gives courts a wider range of disposals than the 1964 Act, ranging from compulsory admission to hospital with restrictions on discharge to an absolute discharge.

A recent review of the Criminal Courts of England and Wales ("The Auld Report," 2001) recommended that new legislation be introduced to require a judge rather than a jury to determine the issue of fitness to plead. The review argued that the complex technical issues involved in determining fitness required the skills of a judge rather than a jury. However, at the time of writing, the legislation has not been reformed and fitness-to-plead trials in England and Wales are still heard by a jury.

In the UK, the number of cases found unfit declined after World War II. Before 1957 a finding of unfitness to plead represented one of the few ways a person who had committed murder could escape a conviction for which (until 1965) the mandatory penalty was execution. The introduction of the concept of diminished responsibility in the Homicide

Act 1957 (which enabled a charge of murder to be reduced to the noncapital offense of manslaughter under certain circumstances) led to a dramatic fall in the number of findings of unfitness. The limited disposal options outlined in the Criminal Procedure (Insanity) Act 1964 meant that those found to be under disability in bar of trial could potentially be detained in hospital for a longer term than they would have served if they had pleaded guilty and received a sentence of imprisonment. This serious consequence further reduced the number of fitness cases and the issue was usually only raised in grave circumstances. The Criminal Procedure (Insanity and Unfitness to Plead) Act 1991 extended the disposal options available to courts and made a number of lesser outcomes possible for those who were found unfit to plead. It is possible that this change may lead to a rise in the number of fitness hearings as the issue could begin to be raised in less serious cases. Home Office statistics suggest that there has been an increase in the number of patients admitted to hospital with restrictions under the legal category of unfit to plead over this period. In 1991 six patients were admitted to hospital compared with 44 patients admitted in 2001.

## The Law on Fitness to Stand Trial in Commonwealth Countries

Countries formerly in the British Commonwealth retain the concept of fitness to plead. For example, in Canada, the Criminal Code permits the court, the accused, or the prosecution to determine whether an accused is fit to be tried. The criteria have also now been incorporated into the Criminal Code of Canada (1985, Section 2) and an individual is unfit to stand trial if he/she is:

> unable on account of mental disorder to conduct a defence at any stage of the proceedings before a verdict is rendered, or instruct counsel to do so, and, in particular, unable on account of mental disorder to:
>
> i. understand the nature and object of the proceedings,
> ii. understand the possible consequence of the proceedings, or
> iii. communicate with counsel.

It is presumed that an accused is fit to stand trial and lack of fitness must be proven on the balance of probabilities. It is not necessary that an accused be able to act in his/her own best interests or to be able to apply analytical reasoning, but it is necessary that he/she have "limited cognitive capacity to understand the process and to communicate with counsel" (*R. v. Whittle*, 1994). A person who satisfies these minimum standards may still be found at trial to have a mental disorder defense.

An individual found unfit to stand trial is subject to a disposition hearing. The Crown may not have proven beyond a reasonable doubt that the accused committed the criminal act and, as a consequence, judges have the power to postpone the determination of fitness until the Crown has made its case and the accused has been found not to be entitled to an acquittal or a discharge on grounds of mental disorder. If the accused is found unfit to stand trial, the prosecution must establish a *prima facie* case against the accused every 2 years until the accused is either found fit to be tried or acquitted because the prosecution cannot establish the case. These safeguards are designed to ensure that an innocent accused is not subject to detention in the same manner as an accused who committed the offense but was found not guilty by reason of mental disorder.

It was the case of *R. v. Taylor* before the Ontario Court of Appeal in 1992 that brought about the changes in Canadian law. In this case, a paranoid schizophrenic man was initially found unfit and detained under the jurisdiction of the Lieutenant Governor's Review Board, the overseeing body at the time. Taylor was subsequently found fit but not guilty by reason of insanity, though a new trial was ordered when another Supreme Court case (*R. v. Swain*) held that the Crown could not lead evidence of insanity. Taylor was again found unfit. The irony of the case was that Taylor was a qualified lawyer who had an excellent understanding of the judicial system but was unable, because of his paranoid delusions, to participate in the proceedings in his own best interests. The Court of Appeal quashed this decision of the Review Board and a new trial was ordered again. The Supreme Court reviewed the statutory criteria and concluded that the proper test in Canada is the "limited cognitive capacity" test and rejected the "analytic capacity" test, a clearly higher threshold. The court noted that "too high a threshold for fitness will result in an increased number of cases in which the accused will be found unfit to stand trial even though the accused is capable of understanding the process."

Using the "limited cognitive capacity" test an accused need do no more than meet minimal requirements as in the Criminal Code. This was reinforced in *R. v. Whittle*.

An "analytic capacity test" would require that the individual, in addition to demonstrating adequate understanding of the court processes and of his/her own predicament, be able to act in his/her best interests. This had been applied in a number of other cases previously.

Criticism of the "limited cognitive capacity test" have included the allegation that the courts have failed to appreciate the extent to which distorted mental processes can interfere with an individual's ability to enlist normal self-preservation, a function not dependent on cognitive abilities but on motivation, insight, affect, and volition.

In Canada the law presumes that the evaluation for fitness, unless the accused would not meet the criteria for bail, can be undertaken out of custody. However, most cases are assessed in custody, often on a forensic psychiatric unit as, typically, an individual who is undergoing a fitness assessment will be sufficiently mentally disturbed to make this placement desirable.

Once an individual is found unfit to stand trial, the court may hold a disposition hearing to determine where the accused would best be placed. If the court does not make this determination, then the provincial review boards (constituted under the criminal code) must hold a hearing within 45 days. Such an individual will often be remanded to a designated mental hospital. One particularly useful provision under the Canadian criminal code is that an accused may undergo psychiatric treatment in order to restore fitness, even when he/she does not give consent, on application by the prosecution.

## Competence to Stand Trial in the USA

In the USA, the notion of fitness or competence to stand trial was first given specific constitutional support by a series of Supreme Court decisions beginning in 1960 with the case of *Dusky* v. *USA* where, for the first time, the court provided criteria for competence to stand trial:

> The test must be whether he [the defendant] has sufficient present ability to consult with his lawyer with a reasonable understanding and whether he has a rational as well as factional understanding of the proceedings against him.

These criteria, though somewhat vague, comprise a cognitive component (capacity to comprehend relevant legal concepts and procedures) and a volitional component (capacity to utilize this information appropriately in one's own defense or function appropriately in the court proceedings).

Operationalizing these criteria has subsequently proven challenging.

Thus, in *Weiter* v. *Settle* (1961), a Missouri court developed a number of specific criteria and clinicians also attempted to develop checklists and other instruments to guide evaluators in providing uniformity among evaluations.

The Dusky test was superseded by the comprehensive Crime Control Act of 1984, which, although it only applies to federal crimes, reflects similar competency standards throughout the USA. Here,

> The defendant is presently suffering from a mental disease or defect rendering him mentally incompetent to the extent that he is unable to understand the nature and consequences of the proceedings against him or to assist properly in his defense.

In the USA, once a defendant is found incompetent to stand trial, he/she is usually sent to a forensic psychiatric hospital where he/she is treated until he/she becomes fit. Although these hospital admissions are usually limited to a few months, they can be extended indefinitely in cases of murder. In the US Supreme Court decision of *Jackson* v. *Indiana* in 1972, the court held that, "a person charged by a state with a criminal offense who is committed solely on account of his incapacity to proceed to trial cannot be held more than the reasonable period of time necessary to determine whether there is a substantial probability that he will attain the capacity in the foreseeable future." This has been widely interpreted to mean that the duration of commitment for treatment for competence to stand trial is limited to the maximum sentence provided for the crime charged, though some states, for example Wisconsin, limit commitment to the maximum sentence or 12 months, whichever is less.

Although the number of accused found to be permanently incompetent in the USA is very small, the limitations on commitments of these individuals, if charged with serious crimes, presents problems for the criminal justice system. This is because the states have limited options after the statutory maximum period of commitment for treatment to competence. Although release is certainly possible, in the case of serious crimes this is not usually a practical or reasonable alternative. Such defendants are typically committed under either civil commitment or guardianship statutes with a consequence that they may be subject to stricter criteria for continued commitment than if they had been detained under criminal commitment.

Subsequent Supreme Court decisions have involved other procedural matters. Thus it was held in *Godinaz* v. *Moran* (1993) that the ability of an accused to waive his/her constitutional rights required a higher competency than that required for fitness to stand trial, that is, the capacity to make reasoned choice among alternatives. Moran had originally pleaded not guilty to three counts of murder and was found competent to stand trial under the Dusky standard. He dismissed his lawyers and pleaded guilty, claiming that he would produce mitigating evidence at sentencing. Finding Moran "intelligent and knowing," the judge granted his request but found him guilty and sentenced him to death. Moran appealed and argued that he had been incompetent to represent himself. The Supreme Court held that the standard for waiving counsel is no higher than to stand trial. The competence involved is that of waiving a right, not the competence to represent oneself. It did hold that the waiver must be knowing (or intelligent) and voluntary.

In another murder case, the accused was found competent several times and, after being convicted and sentenced to death, appealed on the ground that the law placed too great a burden on the defendant. The state court of appeals affirmed this, holding that the state has a great interest in a speedy trial and that a truly incompetent defendant can easily establish his/her incompetence. However, the Supreme Court reversed this decision, finding that a burden higher than preponderance of the evidence violates the principle of "due process." The assignment of the legal burden indicated society's determination of the confidence the fact-finder should have in the factual accuracy of conclusions for a particular type of adjudication. A consequence of an erroneous decision is therefore much greater than the consequences to the state with respect to competence to proceed.

Unlike the UK, in the USA the absolute numbers of individuals found incompetent to stand trial has risen but it seems unlikely that comparative or percentage data have changed. On average, only 30% of defendants referred for competence evaluations are found to be incompetent and the great majority of those assessed are found to be competent. It has been found that a cluster of bizarre behavior at the time of the offense – psychosis, irrational behavior associated with substance abuse, and impaired orientation – correctly predicted 90% of competence determinations. Others have also found that psychosis and mental retardation are highly correlated with incompetency findings. Incompetent defendants are also more likely to be nonwhite and unmarried and to have less education, but most studies do not find these statistically significant. Not surprisingly, assessments of competence to stand trial in the USA are, as in Canada, among the commonest type of court referral for forensic psychiatric services.

## Other Competencies

It must be appreciated that competence or fitness to stand trial is but one of a number of competencies or capacities that an individual must possess in relation to criminal proceedings. These include competence to waive Miranda rights (police cautions regarding statements made to them) and competence to confess, competence to plead guilty, competence to waive representation by counsel, competence to waive a jury trial, competence to waive appeals, competence to be executed, competence to testify, competence to waive extradition, to be evaluated, and to be sentenced.

Some have argued that the evaluation of fitness or competence is the single most significant mental health inquiry pursued in criminal law partly because of its frequency and the fact that financial resources are more than for any other class of forensic activity.

## Competency Screening Tests

Basic though it may appear to be, a number of forensic mental health researchers have spent a great deal of time and energy on the problem of operationalizing and assessing fitness or competency. Instruments such as the Competency Screening Test, Competency to Stand Trial Assessment Instrument, the Fitness Interview Test, and others have all been published and in some jurisdictions are widely used. This is particularly the case in the USA where studies have consistently indicated that evaluations of competency often fall far short of professional standards. As a result, guidelines have been offered, including the use of recognized instruments, the acquisition of all relevant information, taking the context seriously, and careful testing of conclusions and substantiation with clear data and reasoning.

Alternatively, it could be argued that competency or fitness assessments are in many cases the means whereby courts essentially divert individuals who are obviously psychiatrically disturbed out of the courtroom and into mental health facilities. Certainly in Canada this phenomenon is widely seen, especially in cases involving relatively minor criminal behavior.

## See Also

**Detainees:** Fitness to be Interviewed; **Forensic Psychiatry and Forensic Psychology:** Criminal Responsibility

## Further Reading

Grubin DH (1991) Unfit to plead in England and Wales, 1976–1988. A survey. *British Journal of Psychiatry* 158: 540–548.
Home Office and Department of Health & Social Security (1975) *The Report of the Committee on Mentally Abnormal Offenders ("The Butler Report")*.
Johnson S, Taylor R (2002) *Statistics of Mentally Disordered Offenders 2001*. Home Office.
Schneider R, Bloom H (1995) Taylor decision not in the best interests of some mentally ill accused. *Criminal Law Quarterly* 38: 183–205.

# H

**Hair Analysis** *See* **DNA:** Hair Analysis; **Substance Misuse:** Hair Analysis

# HEAD TRAUMA

Contents
**Pediatric and Adult, Clinical Aspects**
**Neuropathology**

## Pediatric and Adult, Clinical Aspects

**P Marks**, The General Infirmary at Leeds, Leeds, UK

### Introduction

This article considers the clinical and pathological features of head injury in adults and children.

Globally head injury is a major problem for health services, not only in the industrialized but also in the developing world. Every year in the UK, about 1 million patients are admitted to hospitals with head injuries of varying severity. Sixty-three percent of adults who sustain a moderate head injury and 85% who sustain severe head injuries will be disabled 1 year afterwards. Patients are frequently left with significant psychological and physical problems, which have major social and economic ramifications. A large proportion of patients who sustain head injuries of significance will not be able to reintegrate into their former lives and occupations and will remain unemployed in perpetuity. The cost of head injury to society at large is enormous and a considerable burden is placed not only upon the acute hospital services but also upon rehabilitation facilities and social services.

### Epidemiology

There are of course many ways in which head injuries can occur, but in the UK 41% of injuries are attributable to falls, 30% to assaults, and 13% occur as a result of road traffic accidents (**Figure 1**). In the UK, head injuries account for 1% of all annual deaths, but importantly this figure represents 15–20% of all deaths occurring in the 5–35-year age group.

### Classification of Head Injuries

A variety of systems and methods have been devised for the classification of head injury. One of the most logical and straightforward is that devised by The Working Party on the Management of Head Injuries proposed by the Royal College of Surgeons of England in 1999. Three categories are outlined:

1. Minor head injuries are defined as those when patients are admitted to hospital for less than 48 h.
2. Intermediate head injuries are defined as those when patients are admitted to hospital for more than 48 h but do not require intensive care or cranial surgery.
3. Severe head injuries are defined as those patients who require intensive care or operative neurosurgical interventions.

This classification is clinical and based on the state of the patient at presentation but does not take into account the eventual outcome.

**Figure 1** Road traffic accidents, especially involving motor cyclists, are common causes of head injury.

## The Pathology of Head Injury

Brain damage following head injury is conventionally divided into primary damage, which occurs at the moment of impact, and secondary damage, which results from processes that are initiated at the time of impact.

Primary damage includes scalp lacerations, skull fractures, contusions and lacerations of the brain, diffuse axonal injury, and intracranial hemorrhage. Secondary damage includes brain swelling, raised intracranial pressure, ischemia and hypoxia, infection, and epilepsy.

Another important distinction to make is between closed nonmissile head injury and penetrating head injuries.

### Primary Damage

**Scalp wounds**  The scalp is very vascular and it should be appreciated that wounds may bleed profusely and this can result in massive external blood loss. Scalp wounds are important as they may indicate the site of injury. Their size and location should be recorded carefully. They may overlie a depressed fracture of the skull, thereby making the injury compound.

**Skull fractures**  Skull fractures are present in 3% of people attending an accident and emergency department. Many studies in adults have shown that the more severe a head injury, the more likely it is to be associated with a fracture. Thus, 65% of patients who are admitted to neurosurgical departments have skull fractures and 80% of fatal head injuries will have evidence of a fracture. Fractures occur in 62% of patients with severe head injuries and extend into the skull base in 77% of those patients. Isolated fractures of the skull base occur in 5% of patients who have sustained a severe head injury. By definition, a depressed fracture is said to have occurred if the fragments of the inner table of the skull are depressed by at least the thickness of the diploe. A patient who sustains a head injury that is associated with a skull fracture has a greater chance of having an intracranial hematoma than one who has not sustained a skull fracture.

A depressed fracture is compound if there is an overlying scalp laceration. Such injuries are said to be "penetrating," if there is in addition a breach in the dura mater. It should be remembered that basal skull fractures involving the paranasal air sinuses or middle ear cleft are technically compound and such injuries may be associated with cerebrospinal fluid (CSF) rhinorrhea and otorrhea, respectively. Fractures of the middle cranial fossa can be associated with CSF rhinorrhea rather than otorrhea, if CSF passes through the eustachian tube into the nasopharynx.

**Contusions and lacerations of the brain**  Contusions represent areas of focal brain damage and are essentially areas of bruising of the brain. Contusions occur when the brain impacts against the bony protuberances that make up the skull base and, to a lesser extent, areas within the skull vault (**Figure 2**). A number of studies have shown that, no matter where the point of impact is on the skull, contusions tend to predominate in the frontal and temporal lobes. A contusion typically involves the crest of a gyrus, which will appear hemorrhagic and swollen on macroscopic examination. Old contusions in head-injury survivors appear as shrunken, yellowish-brown areas known as "plaques jaunes." The significance of contusions is their capacity to excite cerebral edema in the adjacent brain and by so doing cause a rise in intracranial pressure (**Figure 3**). A coup contusion occurs at the site of impact, whereas a

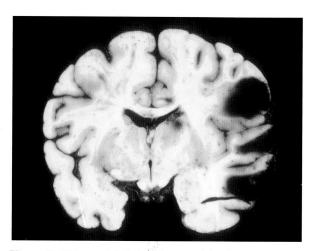

**Figure 2** This man fell downstairs one night after coming back from a bar and was found dead the following morning. This coronal section shows frontal and temporal contusions.

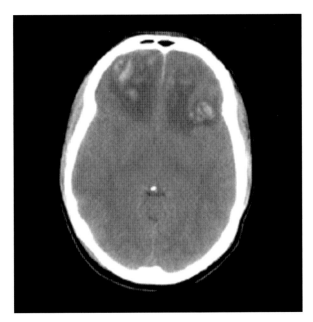

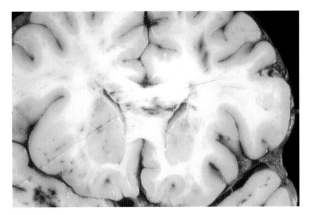

**Figure 4** This young woman was involved in a high-speed road traffic accident. She lost consciousness at the scene and never regained it. At autopsy she had typical features of diffuse axonal injury. Note the typical area of hemorrhage within the corpus callosum.

**Figure 3** This computed tomography head scan shows bilateral frontal contusions. Note the edema surrounding the contusions as well as effacement of the normal sulcal pattern and basal cisterns.

contrecoup contusion occurs at a point diametrically opposite to the point of impact. Typically with contusions, the leptomeninges remain intact but if they are torn, a laceration of the brain will occur. An area of confluent contusions in which the leptomeninges have been torn and bleeding has occurred into the subdural space is often referred to as a "burst lobe." Given the known predominance of contusions in the frontal and temporal lobes of the brain, burst frontal and temporal lobes tend to predominate.

Various attempts have been made to classify contusions, some of which are useful in interpreting the pattern of injury, but others tend to be obfuscating or noncontributory. Useful concepts include fracture contusions that occur at the site of a fracture, and herniation contusions that occur along the medial aspect of the temporal lobes or on the cerebellar tonsils. One of the more confusing terms that may be encountered is the "gliding contusion," which occurs as a result of rotational injury and typically involves the superior surfaces of the cerebral hemispheres. The distinction between a gliding contusion and diffuse axonal injury can sometimes be difficult to make.

**Diffuse axonal injury**  Sabina Strich, who was working in Oxford in the 1950s, was the first to describe the pathological features of what is now referred to as diffuse axonal injury (DAI). This term was coined by Hume Adams in Glasgow and is now universally accepted. Sabina Strich studied a cohort of patients who had sustained severe head injuries, many of

whom had remained in a persistent vegetative state until death or were certainly severely disabled. At autopsy, she observed a characteristic concatenation of macroscopic and microscopic lesions, the precise appearances of which depended upon the interval between the injury and death. Lesions of DAI injury typically occur in two stereotyped anatomical sites:

1. Within the corpus callosum, typically to one side of the midline and extending over a variable anteroposterior distance (**Figure 4**)
2. Within the dorsolateral quadrant of the rostral brainstem, typically in the vicinity of the superior cerebellar peduncles (**Figure 5**). If a head-injured patient who has sustained a DAI survives for only a few days, lesions in the anatomical locations described above usually have a hemorrhagic appearance, but with the passage of time all that may be visible macroscopically is a shrunken area of scarring. As is implicit in the name, DAI is "diffuse" and will not merely be confined to the dorsolateral quadrant of the brainstem and the corpus callosum.

Microscopically, evidence of diffuse damage may be noted throughout the brain. Histologically, the appearances of DAI again vary according to the length of survival following head injury. If death occurs within a few days of injury, the characteristic appearance of retraction balls will be seen in silver-stained preparations (**Figure 6**). These balls represent an extravasation of axoplasm from torn axons. If the patient survives for 2–4 weeks, microglia will infiltrate the areas involved, forming what is often referred to as microglial stars. Astrocytes and lipid-filled macrophages will also be seen amongst these clusters of microglia. In patients who survive for a

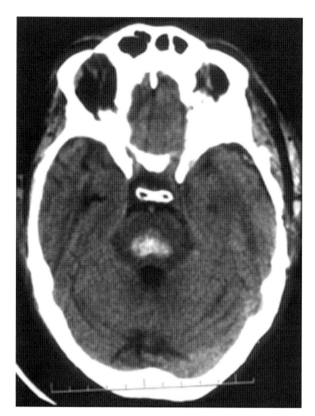

**Figure 5** An area of hemorrhage is seen in the midbrain that is typical of diffuse axonal injury. This young motorcyclist remained in a persistent vegetative state after a head injury.

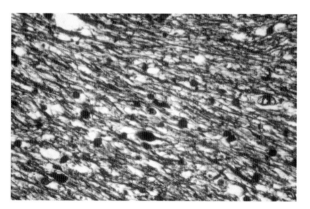

**Figure 6** This photomicrograph shows a section through the corpus callosum stained with a silver preparation. Retraction ball formation is well demonstrated. Original magnification ×400.

prolonged time, stains for myelin will show demyelination of the involved tracts. In severe cases of diffuse axonal injury, ventricular dilatation is often pronounced due to loss of adjacent white matter. Patients who have sustained diffuse axonal injuries form a distinct clinicopathological group. They tend to be unconscious from the time of impact and remain so and have a low incidence of skull fracture, contusion, and intracerebral hematoma. Moreover, the

likelihood that such patients will have raised intracranial pressure is significantly lower than in those who sustain contusional injuries.

## Secondary Brain Damage

It must be accepted that other than preventive measures, nothing can be done to influence the extent of primary brain injury. The goal of all clinicians treating patients who sustain head injuries should be to prevent or minimize secondary brain damage by appropriate and timely intervention. It is convenient to classify the etiology of secondary events that cause brain damage into intracranial and extracranial insults.

## Extracranial Insults

### Hypoxemia

This may be attributable to damage to the brainstem which results in decreased respiratory drive or centrally mediated pulmonary edema. Furthermore, pulmonary complications such as pneumothorax, aspiration pneumonia, hemopneumothorax, or rib fractures, particularly when associated with a flail segment of the chest wall, can all contribute to hypoxemia. This often leads to a decrease in the patient's level of consciousness and moreover can in itself contribute further to cerebral edema. Head injuries are often associated with multiple trauma, which is frequently associated with serious internal or external blood loss. This can result in the development of hypotension leading to decreased cerebral function. The combination of hypoxemia and hypotension is particularly lethal and must be recognized and treated promptly if the patient is to survive. Hypotension can result in neuronal necrosis or in areas of boundaries zone infarction in the watershed areas of profusion between the main arterial territories.

## Intracranial Insults

### Intracranial Hematoma

These should be regarded as secondary phenomena even though the initiating event that results in their development occurs at the time of injury. The accumulation of a hematoma takes time and the injurious effects of such lesions are attributable to their capacity to produce raised intracranial pressure and internal herniations of the brain, e.g., subfalcine, transtentorial, and cerebellar tonsil herniation.

### Extradural Hematoma

Classically these arise from damage to the middle meningeal artery (**Figure 7**). In fact, approximately

70% of extradural hematomas are due to arterial bleeding and the remainder are due to damage and resultant bleeding from the venous sinuses of the dura mater. Extradural hematomas are typically situated in the temporoparietal region and are associated with a fracture of the temporal bone with resultant damage to the middle meningeal artery. They may, however, be bilateral or occur within the posterior cranial fossa. A skull fracture is present in 85% of cases in adults.

Extradural hematomas are often associated with minimal primary brain damage and consequently with timely surgical intervention, they are associated with a good prognosis. Unfortunately, the overall mortality from extradural hematomas is in the region of 30% and this relates to delays in diagnosis and transfer to neurosurgical facilities as well as their development in those patients who do have more severe primary brain damage.

One of the important points for the pathologist to note at the time of autopsy is that artefactual extradural hematomas can occur in fire-related deaths where the head has been subject to intense heat. The effect of such heat is to produce fissure fractures of the skull and, as a result of this, blood may extravasate into the extradural space following contraction of the meninges. The macroscopic appearances of such a hematoma are distinct from those of extradural hematomas of traumatic origin. In those extradural hematomas that are associated with fire damage, the hematoma tends to be pink and spongy, compared with the dark-red appearance of lesions of traumatic origin. Despite this, interpretation of extradural hematomas in the presence of fire damage can be difficult and may obviously raise the possibility of criminal activity, where it becomes important to distinguish the possibility of the victim having sustained a blow to the head, which was followed by an attempt to destroy the body by incineration.

### Subdural Hematomas

These are classified as intradural lesions along with intracerebral hematomas of traumatic origin. Subdural hematomas are more common than extradural hematomas and typically occur when veins that traverse the subdural space en route to the venous sinuses of the dura mater are disrupted (**Figure 8**). Subdural hematomas are in general associated with a far greater degree of primary brain damage than extradural hematomas. In 13% of cases, however, subdural hematoma is "pure," and in these circumstances there is little evidence of other primary brain damage. Macroscopically, the hematoma tends to envelop the entire hemisphere and is therefore more extensive than its extradural counterpart. Acute subdural hematomas may also develop from hemorrhage from a brain laceration or torn cortical artery.

The overall mortality of acute subdural hematoma is considerably greater than that of extradural

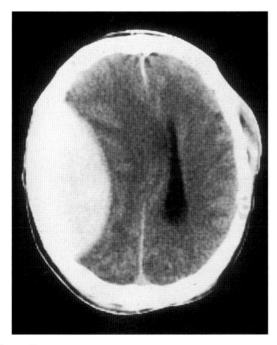

**Figure 7** A computed tomography scan showing a large right-sided extradural hematoma. There is midline shift with subfalcine herniation. Note also the left-sided extracranial soft-tissue swelling.

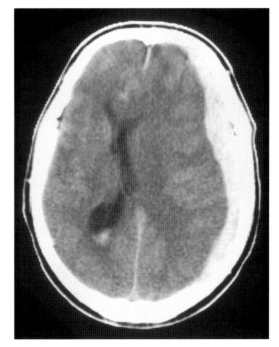

**Figure 8** This man fell off some scaffolding at work. His Glasgow Coma Scale on arrival to hospital was 6. This computed tomography scan shows a left acute subdural hematoma causing midline shift and subfalcine herniation.

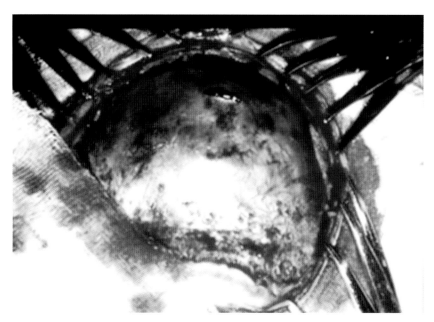

**Figure 9** An operative photograph of the man shown in **Figure 8**. The dura is tense and blue due to the underlying acute subdural hematoma, which can be seen to extrude through a tear in the dura.

hematomas and this is largely a reflection of the greater degree of primary brain damage with which the hematoma is associated. Surgical evacuation at craniotomy is the treatment of choice (**Figure 9**).

It is important to distinguish a chronic subdural hematoma from its acute subdural counterpart. They tend to form a distinct clinical and pathological entity and are often associated with a minor degree of head trauma, which is often forgotten by the patient. In many instances, loss of consciousness did not take place (**Figure 10**).

Any condition that results in an increase in the disparity between the volume of the brain and the volume of the cranial cavity can predispose to the development of a chronic subdural hematoma. Conditions such as chronic alcoholism, degenerative brain disease leading to dementia, and senescence may all be associated with the development of a chronic subdural hematoma. Moreover, chronic epileptics who have cerebral atrophy are also predisposed to developing chronic subdural hematomas not only due to the increased disparity between the volume of the brain and the intracranial cavity but also because of the possibility of repeated head trauma that may occur during seizures.

### Intracerebral Hematomas

Hemorrhages that form discrete hematomas within the brain substance as opposed to contusions tend to predominate in the frontal and temporal lobes and

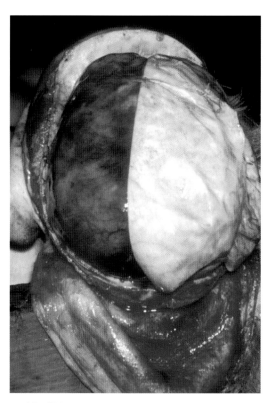

**Figure 10** This elderly woman was found dead at home. She had been complaining of headache and was noted to drag her right leg when last seen alive. Six weeks earlier she attended hospital because she had banged her head on an open cupboard door. This photograph shows the typical features of a chronic subdural hematoma.

need to be considered separately. They tend to be multiple and may also occur in the basal ganglia. It is well recognized that traumatic intracerebral hematoma may develop several days after the initial injury and, in these circumstances, the lesion is referred to as a delayed intracerebral hematoma, or the apoplexy of Bollinger. From a medicolegal standpoint, if a patient develops such a hematoma and subsequently dies, important legal consequences may flow from the initial injury or assault.

## Brain Damage Secondary to Raised Intracranial Pressure

Such damage is a common sequel to nonmissile head injury. Internal herniation of the brain may occur. In subfalcine herniation, an expanding lesion involving one hemisphere causes the cingulate gyrus on the medial aspect of that hemisphere to herniate beneath the free edge of the falx cerebri. In transtentorial herniation, the parahippocampal gyrus on the medial aspect of the temporal lobe is forced through the tentorial hiatus and this causes compression of three important structures, namely the brainstem, the oculomotor nerve, and the posterior cerebral vessels. Compression of the brainstem will result in distortion of the reticular activating system and a depression in the level of consciousness. Compression of the corticospinal tract within the brainstem will result clinically in a contralateral hemiparesis as the pyramidal tract has not decussated at that stage. Compression of the oculomotor nerve will result in ipsilateral pupillary dilatation, due to the now unopposed sympathetic innervation of the pupil. When the posterior cerebral vessels are compressed, a situation that is seen in agonal cases, infarction of the calcarine area of the occipital lobe will take place.

Masses within the posterior cranial fossa will result in herniation of the cerebellar tonsils through the foramen magnum.

The effect of such internal herniation is to cause obliteration of the normal basal cisterns and the development of pressure gradients between one intracranial compartment and another. Vascular damage to the herniated areas of the brain can be seen. The finding of necrosis within the parahippocampal gyri will allow the pathologist to express a view as to whether the intracranial pressure was raised during life. In fatal cases, secondary hemorrhages or areas of infarction may be seen within the brainstem and these are known as Duret hemorrhages.

## Brain Swelling

This is a well-recognized phenomenon following head injury. The significance of brain swelling is

that it may contribute to a rise in intracranial pressure as described elsewhere. Brain swelling may be produced by three different mechanisms:

1. Swelling of the white matter adjacent to contusions, which is considered to be due to leakage of fluid from damaged vessels and loss of local arteriolar tone.
2. Diffuse swelling of the hemisphere or of the whole brain. Unilateral hemispheric swelling may occur in association with an overlying acute subdural hematoma, and following its evacuation the brain can sometimes swell very rapidly and dramatically into the space formerly occupied by the hematoma.
3. Swelling of the entire brain may take place in children. The mechanism by which this occurs is uncertain but the immaturity of the blood–brain barrier may be important. It is extremely important to appreciate that, whatever the mechanism producing brain swelling, it can be exacerbated by extracranial events such as hypotension and hypoxia. A vicious circle can then occur, leading to an increase in brain swelling, which then contributes further to a rise in intracranial pressure.

## Hydrocephalus

This may occur after head injury and can either be communicating or noncommunicating. Communicating hydrocephalus is more frequently observed following head injury and results from the presence of blood within the subarachnoid spaces, which leads to a derangement of flow and absorption of cerebrospinal fluid (CSF). Characteristically, this complication may develop some 10–14 days following injury and will be clinically apparent when there is a failure to improve after initial progress has been made or where frank deterioration occurs.

Noncommunicating hydrocephalus may develop acutely secondary to a posterior fossa hematoma that causes compression and obstruction of the cerebral aqueduct of Sylvius or the fourth ventricle itself.

Treatment may involve the insertion of a ventriculoperitoneal shunt or similar CSF-diverting procedure.

## Penetrating Head Injuries

These are classified into two types.

1. Missile injuries from bullets and shrapnel wounds
2. Stab injuries that may result from domestic and industrial accidents, self-inflicted wounds, and criminal assault.

In the USA eight per 100 000 persons die as a result of penetrating head injuries. Half of all homicides in persons under the age of 45 occur as a result of brain injury and 35% of these are attributable to gunshot wounds. In the UK the incidence of gunshot wounds is significantly less.

### Mechanisms of Injury

Projectiles traveling at low velocities and stab wounds cause damage that is confined to the tract that they produce within the brain. High-velocity missile injuries on the other hand cause diffuse damage which extends beyond the tract. The explanation of this phenomenon lies in simple Newtonian mechanics. The kinetic energy (KE) of a projectile is given by $KE = 1/2 \, mv^2$, so it will be readily appreciated that the kinetic energy of a projectile is chiefly influenced by its velocity, that depends on a square function. The distance the projectile travels and the energy it has expended in doing so will determine the amount of energy that is transferred to biological tissue. Wounds sustained at point-blank range will invariably be more destructive than those sustained 1.5 km (1 mile) from the muzzle of a firearm. Conventionally, projectiles are classified as being either low or high velocity. The speed of sound in air is $333 \, \mathrm{m \, s^{-1}}$ and this is the dividing line between low and high velocity projectiles. Pistols and revolvers have a muzzle velocity of $250 \, \mathrm{m \, s^{-1}}$, whereas most high-power military rifles have a muzzle velocity in the region of $750 \, \mathrm{m \, s^{-1}}$. Shrapnel injuries are classified as being high-velocity, as projectiles from bombs or grenades are usually traveling faster than the speed of sound.

### Missile Injuries to the Cranium

A projectile will pass through the cranium in a path determined by its velocity, trajectory, and the structures it encounters. A projectile may lodge in the brain parenchyma or may ricochet off the inner table of the skull, causing damage on its secondary or sometimes tertiary paths. If the missile has sufficient kinetic energy, it may pass through the brain and produce an exit wound. Such wounds are invariably more irregular and disruptive to tissue than the entry wound. Damage to the scalp is caused by a laceration from the projectile, which may be compounded by pressure waves and powder burns if the weapon is discharged at close quarters. A common misconception is that projectiles are sterile, having been fired from a rifle or revolver. This is completely fallacious and bacteria will invariably pass into the cranial cavity as a result of the wound. The interaction between the projectile and the skull produces a comminuted fracture and the in-driven bone may act as secondary projectiles, producing further damage in their own right. Projectiles produce damage to the brain parenchyma in three ways:

1. Penetration, in which damage is produced along the tract, extends only to a short distance on either side of the tract. This type of injury is typically associated with low-velocity projectiles.
2. Shock waves. These longitudinal waves travel in front of the missile at speeds in excess of $333 \, \mathrm{m \, s^{-1}}$. This type of energy produces structural damage beyond the macroscopic tract of the projectile and explains the functional damage remote from the macroscopic pathway of the bullet.
3. Cavitation. This is a particularly disruptive force, the size of the cavity being proportional to the kinetic energy of the missile. Tissue damage is attributable to the brain parenchyma being pushed centrifugally from the surface of the missile. Tissues are damaged by the blast effect and the compression against unyielding dural and bony structures. As the cavity is formed, the pressure within it falls below atmospheric pressure and as a result debris, including bacteria, is drawn into the wound. Following this, the pressure within the cavity can rise and in certain circumstances can result in total destruction of the skull.

The damage produced by the missile is a potent source of brain swelling and edema, which can cause intracranial pressure to rise very rapidly. High-velocity missiles tend to produce a higher and more rapid rise in intracranial pressure than low-velocity projectiles.

## Posttraumatic Epilepsy

This is characteristically divided into early posttraumatic seizures, which occur within 7 days of head injury, and late posttraumatic epilepsy, which occurs at any point thereafter. In addition, some authorities also recognize a third category, entitled immediate posttraumatic epilepsy, which occurs within 1 min to 1 h after head injury.

### Early Posttraumatic Epilepsy

There is a 30% incidence in severe head injury and approximately 1% incidence in mild to moderate injury. In pediatric practice, 2.6% of children under the age of 15 who sustain a head injury which causes a brief loss of consciousness or amnesia will experience an early posttraumatic fit.

Early posttraumatic epilepsy may be associated with the development of adverse events such as a rise in intracranial pressure, alterations in blood

**Table 1**   Risk factors for the development of posttraumatic epilepsy

1 Penetrating head injuries
2 Depressed skull fractures
3 Dural tears
4 Early posttraumatic epilepsy
5 Presence of intracranial hematoma and/or structural brain damage
6 Long duration of posttraumatic amnesia

pressure, and the release of excessive neurotransmitter substances.

### Late Posttraumatic Epilepsy

By definition, this occurs more than 7 days after a head injury. It has been estimated that the incidence of late posttraumatic epilepsy overall is somewhere between 10% and 13% within 2 years of significant head trauma. The incidence of late posttraumatic epilepsy is higher following severe head injury than with moderate or mild trauma. Although the incidence of early posttraumatic epilepsy is higher in children, the development of late seizures is less frequently observed in children.

Penetrating cranial trauma is associated with a higher incidence of posttraumatic epilepsy than closed-head injury. The overall incidence is 15% in patients who are followed up for a period of 15 years. The majority of patients who have not had a seizure within 3 years will not go on to develop fits. **Table 1** outlines the major risk factors for developing posttraumatic epilepsy.

Anticonvulsant medication can be used to prevent early posttraumatic seizures in those considered to be at higher risk. Prophylactic use of anticonvulsant medication does not reduce the incidence of late posttraumatic fits however.

### Outcome and Prognosis

Age is a major factor that determines the degree of recovery following head injury. In broad terms, infants recover better than children, and children better than adults. A number of factors have been shown to be associated with a poor prognosis following head trauma. These include:

1. A persistent rise in intracranial pressure of more than 20 mmHg despite hyperventilation
2. Increasing age
3. Impaired or absent pupillary responses or eye movements
4. Hypotension
5. Hypercapnia
6. Hypoxemia or anemia

7. The presence of a mass lesion requiring surgical removal
8. Raised intracranial pressure during the first 24 h after injury.

It has also been shown that the presence or absence of the basal cisterns as visualized on the presenting computed tomography scan is an important prognostic indicator. In general, effacement of the basal cisterns is associated with a poor outlook. The Glasgow Outcome Scale (GOS) is often used to assess the outcome following a head injury and the categories of this scale are shown in **Table 2**.

One of the questions that is invariably asked by patients, their relatives, and lawyers acting in personal injury claims, is over what period of time can improvement be expected to take place? It is generally expected that natural recovery following a head injury will take place for up to 2 years and any problems that remain thereafter can be regarded as being fixed or permanent. Moreover, the maximum rate of recovery tends to take place within the first 6 months and, after this, recovery occurs at a much slower pace. Furthermore, if a patient has scored 4 on the GOS at 6 months it is most unlikely he/she will score 5 at the end of the ensuing 18 months.

### Postconcussional Syndrome

This is a characteristic condition that follows head injury. It is characterized by a variety of symptoms that can be divided into somatic, cognitive, and psychosocial problems. Paradoxically, it is often the milder head injuries that are associated with the greater severity of symptomatology. Symptoms such as headache, dizziness, blurring of vision, tinnitus, poor concentration, impairment of short-term

**Table 2**   Glasgow Outcome Scale

1 Dead
2 Persistent vegetative state
3 Severely disabled
4 Moderately disabled
5 Good recovery

Notes: A persistent vegetative state denotes a patient who remains unresponsive, mute, and in whom there is no psychological meaningful response due to inactivity of the cerebral cortex. Subcortical and brainstem centers still function to some degree and sleep/wake cycles are evident.
Severely disabled survivors: this denotes patients who are reliant on the help of others for one or more of the activities of daily life.
With moderate disability, patients are independent for the activities of daily living but are unable to return to their previous occupation or level of activity.
With a good recovery, patients are able to return to their premorbid level of functioning and occupation.

memory, loss of libido, alteration of the sleep/wake cycle, and intolerance of noise are frequently described. The treatment of postconcussional syndrome is difficult but a number of studies have shown that a full explanation of the problems the patient is likely to have at the time of discharge from hospital can go a long way towards reducing the duration of these symptoms.

## The Role of the Clinical Forensic Physician in the Assessment of Nonfatal Head Injuries

The role of the clinical forensic physician or medical examiner falls into three categories:

1. The acute assessment of the head-injured patient
2. The assessment of an accused who may have sustained a head injury and who has also taken alcohol or illicit drugs
3. The preparation of medical reports as directed by the court or insurance companies.

In the emergency setting, the standard principles of maintaining the airway, ensuring that breathing is occurring and the circulation is maintained are of paramount importance and cannot be overemphasized. Attention should be paid to these factors while the emergency services are arriving. The details of such resuscitative measures are well known and are essentially beyond the scope of this article but the interested reader is referred to the ATLS manual for further information.

In practice, the initial neurological assessment of a head-injured patient is of extreme importance not only because it enables the severity of the injury to be gauged but also because it provides a baseline from which improvement or deterioration can be measured.

Three baseline parameters should be recorded:

1. Glasgow Coma Scale (GCS) (**Table 3**)
2. Pulse rate and blood pressure
3. Presence or absence of focal neurological deficit.

When called to see a detainee in custody who is unconscious or drowsy, the clinical forensic physician should have a high index of suspicion that the individual may have sustained a head injury. Assurances from the police that the accused has taken a large amount of alcohol or illicit drugs should increase the index of suspicion rather than decrease it. Many prisoners meet an untimely end when persisting drowsiness or unconsciousness is attributed to the ingestion of alcohol or drugs, when in fact an extradural or subdural hematoma is present but only diagnosed correctly at the time of autopsy. If in doubt,

**Table 3**  The Glasgow Coma Scale

|  | Score |
| --- | --- |
| *Eye opening* | |
| Spontaneous | 4 |
| To speech | 3 |
| To painful stimulus | 2 |
| None | 1 |
| *Best motor response* | |
| Obeys commands | 6 |
| Localizes painful stimulus | 5 |
| Withdraws (normal flexion) | 4 |
| Flexes abnormally | 3 |
| Extension | 2 |
| No response | 1 |
| *Best verbal response* | |
| Oriented | 5 |
| Confused | 4 |
| Says inappropriate words | 3 |
| Makes incomprehensible sounds | 2 |
| No verbal response | 1 |

**Table 4**  Criteria for immediate hospital transfer irrespective of Glasgow Coma Scale score

- Unequal pupils
- Unequal motor examination
- An open-head injury with leaking cerebrospinal fluid or exposed brain tissue
- Neurological deterioration
- Depressed skull fracture

assume that the patient has sustained a head injury and arrange for immediate transfer to hospital, where appropriate assessment by a neurosurgeon can take place. **Table 4** shows the criteria for immediate hospital transfer irrespective of GCS. **Table 5** outlines the criteria for transfer and admission to hospital after a recent head injury.

It is also vitally important to assume that all patients who have sustained a head injury have also sustained an injury to the cervical spine until proven otherwise. Practically, this means that the neck should be immobilized prior to any movement or transferred by the application of a collar, placement of sandbags adjacent to the neck, and taping the forehead to the stretcher. Appropriate imaging can then confirm or refute the presence of a cervical spine injury. It is important to appreciate that an injury to the cervical spine has not been excluded unless the C7/T1 junction has been adequately demonstrated.

The clinical forensic physician is often called upon to write medical reports for the court on patients who have been examined. Many books and courses are devoted to this important area of practice, but when reporting on head-injured patients the following factors should be taken into consideration:

**Table 5** Criteria for hospital admission after a recent head injury

- Confusion or other depression of the level of consciousness at the time of examination
- Skull fracture or clinical suspicion if X-rays are not available
- Neurological signs or headache or vomiting
- Difficulty in assessing the patient, e.g., alcohol, drugs, the young, epilepsy
- Other medical conditions, e.g., diabetes mellitus, hemophilia
- The patient's social condition or lack of a responsible adult to continue observation

Posttraumatic amnesia with full recovery is not an indication for admission. If a person remains in police custody, written instructions about possible complications and the action to be taken should be left with the custody officer.

1. Date and time of the injury
2. Mechanism of the injury
3. Whether the injury resulted in loss of consciousness
4. The presence of other injuries
5. Neurological assessment, including the presenting GCS
6. Whether alcohol or illicit drugs were taken
7. Whether the patient had a fit
8. Significant past medical history, including other closed-head injuries and the presence of preexisting epilepsy
9. The treatment the patient received, including the period of hospitalization
10. An estimation of the period of posttraumatic amnesia.

If supplementary medical reports are required to deal with the condition and prognosis of the patient, the continuing symptoms that are attributable to the injury should be recorded in detail.

It may be difficult to give a definitive prognosis, but the period over which natural recovery can take place should be emphasized. Where specialist information is required, from a neurosurgeon, neuropsychologist, or other practitioner, a recommendation that the patient should be seen by such experts before a final opinion can be offered is often helpful to the instructing lawyer or insurance agency.

## Pediatric Head Injury

Although many of the principles governing the pathology and management of head injury in adults can be applied with some modification to childhood head injury, there are important differences. From the epidemiological standpoint, it should be appreciated that children often have milder head injuries than adults. Despite this, 75% of children hospitalized through trauma will have a head injury. In the

pediatric age group, the overall mortality for all severities of head injury requiring hospitalization has been reported as being between 10% and 13% but it is important to distinguish that with severe head injuries in children who are presenting with decerebrate posturing, the mortality can be as high as 71%.

The type of injury that children sustain is also distinct in some cases from those that affect adults. Birth injuries occur with skull fractures, cephal hematoma, subdural and extradural hematomas. The possibility of child abuse should not be forgotten in the pediatric age group and the peculiar phenomenon of growing skull fractures or leptomeningeal cysts should also be considered.

In addition, the response to injury can be somewhat different in children. The main differences are that posttraumatic seizures are more likely to occur within the first 24 h in children than in adults. In addition, malignant cerebral edema following head injury is a well-recognized phenomenon in young children who have sustained cranial trauma. The degree of swelling may be disproportionate to the apparent severity of the injury. The likely mechanism of such diffuse cerebral swelling, which is often refractory to all forms of treatment, is expected to be hyperemia.

As far as outcome is concerned, children in general do better following head injury than adults, although there is some evidence that very young children who are of preschool age do not fare as well as schoolchildren.

## Head Injury and Child Abuse

Approximately 10% of children under the age of 10 years who attend hospital following alleged accidents are in fact the victims of nonaccidental injury. It is interesting to note that most children who are assaulted are below the age of 3, an age group in which accidental head injury has a low incidence. The attending clinician should have a high index of suspicion but obviously needs to proceed with the utmost tact. Factors that should alert a clinician to the possibility of child abuse include:

1. Retinal hemorrhages
2. Other injuries of differing ages
3. Bilateral chronic subdural hematomas in children less than 2 years of age
4. Significant neurological damage with minimal signs of external trauma. Infants and children who are shaken sustain acceleration and deceleration injuries to the head. Forces which are proportionally larger in children due to the large size of the head relative to the body tend to occur and this problem is exacerbated by the relative

underdevelopment of the cervical musculature. The characteristic features of the shaken-baby syndrome include retinal hemorrhages, subdural hematomas, traumatic subarachnoid hemorrhage, and very little in the way of signs of external trauma. The attending clinician should look for finger marks on the chest and multiple rib fractures where the child's torso may have been held during the shaking process. In fatal cases death is usually attributable to raised intracranial pressure which is refractory to ventilation and osmotic diuretics.

## See Also

**Children:** Physical Abuse; **Coma, Definitions and Differential Diagnoses:** Pediatric; Adult; **Falls from Height, Physical Findings:** In Adults; **Head Trauma:** Neuropathology; **Injury, Fatal and Nonfatal:** Sharp and Cutting-Edge Wounds

## Further Reading

Gean AD (1994) *Imaging of Head Trauma.* Raven Press.
Marion DW (1998) *Traumatic Brain Injury.* New York: Thieme.
Marks PV (1994) Acute head injury: assessment and practical management. *Journal of Clinical Forensic Medicine* 1: 43–46.
Marks PV (2003) Head injury – fatal and non-fatal (and other neurologic causes of sudden death). In: Payne-James J, Busuttil A, Smock W (eds.) *Forensic Medicine – Clinical and Pathological Aspects,* pp. 321–335. Greenwich Medical Media.
Marks PV, Lavy CBD (1992) *A Practical Guide to Head Injury Management.* London: WB Saunders.
Narayan RK, Wilberger JE, Povlishock JT (1996) *Neurotrauma.* McGraw-Hill.
*Report on the Working Party on the Management of Patients with Head Injuries* (1999) London: Royal College of Surgeons of England.

# Neuropathology

**M Case**, St. Louis University Health Sciences Center, St. Louis, MO, USA

## Introduction

Head injuries account for a significant portion of the cases examined by the medical examiner and account for approximately half of all trauma deaths. Head injuries result most often from vehicular accidents, gunshot wounds, falls, assaults, and child abuse. Head-injury rates are greatest in urban areas, where rates are as high as 32/100 000; 50% of head injuries result from traffic accidents, 20–40% from gunshot wounds, 10% from falls, and 5–10% from assaults. Certain procedures for the examination of the central nervous system are discussed in this article because these are essential to document injuries and evaluate the forensic issues. Forensic issues associated with head injuries include mechanisms of injury, timing of injury, onset of symptoms, and survival after injury. Pediatric head injury, particularly abusive injury, is considered in a separate section.

## Examination Procedures

It is essential that the head and brain be examined in a planned and consistently uniform manner so that injuries can be recognized and thoroughly documented. Examination of the brain usually follows a systematic examination of the face, scalp, and neck with documentation of any abnormalities. The pathologist must be present when the cranial cavity is opened to make observations about the presence or absence of epidural or subdural blood.

## External Examination

The examination of the nervous system begins with the external appearance of the face, scalp, and neck. Observation and documentation of all injuries to the face, scalp, and neck should be made in a systematic manner. Injuries in the scalp should be examined after shaving the adjacent hair.

Certain external features may be indicative of internal injury, particularly basilar skull fracture, and should direct attention to those sites:

- Periorbital ecchymosis is the blue or purple discoloration of the periorbital soft tissues caused by fracture of the overlying orbital plate of the anterior cranial fossa (**Figure 1**).
- Mastoid ecchymosis or the battle sign is blue or purple discoloration over the mastoid area caused by fracture of the petrous portion of the temporal bone.
- Blood running from the ear is also caused by fracture of the petrous portion of the temporal bone.

### Blunt Trauma of the Head

Blunt-force trauma is frequent about the face, neck, and scalp and should be thoroughly documented. Abrasions are areas in which the skin surface has been scraped away and are especially seen over the prominences of the forehead, nose, cheeks, and chin.

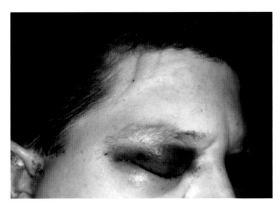

**Figure 1** The right periorbital region in a case of gunshot wound from the right to the left temporal area where there were bilateral periorbital ecchymoses.

Certain patterns of abrasion may indicate a mechanism for the injury. Dicing abrasions are small edged or rectangular abrasions caused by fragments of the tempered glass of the side windows of automobile doors.

Contusions are bruises in which blunt force has damaged underlying small vessels with bleeding into the soft tissue, producing an area of discoloration at the skin surface. Contusions also point to sites of blunt force that may be related to underlying intracranial injury and are important to describe and document. Blunt trauma to the scalp frequently does not produce an externally evident contusion due to the multilayered nature of the scalp and its ability to absorb energy. At autopsy, however, impact sites can be readily noted as hemorrhage within the galea of the reflected scalp. To age these injuries, sections should be taken for microscopic examination.

Lacerations are blunt-force injuries in which the skin surface is torn open, the wound edges are abraded, and the depth of the wound contains tissue bridges. A variety of patterns of lacerations can be recognized, such as those that result from linear objects and hammers. Care should be taken to distinguish sharp wounds from lacerations.

## Internal Examination

### Examination of the Scalp

An incision across the top of the head from mastoid to mastoid area allows the scalp to be reflected forward and backward so that the undersurface of the galea is able to be closely inspected. Any injury evident from the outside can be even more closely viewed from the inside.

### Examination of the Skull

Impact injury to the head frequently produces bleeding into the periosteum of the calvarium. In order to

examine the skull properly, the periosteum should be peeled away, along with the temporalis muscles. Fractures of the skull can then be fully visualized, described, and documented. When the calvarium is opened, the presence of epidural or subdural blood should be noted and documented. Description of the location, amount, and condition of the blood is pertinent. Note should be made of the fit of the brain within the cranial cavity: does it fit tightly due to brain swelling or loosely due to atrophy? After removing the brain, the dura must be gently removed from the cranial fossae so those bones can be examined for fracture.

### Skull Fractures

Fracture of the skull denotes that sufficient force has been applied to the head to exceed the ability of the bone to bend without breaking. Fracture may or may not be accompanied by intracranial injury, but in the more common circumstances it does indicate that the head has received an impact. In describing fractures, anatomic location, length, additional fracture lines, and features such as depression should be included.

### Linear Fracture

Linear fractures are the most common fractures at all ages and account for approximately 70% of all fractures. They occur in both the calvarium and the skull base. They are caused by broad-based forces striking the head over a wide area and are common in accidents, such as traffic accidents and falls. A linear fracture is a simple crack and may have additional extensions of stellate form, in which case it should be considered a complex linear fracture (**Figure 2**).

### Depressed Fracture

Depressed fractures are those in which the bone is displaced inward and may impinge upon the dura and brain, creating complications from cortical contusion and laceration. Depressed fractures are caused by a forceful impact striking over a small area and occur in circumstances such as falls on to a protruding object and impact with instruments such as hammers.

### Comminuted Fracture

A comminuted fracture is one in which the bone fractures into fragments and is caused by a significant force striking over a broad area. Comminuted fractures occur in crushing head injuries and from repeated blows to the head by a blunt object.

### Diastatic Fracture

A diastatic fracture results when a suture is forcefully opened, and it requires significant force. These

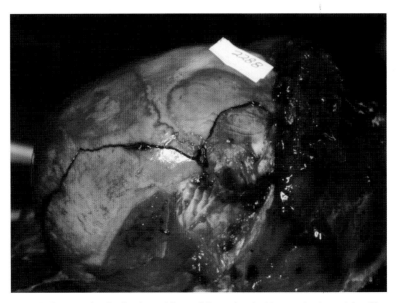

**Figure 2**  Linear fracture of right frontoparietal calvarium with overlying subgaleal hemorrhage sustained in a vehicular accident.

fractures usually occur early in life but may be seen at any time and are particularly common in traffic accidents. Marked brain swelling frequently causes sutural separation in young children before the sutures are fused, and these separations are not fractures.

## Compound Fracture

Compound fractures describe fractures underlying laceration of the surface soft tissues and create the possibility of complications from contamination of these wounds.

## Basilar Skull Fractures

Fractures can originate in the base or the calvarium and extend from one to the other. Fractures of the skull base are prone to a variety of complications due to the possibility of lacerating vessels or nerves leaving the brain. Several recognizable patterns of basilar fracture are common in forensic practice. Fractures of the orbital plates associated with periorbital hemorrhages are common and are caused by gunshot wounds to the head, falls on to the back of the head, and vehicular accidents. These fractures are sometimes called contrecoup fractures and do not indicate additional trauma at the site of fracture. The hinge fracture is a fracture extending across the middle cranial fossae through the petrous portions of the temporal bones, so bleeding is to be expected from the ear(s) (**Figure 3**). Hinge fractures result from very forceful impacts and are most common in vehicular accidents. The ring or circle fracture is a fracture around the foramen magnum through the middle and posterior fossae. Ring fractures are most

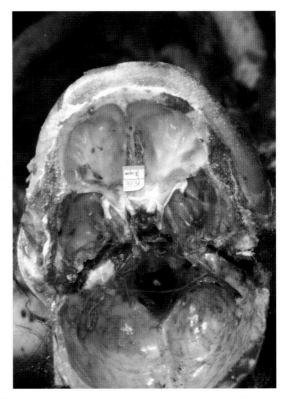

**Figure 3**  Hinge fracture through petrous portions of temporal bones separating the front and posterior parts of the skull base caused by a vehicular accident.

commonly caused by severe hyperextension of the head on the neck during a traffic accident. A less common mechanism is landing on the feet from a high fall or jump so that the vertebral column is driven upward into the skull base.

# Immediate-Impact Brain Injuries

## Contusions

Brain contusions are bruises of the cortical surface that damage the surface from the outside inward, producing disruption of tissue and vessels. The resulting lesion is a wedge-shaped, devitalized area of punctate and streak hemorrhages extending through a variable depth of the cortex. With greater forces or in patients with bleeding problems, hemorrhage may extend into the adjacent subcortical white matter (**Figure 4**). Subarachnoid bleeding in the adjacent

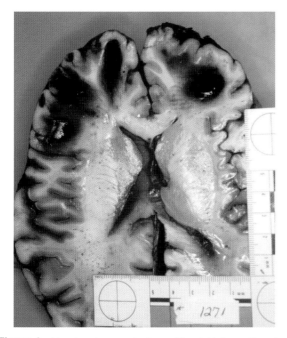

**Figure 4** Massive deep contusions of frontal lobes with extension of contusion hemorrhages into the subcortical white matter.

leptomeninges always accompanies contusion. In surviving patients, contusions undergo changes related to the inflammatory response, with removal of necrotic tissues resulting in a cavitated scar with surrounding gliosis and hemosiderin staining of the leptomeninges. Contusions may be classified into a number of useful categories based on the mechanism of the injury.

## Fracture Contusion

Contusions that occur at the site of skull fracture should be called fracture contusions (**Figure 5**). If the fracture lacerates the brain, the lesion is a fracture laceration.

## Coup Contusion

A coup contusion is caused by a blow to the stationary head with an intact skull at the site of impact. The contusion occurs beneath the point of impact on the convex and lateral surfaces of the brain. They tend to be much less severe than contrecoup contusions.

## Contrecoup Contusion

A moving head impacting a surface in certain falls will result in a common pattern of contusion called the contrecoup contusion. The circumstances of such falls include an adult abruptly losing balance and falling from standing height backwards or to the side, falling downstairs, or jumping from a moving vehicle. Falls from heights greater than 5–6 m typically do not demonstrate this pattern of contusion. Children younger than 4 or 5 years of age do not demonstrate this pattern of contusion. The mechanism of injury is not certain but is most easily understood by Holbourn's rotational shear force

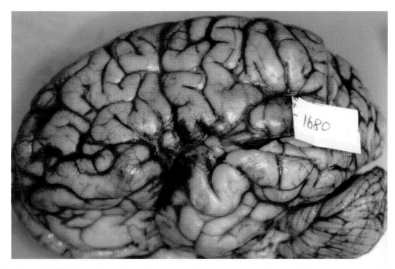

**Figure 5** Fracture contusion of left inferior frontal and superior temporal gyri with overlying subarachnoid hemorrhage.

theory developed from studies of brain movement in relationship to head movement. Movements of the head that cause the brain to impact the rigid shelves of bone of the anterior and middle cranial fossae create contusions over the orbital surfaces of the frontal lobes, the frontal poles, the temporal poles, and the lateral surfaces of the temporal lobes (**Figure 6**). Remarkably, the greatest extent of contusion is found opposite the point of impact to the head. Contrecoup contusions are frequently massive deep contusions and may cause hemorrhage to burst through the cortex and leptomeninges into the subdural space, resulting in overlying subdural hemorrhage or the "burst lobe."

### Herniation Contusion

Herniation contusions result from massive forces thrusting the brain against the skull base or a dural boundary and are frequently the result of gunshot wounds at a distance from the contusion. These contusions are seen over the hippocampal, parahippocampal, and occipitotemporal gyri.

### Crushing Head Injury

A crushing head injury refers to a stationary head impacted one or more times by massive forces causing comminuted fractures of the skull with fragments of bone contusing and lacerating the brain. The resulting contusions should be described as fracture

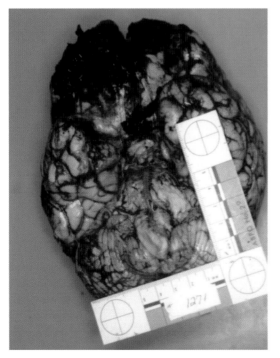

**Figure 6**   Contrecoup contusions of orbital surfaces greater on the right than on the left with bursting of blood through arachnoid membrane into subdural space.

contusions. Examples of these injuries include homicidal assaults with weapons such as choppers or cleavers or crushing of the head by an automobile wheel or industrial apparatus. Because the head is stationary, consciousness may be maintained during these injuries until brain swelling causes significant increased intracranial pressure.

### Falls from a Great Height

Falls from a height greater than 5–6 m may be considered a "great height" because it is at this point that falling head injuries lose the contrecoup pattern of contusion and the injury consists of multiple skull fractures with fracture contusions and lacerations of the brain. These injuries look much like the crushed head injury.

### Diffuse Axonal Injury

Diffuse axonal injury (DAI) refers to diffuse damage to the axonal processes and may result from either traumatic injury or hypoxic–ischemic injury. Traumatic DAI (TDAI) is an injury caused by forces that move the head and result in inertial damage to axonal processes and the vascular adnexae. Such forces may be either impact to the head or impulse shaking mechanisms in which the head is abruptly accelerated and decelerated. These mechanisms cause the brain to move abruptly within the cranial cavity somewhat differently than the more rigid skull moves. Differential movement of the brain causes disruption of axonal processes from the periphery of the brain inward, particularly at sites where the adjoining tissues are nonuniform. As axonal processes are torn, nearby small vessels also tear and these vascular injuries produce the grossly recognizable lesions seen in TDAI. Streak hemorrhages occur diffusely within the brain, most notably in the subcortical white matter, corpus callosum, deep gray structures of the basal ganglia, and the lateral extensions of the rostral brainstem. As axonal processes are disrupted at deeper levels, clinical symptoms reflect this damage to neuronal connections. When significant axonal damage occurs at the level of the deep gray structures and upper brainstem, the clinical appearance is immediate unconsciousness (traumatic unconsciousness). The inertial movement of the brain that tears the axonal processes also tears the vascular adnexae of the brain. These adnexae are the bridging veins that, when torn, result in subdural bleeding. In most cases of TDAI, there are at least small amounts of blood in the subdural space. TDAI most commonly occurs in victims of traffic accidents where severe acceleration–deceleration forces are encountered. Less commonly, TDAI is seen in other types of incidents, such as falls and assaults.

## Brainstem Avulsion

Brainstem avulsions are tears at the pontomedullary or cervicomedullary junction, usually caused by extreme hyperextension of the head in a vehicular accident. The disruption may be partial or complete, and the survival period depends on the completeness of the tear. These injuries are associated with overlying subarachnoid hemorrhage. These injuries occur in conjunction with TDAI.

## Penetrating Injuries

### Gunshot Wounds of the Head

Gunshot wounds of the head are very common injuries. Penetrating wounds are those in which the missile enters the head and does not exit. Perforating wounds are ones in which the missile enters the head, passes through, and exits the head. The behavior of a missile passing through the head depends on a number of factors, including the type of weapon, the caliber of the missile, the bullet construction, and the range of fire. For shotgun wounds of the head, the behavior depends primarily on the range of fire; at close and contact ranges, these wounds will usually be perforating and devastating. Gunshot wounds to the head caused by high-velocity missiles at close and contact range also tend to be perforating. Of gunshot wounds to the head caused by handguns, at close and contact range, approximately 30% will perforate the head and about 30% will perforate the skull. Many low-velocity missiles ricochet within the head to create secondary pathways, whereas others come to rest beneath the skull or the scalp.

Bullets passing through bone of the skull typically do so with a widening cone of fracture of the bone. An entrance wound will thus demonstrate a wider bevel on the inner table and an exit wound will demonstrate a wider bevel on the outer table. An exception is the tangential wound, which demonstrates a combination of the two patterns, reflecting the fact that a fragment entered and a fragment exited – the keyhole defect.

Low-velocity bullet wounds of the brain consist of fracture contusions surrounding the entrance and exit defects of the brain, and these wounds cannot be distinguished from each other (**Figure 7**). Bullet wounds tend to show subarachnoid hemorrhage over most of the brain. The pathway through the brain consists of macerated brain mixed with blood and possibly bone fragments. The bone fragments will be closer to the entrance wound. High-velocity wounds are very damaging at any distance. These wounds often result in the head tearing open with extensive fractures, and at close range they may cause the brain to be extruded. Shotgun wounds at close or contact range are also very damaging and result in massive injuries, often with extrusion of the brain.

### Stab Wounds of the Head

Stab wounds of the head are much less common than gunshot wounds and are more likely to penetrate in the thinner portions of bone, such as the squamous portion of temporal bone or the orbits. The effects of a stab wound to the head are related to the direct damage from severing tissues as well as resulting hemorrhage and later infection (**Figure 8**).

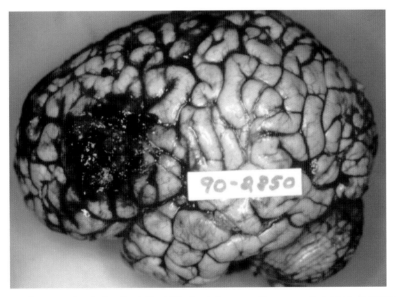

**Figure 7**  Low-velocity gunshot wound entering the left middle frontal gyrus with surrounding fracture contusions and subarachnoid hemorrhage.

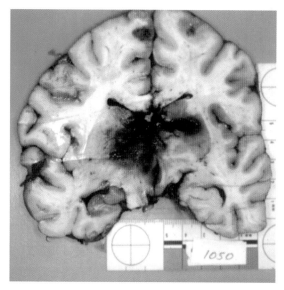

**Figure 8**  Stab wound that passed through the right eye into the right basal ganglia producing hemorrhage of both basal ganglia.

## Intracranial Hemorrhage

### Epidural Hemorrhage

Epidural hemorrhage is bleeding that occurs beneath the skull and over the dura. It is always related to impact to the head, and in approximately 85% of cases there is fracture of the skull. In younger skulls, impact without fracture may produce cranial distortion and strip the dura off the bone with epidural bleeding. Bleeding is usually from a branch of the middle meningeal artery but may be of venous origin from a sinus or diploic vein. Fewer epidural hemorrhages are seen in the very young and the elderly because the dura is so firmly adherent to the bone and difficult to strip off. Epidural hemorrhage tends to lie over the cerebral convexities but may also occur at the base. Because epidural hemorrhages lie above the dura, they tend to take on a lens-like configuration and produce a sharply outlined impression on the underlying brain, with the gyri being markedly flattened out. Brain beneath an epidural hemorrhage frequently demonstrates fracture contusions caused by the accompanying fracture.

Bleeding in an epidural hemorrhage varies from small insignificant amounts to large amounts that may produce a space-occupying mass. The amount of epidural hemorrhage needed to be significant as a mass lesion depends on the location of the bleeding. In an adult, epidural blood over the cerebral convexity greater than 100 ml is significant, whereas much less blood in the posterior fossa causes a mass effect.

Epidural hemorrhage as an isolated injury should have little morbidity or mortality because it can be easily removed surgically if it causes increased intracranial pressure and, if small, may resolve on its own. Epidural hemorrhages associated with other brain injuries have a much worse prognosis.

### Subdural Hemorrhage

Subdural hemorrhage is bleeding beneath the dura and over the surface of the arachnoid membrane. Nontraumatic causes of subdural bleeding are ruptured berry aneurysms and hypertensive hemorrhages that rupture through the subarachnoid membrane into the subdural space. Traumatic subdural hemorrhage is very common and may result from tearing of a venous sinus or an arachnoid artery but most often results from tearing of bridging veins. Subdural hemorrhage does not require an impact to the head; it requires only that the head be accelerated or decelerated so that the brain moves abruptly within the intracranial compartment and puts strain on the bridging veins to the point of tearing.

Subdural bleeding lies over the cerebral convexities as well as the base and tends to be unilateral in adults (**Figure 9**). The amount of blood required to produce a mass effect depends on the age of the individual and state of development of the brain. In infants and young children, very small amounts of subdural blood may be significant as a marker of diffuse brain injury. Young children may develop increased intracranial pressure

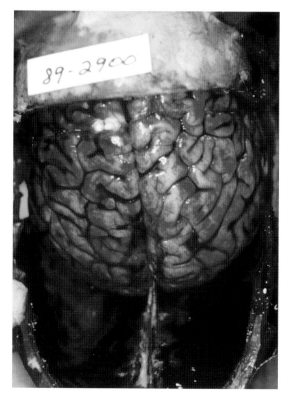

**Figure 9**  Thin film of acute subdural blood over both cerebral convexities and lying within the skull cap.

**Figure 10** Thick layer of fresh subarachnoid hemorrhage over both cerebral convexities caused by chopper blows to the head.

when the amount of blood reaches 30–50 ml. In adults, 100–150 ml of subdural blood produces mass effect. Individuals with brain atrophy from age or alcoholism may require greater amounts of blood.

The cortical surface beneath a layer of subdural blood frequently demonstrates foci of subarachnoid hemorrhage because the torn bridging veins are invested with a layer of arachnoid and, when torn, small amounts of subarachnoid bleeding also occur. The brain surface may be flattened in a crescent shape beneath a collection of subdural blood but will not be as uniformly flattened as seen with epidural hemorrhage.

Blood that remains in the subdural space over time may transform into a chronic membrane in certain circumstances, but not in all cases. Most subdural blood in a previously normal brain will resolve rather rapidly or be rapidly organized. The classic chronic subdural membrane develops in certain patients who have a low intracranial pressure as a result of brain atrophy (elderly or alcoholic patients) or hydrocephalic patients who have been surgically shunted. In these patients, small amounts of bleeding into the subdural space induce an ingrowth of granulation tissue from the dural side. Minor trauma may result in microbleeding in the fragile microcapillaries of the granulation tissue. A repeated cycle of induced growth and bleeding may result in a thick classic membrane in this group of individuals.

## Subarachnoid Hemorrhage

Subarachnoid hemorrhage is bleeding into the subarachnoid space usually occupied by the cerebrospinal fluid. Natural causes of subarachnoid hemorrhage are ruptured berry aneurysms and vascular malformations. Trauma frequently causes subarachnoid bleeding,

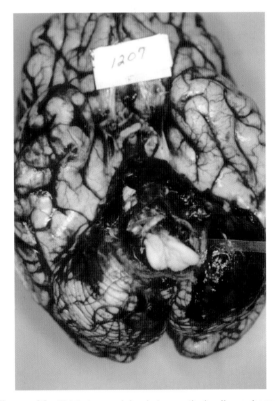

**Figure 11** Thick layer of fresh traumatic basilar subarachnoid hemorrhage over the ventral surface of the brainstem and cerebellum.

which is seen in association with contusions, lacerations, and gunshot wounds (**Figure 10**).

Traumatic basilar subarachnoid hemorrhage is a rare injury, most often caused by damage to a vertebral artery at C1 and related to lateral movement of the atlas if the head or neck is struck firmly. Tearing of the vertebral artery or dissection of the vascular lamina can result in blood tracking upward to lie in a thick layer over the ventral surface of the brainstem and cerebellum (**Figure 11**).

## See Also

**Deaths:** Trauma, Head and Spine

## Further Reading

Adams JH, Graham DI, Scott G, *et al.* (1980) Brain damage in fatal nonmissile head injury. *Journal of Clinical Pathology* 33: 1132–1145.

Adams JH, Graham DI, Murray LS, *et al.* (1982) Diffuse axonal injury due to nonmissile head injury in humans: an analysis of 45 cases. *Annals of Neurology* 12: 557–563.

Adams JH, Doyle D, Ford I, *et al.* (1989) Diffuse axonal injury in head injury: definition, diagnosis and grading. *Histopathology* 15: 49–59.

Contostavlos DL (1971) Massive subarachnoid hemorrhage due to laceration of the vertebral artery associated with fracture of the transverse process of the atlas. *Journal of Forensic Science* 16: 16–56.

Contoslavlos DL (1995) Isolated basilar traumatic subarachnoid hemorrhage: an observer's 25 year reevaluation of the pathogenetic possibilities. *Forensic Science International* 73: 61–74.

Dawson SL, Hirsch CS, Lucas F, *et al.* (1980) The contrecoup phenomenon: reappraisal of a classic problem. *Human Pathology* 11: 155–166.

DiMaio VJM (1999) *Gunshot Wounds – Practical Aspects of Firearms, Ballistics and Forensic Techniques*, 2nd edn. Boca Raton, FL: CRC Press.

Geddes JF, Whitwell HL, Graham DI (2000) Traumatic axonal injury: practical issues for diagnosis in medicoleogal cases. *Neuropathology and Applied Neurology* 26: 105–116.

Gennarelli TA, Thibault LE (1982) Biomechanics of subdural hematoma. *Journal of Trauma* 22: 680–686.

Kraus JF (1993) Epidemiology of head trauma. In: Cooper PR (ed.) *Head Injury*, 3rd edn., pp. 1–26. Baltimore, MD: William & Wilkins.

Lindenberg R, Freytag E (1960) The mechanism of cerebral contusions. *AMA Archives of Pathology* 69: 440–469.

Rivas JJ, Lobato RD, Sarabia R (1988) Extradural hematoma: analysis of factors influencing the courses of 161 patients. *Neurosurgery* 23(1): 44–51.

Sahuquillo Barris J, Lamarca-CIURO J, Vilalta-Castan J, *et al.* (1988) Acute subdural hematomas and diffuse axonal injury after severe head injury. *Journal of Neurosurgery* 68: 894–900.

# HEALING AND REPAIR OF WOUNDS AND BONES

**P Betz**, University of Erlangen-Nuremberg, Erlangen, Germany

## Introduction

Wound healing and its physiology are principally of clinical interest. From the forensic point of view, the different phases of the healing process that occur chronologically but overlap, as described in 1867 by Cohnheim, provide information that is helpful when estimating wound age.

The timing of wounds is a classic problem in forensic histopathology and the literature on this topic is not easy to understand. This article discusses the physiological course of healing of human skin wounds and bone fractures from a forensic perspective. In addition, the associated morphologically detectable reactions of cellular and extracellular matrix components that are useful for age estimation are discussed.

## Physiology of Skin Wound Healing

Wounds are a type of inflammation and their healing is characterized by an initial vascular phase, cellular reactions, and proliferative changes.

### Early Vascular Phase

Immediately after severe tissue trauma, fibrin occurs in the damaged area as a result of the clotting process. However, fibrin can be induced up to 6 h after death, so fibrin detection does not unambiguously provide evidence of the vitality of a wound, even though some authors assume that vital fibrin reactions can be distinguished from postmortem ones by morphological criteria.

Every relevant tissue alteration is followed by an early vascular reaction leading to reduced tissue perfusion and enhanced vascular permeability. In this phase of decelerated blood flow, an interaction between hematogenous leukocytes and endothelial cells takes place, mediated by different cell adhesion molecules. In addition, proinflammatory cytokines such as interleukins (IL-1$\beta$, IL-6, IL-8), growth factors (transforming growth factor TGF-$\beta_1$ or TGF-$\alpha$, basic fibroblast growth factor), and tumor necrosis factor (TNF-$\alpha$) act as peptide mediators and initiate a very early inflammatory response. The cascade of cytokines also regulates the induction of cell adhesion molecules and selectins (E-selectin, L-selectin, P-selectin) on activated endothelial cells and is therefore involved in the migration of leukocytes out of the vascular space. In this context, the interstitial cell adhesion molecule (ICAM-1) acts as a ligand of the leukocyte function-associated antigen (LFA-1), whereas the vascular cell adhesion molecule (VCAM-1) is a ligand of the very late activation antigen 4 (VLA-4). Different selectins are responsible for the attachment of the leukocytes at the vascular endothelium. After margination, the leukocytes actively permeate the vessel wall, attracted by several chemotactic agents such as degraded proteins, complement complexes, lymphokines, leukotrienes, thromboxanes, fibrin, and fibronectin.

Fibronectin is involved in leukocyte migration because of its chemotactic properties but it also provides a provisional matrix for migration of the leukocytes. It is synthesized by fibroblasts, endothelial cells, macrophages, and keratinocytes and shows a high affinity to collagen subtype III. Fibronectin enhances the attachment of fibroblasts and endothelial cells and seems to be involved in angiogenesis as well as in the contraction of the granulation tissue (**Figure 1**).

### Cellular Reactions

On such a provisional matrix polymorphonuclear (PMN) cells infiltrate, followed by macrophages; chemotactic agents such as degraded proteins, complement, lymphokines, and thromboxanes are attracted to the damaged area. The PMN cells contribute to erythrocytes' lysis and phagocytosis of necrotic tissue by the release of proteinases and lysozyme. They also influence the permeability of the capillaries.

Although the migration of neutrophils and macrophages begins simultaneously, the reduced mobility of macrophages explains their later appearance in the wound area. However, neutrophils, which predominate in the early phase of the cellular reaction, quickly disappear from the lesion area, so that macrophages now dominate. These cells also release hydrolytic enzymes, complement and arachidonic acid derivates and are mainly responsible for the phagocytosis of necrotic tissue. Depending on the material incorporated, several subtypes can be identified after a few days. Lipophages show a typical foam-like cytoplasm while erythrophages are characterized by the presence of incorporated erythrocytes (**Figure 2**).

Inside the macrophages, the erythrocytes and their hemoglobin are degraded. This degradation process is induced by microsomal hemoxygenase and siderin results. This pigment, which is blue, can be detected in Prussian blue-stained sections and it is easily distinguished from crystallized bilirubin, so-called hematoidin. In contrast to hemosiderin, this pigment seems to be quickly reabsorbed and it is infrequently seen during wound healing.

Macrophages can be divided into subtypes with respect to their different phagocytic activities, but also according to the time-dependent expression of different immunohistochemically detectable antigens, for example, early (27 E 10), intermediate (RM 3/1), late (25 F 9), and chronic (G 16/1)-stage inflammation markers.

Although lymphocytes are mainly involved in chronic inflammation, they also play a part in healing wounds, although this is the subject of debate. Different definitions of a positive result and difficulties in distinguishing lymphocytes from neutrophils may be the reasons for reported differences. Therefore, only

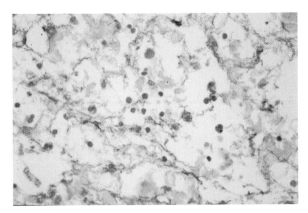

**Figure 1**  Human skin wound 12 h postinfliction. Typical network-like structures react positively for fibronectin and contain numerous neutrophil granulocytes (avidin-biotin complex (ABC), paraffin section, 380×).

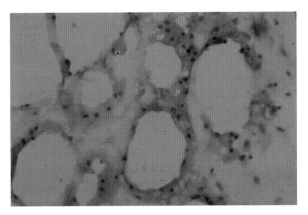

**Figure 2**  Human skin wound 5 days postinfliction: lipophages (frozen section, Sudan, 190×).

relevant lymphocytic infiltrates should be regarded as a reactive change.

In the area of the lesion, leukocytes, mainly PMN, and activated monocytes release proteins such as monokines and growth factors that, in combination with other factors such as fibrin degradation products, stimulate the proliferation and activation of fibroblasts.

## Proliferative Changes

Proliferation can be detected by demonstration of the nuclear antigen Ki 67, which is expressed in the $G_1$-, $G_2$-, S-, and M-phases of the cell cycle and also occurs during physiological regeneration. Under pathological conditions, for example in wound healing, enhanced proliferative activity can be observed.

Cell proliferation in physiological or pathological conditions is closely associated with apoptosis. Apoptotic changes can be demonstrated by detection of the *p53* tumor suppressor gene, which arrests the cell in the $G_1$- or $G_2$-phase to enable DNA reparation. If the reparation processes are unsuccessful, *p53* initiates apoptosis and as a result DNA fragments can be found.

Fibroblasts proliferate, but also migrate into the wound area attracted by the chemotactic properties of collagen fragments, fibronectin, complement, and lymphokines. The activation of fibroblasts is mediated by fibrin or fibrin degradation products, respectively; but also by growth factors, thrombocytes, and macrophages. Activated fibroblasts are characterized by enhanced enzyme activities detectable by enzyme histochemical techniques. Under forensic conditions, a time-dependent increase in the activity of adenosine triphosphatase, nonspecific esterase, aminopeptidase, and acid as well as alkaline phosphatase has been investigated (**Figure 3**).

Additionally, activated fibroblasts synthesize several extracellular matrix components such as cell adhesion molecules like tenascin, which are mainly expressed during embryogenesis, and also in malignant tumors and during wound healing. Due to its typical structure combining domains of epidermal growth factor, fibronectin, and fibrin, tenascin seems to be involved in cell migration and in the regulation of cell adhesion as well as acting as a mitogenic stimulus.

Some fibroblasts differentiate into myofibroblasts which are contractile due to their actin content. They are involved in the stabilizing and contracting the granulation tissue by the expression of different basement membrane components such as laminin, heparan sulfate proteoglycan, and collagen type IV.

Fibroblasts also synthesize proteins to replace necrotic tissue, in particular different collagen subtypes. Collagens are proteins of the extracellular matrix with different molecular structures and are responsible for different biological functions. Collagen I is characterized by considerable mechanical properties while collagen III seems to be involved in wound contraction. Collagen V participates in the migration of capillary and endothelial cells during angiogenesis and mediates cell–substrate adhesion by binding on heparan sulfate proteoglycan. Collagen VI mediates the attachment of interstitial structures in the connective tissue and cell-binding activities (**Figure 4**).

At the same time as the damaged connective tissue is being repaired, keratinocytes are stimulated and activated in order to cover the epidermal defect by migration and proliferation. Migrating keratinocytes, which also contain actin-like contractile elements, are derived from intact superficial keratinocyte layers and from adjacent skin appendages. They also use a provisional matrix of fibrin and fibronectin, which is replaced by a basement membrane after

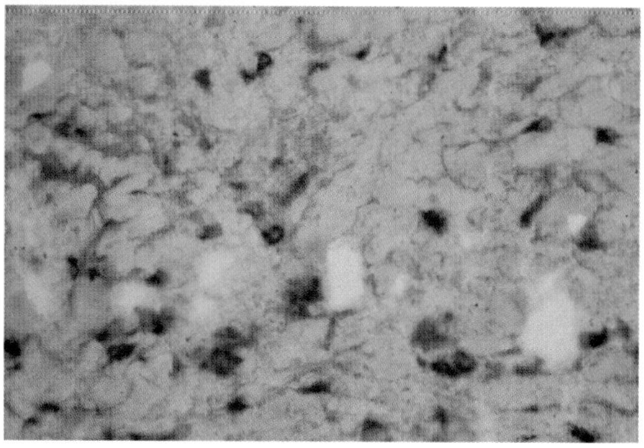

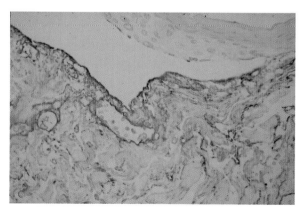

**Figure 3**  Human skin wound, 4 h postinfliction. Enhanced activity of nonspecific esterase in fibroblasts (frozen section, 380×).

**Figure 4**  Human skin wound, 11 days postinfliction. Fibroblast-associated networks positively react for collagen type VI (ABC, paraffin section, 190×).

reepithelialization is complete. The basement membrane collagen types IV and VII are responsible for the mechanical stabilization of the newly built epidermis, whereas laminin and heparan sulfate proteoglycan are involved in cell–cell and cell–substrate interactions. The basement membrane components are mainly synthesized by the migrating keratinocytes, in contrast to the interstitial collagen subtypes, which are produced by fibroblasts (**Figure 5**).

Afterwards, the keratinocytes differentiate: the keratinocytes can be seen by the expression of keratin subtypes or other markers such as involucrin, filaggrin, and transglutaminase.

The initial cell-rich granulation tissue characterized by numerous fibroblasts and developing blood vessels is finally transformed into a permanent scar. During this process, enhanced apoptosis is responsible for cell reduction.

## Bone Fracture Healing

Bone tissue is also continuously remodeled under physiological conditions, and the replacement of the organic and mineral bone matrix is rapidly enhanced during fracture healing. The remodeling process is mainly mediated by two cell types. Osteoclasts, derived from progenitor cells in the monocyte/macrophage system, are responsible for bone degradation by proteolysis of mineral and organic matrix. Osteoblasts are derived from progenitor cells normally located at the endost. These progenitor cells, mediated by cytokines, differentiate into osteoblasts or myelopoietic cells. Osteoblasts synthesize collagen type I but also temporarily subtypes III, V, and VI, as well as noncollagenous proteins during initial new bone formation. The balanced interaction between osteoclasts and osteoblasts in normal bone remodeling is significantly altered in fracture healing.

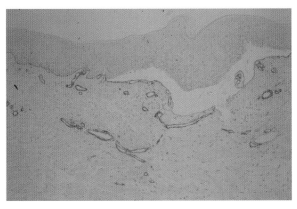

**Figure 5** Human skin wound 3 weeks postinfliction. Rearrangement of the epidermal basement membrane, collagen type IV (ABC, paraffin section, 70×).

## Physiological Course of Fracture Healing

Immediately after trauma, the fracture zone is filled by an extensive hematoma due to ruptured vessels of the periosteum and the opened bone marrow. This initial blood clot contains factors such as blood platelets. The thrombocytes release TGF-$\beta$, inducing the proliferation and differentiation of precursor cells into osteoblasts and chondrocytes. The bone morphogenic proteins (BMPs), also a part of the TGF-$\beta$-superfamily, additionally act on precursor cells. Furthermore, leukocytes (mainly PMN) are attracted to degrading necrotic tissue. Fibronectin degradation products mediate the migration of monocytes/macrophages and histiocytes as well as fibroblasts, leading to the formation of a granulation tissue that completely fills the fracture zone. Parallel to the increasingly condensing connective tissue ("fiber callus"), the fracture gap is usually widened. The bone margins that are irregular as a result of the fracture are smoothened by enhanced bone resorption, mediated by increased osteoclastic activity. This bone resorption is also essential for final stabilization of the fracture due to the removal of necrotic tissue and of sharp and irregular edges. The widening of the fracture zone results in an increased area of bone contact and contributes to the stability of the fracture zone since instable fractures undergo chondroid metaplasia. The resulting fibrocartilage callus is still biomechanically insufficient. The cartilage callus is secondarily transformed into an osseous one that is initially made up by woven bone but gradually replaced by maturing lamellar bone. Finally, this osseous callus proceeds to an increasingly maturing bone tissue completely bridging the fracture zone. Such a bridging callus can persist for a long time, particularly when the fracture ends are dislocated.

## Principles of Forensic Wound-Age Estimation

As discussed, every phase of the healing process is characterized by the chronologic but overlapping appearance of several reactive changes and the time-dependent detection of these features is the basis of all wound-age estimations.

Even though the age of a certain lesion cannot be determined precisely due to various factors influencing the rapidity of the reparation process, such as individual age, malnutrition, malignant, or severe metabolic disorders, the postinfliction interval of a wound can be estimated by different criteria.

The earliest appearance of such a variable established in systematic investigations determines the minimum age of a lesion with a positive reaction. If a variable regularly occurs in a specific time interval ("regular appearance"), i.e., such a reaction can be detected in every control specimen investigated, a postinfliction interval of less or more than that specific time interval is indicated. The latest appearance of a reaction can principally contribute to the estimation of advanced wound ages. However, this criterion is considerably influenced by the initial extent of the wound area and therefore it is of limited diagnostic value. From a practical point of view, it is almost exclusively the earliest appearance of reactive changes that is of forensic relevance since the diagnostic value of a positive finding considerably exceeds that of negative results, which may be absent in a section of a specimen but present in other parts of the lesion.

Several morphological features that are useful for wound age estimation can be detected by routine histological, enzyme histochemical, or immunohistochemical techniques. Routine histological staining procedures, for example, hematoxylin and eosin staining or the Prussian blue reaction, can easily be performed but a specific and unambiguous detection of several reactive changes is not always possible. The number of variables that can be demonstrated by enzyme histochemistry is also reduced and an irregular appearance of positive findings must be taken into consideration even though the advantage can be seen in the resistance to putrefaction. Immunohistochemistry is more sensitive to autolysis, depending on the antigen investigated, but allows specific detection of numerous parameters expressed during the healing process.

One of the most important conditions for a forensically useful age estimation of wounds is clear evidence of a positive reaction. Morphological features similar to postmortem changes are without diagnostic value.

Immunohistochemically detectable reactions must be evaluated critically with respect to nonspecific background staining or other artifacts. Typical network-like structures distant from the wound margins and outside the bleeding zone can be regarded as positive for the immunohistochemical detection of fibronectin, tenascin, or interstitial collagens, for example. Furthermore, the collagen reaction must be associated with fibroblasts because of the presence of destroyed connective tissue fibers in the damaged area. Negative as well as positive controls to prove the specificity of a reaction are necessary. Specimens showing relevant background staining cannot be evaluated.

The quality of the sections is of importance and it is only in optimally thin sections that a reliable evaluation is possible. In addition, a sufficient number of specimens per skin wound (in our opinion at least three specimens) must be investigated to confirm a negative finding. However, as mentioned above, conclusions based on positive findings are to be preferred. Therefore, **Tables 1–4** give details of the earliest appearance of a useful variable.

**Table 1** Variables of vitality of human skin wounds (postinfliction interval <30 min)

| Variable | Earliest occurrence |
| --- | --- |
| Transforming growth factor-$\beta$1, interleukin-8, P-selectin | Minutes |
| Basic fibroblast growth factor, defensin 3 | 10 min |
| Fibronectin | 10–20 min |
| Interleukin-1$\beta$, tumor necrosis factor-$\alpha$ | 15 min |
| Interleukin-6 | 20 min |
| Neutrophil granulocytes | 15–30 min |

**Table 2** Variables of shorter postinfliction intervals in human skin wounds (30 min up to 24 h)

| Variable | Earliest occurrence |
| --- | --- |
| Vascular cell adhesion molecule-1, E-selectin, L-selectin | 30 min |
| Interstitial cell adhesion molecule-1 | 50–60 min |
| Enhanced enzyme activity in fibroblasts | Hours |
| Macrophages | 2–3 h |
| Macrophages > neutrophils | 20 h |

**Table 3** Variables of advanced postinfliction intervals in human skin wounds (>24 h)

| Variables | Earliest appearance |
| --- | --- |
| Fibroblast proliferation | 1.5 days |
| Fibroblast apoptosis | 1–2 days |
| Myofibroblast expression of laminin, heparan sulfate, proteoglycan | 1.5 days |
| Tenascin | 2 days |
| Migrating keratinocytes | 2 days |
| Collagen III | 2–3 days |
| Collagen V, VI | 3 days |
| Lipophages, erythrophages | 3 days |
| Siderophages, hemosiderin | 3 days |
| Granulation tissue | 3 days |
| Myofibroblast expression of collagen IV | 4 days |
| Basement membrane fragments | 4 days |
| Myofibroblast expression of $\alpha$-actin | 5 days |
| Complete reepithelialization (of surgical wounds) | 5 days |
| Macrophage marker RM 3/1 | 7 days |
| Hematoidin, lymphocyte infiltrates | 8 days |
| Complete basement membrane (in surgical wounds) | 8 days |
| Macrophage marker 25 F 9 | 11 days |
| Macrophage marker G 16/1 | 12 days |
| Complete staining for keratin 5 (in surgical wounds) | 13 days |

**Table 4**  Course of normal fracture healing

| Variable | Estimated earliest occurrence |
| --- | --- |
| Hematoma | Seconds |
| Neutrophil infiltration | 12–48 h |
| Fibrohistiocytic proliferation | 2–8 days |
| Collagen formation (fiber callus) | 2–8 days |
| Chondroid metaplasia (cartilage callus) | 1–4 weeks |
| Woven bone formation (osseous callus) | 1–4 weeks |
| Lamellar bone maturation | 5–9 weeks |

Practical guidelines for the evaluation of immuno-histochemical features have been established on the basis of extensive studies on human skin wounds, and have led to a considerable list of variables contributing to a forensic age estimation. The data reported for the time-dependent changes during fracture healing have not yet been confirmed in a similar way in forensic circumstances. Nevertheless, they can be regarded as a point of reference for the timing of bone fractures.

## Further Reading

Betz P (1994) Histological and enzyme histochemical parameters for the age estimation of human skin wounds. *International Journal of Legal Medicine* 107: 60–68.

Betz P (1995) Immunohistochemical parameters for the age estimation of human skin wounds. *American Journal of Forensic Medicine and Pathology* 16: 203–209.

Betz P (2003) Pathophysiology of wound healing. In: Payne-James J, Busuttil A, Smock W (eds.) *Forensic Medicine. Clinical and Pathological Aspects*, pp. 81–90. London: Greenwich Medical Media.

Brinkmann B, Madea B (2004) *Handbuch Gerichtliche Medizin*, vol. 1, pp. 297–333. Berlin: Springer.

Cohnheim J (1867) Über Entzündung und Eiterung. *Virchows Archiv [A]* 40: 1–79.

Dreßler J, Bachmann L, Koch R, Müller E (1998) Enhanced expression of selectins in human skin wounds. *International Journal of Legal Medicine* 112: 39–44.

Hausmann R, Nerlich A, Betz P (1998) The time-related expression of p53 protein in human skin wounds – a quantitative immunohistochemical analysis. *International Journal of Legal Medicine* 111: 169–172.

Laiho K, Tenhunen R (1984) Hemoglobin-degrading enzymes in experimental subcutaneous hematomas. *Zeitschrift für Rechtmedizin* 93: 193–198.

Nerlich A (1998) Pathomorphological and pathophysiological aspects of fracture healing and their application to historic fractures. *Journal of Comparative Human Biology* 49: 156–171.

Pollack SV (1979) Wound healing. A review: I. The biology of wound healing. *Journal of Dermatology and Surgical Oncology* 5: 389–393.

Raekallio J (1970) *Enzyme Histochemistry of Wound Healing*. Stuttgart, Germany: Fischer.

Raekallio J (1973) Estimation of the age of injuries by histochemical and biochemical methods. *Zeitschrift für Rechtmedizin* 73: 83–102.

# HISTOPATHOLOGY

**P Fornes**, University of Paris, Paris, France

## Introduction

In the guidelines for the performance of hospital autopsies, it is always stated that an autopsy is incomplete without histological examination of all major organs. It would not be realistic to claim that the same is true of the forensic autopsy. For example, the autopsy of a shotgun wound of the head or heart may not require further histological examination. With few exceptions, histology should be performed in every case. Because of the increasing scrutiny of media and lawyers in forensic issues, forensic histopathology becomes an essential link in the chain of a suspicious death investigation. Yet, in many jurisdictions, such comprehensive practice is limited by time, cost, and above all lack of experts in forensic histopathology. As a matter of fact, most textbooks of forensic medicine devote little attention, if any, to the microscopic features of forensic pathology, and textbooks of surgical pathology do not deal with forensic issues, such as asphyxia and dating of injuries.

Histology is essential:

1. to confirm the nature of lesions found by the naked eye, and to assess their extent and severity accurately
2. to identify those lesions not visible to the naked eye
3. to date injuries.

Moreover, histological slides and paraffin blocks preserve the evidence, because they are stored permanently.

In this article, recommendations for organ sampling and technical procedures are proposed. Some of the most common forensic situations, in which histology is essential, are examined. Limitations of microscopic examination are also discussed.

## Technical Procedures

Autopsy techniques and methods of dissection of organs are beyond the scope of this article.

Ten percent formalin solution, a 4% solution of gaseous formaldehyde in water, is the most widely used fixative, and can be recommended for most purposes.

With the exception of the brain, which should be fixed whole before being sliced, and the heart, which is also fixed whole following dissection, it is emphasized that the smaller the specimen, the sooner the fixation will be completed. Specimens should not be thicker than 6–8 mm. The minimal acceptable volume of fixation fluid is about 5 times the volume of the specimen. Specimens must be rinsed before fixation to remove clots. After fixation, small samples are taken from the specimen, dehydrated, and embedded in paraffin. Three-μm thick sections are obtained from the paraffin blocks with a microtome, and stained with hematoxylin and eosin (H&E). Additional stains are often required. They should be mentioned in the pathology report. Perls's stain is used to detect iron-laden macrophages, especially in meningeal membranes, lungs, liver, and spleen, because iron deposits may be underestimated by H&E stain (**Figures 1** and **2**). Sirius red or Masson's trichrome stains are often useful in assessing fibrosis, which may also be underestimated by H&E stain. Reticulin fibers can be stained by Gordon–Sweet stain (**Figure 3**). This stain is essential in examining lungs for signs of asphyxia, or when the body is putrefied. In lungs, foreign bodies should be searched for with a polarized light microscope (**Figure 4**). Deposits of starch, talc, or other refractive materials are frequent in the lungs of long-standing drug users (**Figure 4**).

Since the 1990s, advances in histopathological techniques, such as enzyme histochemistry and immunohistochemistry, have been applied to forensic practice. These techniques, used mainly in dating wounds, are discussed later in this article. However, changes in tissues, whether due to disease or injury, are subject to numerous variables, and any conclusion drawn from such studies must be hedged about with qualifications.

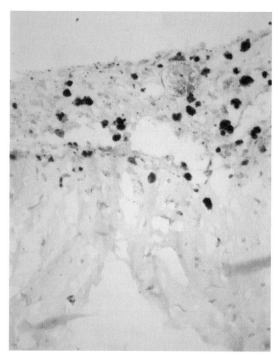

**Figure 1** Iron-laden macrophages revealed by Perls's stain, indicating previous bleeding in dura. Original magnification ×400.

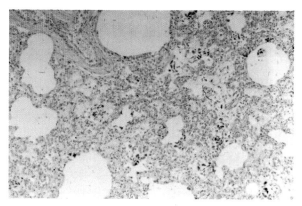

**Figure 2** Siderophages revealed by Perls's stain in the lungs of an abused infant. They have been suggested to be a marker of previous repetitive hypoxic events. Original magnification ×100. Courtesy of A. Dorandeu, MD.

## Organ Sampling: Practical Application

### Brain, Dura, and Spinal Cord

The brain is weighed fresh, but should not be sliced before fixation. This unfailingly leads to distortion of the cut surface during subsequent fixation. Deleterious effects are particularly severe in the case of

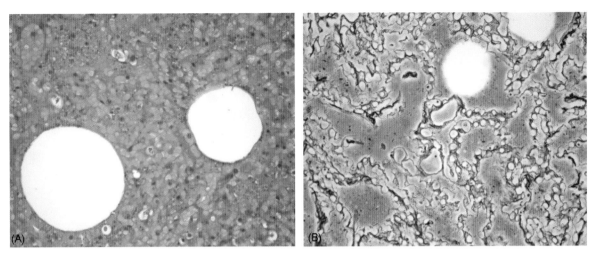

**Figure 3** Alveolar architecture may not be analyzable in a putrefied body ((A), hematoxylin and eosin). Gordon-Sweet stain for reticulin fibers reveals basal membranes (B). Marked congestion is evident, as well as gas bubbles. There were no alveolar wall ruptures. Sudden death ensued. The male victim was found with high cocaine metabolite blood levels. Original magnification ×200.

abundant edema or large hematoma. The same rule applies to fetal and infantile brains, because of their pronounced softness.

The examination of the brain at the autopsy table should be confined to significant surface features, such as subarachnoidal hemorrhage. Blood in the subarachnoid space is best cleared away before fixation, after noting its apparent origin – a contused area, or a ruptured aneurysm.

Flattening of cerebral convolutions and marks of tentorial or foraminal herniation are indicative of cerebral edema. However, as experienced, pathologists tend to overestimate edema in the fresh brain. Because edema indicates a prolonged survival time, overestimation may have important unfortunate medicolegal implications. For this reason, we recommend edema is only assessed in the fixed brain and at histology.

Acute meningitis should only be assessed in the fresh brain when purulent exudate is readily visible in the subarachnoid space. Otherwise, one should be cautious not to misdiagnose turbid edema with meningitis. Histology is the gold standard for the diagnosis of meningitis, in addition to microbiology performed on the cerebrospinal fluid and/or small brain samples (**Figure 5**).

The brain is fixed whole in formalin solution. A 4-week fixation in formalin is recommended before dissection. The number and sites of samples taken for histology depend upon gross findings.

When the brain appears grossly normal, samples should be properly selected depending on suspected pathology: degenerative conditions, such as Alzheimer disease, metabolic/toxic encephalopathy, encephalitis, epilepsy, hypoxia, or traumatic axonal injury.

Beta-amyloid precursor protein (beta-APP) antibody is widely used as a marker for axonal injury with positivity 1.5–2 h after its occurrence (**Figure 6**). Recent work on infant head injury has indicated that the major type of brain damage seen is due to hypoxic–ischaemic damage with focal axonal injury at the craniocervical junction.

It must be borne in mind that axonal injury may not only be caused by trauma, but is also a marker of damage from other causes, and, in the context of head injury, occurs frequently in association with raised intracranial pressure and ischemic injury.

Perls's stain may reveal iron deposits indicating previous bleeding in dura, leptomeningeal membrane, or parenchyma (**Figure 1**). A trauma may have been involved; however, minimal repetitive bleedings may have been spontaneous due to certain vascular malformations, such as telangiectasia or angiomas.

The differential diagnosis of intracerebral hematoma depends on whether it is natural or traumatic; if it is natural, the relationship or otherwise to any trauma can be problematic. It is important in these cases to have other pathological evidence of hypertension and/or traumatic brain injury. Histology may also be of help in differentiating hypertensive hemorrhage from that associated with amyloid. Amyloid tends to have a lobar distribution and can be easily identified histologically with Congo red or thioflavin T stains.

Gliosis, macrophages, and neovessels may give an indication of the age of the injury. CD 68 antibody for microglial cells may aid in injury aging, as well as

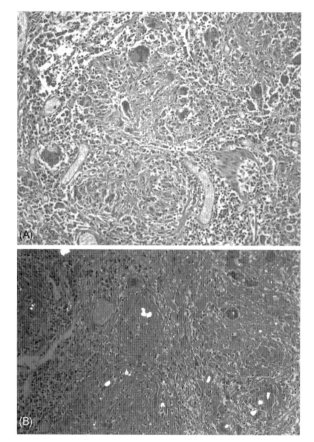

**Figure 4** Sudden death in a 32-year-old male. Histology showed (A) pulmonary and hepatic massive sarcoid-like granulomatous inflammation. Original magnification ×200; stain: hematoxylin and eosin. Polarized light microscopy revealed numerous foreign bodies in giant cells (white spots), suggesting long-standing drug use (B); original magnification ×200; stain: hematoxylin and eosin. Toxic blood concentration of buprenorphine was found in combination with low levels of benzodiazepines and neuroleptics. The chronic drug-induced pulmonary condition associated with acute intoxication caused the death.

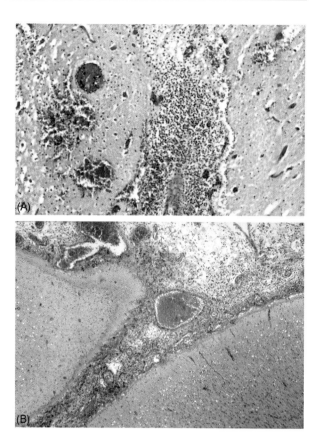

**Figure 5** (A) Suspected child abuse in a 5-month-old infant with leptomeningeal hemorrhage associated with parenchymal hemorrhagic areas. Histology showed hemorrhagic meningoencephalitis. *Escherichia coli* was found in postmortem brain samples. Original magnification ×100; stain: hematoxylin and eosin. Courtesy of MD Piercecchi, MD. (B) Suspected child abuse in a 10-month-old infant with leptomeningeal hemorrhage. There was no skull fracture. Histology showed subacute leptomeningeal hemorrhage, parenchymal contusions, and edema. Original magnification ×100; stain: hematoxylin and eosin. Other autopsy findings, including bruises and history confirmed child abuse. Note the misleading apparent similarity between pathologic features.

highlight older injury. However, one must be cautious in assessing the age of a brain lesion. When there are several lesions, comparisons of histologic features may help in determining whether repetitive traumas have been inflicted. This issue is of paramount importance, especially in suspected child abuse cases.

In the absence of macroscopic lesions in an epileptic brain, gliosis and loss of neurons should be searched for in the hippocampus, neocortex, and cerebellum. Samples from hippocampus and cerebellum are systematically selected, because they are known to be vulnerable to hypoxia. The sites most likely to show cell loss and gliosis in the hippocampus are the Sommer sector of the pyramidal cell layer, and the end folium.

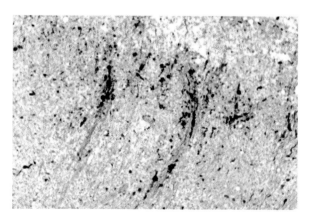

**Figure 6** Traumatic axonal injury evidenced by beta-APP antibody, in the brain of a woman who died 3 h after a traffic accident. Original magnification ×200; stain: hematoxylin and eosin. Courtesy of MD Piercecchi, MD.

When the brain appears normal, both grossly and histologically, despite evidence of skull trauma, such as fracture or scalp hematoma, the pathologist may hypothesize that death occurred before lesions were visible. Dissection of a vertebral artery or spinal cord trauma should also be considered. The spinal cord is only kept for histological examination when traumatic lesions are suspected. Degenerative, tumoral, or inflammatory lesions are exceptional in forensic practice.

Dura should be systematically kept for histology, even when it appears normal to the naked eye. Although ochre areas are usually present in cases of previous trauma, Perls's stain may sometimes reveal small iron deposits invisible to the naked eye.

### Eyes and Optic Nerves

Retinal hemorrhage, subdural hemorrhage, and cerebral edema have been considered diagnostic for a shaken-baby infant, since the syndrome was described in the 1970s. When nonaccidental injury in infants and young children is suspected, careful histological examination of retinal hemorrhages is of critical importance, although there remains debate about the significance of some findings. The question of whether retinal hemorrhages are of reliable diagnostic value in the controversial shaken-baby syndrome has not received a definite and clear-cut answer. Some authors have emphasized the diagnostic value of the distribution and pattern of these hemorrhages.

The International Retinal Hemorrhages Research Network has assembled a protocol for ocular examinations which provides detailed descriptions of technique and observations identified as having value in distinguishing between nonaccidental and accidental injuries.

### Larynx

The organ block examined fresh should contain the floor of the mouth, tongue, soft palate, tonsils, trachea, larynx, cervical esophagus, neck muscles, carotid arteries, jugular veins, and the thyroid gland. The hyoid bone is examined for fracture and hemorrhages, and kept for histology. Soft tissues surrounding bone/cartilage are dissected and examined for hemorrhages, and also kept for histology. The larynx is opened along the posterior midline with scissors, and the lateral portions are pulled apart to expose the mucosa. This maneuver should be cautious, so as not to break an ossified laryngeal cartilage. The larynx should be kept for histology. As experienced, some lesions involving the mucosa, such as edema and inflammatory infiltrates, may not appear at gross examination. Hyperplastic inflamed tonsils, epiglottitis, or laryngitis may cause asphyxia (**Figure 7**). In forensic practice, interpretation of cervical hemorrhages and/or suspicious mobility of hyoid or thyroid horns is sometimes difficult. X-rays of the larynx and hyoid bone do not usually provide a clear-cut answer, when interpretation of gross findings has been impossible. Histology is the gold standard in demonstrating hemorrhagic fracture. Furthermore, as previously emphasized, histologic slides keep the evidence intact.

### Heart and Aorta

Thorough examination of the heart, both grossly and histologically, is essential in forensic practice. Anatomy and detailed methods of dissection of

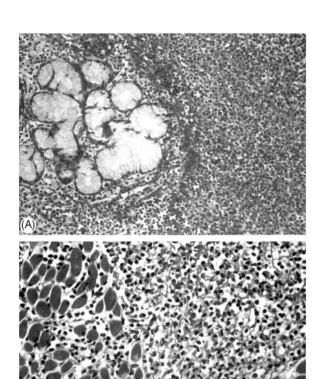

**Figure 7** Homicide suspected in a 3-month-old infant found with rib fractures, bruises, and obstructive asphyxia. At gross examination, retropharyngeal hemorrhagic features suggested that a foreign body or fingers might have been used. The infant's father denied killing his child and said he attempted to resuscitate him. Histology showed that obstructive asphyxia had been caused by retropharyngeal and cervical infectious suppurative cellulitis. It was concluded that death was natural. Note the retrolingual salivary glands and cervical muscular inflammatory involvement ((A) and (B), respectively). Original magnification ×200; stain: hematoxylin and eosin.

the heart are beyond the scope of this article. Only general recommendations are proposed.

The heart should be dissected fresh. First, epicardial coronary arteries should be cut in cross-section at 3–5-mm intervals. Calcified vessels that cannot be readily cut with a scalpel should be stripped off the heart and decalcified for at least 24 h before cutting. A four-point system is applied, by 25% increments of narrowing in cross-sectional area. Stenosis of at least 75% is considered significant/severe. A 90%/pinpoint stenosis is considered critical. The narrowest segments and suspected thromboses are sampled for histology.

In our opinion, the short-axis method of cardiac dissection, the so-called bread slice method, is the method of choice. Cuts of 1.0 cm thick are made, parallel to the atrioventricular groove, starting from the apex. The basal third of the ventricles is left attached to the atria, in order to preserve the attachment of the chordae. The basal portion is then opened according to the inflow–outflow method.

The short-axis method, as opposed to the inflow–outflow method, allows accurate assessment of ventricular cavity dilatation and mapping of scar fibrosis and/or acute infarction.

The heart is weighed at the end of the dissection after removal of clots, and should be fixed whole for histological examination. A normal heart weight is less than 0.45% of body weight in the male, and less than 0.42% in the female.

Four samples are systematically taken from the left ventricle, in the anterior, lateral, posterior/inferior, and septal walls, as well as two samples from the right ventricle in the anterolateral and posterior walls. Additional samples are taken in pathological areas.

In a typical medical examiner practice, approximately 50% of deaths are natural, and most are sudden deaths. Clinicians and epidemiologists define sudden death as natural, unexpected, and occurring within 1 h of the onset of symptoms. For medicolegal purposes, this definition is recommended, because it includes only those deaths due to electrical disturbances, and therefore allows accurate diagnoses. Studies using a time interval of 6 h include other mechanisms of death such as acute heart or respiratory failure.

Coronary heart disease accounts for 80% of sudden cardiac deaths. Most sudden deaths related to myocardial infarction occur within the first hour of its onset.

Based on autopsy studies, it has been determined that greater or equal to 75% cross-sectional luminal narrowing is a useful figure for separating significant stenosis that may result in acute myocardial ischemia from noncritical stenoses. Myocardial infarction is almost always caused by thrombotic occlusion of an epicardial coronary artery upon a ruptured atherosclerotic plaque. The acute infarction may not be visible to the naked eye, due to the short time elapsing between onset of symptoms and death, even if the triphenyl tetrazolium chloride or other gross histochemical technique tests are employed. These techniques are not recommended in forensic practice, because many flaws may affect the results. Infarction is visible to the naked eye approximately 24 h after its onset. The histology of the myocardium in early infarction may also be negative as far as classical findings are considered, e.g., coagulative necrosis and accompanying inflammatory infiltrates. These histologic lesions are detectable approximately 12 h after infarction. Contraction band necrosis may be detectable a few hours earlier (**Figure 8**). However, one should be cautious in interpreting contraction band necrosis, since it may also be explained by reperfusion damage following resuscitation attempts. When histology is negative, C5b-9 complement compound may prove a helpful immunohistochemical marker in assessing and dating early necrosis (**Figure 9**).

Transient myocardial ischemia, occurring in the setting of stable/unstable and vasospastic angina pectoris, may also trigger fatal arrhythmias in the absence of overt myocardial damage.

In forensic practice, coronary artery thromboses are relatively rare. Lethal ventricular arrhythmias occur most frequently in patients with myocardial scars resulting from previous myocardial infarction, due to a slowing of conduction and the onset of reentry circuits at the border between normal and

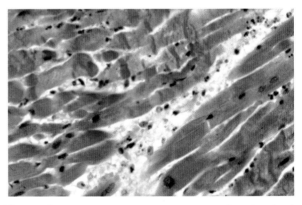

**Figure 8** Myocyte necrosis with contraction bands in early myocardial infarction. There were no resuscitation attempts. Note the rare neutrophils in the interstitium. Original magnification ×400; stain: hematoxylin and eosin.

fibrotic myocardium. Neurovegetative influences, whether emotion or effort, may have a triggering role.

Histology of epicardial and intramyocardial coronary arteries may also reveal amyloidosis (**Figure 10**), necrotizing angiitis, Kawasaki disease, giant-cell arteritis, or thrombotic microangiopathy. Coronary artery dissection, either spontaneous or following invasive procedures, may be a cause of sudden death. A left ventricular mural thrombus, bacterial endocarditis with friable septic vegetations, tumors, such as myxoma or papilloma, and noninfective thrombotic endocarditis may be causes of coronary embolism and sudden death.

Myocarditis is defined, according to the Dallas Criteria, as an inflammatory infiltrate of the myocardium with necrosis and/or degeneration of myocytes not typical of the ischemic damage associated with coronary artery disease (**Figure 11**). According to the same criteria, the term borderline myocarditis is used, when the inflammatory infiltrate is too sparse or damage to the myocyte is not demonstrable by light microscopy, or both. A sparse population of lymphocytes up to a mean of fewer than five lymphocytes per field ($\times 400$) should be considered normal.

Myocarditis may be a cause of cardiac failure, but sudden death is likely to be a more frequent manifestation, albeit underestimated, particularly in the young. Sudden death may occur in both the active and healed phases as a consequence of ventricular arrhythmias. The gross appearance of the heart may be normal. In the acute phase, histology discloses a patchy inflammatory infiltrate, associated with myocardial necrosis. The inflammatory infiltrate is most often purely lymphocytic. Evidence of myocardial infection, whether viral, fungal, bacterial, or parasitic, is rarely found. Giant-cell myocarditis, sarcoidosis, and eosinophilic myocarditis are rare. When myocarditis is suspected in an otherwise grossly normal heart, at least 10 blocks should be selected in the left ventricle and five in the right, because patchy inflammatory infiltrates and necrosis may be overlooked.

Hypertrophic cardiomyopathy is a primary disease of cardiac muscle, which is usually genetically transmitted, and is characterized by a hypertrophied but nondilated left ventricle in the absence of another cardiac or systemic disease that may cause left ventricular hypertrophy, such as hypertension, coronary artery, or valve diseases. Genetic mutations involving, among others, the beta-myosin heavy chain, troponin T, alpha-tropomyosin, and myosin-binding protein C genes have been identified. The natural history of hypertrophic cardiomyopathy is often marked by sudden death.

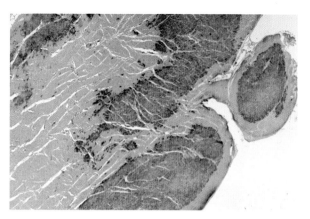

**Figure 9** A subendocardial infarction a few hours old, evidenced by C5b-9 complement compound. Hematoxylin and eosin-stained slides did not show evidence of necrosis. Mapping of necrosis can also be of use in differentiating ischemic necrosis from myocarditis. Original magnification $\times 40$.

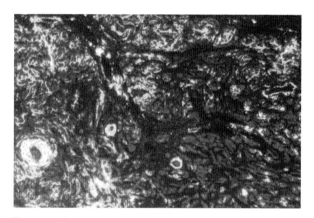

**Figure 10** Cardiac amyloidosis evidenced by thioflavin T immunofluorescence in a 45-year-old woman, who died suddenly. A slightly increased heart weight was the only autopsy finding. There was no known medical history. Original magnification $\times 400$; stain: hematoxylin and eosin.

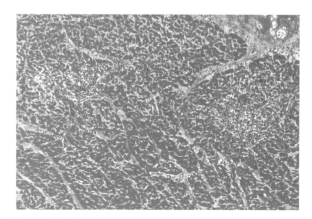

**Figure 11** Sudden death. Patchy inflammatory infiltrates in an otherwise normal heart. Myocarditis may be overlooked if numerous ventricular samples are not examined histologically. Original magnification $\times 40$; stain: hematoxylin and eosin.

Histologically, myocytes are spatially arranged in a chaotic manner (**Figure 12**). Myocyte disarray, interstitial and scar fibrosis cause intraventricular conduction instability. Postischemic scar fibrosis is caused by small-vessel disease, which is characterized by abnormal intramural coronary arteries with thickened walls and narrowed lumina, often associated with fibrosis. Myocyte disarray is sometimes the only marker of the disease; the heart weight and gross pattern are otherwise normal. In most cases, hypertrophy is asymmetrical, with predominant septal wall involvement. However, symmetrical forms of primary hypertrophic cardiomyopathy have been reported. Myocyte disarray is absent. Such forms should only be considered primary when any other cause of hypertrophy, including hypertension, has been ruled out.

Fat is a normal component of the right ventricle. However, in some hearts, the proportion of fat is dramatically increased, especially in obese and/or old women. As opposed to this pattern, arrhythmogenic right ventricular cardiomyopathy (ARVC), also known as right ventricular dysplasia, is characterized by fibrofatty replacement of the right ventricular myocardium (**Figure 13**). The left ventricle may also be affected. The patients are often young people, and sudden death is often the first manifestation of the disease. Clinical findings suggest a familial occurrence with autosomal dominant inheritance, various penetrance, and polymorphic phenotype expression. The intraventricular conduction delay, consequent to fibrofatty replacement, is a source of electrical instability, due to reentrant phenomena. At gross examination, heart weight is usually within the normal range. The pathological diagnosis of ARVC is assessed in the presence of gross and/or histological evidence of regional or diffuse transmural fibrofatty replacement of the right ventricular free wall. Rare sudden deaths have been reported in individuals with only extensive fatty replacement. This diagnosis should be assessed, when any other cause of death, including toxic death, has been ruled out.

At least five samples from the right ventricle should be taken, especially in the anterior wall, as well as in the posteroinferior wall, at the apex and infundibulum (triangle of dysplasia). Focal myocarditis or lymphocytic infiltrate is sometimes observed.

In some cases, where the heart is both grossly and histologically normal, and circumstances of the death suggest an electrical event, conduction tissue should be histologically examined. Interpretation of findings is very difficult. It should be emphasized that the mere observation of histological changes involving the conduction tissue or an accessory atrioventricular (AV) connection does not allow any surmises about electrical or clinical significance, in the absence of an electrocardiogram (ECG) recording or electrophysiological data. Fibromuscular dysplasia of the AV node, tumors, fibrosis, and myocarditis, among others, may cause sudden death.

In some cases, sudden cardiac death remains unexplained even after a thorough macroscopic and microscopic examination, including the conduction system. The long QT syndrome, Brugada's syndrome, or polymorphic ventricular tachycardia are causes of sudden death with no structural lesions. However, these diagnoses cannot be assessed without ECG recording.

Pathologists should bear in mind that there is no close correlation between cardiac histological features and clinical events. In other words, sudden cardiac death may occur in persons with a heart that appears "too good to die," whereas a noncardiac death may occur in others with a heart "too bad to survive." Thorough histological examination of all organs and toxicological analyses are therefore required in assessing the cause of death.

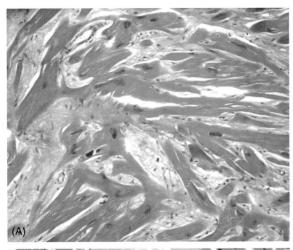
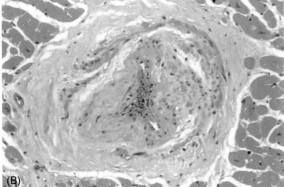

**Figure 12** Myocyte disarray (A) and abnormal intramyocardial coronary artery (B) in hypertrophic cardiomyopathy. Original magnification ×200 (A), ×400 (B); stain: hematoxylin and eosin.

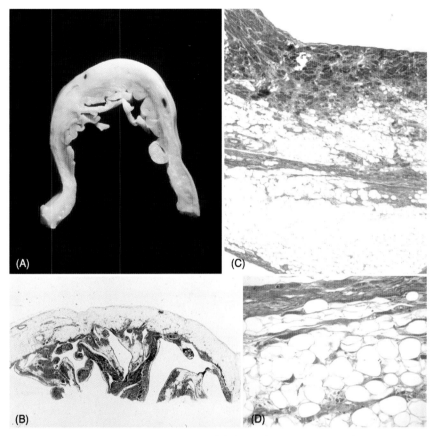

**Figure 13** Right arrhythmogenic ventricular cardiomyopathy. (A) Gross features: massive fatty replacement of right ventricular myocardium. (B–D) Corresponding histologic features showing both diffuse transmural fat and fibrosis. Photograph of mounted slide (B) and original magnifications ×40 (C), ×400 (D). Stain: Masson's trichrome.

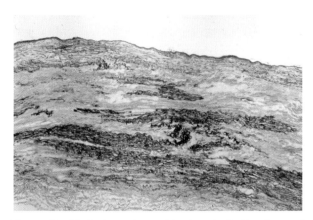

**Figure 14** Marfan's syndrome. Massive elastic fiber loss and fragmentation in the aortic media. Original magnification ×200; stain: orcein.

Aortic dissection and aneurysm may be idiopathic or a complication of Marfan syndrome. The tunica media exhibits significant changes in terms of degenerative cysts, the so-called cystic medial necrosis, severe disruption of elastic fibers, and loss of smooth-muscle cells (**Figure 14**). The defective gene

encodes fibrillin-1, which is the major constituent of microfibrils of the extracellular matrix.

**Lungs**

Interpretation of gross findings is often difficult. Pulmonary lesions are often patchy and histologic features are usually heterogeneous. Moreover, many lesions, such as granulomas, or related to chronic/acute asthma, are not visible to the naked eye. For these reasons, we recommend at least 12 samples are taken, including one in each proximal region near the hilus, one in the central region, and one at the periphery of every lobe. More samples should be taken when necessary, especially when obstructive asphyxia/drowning is suspected.

In obstructive asphyxiation, extensive hemorrhagic edema is present in the interstitium and alveolar spaces. The hemorrhagic feature and the interstitial edema are strong arguments against postmortem edema. However, although suggestive of obstructive asphyxia, lesions are not specific and should be interpreted in the light of autopsy findings and toxicological data.

Histologic investigation of bodies found in water should not be confined to the lungs, but requires complete histologic examination of all organs in order to differentiate between death by drowning and other causes of death. This task is difficult, because there are no pathognomonic gross or histologic findings on which to base the diagnosis. Varying amounts of water may have been aspirated. Thus, the length of time before irreversible hypoxia occurs might be different. The circumstances of the death also influence other pathophysiologic effects. One victim may die in water from physical exhaustion. Another may fall into the water, and die suddenly. Accidental drowning is likely to differ from suicidal drowning, in which victims may be intoxicated with drugs or alcohol. Moreover, histologic examination is often complicated by putrefaction. The diagnostic problem is further complicated by the heterogeneous distribution of changes in the lungs. Multiple sections must be examined, and stained for reticulin fibers. Examination of the reticulin network is particularly useful when the body is putrefied (**Figure 3**). The most important histologic findings in the lungs are interstitial congestion, edema, alveolar macrophages, alveolar hemorrhage, and emphysema aquosum (**Figure 15**). The latter is characterized by acute dilatation of the alveoli with extension, elongation, and thinning of the septa, and compression of the alveolar capillaries. It should be noted that some drowned victims die of laryngospasm without actually aspirating fluid.

In other organs – especially the brain, heart, and liver – there is marked acute congestion, associated with perivascular hemorrhage. These changes are indicative of hypoxia, but are not specific. Thorough examination of the heart is important to determine whether heart disease has been involved in the death.

Diatom analysis is one of the biologic tests used to assess the diagnosis of drowning. The forced entry of diatoms into the circulatory system results in embolization into internal organs. Diatom identification and quantification require long experience to avoid mistakes. Diatoms found in the lungs, bone marrow, and other organs are compared to those found in water where the body was found.

It has been suggested that the presence of siderophages in the lungs of infants who die unexpectedly should be considered a marker of a previous hypoxic event, or repetitive asphyxia, which may preclude a diagnosis of sudden infant death syndrome. Because iron-laden macrophages may be underestimated or overlooked on routine examination with H&E, Perls's stains should be used routinely in the investigation of unexplained infant deaths (**Figure 2**).

In asthma, airway obstruction is peripheral and diffuse. Histology discloses eosinophils, typical thickening of bronchial basal membrane and plugs in the bronchial lumen, due to hypersecretion of the mucinous glands (**Figure 16**).

Histology of the respiratory tract (trachea, bronchi, and lung tissue) in fire deaths is essential in determining whether the victims died before or during the fire. Vital lesions include swelling and superficial coagulation necrosis of the cylindrical epithelium, deposits of soot at the surface of the laryngeal and bronchial epithelium, and in alveolar spaces.

## Genital Organs

The genital organs are kept for histology if findings at the death scene or autopsy findings raise the slightest doubt of a possible sexual assault. In addition, the perineum and the anorectal segment should also

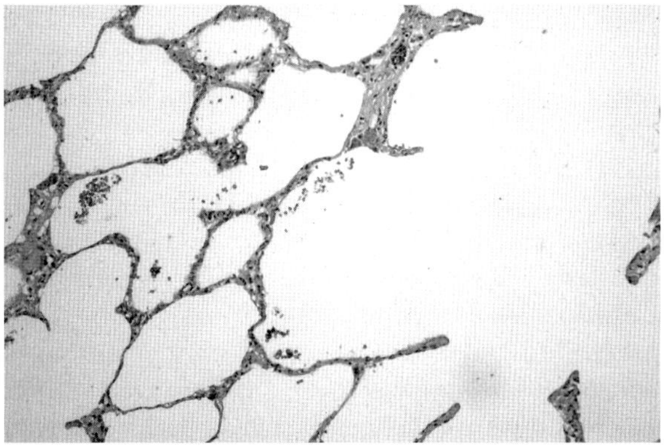

**Figure 15** ''Emphysema aquosum'' in a drowning case. Elongated and ruptured alveolar walls and enlarged alveolar cavities. Original magnification ×200; stain: hematoxylin and eosin.

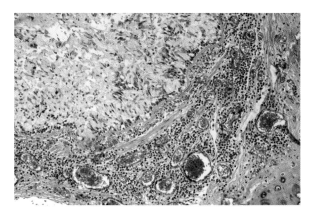

**Figure 16** Death from asthma. The bronchial lumen is occluded by mucus containing desquamative epithelial cells. The basal membrane is thickened. The dense inflammatory infiltrate is almost exclusively eosinophilic. Original magnification ×400; stain: hematoxylin and eosin.

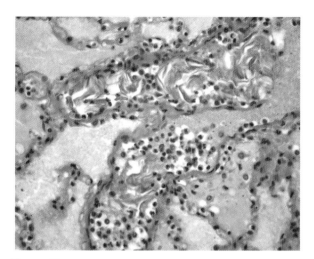

**Figure 17** Maternal death shortly after delivery. Massive amniotic embolism. Original magnification ×400; stain: hematoxylin and eosin.

be kept for histology. Multiple sections should be examined for hemorrhage and ulcerative lesions.

Genital organs are also kept for histology in investigating a maternal death. Amniotic embolism is a possible cause of death in this context (**Figure 17**).

## Bones

In infants/children, all acute or healed fractures should be histologically examined for aging.

Hemorrhage is present at the site of the fracture and extends into the surrounding muscles. The tissue damage stimulates an inflammatory response. Following neutrophilic infiltration, macrophages remove the fibrin, red cells, inflammatory exudates, and debris. Globules of fat and bone marrow are released and may enter disrupted vascular spaces and become embolic. The inflammatory phase lasts about 3 days. Following this phase, there is an ingrowth of capillary loops and fibroblasts forming granulation tissue, which appears by 4 days. By about 7 days, there are abundant fibroblasts. At this stage, there is usually a proliferation and infiltration of osteogenic cells in the periosteum at the periphery of, and not into, the fracture line. Within 1 week, small areas of new bone are visible. The growth of woven bone represents a temporary repair corresponding to union by primary callus formation at about 30 days. In the reorganization of remodeling phase, the trabeculae of woven bone gradually undergo resorption and are replaced by lamellae of bone, which are laid down in parallel plates corresponding to the lines of stress in the bone. This period of consolidation into mature lamellar bone may take as long as 1 year. It must be borne in mind that bone repair is faster in children than in adults.

**Table 1** Main histological and immunohistochemical features in skin wounds

|  | Earliest appearance | Regular appearance |
| --- | --- | --- |
| Neutrophils | 15–30 min | >15 h |
| Macrophages | 2–3 h | >3 days |
| Macrophages > neutrophils | 20 h | >11 days |
| Siderophages/hemosiderin | 3 days | |
| Granulation tissue | 3 days | |
| Lymphocyte infiltrates | 8 days | |
| P-selectin | minutes | 7 h (latest appearance) |
| Fibronectin | 10–20 min | >4 h |
| E-selectin | 1 h | 17 days (latest appearance) |
| ICAM-1 | 1.5 h | 3.5 days (latest appearance) |
| Tenascin | 2–3 days | >5 days |
| Collagen III | 2–3 days | >6 days |
| Collagen V | 3 days | >6 days |
| Collagen VI | 3 days | >6 days |
| Collagen I | 4–6 days | >6 days |
| Myofibroblasts (mf) | 1.5 days | |
| Positive for laminin (mf) positive for alpha-actin | 5 days | |
| Cytokeratin 5. Complete staining of the epidermis | 13 days | >23 days |

Adapted from Betz P (1995) Immunohistochemical parameters for the age estimation of human skin wounds. *American Journal of Forensic Medicine and Pathology* 16: 203–209.

## Skin

The lesion surrounded by normal skin is sampled for histology.

Dating wounds and bruises is an essential but difficult task in forensic practice. The acute inflammatory reaction is characterized by sequential chronological events, which can be detected by routine histology and enzyme or immunohistochemical techniques. Various factors, including the age of the victim, site, size, or mechanism of injury, are to be taken into consideration in estimating the age of a lesion. Only published human autopsy series should be used as guidelines. **Table 1** details the main histological features in skin wounds.

Morphological alterations are preceded by functional enzyme-related changes. Thus, it is to be expected that the demonstration of enzymes and other substances causing changes could reveal earlier reactions than could the visualization of the resulting histologically demonstrable alterations. Main developments in this aspect of vitality diagnosis are due to studies by Raekallio. Using enzyme histochemistry methods, he identified two clearly delineated zones of differing enzymatic activity around a vital wound: a central zone and a peripheral zone. The central zone is an area 200–500 μm wide that is located at the edges of a vital wound and shows a gradual decrease in enzymatic activity. This decrease can be detected between 1 and 4 h after wound infliction. This enzymatic response has been called the "negative vital reaction." It is recognized as the maximum tissue destruction zone. The peripheral zone is an area 100–200 μm wide circumscribing the central zone. This area shows a remarkable increase in enzymatic activity 1 h after wound infliction. This response has been called the "positive vital reaction." The second important finding of Raekallio was the realization that the increase in enzymatic activity in the peripheral zone occurs over a specific time interval, and this time interval is different for each enzyme. Furthermore, these enzymatic activities possess good postmortem stability and can be seen up to 5 days after death. For these reasons, enzymatic activity is useful in determining the age of a wound. Both the central and the peripheral zones are not present in postmortem wounds, at least those inflicted 1 h or more after death. **Table 2** details the main enzymatic histochemical features in skin wounds.

The immunohistochemical detection of antigens expressed during the early vascular phase of wound healing, in which cellular reactions are still absent, also provides important information on the intravital origin of lesions, i.e., that the wounds have been inflicted in life and not after death. However, the diagnostic value of immunohistochemistry for forensic purposes should be treated with caution. For example, it was shown in immunohistochemical studies that fibrin deposits can be demonstrated up to 6 h after death. Therefore, postmortem fibrin in bruises cannot be distinguished with certainty from antemortem fibrin.

**Table 1** displays the sequential events detected by immunohistochemical techniques.

**Table 2** Enzyme histochemical vital reactions in antemortem human skin wounds

| Enzyme activity | Increase in the peripheral zone (h) | | Decrease in the central zone (h) | |
| --- | --- | --- | --- | --- |
| | From | To | From | To |
| Adenosine triphosphatases | 1 | 2 | 1 | 2 |
| Esterases | 1 | 2 | 1 | 4 |
| Aminopeptidases | 2 | 4 | 2 | 8 |
| Acid phosphatases | 4 | 6 | 4 | 8 |
| Alkaline phosphatases | 8 | 12 | 4 | 8 |

Adapted from Raekallio J (1980) Histochemical and biochemical estimation of the age of injuries. In: Perper JA, Wecht CH (eds.) *Microscopic Diagnosis in Forensic Pathology*. Springfield, IL: Charles C. Thomas.

Although it is often difficult to assess accurate aging, comparisons of histologic features may help to determine whether repetitive traumas have been inflicted. This issue is of paramount importance in suspected child abuse.

Biochemical markers have also been investigated. Histamine and serotonin are both vasoactive compounds known to participate in the initial stages of the acute inflammatory reaction. Norepinephrine (noradrenaline), cathepsin D, and prostaglandins have also been investigated. It should however be borne in mind that these techniques require long experience to avoid errors.

Burns, whether thermal, chemical, or electrical, are sampled to determine vitality and mechanism. Enzyme histochemistry has also been applied to demonstrate earlier changes in antemortem burns than was possible with histological methods.

Histologically, at 4 h, a few neutrophils migrate outside the vessels. In 6-h burns there is obvious leukocytic infiltration of the peripheral zone. The concentration of neutrophils increases progressively and is highest at 48–72 h, when, in addition to the neutrophils, there are macrophages and fibroblasts. In the epidermis, by 12–24 h after burning, there is some necrosis and degeneration of the epidermal cells in the central zone located immediately beneath the heated area. In the peripheral zone, surrounding the central area, the epidermal cells start to stretch and their nuclei start to elongate, heralding the onset of epithelial migration. In burns 48–72 h old, migration of the epidermal cells is pronounced. The epithelial cells of the dermal appendages, such as the hair follicles, undergo changes similar to those of epidermal cells. As healing progresses there is increased proliferation of both epithelial and connective tissue elements, but these are not striking until 72 h or more after burning.

The depth and extent of burns are clinically estimated using the "rule of nines." The histological changes associated with the four degrees of burn severity are as follows.

**First-degree burns** There is dilatation of capillaries, condensation of nuclear chromatin, some necrotic epidermal cells, and edema of the subepidermal connective tissue.

**Second-degree burns (blisters)** There is subepidermal edema with blister formation, varying degrees of epidermal cell necrosis, and reduced staining reaction of epidermal cell nuclei. In the upper part of the dermis, there is hyperemia, edema, and a minimal perivascular accumulation of neutrophils, macrophages, and occasional lymphocytes. Neutrophils have usually migrated into the dermis after 16 h.

**Third-degree burns (complete destruction of skin)** There is loss of epidermis and necrosis of the dermis (including the deeper layers); coagulation of collagenous fibers; necrosis of skin appendages; hyperemia of neighboring capillaries; along the edge of adjacent intact epidermis an elongation of cells and cell nuclei can be seen (palisade formation); the necrotic areas become demarcated by neutrophils after 6–24 h; dermal inflammation tends to lag by several days, although the subcutaneous tissue shows inflammatory cell infiltration by the second day.

**Fourth-degree burns (charring)** There is complete destruction of skin and subcutaneous tissue, sometimes with exposure of bone.

There are two forms of death from electrocution: (1) deaths caused through contact with electrical conductors and (2) those caused by lightning stroke. The pathological changes in both are similar. Histologically, the cells of the epidermal basal layer show marked nuclear elongation (**Figure 18**). Vacuolization can be seen in the cells of the spindle cell layer, and sometimes blisters. The typical elongation of the cell nuclei can be seen in the dermis. Metallic particles can be helpful in assessing an electrical burn.

In some cases, histology may be useful in distinguishing between entry and exit gunshot wounds. Attempts have been made to evaluate the presence or absence of soot associated with an entry wound by microscopic examination.

## Other Organs

One sample of the thymus is kept systematically in infants/children. One sample is taken from the liver, kidneys, spleen, and pancreas. More samples may be required by pathological gross findings. Adrenal glands are kept whole. Samples from esophagus, stomach, and intestines are only kept when gross examination shows abnormalities.

## Ten Practical Key Points in Forensic Histology

1. The brain, heart, larynx, and samples of other organs should be systematically kept in formalin solution in all cases.
2. Histology is essential:
   a. to confirm the nature of lesions found by the naked eye, and to assess their extent and severity accurately
   b. to identify those lesions not visible to the naked eye
   c. to date injuries
   d. because histological slides can be stored permanently and therefore preserve the evidence.
3. The brain should not be sliced fresh. It should be kept whole. A 4-week fixation in formalin is recommended before dissection.
4. The heart should be dissected fresh, and fixed whole.
5. Multiple lung samples should be examined histologically, especially when asphyxia/drowning is suspected. Stains for reticulin fibers should be used in those cases.
6. Iron deposits may be missed or underestimated by H&E stain, and therefore should be searched for by Perls's stain.
7. In suspected infant head injury, with or without impact, histological examination of eyes is mandatory. Beta-APP is a useful immunohistochemical marker for traumatic axonal injury.
8. Enzyme and immunohistochemistry for dating wounds and ecchymoses require a long experience. Otherwise, we do not recommend these techniques.
9. Histology should not be performed in "blinded conditions," i.e., with no knowledge of the autopsy findings.
10. The cause of a death should never be based on histological findings only, but also on scene investigation data, medical records, autopsy findings, and laboratory analyses, especially toxicology.

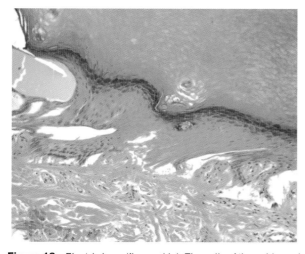

**Figure 18** Electric burn (finger skin). The cells of the epidermal basal layer show marked nuclear elongation. The diagnosis should be systematically confirmed by the technical expertise of the suspected electrical equipment or device. Original magnification ×400; stain: hematoxylin and eosin.

## See Also

Immunoassays, Forensic Applications; Serology: Overview; Blood Identification; Bloodstain Pattern Analysis

## Further Reading

Esiri MM (ed.) (1996) *Oppenheimer's Diagnostic Neuropathology. A Practical Manual*, 2nd edn. Oxford, UK: Blackwell Science.

Gilliland MGF, Luthert P (2003) Why do histology on retinal hemorrhages in suspected non-accidental injury? Expert opinion. *Histopathology* 43: 592–602.

Hernandez-Cueto C, Girela E, Sweet D (2000) Advances in the diagnosis of wound vitality. a review. *American Journal of Forensic Medicine Pathology* 21: 21–31.

Janssen W (ed.) (1984) *Forensic Histopathology.* Berlin: Springer.

Karch SB (ed.) (2002) *Pathology of Drug Abuse*, 3rd edn. Boca Raton, FL: CRC Press.

Leetsma JE (ed.) (1988) *Forensic Neuropathology.* New York: Raven Press.

Ludes B, Coste M (eds.) (2000) *Diatomées et Médecine Légale.* Paris: Tec et Doc Lavoisier.

Payne-James J, Busuttil A, Smock W (eds.) (2003) *Forensic Medicine. Clinical and Pathological Aspects.* London: Greenwich Medical Media.

Perper JA, Wecht CH (eds.) (1980) *Microscopic Diagnosis in Forensic Pathology.* Springfield, IL: Charles C. Thomas.

Pollanen MS (ed.) (1998) *Forensic Diatomology and Drowning.* Amsterdam: Elsevier.

Plunkett J (1999) Shaken baby-syndrome and the death of Matthew Eappen. *American Journal of Forensic Medical Pathology* 20: 17–21.

Silver MD, Gotlieb AI, Schoen FJ (eds.) (2001) *Cardiovascular Pathology*, 3rd edn. New York: Churchill Livingstone.

Whitwell HL (ed.) (2004) *Forensic Neuropathology.* London: Arnold.

# HISTORY OF FORENSIC MEDICINE

**J Payne-James**, Forensic Healthcare Services Ltd, London, UK

## Introduction

Forensic medicine, legal medicine, and forensic pathology are terms that have been used interchangeably around the world. It now seems appropriate to use the terms forensic medicine and legal medicine together to indicate all branches of medicine and related specialties, that interact with legal processes, either directly or indirectly. The actual usage of the terms may vary from country to country. Forensic medicine can be divided into forensic pathology, which investigates unnatural, unexpected, or violent death, and clinical forensic medicine (a term that has become widely used only in the last two decades), which is used to refer to that branch of medicine which involves an interaction between the living person, medicine, and legal processes. In broad terms a forensic pathologist does not (in general) deal with living individuals, whereas a forensic physician does not deal with the deceased. There are many medical practitioners who are involved in both clinical and pathological aspects of forensic medicine. Many practitioners have qualifications or training in medicine, law, and forensic science. There are many areas where both clinical and pathological aspects of forensic medicine overlap, and this is reflected in the history and development of the specialty as a whole.

The term forensic pathologist is used generally to describe those pathologists who undertake autopsies performed on the instructions and request of legal bodies responsible for the investigation of sudden, suspicious, obscure, unnatural, litigious, or criminal deaths. The legal bodies that may make these requests may be agents of the state, the judiciary, the police, lawyers representing those arrested for murder, those involved in legal action, health and safety organizations, and many other possible sources. The forensic pathologist undertakes the examinations to assist and advise the state or other investigating agencies in the interpretation of the findings and to recommend further relevant investigation. The practitioners of clinical forensic medicine have been given many different names over the years, but the term forensic physician has now become accepted. Other names that have been used include police surgeon, forensic medical officer, and forensic medical examiner. The extent and range of the role of a forensic physician is variable – many may limit themselves to specific aspects of clinical forensic medicine – for example, sexual assault or child abuse. **Table 1** illustrates those cases in which the expertise of a forensic physician may be required. Some practitioners of clinical forensic medicine may only perform part of these functions, whilst others may have a more extensive role, which may be dependent on geographical location and local statute. Part of a forensic pathologist and forensic physician's remit must be to have a good knowledge of "medical jurisprudence" – the application of medical science and related specialties to the law. The function and role of forensic pathologists and forensic physicians can differ widely or overlap, depending on local judicial systems or statute, and in many cases result in the need for a special understanding of medical law and medical ethics.

The origins of forensic and legal medicine go back many centuries although the terms forensic medicine and medical jurisprudence date back to the earliest part of the nineteenth century. In 1840 Thomas Stuart Traill pointed out that "it is known in Germany, the country in which it took its rise, by the name of State Medicine, in Italy and France it is termed Legal Medicine; and with us it is usually denominated Medical Jurisprudence or Forensic Medicine."

In China, pharmacology and pharmacognosy were written about from 3000 BC. In 1975 Chinese archeologists discovered a number of bamboo pieces that had information on the rules and regulations for examining injuries – these dated from about 220 BC. The Hammurabi Code (named after the king of Babylon – now in modern Iraq), dated back to about 2200 BC and dealt specifically with the rights and duties of physicians, including medical malpractice. Penalties ranged from cutting off the hands of the offending physician to monetary compensation.

The laws of Manu (India) date back to around 10 BC and dealt with issues still particularly relevant today, including the competence of witnesses in courts. In Egypt, laws regulated the medical profession and physicians had to follow strictly the methods used by ancient physicians. Stab wounds were categorized and closed head injuries with skull fractures described. Papyri related to Roman Egypt dating from the latter part of the first to the latter part of the fourth century AD contain information about

**Table 1** Possible roles of a forensic physician[a]

| Role |
| --- |
| • Determination of fitness to be detained in custody |
| • Determination of fitness to be charged: competent to understand charge |
| • Determination of fitness to be interviewed by the police or detaining body |
| • Advise that an independent person is required to insure rights for the vulnerable or mentally disordered |
| • Assessment of alcohol and drug intoxication and withdrawal |
| • Comprehensive examination to assess a person's ability to drive a motor vehicle, in general medical terms and related to alcohol and drug misuse |
| • Undertake intimate body searches for drugs |
| • Documentation and interpretation of injuries |
| • Take and advise on appropriate forensic samples |
| • Assess and treat personnel injured whilst on duty (e.g., police personnel) including needlestick injuries |
| • Pronounce life extinct at a scene of death and undertake preliminary advisory role |
| • Undertake mental state examinations |
| • Examine adult complainants of serious sexual assault and the alleged perpetrators |
| • Examine alleged child victims of neglect, physical, or sexual abuse |
| • Examine victims and assailants in alleged police assaults |
| • Give expert opinion in courts and tribunals |
| • Investigation of deaths in custody |
| • Pressure group and independent investigators in ethical and moral issues: victims of torture, war crimes, female genital mutilation |
| • Refugee medicine (medical and forensic issues) |
| • Asylum-seeker medicine (medical and forensic issues) |
| • Implement principles of immediate management in biological or chemical incidents |

[a]This table illustrates the role of forensic physicians in the UK; roles vary according to geographical location.
For all these examinations a forensic physician must accurately document findings and when needed produce these as written reports for appropriate civil, criminal, or other agencies and courts. The forensic physician will be also able to present the information orally to a court or other tribunal or forum.

forensic medical examination or investigation. In Persia (now Iran), there was an official scale of medical fees and a restriction of medical practices to certain castes and classes of the community, and penalties were meted out for medical malpractice. Injuries were subdivided into several groups; abortion was a serious crime.

Amundsen and Ferngren have assessed the evidence for the role of physicians as expert witnesses in classical Greece and concluded that forensic medicine was used by Athenian courts and other public bodies and that the testimony of physicians in matters of a medical nature was given particular credence. In the Roman Republic the *Lex Duodecim Tabularum* (449 BC) made minor reference to medicolegal matters including length of gestation (to determine legitimacy), disposal of the dead, punishments dependent on the degree of injury caused by an assailant, and poisoning. The *Lex Aquillia* of 572 BC dealt with the lethality of wounds. The "*novus actus interveniens*" in relation to deaths from wounds was brought into play and declared as a break in causation. Sulla's "Lex Cornelia" (138–78 BC) declared that a physician should be exiled or executed if it was established that he had caused the death of his patient. The body of Julius Caesar (100–44 BC) after his murder in the forum was examined by the physician Antistius who declared that there were 23 stab wounds, only one of which was a fatal wound. The Emperor Justinian (AD 483–565) in his "Digest" recorded that "physicians are not ordinary witnesses, but give judgment rather than testimony."

Between the fifth and the tenth centuries, the so-called Dark Ages, the "Leges Barbarorum" of the Goths, Visigoths, and Vandals laid down clearly when medical experts were called for. "Wergeld" (blood money) was payable to the victim or on death to relatives of the decedent by the perpetrator – and these principles apply in certain cultures today. The first Holy Roman Emperor, Charlemagne (742–814) had his bishops produce the "Capitularies" in which the need for expert medical testimony was required in wounding, abortion, rape, incest, infanticide, and suicide.

In 1209, the influence of the Church was formalized by Pope Innocent III with the appointment of physicians to the courts. In 1234 Gregory IX in his "Compilatio Decretalium" collected all decisions and edicts in relation to medicolegal matters and these held sway in France until 1677.

Traill stated that "Medical Jurisprudence as a science cannot date farther back than the 16th century" and identified George, Bishop of Bamberg

who proclaimed a penal code in 1507, as the originator of the first examples of codes where medical evidence was a necessity in certain cases. However, it was the *Constitutio Criminalis Carolina* – the code of law published and proclaimed in 1553 in Germany by Emperor Charles V – that originated legal medicine as a specialty. Within these codes of 1553, expert medical testimony became a requirement rather than an option to give opinions in cases of murder, wounding, poisoning, hanging, drowning, infanticide, and abortion. In 1575, the military surgeon Ambrose Paré produced his book on medicolegal reports; he also wrote about deaths from lightning, antemortem versus postmortem injuries, and poisoning by carbon monoxide and corrosives.

In 1595 Andreas Libavius produced his medicolegal text in which he specifically describes cruentation, the phenomenon in which blood flowed from a decedent's wounds if he were to be touched by the murderer postmortem. James VI of Scotland subscribed to this practice in his book "Daemonologie." In that year the text "*Methods Testificandi*" was published by Codronchius, a physician from Imola, and in the following year Fortunatus Fidelis published "De Relationibus Medicorum" from Palermo. The French physician, Séverin Pineau wrote his book on defloration and virginity, and he discussed at some length the existence of the hymen. Paulus Zacchias (1584–1659), principal physician to the popes Innocent X and Alexander VII, expert before the "Sacra Romana Rota" (the highest papal court of Appeal) published the major seven-book series "Quaestiones Medico-legales." He is still hailed as the father of legal medicine.

Certainly medicolegal autopsies were well documented in parts of Italy and Germany five centuries before the use of such procedures by English coroners. The use of such expertise was not limited to deaths or to Europe. Cassar describes the earliest recorded "Maltese medicolegal report" from 1542, in which medical evidence established that the male partner was incapable of sexual intercourse and this resulted in a marriage annulment.

These historical references of medical expertise being used in the context of law prior to the eighteenth and nineteenth centuries confirm the longstanding need and status of forensic or legal medicine in many jurisdictions.

A number of books and treatises were published in the English language in the eighteenth century concerning forensic medicine and medical jurisprudence. What is remarkable is that the issues addressed by many of the authors are ones that would not be out of place in a contemporary setting. It seems odd that many of these principles are restated today as though new. In the course of the next two centuries, several medicolegal texts appeared in Germany and France; chairs of medical jurisprudence were installed in Paris, Strasbourg, and Montpellier with such major authorities as Mahon and later Orfila and Tardieu in Paris, Chaussier in Dijon, Foderé in Strasbourg, Johann Ludwig Casper in Berlin, and Eduard Ritter von Hofmann in Vienna.

In 1783 William Hunter published essays related to the findings in murder of bastard children, and this may be the first true "forensic medicine" publication from England. The first larger work (*Elements of Medical Jurisprudence*) was published in 1788 by Samuel Farr, itself translated from 1767 Fazelius of Geneva's publication *Elemental Medicinae Forensis*. Davis refers to these and to *Remarks on Medical Jurisprudence* by William Dease of Dublin, and OW Bartley of Bristol's *Treatise on Forensic Medicine or Medical Jurisprudence*. Both these Davis considers of poor quality and he makes the statement that the "first original and satisfactory work" was George Male's *Epitome of Juridical or Forensic Medicine*, published in 1816. A second edition was published in 1821. Male was a physician at Birmingham General Hospital and may be considered the father of English medical jurisprudence. However, the first course of lectures to medical students on legal medicine were given in Britain by Andrew Duncan (senior), then Professor of Physiology in Edinburgh, in 1789. These were published in 1792 as the *Heads of Lectures on Medical Jurisprudence or the Institutiones Medicinae Legalis*. Duncan's eldest son occupied the first chair of medical jurisprudence and medical police created by central government as a Regius Chair with royal patronage in 1807. Chairs were later established in Glasgow (1839) – Robert Cowan, and in Aberdeen (1857) – Francis Ogston. In England the first professor was John Gordon Smith (1773–1832) and later George Edward Male (1779–1845). Others followed later in the London medical schools. In 1856 a course in medical jurisprudence was an essential prerequisite for admission to the Faculty of Advocates in Edinburgh.

In 1813 in New York, Benjamin Rush (1745–1813), another Edinburgh medical graduate and a signatory of the Declaration of Independence, wrote on medical jurisprudence. In 1804, an Edinburgh-trained physician, JA Stringham (1775–1813), was appointed as a lecturer in medical jurisprudence at the College of Physicians and Surgeons of New York and was appointed to a Chair in 1813.

Texts on forensic medicine began to appear more rapidly with much broader content. John Gordon Smith in his book *The Principles of Forensic Medicine Systematically Arranged and Applied to British Practice*, published in 1821, stated that "Forensic Medicine – Legal, Judiciary, or Juridical Medicine – and Medical Jurisprudence are synonymous terms." **Figure 1** reproduces the forms from his book used to document information about neonatal deaths and stillborn babies. Smith refers in his Preface to the earlier books and notes: "It is but justice to mention that the American schools have outstripped us in attention to Forensic Medicine" – and he may have been referring to the work of Theodric Romeyn Beck and others. TR Beck and his brother JB Beck (both pupils of Stringham) became leaders in their field by their publications and lecturing. TR Beck published the first American textbook 2 years later.

John Gordon Smith wrote:

> Every medical practitioner being liable to a subpoena, should make it his business to know the relations of physiological and pathological principles to the facts on which he is likely to be interrogated, and likewise the principal judiciary bearings of the case. The former of these are to be found in works on Forensic Medicine; the latter in those on Jurisprudence. Alfred Taylor in his book *A Manual of Medical Jurisprudence* defined medical jurisprudence as "that science, which teaches the application of every branch of medical knowledge to the purpose of the law."

There was a clear demand for such books, and Traill's *Outlines of a Course of Lectures on Medical Jurisprudence* (published in 1840 when he was Regius Professor of Jurisprudence and Medical Police at Edinburgh) was the second edition of a book initially published in 1834. It was in Edinburgh in 1807 where the first Chair of Forensic Medicine was established in the UK, with subsequent nonprofessorial academic forensic medicine posts at Guy's Hospital and Charing Cross Hospital, London. In 1839 and 1875 respectively academic chairs of medical jurisprudence were created in Glasgow and Aberdeen.

The relevant areas of interest to forensic medicine and medical jurisprudence were gradually becoming better defined. **Table 2** summarizes the chapter contents of John Gordon Smith's 1821 text. It will be noted that almost two centuries ago much of the content is completely recognizable and relevant to forensic physicians and forensic pathologists even today. So by the end of the nineteenth century, in Europe, the UK, and America and those related jurisdictions a framework of forensic medicine was established that persists today.

## FORMS, *referred to at Page 340.*

**A.**   *Statement of the Examination of*   new-born Children, *who died* AFTER RESPIRATION.

| Sex of the Subject. | Period of Gestation when born. | Duration of Life, after Birth. | State and Appearance of the Subject. | Weight of the whole Body. | Colour of the Lungs *in situ.* | Relative Situation of the Lungs as to the Pericardium. | Weight of the Lungs alone. | Their State as to Buoyancy in Water while entire. | The same when divided. | Miscellaneous Remarks *. |
|---|---|---|---|---|---|---|---|---|---|---|
| | | | | | | | | | | |

**B.**   *Statement of the Examination of*   STILL-BORN *Children.*

| Sex. | Period of Gestation. | General State, &c. | Weight of the Body. | Colour of the Lungs *in situ.* | Relative Situation. | Weight of the Lungs. | Their State in Water when entire. | The same when divided. | Miscellaneous Remarks *. |
|---|---|---|---|---|---|---|---|---|---|
| | | | | | | | | | |

\* In this column should be recorded the state of the lungs when cut into, as to the crepitus or absence of it, and also as to hæmorrhage—with any other observations that may be furnished by peculiar cases. The result of a few such cases, accurately recorded by a number of practitioners, would be acceptable to the profession.

**Figure 1**   Copies of forms used in John Gordon Smith's 1821 text *The Principles of Forensic Medicine Systematically Arranged and Applied to British Practice*, concerning neonatal deaths and stillborn children. Reproduced from Smith JG (1821) *The Principles of Forensic Medicine Systematically Arranged*. London, UK: Thomas and George Underwood.

## Contemporary Forensic Pathology

Forensic pathology is practiced by those in general with a background in histopathology or anatomical pathology. The forensic pathologist's work is directed to assisting in predominantly judicial or legal processes by establishing manner, time, and cause of death. Their pathological skills must be supported by an ability to integrate the medical aspects of the workload with toxicological, scientific, and legal issues. Forensic pathologists are assigned a variety of names around the world, for example, legal medicine specialists, medical examiners – but all are primarily involved in the investigation of death – by the use of autopsy and associated procedures. Forensic pathologists may work in academic departments, state or government institutions, or independently. It is to be expected that their work and the reporting of their work is and is seen to be independent of any body or organization, whether police or governmental, and free from political interference. A forensic pathologist may be expected to have special knowledge in the following areas: anatomy, cytopathology, hematology, microbiology, immunology, chemical pathology, and toxicology. Many forensic pathologists around the world will also have special relationships with public health, occupational health, and community health issues, reflecting for some, the

**Table 2** Sample chapter contents of John Gordon Smith's 1821 text *The Principles of Forensic Medicine Systematically Arranged and Applied to British Practice*

Of sudden death in the healthy state
- The phenomena of death
- States of the living body resembling death
- Tests of the reality of death
- Sudden death without cause of crimination
- Sudden death from intrinsic or morbid causes

Death by personal agency or homicide
- Mineral poisons
- Vegetable poisons
- Occult poisoning
- Suffocation
- Drowning
- Hanging
- Smothering

Death by spontaneous agency or suicide

Infanticide

Questions arising from injuries done to the person not leading to the extinction of life
- Mutilation
- Rape

Disqualifications for the discharge of social or civil functions
- Mental disqualification
- Mania

Sexual identity

Personal identity

---

historical origins of the workload. Many forensic pathologists will also have workloads relating to the clinical aspects of forensic medicine.

## Contemporary Clinical Forensic Medicine

It is only in the last two decades that research and academic interest in clinical forensic medicine has become an area of much more focused interest and research. A working definition has been suggested as: "clinical forensic medicine includes all medical (healthcare) fields which may relate to legal, judicial, and police systems." In part this increased relevance relates to much wider awareness of human rights abuses and civil liberties which in turn have directed much attention to the conditions of detention of prisoners, and to the application of justice to both victim and suspect. The differing and potentially conflicting roles that a forensic physician may have when attending a prisoner or other person detained by the state or other body have been recognized by identifying three possible facets of medical care: (1) the role of medico-legal expert for a law enforcement agency, (2) the role of a treating doctor, and (3) the examination and treatment of detainees who allege that they have been mistreated by the police during their arrest,

during interrogation, or during the various stages of police custody. This conflict is well recognized by forensic physicians.

Table 3 is a summary of responses to a questionnaire on various aspects of clinical forensic medicine undertaken in late 2002/early 2003. It shows with clarity the range of different standards and procedures in a number of the most important aspects of forensic medicine and may be summarized as follows.

- A wide variety of differing patterns of clinical forensic medicine practice may be seen on an international basis – but there appears to be recognition of the need to have appropriate personnel to undertake the roles required.
- Informal/*ad hoc* arrangements to deal with medical and forensic care of detainees and victims appears to be common – often with large centers having physicians specially trained or appointed whilst rural or outlying areas are reliant on nonspecialists.
- In several countries the emphasis of care and assessment appears to be the examination and assessment of the alleged victim rather than the alleged suspect rather than there being an equality of approach – this potentially compromises justice.
- The standard of medical care of detainees in police custody is variable – although there appears to be more recognition of the human rights aspects of care of those in police custody.
- There are no international standards of practice or training – international standards are still lacking, but more countries appear to be developing national standards.
- There are apparent gaps in the investigation of police complaints in some countries – this remains the case.
- Statistics of deaths in custody are not always in the public domain – this remains the case – and the investigation of deaths in police custody may still not be independently undertaken.

## Summary

Forensic medicine arises from a long tradition of links between the law and medicine and now embraces a wide variety of needs and skills intertwining medicine, pathology, science, the law, and ethics. Each practitioner, whether clinical, pathological, or both, should be aware of their responsibilities, not only to their patient or the deceased, but to society as whole, and be able to utilize their medical expertise in the pursuit of fairness and justice within the framework of legal requirements and ethical values.

**Table 3** Responses to a questionnaire addressing various aspects of custody medicine around the world – 2003

| Question | Australia | England & Wales | Germany |
|---|---|---|---|
| Is there a formal system in your country (or state) by which the police and judicial system can get immediate access to medical and/or forensic assessment of individuals detained in police custody (prisoners)? | Yes (within the state) Two tiered system addressing general health issues and forensic medical services | Yes. Forensic physicians (forensic medical examiners) are contracted (but not generally employed) by both police and courts to undertake this. The Police & Criminal Evidence Act 1984 made particular provision for this and for prisoners to request to see a doctor. Police surgeons do not necessarily have specific forensic training or qualifications | Yes – only after a court order has been granted |
| Who examines or assesses individuals detained in police custody to determine whether they are medically fit to stay in police custody? | Nurses or medical practitioners who are employed or retained by police. | Forensic physicians, Police and Criminal Evidence Act 1984. Recent changes to PACE Codes of Practice suggest that an appropriate 'healthcare professional' may be called. | Normally a police surgeon but if not any qualified doctor. |
| If a prisoner is suspected of being under the influence of drugs or alcohol in police custody, is it usual for them to be examined by a doctor (or other healthcare professional) to determine whether they are fit to remain in custody? | Yes, but it will be largely dependent on any health concerns. (e.g abusive, intoxicated person - unlikely to access medical attention, but impaired conscious state - always access medical attention) | Yes, if there are associated health concerns, or if there is a specific need to determine fitness to interview when either intoxication or withdrawal may render an interview invalid. Specific guidelines are published on care of substance misuse detainees in police custody | Yes |
| Does your country/state have specific codes/ laws/statutes or regulations that make provision for the welfare of individuals in police custody? | Yes | Yes | Yes |
| Who undertakes the forensic medical examination and assessment of alleged *victims* of sexual assault? | Forensic Medical Officers | Forensic physicians or sexual offence examiners or doctors employed within specialist sexual offences units | Either a gynaecologist or a medicolegal doctor |
| Who undertakes the forensic medical examination and assessment of alleged *perpetrators* of sexual assault? | Forensic Medical Officers | Forensic physicians | Medicolegal doctor |

| Hong Kong | India | Israel | Malaysia |
|---|---|---|---|
| Yes. The formal and generic mechanism is for the individual to be taken to an Emergency Department of a nearby hospital. Rarely they may be sent for a specific purpose to a specialist forensic doctor | Yes. Under a Section of the Criminal Procedure Code (Cr. P.C.), a police officer can immediately bring an arrested person to a doctor for examination. If the arrested person is a female, only a female registered medical practitioner can examine her. The accused/ detained person can himself contact the doctor and have himself examined. | Yes | No organised forensic clinical services available. Subjecting the detainees for examination is at the discretion of the agencies. If the need arises, usually doctors who have no training in clinical forensic medicine undertake such examinations. In larger institutions senior doctors and at times forensic pathologists may examine them. |
| Currently the duty police officer looks and asks if medical attention is required. Most duty officers are quite liberal in referring the individuals to the Emergency Department. | A Government doctor | Police surgeons | Generally not unless they become ill. Any government doctor in the nearest hospital may undertake such an examination. |
| Yes, they will most certainly be sent to the Emergency Department. Registered addicts, will occasionally be taken to a Methadone Clinic if they are suffering from withdrawal. | Yes | Yes | Not routinely |
| There are generic guidelines for all in custody none specific to the police. | The Protection of Human Rights Act 1993, stipulates detailed provisions regarding this. | Yes | Yes. 'Inspector General's Standing Order' |
| Forensic pathologists/doctors mainly. Accident & Emergency doctors occasionally and family planning doctors. The latter when the victims do not wish to report the incident to police | Different centres have different protocols (eg in this institution, gynaecologists – mainly females) | Forensic pathologists | In major hospitals there may be fixed protocols. Some forensic physicians, primary care physicians, emergency medicine physicians and gynaecologists undertake such examinations. In smaller hospitals non-specialist physicians do the examinations. In some cases forensic pathologists. |
| Forensic pathologists/doctors mainly. | Different centres have different protocols (in this institution, forensic medicine specialists). A bizarre situation, where the victim goes to the gynaecology department, while the accused in the same case comes to us | Forensic pathologists | See above |

Continued

| Question | Netherlands | Nigeria | Scotland | Serbia |
|---|---|---|---|---|
| Is there a formal system in your country (or state) by which the police and judicial system can get immediate access to medical and/or forensic assessment of individuals detained in police custody (prisoners)? | Yes | Yes (for medical reasons) dependent on the availability of the physician. | Yes. Police retain services of doctors not all necessarily qualified in clinical forensic medicine. | Yes – via the public healthy system. Generally for treatment purposes. Also, if considered necessary for evidence collection (by the investigator appointed under the Criminal Procedure Act – CPA) the police will refer to prosecutor in charge seeking for his/her permission to call a forensic doctor. |
| Who examines or assesses individuals detained in police custody to determine whether they are medically fit to stay in police custody? | Generally speaking: Public Health Officers, who are qualified in clinical forensic medicine | Any doctor attached to Prison Services, the Police or doctors in the local Hospitals, depending on who is available. | Forensic physicians – these doctors are not employees. Nursing schemes have been mooted but not yet been implemented | If there is an obvious health problem, or if they have certain diseases that need medical attention, police will take them to a public health care facility or, in the case of emergency, call ambulance. |
| If a prisoner is suspected of being under the influence of drugs or alcohol in police custody, is it usual for them to be examined by a doctor (or other healthcare professional) to determine whether they are fit to remain in custody? | Yes | No | Only when a need is established or the prisoner requests medical assistance. Profound intoxication or suspicion of head injury would be an indication for examination | Intoxicated detainees may be requested to provide a blood or other appropriate samples for analysis. The request can be refused. Samples are arranged outside police premises, usually in the public health institutions. |
| Does your country/state have specific codes/laws/statutes or regulations that make provision for the welfare of individuals in police custody? | Yes | Not aware of any | Local procedures for each police force based on central guidance, but there is no statute | No |
| Who undertakes the forensic medical examination and assessment of alleged *victims* of sexual assault? | Generally Public Health Officers, qualified in clinical forensic medicine | Primary care physicians (GPs) and Medical Officers in local hospitals. | Usually Forensic physician, some may be admitted to hospital and b examined by hospital staff. | There is no standard procedure for the examination of alleged victims of sexual assault. There are no protocols for the examination of victims, or for collection of forensic samples . |
| Who undertakes the forensic medical examination and assessment of alleged *perpetrators* of sexual assault? | Generally speaking: Public Health Officers, who are qualified in clinical forensic medicine | See above | Forensic physician (although experienced police surgeons are not readily available in some sparsely populated areas, and the inexperienced are often reluctant to embark on such an examination). | In practical terms rarely done although the CPA allows examination of alleged perpetrators of any crime (including sexual assault) for forensic purposes even without their consent if the examination itself is not considered harmful for them. |

| South Africa | Spain | Sweden | Switzerland | US |
|---|---|---|---|---|
| Yes, but not in all the parts of the country. | Yes, any individual detained in police custody has the right to be examined by a doctor. In certain cases has the right to have a forensic assessment by the Forensic Surgeon Corps of the Ministry of Justice. | Yes. | Yes. | Yes. Medical assessment is performed by a nurse or family physician at the jail. Forensic issues can be addressed by the on-call clinical forensic nurse if the detained individuals are not in the jail but in the hospital. |
| Not always – psychiatrist in some cases. | When a person is under arrest (without having being put under regulation), he asks for being examined by a doctor, he is usually transferred to the Spanish Health Public System doctors. The forensic surgeon takes part, exceptionally. | So called "police doctors", who usually are general practitioners. | The "prison doctor": either a doctor of internal medicine of University Hospital or in rural regions the district physician (acute cases) A forensic doctor of the Institute of Legal Medicine of the University of Zürich (not urgent cases, "chronic cases") | Jail nurse or physician (family medicine trained) |
| Yes, but not common practice. | Yes, he is often to be examined and even blood samples to be extracted (with his previous consent) if the prisoner is involved in some aggression, homicide or car driving, for example. | Yes. In most custody suites a nurse is employed nurse who will call a doctor. | Yes, see above | Examined by the jail nurse 24 hours/day or by jail physician 0800 to 1700. After that prisoner would be transferred to the University Hospital Emergency Department. |
| Yes | Yes, there are specific rules in Constitution and in the Penal Code. | Not known. | Yes | Yes |
| Medical practitioner | A forensic surgeon (médico forense) and a gynaecologist (if the victim is female) or a proctologist (if the victim is male). | The police are free to engage any doctor to do this. In cases of assault on adults the examination is undertaken by specialists in forensic medicine in a small fraction of the cases. A specialist in paediatric medicine or surgery always examines children, often but not always, together with a specialist in forensic medicine. | Physicians of Institute of Legal Medicine of University of Zurich (District Physician) Physicians of University Department of Gynecology, University Hospital Zurich | Sexual Assault Nurse Examiners, Emergency Department physicians |
| Medical practitioner | A forensic surgeon. | Similar to the procedures of adult victims | Physicians of Institute of Legal Medicine of University of Zurich (District Physician) | Sexual Assault Nurse Examiners, Emergency Department physicians |

Continued

**Table 3**  Continued

| Question | Australia | England & Wales | Germany |
|---|---|---|---|
| In cases of sexual assault is it always possible for victim, perpetrator or both to be examined by a doctor of the same gender if that is requested? | Generally, yes. | Generally, yes – but not always possible | Yes |
| Who undertakes the forensic medical examination and assessment of alleged child victims of *sexual* assault? | Forensic Medical Officers *or* paediatricians | Forensic physicians and/or paediatricians. Ideally joint examinations (guidelines for the assessment have been issued) | Either pediatrician gynaecologist or medicolegal specialist. |
| Who undertakes the forensic medical examination and assessment of alleged child victims of *physical* assault? | Forensic Medical Officers *or* paediatricians | Forensic physicians and/or paediatricians. | Pediatrician or medicolegal specialist |
| Is there a system in your country/state whereby individuals detained in police custody who appear to have (or have) psychiatric disorder or mental health problems or learning disability – may be assessed? | Yes | Yes | Yes |
| In your country/state are there specialised units or locations where victims of sexual assault are examined or assessed? | Yes | Yes – but not full geographical coverage – tends to be in urban centres | No |
| In cases of alleged assault by police who examines *the police personnel*? | Forensic Medical Officers (report & documentation of injuries) Police Medical Officers (for any occupational health and safety issues) | Forensic physicians | An independent medical doctor |
| In cases of alleged assault by police who examines *the complainant*? | Forensic Medical Officers (report & documentation of injuries) | Forensic physicians | An independent medical doctor |
| In your country/state – is there a person, a body or an organisation that investigates complaints against the police? | Yes | Yes. The Police Complaints Authority. Replaced by the Independent Police Complaints Commission (IPCC) in 2004 | State Prosecutor |
| If your country has a person, a body or an organisation that investigates complaints against the police, a) is it completely independent of the police? – and b) who funds it? | a) Two bodies Police - Internal Investigations Government body - Ombudsman's Office b) Government funded | a) the PCA is independent of the police. Police forces also appoint other police forces to investigate b) the Government | a) Yes b) Judicial system |

| Hong Kong | India | Israel | Malaysia |
|---|---|---|---|
| No, There is currently only 1 full-time female forensic doctor able to do this. | Yes, if requested, a doctor of the same gender would be arranged. This would generally apply only to the victim (female gynaecologists examine the victim anyway) The wishes of the accused are not always observed. It is highly unusual for a female to examine a male accused. | Not always | It may be accommodated if possible |
| Forensic pathologists/physicians, pediatricians, obstetricians and gynaecologists doctors. Sometimes jointly. | Female children – gynaecologist, preferably female (which is generally the case anyway) Male children – forensic personnel of either sex | Forensic pathologists and paediatricians | Wherevever possible by paediatricians or gynaecologists. Smaller hospitals by non-specialist physicians. |
| Pediatricians. Sometimes forensic pathologists/physicians. Sometimes jointly. | Forensic medicine departments | Forensic pathologists and paediatricians | Paediatrician smaller hospitals by non-specialist physicians |
| Yes. They are likely to be referred to psychiatrists or in the case of learning disability to social workers and/or clinical psychologists. | Yes, in theory. This may not be strictly observed, until and unless there is a court order which may need to be obtained by relatives. | Yes | Yes |
| There are purpose built video interview and medical examination suites. These tend to be used only when there is a strong likelihood of prosecution. Often done in pediatric wards. | No | Yes | Some major hospitals have 'One stop centers' with protocols for managements, both short term and long terms. |
| The majority are examined by emergency medicine physicians. Some are examined by forensic pathologists/ physicians | No experience of this – if needed probably forensic pathologist | Forensic pathologist | Any available physician |
| The majority are examined by emergency medicine specialists. Some are examined by forensic pathologists/ physicians | Forensic pathologist | Forensic pathologist | See above |
| Yes. All complaints are handled by the Complaints Against Police Office (CAPO) (part of the police) but all cases are then reviewed by a statutory board the Independent Police Complaints Council (IPCC). | Yes. Via the Police Commissioner. Or to the magistrate. Probably rarely used. | Yes | There are human rights groups. Police also conduct investigations against their own staff |
| a) CAPO – No. Police establishment b) IPCC – Yes. Funded by taxpayer | a) Police Commissioner is from the police stream itself. Magistrates are completely independent of the police. b) Government. | a) Yes b) Ministry of Justice | b) there are NGOs who back the victims and provide support. Police conducts its own investigations. Outcome of the investigation depends on various factors (same in many countries) |

Continued

| Question | Netherlands | Nigeria | Scotland | Serbia |
|---|---|---|---|---|
| In cases of sexual assault is it always possible for victim, perpetrator or both to be examined by a doctor of the same gender if that is requested? | Usually but not always | No | Not always, but every effort is made to comply with an examinee's wishes | There is no statutory provision that regulates free choice of either victim or perpetrator to be examined by a doctor of preferred (same) gender. |
| Who undertakes the forensic medical examination and assessment of alleged child victims of *sexual* assault? | Generally speaking: Public Health Officers qualified in clinical forensic medicine | Same as above | In the larger centres joint paediatric/forensic physician examinations common. Others centres it varies. | Physicians with forensic training are rarely involved in initial examination and assessment. Forensic physicians tend to get involved at a later stage of investigation. |
| Who undertakes the forensic medical examination and assessment of alleged child victims of *physical* assault? | Generally speaking: Public Health Officers, qualified in clinical forensic medicine | Same as above. | Mostly paediatricians but some evidence is based on findings of family physicians | Formerly. Few forensic pathologists were involved Situation is somewhat improved, but still poor cooperation between clinicians and forensic doctors. |
| Is there a system in your country/state whereby individuals detained in police custody who appear to have (or have) psychiatric disorder or mental health problems or learning disability – may be assessed? | Yes | Yes | Variable picture. Screening by forensic physician. On call psychiatrist or mental health team in some areas. No s12 procedure. Some courts have regular pretrial psychiatric attendance | Not when in police custody (within 48 hours after arrest). If suspect is detained on the order of the investigative judge, then may be examined by psychiatrist and/or psychologist upon need. |
| In your country/state are there specialised units or locations where victims of sexual assault are examined or assessed? | Sometimes but not always | No | Specialised units widely available, often on police premises. Children usually in hospital | No |
| In cases of alleged assault by police who examines *the police personnel*? | Generally speaking: Public Health Officers, qualified in clinical forensic medicine | Physician attached to the Police Service - could be a uniformed officer. | Forensic physician (unless urgent transfer to hospital) | Physicians working for public health care system. |
| In cases of alleged assault by police who examines *the complainant*? | Generally speaking: Public Health Officers, qualified in clinical forensic medicine | Medical Officer in the local hospital; (if he is lucky to have the opportunity and guts to complain) | Forensic physician (unless urgent transfer to hospital) | See above |
| In your country/state – is there a person, a body or an organisation that investigates complaints against the police? | Yes | A Tribunal would be set up if the issue is considered to be of significant national interest. | The Procurator Fiscal (public prosecutor – legally qualified civil servants). Complaints must be referred by police where any criminality is alleged | There is a Commission for Complaints within the police services as a first tier. Within the Ministry of Interior there is a second tier. Victims of police assault can also report directly to the Court of Law in accordance with the Penal Code, and CPA. |
| If your country has a person, a body or an organisation that investigates complaints against the police, a) is it completely independent of the police? – and b) who funds it? | a) yes (directly under the national prosecutor's office) b) Ministry Of Justice | a) No b) Government | a) No. Complaints are investigated by police unless criminality is suspected, when immediate report to regional Procurator Fiscal is mandatory; b) cases taken by the Procurator Fiscal are centrally funded | a) No. As part of the police and Ministry of Interior the Commission, on both tiers, is not independent from the police. |

| South Africa | Spain | Sweden | Switzerland | US |
|---|---|---|---|---|
| Yes | No. It depends on the doctor on duty. | No. | Yes | No. If available, an attempt will be made to have same sex examiner but not always possible. |
| Medical practitioner | A forensic surgeon and a paediatrician. | As for adults. | ≤16 years: female gynecologist at University Children Hospital >16 years as adult | Emergency department physician |
| Medical practitioner | Forensic surgeon and a forensic paediatrician. | As for adult | ≤16 years: doctors at University Children Hospital (Trauma-X group) >16 years: doctors of Institute of Legal Medicine of University of Zurich (District Physician) | Forensic nurse and forensic physician |
| Yes | Yes. If mental health problems apparent case is remitted to a judge and is examined by a forensic surgeon and a psychiatrist. | It's part of the "police doctors" duties, but many custodies do have access to psychiatric consultants. | Those who have known disorders are followed by a specialized forensic psychiatric psychological service. Others are reported by the guards | Yes |
| Yes | Victims of sexual assault, are examined in gynaecology or paediatrics units of large hospitals. | No | Yes, but only in some cities. In other cases system as with responses above | Yes |
| Medical practitioner | A forensic surgeon as member of the Ministry of Justice (completely independent of the Police) | Advised that a specialist in forensic medicine should do it. | Physicians of Institute of Legal Medicine, University of Zurich (District Physician) | Emergency department physician or police department's physician |
| Medical practitioner | A forensic surgeon and a gynaecologist or an urologist. | See above | Physicians of Institute of Legal Medicine, University of Zurich (District Physician) | Emergency department physician, forensic nurse or forensic physician |
| Independent Complaint Directorate (ICD) | The correspondent court of first instance (the one on duty at the moment when the facts are reported) | Yes | Yes | Internal Affairs unit of police department |
| a) Yes, (seemingly) b) international organizations | a) Yes. The Police are subordinate to the Court of First Instance. b) The Judge, the judicial Secretary, the district Attorney and the forensic surgeon. | a) No. It's a special unit within the police. b) State | a) Yes b) the state of Zurich | No |

Continued

**Table 3**  Continued

| Question | Australia | England & Wales | Germany |
|---|---|---|---|
| In your country/state, is there person, a body or an organisation that investigates deaths of individuals whilst in police custody? | Yes | Yes – the PCA (A IPCC - from 2004) | State prosecutor and Forensic Legal medicine |
| If the answer to the previous question is yes – a) is that person, body or organisation independent of the police, and b) who funds that organisation? | a) Three bodies Police - Homicide Squad & Internal Investigations Coroner's Office Ombudsman's Office b) Government | a) Yes b) Government | a) Yes b) State |
| In your country/state are statistics published about deaths that have taken place in police custody? | Yes | Yes | Yes |
| If the answer to the previous question is yes – where, when and how often are those statistics published and do they include an analysis of cause of death (e.g., self-harm, drugs, other violence)? | Coroners Report - all cases Australian Institute of Criminology - annually Complete analysis in all cases. | Annual report of the PCA with breakdown of causes and circumstances of death | Granzow, Püschel, Arch-Kriminol. 1998 Jan-Feb; 201(1-2): 1-10 Includes an analysis of cause of death |
| Does your country/state have a recognised (recognised by your medical professional body) specialty or sub-specialty of medicine for those working in a) clinical forensic medicine or b) forensic pathology? | a) No b) Yes | a) No b) Yes (as part of the discipline of pathology) | a) No - only in some states in Germany b) Yes |
| Can you supply with the details a) of the main organisation that represents the interests of such practitioners and b) the number of practitioners represented? | a) Royal Australian College of Pathologists b) Approx 50 | a) Association of Forensic Physicians (approx 1000) b) British Association in Forensic Medicine (approx 300 – only 40 or so full-time) | a) German Society of Legal Medicine b) ca. 400 |

| Hong Kong | India | Israel | Malaysia |
|---|---|---|---|
| Yes, The Coroner with a mandatory inquest held in public and with a jury. However, the investigations are conducted by the police. | Yes, the magistrate does it. Police cannot investigate such deaths. | Yes | All deaths in custody are subjected to inquest by the magistrate according to Malaysian Criminal Procedure Code |
| a) The Coroner – Yes – Funded by Judiciary b) The Police – No | a) Yes, independent of the police b) Government pays the salary | a) Yes b) Ministry of Justice | a) magistrate is independent b) there is no fulltime coroner, magistrate acts as the coroner in normal deaths except custodial deaths where the magistrate acts directly. Most of the deaths are investigated by the police, coroner does not play a visible role. Inquest system needs improvement. |
| Yes. In the Coroners Annual Report | Yes, There is a publication called "Crime Statistics", which I think is published by the Home Ministry | No | Police HQ maintains all data |
| The number of occurrences, the custodian department and the verdicts of the inquests are summarised but no details of death itself. | Yearly publication. The figures may be inaccurate or incomplere. | No | Not known whether it is regularly published, but data available |
| a) Yes & No b) Yes. There is laid out training for forensic pathology under the Hong Kong College of Pathologists which includes clinical forensic medicine aspects. There is also statutory specialty registration but again only in forensic pathology. | a) There is just one super-specialty called forensic medicine, which caters for both (a) clinical forensic medicine as well as (b) forensic pathology | a) Yes b) Yes | a) No b) No |
| a) N/A b) Hong Kong College of Pathologists, Forensic Pathology Panel – 18 | a) Indian Academy of Forensic Medicine (IAFM) b) About 500 people are represented. For more information on IAFM, please visit its website at http://www.fortunecity.com/campus/electrical/314/iafm.html | a) Israel Association of Pathologists b) 12 | a) Hospital forensic pathologists come under the Ministry of Health. Others are in the University Departments of Pathology. Forensic Unit comes under pathology. Clinical forensic medicine is mostly a neglected subject |

Continued

| Question | Netherlands | Nigeria | Scotland | Serbia |
|----------|-------------|---------|----------|--------|
| In your country/state, is there person, a body or an organisation that investigates deaths of individuals whilst in police custody? | Yes | A uniformed police pathologist, rarely a hospital pathologist and in some cases a Medical Officer. | All investigations are under supervision of Procurator Fiscal; there is always a public 'fatal accident inquiry' before a judge | In the case of death in police custody, but also during the police action or allegedly as a result of police action, or while person is in penitentiary, District Court that has territorial jurisdiction should order full postmortem, as well as other investigations. |
| If the answer to the previous question is yes – a) is that person, body or organisation independent of the police, and b) who funds that organisation? | a) Yes | a) It depends on who does the case. b) Government | All investigations are under supervision of PF; there is always a public 'fatal accident inquiry' before a judge | a) Yes, it is a Court of Law. b) State and Government. |
| In your country/state are statistics published about deaths that have taken place in police custody? | Yes | No | | Not aware of any statistics. |
| If the answer to the previous question is yes – where, when and how often are those statistics published and do they include an analysis of cause of death (e.g., self-harm, drugs, other violence)? | The prosecutor. receives complete autopsy results | Not applicable | | N/A |
| Does your country/state have a recognised (recognised by your medical professional body) specialty or sub-specialty of medicine for those working in a) clinical forensic medicine or b) forensic pathology? | a) No b) No | a) Yes b) Yes Recognition (by the Nigerian Medical Council and Postgraduate Medical College) is strictly as a subspecialty of pathology. | a) as for England & Wales – only that the craft is recognised by British Medical Association b) Yes – as part of pathology | a) Yes b) Yes Specialisation is designated as 'Forensic Medicine' covering both issues. There are no separate specialisations. The model was imported from Germany and France at the beginning of the last century when the first medical faculties were founded in the country. |
| Can you supply with the details a) of the main organisation that represents the interests of such practitioners and b) the number of practitioners represented? | a) b) | a) There is no professional body that represents these very few specialists b) There are two DMJ Clin. graduates: No Forensic Pathologist (including me) is in Nigeria. | a) AFP and BMA for CFM in UK. Pathologists by BAFM and BMA – the British Medical Association has Forensic Medicine Committee b) AFP 1000 BAFM 100 | a) Yugoslav Association of Forensic Medicine b) Approximately 40-50 members. |

| South Africa | Spain | Sweden | Switzerland | US |
|---|---|---|---|---|
| Both ICD and forensic pathologist/medical practitioner | Yes. The Court of First Instance (of criminal investigation). | Yes | Yes, the district attorney and the Institute of Legal Medicine | Yes, Medical Examiner |
| a) Yes b) International Organization | a) Yes. doctors who assist individuals detained and prisoners, are specialists, totally independent of police. b) It is funded by health system doctors (Health Public National System), forensic surgeons (Ministry of Justice) and prisons doctors (Ministry of Justice). | a) Yes. b) The department of justice. | a) Yes (Department of Justice) b) the state of Zurich | a) yes b) county government |
| Not aware of any statistics | No | No | No | yes |
| See above | See above | See above | In the state of Zurich: All cases are investigated by the Institute of Legal Medicine to establish the cause and manner of death | annually |
| a) Yes – utilising a Diploma or Masters degree b) Yes, recognised registered speciality. | a) Yes & No. Each forensic surgeon has undertaken a competitive exam in the Supreme Court - Ministry of Justice. Some, also are specialist in legal and forensic medicine granted by the Ministry of Education. The Ministry of Justice has recognized both for forensic surgeons working in Institutes of Legal Medicine. | a) Yes. b) Yes. | a) Yes b) Yes. The specialist title of ''Legal Medicine'' covers both sub-specialities. | a) no (courts have recognized CFM as a medical specialty) b) yes |
| a) Department of Health in collaboration with international organizations (I have attended such a meeting). b) About 80 practitioner | Forensic surgeons form groups in some professional Associations nationwide like the Asociación Nacional de Médicos Forenses, Asociación Andaluza de Médicos Forenses, Asociación Estatal de Médicos Forenses, Asociación Gallega de Médicos Forenses., etc. About 300 forensic surgeons are represented by those Associations. The number of licensed medicolegal-experts in Spain is currently 450 and acting medico-legal experts about 150. | a) The National Forensic Board, under the Department of Justice is responsible for all examinations in the fields of forensic pathology (death investigations), forensic psychiatry, forensic medicine and forensic genetics. All specialists who are active in these fields are employed by this organisation. Competition in these fields is free but does, with the exception for investigations of living victims and perpetrators, not occur. b) There are approximately 25 specialists in forensic medicine in Sweden today. | a) Swiss Society of Legal Medicine (www.legalmed.ch) b) 40 | a) NAME, National Association of Medical Examiners b) 400 |

Continued

**Table 3** Continued

| Question | Australia | England & Wales | Germany |
|---|---|---|---|
| Can you give a rough estimate of a) the population of your country/state, b) the number of medical practitioners working in clinical forensic medicine, c) forensic pathology? | a) State - 5 Million b) ~50 c) ~10 | a) 60 million b) ~2000 c) ~40 | a) Germany 80 Million/NRW State 16 Mill. b) Germany 150/State 50 c) Germany 250/State 50 |
| Are specific qualifications available for a) clinical forensic medicine or b) forensic pathology? | a) Yes b) Yes | a) DMJ (Clin), DFM, MMJ b) MRCPath DFM DMJ (Path) | Yes but are the same |
| Are such qualifications mandatory in order to practice in a) clinical forensic medicine or b) forensic pathology? | a) Yes in full time practice (only) b) Yes | a) No b) Yes | a) Yes b) Yes |

| Hong Kong | India | Israel | Malaysia |
|---|---|---|---|
| a) 6.5 million b) None fulltime. Over 1000 in different ways c) 18 this group does most of the criminal cases relating to clinical forensic medicine | a) 1.05 Billion b) There is no data available on it. In peripheral regions, such as small towns and villages, even general duty doctors fulfil the work of clinical forensic medicine and forensic pathology. c) same as above. | a) Six million b) Eight c) Same eight | a) 20 million b) 1 trained forensic physician c) ∼20 forensic pathologists |
| a) DMJ (Clin)(Lond.) b) DMJ (Path)(Lond.), FHKCPath, FHKAM | a) Yes, three year post-graduate course in Forensic Medicine, which can only be done by a graduate in medicine and surgery. There is an entrance test for this course. b) Same as above | a) No b) Yes | a) No b) Master of Pathology (Forensic) – 4 year course |
| a) No b) Yes | a) No, as stated above, they are not mandatory. Although a great prestige is accorded to the report of people who have such a qualification. b) same as above. | a) No b) Yes | a) and b) ordinary doctors undertake a large part of routine autopsies and clinical cases. Depending on the availability, difficult or complicated cases are handled by specialists. |

| Question | Netherlands | Nigeria | Scotland | Serbia |
|---|---|---|---|---|
| Can you give a rough estimate of a) the population of your country/state, b) the number of medical practitioners working in clinical forensic medicine, c) forensic pathology? | a) 16 million b) ~350 c) ~5 | a) ~120 million b) One part time; a uniformed Police Officer c) Six- all currently outside Nigeria; one of the six has retired. | a) ~5.25 million; b) ~150 and c) ~12 (these are mainly university staff). | a) 7.5 million b) ~40–50 c) ~40–50 |
| Are specific qualifications available for a) clinical forensic medicine or b) forensic pathology? | a) yes b) yes | a) All trained in the UK, Germany and USA. There are no local training programmes. | All UK qualifications e.g., DMJ DFM (not compulsory); pathologists MRCPath DFM DMJ and one available from the RCP (Ed) | Not qualifications but training program |
| Are such qualifications mandatory in order to practice in a) clinical forensic medicine or b) forensic pathology? | a) not yet b) not officially | a) No b) Locally trained histopathologists and medical officers unfortunately often assume this role. | a) No b) Yes | a) No b) Yes. |

The author is grateful to the following people for their assistance taking their time to answer the questions put to them – any errors of
David Wells, Steve Craven, Kadenathan Nadesan, Jose Blanco Pampin, Bernd Brinkmann, Walter Bär, Barend Cohen, Tzipi Kahana,

| South Africa | Spain | Sweden | Switzerland | US |
|---|---|---|---|---|
| a) 42 Million b) ~180 (majority of them are part-time basis) c) ~25 | a) 0.5 million b) ~9 c) ~9 | a) Nine million b) 35 (10 non-specialists in training) c) FM = FP in Sweden | a) 7.2 million b) and c) 70 (most of us do both clinical forensic medicine and forensic pathology) | a) 4 million in state b) 15 c) 14 |
| a) No, but being established b) Yes | The are national test (competitive examinations on Supreme Court-Ministry of Justice) to be admitted in the National Corps of Forensic surgeons (Cuerpo Nacional de Médicos Forenses). The professionals are the ones who carry out both clinical forensic medicine and forensic pathology. | a) Yes b) Yes | a) and b) : Yes qualifications that cover both fields | a) no b) yes |
| a) No b) Yes, but still unqualified are working. | a) Yes b) Yes | a) Yes b) Yes | a) Yes (but only at University Institutes) b) Yes (but only at University Institutes) | a) no b) yes |

interpretation or abbreviations are the authors: David McLay, John Obafunwa, Antti Penttila, William Smock, Anil Aggrawal, Philip Beh, IngemarThiblin, Djordje Alempijevic, Banwari Meel.

## Further Reading

Amundsen DW, Ferngren GB (1977) The physician as an expert witness in Athenian Law. *Bull History of Medicine* 51: 202–213.

Amundsen DW, Ferngren GB (1979) Forensic role of physicians in Roman law. *Bulletin of the History of Medicine* 53: 39–56.

Brittain RP (1967) Origins of legal medicine: Roman law – *Lex Duodecim Tabularum. MedicoLegal Journal* 35(2): 71–72.

Chaiullé SE (1949) Origin and progress of medical jurisprudence 1776–1876. *Journal of Criminal Law and Criminology* 40: 4.

Clark M, Crawford C (1994) *Legal Medicine in History.* Cambridge, UK: Cambridge University Press.

Editorial (1993) Three-faced practice: doctors and police custody. *The Lancet* 341: 1245–1247.

Forbes TR (1985) *Surgeons at the Bailey: English Forensic Medicine to 1878.* New Haven, CT: Yale University Press.

Guy WA (1844) *Principles of forensic medicine.* London: Henry Renshaw.

Hunter W (1783) *On the Uncertainty of the Signs of Murder in the Case of Bastard Children.* London.

Payne-James JJ (1994) Clinical forensic medicine. *Journal of Clinical Forensic Medicine* 1: 1.

Payne-James JJ (1997) *Questionnaire for lecture 'Global Clinical Forensic Medicine', 4th Annual Clinical Forensic Medicine Postgraduate Conference.* Louisville, KT.

Payne-James JJ, Busuttil A (2003) History of forensic medicine. In: Payne-James JJ, Busuttil A, Smock W (eds.) *Forensic Medicine: Clinical and Pathological Aspects.* Greenwich Medical Media: London.

Smith JG (1821) *The Principles of Forensic Medicine Systematically Arranged and Applied to British Practice.* London: Thomas and George Underwood.

Traill TS (1840) *Outlines of a Course of Lectures on Medical Jurisprudence,* 2nd edn. Edinburgh, UK: Adam and Charles Black.

# HISTORY OF TORTURE

**M Peel**, Medical Foundation for the Care of Victims of Torture, London, UK

## Introduction

Colloquially speaking, torture is the deliberate infliction of severe physical or psychological pain. As such, it includes domestic and elder violence, child abuse, and criminal torture following kidnapping. It encompasses physical forms of torture such as beating, burning, cutting, and suspending. Psychological torture includes threats, humiliation, mock execution, and witnessing others being tortured. Torture may have a sexual component which ranges from enforced nudity to rape. It is usually associated with detention, legal or otherwise, and conditions are often appalling, adding to the trauma. The Rome Statute of the International Criminal Court (article 7.2e) uses the phrase "in the custody or under the control of the accused" to demonstrate that torture can be committed beyond a situation of simple detention. The irony is that the perpetrator is usually someone who has a duty to protect the victim.

Because of the victim's powerlessness, torture always has a psychological component, and often a physical component. The psychological pain is also frequently associated with losing the ability to trust, and a belief in the world as a just place, as well as feelings of guilt when others are tortured as well. Sometimes perpetrators intend to destroy the psyche of the victim, but the psychological damage is often an unintended consequence of creating fear through physical abuse.

For the purposes of forensic medicine, the term is generally restricted to situations in which the torture is perpetrated by a person acting on behalf of a state (the perpetrator, known as a state agent) or a *de facto* state. A *de facto* state is, for example, a rebel group in effective control of territory, that assumes the authority to arrest, detain, and punish. The United Nations Convention Against Torture and Other Cruel, Inhuman or Degrading Treatment or Punishment 1984 (UNCAT) requires that, to fall within the definition of torture, the act must be committed by or with the consent of a public official, even where that consent appears to be implicit – for example, where state officials "turn a blind eye," or fail to investigate an offence. The act must be deliberate and aimed at that individual, rather than an act of random violence. There are no circumstances in which a state can justify torture, even in an emergency, which is why states are keen to deny allegations.

International conventions also stress that the act must be purposeful. UNCAT says that it must be for such purposes as obtaining a confession, punishing, intimidating, or coercing that person or a third party. The phrase "such purposes as" means that this list is not exhaustive. The Inter-American Convention to Prevent and Punish Torture 1985 uses the phrase "or for any other purpose." Purpose means that the state had a reason for committing the offence. It must not be confused with the motive of the individual perpetrator. For example, rape in detention by guards is a form of torture. The motive (of the perpetrator) will probably be a mixture of power, lust, and a desire to humiliate, whereas the purpose (of the authorities) in condoning the act is generally to intimidate or coerce the victims and others. Acts causing severe pain and suffering that do not have this purpose may still be considered by courts to be inhuman and/or degrading treatment.

## Torture in the Past

### Early History of Torture

Plato surmises that the earliest societies were communities that settled into an agricultural life. They were attacked by warrior tribes who, on defeating the community, set themselves up as its oligarchic rulers. They defined the class structure with themselves at the top, and slaves, mostly those who had been defeated in war, at the base. As Greek society developed, independent judges were called on to adjudicate in disputes between families, and rules of evidence were established. Someone from a free family had a reputation and status to lose, and so his word could be trusted (as could, to a lesser extent, her word). However, the evidence of a slave was considered to be unreliable, and had therefore to be extracted under torture.

This rationale continued into the early Roman times, when it slowly became extended in two ways. First, the scope of those who could be tortured was extended to the lower grades in society who were not slaves. Second, anyone could be tortured in cases of alleged treason. As the power of the state became centralized in a single person, the crimes of treason and lèse-majesté (disrespect to the ruler) became merged, and a wide range of accusations were permitted to be investigated using torture, irrespective of the social status of the accused. Thus, torture also began to be used to intimidate those who might otherwise dissent against totalitarian rule.

Methods of torture included beatings with rods and whips, the use of primitive frames in which major joints were distended, and the crushing of individuals under piles of stones. Roman law distinguished between *quaestio*, which was the criminal judicial process, incorporating torture, and *tormentum*, the aggravated death penalty, although in practice the difference between these two was not clear. It was recognized that slaves often died during the *quaestio* (perhaps to prevent them retracting the statement once the torture was over), but this was not the purpose of the exercise.

Jurists have been aware of the unreliability of information gained from torture at least since the time of Aristotle. Lawyers are recorded variously as saying, on the one hand, that information gathered through torture was reliable if the torture had been conducted "properly," and on the other hand, that under torture all but the strongest would give whatever information the interrogator wanted to hear – and that the strongest would die rather than give out the wanted information. The *Digest of Justinian*, a third-century collection of older jurisprudence, states:

> It was declared by the imperial constitutions that while confidence should not always be reposed in torture, it ought not be rejected as absolutely unworthy of it, as the evidence obtained is weak and dangerous, and inimical to the truth; for most persons, either through their power of endurance, or through the severity of the torment, so despise suffering that the truth can in no way be extorted from them. Others are so little able to suffer that they prefer to lie rather than to endure the question, and hence it happens that they make confessions of different kinds, and they not only implicate themselves, but others as well.

## Medieval and Renaissance Periods

At the beginning of the twelfth century in Europe, criminal accusations and disputes were settled by oath, ordeal, and trial by combat, on the grounds that God would ensure the success of those in the right. As judicial systems developed, means were required of providing objective proof of guilt, either for a judge sitting alone or alongside a jury. Although there were other "partial proofs," the only conclusive proof was either from two eyewitnesses or a confession. In this context, confession became the most important proof, "the queen of proofs," in both canon and lay courts, especially when the penalty was death – which was the case in a large number of crimes.

Torture therefore returned to the legal arena, although less so in England than in the rest of Europe.

It was used principally on the accused rather than witnesses. Confessions were supposed to be voluntary, not coerced, and should be repeated outside the torture room (but with the threat of further torture if the confession was retracted). Torture could be used to show that the accused had information that could be known only by the criminal. A credible threat of torture helped priests "persuade" people of the importance of confession before a good Christian death. Again there was a class divide. Those whose oaths could be trusted did not need to undergo torture, only those of low social class or with a bad reputation. It was not thought to be unjust to cause severe physical pain to someone on a mere accusation, as God would help the just to resist. Anyway, it was believed that, as the victim had brought him/herself to the attention of the authorities, he/she must have done something wrong, so the pain of torture was not completely undeserved.

Nevertheless, there was disquiet. Many quoted St Augustine, who in the fourth century had written in *The City of God*:

> What shall I say of torture applied to the accused himself? He is tortured to discover whether he is guilty, so that, though innocent, he suffers most undoubted punishment for a crime that is still doubtful, not because it is proved that he committed it, but it is not ascertained that he did not commit it ... For if he has chosen ... to quit this life rather than to endure any longer such tortures, he declares that he has committed the crime which in fact he has not committed.

The psychological aspect of torture has always been recognized, with grandiose machines being made in classical times intended as much to frighten as to hurt. This was systematized in the Spanish Inquisition, which started in 1478. There were four separate stages. In the first, the victim was threatened with torture and the intended means described. In the second stage he/she was shown the torture equipment. In the third, he/she was attached to it. Only in the fourth stage was the equipment used.

The legal constraints on torture were well known, but it was also recognized that they were in practice largely ignored. A lot depended on the character of the judges, who were highly variable. That torture was an effective way of gaining confessions was acknowledged, but the quality of those confessions was unclear. Guy Fawkes, accused of instigating the English gunpowder plot against James I and parliament, was tortured in 1605–1606. The change in his signatures before and after the torture testifies to the physical and psychological damage done to him. He confessed and named his co-conspirators. Recent historical study suggests that, although they were definitely the people that the Lord Chancellor wanted to prosecute, not all of them were likely to have had any significant role in the conspiracy.

### Enlightenment Thinkers

The "abuse" of torture by the *anciens régimes* of Europe was one of their great criticisms during the enlightenment. Torture had been used to intimidate, oppress, and to gain false confessions. There were many cases published in which the crime confessed could not have been committed by the accused, or had not even happened at all. The church was no longer considered to have the right to punish heresy, witchcraft, and other religious crimes. Torture was considered to be the greatest human rights abuse by writers such as Cesare Beccaria in 1764. The abolition of torture was one of the great successes of this period. Governments abolished torture as other means of investigation replaced confession, and new, less severe forms of punishment augmented the death penalty and mutilation. In 1874, Victor Hugo announced that "torture has ceased to exist." Sadly, officially sanctioned torture was to return to Europe within less than 50 years.

### Other Societies

Throughout the centuries torture has not been confined to Europe. For example, ancient Egyptian and Persian societies used violence to discourage rebellion. Although Islamic law does not recognize the validity of confession obtained by coercion, the Ottoman empire employed torture throughout its existence. In Japan there were prescribed forms of torture to gain confessions in criminal cases until they were abolished in 1879.

## Torture in the Recent Past

Widely accepted allegations of torture have been widespread since the end of the Second World War. It has been said that the prohibition of torture under international human rights law is so widely accepted because virtually every nation state has accused another of the practice. Some of the best-documented examples are described below. However, there are many other examples worldwide that have not been so well documented, because they have not occurred in situations where there was such democratic accountability.

### Anticolonialism and Algeria

It had become recognized, especially in England, that torture was principally a political device and not a legal one. As states became more powerful in the nineteenth century, the political control of the police became stronger in many countries. Although this was often done in the name of "the people," there was blurring about what was in the best interests of the state, the people, and the ruling elite, with the elite often deciding, and suppressing those who disagreed. Torture returned during the First World War, and reached a zenith under totalitarian regimes, especially those of Hitler and Stalin, where torture was used to gain confessions that were politically expedient, without any interest in their veracity.

After 1945 the United Nations (UN) had determined to abolish torture again from the world. The Universal Declaration of Human Rights (1948), the Geneva Conventions (1949), the International Covenant on Civil and Political Rights (1966), UNCAT (1984), as well as a number of regional human rights conventions, all prohibit torture, and every member state of the UN accepts this principle. However, as has been the case throughout history, there remains a huge gap between the legal constraints on torture and the practice on the ground.

Torture was also used by most colonial governments to suppress local opposition. This came to light in Algeria in the mid-1950s, in reports by victims such as Henri Alleg, whose testimony was endorsed by the writer and philosopher Jean-Paul Sartre. Official accounts explained (as always) that the events were an aberration by individuals, and in particular, foreign individuals. Most notably the Wuillaume report (1955) declared that the cruelty (e.g., beatings, electric shocks, forced distension of the stomach) was not "excessive." This was all challenged, and it became clear that the torture was widespread and officially sanctioned. In his memoirs, 20 years after the events, General Jacques Massu acknowledged the torture but argued that it was necessary because of the exceptional nature of the situation.

Many commentators pointed out the large gap between humane treatment of detainees and torture. This is important because any deliberate move to treat detainees harshly ("ill treatment" rather than "torture") is nevertheless likely to end in extreme abuses. Torture starts by dehumanizing the victim, and almost immediately it dehumanizes the perpetrators as well. Reports from countries such as Greece at the time of the Colonels (1967–1974) show how military recruits were themselves humiliated and tortured in order to desensitize them to torturing others. Perpetrators always create myths that their victims are subhuman. Ultimately, torture dehumanizes the society that condones it.

### Latin America

In the 1960s and early 1970s military dictatorships were established in many of the countries of Central and South America, including Argentina, Brazil, Chile, El Salvador, and Uruguay. In these countries, abduction and torture by the authorities were systematic, and the term "disappearance" came into existence to describe those who had died during the process and whose bodies were hidden. Those who survived were often left physically and psychologically damaged by their experiences. As always, although those who justified the acts claimed that they were necessary to gain information to protect the state (or at least its rulers), the clear purpose was to intimidate any potential opposition.

Considerable state resources were put into designing and equipping clandestine detention centers, in order to maximize their impact. Training of security agents was extensive. Healthcare professionals were often involved in the torture. Experiences and techniques were shared, notably at the US-sponsored School of the Americas, which was based in Panama until 1984.

Techniques included a range of devices using electricity, including metal bedframes (*la parilla*), and modified electrical cattle prods (*picana eléctrica*). Different forms of suspension were used, and both "wet" and "dry" asphyxiation. *Teléfono* was the simultaneous slapping of both ears with the intention of permanently damaging the eardrums. Victims were often naked, with the ever-present threat of sexual assault, and beatings and electric shocks were often applied to the genitals. Rape, mostly of women but also of men, was regularly reported.

### UK versus Ireland and the "Five Techniques"

In the mid-1970s, the UK government was accused of ill-treating detainees in Northern Ireland as part of the process of interrogation. Specifically, they acknowledged that they used five techniques together to try to disorientate them. These were:

1. wall-standing: forcing detainees to remain for periods of some hours in a "stress position," described by those who underwent it as being "spread-eagled against the wall, with their fingers put high above the head against the wall, the legs spread apart and the feet back, causing them to stand on their toes with the weight of the body mainly on the fingers"
2. hooding: putting a black or navy-colored bag over the detainee's head and, at least initially, keeping it there all the time except during interrogation
3. subjection to noise: pending interrogation, the detainee was held in a room where there was a continuous loud and hissing noise
4. deprivation of sleep: pending interrogation, the detainee was deprived of sleep

5. deprivation of food and drink: subjecting the detainee to a reduced diet during his/her stay at the center and pending interrogations.

In the subsequent case at the European Court of Human Rights, the court noted:

> The five techniques were applied in combination, with premeditation and for hours at a stretch; they caused, if not actual bodily injury, at least intense physical and mental suffering to the persons subjected thereto and also led to acute psychiatric disturbances during interrogation. They accordingly fell into the category of inhuman treatment within the meaning of Article 3 [of the European Convention on Human Rights]. The techniques were also degrading since they were such as to arouse in their victims feelings of fear, anguish and inferiority capable of humiliating and debasing them and possibly breaking their physical or moral resistance.

Although at this time the court said that these techniques were inhuman and degrading but not torture, it is important to note that in 1999 the Court (in *Selmouni* v. *France*) said:

> [T]he Court considers that certain acts which were classified in the past as "inhuman and degrading treatment" as opposed to "torture" could be classified differently in future. It takes the view that the increasingly high standard being required in the area of the protection of human rights and fundamental liberties correspondingly and inevitably requires greater firmness in assessing breaches of the fundamental values of democratic societies.

From a forensic perspective, the significance of this case is that several medical examinations of the complainant showed new injuries that supported his allegations of ill treatment in the police station. The court described the duty of care in custody in this way:

> The Court considers that where an individual is taken into police custody in good health but is found to be injured at the time of release, it is incumbent on the State to provide a plausible explanation of how those injuries were caused.

### Israel and "Moderate Physical Pressure"

In 1987 the Israeli Government set up the Landau Commission to investigate the methods of interrogation used by the General Security Service. They said that it was acceptable to use "moderate physical pressure" to gain information considered necessary to preserve public safety. Such methods were described by the Commission but were never made public. Accounts sent to UNCAT (the Committee) by those who had been interrogated included the following methods, which were neither confirmed nor denied by Israel:

1. restraining in very painful conditions
2. hooding under special conditions
3. sounding of loud music for prolonged periods
4. sleep deprivation for prolonged periods
5. threats, including death threats
6. violent shaking
7. using cold air to chill.

In 1998 the Committee concluded that these methods, together or, under certain circumstances, separately, did indeed constitute torture. The following year the Israeli government passed a new basic law, proscribing such practices, although there are still criticisms that the law has not been properly implemented.

## Current Situation

After the coordinated torture of the later part of the Cold War came the mindless brutality that set the context for most torture in the 1990s. In many countries of Africa civil wars were fought over control of natural resources, with one or both sides killing, torturing, and destroying more or less randomly. Guerrilla wars were fought, for example, by the Tamils in Sri Lanka and the Kurds in Turkey, where the state suppressed entire ethnic minorities rather than just the fighters. Then there were countries such as Algeria and the former Zaire, where unpopular governments were using the state security system simply to maintain power.

Most torture comprised beatings, suspension, burns with cigarettes, cuts with bayonets, and electric shocks. Sexual assault and rape of men and women were commonplace. Healthcare professionals were rarely involved. In its annual report for the year 2000, Amnesty International described torture as occurring in 166 of the 193 member states of the UN, with sporadic incidents in other countries. The principal purpose was to intimidate those protesting against repressive regimes, although extortion by police and soldiers was another important driving force.

At the time of writing, the nature of torture seems to be changing again. After the destruction of the World Trade Center on September 11, 2001 came the "war on terror of global reach," and the return of torture and certain techniques of ill treatment as a means of attempting to gain information. This was called by its proponents "torture lite," meaning the use of psychological pain, and sometimes physical pain, designed to come just under the point at which it would breach international proscriptions of torture. Alleged methods included disorientation by exposure to prolonged periods of bright artificial light and loud sounds, irregular provision of food and drink, and the forced adoption of uncomfortable postures for prolonged periods. These are very similar to those criticized in the cases of the UK and of Israel. Medical attention for wounds was delayed. Threats were made against family members, including children. Complex deceptions were enacted, and there were credible threats (perhaps fulfilled) of transfer to the authorities of a state where violent torture was commonplace.

## Conclusions

Torture has existed for several thousand years. It has been repeatedly heralded as a way of gaining confessions and information, which it is. However, what is cynically or negligently overlooked is that the confessions and information gained by torture are unreliable. The physically and psychologically strong die before giving out useful information, while the weak confess to anything, even though they probably know nothing. Torture is not an effective means of gaining truthful confessions or information, but a means for insecure governments to maintain control. It often leads to significant psychological disability, and sometimes permanent physical disability as well. There is no legal, moral, or even practical justification for torture.

## See Also

**Human Rights, Controls and Principles**; **Torture:** Physical Findings; Psychological Assessment; **War Crimes:** Pathological Investigation

## Further Reading

Basoglu M (1992) *Torture and its Consequences: Current Treatment Approaches.* Cambridge, UK: Cambridge University Press.
British Medical Association (2001) *The Medical Profession and Human Rights: Handbook for a Changing Agenda.* London: Zed Books.
Peel M, Iacopino V (2002) *The Medical Documentation of Torture.* London: Greenwich Medical Media.
Peters E (1996) *Torture: Expanded Edition.* Philadelphia, PA: University of Pennsylvania Press.
United Nations High Commissioner for Human Rights (2001) *The Manual on Effective Investigation and Documentation of Torture and Other Cruel, Inhuman or Degrading Treatment of Punishment (The Istanbul Protocol).* Geneva, Switzerland: United Nations.

# HISTORY OF TOXICOLOGY

**A Aggrawal**, Maulana Azad Medical College, New Delhi, India

## Introduction

The word "poison" immediately conjures up images of cloak-and-dagger conspiracies, diabolically sneering poisoners, unfaithful and murderous wives, mad and cruel kings, and greedy nieces and nephews. No other single subject has a history as full of intrigue and romance as that of poison. As is the case with every subject, the study of the history of poisons provides valuable insights. The oft-quoted maxim "those who do not study history may be condemned to repeat it," applies very aptly to poisons.

What exactly is a poison? A poison can be defined as a substance that is capable of destroying life or causing illness fairly quickly, on a biochemical basis, when introduced into, or absorbed by, a living system in small quantities. Thus, liberal consumption of saturated fats may be responsible for death by coronary atherosclerosis after a few decades; however, it cannot be called a poison because the death, although surely associated with saturated fats, is not quick. Similarly, a bubble of oxygen introduced into the vein of a human being, although capable of killing the person immediately by air embolism, cannot be construed as poison because it does not kill on a biochemical basis. Nor can a sharp pin or needle be called a poison when ingested because it would kill by physically rupturing the gastrointestinal tract. Although approximately 0.25 kg of common salt would kill a human being fairly quickly when ingested, on a biochemical basis, it could still not be construed as a poison because the lethal quantity is very high. Thus, the three most important qualifying characteristics of a poison are its speed of action, action on a biochemical basis, and its lethality in small doses. Poisons that rank high on all three scales, such as cyanide, arsenic, and phosphorus, have dominated popular imagination since time immemorial. Toxicology is the science dealing with the study of poisons.

## Poisons in Mythology

Poison has been called the cowardly person's weapon. Its secretive nature has held a peculiar fascination for humanity. Since earliest times, the magic, myth, and legend of poison have been linked to hunting, crime, punishment, politics, romance, and, of course, medicine and the development of antidotes.

Toxicology has been known from very early times in all cultures. According to Indian mythology and tradition, the origin of poisons is attributed to Lord Brahma, who is one of the Holy Trinity of Indian gods (the Hindu Holy Trinity comprises Lord Brahma, the creator of the universe; Lord Vishnu, the preserver; and Lord Shiva, the destroyer of the universe). It is said that after the creator of the universe was offended by a devil (asura) named Kaitabha, he created poison to kill him. He was, no doubt, successful in destroying the demon with his new weapon, but its evil spread over the whole world. So much so that, to minimize its bad effects, Brahma had to distribute it through the vegetable, animal, and mineral kingdom and also create its antidote. Brahma thus distributed poisons into three categories: animal, mineral, and vegetable. Brahma is often cited as the first to classify poisons in this manner. Later, the Greek physician Dioscorides (AD 40–80) developed this classification independently (**Table 1**).

One of the foremost Indian experts in the science of toxicology was Kashyapa, a physician who lived in the times of Buddha (sixth-century BC). Kashyapa was a follower of the Brahmanic religion at first but was later converted to Buddhism. He was a successful curer of snakebite. A famous tale relating to his curative powers is frequently narrated. King Parikshita had been cursed that he would die of snakebite, but Kashyapa had taken it on himself to cure the king when the curse befell him. On the destined day when Takshaka, the king of serpents, was going to bite Parikshita, he met Kashyapa on the way and challenged him by showing his remarkable powers. It was perhaps his idea to frighten Kashyapa so that he would take back his vow. He bit a fully blossomed tree, and in front of everyone's eyes the tree turned to ashes. However, to everyone's surprise and to the shame of Takshaka, Kashyapa, using his wonderful charms and medicines, restored the tree to its original blossom. Unfortunately, Kashyapa was soon "bought over" by Takshaka, and Takshaka finally succeeded in killing Parikshita by his fatal bite.

Sure enough, this tale is mythological, but it does show the expertise of ancient Hindu doctors in the science of toxicology. The famous Indian surgeon Sushruta (seventh-century BC) defined agadatantra, which is akin to the modern term toxicology. It dealt with the diagnosis and treatment of any person bitten

**Table 1** A list of 125 major events in the history of criminal poisoning and toxicology

| No. | Year | Event |
|---|---|---|
| 1. | 16 000 BC | Hunters in Kenya used poison to kill |
| 2. | 4500 BC | Sumerians living in Mesopotamia (modern-day Iraq) worshipped Gula, a deity of noxious poisons. Gula is the earliest-known deity associated with poisons |
| 3. | 4000 BC | A Sumerian tablet of this period refers to the poppy as equivalent to ''joy'' plus ''plant,'' an allusion which indicates that Sumerians were aware of poppies and their effects |
| 4. | 3100–3000 BC | People in Egypt and Nubia used poisoned arrows |
| 5. | 3000 BC | Menes, the first Egyptian Pharaoh (king), cultivated and studied medicinal and poisonous plants |
| 6. | 2737 BC | The *Book of Drugs* appeared in China and described marijuana, alluding to its commercial and medical uses. The Chinese used marijuana to treat gout, malaria, and absent-mindedness |
| 7. | 2500 BC | Coca leaves (*Erythroxylon coca*), the source of cocaine, and a chewed wad of coca found near gravesites dating to this period show that coca was known to people of this era |
| 8. | 2000 BC | Chinese Emperor Shen Nung experimented with poisons and their antidotes and wrote a treatise on herbal medicine |
| 9. | 1600 BC | The *Smith Papyrus* cites the use of charms against snake poison |
| 10. | 1500 BC | The *Ebers Papyrus* (discovered in Thebes in 1872, by the German Egyptologist Georg Moritz Ebers (1837–1898)) mentions over 800 recipes (829 in all), many containing recognizable and identified poisons. Antimony, copper, lead, turpentine, verdigris, hyoscyamus and opium were used as poisons |
| 11. | 1400 BC | The *Hearst Medical Papyrus* (discovered in upper Egypt in 1899) refers to both poisons and therapeutic agents |
| 12. | 1200–900 BC | Hymns of the Rg Veda and Atharva Veda mention the use of poisoned arrows in war. Tubers of aconitum were mentioned as the major poison source |
| 13. | *c.* 850 BC | Homer wrote *The Odyssey*, in which he mentioned how Ulysses smeared his arrows with a number of poisons, including snake venoms and extracts of *Helleborus orientalis*. Circe, one of the first great sorceresses, is described as using poisons to subdue men |
| 14. | Seventh century BC | The famous Indian surgeon Sushruta defined agadatantra, a term akin to the modern term ''toxicology.'' The science of agadatantra deals with the diagnosis and treatment of any person bitten by poisonous insects or venomous reptiles or affected by any natural, artificial, or compound poison |
| 15. | 600 BC | The Indian physician Charaka detailed the poisons found in India in his *Charaka Samhita* |
| 16. | 525 BC | Psammentius, the king of Egypt, was forced to drink ''bull's blood,'' which killed him. ''Bull's blood'' was believed to be a poisonous substance at that time |
| 17. | Sixth century BC | One of the foremost Indian experts in the science of toxicology, Kashyapa, flourished during the times of Buddha. He was able to cure snakebites successfully |
| 18. | *c.* 500 BC | Han Chinese were using poisoned arrows |
| 19. | Fifth century BC | Hippocrates (460–*c.* 370 BC), the ''father of medicine,'' suggested methods of managing poisoned patients that rely primarily on limiting the absorption of toxic agents |
| 20. | 400 BC | 1. Hydrocyanic acid was known as a poison. This acid was being distilled from the kernels of peach and other cyanogenetic plants at this time<br>2. Persian Queen Parisatys eliminated her daughter-in-law by dexterously poisoning the knifeblade she used to carve meat for her dinner<br>3. Book of Job speaks of poison arrows (Job 6:4)<br>4. The historian Ctesias first described the mythological animal, the unicorn. It was believed that those who drank from its horn were protected from stomach trouble, epilepsy, and poison. According to Ctesias, the unicorn was very fleet of foot and difficult to capture. The actual animal behind Ctesias' description was probably the Indian rhinoceros. The unicorn's horn was to gain reputation as a poison remedy once again during the Middle Ages |
| 21. | 399 BC | The Athenian philosopher Socrates (*c.* 470–399 BC) was executed by asking him to drink a cup of poison hemlock (*Conium maculatum*). Poison hemlock (also known as ''spotted hemlock'') was widely used by the state as a method of execution at this time |
| 22. | Fourth century BC | 1. Aristotle (384–322 BC) described the preparation and use of arrow poisons<br>2. Theophrastus (*c.* 370–286 BC) referred to poisonous plants in his *De Historia Plantarum*. The ninth book of this encyclopedia mentions several poisonous plants such as aconite, hellebore, mandrake, and henbane |
| 23. | 331 BC | A series of deaths occurred in Rome, which were earlier attributed to pestilence. A slave revealed that the deaths were actually the result of a poison administered by a group of matrons. A search of women's houses revealed concoctions, which the women were ordered to consume. They all perished. Further investigations revealed 170 accomplices, who were tried and all found guilty. According to the Roman historian Livy (59 BC–17 AD), this was the first poisoning trial in Rome |
| 24. | 325 BC | Diodorus Siculus, in his account written during Alexander the Great's campaign in western India, mentioned that Hindus prepared a decoction of poison by decomposing snakes |
| 25. | 322 BC | Athenian statesman Demosthenes (385–322 BC), one of the greatest Greek orators, committed suicide by taking poison hidden in his pen to escape his enemies |
| 26. | Third century BC | Apollodorus of Alexandria writes *Peri therion (On poisonous animals)*, a definitive work on animal poisons. This work is later lost, but revived by Nicander of Colophon in his poems. |

**Table 1** Continued

| No. | Year | Event |
|-----|------|-------|
| 27. | Second century BC | Nicander of Colophon (204–135 BC), working in the intellectual atmosphere created by Attalus III, wrote two poems, *Theriaca* (a 1000-line poem, dealing with poisonous animals) and *Alexipharmaca* (a 600-line poem, dealing with antidotes), that are among the earliest works on poisons. Theriac is a term derived from the word theria (dangerous or poisonous beasts). *Theriaca* is one of the earliest works on poisonous animals |
| 28. | 200 BC | First known instance of mass poisoning. Some 190 matrons, mostly of patrician birth, were executed for poisoning |
| 29. | 183 BC | Carthaginian general, Hannibal, one of the foremost military commanders in history, took his own life with cyanide |
| 30. | 138–133 BC | Attalus III, the last king of Pergamon in Asia Minor, cultivated poisonous plants, and experimented on condemned prisoners |
| 31. | First century BC | The king of Pontus (in modern Turkey), Mithridates VI (lived *c.* 132–63 BC; reigned 120–63 BC), was fanatically fearful of poisons and developed one of the first known universal antidotes, mithridatum |
| 32. | 81 BC | The Roman dictator Sulla issued *Lex Cornelia*, the first known law in human history against poisoning. According to this law, poisoners, if they belonged to the nobility, would face exile or loss of property; if they belonged to the lower ranks, they would be thrown to the wild beasts |
| 33. | 30 BC | Cleopatra (69–30 BC) committed suicide (August 30) using the venom of an asp |
| 34. | 14 AD | Laurel water on figs was used by Livia (58 BC–AD 29) to kill her husband Augustus (31 BC–14 AD). Many historians however think that this is not true |
| 35. | 54 AD | Locusta, one of the most infamous poisoners of all time, was hired by Agrippina, Nero's mother, to poison Claudius, her husband and Nero's stepfather, with poisonous mushrooms. Some versions assert that the poison used was arsenic |
| 36. | 55 AD | Locusta fooled Britannicus, Nero's stepbrother, into drinking a soup laced with arsenic. An unusually hot soup was prepared which was officially tasted, but then required additional cooling before the intended victim took it. During the time of additional cooling, arsenic was slipped into the soup |
| 37. | First century AD | 1. The Roman naturalist and historian Pliny the Elder (*c.* AD 23–79), wrote *Naturalis Historia* in 37 volumes. Books XX–XXXII deal with medicine. They described the biologic effects of poisonous plants and animals. Curiously, Pliny the Elder died of a poisonous gas in 79 AD – from exposure to fumes from the eruption of Mount Vesuvius<br>2. Andromachus (AD 37–68) refined mithridatum. The new recipe became known as theriac of Andromachus<br>3. The Greek surgeon Pedianos Dioscorides of Anazarbus – generally known simply as Dioscorides – (AD 40–80), and widely considered as the father of materia medica, compiled the first herbal in which he described 1000 simple drugs, 600 plants, and 35 animal products. His *De Materia Medica*, written in Greek, remained an authoritative text for the next 1600 years<br>4. Roman Emperor Trajan (98–117 AD) was so wary of wolfsbane plant (*Aconitum napellus*, referred to by Ovid as "stepmother's poison") that he banned its growth in Roman domestic gardens |
| 38. | Second century AD | Greek physician Galen (?131–201) prepared nut theriac – a remedy against bites, stings, and poisons – for Roman emperors. He wrote *De Antidotis I et II*, which provided recipes for different antidotes, including mithridaticum and panacea |
| 39. | 640 AD | Paul of Aegina wrote *Epitomae Medicinae Libri Septem*. Book five deals with toxicology, specifically bites and wounds of animals |
| 40. | Ninth century | Ibn Jabir wrote *Book on Poisons*. Al-Tabari (born *c.* 810) wrote the *Paradise of Wisdom*. Ibn Wahshiya (late ninth century) wrote *Book on Poisons*. All three books deal with poisons |
| 41. | 10th century | 1. Parts of *Liber Continens* of al-Razi (860–932) and *Canon Medicinae* of ibn Sina (980–1037) deal with poisons<br>2. An Arabian leader Hassan-Ibn-Sabbah wielded power by providing his followers with hashish, a potent form of marijuana |
| 42. | 1198 | Moses Maimonides (1135–1204), a Jewish philosopher and physician in the service of the Sultan of Egypt, wrote *Treatise on Poisons and Their Antidotes*. He discussed suctioning to remove superficial poisons and emesis to reduce absorption. However, antidotes like theriac and mithridatium were still recommended |
| 43. | 1216 | John, King of England (1167–1216) was murdered by toad toxins (October 18–19) |
| 44. | 13th century | 1. English philosopher Roger Bacon (1214–1294) recommended potable gold (gold dissolved in acid) for poisoning. It was in fact supposed to be a panacea<br>2. Petrus of Abano (1250–1316), a professor of medicine at the University of Padua, wrote *De Venenis*, a book on poisons, which would remain popular for many generations |
| 45. | 1419 | Members of a group known as the Venetian Council of Ten carried out murders by poison for a fee |
| 46. | 1499 | Amerigo Vespucci, the famed explorer, described natives chewing coca leaves |
| 47. | 1527 | Philippus Aureolus Theophrastus Bombastus Von Hohenheim (Paracelsus 1492–1541), the unconventional and indefatigable medical practitioner, publicly burned the books of Avicenna and Galen (on June 24), thus heralding the new age of experimental toxicology. His use of mercury in the treatment of syphilis led to accusations by his detractors of poisoning, to which he wrote the *Third Defence*, which includes the famous phrase, "What is there that is not poison? All things are poison and nothing is without poison. Solely the dose determines that a thing is not poison." |

Continued

**Table 1** Continued

| No. | Year | Event |
| --- | --- | --- |
| 48. | 1533 | Catherine de Médicis (1519–1589), one of the greatest poisoners in France, married the Dauphin (later Henry II). Pope Clement VII, her uncle presented Francis I (bridegroom's father) with a piece of unicorn's horn. Unicorn's horn – first described by the historian Ctesias in around 400 BC – once again found favor as a universal remedy for poisons. So afraid of poisoning were kings at this time that unicorn's horn became part of official regal dowry. A legend was rife at this time that the unicorn purified poisoned waters with its horn so that other animals might drink. Since it was very costly, it could only be used by the kings and nobles. It was probably the tusk of a marine mammal – the narwhal, or perhaps the tusk of a rhinoceros |
| 49. | 16th century | Bezoar stones were very popular as universal remedies against poisons. These were actually fossilized concretions formed within intestines of animals, containing calcium phosphate and carbonate and not infrequently fragments of unaltered bone. They could be animal gallstones too. Charles IX of France (1550–1574) (son of the famous French poisoner Catherine de Médicis) was very proud of his possession of a bezoar stone, and though the noted surgeon Ambroise Paré (1510–1590) of Paris told him of its uselessness, he wouldn't believe him. He actually conducted an experiment on a condemned criminal, who was first given bichloride of mercury, and then the bezoar stone. The prisoner died an agonizing death within 7 h |
| 50. | 1534 | Pope Clement VII (1478–1534) was murdered (on September 25) with poisonous mushrooms (*Amanita phalloides*) |
| 51. | 1542 | The last legal execution by boiling was performed on Margaret Davie, who had ''pouysoned three households that she dwelled in'' |
| 52. | 1543 | 15 December: a Franciscan monk called John of Ragusa offered the Venetian Council of Ten a selection of poisons, and stated his terms for killing various eminent personages. The rate offered was 500 ducats for the Great Sultan, 150 for the King of Spain, 100 for the Pope, 60 for the Duke of Milan, and 50 for the Marquis of Mantua. The offer was accepted the next year. Results are not known |
| 53. | 1566 | The Paris Parliament prohibited the use of antimony, because of its rising use as a homicidal poison |
| 54. | 1596 | Edward Squires was hired by Spain to poison Queen Elizabeth I by smearing an opium-based poison on the pommel of her saddle |
| 55. | 1613 | The Countess of Somerset was found guilty of using corrosive sublimate (mercuric chloride) to murder Sir Thomas Overbury while he was imprisoned in the Tower of London |
| 56. | 1659 | Hieronyma Spara of Rome – an astrologer, a sorceress, and a poisoner – was conducting a lucrative business selling poisons to young married women keen to do away with their husbands. She formed a society in which she taught women how to murder their husbands by means of poison. Her poison was a special concoction known as aquetta di Perugia. She was executed the same year |
| 57. | 1662 | Louis XIV (1638–1715), king of France (1643–1715), issued a decree forbidding apothecaries to sell poisons to anyone unknown to them. In addition, purchasers were required to sign a register |
| 58. | 1666 | Many American soldiers died of accidental poisoning with *Datura stramonium* (jimsonweed). The incident occurred in the early American colony, Jamestown, Virginia, when a shortage of food led them to scavenge among the fields for something to eat. Jimsonweed is a corruption of Jamestown weed |
| 59. | 1667 | Madame de Montespan, the mistress of King Louis XIV, attempting to poison her rival and the King, started buying poisons from La Voisine. Continued buying till 1680, when La Voisine was finally burnt at the stake |
| 60. | 1676 | Marquise de Brinvilliers of France (July 22, 1630–July 16, 1676), one of the worst mass poisoners in history who is supposed to have killed over 100 people with arsenic, was decapitated on July 16 |
| 61. | 1679 | 1. Louis XIV, fearing for his own life, instituted la Chambre Ardente (the fiery room), or la Chambre de Poison, a special court to try poisoners (April 1679). The Affaire des Poisons (the affair of the poisons), one of the most sensational criminal cases of seventeenth-century France, revealed that nobles, prosperous bourgeois, and the common people alike had secretly been resorting to female fortune-tellers – at that time numerous in Paris – for drugs and poisons, for black masses, and for other criminal purposes |
| | | 2. Jean-Baptiste Racine (1639–1699), French dramatic poet and historiographer, was accused by Catherine Deshayes (La Voisine) of having poisoned his mistress and star actress, the Marquise du Parc, but no formal charges were laid and no consequences ensued |
| 62. | 1680 | Catherine Deshayes (1638–1680) a.k.a La Voisine, was tried for poisoning several thousand people, including over 2000 infants. La Voisine's daughter and accomplices testified that even King Louis XIV's mistress Mme de Montespan had been buying poisons from her (since 1667). Montespan was trying to poison her young rival Mlle de Fontanges. King Louis suspended the public proceedings after the accusations against Mme de Montespan but ordered the continuation of the inquiry. La Voisine was found guilty and burnt at the stake on February 23, 1680, thus ending the career of one of the worst mass poisoners of all time |
| 63. | 1719 | Madame Giulia Toffana (c. 1635–1719), another mass poisoner, was executed at Naples |
| 64. | 1752 | Mary Blandy, a 31-year-old spinster, was tried at Oxford for murdering her father with arsenic. She was found guilty and hanged |
| 65. | 1765 | Fontana of Italy studied the effect of viper venom and other toxic substances on animals and concluded that drugs act on one type of body tissue |

**Table 1** Continued

| No. | Year | Event |
|---|---|---|
| 66. | 1769 | Secundus designed a stomach pump, making it easier to wash out poisons |
| 67. | 1773 | Scheele described the nature of charcoal adsorption. Lowitz (1785) confirmed findings |
| 68. | 1775 | Karl Wilhelm Scheele (1742–1786) discovered that he could change arsenious oxide to arsenious acid, which in contact with zinc produced arsine. This discovery later played a great part in the forensic detection of arsenic |
| 69. | 1776 | Thomas Hickey unsuccessfully attempted to assassinate George Washington by poisoning his dish of green peas. Hickey was hanged, and became the first American executed for treason |
| 70. | 1787 | Mathieu Joseph Bonaventure Orfila (1787–1853), the French toxicologist who is widely regarded as the father of toxicology, was born on April 24 |
| 71. | 1799 | Humphrey Davy described the effect of laughing gas on the human body |
| 72. | 1805 | 1. German apothecary Sertürner isolated morphine from opium |
| | | 2. Philip Physick, an American surgeon, employed the pump designed by Secundus (36 years earlier) to attempt gastric lavage. He washed out the stomachs of two children who had ingested opium |
| 73. | 1809 | Poisoner Mary Bateman, "the Yorkshire witch", was executed |
| 74. | 1813 | 1. Orfila published his *Traité des Poisons*, which would soon become an authoritative work on toxicology |
| | | 2. M. Bertrand, a French chemist, heroically demonstrated the antidotal power of activated charcoal, by ingesting an overdose of arsenious trioxide mixed with charcoal. He survived |
| 75. | 1819 | Caventou and Pelletier isolated strychnine from *Nux vomica* |
| 76. | 1820 | Desosse found quinine in the bark of cinchona tree. Runge found caffeine in coffee |
| 77. | 1826 | Giesecke discovered coniine in hemlock |
| 78. | 1828 | Possell and Reimann isolated nicotine from tobacco |
| 79. | 1829 | Sir Robert Christison (1797–1882), Professor of Forensic Medicine at Edinburgh, published *Treatise on Poisons*, which for many years was regarded as the standard work on toxicology in the English language |
| 80. | 1830 | French chemists isolated amygdalin from bitter almonds |
| 81. | 1831 | Touery, a French pharmacist, made a dramatic demonstration of the antidotal powers of activated charcoal before the French Academy of Science. He ingested 10 times the lethal amount of strychnine, and then took activated charcoal. He survived. He thus reenacted the heroic demonstration made 18 years previously by his countryman M. Bertrand, only this time the demonstration was made before a respectable scientific body |
| 82. | 1832 | 1. Codeine purified from opium |
| | | 2. *Poisons and Asphyxia* by Henry Coley was published in New York. This was one of the earliest books to discuss toxicology scientifically |
| 83. | 1833 | Mein extracted atropine from deadly nightshade |
| 84. | 1836 | An English chemist James Marsh (1794–1846) developed the Marsh test for detecting arsenic in human tissues. This proved a boon for forensic toxicologists, who till now had no test to prove the presence of arsenic in human tissues. The "age of arsenic" (15th–18th century) came to an end |
| 85. | 1838 | Duflos described wet ashing. This technique was later developed by Fresenius and von Babo in 1844 |
| 86. | 1839 | Orfila became the first toxicologist to extract arsenic from human organs (in the case of the assassin–suicide Soufflard). Previously only the gastrointestinal contents were used for analysis |
| 87. | 1840 | 1. Marsh test was practically put to use, for the first time, in the great arsenic homicide case of Lafarge. Marie Lafarge was suspected of poisoning her husband Charles Lafarge with arsenic. She was found guilty and sentenced to life imprisonment |
| | | 2. Burton reported a blue line on the gums in victims of chronic lead poisoning. This came to be known as the Burtonian line, and became a very important diagnostic sign of chronic lead poisoning |
| 88. | 1842 | German chemist Hugo Reinsch introduced Reinsch's test – a new test to detect arsenic |
| 89. | 1844 | Fresenius and von Babo devised a scheme for the systematic search for all mineral poisons. They used wet ashing with chlorine |
| 90. | 1850 | Quantitative determination of metals in organs became possible. Metal is weighed as the sulfate or oxide |
| 91. | 1851 | 1. The UK passed the Arsenic Act, in an attempt to control the availability of arsenic, which was being commonly used for homicides. |
| | | 2. Belgian toxicologist Jean-Servais Stas (1813–1891) developed the first ever method to detect alkaloids from biological specimens, while investigating the alleged poisoning of Gustave Fougnies by nicotine |
| 92. | 1852 | Marie Lafarge (see entry for 1840) was released by Napoleon III, but died the same year |
| 93. | 1853 | Alexander Wood perfected the hypodermic syringe, paving the way for emergence of morphine addicts. Ironically, his aim was to reduce opiate addiction by circumventing the oral route |
| 94. | 1862 | The electrolyte deposition method was first used for quantitative determination of metals in organs. Previously sulfate or oxide of metal was the weight for such quantitative determination |
| 95. | 1865 | Microsublimation was first demonstrated by Helwig |
| 96. | 1867 | 1. Theodore Wormley published *Microchemistry of Poisons* |
| | | 2. Schmiedeberg developed a method to determine levels of chloroform |
| 97. | 1868 | Hofmann developed isonitrile reaction for chloroform |

Continued

**Table 1** Continued

| No. | Year | Event |
|---|---|---|
| 98. | 1870 | Lieben developed the iodoform test for alcohol |
| 99. | 1874 | Selmi showed that a substance (reported to be morphine) isolated from the organs of a body that had been buried 2 weeks was in reality a morphine-like ptomaine or cadaveric alkaloid. Many other alkaloid-like ptomaines have since been discovered |
| 100. | 1880 | Fodor developed a method of quantitative determination of carbon monoxide in the blood |
| 101. | 1887 | L. Edeleano, a German scientist, synthesized amphetamine, the first member of this class to be synthesized |
| 102. | 1888 | Schwartz developed the resorcin reaction for chloroform |
| 103. | 1898 | 1. Eduard Schiff, a dermatologist, showed that arsenic might be found with astonishing frequency in hair. He suggested that hair should be tested as a standard step in any investigation of possible poisoning |
|  |  | 2. Bayer marketed heroin as a substitute for morphine. Ironically, the idea was to reduce addiction, but heroin would emerge as a greater scourge |
| 104. | 1906 | Nicloux published a micromethod for the quantitative determination of alcohol in blood |
| 105. | 1910 | Russian botanist Mikhail Semyonovich Tsvet (1872–1919) published his book describing adsorption chromatography. This technique and its modifications were to become very important later in the detection of poisons |
| 106. | 1913 | J.J. Thomson (1856–1940), the discoverer of electrons, built the first mass spectrometer, known as the hyperbola spectrograph |
| 107. | 1927 | Gordon Alles discovered the major physiological effects of amphetamine by self-administering this drug |
| 108. | 1932 | Swedish scientist Erik Matteo Prochet Widmark (1889–1945) measured ethyl alcohol in the blood to calculate intoxication |
| 109. | 1944 | Gas chromatography, a strong technique to detect poisons, was first carried out in Austria by the chemist Erika Cremer |
| 110. | 1947 | Sir Bernard Spilsbury (1877–1947), who was depressed during the last years of his life, took his own life by gassing himself with coal gas (December 17) |
| 111. | 1954 | R.F. Borkenstein, captain of the Indiana State Police, invented the breathalyzer for field sobriety testing |
| 112. | 1956 | 1. Golay first showed wall-coated open tubular (WCOT) columns for gas chromatography to be theoretically ideal |
|  |  | 2. The infamous Minamata Bay disaster (poisoning due to methyl mercury) struck Japan. More than 17 000 were affected |
| 113. | 1957 | Kenneth Barlow, a 38-year-old male nurse, killed his wife by insulin. This was the first known case of murder using this novel drug. He was found guilty and sentenced to life imprisonment |
| 114. | 1958 | The infamous Kerala food-poisoning tragedy occurred in Kerala, India. Wheat flour and sugar had inadvertently been stored in the same cabin on a ship as parathion, and the parathion leaked into the flour and sugar. Over 1000 people were poisoned subsequently, of whom more than 100 died |
| 115. | 1962 | Rachel Carson published *Silent Spring*, in which she successfully argued the case against pesticides. Although highly controversial, the book stimulated an organized approach to the study of chemical effects on ecosystems |
| 116. | 1968 | American Academy of Clinical Toxicology (AACT) established. First issue of *Clinical Toxicology* appeared |
| 117. | 1978 | Georgi Markov, a 49-year-old Bulgarian defector to the UK, was shot at the back of his right thigh, on September 7, with a pellet of ricin. He died 4 days later on September 11. This was the first known case of assassination with ricin |
| 118. | 1983 | Using protocols written by David L. von Minden, the US Navy adopted SIM (Single Ion Monitoring) gas chromatography–mass spectrometry confirmation of the THC metabolite of marijuana, establishing the procedure as the "gold standard" for drug confirmation in the USA |
| 119. | 1984 | 2000 people died in Bhopal, India due to accidental release of methyl isocyanate (MIC) from a small pesticide division of Union Carbide Company manufacturing carbaryl (December 2) |
| 120. | 1988 | George Trepal, a member of Mensa, killed his neighbor Peggy Carr by tampering with her Coca-Cola bottles and mixing in thallium. One of her sons was permanently disabled by the effects of thallium. Trepal was convicted of first-degree murder and sentenced to death in 1991 |
| 121. | 1991 | President Zachary Taylor's (1784–1850) body was exhumed on June 17 to test for arsenic poisoning. It was increasingly suspected that he had been poisoned by the pro-slavery faction. Nothing was found however |
| 122. | 1992 | A report of the first and only poisonous bird, the hooded pitohui (*Pitohui dichrous*), was published in *Science*. It was found in Papua New Guinea: the skin and feathers of this bird contain almost the same homobatrachotoxin as the poison-arrow frogs |
| 123. | 1997 | Thirty-nine unidentified flying object cult members committed suicide with phenobarbital and vodka (March 26) |
| 124. | 2000 | Dr. Harold Shipman – one of the most notorious mass poisoners of modern times – was convicted at Preston, UK on January 31, of murdering 15 of his patients by administering lethal doses of diamorphine (pharmaceutical heroin). Investigations indicated that, during his working life, he killed about 220–240 of his patients. Shipman hanged himself at Wakefield Prison on January 13, 2004 |
| 125. | 2003 | V.V. Pillay, one of the greatest Asian toxicologists, published his definitive *Comprehensive Medical Toxicology*. A number of poisons native to Asia and their treatments are described |

by poisonous insects or venomous reptiles or affected by any natural, artificial, or compound poison.

Another popular Indian legend related to poisons is about Lord Shiva, whose neck turned blue when he drank the deadly poison produced by the churning of the ocean, through which he saved the world from destruction. For this reason, Lord Shiva is also known in India as Neelkanth (one with a blue throat).

## Historical Beginnings

Modern humans (*Homo sapiens*) appeared in Africa and possibly in Asia perhaps about 100 000 years ago and eventually migrated to Europe. Among these European peoples, the best known are the Cro-Magnons. The emergence of fully modern humans in other areas of the world seems to have occurred 30 000–15 000 years ago and involved various migrations and the intermingling of different populations. Humans learned to write and record their experiences in about 5000 BC. The history of toxicology from 100 000 to 5000 BC can only be extrapolated from available anthropological evidence.

Primitive humans must have observed that animals intuitively avoided certain plants. This may have aroused curiosity, and it must have required only a little experimentation to discover that the juices of these plants could kill easily. Poisonous plants such as curare, strophanthus, oleander, aconite, calotropis, *Abrus precatorius*, and *Ricinus communis* must have been the first to be noticed.

Since early humans were essentially hunters, the next logical step was to smear the tips of their arrows with the juices of these plants. The observation that animals could be killed faster with this method must have given them a sense of immense power. Even today, many tribal people hunt with poison-tipped arrows. Many Amazon tribes hunt with darts smeared with the juice of *Strychnos toxifera* (curare) or other similar plant poisons. They even grade the strength of their poison according to the number of trees a monkey can jump through before falling from a poisoned dart. If a monkey falls after jumping through just one tree, it is called one-tree poison, which is considered strong enough for hunting. If a monkey jumps through as many as three trees before falling, it is a three-tree poison, which is too weak for hunting.

The observation of present-day tribes preparing poisons from poisonous plants is akin to viewing the past through a time machine. Cultural anthropologists inform us that not much has changed in their practices over the centuries. Amazon Indians strip the bark of poisonous trees (e.g., *S. toxifera*), pound it, mix water thoroughly with the fibrous pulp, and boil to concentrate it. Finally, they add juices of other trees (e.g., the kiracaguero tree) to produce a sticky syrup, which can easily be smeared on the tips of their arrows. These tribes have been known to mix other poisonous substances in the concoction, including the fangs and livers of venomous snakes and spiders and even the stingers of poisonous ants.

Present-day tribes throughout the world carry out similar practices. The Bushmen of the Kalahari desert use the intestine of a caterpillar for poisoning their arrows, whereas the Chocos of Colombia tip their darts with a poison excreted from the skin of small but brilliantly colored frogs. The frogs are stimulated to perspire, their sweat is collected, and darts are dipped into the sweat. A few frogs yield sufficient poison for more than 100 arrows. Pygmies poison their arrows with red ant substances.

The realization that those very same animal products and plant juices could help kill human beings too must have aroused latent homicidal tendencies. At last there was a weapon which could enable you to strike surreptitiously without coming into the forefront. All that was needed was somehow to mix the juices into the enemy's food. Thus arose the first homicidal poisoner.

Nobody knows who was the first homicidal poisoner, or even when, where, and what poison was used, because there are no written records. However, reasonable guesses can be made. There was no single first homicidal poisoner; there were probably several, spread over a large triangular area ranging from China and India in the orient to Greece and Italy in the occident and Egypt in the south. These are the regions that saw the emergence of the earliest "intelligent" civilizations, and it is only reasonable to assume that these civilizations were the first to discover the use of poison to their advantage. These are also the regions rich and abundant in the previously mentioned toxic plants and animals.

## The Toxicology of the Egyptians

Humans learned to write in about 5000 BC, and from this point onward, the history of toxicology is clearer. The earliest of all poison recipes can be gleaned amid Egyptian papyrus rolls dating back to about 4500 BC, now preserved in the Louvre museum in Paris. Three millennia before Christ, Menes, the first of the Pharaohs, is reported to have cultivated and studied poisonous and medicinal plants and to have accumulated animal, mineral, and vegetable poisons. In *Ebers Papyrus*, more than 800 recipes are described, many containing recognizable and identified poisons: for example, hemlock, aconite, opium, and some toxic heavy metals, such as lead and antimony. Some of the pharaohs are known to have experimented with poisons, perhaps for practical matters of government and state.

## Toxicology in the Greek Period

The mythology and literature of classic Greek history show a considerable knowledge of poisons, although in ancient Greece autopsies were not performed. In the *Odyssey of Homer*, Helen is described as discreetly introducing into the wine of Telemachus and Menelaus a drug that acted as a powerful anodyne. In Greek legend, Hecate was knowledgeable about aconite, Medea was familiar with the properties of colchicum, and Hercules is said to have met his end from wearing a shirt after his wife had impregnated it with poison. The first professional treatment of toxicology appears in various Greek writings in approximately the third and fourth century BC. Thus, Theophrastus (370–286 BC), a pupil of Aristotle, included numerous references to poisonous plants in his work *De Historia Plantarum*. Nicander of Colophon (204–138 BC) wrote two treatises, which are the most ancient works devoted entirely to poisons. One was on snake poisons and the other on plant poisons, including opium, henbane, poisonous fungi, colchicum, aconite, and conium. Nicander classified poisons into those that killed quickly and those that killed slowly, and he recommended emetics in the treatment of poisoning, a recommendation that is valid even today.

The Greek physician Dioscorides (AD 40–90) classified poisons as: (1) animal poisons, such as from cantharides, toads, and snakes; (2) poisons from plants, including opium, hyoscyamus, mandrake, hemlock, aconite, cherry laurel, and yew; and (3) mineral poisons, including arsenic, copper, mercury, and lead. This simple classification (which, according to Indian mythology and tradition, was first used by Brahma) remained in use for many centuries and is still vaguely recognizable in modern classifications of poisons.

Poisons were used by the Greeks as a means of capital punishment, the best-remembered case being that of Socrates (who was made to drink from a cup of poison hemlock; similar cups of poison were offered to Plutarch, Midas, and Themistocles, among others). It was also used as a means of political assassination, although this was developed on a much greater scale by the Romans subsequently. Thus started the search for antidotes for poisons. In fact, it became a practical necessity if the king wished to survive in office.

## Ancient Rome

From simple hunting to complicated court crimes, poison was dexterously used and women in ancient times were adept in the art of poisoning. In approximately the second-century BC, the Roman Senate is believed to have executed about 190 such women who are said to have hailed from noble families but were driven by jealousy, hatred, and revenge (**Table 1**).

In those days, little value was attached to human life and many people lived in fear of poisoning. This gave birth to amulet vendors, who developed charms and talismans to work as antidotes for poison.

The Persian Queen Parisatys (400 BC) eliminated her daughter-in-law by dexterously poisoning the knife blade she used for carving meat for her dinner. Locusta was another mastermind in the art of poisoning. She was commissioned by Nero's mother, Agrippina, to poison her husband, Emperor Claudius (54 AD).

Indeed, she received royal patronage and was appointed the State Poisoner. In pursuit of her art, she was liberally offered slaves on whom to try out her poisonous prescriptions, and her nefarious activities were kept alive through a school of well-trained students.

## The Age of Arsenic

Italy was known for the Renaissance and its poisoners. Poisoning was rife throughout society, and there were many incredible stories relating to it. There were stories of poisons that could be smeared on the pages of a book so that anyone reading it would be poisoned through the pores of his or her fingers.

Arsenic was the favorite choice of all poisoners during this period because it had many qualities of an ideal homicidal poison. It was colorless, odorless, and tasteless; its symptoms resembled those of a natural disease, cholera; it was required in very small quantities (a pinch of arsenious oxide could kill as many as five people); it was readily available (it was used by arsenophagists to increase their sexual vigor and by women to improve their complexion); and no scientific test was known to detect it. In 1740, the celebrated English novelist Henry Fielding (1707–1754) appealed to scientists to make this poison visible in some way but was told that there was no way to do this.

So dreaded was this poison that it became variously known as the "king of poisons," "the poison of poisons," and "le poudre de succession" (inheritance powder). The period between the fifteenth and eighteenth centuries can rightfully be called "the age of arsenic" because poisoning with arsenic was rife during this period. Other poisons were undoubtedly used as well, although to a lesser extent. This period may also be referred to as "the age of indiscriminate poisoning." People were poisoning their enemies seemingly for trivial reasons, simply because they knew they could get away with it.

The Borgias, a notorious Spanish family living in Italy, were the most feared poisoners during this time. So feared were they that a number of anecdotal stories were told about them. It was said that they had a special ring with a tiny poisoned spike. Anyone shaking hands with them would be clandestinely punctured and killed. One member of this family, Cesare Borgia (1476–1507), is reputed to have killed hundreds of his enemies with arsenic.

By the sixteenth century, Italian women had the reputation of being at the forefront of poisoning. It is said that they even prepared poisons for sleeping persons. These women did not hesitate to poison their husbands. Toffana was one such woman; she was popular in Naples for creating the perfect poison, called aqua toffana or aquettaa-di-Napoli, which was a tasteless, colorless, and odorless liquid. Six drops were enough to kill a person in a few hours. The Italians were so popular as poisoners that the British coined words such as "italianated" or "italianation" for secret poisonings.

The French were not lagging far behind in the world of poisons. Marie Madeleine d'Aubray (1630–1676; also variously known as Marquise de Brinvilliers or Madame de Brinvilliers) was so beautiful that no one suspected that she was engaged in poisoning, which she practiced on patients in hospitals she often visited on the pretext of charity. She was guillotined in 1676 after she had taken several lives, including those of her husband, father, two brothers, and one sister, in addition to the lives of her lovers and onlookers who stood in her way.

The age of arsenic was finally brought to an end by two celebrated toxicologists, a Spaniard turned Frenchman, Mathieu Joseph Bonaventure Orfila (1787–1853), and an Englishman, James Marsh (1794–1846). Marsh developed the celebrated Marsh test in 1836, by which arsenic could be detected very easily. Orfila used this test in a criminal case just 4 years later and won a conviction.

## Antidotes through the Ages

The most famous example of an antidote was that devised by King Mithridates VI. He was king of Pontus in Asia Minor, living from 132 to 63 BC. The Roman scholar Pliny the Elder (AD 23–79) wrote extensively about him. Mithridates experimented with poisons, testing them on condemned criminals,

and he also tried various antidotes to the poisons on these prisoners, either before they were poisoned or immediately after they were poisoned, to determine whether the antidotes were effective. In this way, he discovered various antidotes or what he considered to be antidotes against different poisons, and he compounded them together in order to produce a universal antidote that could neutralize any poison.

Adopting an overcautious approach, he then began taking this supposed universal antidote daily. It is often stated that the original recipe had more than 36 ingredients (according to the Greek physician Galen (AD 130–200) there were 54). Eventually, Mithridates was defeated by the Roman general and statesman Pompey (106–48 BC) and "holed up" in his fortress. He massacred his wives, concubines, and daughters and then took poison. However, protected as he was by a daily dose of his magnificent antidote, the poison failed to act. The antidote by this time was known as mithridatium. He had to get his Celtic soldier servant to stab him to death with his sword.

After Mithridates' defeat and death, Pompey discovered Mithridates' notebooks on antidotes for poisons, and so mithridatium became known in Rome. The Roman emperor Nero (AD 37–68) showed a great interest in poisons. Andromachus, one of Nero's personal physicians, improved the formula and it then became known as theriac of Andromachus, containing 64 ingredients, including the flesh of vipers. For some reason, people have always thought that the flesh of vipers is a good antidote to poison. Perhaps this thought arose because the snakes are poisonous but they do not die of their poison, so it is rather reasonable to think that the snakes' flesh acts as an antidote. Viper's flesh was a very common ingredient of any antidote developed in ancient times.

In the course of time, theriac became not only an antidote against poison but also a panacea against all diseases, and it was in medical use until the eighteenth century. To prevent fraud, in many cities, including Venice, Montpellier, Toulouse, and Strasburg, theriac was carefully compounded and prepared in public under official supervision. Even today, theriac jars can be seen in museums.

Other universal antidotes to poisons that survived and remained in popular use for centuries include bezoars (stomach stones) found in certain animals, particularly ruminants and some varieties of goats. These were first used in the Middle East and were introduced into Europe by the Arabs, who continue to have some faith in them even to this day. These stones were pulverized and put into wine to treat cases of poisoning, but small stones were also

**Table 2** Twenty-five most notorious homicidal poisons and their major proponents

| No. | Poison | Major proponent | Details of the case |
|---|---|---|---|
| 1. | Aconite | Dr. George Henry Lamson (1853–28 April 1882) (male, UK) | Lamson, an English physician, was a morphine addict and needed funds. On December 3, 1881, Lamson visited his 18-year-old invalid brother-in-law, Percy Malcolm John, who lived at Blenheim House School at Wimbledon. In the presence of the school principal, Lamson gave his brother-in-law a capsule and a ready-cut piece of Dundee cake. He had bought aconitine, a little known vegetable poison at that time, from a manufacturing chemist on November 24, and had put it in the cake. Soon after giving the cake, he left, saying he had to take a train to Paris. Percy fell ill within 10 min of his departure and died later that night. Lamson was found guilty and executed at Wandsworth prison, after confessing to the chaplain |
| 2. | Antimony | Dr. William Palmer (a.k.a. the Rugeley poisoner) (male, UK) | Dr. Palmer killed at least 14 people with antimony at the place of his residence, Rugeley (hence the name Rugeley poisoner). The death of his last victim John Parsons Cook aroused suspicion. An autopsy was ordered and small traces of antimony were found in the dead body. Palmer was found guilty and hanged outside Stafford Gaol on June 14, 1856 |
| 3. | Arsenic | Mary Ann Cotton (1833–24 March 1873) (female, UK) | It is difficult to find a single major proponent of arsenic, which has been called the "king of poisons." Mary Ann Cotton was believed to have killed at least 20 people with arsenic. This included her husband, lover, her own young baby, stepsons, and many others. She was tried for the poisoning of her stepson. Her defense was that the dead boy had been poisoned accidentally by arsenic contained in green floral wallpaper used in his home. She was found guilty and executed by hanging on March 24, 1873. She had a young baby, who was forcibly taken away from her 5 days before her execution. Hieronyma Spara (died 1659), La Toffana (c. 1635–1719), and Catherine Deshayes (a.k.a. La Voisine) (1638–1680), may also be considered as major proponents of arsenic, but there is no unanimity among historians regarding the poisons they used |
| 4. | Bacteria | Henri Girard (1912–1918) (male, France) | A number of bacteria have been used for murder. These include typhoid (Henry Girard, France), diphtheria (Arthur Warren Waite, USA) and plague (Pakur murder case). Henry Girard killed Louis Pernotte of France with typhoid cultures on December 1, 1912, and then killed Mme Monin in April 1918. He escaped justice, as he swallowed his own culture of bacteria and died. He is known as the first scientific murderer |
| 5. | Cantharidin (Spanish fly) | Arthur Kendrick Ford (male, UK) | On April 26, 1954, 44-year-old Ford, office manager of a wholesale chemist's firm in London's Euston Road, having a charge of 26 people (22 women and 4 men), gave some of his female staff coconut candies laced with cantharidin. The idea was to make them sexually inclined towards him. Two women, Betty Margaret Grant (27) and June Florence Malins (19), died the next day. Ford was convicted of manslaughter and sentenced to 5 years in prison |
| 6. | Chloroform | Adelaide Bartlett (female, UK) | 19-year-old Adelaide married Edwin Bartlett in 1875. In 1885, she fell in love with Rev. George Dyson, and, in collusion with him, killed her husband with chloroform. On autopsy, a large quantity of chloroform was found in Bartlett's stomach. Dyson was known to have bought chloroform from various chemists just before the murder. However Dyson was never tried, and even Adelaide Bartlett was acquitted by jury for lack of sufficient evidence |
| 7. | Copper | Pierre-Désiré Moreau (male, France) | Moreau, a 32-year-old Parisian, killed his two wives with copper sulfate, with the aim of receiving their dowry. He was guillotined in Paris on October 14, 1874 before a large crowd |
| 8. | Cyanide (HCN, prussic acid) | Richard Brinkley (male, UK) | A carpenter by trade, Brinkley first killed a 77-year-old widow, Johanna Maria Louisa Blume, after fraudulently getting her signatures on her will, giving all her property to him. When the dead woman's daughter refused to part with property (she employed a solicitor instead), he went on to eliminate two witnesses, whose signatures were also taken fraudulently. By an error a different couple was killed, taking his total toll with cyanide to three. Brinkley was hanged at Wandsworth Prison on August 13, 1907 |

**Table 2** Continued

| No. | Poison | Major proponent | Details of the case |
|-----|--------|-----------------|---------------------|
| 9. | Digitalis | Dr. Edmond de la Pommerais (male, France) | Pommerais had a modest medical practice in Paris in 1859. In 1861, he married the rich Mlle Dubisy, and her mother died shortly afterwards. A little later Pommerais' mistress Mme Séraphine de Pawr also died, apparently of cholera. When Pommerais applied for her insurance money of half-a-million francs, the company began an investigation, which led to exhumation of Mme de Pawr's body. Massive amounts of digitalis were found in her body. Pommerais was guillotined in 1864. He continued pleading his innocence until the end |
| 10. | Gas | Reginald Ivor Hinks (male, UK) | Born in 1901, Hinks was a Hoover salesman in Bath, UK, in 1933. He married Constance Anne Pullen, a divorcée with one child, who lived with her 85-year-old father James Pullen. After moving into Pullen's house, Hinks murdered the old Pullen by shoving his head against the gas oven; the old man died of gas poisoning. Hinks was hanged at Bristol on May 4, 1934 |
| 11. | Glibenclamide (oral hypoglycemic agent) | Reverend P (1978–1979) (male, Sri Lanka) | Reverend P, an Anglican priest in his early 60s, developed adulterous relations with Mrs. I. His problem was to remove his wife (Mrs. P) and Mrs. I's husband (Mr. I). This he safely did with glibenclamide, an oral hypoglycemic agent. He was a diabetic, and shortly before the murders, he had made a visit to the UK (in 1978), where he had bought 100 tablets of glibenclamide. The first to go was Mr. I (on August 10, 1978). Mrs. P was next to go on March 19, 1979. Both Reverend P and Mrs. I were found guilty and sentenced to death. On appeal Mrs. I was acquitted for lack of evidence. Reverend P received a presidential pardon, and was imprisoned for life.<br>This case, which appeared in *Medicine, Science and the Law* 1999; 39: 354–358, only gives the initials of the characters instead of their full names |
| 12. | Heroin (pharmaceutical) | Dr. Harold Frederick Shipman (male, UK) | Between 1990 and 2000, Shipman murdered an estimated 240 of his patients with diamorphine (pharmaceutical heroin). Shipman was convicted on January 31, 2000, at Preston, UK, of murdering 15 of his patients and of forging the will of one of them. He was sentenced to 15 concurrent terms of life imprisonment and told by the judge that in his case life imprisonment would mean that he would remain in prison until his death. Shipman hanged himself at Wakefield prison on January 13, 2004 |
| 13. | Hyoscine | Dr. Hawley Harvey Crippen (male, UK) | Crippen, an American doctor, came to England in 1900, with his second wife Cora Turner. He fell in love with his secretary, Ethel le Neve, and murdered Cora early in 1910, using hyoscine. Hiding her remains in the cellar, both Crippen and his secretary fled to Antwerp. He was brought back to England, tried, and found guilty and hanged on November 23, 1910 |
| 14. | Insulin | Kenneth Barlow (1957) (male, UK) | On May 3, 1957, Kenneth Barlow, a 38-year-old male nurse called a doctor to his house in Thornbury Crescent, Bradford (at 11.30 p.m.), saying that he suspected his wife had drowned in her bath. Attempts at artificial respiration had proved to be of no avail. A postmortem examination revealed four needle marks in the woman's buttocks (two in each buttock). Police suspected Barlow, because there were no signs of splash in the bathroom and his pyjamas were quite dry (contradicting his statement that he had given artificial respiration to his wife). Eventually insulin was detected at the injection sites.<br>A novel defense put up by Barlow was that, just before death, his wife's body had discharged insulin in great quantities, reacting to a state of fear. However such physiological responses could not raise the levels of insulin to the level found in the dead woman's buttocks. Barlow was found guilty and sentenced to life imprisonment |
| 15. | Morphine | Dorothea Nancy Waddingham (1935) (female, UK) | Waddingham was a 36-year-old self-styled nurse, who killed 89-year-old Mrs. Baguley and her 50-year-old daughter Ada Baguley with morphine in 1935. She had seen to it that Mrs. Baguley had first made a will in her favor. She was found guilty and hanged on April 16, 1936 at Winson Green Prison, Birmingham |

Continued

**Table 2** Continued

| No. | Poison | Major proponent | Details of the case |
|---|---|---|---|
| 16. | Mushrooms, poisonous (*Amanita phalloides*) | Julia Agrippina (16–59 AD) (female, Rome) | Agrippina was supposed to have killed a number of people with poisonous mushrooms (between 49 and 59 AD), including her two husbands, Passienus Crispus and Claudius I. She was helped by the court poisoner, Locusta, in her royal poisonings |
| 17. | Nicotine | Hippolyte de Bocarme (1851) (male, Belgium) | Bocarme was a Belgian nobleman who murdered his brother-in-law (wife's brother) Gustave with nicotine. He was tried at the Palais de Justice in Mons on May 27, 1851 and found guilty. He was guillotined in July 1851 |
| 18. | Parathion (E-605) | Christa Ambrose Lehmann (female, Germany) | In February 1954, Lehmann bought five chocolate truffle candies, lacing one of them with parathion, a newly developed insecticide. She intended to give it to a female neighbor, who regarded Lehmann as an unwanted intruder. The unsuspecting neighbor preserved the candy for her daughter, who ate some and accidentally dropped some of it on the floor, whereupon a pet dog seized upon it, and ate it. Both the young girl and the pet dog died within a short time. Lehmann was found guilty and sentenced to life in prison. While in police custody, she confessed to having murdered her husband and father-in-law with the same poison |
| 19. | Phosphorus | Louisa May Merrifield (1953) (female, UK) | Louisa Merrifield, in collusion with her husband, killed their employer Mrs. Sarah Ann Ricketts on April 14, 1953 with rat poison containing phosphorus. Louisa and her 71-year-old husband Alfred were tried for murder. Alfred was released, but Louisa was found guilty and hanged at Manchester's Strangeways prison on September 18, 1953 |
| 20. | Ricin | The KGB (suspected) | On September 7, 1978, Georgi Markov, a 49-year-old Bulgarian defector to the UK, was waiting for his evening bus home on Waterloo Bridge, London, when he was shot at the back of his right thigh with a pellet of ricin. The firing device was an umbrella, in which presumably a gas-powered device had been fitted. He died 4 days later on September 11. Pathologist M. Rufus Crompton conducted an autopsy on September 12, and preserved large blocks of tissue from the left and right thigh. A tiny hollow pellet made of 90% platinum and 10% iridium was recovered from the block from the right thigh. A mere 1.52 mm in diameter, it had two holes (0.34 mm wide) cut through it. No trace of ricin was ever found in Markov's corpse, but his symptoms pointed to ricin poisoning. It was presumed that the metal ball was full of ricin, a deadly poison lethal in very small quantities. The pellet could contain about 2 mg ricin, which is enough to kill a human being. After the collapse of communism in 1991, the new Russian government admitted that their predecessors had sanctioned several assassinations of Bulgarian defectors, including Georgi Markov |
| 21. | Seconal | John Armstrong (1955) (male, UK) | John Armstrong was a 25-year-old Royal Navy sick berth attendant, who killed his 5-month-old son with seconal. At autopsy red skins were recovered from the dead child's stomach and windpipe. At first thought to be the skins of some poisonous berry, they soon turned out to be the remains of the gelatine capsules of the drug seconal. Both John and his wife Janet were arrested and tried for murder. Janet was acquitted. John was pronounced guilty, but was reprieved |
| 22. | Strychnine | Ethel Lillie Major (1934) (female, UK) | Ethel Lillie Major killed her husband Arthur Major by mixing strychnine in his food. On May 22, 1934, Arthur ate some corned beef and was soon taken ill. Ethel had access to strychnine, which her father, an ex-gamekeeper, kept with him to eliminate vermin. While eating, Arthur had complained about the bad taste of corned beef and had thrown some of it to his neighbor's dog, who quickly lapped it up and died on May 23 after suffering muscular spasms. |
| | | | Arthur died on May 24, 1934 at 10.40 p.m. after suffering from severe convulsions and spasms. On postmortem examination, strychnine was found in his body. Ethel was found guilty and executed at Hull Prison on December 19, 1934 |

**Table 2** Continued

| No. | Poison | Major proponent | Details of the case |
|-----|--------|-----------------|---------------------|
| 23. | Succinylcholine | Dr. Carl Coppolino (1967) (male, USA) | Carl Coppolino was a poor boy, who married Carmela, a doctor's daughter, and both went on to become doctors. Carl became an anesthesiologist. In 1962, Carl became infatuated with one Marjorie Farber, the 48-year-old wife of a retired army colonel. He killed Colonel Farber in 1963, with succinylcholine, an injection he had instructed Marjorie to administer. In 1965, he became infatuated with Mary Gibson, a 38-year-old divorcée. Within months – on August 28, 1965 – Carmela died, and within 5 weeks of her death Carl married the rich divorcée Mary Gibson. The bodies of both Colonel Farber and Carmela were exhumed. A puncture mark was found on Carmela's body. After a great deal of scientific testimony, Carl was found guilty of second-degree murder, and imprisoned for life |
| 24. | Thallium | George Trepal (1988) (male, USA) | Trepal killed his neighbor Peggy Carr by spiking her Coca-Cola bottles with thallium, because their household listened to loud music, and Carr's dogs chased Trepal's cats. Both these things disturbed Trepal. He was found guilty and sentenced to death |
| 25. | Venom (snake) | Dr. Grimesby Roylott (male, literary character, England) | Homicide with snakes appears such a natural death that no culprit has been found to date, although undoubtedly there should be several – certainly in Asian countries, where death with snakebites is so common that it does not raise an eyebrow. Sir Arthur Conan Doyle, in his story *The Adventure of the Speckled Band*, tells us how Dr. Grimesby Roylott kills one of his stepdaughters, Julia Stoner, with a snake (swamp adder). Two years later he tries the trick on the other stepdaughter, Helen (Julia's twin), but is accidentally bitten by the snake himself. Holmes and Watson find him dead in his room, with the snake coiling his head like a speckled band |

mounted and worn as amulets as a protection against poison.

Another universal antidote was terra sigillata, a special clay earth from the island of Lemnos. To prevent fraud, this special clay was prepared in tablets and stamped with a seal, thus giving the substance its name. Later, other sources of similar earth were found in different areas of Europe, and in the sixteenth and seventeenth centuries mugs were made from it, from which anyone could drink without fear of poisoning.

## Modern Era

*We can never be fully in possession of a science until we know the history of its development.*

Charles Greene Cumston

The period since the mid-1850s has seen great progress in the analysis of poisons. Today, with modern techniques and instrumentation, the most minute traces of alien compounds can be detected, not only from tissues and organs collected at the time of postmortem examination but also in biological samples such as blood and urine collected during life. The study of antidotes has become more scientific. We have moved from the age of mithridatium, bezoars, and terra sigillata to the age of physiological antidotes and chelating agents. A number of medical journals are devoted solely to the study of toxicology. Toxicology is taken up by promising young students as a career. It is no longer the murky, shady, crime-infested vocation of the poisoners; instead, it has become a true science pursued by brilliant investigators.

The number of poisoners in the modern world has certainly decreased, but by no means have they vanished altogether. Sporadic cases of homicidal poisonings still occur. **Table 2** provides an idea of the amazing variety of poisons that poisoners have used during the past century. However, due to modern analytical methods, each one of them was apprehended and prosecuted.

Modern analytical methods in toxicology have also enabled historians to rewrite history. When the 12th president of the USA, Zachary Taylor (1784–1850), died, it was believed that he died of gastroenteritis. However, since he was opposed to slavery, it was increasingly suspected that he had been poisoned by people from the pro-slavery faction. It was believed that he was poisoned with arsenic since his symptoms were very similar to arsenic poisoning. The emergence of highly sensitive analytical techniques in toxicology convinced the coroner of Jefferson County, Kentucky, to allow his body to be exhumed on June 17, 1991. Gutzeit test, neutron activation analysis, and X-ray microanalysis done on hair and nail samples showed that Taylor had not been poisoned with arsenic.

Such was not the case with Napoleon Bonaparte (1769–1821), however. A neutron activation analysis of his locks of hair showed high levels of arsenic, and many historians now think that Napoleon may have been poisoned with arsenic by his enemies while he was exiled on the island of St. Helena. Similarly, analysis of locks of Newton's (1642–1727) hair show that he may have suffered from mercury poisoning during the years 1692 and 1693. He recovered though, and he lived to be 85 years old.

## See Also

History of Forensic Medicine; Mass Poisonings; Toxicology: Overview; Venom

## Further Reading

Aggrawal A (1997) Poisons, antidotes and anecdotes. *Science Reporter* 26–29. [Also available online at http://prof_anil_aggrawal.tripod.com/poiso001.html].

Aggrawal A (2002) Poisons and antidotes through the ages, with special reference to Indian history and mythology. *Mithridata (Toxicological History Society Newsletter)* 12(2): 13–18.

Aggrawal A (2003) 250 greatest forensic scientists of all time. *Anil Aggrawal's Internet Journal of Forensic Medicine and Toxicology* 4(2): http://www.geradts.com/~anil/ij/vol_004_no_002/others/250.html; accessed October 29, 2003.

Aggrawal A (2004) Agrippina, the first forensic odontologist and the greatest poisoner in ancient Rome. *Mithridata (Toxicological History Society Newsletter)* XIV(1): 6–11.

Borzelleca JF (2001) The art, the science, and the seduction of toxicology: an evolutionary development. In: Hayes AW (ed.) *Principles and Methods of Toxicology,* 4th edn, pp. 1–21. London: Taylor & Francis.

Gallo MA (2001) History and scope of toxicology. In: Klaassen CD (ed.) *Casarett and Doull's Toxicology: The Basic Science of Poisons,* 6th edn, pp. 3–10. New York: McGraw-Hill.

Jones RG (ed.) (2002) *The Mammoth Book of Women Who Kill.* London: Robinson.

Pillay VV (2003) *Comprehensive Medical Toxicology.* Hyderabad, India: Paras.

Smith S (1952) Poisons and poisoners through the ages. *Medicolegal Journal* 20: 153–167.

Thompson CJS (1899) *Poison Romance and Poison Mysteries.* London: Scientific Press.

Thompson CJS (1931) *Poisons and Poisoners.* London: Harold Shaylor.

Trestrail JH III (2000) *Criminal Poisoning.* Totowa, NJ: Humana.

Trestrail JH III (2000) *Mithridata: The Newsletter of the Toxicological History Society – The First Ten Years (Jan 1991–July 2000).* Grand Rapids, MI: Center for the Study of Criminal Poisoning.

Wax PM (1994) Historical principles and perspectives. In: Goldfrank LR, Flomenbaum NE, Lewin NA, *et al.* (eds.) *Goldfrank's Toxicologic Emergencies,* 5th edn, pp. 1–20. Norwalk, CT: Appleton & Lange.

Wilson C (1989) *Written in Blood – A History of Forensic Detection.* London: Equation.

# HUMAN RIGHTS, CONTROLS AND PRINCIPLES

H McKelvie and B Loff, Victorian Institute of Forensic Medicine, Southbank, VIC, Australia

## Introduction

International human rights law and international humanitarian law (IHL) are two different but related areas of law with the common goal of safeguarding the fundamental rights of the individual. International human rights law focuses on the relationship between the state and the individual. All human rights are considered to be interdependent, indivisible, and interrelated. The law applies to all people simply because they are human, and is therefore universal and inalienable. Humanitarian law focuses on issues arising in times of armed conflict, when many human rights may be restricted. It seeks to limit the effects of armed conflict on those who are not, or are no longer, participating in hostilities, and to restrict the means and methods of war to the attainment of the objectives of the conflict. These two branches of public international law are contained in international treaties and conventions and in what is known as "customary law" – a rule of conduct that as a result of long and consistent practice has come to be considered by states to be legally binding. The International Bill of Rights comprising the Universal Declaration of Human Rights (UDHR), the International Covenant on Civil and Political Rights, and the International Covenant on Economic, Cultural and

Social Rights forms the framework for human rights thinking and practice. The Geneva conventions and their additional protocols are the primary documents underpinning IHL.

This article will provide a brief overview of both these branches of international law, including their history and current status and the institutions involved in implementing and enforcing them. In providing this overview, the authors acknowledge the information provided by the International Committee of the Red Cross (ICRC), the British Red Cross, and the United Nations (UN) Office of the High Commissioner for Human Rights.

## International Humanitarian Law

### What Does International Humanitarian Law Cover?

There have been laws governing the conduct of war as long as there has been war. Today IHL is regarded in the main as comprising of six major treaties (the four Geneva conventions and their two protocols) that include over 600 "articles" or "provisions" and a complex web of customary laws. The nuances of these laws are the province of diplomatic services and international legal experts, but can be summarized in a few basic rules:

- Civilians and those who are no longer taking part in hostilities must be respected, protected, and treated humanely. This includes the provision of care for the wounded, sick, and shipwrecked.
- Prisoners must be treated humanely and protected from acts of violence, particularly torture, and should be afforded the fundamental protections of the judicial process.

The use of force in armed conflict must be limited to achieving the objectives of the conflict and no superfluous injury to people or damage to property should be inflicted.

There are other bodies generating international standards and norms that may be characterized as coming under the umbrella of IHL. Indeed, the charter of the UN states that one of the purposes of the UN is to maintain peace and security. The Security Council, as is well recognized, carries the primary responsibility for this task. The convention on prevention and punishment of the crime of genocide (that entered into force in 1951) may be particularly pertinent during times of war. If the Security Council determines that genocide is taking place, the international community is bound, in theory at least, to intervene.

The optional protocol to the convention on the rights of the child relating to the involvement of children in armed conflict adopted by the General Assembly is another example of law that focuses upon humanitarian concerns. The Security Council has, in addition, recently passed a resolution dealing with children in armed conflict. The ILO also has something to say about children and war. Its convention relating to the prohibition of the worst forms of child labor deals with the recruitment of children for use in armed conflict.

There are multilateral treaties in force that encompass matters including the nonproliferation of nuclear weapons, chemical weapons, antipersonnel mines, and excessively injurious conventional weapons. The International Criminal Court (ICC) will, unlike the International Tribunals for the Former Yugoslavia and for Rwanda, provide a standing venue for dealing with war crimes, and its future jurisprudence should enlarge the existing body of humanitarian law.

### When Does International Humanitarian Law Apply?

IHL applies in all armed conflicts whatever their origin or cause. The rules of IHL must be respected whether or not the persons in need of protection are victims of what is considered a "just war." However, IHL does distinguish between different types of armed conflict. The four Geneva conventions deal extensively with international armed conflicts, which are those between nation states. Wars of national liberation, where people are fighting against a colonial power as an exercise of self-determination, are also recognized as international conflicts under Protocol I, which was added to the Geneva conventions in 1977. Civil wars within a state (which constitute the majority of conflicts going on in the world at the present time) are considered conflicts of a "non-international character." They are subject to a "simpler" version of the IHL rules (contained in Article 3 common to all four of the Geneva conventions, and basically reflected in the summary above).

### The History of International Humanitarian Law

Like human rights law, IHL has its origins in the principles of early religions, as well as the customs of warfare recognized by ancient civilizations. For example, the Catholic saints Augustine and Thomas Aquinas, and in Islam, the prophet Mohammed addressed the question of "just means" to be employed during warfare. Conventions for combat, the treatment of civilians and captured enemy soldiers were also subject to unwritten rules of humane conduct amongst ancient civilizations. In the seventeenth century, the Dutch jurist and political thinker Hugo Grotius also made a lasting contribution to the development of IHL with his text *On Laws of War and Peace*, which defined what should be regarded as justifiable and unjustifiable wars and which appealed to heads of state to restrain their conduct during wartime.

In the nineteenth century, at the instigation of a young Swiss man, Henri Dunant, IHL began to be codified. In June 1859, Dunant found himself, more or less by accident, amongst 40 000 Italians, French, and Austrians wounded after the battle of Solferino in northern Italy. His efforts and those of a few other volunteers to ease the suffering of the wounded inspired him to write a booklet (*Un Souvenir de Solferino*), published in 1862, which suggested that national societies should be formed to care for the victims of war, without discrimination on the basis of race, nationality, or religion. He also made a further proposal that states should make a treaty recognizing the work of these national organizations, to guarantee better treatment for those wounded in war.

With the aid of four colleagues, Dunant then established the International Committee for Aid to the Wounded (which was subsequently renamed the International Committee of the Red Cross (ICRC)). A diplomatic conference convened by the Swiss government in Geneva in 1864 saw the meeting of several newly formed national societies, based on Dunant's ideas, and the adoption by 16 European states of the Convention for the Amelioration of the Condition of the Wounded in Armies in the Field. This document was the first Geneva Convention, which formally laid the foundations of IHL. It enshrined the principles of universality and tolerance without distinction between race, nationality, or religion. It also established the now almost universally recognized Red Cross emblem to distinguish military medical personnel. (The other well-known emblem of the Red Crescent was adopted by the Ottoman Empire in 1876 during the war with Russia. It was recognized in the 1929 Geneva Convention.)

The codification of IHL continued with a new draft in 1868 extending the principles contained in the convention to maritime conflicts. In the same year, the St. Petersburg Declaration was made, renouncing the use of explosive bullets. In 1899 and 1907, two international peace conferences were held at The Hague, which resulted in a series of conventions being adopted that defined the laws and customs of warfare, and forbade certain practices, including: bombardment of undefended towns, and the use of poisonous gases and soft-nosed bullets.

During World War I, adherence to the Geneva Convention and the operations of the ICRC were seen to have some effect in protecting lives and ameliorating suffering, but it was recognized that the Convention needed strengthening. In 1925, a Protocol was adopted prohibiting the use of asphyxiating and poisonous gases. In 1929, a further conference in Geneva adopted a convention with more robust provisions about treatment of the sick and wounded. A second convention was adopted regarding the treatment of prisoners of war.

The four Geneva conventions of 1949, which are still in force today, are the legacy of the Spanish Civil War and World War II. The atrocities perpetrated during those conflicts prompted the international community to renew its commitment to improving the protection of war victims. In particular, agreement was needed on rules to prevent a recurrence of the genocidal actions of the Nazis in interring and exterminating 6 million Jews, gypsies, and others. The inadequacy of the original Geneva conventions was highlighted by the lack of action taken to denounce the Nazi concentration camps or intervene on behalf of the Holocaust victims interred in them. The ICRC has acknowledged its moral failure in this context, and has expressed regret for its possible omissions and errors of the past, but has never formally apologized.

Each of the four conventions of 1949 deals with a different category of protected person:

- first convention: care of the wounded and sick members of the armed forces in the field
- second convention: care of the wounded, sick, and shipwrecked members of the armed forces at sea
- third convention: treatment of prisoners of war
- fourth convention: protection of civilians during war. It outlaws torture, collective punishment, and the resettlement by an occupying power of its own civilians on territory under its military control (which specifically deals with the issue of the concentration camps).

These four conventions did not attempt to incorporate the "Hague law," dealing with the customs of warfare developed at the Peace Conferences of 1899 and 1907. Since they were drawn up, new technologies and new weapons have been developed and the number of states has more than doubled with the process of decolonization, which brought with it new types of conflict – wars of national liberation. In addition, an increasing number of civil wars necessitated increased protections for victims of these non-international armed conflicts. These challenges were met at a diplomatic conference convened in Geneva in 1974. Over a three year period two new treaties were developed, which became the protocols additional to the Geneva conventions. These two protocols deal with protection of individuals in international armed conflicts and those between the armed forces of a government and dissidents or other organized groups in control of part of its territory.

IHL continues to develop with further conventions being agreed, for example:

- the 1980 Conventional Weapons Convention and its four protocols
- the 1993 Chemical Weapons Convention
- the 1997 Ottawa Convention on antipersonnel mines
- the 2000 Optional Protocol to the Convention on the Rights of the Child on the involvement of children in armed conflict.

### Implementation and Compliance

As with all international legal conventions and treaties, it is up to individual states to become party to them by a process of signature and ratification or accession. (A treaty is open for signature for a certain time after the conference that has adopted it. Signature is not binding until it is also ratified, usually following a process in the domestic parliament. If the time for signature and ratification has passed, a state may still become a party to the treaty by the single act of accession.) For example, there are 191 parties to the Geneva conventions of 1949; 161 are party to the first protocol and 156 to the second.

States that are party to a treaty or convention are legally obliged to comply with its provisions and all states must respect those provisions that are accepted as customary law (whether or not they are parties to a treaty that covers the same provisions). All states are expected to respect their international commitments and this includes taking necessary measures to implement international laws effectively. Under the Geneva conventions and the additional protocols, party states are required to undertake a number of specific measures to facilitate compliance. Some are peacetime measures and others are to be taken in times of armed conflict. The following are two examples of the many measures contained in the conventions and protocols:

- Instruction and training of the armed forces. It is imperative for effective implementation that the rules of the Geneva conventions and the additional protocols are provided to members of the armed forces in a form that can be clearly understood and relevant to their rank and function.
- Translation to domestic legislation. States (parties) must enact their own domestic legislation that gives effect to the provisions of the conventions and protocols, to guarantee they fulfill their international obligations. For example, grave breaches of

IHL (also known as "war crimes") must also be crimes under domestic law, and capable of being prosecuted in domestic courts.

The international community has in recent years taken further steps to encourage compliance. By establishing two international tribunals to prosecute war crimes perpetrated during conflicts in Rwanda and the former Yugoslavia, it is hoped that the prospect of being held accountable for violation of IHL will be a real disincentive to those contemplating future violations. In 1998, an international treaty, known as the Rome Statute, created the ICC.

### Violations of IHL

Unfortunately, being a party to a convention or treaty and undertaking implementation measures are not of themselves guarantees of compliance. Despite war no longer being an acceptable way to settle differences between states (as clearly stated in the UN Charter of 1945), armed conflicts happen, and there are countless examples of IHL being violated. This is especially true in the context of the increasing number of wars waged within national and regional borders, noted earlier. Sadly, these conflicts often involve deliberate attacks on local citizens and displaced persons. These may take the form of physical and sexual violence, terror, starvation, and "disappearances," as well as destruction of infrastructure like homes, water sources, or hospitals. These attacks aim to weaken enemy forces by targeting host or supportive communities, to gain territorial control or access to natural and other resources, or are simply random acts of violence.

In 2003, the UN Secretary General Kofi Annan reported on the unacceptably high toll of injuries and deaths amongst innocent citizens caught up in violent conflicts around the world. He highlighted particular examples with the conflicts in:

- the Sudan – where aid workers have collectively been dismayed by the pattern of attacks on civilians, humanitarian workers, and facilities, including attacks on civilians at or near food distribution sites
- Afghanistan – where several different groups of nonstate combatants control territory, creating major difficulties for provision of aid and humanitarian protection for civilian victims of the conflict
- the Democratic Republic of the Congo – where war in the east of the country, motivated by the illegal exploitation of natural and mineral resources, has had appalling humanitarian consequences, including the deaths of over 3 million people.

In a further example of IHL violation, international attention has also been drawn to the situation in Guantanamo Bay in Cuba where the USA is using its Camp X-Ray naval base as a holding facility for alleged Al Qaeda, Taliban, and other detainees who have come under US control during the "war on terrorism." Rather than classifying these detainees as prisoners of war, the USA has adopted the term "illegal combatants." This has been done to avoid the need to adhere to the requirements of the Geneva conventions which include repatriation of prisoners at the end of a war. Some of these detainees have been held without charge for over two years, prompting calls for an end to their seemingly indefinite detention beyond the reach of the law.

### Prosecuting IHL Violations

As already noted, the international community has taken steps to hold to account perpetrators of major humanitarian law breaches. Formal prosecution trials were first held by the international community in November 1945 in Nuremberg, Germany. The so-called International Military Tribunal was set up by the victorious Allies (the USA, France, the UK, and the Soviet Union) at the end of World War II. Prosecutors from these four countries indicted a total of 22 Nazi German officials on three basic charges: (1) conspiring and ultimately launching an "aggressive war;" (2) committing war crimes; and (3) committing "crimes against humanity." The trials lasted 11 months. Of the 21 defendants in custody, a total of 11 were sentenced to death, three were acquitted, and the rest received prison terms. Ten men were hanged in November 1946; one of those sentenced to death, Hermann Göring, committed suicide hours before his scheduled execution.

More recently, the UN Security Council passed resolutions to establish the International Criminal Tribunal for the former Yugoslavia (ICTY) (1993) and the International Criminal Tribunal for Rwanda (ICTR) (1994). The ICTY has a mandate to:

- bring to justice persons allegedly responsible for serious violations of IHL during the conflict in the former Yugoslavia since 1991
- render justice to the victims
- deter further crimes
- contribute to the restoration of peace by promoting reconciliation in the former Yugoslavia.

To date, 91 accused have appeared in proceedings before the tribunal with a range of outcomes, including 20 convictions, five acquitted/found not guilty, 21 indictments withdrawn, and 14 accused have died. There are several trials that are ongoing, including that of former President Slobodan Milosevic.

The ICTY has not been without problems, and has been criticized on a number of fronts including:

1. It is insufficiently resourced and does not have powers of arrest, instead relying on other agencies to apprehend and extradite indictees.
2. Its processes are overly legalistic, which is in part the reason for the length of time taken to complete trials.
3. A disproportionate number of indictees are Serbs.
4. The tribunal was established by the UN Security Council instead of the UN General Assembly, which makes it seem like a court created by the Great Powers in order to try citizens of smaller nations.

The ICTR was established for the prosecution of persons responsible for genocide and other serious violations of IHL committed in the territory of Rwanda between January 1, 1994 and December 31, 1994. More than 70 accused have been indicted, with 13 trials completed (12 convictions and one acquittal). Eight trials are currently in progress involving 20 defendants. Those convicted include Jean Kambanda, the Prime Minister of the Rwandan government during the genocide, who was the first head of government to be indicted and subsequently convicted for genocide. This conviction demonstrates that IHL can be applied to the highest authorities and has helped to create the conditions in which prosecutions could be undertaken against former heads of state General Augusto Pinochet of Chile, President Hissein Habre of Chad, and Slobodan Milosevic of Serbia.

As mentioned earlier (although not without problems), the effectiveness of the ICTY and the ICTR has paved the way for a permanent court. The ICC was established by the Rome Statute of July 17, 1998, when it was adopted by 120 states. The statute came into force on July 1, 2002, when the 60th state ratified it. The ICC is the first ever permanent, treaty-based, international criminal court established to promote the rule of law and ensure that the gravest international crimes (genocide, crimes against humanity, and war crimes) do not go unpunished. A number of legal and practical steps have yet to be taken before the ICC begins operating some time after September 2004. The ICTY and the ICTR were set up more swiftly within the framework of the UN, whereas the ICC will be established as a new international organization.

### Role of the ICRC

The organization founded by Henri Dunant in 1863 has evolved into the primary voice for victims of war and an international advocate for adherence to IHL. The mission of the ICRC states that it

> is an impartial, neutral and independent organization whose exclusively humanitarian mission is to protect the lives and dignity of victims of war and internal violence and to provide them with assistance ... in situations of conflict. It also endeavours to prevent suffering by promoting and strengthening humanitarian law and universal humanitarian principles.

The Geneva conventions confer special status on the ICRC to undertake these activities. This includes parties to an international conflict being obliged to allow ICRC delegates access to occupied territories, prisoner-of-war camps, and areas where civilians may be detained. Its unique role has further international recognition in the form of its observer status at the UN General Assembly. Although it has a worldwide reach through its network of workers and volunteers in the Red Cross and Red Crescent movements, the ICRC has maintained its character as a private institution, governed by Swiss law and with Swiss citizens constituting its governing body. Its funding comes from voluntary contributions from states that are party to the Geneva conventions, from national Red Cross and Red Crescent societies and private donors. It is therefore able to play an international role, independent of governments that are not in a position to influence its activities. It acts as a neutral intermediary between the two (or in some cases, several) sides to a conflict, utilizing an approach of confidential diplomacy. Where this approach is ineffective, the ICRC can make public appeals to the combatants, although this approach is rarely employed. Over 125 years the ICRC has had some success in persuading states and other parties to respect humanitarian law in the midst of armed conflict.

### Médecins Sans Frontières (Doctors without Borders)

Not all of those working for the Red Cross were content with its neutral approach. During the Biafran war between 1968 and 1970, some doctors working for the Red Cross became frustrated with the obligation to maintain silence in the face of what they were confronted with. In 1971, Dr. Bernard Kouchner founded Médecins Sans Frontières (MSF) with the intention that it should both provide medical assistance and speak out about human rights abuses. In 1987, Dr. Kouchner published *Le Devoir d'Ingérence* (The Duty to Intervene), which posited the view that liberal democracies were morally obligated to override the sovereignty of a state abusing human rights. He eventually became Minister for Health in France.

MSF is now a well-recognized international humanitarian aid organization with over 2500 volunteers providing emergency medical assistance to populations in danger in more than 80 countries. In carrying out its humanitarian assistance, MSF seeks also to raise awareness of crisis situations; MSF acts as a witness and will speak out, either in private or in public about the plight of populations in danger.

## International Human Rights Law

### Origins of International Human Rights Law

The classical doctrine of natural law can be seen as a starting point for the development and understanding of international human rights law. The doctrine dates from ancient Greece. During the thirteenth century Thomas Aquinas described four types of law: (1) eternal law (laws that govern the nature of an eternal universe); (2) natural law, being that part of eternal law discoverable through processes of reasoning; (3) divine law, revealed in scripture (necessary to observe in order to achieve salvation); and (4) human law, consisting of rules supportable by reason articulated by human authorities for the common good. These laws derive their authority from natural law. This leap in thought is of course controversial. He also suggested that any human law in conflict with natural law was not binding, but obedience to it may still be appropriate to avoid civil disturbance.

This concept evolved to become intermingled to different degrees with social contractarian philosophy. Thomas Hobbes in the seventeenth century described the life of humans in a state of nature as "solitary, poor, nasty, brutish, and short." By social contract citizens surrendered their natural liberty to the unlimited power of the state sovereign to ameliorate their nasty condition. John Locke, arguing at a slightly earlier date, suggested that some natural rights survived within the social contract and when not observed provided the basis upon which governments could be changed. In a complex amalgam of contract and nature, Jean-Jacques Rousseau insisted that there were some natural rights that no positivist law could take away. Legal positivists do not believe that law is discoverable through abstract reasoning; some see the law as no more than a series of rules. The utilitarian Jeremy Bentham is regarded as the founder of this school of thought. In any event, the American and French revolutions gave rise to the principles that all men (sic) have the natural rights to life, liberty, and pursuit of happiness, or to life, property, security, and resistance to oppression respectively.

During the seventeenth century Hugo Grotius and Samuel Pufendorf shifted ideas of natural law from the domestic domain to the laws made between princes, the laws of war, and these become the origins of public international law. This more modern amalgam of natural law, legal positivism, and international law are the foundations of twentieth-century human rights law and these laws are, of course, heavily influenced by moral and political debates.

The twentieth century saw major strides in the formalization of human rights. The horrors of the "world wars" motivated the international community to develop structural frameworks for the administration of universally agreed standards. After World War I, the allied powers established the League of Nations, approved as part of the Treaty of Versailles at the Paris Peace Conference in 1919. The mission, as stated in the League's charter, was "to promote international cooperation and to achieve international peace and security." The League was ineffective in stopping the military aggression that led to World War II and it ceased its work during the war, dissolving on April 18, 1946. The UN assumed its assets and carries on much of its work.

The concept of human rights underpins all UN operations. For example, the Preamble to the Charter of the UN contains the "reaffirm[ation] of faith in fundamental human rights, in the dignity and worth of the human person, in the equal rights of men and women and of nations large and small." This sentiment is echoed throughout the Charter in various articles. The importance of human rights as the driving force of UN actions has been consistently promoted by the current Secretary General, Kofi Annan.

### Declarations and Treaties

The UN Charter and the UDHR, adopted by the UN General Assembly in 1948, form the basis of modern international human rights law. Since then the scope of human rights law has gradually expanded, as has the specificity of the articles contained within the various international instruments. There are different types of instruments and mechanisms by which they have effect. Declarations are made by the international community as an exposition of ideal standards. Generally, declarations are not legally binding. The exception to this is the 1948 UDHR. The UDHR is so widely accepted that it is regarded as being "customary" international law. It was originally thought that the fairly broad statements contained in the UDHR would be expanded in a more detailed convention. However, with the coming of the Cold War, this was not to be the case. Thus, two treaties were drafted: the International Covenant on Civil and Political Rights

and the International Covenant on Economic, Social and Cultural Rights. Though approved by the General Assembly in 1966, the two treaties did not come into force until 1977, having taken this time to receive sufficient ratifications. Together these treaties are known as the International Bill of Rights.

Other significant human rights covenants are:

- The Convention on the Prevention and Punishment of the Crime of Genocide (entered into force 1952)
- The International Convention of the Elimination of All Forms of Racial Discrimination (entered into force 1969)
- The Convention on the Elimination of All Forms of Discrimination against Women (entered into force 1981)
- The Convention against Torture and Other Cruel Inhuman or Degrading Treatment or Punishment (entered into force 1987)
- The Convention on Rights of the Child (entered into force 1990)
- The International Convention on the Protection of the Rights of All Migrant Workers and Members of their Families (adopted 1990, not yet in force).

### Monitoring and Compliance

As the main deliberative body of the UN, the General Assembly, made up of 191 member states, is closely concerned with reviewing and taking action on human rights issues that are referred to it by the Economic and Social Council and its Third Committee. (The General Assembly has six main committees. The Third Committee is the Social, Humanitarian, and Cultural Committee.) There are also various bodies that have been established under the umbrella of the UN to monitor compliance with human rights instruments and to investigate alleged breaches. There are both charter-based human rights bodies and treaty-based ones. The charter-based bodies have been established on the basis of provisions contained in the Charter of the UN. They hold broad human rights mandates (in line with the UN Charter) and address an unlimited audience (the entire international community). The Commission on Human Rights and the Subcommission on the Promotion and Protection of Human Rights are both charter-based UN bodies established under the authority of the Economic and Social Committee of the UN. They utilize special rapporteurs, representatives, and expert working groups to investigate, discuss, and report on specific human rights issues. (For example, in 1990 a special rapporteur was commissioned to report on the situation of human rights in Haiti following the overthrow of the constitutionally elected President, Mr. Jean-Bertrand Aristide, and the use of violence and military coercion and the subsequent deterioration of the situation of human rights in that country. Similarly, a special rapporteur was dispatched to Chechnya in 2002 in light of continued reports of widespread violence against civilians and alleged violations of human rights and humanitarian law, in particular, forced disappearances, extrajudicial, summary, or arbitrary executions, torture, arbitrary detentions, ad hoc detention locations, and continued abuses and harassment at checkpoints by Russian state agents.)

Treaty-based bodies derive their existence from specific treaties and hold more narrow mandates based on the issues covered in the relevant treaty, with their audience limited to the countries that have ratified the treaty. The following list provides examples of treaty-based human rights bodies:

- Committee against Torture, established pursuant to Article 17 of the Convention against Torture and Other Cruel Inhuman or Degrading Treatment or Punishment
- Committee on Economic, Social and Cultural Rights, established to supervise the implementation of the International Covenant on Economic, Social, and Cultural Rights. Unlike other treaty bodies, this Committee was not established by the Covenant. The Economic and Social Council created the Committee, following the unsatisfactory efforts of two previous bodies
- Committee on the Elimination of Discrimination against Women, established pursuant to Article 17 of the Convention on the Elimination of All Forms of Discrimination against Women, to supervise implementation of the Convention
- Human Rights Committee, established pursuant to Article 28 of the International Covenant on Civil and Political Rights.

Members of these committees are experts in their areas and are elected by the state parties (except the Committee on Economic Social and Cultural Rights, whose membership is elected by the Economic and Social Council of the General Assembly). Implementation of treaty obligations is monitored at the national level, with the treaty bodies examining reports submitted by state parties. This process may be followed up with dialog with certain countries (up to 100 per year) about the local human rights situation and how it might be improved.

In addition to these formal UN bodies, other mechanisms are employed to monitor compliance with human rights standards. These mechanisms include the Secretary General appointing representatives, working groups, or special rapporteurs on thematic issues, e.g., internally displaced persons;

summary or arbitrary executions; torture; religious intolerance; racism; and violence against women.

The Secretary General can also use his/her "good offices" to intervene confidentially with a member state to raise human rights concerns. This includes such issues as release of political prisoners and commutation of the death sentence. Any such use of the Secretary General's "good offices" is reported to the Security Council.

All these measures do go some way to preventing human rights abuses and ensuring that member states are aware of their obligations. There are some concrete results in the form of, for example, suspension of executions, release of detainees, and changes to domestic legal systems to reflect international human rights treaty obligations.

## Use of International Human Rights Law by Individuals

One notable development in the implementation of human rights law has been in its use by individuals. This is especially true in the context of the European Court of Human Rights, whose jurisdiction is based around the European Convention on Human Rights, to which all 45 member states of the Council of Europe are signatories. The court provides a direct method of complaint by a person claiming to be a victim of a violation of the Convention, usually after he/she has exhausted avenues of legal redress in his/her own domestic courts. Where an infringement is proved, the European Court of Human Rights is able to make a ruling to provide redress against the relevant state. Since it was convened in 1998 (building on the work of the European Commission for Human Rights before it), the court's judgments have provided guidance on how fundamental human rights are to be respected and protected, not only for member states of the Council of Europe, but also other countries, thus becoming a leading mechanism for human rights protection. Its significant role in acknowledging individuals as rights holders has catalyzed a trend that is gradually being followed elsewhere in the world, creating further levels of protection than might have been envisaged as the interstate treaty system was developed.

## Role of the Human Rights Commissioner

In acknowledgment of the increasing significance of human rights in the world arena, the post of High Commissioner for Human Rights was created in 1993 as the principal UN official responsible for these issues, accountable to the Secretary General (this is in addition to the other UN bodies described above). The Office of the High Commissioner for Human

Rights (OHCHR) is based in Geneva in Switzerland, and also has an office at the UN Headquarters in New York. The High Commissioner has a leadership role in the international human rights movement, traveling widely and making public presentations, providing a voice for victims and at the same time engaging in dialog with governments to strengthen cooperation and adherence to human rights principles. The office works with a range of players in the human rights arena – nongovernment organizations involved in aid work, academic institutions and relevant private sector organizations to promote human rights as widely as possible and provide educational opportunities about human rights issues. It also offers administrative services, research, and other expertise and advice to other UN bodies, and to the numerous experts appointed to investigate and report on human rights issues.

## Conclusion

Both human rights law and IHL are crucial expressions of what the international community regards as the fundamental rights of the individual during peacetime and during times of war. During armed conflict, when some human rights may be justifiably suspended (other than those set out in Article 4 of the International Covenant on Civil and Political Rights – this includes the right to life, the right not to be subjected to torture or to cruel, inhuman, or degrading treatment or punishment, the right not to be held in slavery or servitude, the right not to be imprisoned for failure to perform a contractual obligation, the right not to be subject to retroactive penal measures, the right to recognition as a person before the law, and the right to freedom of thought, conscience, and religion), humanitarian law should be employed to protect those civilians and prisoners caught up in the conflict. Of course, the aims of both human rights law and humanitarian law are achieved only as far as they are recognized and acted upon by governments and individuals. This is an ongoing challenge for the UN and the other international agencies devoted to promoting and acting upon them. Providing support for these agencies to fulfill their mandates remains a challenge for us all.

## See Also

**War Crimes:** Tribunals

ISBN 0-12-547970-0